EVOLUTION AND PHYLOGENY OF FLOWERING PLANTS

EVOLUTION AND PHYLOGENY OF FLOWERING PLANTS

Dicotyledons: Facts and Theory

with over 550 illustrations and maps by the author

J. HUTCHINSON
LL.D. (St. Andrews), F.R.S., V.M.H.
Late Keeper of Museums of Botany
Royal Botanic Gardens
Kew, England

1969

ACADEMIC PRESS
London and New York

ACADEMIC PRESS INC. (LONDON) LTD.
Berkeley Square House
Berkeley Square
London, W1X 6BA

U.S. Edition published by
ACADEMIC PRESS INC.
111 Fifth Avenue
New York, New York 10003

Library of Congress Catalog Card Number: 79–82391

PRINTED IN GREAT BRITAIN BY
WILLIAM CLOWES AND SONS, LIMITED
LONDON AND BECCLES

PREFACE

According to Daydon Jackson's GLOSSARY OF BOTANICAL TERMS, **Phylogeny** deals with ancestral history deduced from development, and **Evolution** is the theory according to which complex forms are considered to have been derived from simpler ones.

The Oxford Dictionary defines them as follows: **Phylogeny:** 1, The genesis and evolution of the phylum, tribe or species; ancestral or racial evolution of an animal or plant type (as distinguished from ontogenesis, the evolution of the individual). . . . 3, A pedigree or genealogical table showing the racial evolution of a type of organisms. **Evolution:** section C; The origination of species of animals and plants, as conceived by those who attribute it to a process of development from earlier forms, and not as a process of "special creation".

Chambers's Twentieth Century Dictionary: **Phylogeny:** Evolutionary pedigree or genealogical history. **Evolution:** The act of unrolling or unfolding; gradual working out or development; a series of things unfolded; the doctrine according to which higher forms of life have gradually arisen out of lower.

As this book more or less covers each of these definitions, I have thought it preferable to use both in the title. It is intended as a Companion or Supplement to my FAMILIES OF FLOWERING PLANTS, 2nd Ed., Vol. I, DICOTYLEDONS, published by the Clarendon Press, Oxford, in 1959. In that work the families were described, with a list of the principal genera and the more important economic products, and in the smaller groups short keys to the genera were provided. An artificial key to the families was also given.

There was no room, however, for notes on phylogeny or genera with outstanding characters. These are now provided together with illustrations of many plants of special morphological interest and economic importance, and which sometimes may lead to their identification. The illustration of numerous fruits may thus partly supplement the classical work of Gaertner, DIE FRUCTIBUS ET SEMINIBUS PLANTARUM, published as long ago as 1789–91. For example most of the distinctive fruits, 62 of them, of the large family *Brassicaceae* (*Cruciferae*), 80 of the Order LEGUMINALES, and 21 of the family *Apiaceae* (*Umbelliferae*), are illustrated, as well as drawings of several important medicinal and economic plants. Drawings of the type species of the type genus of most of the larger families are also included.

The illustrations are mostly my own work, and in the general sketch of the plant, perspective has as a rule been neglected in order to show clearly the shapes of leaves and other features which are of importance for at least the species. In some cases, in order to save time, I have not hesitated to make use of published reliable dissections such as those in Baillon's HISTOIRE DES PLANTES and in Hooker's ICONES PLANTARUM. A few, mostly by Miss S. Ross Craig and the late W. E. Trevithick, published in the FLORA OF WEST TROPICAL AFRICA, are included by kind permission of the Crown Agents. I am also indebted to Miss Mary Grierson, botanical artist in the Kew Herbarium, for the drawing of the remarkable Composite, *Wilkesia gymnoxiphium* A. Gray (Fig. 507), endemic in Hawaii.

A few maps, additional to those in the FAMILIES OF FLOWERING PLANTS, are also included, mostly of natural (homogeneous) genera which seem to lend support to the theory of continental drift, especially with reference to the close relationship of the floras of tropical Africa and tropical America.

The suggested phylogeny of each Order is shown more or less as in that great pre-Darwinian work, Lindley's VEGETABLE KINGDOM. For imitating this no apology is necessary, for Lindley was far ahead of his contemporaries in his ideas with respect to the relationships of flowering plant-families. Under each Order reference is given to my FAMILIES OF FLOWERING PLANTS, 2nd Ed., Vol. I, DICOTYLEDONS (1959).

Many of these notes have been written while engaged with my larger work, THE GENERA OF FLOWERING PLANTS. They are intended mainly for students in order to supplement not only my FAMILIES OF FLOWERING PLANTS, but also Rendle's CLASSIFICATION OF FLOWERING PLANTS, Vol. II (1925), and Lawrence's TAXONOMY OF VASCULAR PLANTS (1951), both of which are based on Engler and Prantl's great work, PFLANZENFAMILIEN. It is not intended to compete with either of these excellent books, which have already provided for English readers a great amount of information about flowering plants, both taxonomic and biological. Its compilation owes a great deal to Bentham and Hooker's classical GENERA PLANTARUM.

As in my KEY TO THE FLOWERING PLANTS OF THE WORLD, I have used for the family name that of the type genus, believing that this practice may in time become general, and as sanctioned by the International Rules of Botanical Nomenclature. For examples, *Papilionaceae* gives place to **Fabaceae**, *Compositae* to **Asteraceae** and *Cruciferae* to **Brassicaceae**.

The phylogenetic system as arranged in my FAMILIES OF FLOWERING PLANTS, 2nd Ed., was the outcome of over 60 years' experience in taxonomic botany in the great herbarium and museums at Kew, besides field work in the Canary Islands, the Pyrenees and in southern and central Africa. My knowledge of the families was immensely increased through preparing the FLORA OF WEST TROPICAL AFRICA, in which I was entirely responsible for descriptions and keys of over 1400 genera and 4660 species of flowering plants (except Orchids), a task which occupied about 11 years.

I am indebted to my former colleague Mr. A. A. Bullock, B.Sc., for allowing me to make use of his MS. list of family names which have been published up to the present, and to Mr. G. Ll. Lucas, B.Sc., for reading the proofs. A very large number of the names, no longer recognised, will be found at the foot of the descriptions of the various families. For example, no less than 26 have been proposed for various tribes of *Rosaceae*, and even quite a number for the most natural of all families, *Asteraceae* (*Compositae*).

The subtitle of this present work, DICOTYLEDONS: Facts and Theory, may evoke criticism from those botanists who have little or no use for phylogeny and who may not even believe in evolution. In Dickens' famous story HARD TIMES, Thomas Gradgrind, the schoolmaster, demanded of his pupils nothing but facts. "Now, what I want is Facts. Teach these boys and girls nothing but Facts. Facts alone are wanted in life. Plant nothing else, and root out everything else." This book, therefore, would no doubt have enraged the worthy Thomas, for it is brimful of Theory, which is of necessity founded on facts. As the late John Parkin wrote long ago, "Taxonomy without phylogeny may be likened to bones without flesh" (NATURE **134**, 553 (1934)).

J. H., Kew, 1969

CONTENTS

INTRODUCTION

Seed plants (*Spermatophyta*) are primarily divided by all botanists into two very distinct groups, **Gymnosperms** and **Angiosperms**. To the former belong the Conifers, which have no true flowers and have naked ovules, and to the latter all those with more or less perfect flowers and in which the ovules are enclosed in a carpel or ovary.

Botanists also agree in dividing these true flowering plants into two main divisions, **Dicotyledons** and **Monocotyledons**, characterised by the number of seed-leaves, or cotyledons as they are termed, the Dicotyledons with two, and the Monocotyledons with only one primary leaf. There are also other important differences between the two groups. In the stem of dicotyledonous plants the vascular bundles are arranged in a circle or circles surrounding the pith (well shown in a cross-section of most trees), but in monocotyledons these bundles are scattered and not in rings. Frequently, but not always, the two groups may be recognised by their leaves; in the former the venation is a network between the nerves which usually spread at an angle from the midrib, and in the latter the nerves and often the veins run parallel with the midrib and margin. This book deals only with **Dicotyledons** as arranged and described in my FAMILIES OF FLOWERING PLANTS, 2nd Ed. (1959).

Classification of Dicotyledons

These have been classified in various ways too numerous to record here in much detail, and like the plants themselves their systematic arrangement has gradually been evolved from a small and crude beginning, like Jack's beanstalk, which was at first a tiny plant. In the very early herbals prominence was given to the habit of growth and their uses to mankind.

It has been claimed that King Solomon was the first "Professor of Botany" because he "spake of trees, from the cedar that is in Lebanon, even unto the hyssop that springeth out of the wall".

Theophrastus[1] (about 370 B.C.) has the greatest claim to be called the "father of botany", for he indicated the essential differences between Dicotyledons and Monocotyledons, and he also recognised that different plants grow in dissimilar habitats, such as woodland, marsh, lake, river and other distinct plant-associations. He had a very clear conception of the mode of formation of annual rings in trees, and even recognised that the head of a member of the *Aster* family (*Asteraceae*) consisted of many

---

[1] For genus named after Theophrastus see Fig. 322.

separate flowers. According to the American botanist, Greene, the different types of insertion of floral members such as hypogynous, perigynous and epigynous were clearly recognised by Theophrastus. Greene translated him as follows:

> Some produce the flower around the (base of the) fruit, as do the grape-vine and olive tree. In the greater portion of plants the fruit thus occupies the centre of the flower. But there are not wanting such as support the flower on the summit of the fruit, as do the pomegranate, apple, and rose, all of which have their seed (ovules) underneath the flower. A few bear the flower on the summit of the seed itself, such as thistles, and all that have their flowers in that manner crowded together.

Greene states further that Theophrastus

> learned this springing of the "flower" from the top of the seed to be characteristic of the whole family of the umbellifers, and a few of the rubiaceous plants that he knew, as well as of the thistles and their kindred. . . . At this juncture the sublime old Greek will appear to have lived before his time by more than two thousand years.

For many centuries after the death of the famous Greek, not a single pure botanist appeared on the scene, though several men wrote about agriculture (Cato, Varro and Virgil) and on medicinal plants (like Dioscorides and Galen). Dioscorides lived about A.D. 64. He was a much travelled physician of Asia Minor, and he compiled a textbook which remained the supreme authority for over sixteen centuries. His work was also mainly concerned with medicinal plants, but he recognised many of the better known natural families. A botanical historian asserts, therefore, that it is propagating fable in place of history to affirm that actual families were first recognised and indicated by any Linnaeus, or Adanson, or Jussieu, of the eighteenth century.

Pliny, a contemporary of Dioscorides, also wrote a HISTORIA NATURALIS (A.D. 77), largely compiled from Greek authors. Thereafter, for more than fourteen centuries there is no botanical history. It was not until the sixteenth century that several herbals were published. Brunfels (1530), Fuchs (1542), Bock (1539) and Lobelius (1576) collected plants in their own countries, wrote careful descriptions, and illustrated them by wood engravings, some of great merit. It was early recognised that some plants had much in common with others, such as species of a genus, and wider resemblances of habit and general appearance led to the recognition of larger groups like the Daisy family, Carrot family, Rushes, Grasses and others.

William Turner[1] is the acknowledged "Father of English Botany". He was the author of several botanical works, and wrote the first ENGLISH

[1] For genus named after Turner see Fig. 183.

HERBAL. The first part of this was published in London in 1551, and the second and third parts in Cologne in 1562 and 1568 respectively. Turner was born in 1512 at Morpeth, a small town a few miles north of Newcastle-on-Tyne, Northumberland.

The (HERBAL) HISTORIA PLANTARUM of Valerius Cordus[1] of Wittenberg showed a great advance and is a landmark in descriptive botany.[2] Cordus was born in 1515 at Simsthausen in Hesse, a village between Marburg and Frankenberg. He was educated at Wittenberg University, Prussia. From there he explored the forests and wild mountain glens of Germany, and discovered many new plants. As a result he wrote a HISTORY OF PLANTS when he was twenty-five years old, in which he described between four and five hundred kinds. This was not published until 1561, seventeen years after his death.

In 1583 there appeared a HISTORY OF PLANTS by a Dutch herbalist, Dodonaeus, whose work later formed the basis of several English herbals. Another outstanding name was that of the Italian, Caesalpino, whose work CONCERNING PLANTS also appeared in 1583. In this the study of plants was for the first time separated from their medical uses, though some of his observations are decidedly quaint. He considered that the location of the "soul" of a plant must be at the junction of the stem and root!

A larger work was John Gerard's HERBALL OF GENERALL HISTORIE OF PLANTES, which appeared in 1597. This was mainly based on Dodonaeus' work mentioned above. The plants were arranged in three books, and "sorted as near as might be in kindred and neighbourhood", though the characters employed were very superficial and mixed up with the uses of the plants to man. The first book was mainly devoted to Grasses, Rushes and bulbous plants.

About the middle of the sixteenth century several botanic gardens were established, at Padua in 1545, at Pisa in 1547 and at Bologna in 1567. Towards the end of the century other countries followed suit, at Leiden in Holland, Montpellier in France and at Heidelberg in Germany. Britain was later in the field, the first being at Oxford in 1621, whilst Kew, at first a royal garden, was not officially established until 1841.

The works of Caspar Bauhin,[3] a Swiss pupil of Fuchs, show a great advance. In his INTRODUCTION TO THE WORLD OF BOTANY, published in 1620, and his CATALOGUE in 1623, genera and species were distinguished by names, and frequently only two were employed to represent the genus and species, though this custom was not generally established until 1753. But

---

[1] For genus named after Cordus see Fig. 410.

[2] For an account of this work see T. A. and M. S. Sprague, The Herbal of Valerius Cordus, J. LINN. SOC. BOT. **52**, 1–113 (1939).

[3] For genus named after Bauhin see Fig. 66.

there was still a complete neglect of flower and fruit characters in the arrangement of the larger groups.

When plants began to be studied for their own sake, it became apparent that they must be related in some way to one another. The least observant botanist of the sixteenth century could not fail to notice that a tree like a laburnum had the same kind of flower and fruit as a herb like a pea. One way was to fix arbitrarily on some single organ. With Lobelius[1] the sign of relationship lay in the leaf, with Caesalpino in the seed and fruit. The non-flowering plants were a great puzzle to the early botanists, for microscopes had not then been invented. Belief in spontaneous growth was almost universal, and even up to the end of the sixteenth century botanists thought that Fungi developed from damp soil. Caesalpino believed that seedless plants were "bred of putrefaction". And it was a very long time before it was realised that plants had sex.

However, the dawn of a new era was at hand. An English botanist, John Ray, arranged plants in a better way than any of his predecessors. He was the first fully to appreciate the importance of the presence of one or two seed-leaves. Ray was born at Black Notley in Essex in 1627, and was educated at Braintree and Cambridge University. His greatest work was his HISTORIA PLANTARUM (History of Plants). The first volume of this was published in 1686, the second in 1687, and the third in 1704. His name is commemorated in the Ray Society of London.

Tournefort[2] (1656–1708) was among the last to classify plants as trees, shrubs, and herbs. He is often referred to as the founder of the *genus*, a group of closely related plants or animals. It is true that generic names had been used before his time, but he was the first to provide them with descriptions and to give them a status distinct from the species, a single kind of plant. This marked an important epoch in the history of botany.

Tournefort was born at Aix, in Provence, in 1656. He studied anatomy and medicine at Montpellier and made botanical journeys in southern France and Spain. In 1683 he was appointed Professor of Botany at the Jardin des Plantes, Paris. In 1694 he published his ELEMENS DE BOTANIQUE, of which the INSTITUTIONES is an enlarged Latin edition. Tournefort's system was based solely on the corolla, and was thus artificial, comparing unfavourably with that of Ray, though many of the classes are identical. In 1700 he was sent on a voyage of scientific exploration to Greece and Asia Minor, and returned in 1702 with large natural history collections, including 1356 new species of plants. The work of describing these collections, together with the strain of his professional and medical duties, proved too arduous, and he died in 1708.

---

[1] For genus named after Lobelius see Fig. 500.

[2] For genus named after Tournefort see Fig. 555.

Camerarius, a German (1665–1721), was the first to show that plants had sex, and he proved in his work entitled DE SEXU PLANTARUM EPISTOLA that pollen is necessary for fertilisation and the formation of seeds.

Carl Linnaeus, the "Father of Modern Botany", has been the most lauded botanist of all time. He was born at Rashult, a small village in Småland, Sweden, in May, 1707. At the age of twenty-one he was put in charge of the botanic garden at Lund as assistant to Professor Rudbeck, whose name he afterwards commemorated in *Rudbeckia*, a well-known genus of *Asteraceae* (*Compositae*).

Later Linnaeus went to Holland, where he was engaged by George Clifford, an Englishman, and wrote an account of his garden. Subsequently he returned to Sweden and wrote numerous botanical works, most famous of which was the SPECIES PLANTARUM, published in 1753. In this he established the custom of using only two names for a plant, instead of a descriptive phrase. For example, for the Bulbous Buttercup, instead of *Ranunculus foliis ovatis serratis, scapo nudo unifloro*, he substituted *Ranunculus bulbosus*. Botanists owe a great deal to him for having so firmly established this practice.

Linnaeus was the author of the SEXUAL SYSTEM, published in 1735. In this were recognised twenty-four classes, determined mainly by the number, or some obvious character of the stamens. The classes were again divided into Orders according to the number of styles. For example, plants included in *Monandria* had only one stamen, in *Diandria* two stamens, in *Triandria* three stamens, and so on up to *Dodecandria* with twelve stamens. The simplicity and convenience of this novel system led to its universal adoption, and it held the field for three-quarters of a century or more.

Linnaeus, himself, did not regard this system as more than a temporary convenience, and proceeded to elaborate a more natural one by which plants should be arranged according to their true relationships. This he did not live long enough to complete, though he carried it out partially in his PHILOSOPHY OF BOTANY, published in 1751. He arranged the genera known to him under sixty-seven Orders, to which he gave names but did not distinguish their characters. Some of them are more or less equivalent to natural groups still recognised, such as Palms (*Arecaceae*), Orchids (*Orchidaceae*), Grasses (*Poaceae*), Cone-bearers (*Coniferae*), Daisy-like plants (*Asteraceae*), Buttercups (*Ranunculaceae*) and Pea-like plants (*Fabaceae*), several of which had been recognised by earlier botanists. Many of his other groups, compared with modern standards, were very artificial.

The name of Linnaeus should perhaps have been commemorated by the most gorgeous flower in the world. But he was a modest man, as nearly all truly great men are, and he was well content to have called after him such a dainty and charming little creeping plant as *Linnaea borealis*, the generic name bestowed by Gronovius. Emerson wrote of this plant:

He saw beneath dim aisles, in odorous beds,
The slight *Linnaea* hang its twin-born heads;
And blessed the monument of the man of flowers,
Which breathes his sweet fame through the northern bowers.

Linnaea borealis is a common plant in Sweden, and it is found in the mountains of Scotland, the pine forests of Norway, the steppes of Siberia, and across the colder parts of North America, especially in the region of the Great Lakes.

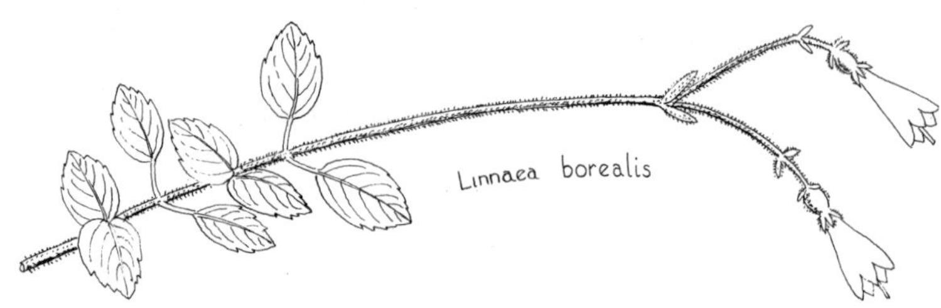

Linnaeus dedicated his CRITICA BOTANICA (1737) to Dillenius as follows (translation):

To the foremost botanist of this age

JO. JAC. DILLENIUS[1]
Doctor of Medicine

Sherardian Professor of Botany in the University of Oxford, Fellow of the Imperial Academy of Natural Science, and of the Royal Society,

Carolus Linnaeus
gives greeting.

---

[1] John James Dillenius was born at Darmstadt in 1687 and was educated at the University of Giessen. In 1719 he published his CATALOGUS PLANTARUM SPONTE CIRCA GISSAM NASCENTIUM, with 16 plates drawn by the author. This attracted much attention, and Dillenius was persuaded by Consul William Sherard to come to England in August 1721. He stayed with William Sherard at Oxford and afterwards in London, and with James Sherard, the Consul's brother, at Eltham, in Kent. His first work in England was the preparation of the edition of Ray's SYNOPSIS STIRPIUM BRITANNICARUM in which he included 24 plates of rare plants.

In 1728 Consul Sherard died, bequeathing his herbarium and library and £3000 to the university of Oxford, to provide a salary for the professor of botany at Oxford, on condition that Dillenius should be the first to be appointed. In 1732 Dillenius published his HORTUS ELTHAMENSIS illustrated by 417 excellent drawings etched by himself, of which Linnaeus wrote "est opus botanicum quo absolutius mundum non vidit". In 1735 Linnaeus spent a month with him at Oxford, after which he dedicated his CRITICA BOTANICA to him as stated above. Dillenius died at the age of 63, and Linnaeus named the genus *Dillenia* in his honour.

Here is a copy of the first description of the genus named after him:

Linnaea. Authore Clariss. Dn. Gronovio.[1]

Cal: Perianthium duplex: P. fructus tetraphyllum: foliolis duobus oppositis, minimis, acutis: reliquis duobus ellipticis, concavis, echinatis, erectis, germen amplectentibus, conniventibus, persistentibus.

P. Floris germini insidens, monophyllum, quinquepartitum, erectum, angustum, acutum.

Cor. monopetala, conica, semiquinquefida, obtusa, fere aequalis, calyce floris duplo major.

Stam: Filamenta quatuor, subulata, fundo corollae inserta; quorum duo minima, duo proxima longiora, corolla breviora. Antherae simplices.

Pist. Germen subrotundum, infra receptaculum floris. Stylus filiformis, rectus, longitudine corollae, ad alterum latus inclinatus. Stigma globosum.

Per. Capsula ovata, glabra, trilocularis, calyce fructus tecta.

Sem. solitaria, subrotunda.

After the death of Linnaeus in 1778, the centre of botanical activity was switched from Sweden to France, where a further advance was soon made in the development of a more natural system. Bernard de Jussieu, Professor and Demonstrator of Botany at the royal garden, adopted the later views of Linnaeus, but continually found it necessary to introduce improvements. So that the system of Linnaeus became little by little the system of Jussieu. Like many other clever but modest men, however, he published nothing about his innovations. This was left to his nephew, Antoine Laurent de Jussieu, who prefaced his own scheme in 1789 by that of his uncle. The nephew introduced many improvements, and his GENERA OF PLANTS is the first system which could claim to be more or less natural. The younger Jussieu arranged plants into fifteen classes, in the first of which he included those without seed-leaves. Among these were the non-flowering kinds, such as Toadstools, Seaweeds, Liverworts, Mosses and Ferns. He divided the remainder into Monocotyledons and Dicotyledons. He subdivided both groups firstly on the presence, absence, or union of the petals, and secondly on the relative position of the floral parts, especially the stamens in relation to the ovary. It is in this system that the terms hypogynous (below the ovary), perigynous (around the ovary) and epigynous (above the ovary), become so conspicuous. Jussieu's system has been more or less the basis for all the systems since proposed.

Next to take the field was a Scotsman, Robert Brown, who solved many points in regard to the structure of the flower and seed. This induced Sir Joseph Hooker, a famous director of Kew, and a close friend of Darwin, to rank Brown second only to Jussieu and to Ray as the expositor of the natural system of plants. Born at Montrose, Scotland, in 1773, Brown was

---

[1] J. F. Gronovius, author of FLORA ORIENTALIS (1755).

educated at Aberdeen and Edinburgh universities. In 1801 he went as naturalist on the expedition under Captain Flinders to Australia, and returned in 1805 with a large collection of plants, representing nearly 4000 species. In 1810 he became librarian to Sir Joseph Banks, a long-time president of the Royal Society, who on his death in 1820 bequeathed to Brown for life the use of his library and collections. In 1827 these were transferred to the British Museum, and Brown went with them as Keeper of the Department of Botany, a post he held until his death in 1858.

Besides his PRODROMUS FLORAE NOVAE HOLLANDIAE (1810), containing descriptions of Australian plants collected by Banks and Solander on Captain Cook's first voyage around the world in 1768–71 and his own collections, Brown published a paper in 1827 entitled THE FEMALE FLOWER IN *Cycadaceae* AND *Coniferae*, in which he announced the important discovery of the distinction between Angiosperms and Gymnosperms.

Like that of the Hookers, the family name of de Candolle occupies a large place in the history of taxonomic botany. A. P. de Candolle's classic work, THÉORIE ÉLÉMENTAIRE DE LA BOTANIQUE, was published in Paris in 1813. He showed that the relationships of plants were best ascertained by the comparative study of the structure and development of their organs (morphology) and not by their functions (physiology), and he defined the principles of a natural system.

De Candolle's famous PRODROMUS SYSTEMATIS NATURALIS REGNI VEGETABILIS was published in Paris from 1824 to 1873. Most of the families were the work of A. P. de Candolle[1] and his son Alphonse, who continued the work after his father's death. It is very rare that a son carries on the work of his father in natural science. The PRODROMUS contained descriptions of most of the known species of Dicotyledons and Gymnosperms, and was a monumental work which has been indispensable to taxonomists ever since.

Further attempts were soon made to improve de Candolle's system. John Lindley,[2] Professor of Botany at University College, London, in 1830 published many original ideas. In Germany Stephan Endlicher[2] added modifications in his GENERA OF PLANTS (1836–40), followed by Eichler[2] (1883). Instead of commencing with families in which both sepals and petals are present, however, they began with a group without petals. In this way they broke away from the Jussieu-de Candolle system, and this idea (a mistaken one from our point of view of evolutionary sequence) was later further elaborated by another great German botanist, Adolf Engler (with K. Prantl), in a comprehensive work entitled DIE NATÜRLICHEN PFLANZENFAMILIEN (The Natural Families of Plants), profusely illustrated and written in German.

---

[1] For genus named after de Candolle see Fig. 37.

[2] More detailed accounts of Lindley, Endlicher and Eichler are given in my FAMILIES OF FLOWERING PLANTS, 2nd Ed. **1**, 14.

The Jussieu-de Candolle system was adhered to, with many improvements, however, by the Kew botanists G. Bentham and J. D. Hooker in their GENERA PLANTARUM, published between the years 1862–80. This great work contains Latin descriptions of all the families and genera known up to the time of publication of the various parts, which are arranged in three volumes. It is regarded as a classic and has been much used throughout the world.

In the GENERA PLANTARUM the Dicotyledons were divided into several large groups mainly determined by one or only a few characters. Thus *Polypetalae* had flowers with free petals, *Gamopetalae* with united petals and *Apetalae* without petals. The *Polypetalae* were then subdivided into smaller groups, those with a hypogynous type of flower, *Thalamiflorae* (examples *Ranunculaceae* and *Magnoliaceae*), those with a disk, *Disciflorae* (examples *Rutaceae* and *Celastraceae*) and those with a perigynous type of flower, *Calyciflorae* (examples *Rosaceae*, *Leguminosae* (*sensu lato*) and *Myrtaceae*). The *Gamopetalae* were subdivided into series, those with inferior ovary and those with superior ovary, and in a similar manner the *Apetalae*.

These divisions did not result in a natural system because certain families were widely separated though clearly more or less closely related. For example, *Caryophyllaceae* (*Polypetalae*), with free petals, are related to *Gentianaceae* and *Primulaceae* (*Gamopetalae*), with united petals, and to *Polygonaceae* (*Apetalae*), without petals.

H. Baillon's HISTOIRE DES PLANTES (1867–95), a work of thirteen volumes, contains descriptions of the families and many genera of flowering plants. He took a very broad view of families; for example he included in *Ericaceae* the *Vacciniaceae*, *Clethraceae*, *Epacridaceae*, *Empetraceae*, *Stypheliaceae*, *Pyrolaceae*, *Monotropaceae*, *Diapensiaceae*, *Lennoaceae*. In *Rubiaceae* he even included *Caprifoliaceae* and *Adoxaceae* (the last mentioned with a ?), all of which were or have been regarded subsequently as separate and distinct families. Its chief merits, however, are the splendid illustrations with accurate dissections drawn by Faguet, some of which I have made use of in the present book. He also published monographs on *Euphorbiaceae* and *Buxaceae*, etc., accompanied by beautifully reproduced plates. Baillon was born at Calais in 1827 and died in 1895.

The German system of Engler and Prantl (1887–98), mentioned above, more or less reversed the sequence of that of Bentham and Hooker, for the groups of Dicotyledons without petals (*Apetalae*); some with catkins ("Amentiferae") were placed first, those with free petals next, and finally those with united petals at the top of the scale, ending with the large family *Asteraceae* (*Compositae*). And the Monocotyledons preceded the Dicotyledons.

Harvey Gibson, in his OUTLINES OF THE HISTORY OF BOTANY (1919), said of the Engler and Prantl system:

I am expressing merely my own personal opinion; still I have no hesitation in prophesying that in years to come botanists will regard Engler's system as having done as much to retard the attainment of a true phylogenetic classification of Angiosperms as Linnaeus' SEXUAL SYSTEM retarded a natural classification, as it was then understood in the eighteenth century.

In my FAMILIES OF FLOWERING PLANTS, the hypogynous flower with free sepals and petals, free stamens and free carpels, was considered to be the most primitive type of present-day flowering plants. After much study and practical work in the naming and description of many plants from all over the world, I came to the conclusion that there seem to be two main lines of evolution of the Dicotyledons, one fundamentally woody, which I called **Lignosae**, and the other fundamentally herbaceous, **Herbaceae**. I would stress the word fundamental, for there are many herbs amongst the **Lignosae**, though they have been clearly derived from woody ancestors, for example in *Fabaceae* (*Papilionaceae*), and some in *Rosaceae* and *Rubiaceae*. But there are very few woody plants in the **Herbaceae**.

The **Lignosae** begin with the Magnolia family, *Magnoliaceae*, and terminate in an evolutionary sense with the *Verbena* family, *Verbenaceae*, which indeed includes one of the most durable timbers, Teak. In between these extremes in an ascending series are, to mention only a few of the larger families, *Annonaceae*, *Dilleniaceae*, *Flacourtiaceae*, *Rosaceae*, *Leguminosae* (in the broader sense), *Araliaceae*, *Moraceae*, *Urticaceae*, *Tiliaceae*, *Euphorbiaceae*, *Ericaceae*, *Myrtaceae*, *Rutaceae*, *Apocynaceae*, *Rubiaceae*, *Bignoniaceae*, *Ehretiaceae* and *Verbenaceae*. Some of these families have flowers with both free and united petals, or without them, and often with both superior and inferior ovaries.

The **Herbaceae** commence with the family *Paeoniaceae*, the Hellebores (*Helleboraceae*), and Buttercups (*Ranunculaceae*), followed by the Poppy family (*Papaveraceae*), the Crucifers (*Brassicaceae*), then *Caryophyllaceae*, *Gentianaceae*, *Saxifragaceae*, *Apiaceae* (*Umbelliferae*) *Campanulaceae*, *Asteraceae* (*Compositae*), *Solanaceae* and *Scrophulariaceae*, and end with the Dead-nettle family, *Lamiaceae* (*Labiatae*). There are relatively few woody or arborescent plants in this phylum, though some may be so due to convergent evolution from the **Lignosae**, especially in the last few climax families.

Certain families of the **Lignosae** contain many important economic plants, besides numerous lovely flowering trees and shrubs. To *Rosaceae* belong the Apple, Pear, Plum, Apricot, Strawberry, Blackberry, Raspberry, Loquat and others, besides many beautiful garden plants, Roses, etc. Closely related to *Rosaceae* is the large Order *Leguminosae*, which is divided into three separate families, *Caesalpiniaceae*, *Mimosaceae* and *Fabaceae* (*Papilionaceae*); the first two of these contain many important timber trees nearly all in the tropics, the last named food and forage plants mostly in more temperate regions, such as the garden Pea, *Pisum sativum*, the Broad

Bean, *Vicia faba*, the Ground Nut, *Arachis hypogaea*, Soy Bean, *Glycine max* and the Clovers, *Trifolium* spp. Dyes and insecticides are also obtained from these families, and many lovely garden plants such as *Wisteria*, *Laburnum*, Lupins, Sweet Peas, etc.

The Oak family, *Fagaceae*, has been of great importance to man, the genera *Quercus* (Oak) and *Fagus* (Beech) providing valuable timbers, as also the related walnut family, *Juglandaceae*. *Sterculiaceae* provides the world with Cocoa, *Theobroma cacaoa*, and *Malvaceae*, Cotton from the seeds of *Gossypium*. The large family *Euphorbiaceae* contains the most valuable rubber plant, *Hevea brasiliensis*, native of Brazil and cultivated mainly in Malaya, and the Castor Oil plant, *Ricinus communis*. The Tea family, *Theaceae*, is essential to the comfort and social life of many peoples, tea being the dried leaves of *Camellia chinensis*, which genus provides some lovely flowering shrubs. The Grape Vine, with all the various wines produced from its fruits, is *Vitis vinifera* (*Vitaceae*), to which genus the lovely Virginia Creeper also belongs.

Especially important to mankind is the Rue family, *Rutaceae*, with the Orange, Lemon, Grapefruit and Lime. Mahogany, one of the most valuable timbers, is *Swietenia mahagoni*, belonging to the large tropical family *Meliaceae*; and to *Anacardiaceae* belongs the Mango, *Mangifera indica*. The Ashes, important timber trees, are species of *Fraxinus*, and the Olive, a valuable commodity in dry Mediterranean countries, is the fruit of *Olea europaea*, family *Oleaceae*. *Apocynaceae* and *Asclepiadaceae* have very few plants of economic importance, but many are highly ornamental and of great morphological interest. *Rubiaceae* is a vast tropical family with only a few species of economic importance, but amongst these few are Coffee, *Coffea arabica* and other spp., and Quinine, *Cinchona* spp., while *Verbenaceae* provide Teak, *Tectona grandis*, the most important hard-wooded tree of Indo-Malaya.

The fundamentally herbaceous phylum, **Herbaceae**, is not so important from an economic point of view, though it provides many decorative plants of great value to horticulture. The Poppy family (*Papaveraceae*) may be mentioned, the Opium Poppy being *Papaver somniferum*, with its significant specific name. The family *Brassicaceae* (*Cruciferae*) has several food plants such as the Cabbage, *Brassica oleracea*, the Cauliflower, the Turnip, *Brassica rapa*, and Watercress, *Nasturtium*, and numerous lovely garden plants such as the Wallflower, *Cheiranthus cheiri*. *Gentianaceae* have many beautiful rock-garden plants, *Gentiana* spp., as also *Primulaceae*, with many lovely species of *Primula* and *Androsace*.

The more climax families of herbs are the Hemlocks, *Apiaceae* (*Umbelliferae*), to which belong Celery, *Apium graveolens*, the Carrot, *Daucus carota*, Parsnip, *Peucedanum sativum*, and Parsley, *Petroselinum crispum*. The Aster family, *Asteraceae* (*Compositae*) is the largest of all, but contains relatively few plants that are medicinal or edible. The most important are the Jerusalem Artichoke, *Helianthus tuberosus*, the Globe Artichoke, *Cynara scolymus*,

Chicory, *Cichorium intybus*, Lettuce, *Lactuca scariola*, Sunflower, *Helianthus annuus* (seeds), and many decorative plants such as the *Chrysanthemum*, *Dahlia* and *Aster*.

Finally, higher up in the evolutionary scale is the Potato family, *Solanaceae*, the Potato, *Solanum tuberosum*; Tomato, *Lycopersicum esculentum*; medicinal plants, the Deadly Nightshade, *Atropa belladonna*, the Henbane, *Hyoscyamus niger*; and of special importance to some men and women the Tobacco plant, *Nicotiana tabacum*. Scented plants and some culinary herbs belong to the completely climax family *Lamiaceae* (*Labiatae*).

The Most Primitive Group of Angiosperms (Flowering Plants)

About the beginning of this century there was much speculation as to whether the catkin-bearers or "Amentiferae", on the one hand, or the *Magnoliaceae*, on the other, should be regarded as the more primitive of angiospermous flowering plants. As already noted the former were placed first in the Engler and Prantl system, the latter in the forefront by Bentham and Hooker, following more or less the example of de Candolle in his monumental PRODROMUS.

An American botanist, Bessey, as early as 1897, was perhaps the first to object to the theory on which Engler and Prantl's system was based. Also H. Hallier, of Hamburg, wrote many papers in order to show that Engler was mistaken in some of his ideas. But the most convincing research into the question in this country fell to the lot of the late E. A. N. Arber and J. Parkin, who announced the results of their investigations before the Fellows of the Linnean Society of London in 1907 in a paper entitled "The Origin of Angiosperms" (J. LINN. SOC. BOT. **38**, 29). These two Cambridge botanists came to the conclusion that the family *Magnoliaceae* represents the most primitive of the existing families of Angiosperms, and that plants without petals, such as the Oaks and Birches, the Nettles, etc., were really reduced types derived from ancestors which possessed petals, and that therefore they were not primitive.

Little more was done in this country until the present author took up the task of attempting to build up a new and more natural system, beginning with the *Magnoliaceae* and related families. For this purpose every genus and species of all families in the Kew Herbarium which seemed to be at all primitive were carefully examined, and a preliminary account was published in the KEW BULLETIN 1924, 114. I feel confident that a botanist who could divest himself of any theory which he might hold already and make a similar study would probably soon see the fallacy of placing the Monocotyledons before the Dicotyledons, as Engler did, and of placing the highly evolved *Poaceae* (*Gramineae*) at the very beginning. And he might also come to the conclusion that the so-called "Amentiferae" would find their rightful place as reduced representatives of *Rosaceae*, *Hamamelidaceae* and other related families.

LINEAR SEQUENCE OF ORDERS
(to be read from below upwards)

A "bird's eye view" of the author's phylogenetic system showing the sequence of the larger Orders and the chief family represented in each of them. A row of asterisks indicates a break in affinity and a more or less climax group from which no further evolution is apparent.

In the Preface to my FAMILIES OF FLOWERING PLANTS (p. viii), I suggested that even widely experienced botanists might find some difficulty in tracing actual relationship between any of the groups belonging to the two divisions, **Lignosae** and **Herbaceae**. After much further research connected with my GENERA OF FLOWERING PLANTS, I remain convinced that the tangle of families, especially as arranged in the latest SYLLABUS of the Engler and Prantl system (12th Ed., 1964), in which the *Archichlamydeae* and *Sympetalae* (*Metachlamydeae*) are still maintained as major groups, are more logically sorted out as shown in this list.

Indeed, an enquiring student might well ask his tutor to point out which families in the two columns are actually related, apart from one or two at the top of the lists, some of which are more likely due to parallel or convergent evolution, such as *Verbenaceae* and *Lamiaceae* (*Labiatae*), and *Araliaceae* and *Apiaceae* (*Umbelliferae*), to take the most obvious examples. For instance, where would he place in the first column (**Lignosae**) the *Brassicaceae* (*Cruciferae*), the *Caryophyllaceae*, the *Gentianaceae* and *Primulaceae* (the latter surely not with *Myrsinaceae*), the *Saxifragaceae* (surely not with *Cunoniaceae*), the *Campanulaceae* and *Asteraceae* (*Compositae*), the *Geraniaceae* (not with *Euphorbiaceae*), and the *Boraginaceae* (*sensu stricto*)?

VERBENALES (*Verbenaceae*)
* * * * *
BIGNONIALES (*Bignoniaceae*)
* * * * *
RUBIALES (*Rubiaceae*)
(*Asclepiadaceae*) ←
APOCYNALES (*Apocynaceae*)
LOGANIALES (*Loganiaceae*)
* * * * *
SAPINDALES (*Sapindaceae*)
MELIALES (*Meliaceae*)
RUTALES (*Rutaceae*)
* * * * *
EBENALES (*Sapotaceae*)
MYRSINALES (*Myrsinaceae*)
RHAMNALES (*Rhamnaceae*)
* * * * *
SANTALALES (*Loranthaceae*)
OLACALES (*Olacaceae*)
CELASTRALES (*Celastraceae*)
* * * * *
MYRTALES (*Myrtaceae*)
GUTTIFERALES (*Hypericaceae*)
* * * * *
ERICALES (*Ericaceae*)
OCHNALES (*Ochnaceae*)
THEALES (*Theaceae*)
* * * * *
EUPHORBIALES (*Euphorbiaceae*)
* * * * *
MALVALES (*Malvaceae*)
TILIALES (*Tiliaceae*)
* * * * *
CACTALES (*Cactaceae*)
* * * * *
CUCURBITALES (*Cucurbitaceae*)
PASSIFLORALES (*Passifloraceae*)
LOASALES (*Turneraceae*)
* * * * *
POLYGALALES (*Polygalaceae*)
VIOLALES (*Violaceae*)
CAPPARIDALES (*Capparidaceae*)
PITTOSPORALES (*Pittosporaceae*)
* * * * *
PROTEALES (*Proteaceae*)
THYMELAEALES (*Thymelaeaceae*)
BIXALES (*Flacourtiaceae*)
* * * * * (*Urticaceae*) ←
URTICALES (*Moraceae*)
* * * * *
CASUARINALES (*Casuarinaceae*)
FAGALES (*Fagaceae*)
HAMAMELIDALES (*Hamamelidaceae*)
* * * * * (*Araliaceae*) ←
ARALIALES (*Cornaceae*)
CUNONIALES (*Cunoniaceae*)
(*Fabaceae*) ←
* * * * * (*Mimosaceae*) ←
LEGUMINALES (*Caesalpiniaceae*)
ROSALES (*Rosaceae*)
DILLENIALES (*Dilleniaceae*)
* * * * *
LAURALES (*Lauraceae*)
ANNONALES (*Annonaceae*)
MAGNOLIALES (*Magnoliaceae*)
LIGNOSAE (fundamentally woody)

LAMIALES (*Lamiaceae*)
BORAGINALES (*Boraginaceae*)
POLEMONIALES (*Polemoniaceae*)
GERANIALES (*Geraniaceae*)
* * * * *
PERSONALES (*Scrophulariaceae*)
SOLANALES (*Solanaceae*)
ASTERALES (*Asteraceae*)
* * * * *
GOODENIALES (*Goodeniaceae*)
CAMPANALES (*Campanulaceae*)
* * * * *
VALERIANALES (*Valerianaceae*)
* * * * *
UMBELLALES (*Apiaceae*)
SARRACENIALES (*Sarraceniaceae*)
SAXIFRAGALES (*Saxifragaceae, sensu herbaceo*)
* * * * *
PLANTAGINALES (*Plantaginaceae*)
PRIMULALES (*Primulaceae*)
GENTIANALES (*Gentianaceae*)
ONAGRALES (*Onagraceae*)
* * * * *
CHENOPODIALES (*Chenopodiaceae*)
POLYGONALES (*Polygonaceae*)
CARYOPHYLLALES (*Caryophyllaceae*)
* * * * *
RESEDALES (*Resedaceae*)
CRUCIALES (*Brassicaceae*)
RHOEADALES (*Papaveraceae*)
* * * * *
PIPERALES (*Piperaceae*)
ARISTOLOCHIALES (*Aristolochiaceae*)
BERBERIDALES (*Menispermaceae*)
(*Ranunculaceae*) ←
RANALES (*Helleboraceae*)
HERBACEAE (fundamentally herbaceous)

GRAMINALES (*Poaceae*)
CYPERALES (*Cyperaceae*)
JUNCALES (*Juncaceae*)
* * * * *
ORCHIDALES (*Orchidaceae*)
BURMANNIALES (*Burmanniaceae*)
HAEMODORALES (*Haemodoraceae*)
* * * * *
CYCLANTHALES (*Cyclanthaceae*)
PANDANALES (*Pandaceae*)
* * * * *
PALMALES (*Arecaceae*)
* * * * *
AGAVALES (*Agavaceae*)
* * * * *
DIOSCOREALES (*Dioscoreaceae*)
* * * * *
IRIDALES (*Iridaceae*)
AMARYLLIDALES (*Amaryllidaceae*)
* * * * *
TYPHALES (*Typhaceae*)
ARALES (*Araceae*)
ALSTROEMERIALES (*Alstroemeriaceae*)
LILIALES (*Liliaceae*)
* * * * *
ZINGIBERALES (*Zingiberaceae*)
BROMELIALES (*Bromeliaceae*)
* * * * *
ERIOCAULALES (*Eriocaulaceae*)
XYRIDALES (*Xyridaceae*)
COMMELINALES (*Commelinaceae*)
* * * * *
NAJADALES (*Najadaceae*)
POTAMOGETONALES (*Potamogetonaceae*)
APONOGETONALES (*Aponogetonaceae*)
JUNCAGINALES (*Juncaginaceae*)
TRIURIDALES (*Triuridaceae*)
ALISMATALES (*Alismataceae*)
BUTOMALES (*Butomaceae*)

Dicotyledons **Monocotyledons**

HYPOTHETICAL PROANGIOSPERMS

Phylum I

LIGNOSAE

Order 1. MAGNOLIALES

(*Fam. Fl. Pl.* **1**, 122)[1]

The family **Magnoliaceae**, as already stated, is here regarded as being the most ancient of living Angiosperms. Not only its floral structure, but its geographical distribution seem to support this view. The headquarters of the family is the Himalaya-Burma-Yunnan region, which perhaps has been the sanctuary of some of the angiospermous flora, where they were spared the devastation of successive ice ages. In this family the large sepals and petals are little differentiated from each other; the stamens are numerous, and, like the free carpels, are spirally arranged on a usually elongated cone-like axis. In addition *Magnoliaceae* are trees and shrubs. Another characteristic, and one which seems to run throughout this group, is the kind of stoma, which is of the so-called "Rubiaceous" type, i.e. the guard-cells are accompanied by special subsidiary cells parallel to the pore (Fig. 1 **B**–**D**). No

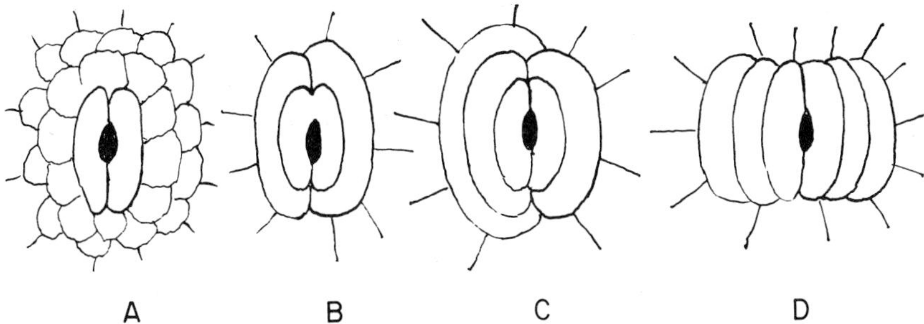

Fig. 1. Types of stomata: **A**, Ranunculaceous. **B**–**D**, Magnoliaceous and rubiaceous (after Solereder).

such subsidiary cells occur in the RANALES (*sensu stricto*), an equally primitive group, even in the few softly woody members such as *Clematis*. This difference in such vital organs as stomata may be of some phylogenetic importance in these more primitive families, associated as it is with a difference in habit.

The genera of *Magnoliaceae* show very little range in floral structure. In tribe *Magnolieae* the anthers are introrse, and the fruits are not winged; in

---

[1] Under each Order heading there will be a reference to the corresponding section in the 2nd Edition of FAMILIES OF FLOWERING PLANTS. This title will be abbreviated for convenience to *Fam. Fl. Pl.* The figure **1** or **2** will indicate volume number, and the final figures will show the relevant pages.

FIG. 2. The Himalayan *Magnolia pterocarpa* Roxb. (*Magnoliaceae*) is perhaps the most ancient species of living angiospermous flowering plants; note the gradual reduction of the leaves towards the floral parts, indicated by the scars. **A**, the free carpels in fruit. **B**, separate carpel with seed hanging by a thread.

Liriodendreae the anthers are extrorse, and the fruits are winged. The type genus *Magnolia* occurs mainly in the Himalaya-China-Japan regions of Asia, and in the eastern states of North America. The species are trees with evergreen or deciduous entire leaves, mostly bisexual and usually terminal flowers, 9 or more sepals and petals, sometimes not clearly differentiated, numerous spirally arranged introrse stamens, numerous carpels with 2 ovules in each (or rarely 4 or 3 in the lower carpels), in fruit dehiscent along the dorsal suture; seeds 1 or 2 in each carpel, hanging by elastic-like threads. Type species *M. virginiana* Linn., eastern United States of North America (Fig. 3).

Elmerrillia and *Michelia* have axillary flowers, the former with a sessile gynoecium and introrse anthers, the latter with a stipitate gynoecium and latrorse or sublatrorse anthers. In tribe *Magnolieae* the genus *Kmeria* stands out in having unisexual flowers. The usual dehiscence of the carpels in this tribe is by a split along the dorsal suture, but in *Talauma* (Fig. 4) it is circumscissile, i.e. by a circular split, the upper portion falling away and leaving the persistent base with the seeds suspended from the main axis. *Aromadendron* has a very advanced type of gynoecium; the carpels are concrescent, fleshy and indehiscent, and the ovules in each are reduced to 2.

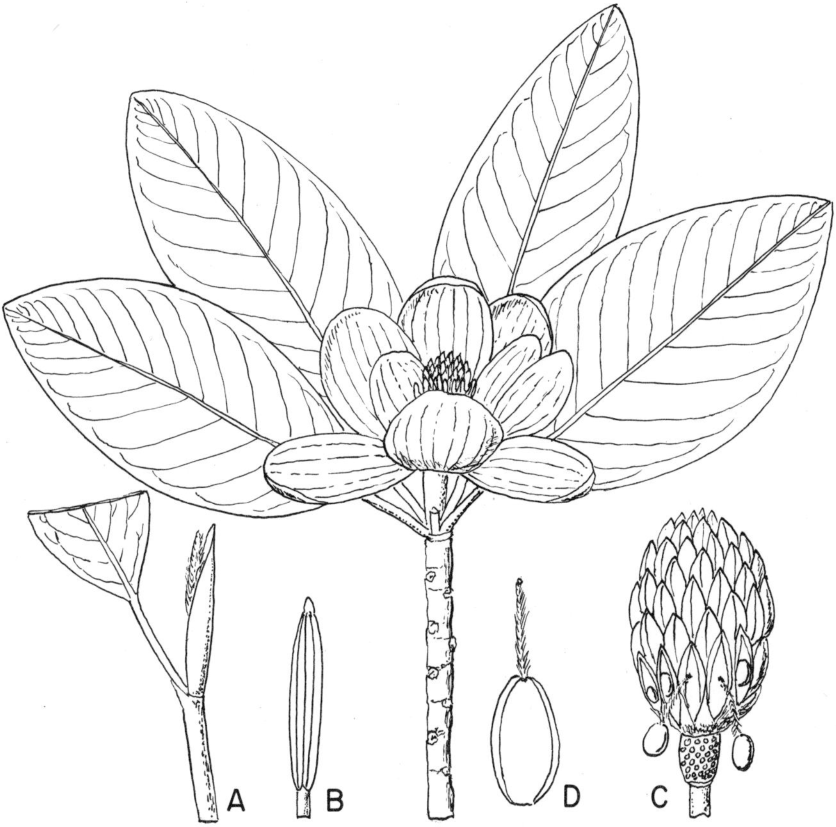

FIG. 3. *Magnolia virginiana* Linn., eastern United States, the type species of the type genus of *Magnoliaceae*. **A**, part of leaf showing stipules. **B**, stamen. **C**, carpels in fruit, showing seeds hanging by threads. **D**, seed.

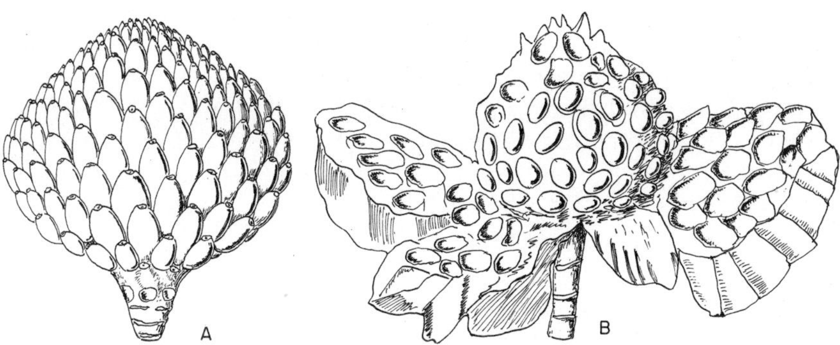

FIG. 4. **A**, carpels of *Talauma ovata* A. St. Hil (*T. fragrantissima* Hook.) (*Magnoliaceae*), Brazil. **B**, the mass opened out showing the seeds partly immersed in the axis.

In *Pachylarnax* (Fig. 5) the carpels are also concrescent, but they open completely along their abaxial suture and partially also along their line of junction. The fruit of this genus is thus equivalent to a woody loculicidal capsule, so common in many more advanced families.

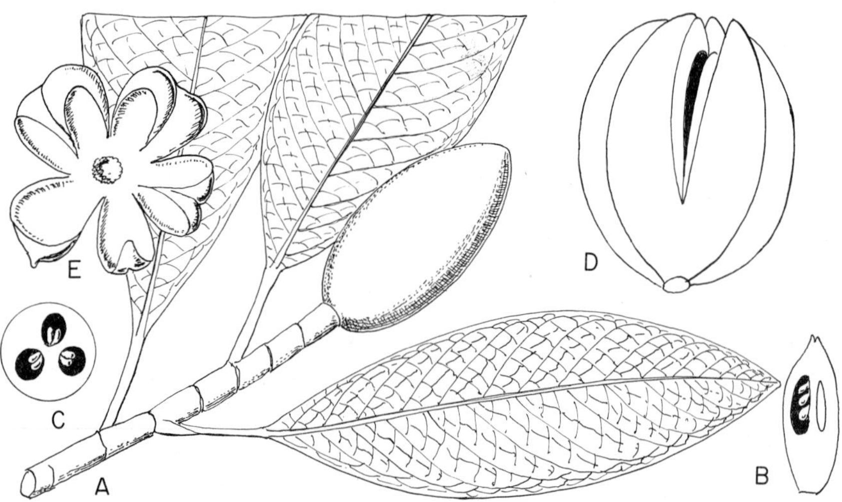

FIG. 5. The genus *Pachylarnax* (*P. pleiocarpa* Dandy), Assam, shown here, is unique in the family *Magnoliaceae* in having a syncarpous, dehiscent fruit. **A**, leaves and flower-bud. **B**, vertical section of ovary. **C**, transverse section of the same. **D**, fruit. **E**, open fruit.

There is only one genus of tribe *Liriodendreae*, namely *Liriodendron* (Fig. 6), and the two known species are so much alike that for a long time they were considered to be the same, though very widely separated geographically, one in the S.E. states of North America, the other in far away central China. No doubt their long isolation accounts for the slight differences observable. There are several other examples of this interesting connection between the floras of the S.E. states of North America and eastern Asia, a subject which has engaged the attention of many botanists.

Certain anatomical characters are common to all *Magnoliaceae*; these are secretory cells, wood prosenchyma with bordered pits, tendency to scalariform perforations in the vessels; the occurrence of diaphragms of stone-cells in the pith; no l-celled hairs or glandular hairs; if present the hairs consist of one row of cells, and the character of the stomata has already been mentioned.

The family is of very little economic importance, apart from its horticultural ornamental value. The wood of *Magnolia grandiflora* Linn., a native of the United States of North America, is known as "Bull Bay", and is used for cabinet and joinery work, though the supply has rapidly diminished.

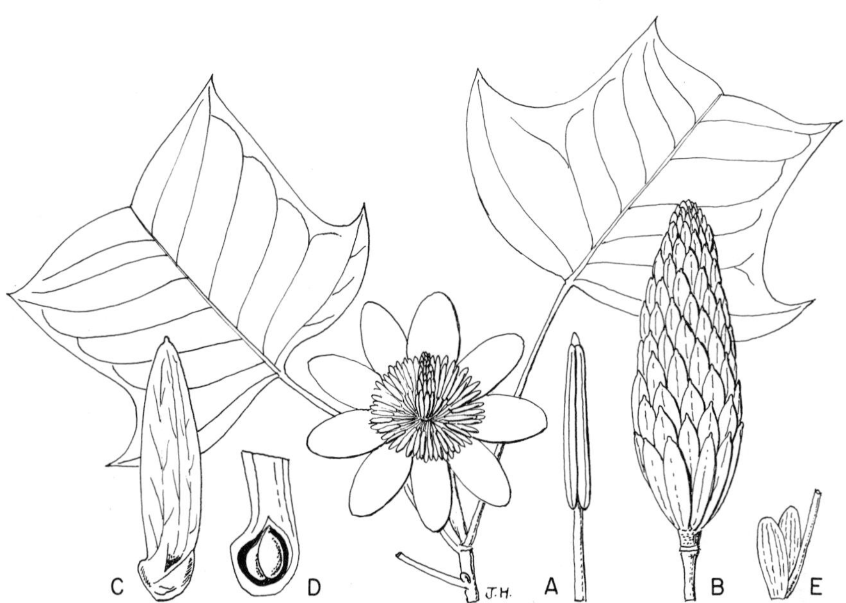

FIG. 6. The Chinese species of Tulip tree, *Liriodendron chinense* Sargent (*Magnoliaceae*). The second known species, *L. tulipifera* Linn., occurs in the far away eastern United States of North America. **A**, stamen. **B**, gynoecium. **C**, one carpel. **D**, part of same showing ovules. **E**, stipules (orig.).

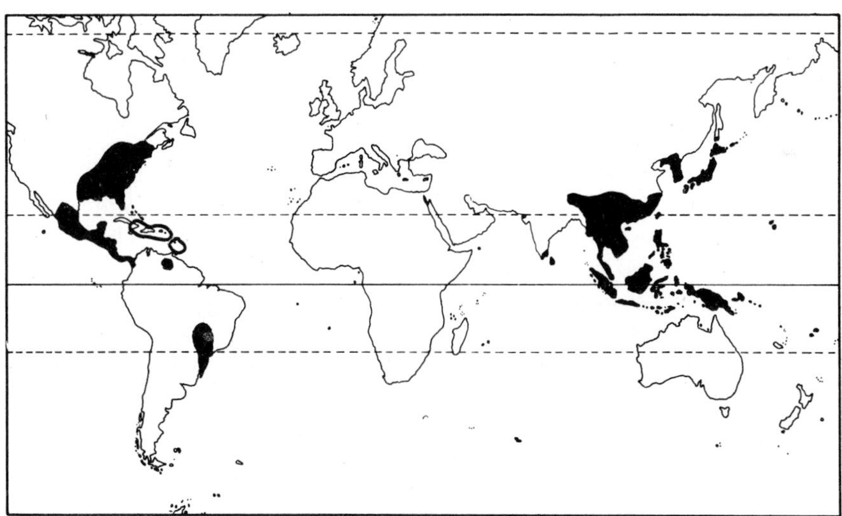

MAP 1. The distribution of *Magnoliaceae* is shown above. Note the discontinuous range in widely separated areas, usually denoting an ancient family. Before successive ages destroyed them, *Magnoliaceae* occurred right across what is now the temperate region of the Northern Hemisphere. Later evolved families have usually a more continuous distribution. (Repeated from my FAMILIES OF FLOWERING PLANTS.)

The Tulip Tree, *Liriodendron tulipifera* Linn., so called because the flowers look like small tulips, is highly ornamental, the leaves becoming yellow in autumn. Its wood is free from knots, is easy to work and takes paint and polish well.

The several families which are closely related to the *Magnoliaceae* are either considerably more advanced (such as *Dilleniaceae*), or more reduced in floral structure.

The single genus *Illicium* of **Illiciaceae**, formerly included in *Magnoliaceae*, has an interesting distribution closely resembling that of *Magnolia* and *Liriodendron*, but is more subtropical. (For map see FAMILIES OF FLOWERING PLANTS, 2nd Ed. **1**, 125.) Its species are very closely related and must be of great age phylogenetically. It occurs in the Northern Hemisphere from Assam to Japan and Korea and south to Borneo in the Old World, and in America in Florida, Mexico and the West Indies. The species are small trees and shrubs with alternate, simple, entire, pinnately nerved leaves without stipules; flowers bisexual, axillary or supra-axillary, rarely on the main stem; sepals and petals numerous to 7, several-seriate, imbricate, inner gradually larger; stamens numerous to 4; carpels 21–5, free and in a single whorl; ovule 1, near the base; fruits follicular, dehiscing adaxially; seeds glossy, with copious endosperm and minute embryo.

Chinese Star Anise, the fruits and seeds of a small evergreen tree in south China, *Illicium verum* Hook. f. (Fig. 7), are aromatic, with a flavour similar to Anise, *Pimpinella anisum* Linn. (*Apiaceae*), the oil from both being used as flavouring agent and carminative.

Winteraceae[1] have carpels in a single whorl, or they are reduced to only one; the leaves have no stipules, and the flowers show a tendency to polygamy. In *Exospermum* (Fig. 8) and *Zygogynum*, however, the carpels are more or less united, especially in fruit. The anatomical characters are mainly those of *Magnoliaceae*, but *Drimys* is remarkable in having no vessels in the xylem, a feature common to the Gymnosperms (probably a so-called relict character), and the wood resembles very much that of the *Araucarieae* tribe of *Pinaceae*. *Winteraceae* have a more tropical and southerly distribution than *Magnoliaceae*. Winter's Bark, *Drimys winteri* Forst., South America, is much used in Brazil as an astringent and stimulant. Captain Winter, from whom it took its name, commanded the "Elizabeth" under Sir Francis Drake, and he used the bark "as a spice and medicine for scurvy".

The type genus of *Winteraceae* is *Drimys* J. R. & G. Forster (*Wintera* Murr.), with about 20 species ranging from the Malay Archipelago to eastern Australia, New Caledonia, and also in Central and South America; they are evergreen trees and shrubs with pellucid-punctate leaves, flowers bisexual or sometimes polygamo-dioecious, the calyx closed in bud and

[1] Including *Drimeaceae* van Tieghem (1900).

FIG. 7. The Chinese Star Anise, *Illicium verum* Hook. f. (*Illiciaceae*), south China. **A**, stamen. **B**, carpels. **C**, the same in fruit (orig.).

bursting irregularly when opening, then deciduous; petals 6 or more, imbricate; anther-loculi lateral; carpels free and berry-like in fruit, with sessile stigmas, seed with shining testa.

In *Zygogynum vieillardii* Baill. the flower is solitary, terminal and sessile; in *Exospermum* and *Zygogynum* spp. there are three together and terminal; a terminal cluster of cymes in *Bubbia* and *Drimys* spp.; carpels united in tribe *Exospermeae*; reduced to one in *Drimys dipetala* F. Muell. and *Zygogynum*

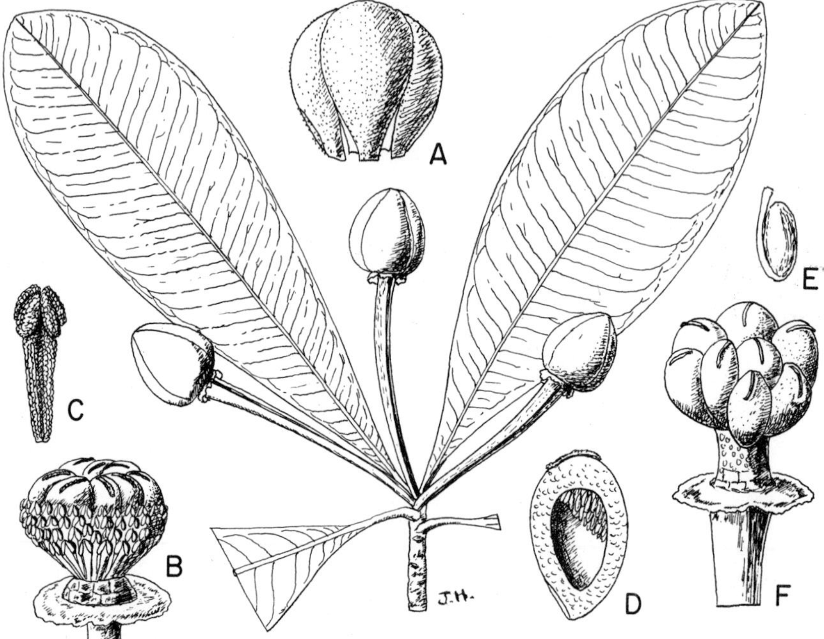

FIG. 8. *Exospermum stipitatum* van Tiegh. (*Winteraceae*), New Caledonia. **A**, petals after falling off. **B**, stamens and carpels. **C**, single stamen. **D**, vertical section of carpel. **E**, seed. **F**, carpels in fruit (orig.).

pomiferum Baill. In my opinion the genus *Degeneria* A. C. Smith (Fig. 9) (*Degeneriaceae*) finds its proper place in *Winteraceae*.[1] (For map of distribution of *Winteraceae* see also FAMILIES OF FLOWERING PLANTS, 2nd Ed. **I**, 127.)

The small but more advanced family **Canellaceae**,[2] glabrous aromatic trees with gland-dotted leaves, has probably descended more directly from the Winteraceous stock than from the BIXALES in which it has usually been included. The stamens are connate into a column (an advanced character) with the anther-loculi outermost, and the embryo is small in abundant endosperm. It is found mainly in tropical America where *Winteraceae* are also abundant.

The type genus is *Canella*, with a single species, a tree with aromatic bark; leaves oblanceolate, punctate; flowers in terminal cymes; sepals 3, imbricate; petals 5, free, imbricate; stamens 10, connate, tube wavy at the top, anthers linear; ovary with 2 parietal placentas and 3 or 2 ovules on each placenta;

[1] See note at foot of p. 128 in my FAMILIES OF FLOWERING PLANTS, 2nd Ed. **I**.

[2] Including *Winteranaceae* O. Warburg (1895).

FIG. 9. **A**, *Degeneria vitiensis* A. C. Smith, Fiji Islands, considered by the present author to belong to *Winteraceae* and related to **B**, *Zygogynum pomiferum* Baill. (orig.).

style short, thick, truncate; fruit a berry, 6–4-seeded; seeds globose, shining, embryo small in oily-fleshy endosperm; cotyledons semi-orbicular. The other four genera have solitary axillary flowers. In *Cinnamosma* the petals are united into a tube, in *Pleodendron* there are 12 petals in 4 series. I am not too happy about the position of this small family.

Canella Bark (*Cortex Canellae*) is that of *Canella winterana* (Linn.) Gaertn., a native of Florida and the West Indies, and is used locally as a condiment, and possesses aromatic, stimulant and tonic properties. The genus *Warburgia*, *W. ugandensis* Sprague, is an important timber in Uganda, the bark used as a purgative, and the resin for fixing handles in tools. The wood of Santal Vert, *Cinnamosma fragrans* Baill., is scented and is exported from Madagascar.

Schisandraceae were also formerly included in *Magnoliaceae*, the absence of stipules being a good spotting and separating character. The tendency to unisexual flowers already slightly developed in the basic family *Magnoliaceae* is here accomplished, the stamens are partially connate or wholly united into a fleshy globose mass, and the fruits are baccate. In this family the eastern Asiatic—eastern United States of America distribution is again repeated, *Schisandra* being found in these two widely separated regions. In *Schisandra* (Fig. 10) the tendency to an elongated floral axis is continued, for the carpels, although in flower arranged in a head, are later in fruit spread along an elongated axis as in many *Magnoliaceae*. In the only other genus of this family, *Kadsura*, the carpels in fruit remain in a globose or ellipsoid head. Anatomists draw attention to the sclerenchyma-cells, in the walls of

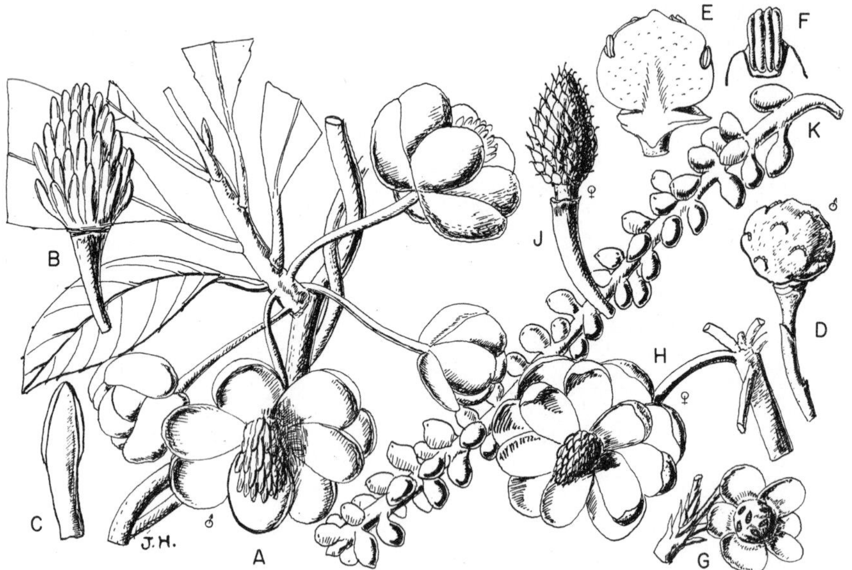

FIG. 10. **A**, male flowers of *Schisandra grandiflora* (Wall.) Hook. f. and Thoms. **B**, stamens. **C**, single stamen. **H**, female flower. **J**, carpels. **K**, fruits. **D**, carpels of *S. propinqua* Hook. f. and Thoms. **E**, vertical section of male flower. **F**, anther. **G**, female flower (*Schisandraceae*) (orig.).

which crystals of oxalate of lime appear to be embedded, and the vascular bundles of the midrib and petiole are arranged in the form of an arc.

Himantandraceae is monotypic, and *Himantandra* occurs from the Moluccas and New Guinea to N.E. Australia. There are only two or three species of these aromatic trees, and they are remarkable for their peltate, scaly indumentum. The leaves have no stipules, the flowers are bisexual, and are at first covered by two calyptrate leathery sepals. The 6 or 7 petals are very similar in size and shape to the numerous stamens which have the anther-loculi separated on each side towards the base of the petaloid connective. The 7–10 free carpels have a solitary pendulous ovule in each. The fruit is remarkable, being gall-like, fleshy and 7–10-locular by the late coalescence of the carpels. This genus is apparently an ancient isolated relic, with no very close living relatives.

Another "relict" monotypic family is **Lactoridaceae**. *Lactoris fernandeziana* Philippi (Fig. 11) is as solitary as was Alexander Selkirk, the prototype of Robinson Crusoe, for it occurs only on the island of Juan Fernandez, off the coast of Chile. Secretory cells in the leaves give rise to transparent dots, the wood contains vessels with bordered pits and simple perforations, and the wood prosenchyma also bears bordered pits. This single genus was classified in the *Piperaceae* by Bentham and Hooker, but it seems to be much

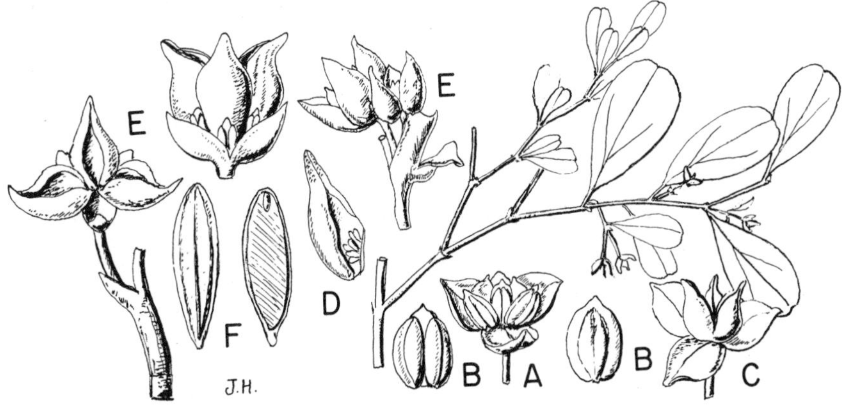

FIG. 11. *Lactoris fernandeziana* Philippi (*Lactoridaceae*), the sole representative of the family, occurs only on the island of Juan Fernandez, where Alexander Selkirk, the prototype of Robinson Crusoe, was marooned. **A**, flower. **B**, stamens, front and back. **C**, sepals and carpels. **D**, one carpel opened out. **E**, fruits. **F**, seed and vertical section of same (orig.).

nearer *Winteraceae*. It is especially interesting because several of the floral characters savour of those of Monocotyledons. There are 3 sepals, but no petals, and the 6 stamens with extrorse anthers are in 2 whorls; carpels 6, nearly free from one another, and with 6 ovules in each carpel arranged in 2 vertical rows. It seems that even in this early stage of the woody phylum there is here and there a strong tendency towards the trimerous type of flower which is so general in Monocotyledons. It is noted later that trimery of the sepals and petals is almost universal in the large and more advanced family *Annonaceae*.

A more highly evolved family of this alliance and with a very restricted distribution is **Trochodendraceae.**[1] There are two genera, *Trochodendron* and *Euptelea*, the former monotypic, the latter with about four species. For the first time in this group the flowers are gathered into an inflorescence in *Trochodendron*, and the leaves are whorled and serrate. There is no perianth, and the carpels are more or less reduced to a single whorl. The family is related to but more advanced than *Winteraceae*, and perhaps provides a direct link between that family and the HAMAMELIDALES. As in *Drimys*, there are no vessels in the wood of *Trochodendron*, no doubt another relict character from the Gymnosperms. In *Euptelea* the vessels have scalariform perforations with exceptionally numerous bars, and in *Trochodendron* the occurrence of branched sclerenchymatous cells in the leaf and axis is noted by the anatomists. They are differentiated as internal hairs and project into the cells. The stomata are surrounded by several ordinary epidermal cells, quite

[1] Including *Eupteleaceae* van Tieghem (1900).

a departure from the so-called rubiaceous type so universal in the *Magnoliaceae*. *Trochodendron aralioides* Sieb. & Zucc. occurs only in the forests of Japan and Formosa, and in the latter island forms pure forest between the Conifer belt and the broad-leaved tree region, where examples are found with trunks as much as 15 ft in diameter.

There is quite a considerable range of structure in these small families which appear to have been derived from the Magnoliaceous stock. It seems

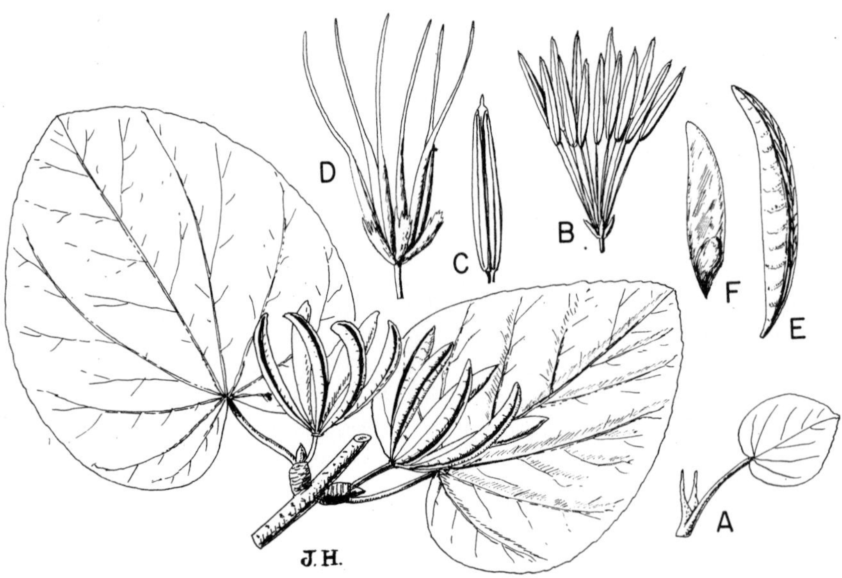

FIG. 12. *Cercidiphyllum japonicum* Sieb. & Zucc. (*Cercidiphyllaceae*), Japan and western China, showing leaves and fruits on short shoots. **A**, stipules and young leaf. **B**, male flower. **C**, anther. **D**, female flower. **E**, carpel in fruit. **F**, seed (orig.).

to culminate in **Cercidiphyllaceae**, another monotypic family represented by the single genus *Cercidiphyllum*. This is a timber tree of China and Japan, with opposite, stipulate leaves, dioecious, axillary flowers, reduced calyx, no petals, and follicular fruits. To me it shows some distant relationship with *Liriodendron*, but also approaches *Hamamelidaceae*, to some members of which it bears considerable external resemblance. Though in this phylogenetic system the HAMAMELIDALES are considered to have been derived from the ROSALES stock, it cannot be ruled out that some of them, at any rate, may have descended more directly from the MAGNOLIALES.

Cercidiphyllum japonicum Sieb. & Zucc. (Fig. 12) is one of the most interesting trees of Japan, and gives to the forests of Yezo their characteristic appearance. It grows on the slopes of low hills in a moist deep rich soil, together with dwarf bamboos. There it attains a height of 100 ft, and often develops clusters of stems 8–10 ft through, and even of greater dimensions in China, where the late E. H. Wilson found an old tree 55 ft in girth. The timber is valuable, soft, straight grained, light yellow, like that of *Liriodendron*. The foliage is bright red in spring and yellow in autumn, and must provide a wonderful sight in its native environment. At Kew and in Britain generally it grows very slowly and is often injured by late spring frosts.

ORDER 2. ANNONALES

(*Fam. Fl. Pl.* **1**, 133)

Families: **Annonaceae, Eupomatiaceae.**

A more advanced group derived from the *Magnoliaceae* is the large family **Annonaceae**,[1] which is almost confined to and largely spread over the whole of the tropics. It is very homogeneous, differing from the *Magnoliaceae* by the absence of stipules and by the ruminate endosperm of the seeds, and many have valvate petals.

Although so primitive and natural a family, nevertheless, within its concept we may note the evolution of a few relatively advanced characters, such as a sympetalous corolla, and a syncarpous ovary with parietal placentation. The development of parietal placentation in so primitive a family shows, therefore, that this type may be more ancient phylogenetically than axile placentation, which is so universal in many of the more advanced and climax families with syncarpous ovaries, such as *Euphorbiaceae* and *Rubiaceae*.

The principal associated "spotting" characters for the *Annonaceae* are the sepals and petals in whorls of three, the anthers (see Fig. 14) usually capped by the enlarged often truncate connective (reminiscent on a small scale of the male cone-scales of the more ancient *Cycadaceae*), and the seeds have always abundant, ruminate endosperm and a very small embryo.

There are some constant anatomical characters for the family. These are the occurrence of secretory cells in the leaf parenchyma, as in *Magnoliaceae*; the almost universal occurrence of solitary or clustered crystals in the epidermis of the leaf; the stomata with subsidiary cells parallel to the pore (as in *Magnoliaceae*); the simple perforations of the vessels; and the absence of

---

[1] Including *Hornschuchiaceae* J. G. Agardh (1858). *Monodoraceae* J. G. Agardh (1858).

external glands. The indumentum, when present, consists of simple, uniseriate, few-celled hairs, of stellate hairs, or more rarely of peltate scales.

On phylogenetic lines the family may be arranged into two groups, the first and much the larger with apocarpous gynoecium, a few of which, such as the type genus *Annona*, become syncarpous only in fruit; and a second, such as *Monodora* (Fig. 13), with a primarily syncarpous gynoecium, with as stated above, parietal placentation. The phylogenetic sequence of these two groups is therefore clear.

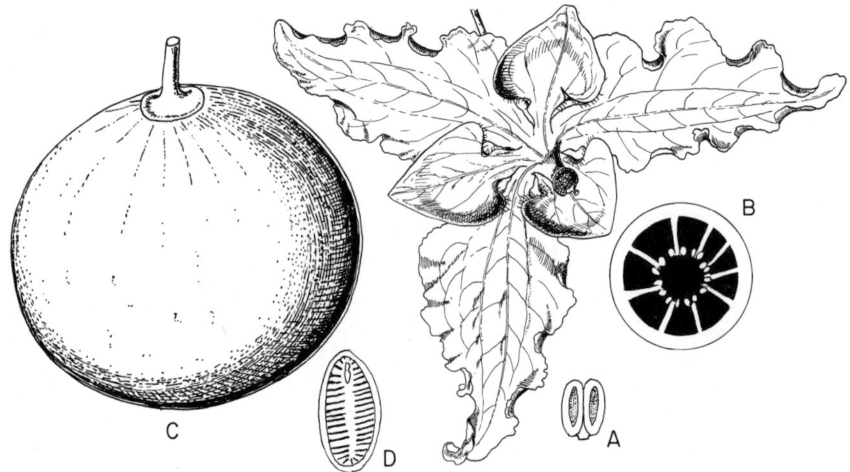

FIG. 13. *Monodora myristica* Dunal, tropical Africa, a very advanced genus of *Annonaceae* with remarkable flowers and a syncarpous ovary showing parietal placentation. **A**, anther. **B**, diagrammatic cross-section of ovary. **C**, fruit. **D**, vertical section of seed showing ruminate endosperm and minute embryo (orig.).

The relative primitiveness of the characters of the subdivisions of the first group, however, is rather conjectural. For example, should stress be laid on the imbrication of the petals within each series of the tribe *Uvarieae*, or should the gradation of the sepals into the outer petals of the *Miliuseae* be indicative of a more ancient group, though in aestivation all the petals in *Miliuseae* are valvate? The student's guess will be quite as good as mine!

The third tribe, *Unoneae*, is clearly the most advanced, for here the petals are valvate, and the outer ones are as large as and similar to the inner, or the latter are smaller or entirely suppressed, indicating reduction.

As in the *Magnoliaceae*, the stomata of the leaves are provided with special subsidiary cells parallel with the pore. The anther-tips (see Fig. 14) are a very striking feature of *Annonaceae*, and they may represent an ancient relict type of structure, i.e. the reduced top of the original foliage leaf. The habit of the genus *Geanthemum* (see Fig. 19) is remarkable, the flowers being borne only on sucker-like underground shoots.

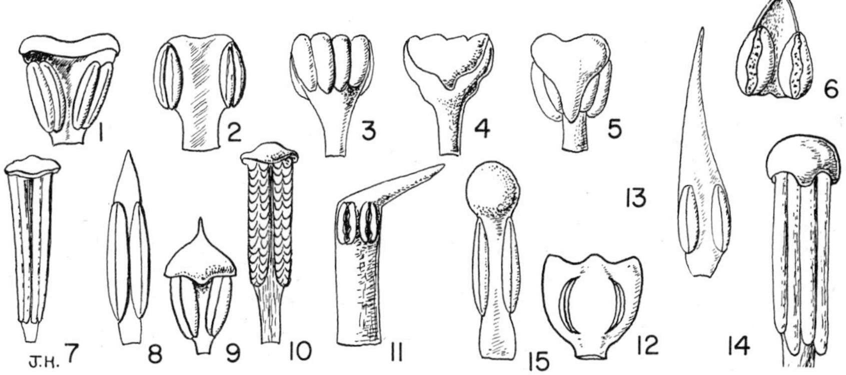

FIG. 14. Types of stamens in *Annonaceae*: **1**, *Polyalthia stuhlmannii* (Engl.) Verdc. **2**, *Popowia congensis* Eng. & Diels. **3** and **4**, *Enneastemon schweinfurthii* (Engl. & Diels) Robyns & Ghesq. **5**, *Enneastemon fornicatus* (Baill.) Exell. **6**, *Orophea thorelii* Pierre. **7**, *Annonidium mannii* (Oliv.) Engl. & Diels. **8**, *Polyalthia oliveri* Engl. **9**, *Artabotrys harmandii* Finet & Gagnep. **10**, *Xylopia africana* (Benth.) Oliv. **11**, *Enneastemon barteri* (Baill.) Keay. **12**, *Sageraea elliptica* (A.DC.) Hook. f. & Thoms. **13**, *Oxandra laurifolia* (Sw.) A.Rich. **14**, *Uvariastrum pierreanum* Engl. **15**, *Asimina triloba* Dunal. The produced connective of the anthers is regarded as an ancient character, probably representing the remnant of the leaf-blade of which the stamen is a modification.

The type genus is *Annona* Linn. (formerly often spelled *Anona*, and hence the family name, *Anonaceae*); trees and shrubs, sometimes with stellate indumentum; flowers solitary or few together and either terminal, leaf-opposed or borne between the nodes; sepals 3, small and valvate; petals 6, in two series or the inner series rudimentary or absent, free or connate at the base, the outer fleshy and valvate, the inner imbricate or valvate; anther-connective dilated into a truncate disk, rarely apiculate, and the numerous carpels are often more or less connate, but especially so in fruit, with 1 basal erect ovule and 1 seed; type species *A. muricata* Linn. (Fig. 15).

The genera most divergent from the type genus are *Geanthemum* (already mentioned), the flowers of which are borne on subterranean shoots (see Fig. 19); the lepidote indumentum of *Meiocarpidium* recalls that of *Himantandra* (p. 12); the recurved hook-like inflorescence of *Artabotrys*; the very large flowers of *Sapranthus*, with a carrion-like odour similar to that of a *Stapelia* or *Aristolochia*. The flowers are dioecious in *Tetrastemma*, *Thonnera* and *Ephedranthus*, monoecious in *Uvariopsis* and *Raimondia*. In *Sphaerothalamus* the calyx enlarges and becomes membranous, enclosing the fruit. The 6 petals in *Monanthotaxis*, *Haplostichanthus* and *Monocyclanthus* are in a single series, and there are only 3 petals in tribe *Xylopineae*, series *Tripetalae*; corolla sympetalous in *Asteranthe*, *Enneastemon*, *Uvariopsis*, *Hexalobus*, *Stormia*, *Disepalum* and some species of *Papualthia*, and in subfamily

FIG. 15. *Annona muricata* Linn., the type species of the type genus of *Annonaceae*, the Soursop or Guanabana of the West Indies. **A**, flower. **B**, fruit spiny, green, up to 12 in. long and 8–10 lb in weight; the white juicy flesh is very aromatic; said to be unrivalled for sherbets and other drinks (orig.).

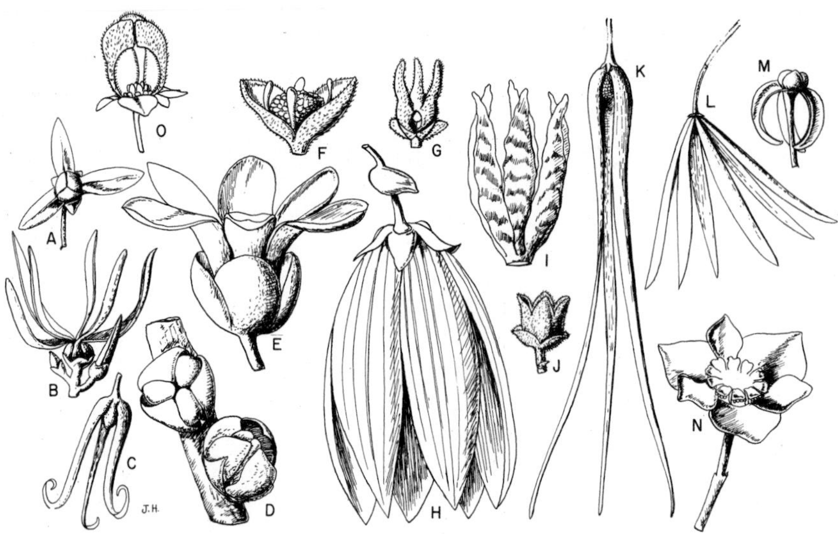

FIG. 16. Diversity of floral types in the family *Annonaceae*. **A**, *Cleistopholis patens* (Benth.) Engl. & Diels, tropical Africa. **B**, *Xylopia aethiopica* (Dunal) A. Rich., tropical Africa. **C**, *Neostenanthera hamata* (Benth.) Exell, tropical Africa. **D**, *Uvaria angustifolia* Engl. & Diels, tropical Africa. **E**, *Sphaerothalamus insignis* Hook. f., Malay Archipelago. **F**, *Disepalum anomalum* Hook. f., Malaya. **G**, *Artabotrys monteiroe* Oliv., tropical Africa. **H**, *Sapranthus nicaraguensis* Seem., Central America, **I**, *Hexalobus senegalensis* A.DC., tropical Africa. **J**, *Uvariopsis zenkeri* Engl., tropical Africa. **K**, *Dasymachalon longiflorum* Finet & Gagnep., Bengal to Assam. **L**, *Polyalthia simiarum* (Ham.) Hook. f. & Thoms., India. **M**, *Cleistopholis staudtii* Engl. & Diels, tropical Africa. **N**, *Popowia seretii* De Wild., tropical Africa. **O**, *Orophea corymbosa* Miq., Malaya (orig.).

FIG. 17. *Goniothalamus grandiflorus* (Warb.) Boerlage (*Oxymitra macrantha* Hemsl.) (*Annonaceae*), grows only in the Solomon Islands. The flowers are borne in clusters on the stem and branches remote from the leaves; note the exceptionally long petals. **A**, stamen. **B**, vertical section of carpel. **C**, vertical section of seed showing ruminate endosperm and minute embryo. **D**, carpels in fruit (orig.).

Monodoroideae; outer petals with long dorsal appendages in *Rollinia*, *Stenanthera*, and a few others. The anthers are transversely locellate in *Porcelia*, *Xylopia*, *Cardiopetalum* and *Hornschuchia*; the connective not produced beyond the loculi in *Geanthemum*, *Tetrastemma*, *Thonnera*, *Raimondia* and

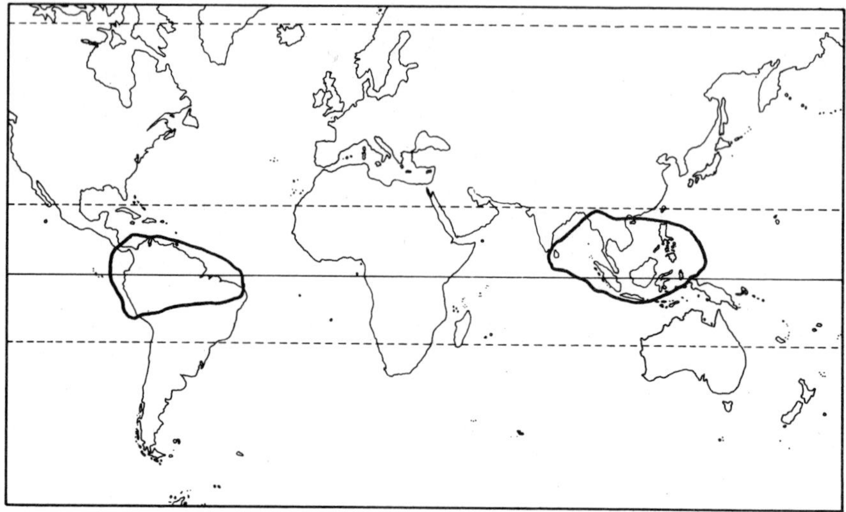

MAP 2. Remarkable example of discontinuous distribution of the natural genus *Anaxagorea* (*Annonaceae*).

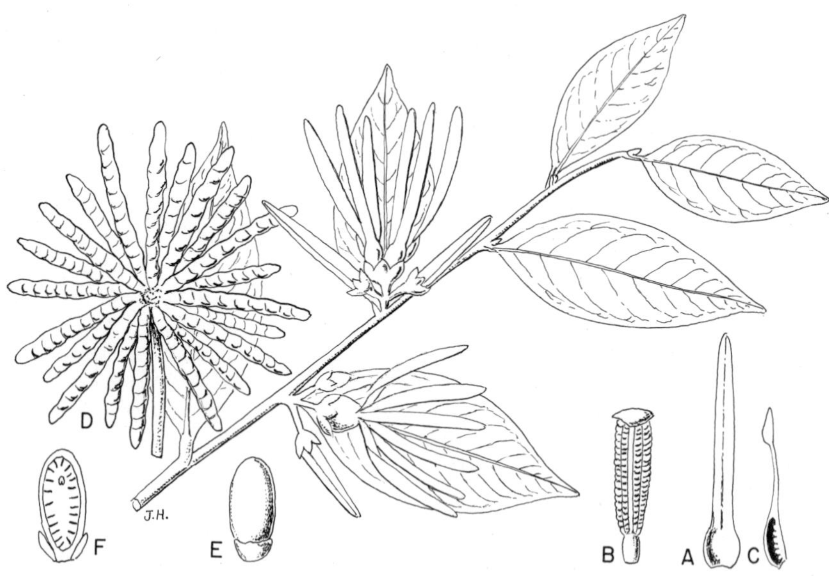

FIG. 18. *Xylopia aethiopica* (Dunal) A. Rich. (*Annonaceae*). **A**, petal. **B**, stamen. **C**, carpel. **D**, fruits. **E**, seed with aril. **F**, vertical section of seed (orig.).

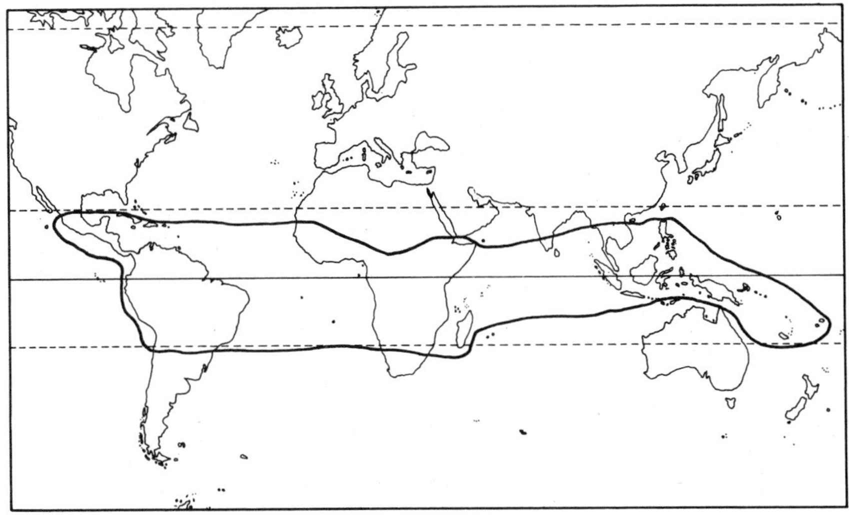

MAP 3. Range of the natural (homogeneous) pantropical genus *Xylopia* (*Annonaceae*).

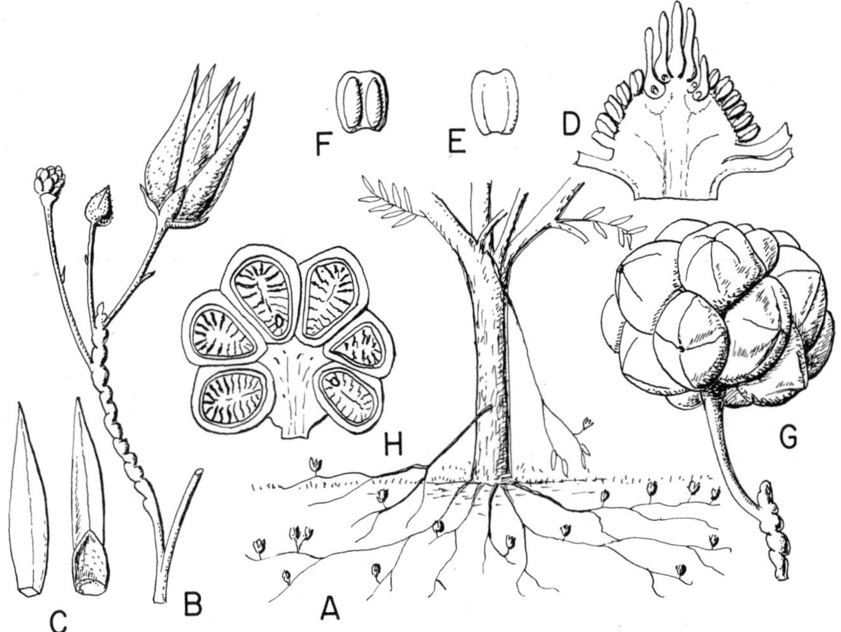

FIG. 19. *Geanthemum rhizanthum* (Eichl.) Safford (*Annonaceae*), Brazil. **A**, showing the remarkable habit with the flowers arising from underground shoots. **B**, inflorescence. **C**, petals. **D**, section of flower. **E** and **F**, anthers. **G**, fruit. **H**, section of fruit (partly after Eichler).

Alphonsea; outer stamens are sterile and subpetaloid in *Fusaea*. The carpels are on an elongated torus (as in *Magnoliaceae*) in *Mischogyne* and *Toussaintia*, united into a 1-locular ovary with parietal placentas in subfamily *Monodoroideae*, and united into a many-locular mass in fruit in subtribe *Annonineae*, *Pachypodanthum* and *Annonidium;* solitary in *Kingstonia*, *Monocarpia*, *Mezzettia* and *Tridimeris*; sunk in the torus in *Pseudannona*; stigmas united in *Piptostigma*; seeds triquetrous and winged in *Richella*.

Annonaceae are nearly confined to the tropics, where they mostly grow at low elevations. For example they are very abundant in the rain-forest of west tropical Africa, but rare in the adjacent and more elevated savannah regions, except along the rivers.

The only genus extending for any distance into the temperate zone is *Asimina*, which reaches as far north as the Great Lakes of North America. Examples of intercontinental distribution or affinity are not numerous in this family, but these few are of considerable interest. The only truly natural genus common to the tropics of both hemispheres is *Xylopia*, which stands out in the family especially by its transversely septate anthers (Fig. 18).

Species of *Annona* have edible fruits, the West Indian *A. reticulata* Linn. and *A. squamosa* Linn. (Custard Apple) (Fig. 20) being the most important. *Xylopia aethiopica* A. Rich. supplied the ancients with Ethiopian pepper. Some of the woods in tropical America, known as "Lancewoods", were formerly in great demand before the advent of mechanical transport.

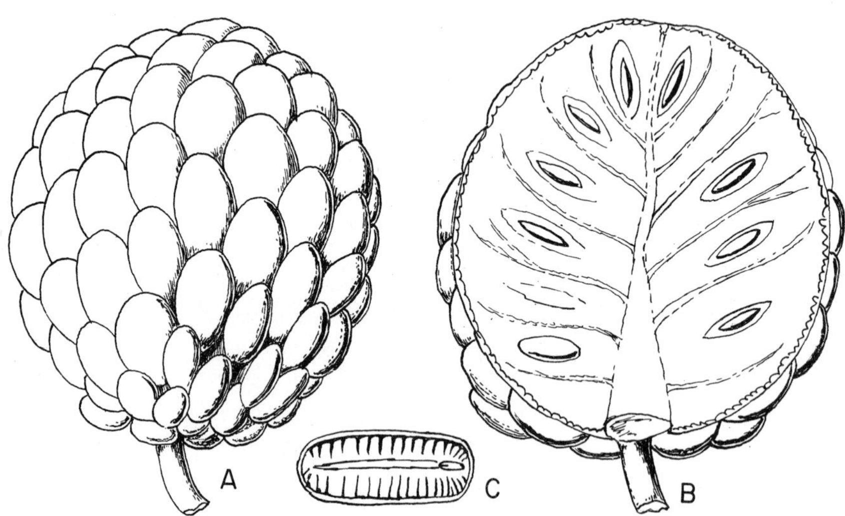

FIG. 20. The Sugar Apple or Sweet Sop, *Annona squamosa* Linn. (*Annonaceae*). **A**, whole fruit. **B**, vertical section. **C**, longitudinal section of seed.

The only other family at all closely associated with *Annonaceae* is **Eupomatiaceae**, which shows a very primitive feature in having the sepals gradually passing into petals; but the carpels are sunk in the large receptacle. Here we have, it seems probable, almost an exact parallelism to the *Cyclanthaceae* in the Order ROSALES, and also to the *Nymphaeaceae* in the herbaceous group RANALES, parallelisms which have sometimes been mistaken for real affinity! There are two species of this interesting family, which is confined to Australia, *Eupomatia laurina* R.Br. in Queensland and New South Wales, and *E. bennettii* F. Muell., only in Queensland. The endosperm of the seed is ruminate, as in *Annonaceae*. This part of Australia harbours some very interesting genera and species of plants isolated from their relatives, such as the Hamamelidaceous genus *Ostrearia*, and the only Australian species of *Rhododendron* is found on the tops of the mountains in the Mt. Bellenden Ker region.

FIG. 21. *Cananga odorata* (Lam.) Hook. f. & Thoms. (*Annonaceae*), native of Indo-China and Malaya, known as Ylang-Ylang; the petals are strongly perfumed and the oil used in European perfumery. **A**, fruits, **B**, section of seed (orig.).

Anatomically *Eupomatiaceae* differ from *Annonaceae* in the following characters: there are no diaphragms composed of stone-cells in the pith; the bast is not stratified into hard and soft; there are typical bordered pits in the wood-prosenchyma.

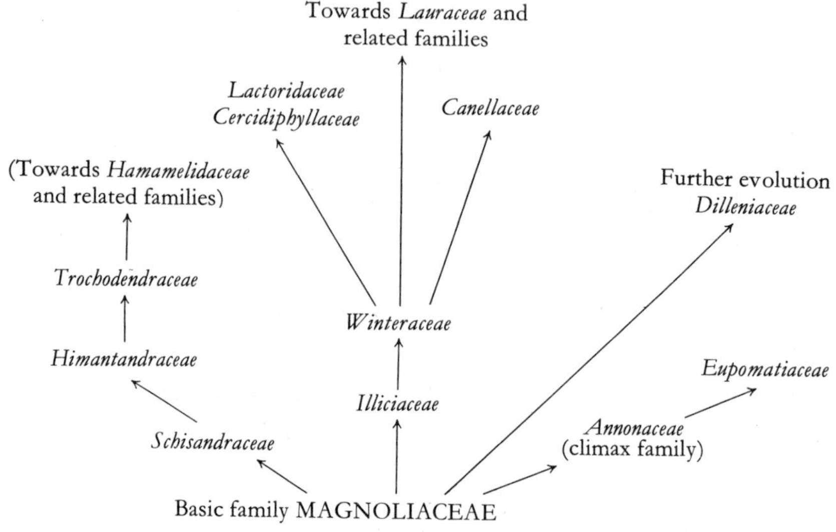

Diagram showing relationships of *Magnoliaceae* and derived families.

Order 3. LAURALES

(*Fam. Fl. Pl.* **1**, 135)

Families: **Monimiaceae, Austrobaileyaceae, Trimeniaceae, Lauraceae, Gomortegaceae, Hernandiaceae, Myristicaceae.**

Phylogeny of *Lauraceae* and closely related families: MAGNOLIACEAE → WINTERACEAE → LAURACEAE → **Myristicaceae** (climax).

Reduced relatives of some of the preceding families seem to be those included in the Order LAURALES, all of which have lost their petals. Some of them, in addition, have more or less perigynous flowers, and the stamens are in whorls with often a characteristic mode of dehiscence of the anthers, by valves. As pointed out further on, the same feature of the anthers occurs in *Berberidaceae*, no doubt a clear case of parallel evolution.

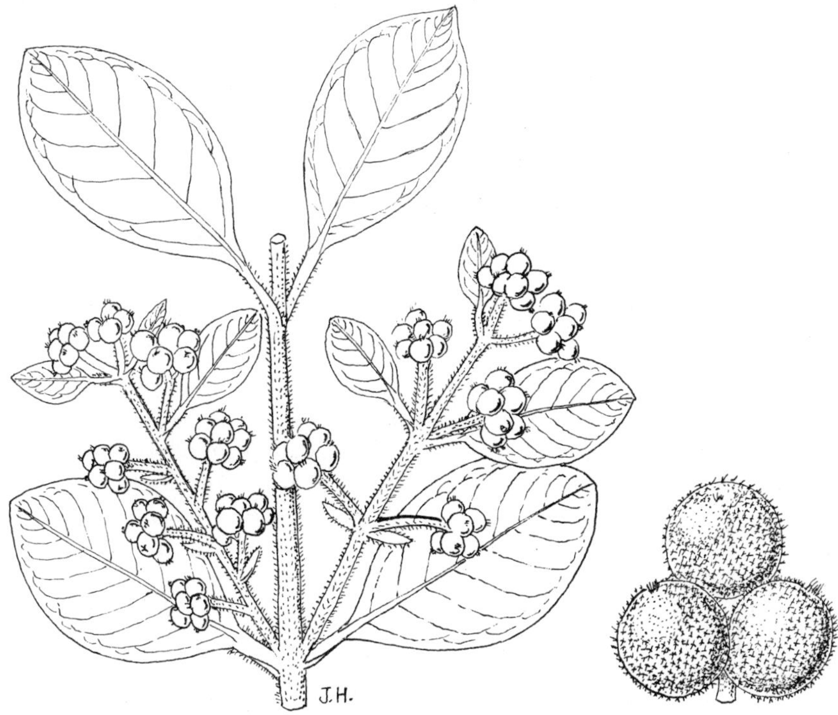

FIG. 22. *Monimia ovalifolia* Thou., Mauritius, in fruit, the type species of the type genus of the family *Monimiaceae*. (Owing to lack of good herbarium specimens, nothing else could be shown.)

The family **Monimiaceae**[1] is fairly well defined and homogeneous, and on the whole seems to be most closely related to *Lauraceae*. Like that family they appear to be reduced apetalous representatives of the MAGNOLIALES, and also especially of the *Winteraceae* and *Annonaceae*, which they resemble in their aromatic, often pellucid-punctate leaves and the absence of stipules. The tendency to perigyny by the cupular expansion of the perianth is very strong in the family, and is a marked advance on the hypogynous MAGNOLIALES. The distribution of the two families is very similar.

The type genus is *Monimia*, shrubs with opposite entire leaves, small dioecious flowers in short axillary cymes, the male flowers with an ovoid or globose calyx at length deeply split into 6–4 valvate lobes, the disk completely lining the tube, numerous stamens in many series, the filaments with a gland on each side at the base, anthers with separate loculi opening by a slit lengthwise, the female calyx globose, soon almost closed, no staminodes,

[1] *Atherospermataceae* R.Br. (1814). *Amborellaceae* Pichon (1948).

and few sessile carpels with slender styles and each with a pendulous ovule; fruit a small drupe enclosed in the persistent calyx. Type species, *M. ovalifolia* Thouars, Mauritius (Fig. 22).

The opposite leaves and the plumose styles of *Doryphora* seem to indicate a development similar to that found in *Clematis* in *Ranunculaceae*, whilst the fruits of *Laurelia* have evolved on similar lines to those of the *Calycanthaceae* in the ROSALES, though the seeds retain their endosperm. The glandular appendages of the filaments and the valvular dehiscence of the anthers of the subfamily *Atherospermoideae* tend to link up *Monimiaceae* with *Lauraceae*, the latter character also being a well-known feature of the family *Berberidaceae*, again no doubt an example of parallelism.

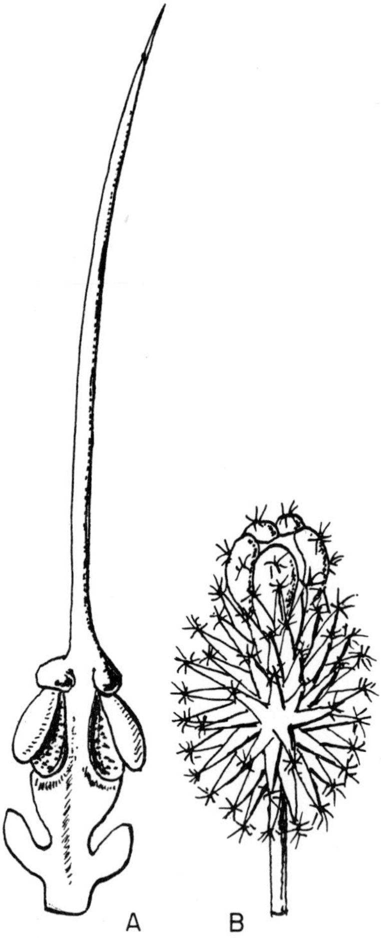

A B

FIG. 23. **A**, remarkable stamen of *Doryphora sassafras* Endl., Australia. **B**, fruit of *Siparuna muricata* A.DC., Peru (*Monimiaceae*).

Divergent from the type genus are a few genera with alternate leaves, such as *Amborella, Tambourissa* spp., and occasionally in *Hennecartia*. The inflorescence is involucrate with two valvate bracts in *Atherosperma* and *Doryphora*; bracts foliaceous in *Bracteanthus*. The flowers are bisexual in *Hortonia*, *Daphnandra*, *Nemuaron* and *Doryphora*. The calyx of *Hennecartia* is flat and disk-like; oblique and like that of *Aristolochia* in *Glossocalyx* (see Fig. 24); the female calyx of *Conuleum* and *Lauterbachia* falls off by a circumscissile slit, whilst the anthers of *Hennecartia* have a mushroom-like produced connective, are connate into a tube in *Tetrasynandra*, and in *Doryphora* the styles are plumose, as noted above.

Anatomical characters of importance are the presence of secretory cells which frequently give rise to transparent dots in the leaves; vessels with scalariform perforations. The type of stoma is not uniform, the guard-cells in some being surrounded by several ordinary epidermal cells or by subsidiary cells parallel to the pore.

Fig. 24. *Glossocalyx longicuspis* Benth. (*Monimiaceae*), west tropical Africa. Note the remarkable anisophylly, the leaves alternately reduced to a single linear blade. **A**, male flower. **B**, stamen. **C**, female flower. **D**, vertical section of female flower. **E**, carpel. **F**, fruit (orig.).

The indumentum consists of simple unicellular hairs, tufted hairs, stellate hairs and peltate scales.

Monimiaceae, like *Annonaceae*, are almost entirely tropical. They are absent from India proper, however, and are very sparsely represented in Africa, though the Mascarene Islands harbour a few distinct endemic genera. Of particular interest is *Laurelia*, a distinct genus of three species, which connects the flora of New Zealand with that of far distant Chile and Patagonia (for map showing distribution of some genera of this family see my FAMILIES OF FLOWERING PLANTS, 2nd Ed. **1**, 136).

Elswehere[1] I called attention to the remarkable case of anisophylly in *Glossocalyx* (Fig. 24), a west African genus of three species. Opposite each normal foliage-leaf is a reduced filiform leaf which is caducous, thus making the leaves appear alternate, as indeed they had previously been described. There are very few economic products. Boldo Leaves, *Peumus boldus* Molin., a Chilean shrub, are fragrant; they contain about 2 per cent of an essential oil, and an extract is used in medicine to assist digestion. The fruit is sweet and edible. The woods of *Doryphora sassafras* Endl., and *Atherosperma moschata* Labill., are attractive and are used for furniture in Australia.

The genus *Austrobaileya*, **Austrobaileyaceae**, with only two known species, has been something of a puzzle as to its true position in our system. Its author, the late C. T. White, suggested that it should be placed near

[1] J. BOT. **80**, 20, with figure (1942).

Magnoliaceae, but the free carpels with a bilobed style, coupled with the opposite leaves, the sepals and petals graded into each other, and numerous petaloid introrse stamens exclude it from that alliance; for want of a better place I have it near *Monimiaceae* (FAMILIES OF FLOWERING PLANTS, 2nd Ed. **1**, 137, Fig. 13).

Lauraceae[1] is an important family from an economic standpoint. They grow mainly in the cooler elevated parts of warm countries and many of them have aromatic bark, wood, leaves or seeds, besides essential oils, valuable timbers and drugs and spices. For example the forest in the cloud belt of Madeira and the Canary Islands is composed mainly of species of

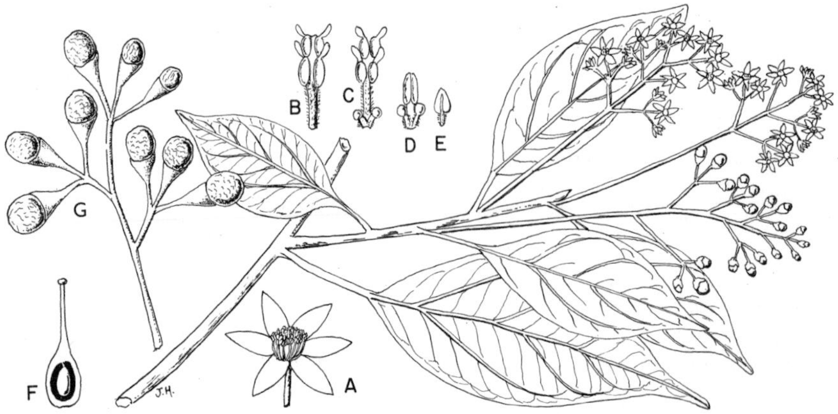

FIG. 25. The Camphor tree, *Cinnamomum camphora* Nees (*Lauraceae*), native of eastern Asia and cultivated in most warm countries. **A**, single flower. **B**, outer, **C**, inner stamens. **D**, outer, **E**, inner staminode. **F**, vertical section of ovary. **G**, fruits (orig.).

Lauraceae, and there is a very interesting story connected with the island of Hierro, the most westerly of the latter group. It was of considerable interest to the early voyagers on account of the supposed existence of a wonderful rain tree called *Garoe* or *Til*, which was credited with the miraculous power of supplying the inhabitants of the whole island with sufficient water for their maintenance. The moisture was collected by the foliage from the clouds and mist, and dripped into a well which was constructed below. The tree was most probably *Oreodaphne foetens* Nees, and sketches of it figured as title pages on some of the early books on natural history, such as Duret, HISTOIRE ADMIRABLE (1605), and Bauhin and Cherler, HISTORIA PLANTARUM GENERALIS (1619). In more temperate countries two of the best-known species of *Lauraceae* are the Sweet Bay, or Bay Laurel, *Laurus nobilis* Linn.

[1] Including *Cassythaceae* Lindley (1833). *Perseaceae* Horaninow (1834).

(see Fig. 28), and the Californian Laurel or Spice Tree, *Umbellularia californica* Nutt. The leaves of the former were used by the ancient Greeks and the Romans to make wreaths with which to crown victorious warriors and athletes. They contain an essential oil, and they are sometimes used for flavouring in culinary work.

Camphor is obtained by distillation from the wood of an evergreen tree, *Cinnamomum camphora* Nees (Fig. 25), a native of Formosa, Japan and China and cultivated in most warm countries. Besides its use in medicine, the wood is employed for furniture and articles made of it are rarely attacked by insects.

Cinnamon is the bark of *Cinnamomum zeylanicum* Nees, a low tree of Ceylon, south India and Burma. For commercial purposes it is coppiced and the shoots cut when two years old. It is used chiefly for flavouring, astringent powders and tinctures.

Sassafras Root is that of *Sassafras officinale* T. Nees & Ebermaier, a tree widely distributed over the eastern United States. All parts of the tree, especially the bark and root, secrete in special cells an aromatic volatile oil which is employed in large quantities as a perfume and flavouring agent, and is used in medicine.

The Avocado Pear is *Persea americana* Mill., and is one of the most useful of tropical American fruits. It can be eaten as a salad, alone or mixed with others, or cooked in various ways as a vegetable, and the best flavoured forms used as dessert.

A celebrated furniture-wood in South Africa is the Stinkwood, *Ocotea bullata* E. Mey. (Fig. 26). It gets its name from the rather objectionable odour of the wood when freshly worked, which fortunately disappears later on. Other useful woods are Nan-mu, *Persea nanmu* Oliv., native of China; Greenheart, *Nectandra rodioei* Hook., Guyana; and several others.

The habit of the genus *Cassytha* (Fig. 27) is unique in the family; leafless parasites with wiry twining stems, recalling *Cuscuta* (*Cuscutaceae*) related to the *Convolvulaceae*. Most of them are found in Australia and the Malay Archipelago, where they attack other plants, fastening their wart-shaped, shield-like or discoid suckers on the young green shoots.

The type genus, *Laurus*, embraces only two species, *L. nobilis* Linn. (Fig. 28), in the Mediterranean region, being the type; trees, leaves alternate, evergreen; flowers bisexual or dioecious, cymose; calyx-segments 4; stamens in the male 12 or more, rarely 8, several of the filaments having a stipitate gland on each side in the middle or near the base, or rarely some eglandular; anthers introrse; staminodes in the female flowers often 4; style short; fruit a berry.

Tribes *Appollonieae*, *Cryptocaryeae*, *Sassafrideae* and *Cinnamomeae*, whose inflorescences are not enclosed by an involucre, seem to represent more primitive types than those where they are enclosed up to or during flowering

FIG. 26. Stinkwood, *Ocotea bullata* E. Mey. (*Lauraceae*), South Africa; now a rare timber, but celebrated for making attractive furniture. **A**, male flowering shoot. **B**, female shoot. **C**, fruit (orig.).

time by an involucre of bracts and in which the flowers are umbellate or solitary within the involucre, as in tribe *Litseae*. Further tribal characters are the 2- or 4-locellate anthers, and whether all the anthers are introrse or those of one or more rows extrorse. In *Cryptocaryeae* the mature fruit

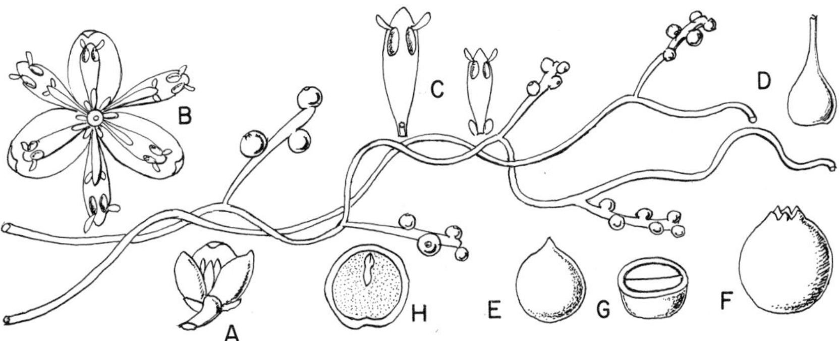

FIG. 27. *Cassytha filiformis* Linn. (*Lauraceae*), tropics generally; unique in the family with its leafless twining habit. **A**, flower. **B**, male flower spread out. **C**, stamen. **D**, ovary. **E**, seed. **F**, fruit. **G**, cross-section of seed. **H**, vertical section of seed (orig.).

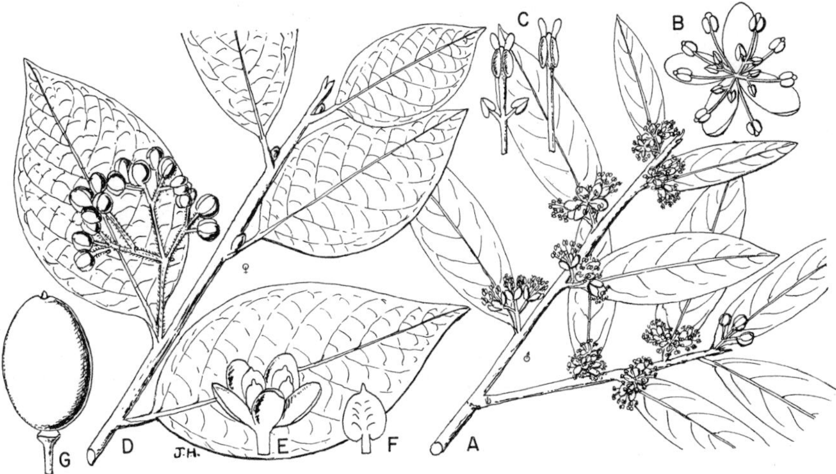

FIG. 28. *Laurus nobilis* Linn., Mediterranean region, the type species of the type genus of the family *Lauraceae*. **A**, male flowering shoot. **B**, male flower. **C**, stamens. **D**, female shoot with flowers. **E**, female flower. **F**, carpel. **G**, fruit (orig.).

becomes more or less completely enclosed by the persistent calyx-tube. This is indeed a difficult family and one still needing the attention of a most careful and experienced taxonomist!

A few outstanding characters may be noted: leaves sometimes subopposite in *Beilschmiedia*; mostly prominently 3-nerved from the base in *Cinnamomum*; flowers arranged in dense heads in *Misanteca*; male and female inflorescences dissimilar in *Endlicheria*; flowers dimerous in *Potameia*; receptacle (or pedicel) of the Malayan genus *Dehaasia* swollen and resembling that of *Podocarpus* (*Taxaceae*); calyx persistent and reflexed in fruit in

Machilus; anthers opening by minute pores in *Micropora*; annular disk present in *Gynandrodaphne*; ovary inferior in *Hypodaphnis*; fruit supported on a double-margined receptacle in *Misanteca*; ruminate cotyledons noted in *Beilschmiedia sikkimensis* King ex Hook. f.

The next family, **Trimeniaceae,**[1] is a small one and was separated from *Monimiaceae* by Gibbs.[2] There are four genera, *Xymalos* Baill. (Africa), *Idenburgia* Gibbs (New Guinea), *Trimenia* Seem. (Fiji) and *Piptocalyx* Oliv. (Australia). They are trees and shrubs or scandent shrubs, with bisexual or polygamous flowers arranged in axillary or terminal inflorescences.

Another small family of this alliance is **Hernandiaceae.**[3] Some were formerly included in *Combretaceae* and *Thymelaeaceae* (Lindley VEG. KINGD.), and *Hernandia* was placed in *Lauraceae* by Bentham and Hooker. In the Engler and Prantl system they are also placed near *Lauraceae*. Even so the family as at present constituted is not a very homogeneous one, the genera showing little real relationship with one another. These are *Sparattanthelium* Mart., *Hernandia* Linn., *Illigera* Blume, *Hazomalamia* Capuron and *Gyrocarpus* Jacq. *Illigera* differs from the others in having digitately compound leaves. In a few there are secretory cells with oily contents which give rise to transparent dots.

The type genus is *Hernandia*, with alternate, ovate, often peltate, exstipulate leaves, monoecious, laxly paniculate flowers, the partial inflorescence composed of 3 flowers surrounded by an involucre of 4–5 foliaceous bracts, the middle flower female, the lateral male; this involucre becomes inflated in fruit and contracted at the mouth, and is often coloured. The calyx-segments are 8-6, subvalvate in each of the 2 whorls; no petals; stamens as many as the outer segments and opposite to them; anthers 2-locellate, opening laterally by valves; often a pair of glands at the base of the stamens; ovary of female flowers l-locular; fruit ribbed; seeds with thick, lobed, subruminate cotyledons. Type species *H. sonora* Linn., India.

In *Gyrocarpus* (Fig. 29, **A**) there are no bracts, and the fruits are crowned by two terminal wings formed by the enlarged calyx-segments, as in most *Dipterocarpaceae*. The fruits of *Illigera* (Fig. 29, **D**) have 2–4 broad lateral wings. In *Sparattanthelium* (Fig. 29, **C**) the fruits are dry and ribbed, and the axis of the infructescence becomes indurated and dichotomously divided.

Important anatomical characters are the possession of secretory cells with oily contents and the excretion of oxalate of lime in the form of small acicular crystals. Cystoliths are characteristic of two genera, *Gyrocarpus* and *Sparattanthelium*. The rather soft woods of this small family are used locally for canoes, catamarans, clogs, drawing boards and musical instruments.

---

[1] Including *Sphenostemonaceae* Erdtman (1952).

[2] Gibbs PHYTOGEOGR. AND FLORA ARFAK MTS. 135 (1917).

[3] Including *Gyrocarpaceae* Dumortier (1829). *Illigeraceae* Blume (1834).

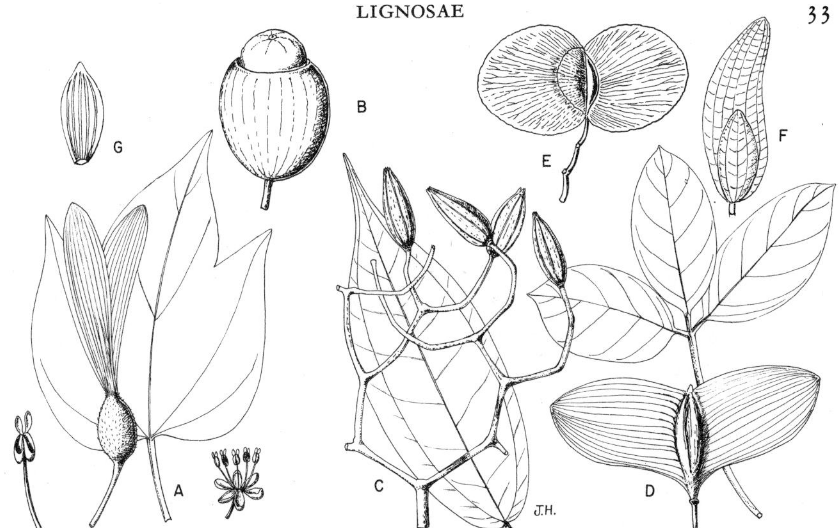

FIG. 29. The fruits of *Hernandiaceae* differ markedly: **A**, *Gyrocarpus jacquinii* Gaertn., leaf, flower, stamen and fruit, tropical America. **B**, *Hernandia peltata* Meisn., Old World tropics. **C**, *Sparattanthelium sprucei* Rusby, Peru. **D**, *Illigera trifoliata* Dunn, India, Malay Peninsula. **E**, *Illigera luzonensis* Merrill, Philippine Islands. **F**, fruiting calyx of *Hazomalamia voyronii* (Jumell) H. Capuron. **G**, fruit (orig.).

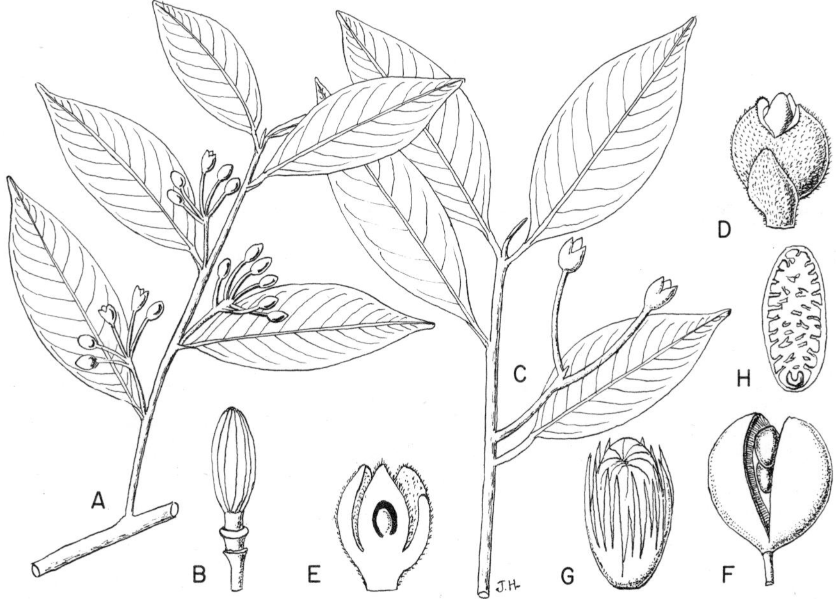

FIG. 30. Nutmeg, *Myristica fragrans* Houtt. (*Myristicaceae*), Malay Archipelago and cultivated; this is the type species of the type genus of the family. **A**, male flowers. **B**, same with calyx removed. **C**, female flowers. **D**, female flower. **E**, vertical section of female flower. **F**, fruit. **G**, seed and aril. **H**, vertical section of seed (orig.).

Our next family is **Myristicaceae**, the Nutmeg family, evergreen trees and shrubs confined to tropical countries, and characterised by their red viscid juice and aromatic properties. Nutmeg and Mace are the seeds and arils of *Myristica fragrans* Houtt., a native of the Malay Archipelago, and cultivated elsewhere; largely used for flavouring and as carminatives. Otoba Nutmeg, *Myristica otoba* Humbl. & Bonpl., is native of South America.

The type genus *Myristica* embraces about 80 species distributed from India to Polynesia, the type species being *M. fragrans* Houtt. (Fig. 30). Trees; leaves mostly white or glaucous beneath, lateral nerves confluent near the margin; flowers dioecious; inflorescence axillary or supra-axillary or sometimes from the axils of old leaves; bracts present; bracteoles embracing the base of the calyx; filaments connate into a column often apiculate above the anthers, these elongated and closely connate; style almost absent, stigmas connate into a sulcate mass; seed with an aril laciniate almost to the base; endosperm ruminate; cotyledons partly connate by the margins then divaricate and forming a disk or saucer.

ORDER 4. DILLENIALES ORDER 5. CORIARIALES

(*Fam. Fl. Pl.* **1**, 143–47)

Families: **Dilleniaceae, Connaraceae, Crossosomataceae, Brunelliaceae** and **Coriariaceae.**

Evolution and further development of **Dilleniaceae** and related families: MAGNOLIACEAE → DILLENIACEAE (**Rosaceae, Flacourtiaceae**).

The only group that seems at all likely to show the origin of the relatively more advanced Order BIXALES appears to be **Dilleniaceae.**[1] Most of the members of this family have free carpels, and the two types of anthers characteristic of *Dilleniaceae*, which serve to subdivide the family, are also repeated in the BIXALES as well as in the tribe *Chrysobalaneae* of *Rosaceae*. So it seems very probable that *Dilleniaceae* are the basic group for BIXALES and most or at least part of the ROSALES. Indeed some of the latter differ from *Dilleniaceae* only by having more or less perigynous types of flowers and seeds devoid of endosperm. Another more distant group derived from the BIXALES is the family *Tiliaceae* and its relatives, some of them very close indeed to *Flacourtiaceae*.

---

[1] Including *Hibbertiaceae* A. G. Agardh (1858).

Dilleniaceae, therefore, is a relatively primitive family, having some direct affinity with *Magnoliaceae*. Here, however, the floral axis has become reduced and is not cone-like, and as a rule the carpels are few and, like the petals, are more or less arranged in a single whorl. The strong parallel nervation of the leaves is characteristic and has been transmitted to and retained in many ROSALES, HAMAMELIDALES, and the "Amentiferae" in a striking manner. The much-imbricate, persistent sepals, the often crumpled petals, and the arillate seeds are the best marks of the family. Probably an aril should generally be regarded as a primitive structure, for it is found in the ancient *Cycadaceae* and *Taxaceae* in the Gymnosperms. In some *Dilleniaceae* it entirely envelops the seed and is often pectinate. A few of the more advanced genera have more or less united carpels, and in *Neowormia*,[1] a genus in the Seychelles Islands, they are completely connate.

In tribe *Hibbertieae* there is a feeble development of a zygomorphic flower, but only with reference to the stamens, which in some species of *Hibbertia* are all to one side of the flower, whilst in *Candollea* some of the stamens are united into bundles and some are free. A striking and unusual character is found in *Davilla*; the sepals are of two kinds, the inner two becoming hard and accrescent and completely enclosing the fruit (Fig. 35). A remarkable modification of the family occurs in *Pachynema* (Fig. 34), with Spartium-like or flattened branches and leaves reduced to scales. It occurs in Australasia. One member of this most advanced tribe, though it has retained numerous stamens, has become reduced in its gynoecium to one carpel! This is the genus *Trisema* (see Fig. 36), containing four species and found in that home of "missing links", New Caledonia. The tribe *Dillenieae* is probably more ancient than the *Delimeae*, for the anthers are linear and more like those of the *Magnoliaceae*.

The type genus is *Dillenia* (type species *D. indica* Linn., see Fig. 31), tropical trees with large leaves, mostly large and showy, lateral, solitary or fasciculate flowers, 5 spreading sepals; 5 large free petals, numerous almost free stamens with linear anthers, the inner erect and introrse, the outer recurved and extrorse, carpels varying from 20 to 5 and adherent to the central axis, numerous ovules, globose fruits, and the seeds have no aril (see also Fig. 32).

The more outstanding divergent genera are *Acrotrema* (Fig. 33), habit herbaceous; *Pachynema* (Fig. 34), stems and branches flattened, and the leaves much reduced and scale-like; stipules large and adnate to the petiole in *Davilla vaginata* Eichl. and *D. wormifolia* Baill.; leaves lyrately lobed in the lower part in *Acrotrema lyratum* Thwaites; inflorescence with somewhat scorpioid-cymose branching in *Schumacheria castaneifolia* Vahl; sepals more than 5 in *Empedoclea* and *Reifferscheidia*; of two kinds in *Davilla*, the inner

---

[1] Hutch. and Summerhayes KEW BULLETIN 388 (1928).

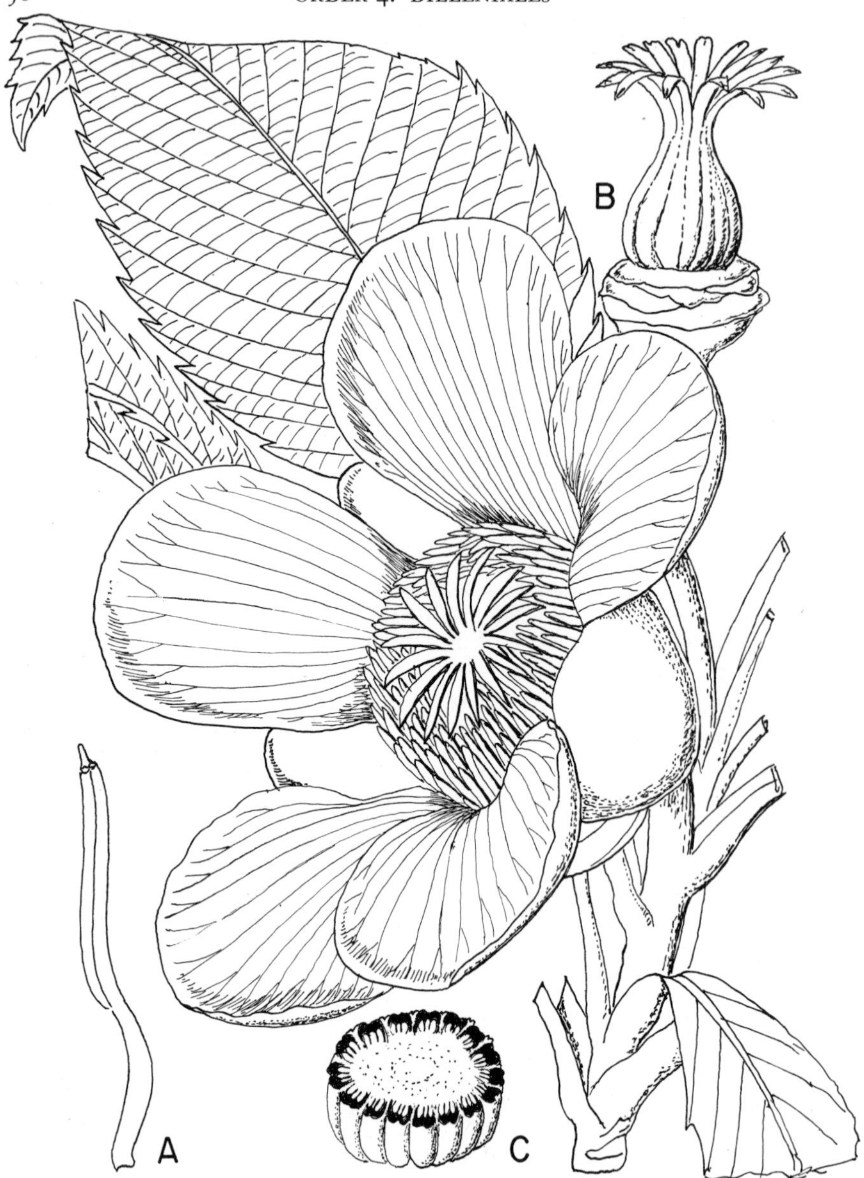

FIG. 31. *Dillenia indica* Linn. (*Dilleniaceae*), Indo-Malaya; the type species of the type genus of the family; note the general resemblance to certain *Magnoliaceae*. **A**, stamen. **B**, gynoecium. **C**, cross-section of gynoecium. (Adapted from BOTANICAL MAGAZINE.)

two hard and accrescent and completely enclosing the fruit and resembling a globose capsule (Fig. 35); petals 3 in *Trisema*; stamens united in *Schumacheria* and in most of the tribe *Hibbertieae*; in two bundles in *Didesmandra*;

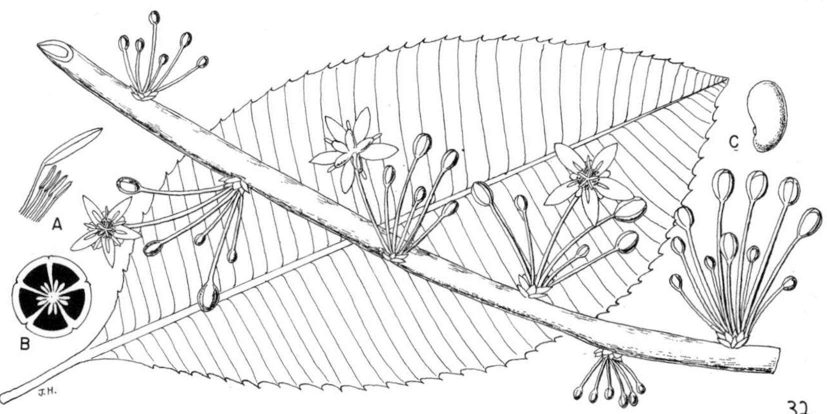

FIG. 32. *Dillenia pentagyna* Linn., India. **A**, showing the two types of stamens. **B**, cross-section of gynoecium. **C**, seed (partly after Roxb.).

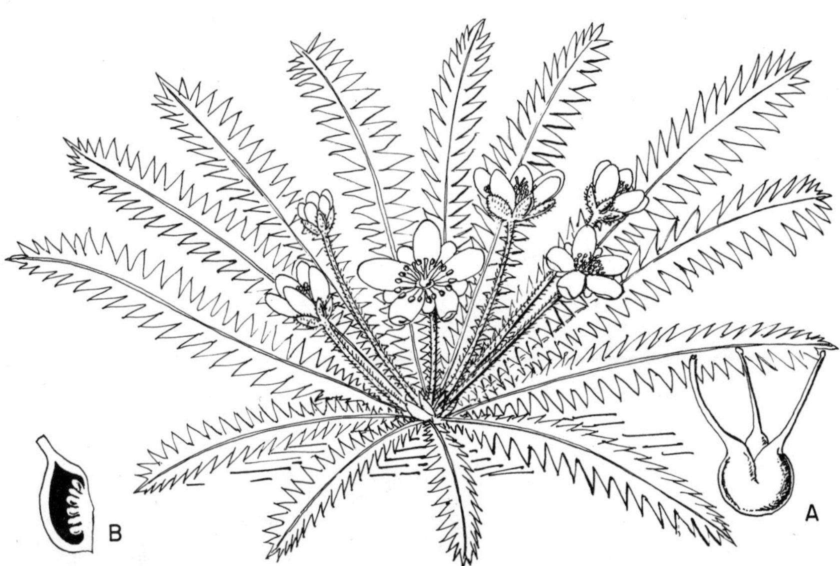

FIG. 33. A herb among the trees and shrubs in the family *Dilleniaceae*; *Acrotrema thwaitesii* Hook. f., a native of Ceylon. **A**, gynoecium. **B**, vertical section of carpel (orig.).

carpels reduced to 1 in *Trisema*, *Delima* and *Doliocarpus* spp.; completely connate in *Neowormia*; seeds with a very large laciniate aril in *Delima sarmentosa* Linn. and *Tetracera* spp.

Dilleniaceae seem to represent an intermediate group leading on to other large and diverse subphyla, including the great ROSALES alliance and families derived from it such as the so-called *Amentiferae*. The affinity of *Dilleniaceae*

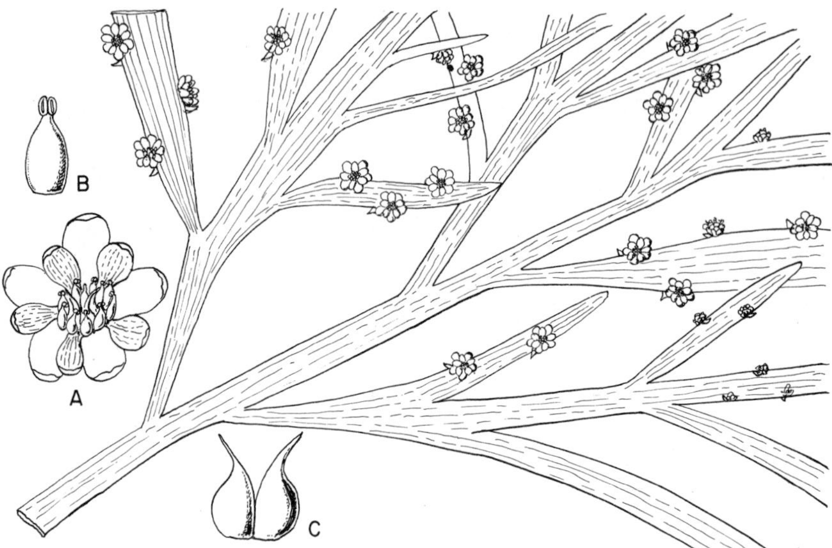

FIG. 34. *Pachynema dilatatum* Benth. (*Dilleniaceae*), northern Australia; branches flattened and leaves reduced to scales. **A**, flower. **B**, stamen. **C**, two carpels in fruit (orig.).

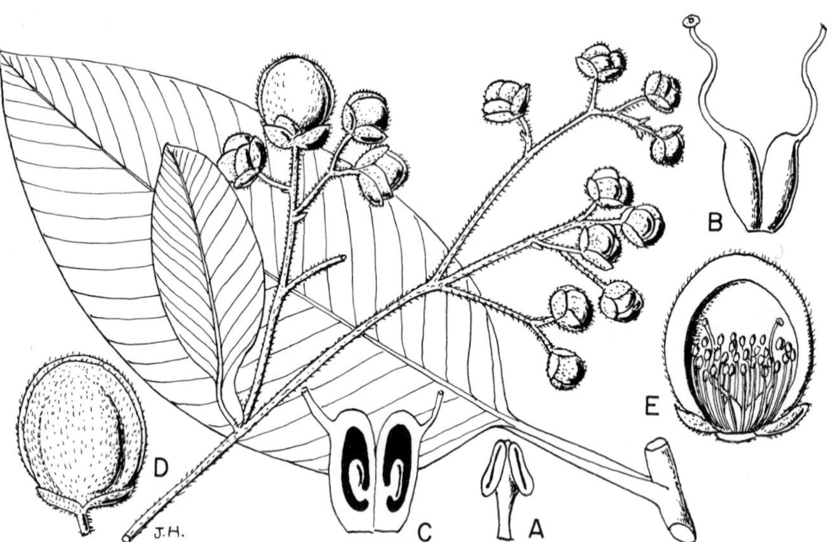

FIG. 35. In the genus *Davilla* (*Dilleniaceae*) the two inner sepals become enlarged and hardened into a purse-like protective envelope around the fruit; *Davilla grandifolia* Moric., Brazil. **A**, anther. **B**, carpels. **C**, vertical section of carpels. **D**, enlarged calyx. **E**, the same with one inner sepal removed. (Adapted from Martius FLORA BRAS.)

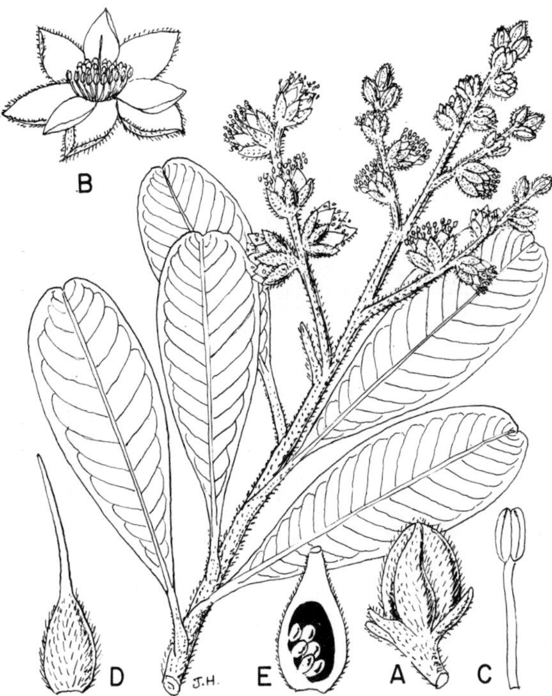

FIG. 36. *Trisema coriacea* Hook. f. (*Dilleniaceae*); note the gynoecium reduced to a single carpel, **D**. **A**, flower bud. **B**, open flower. **C**, stamen. **E**, vertical section of ovary (orig.).

and *Rosaceae* is very marked, the latter family being distinguished by its usually more perigynous or epigynous types of flowers and absence of endosperm from the seeds.

Dilleniaceae are generally distributed in the tropics, with the exception of Africa, where there is only one genus, *Tetracera*. This is the most widespread, occurring almost throughout the area occupied by the family as a whole, and an interesting development is the reduction in habit to suffruticose with woody underground rhizomes in the light forests of Rhodesia. The genus *Acrotrema* (Indo-Malaya) is also composed of herbs with woody rhizomes and radical fern-like leaves. Here we have two clear examples of herbs which have been undoubtedly derived from tree and shrub ancestors.

The genus *Wormia* connects the floras of Madagascar and Indo-Malaya. Of equal phytogeographic interest is *Hibbertia*, common to Madagascar, New Guinea and Australasia, and more largely represented in the last region, with a strong endemic element in New Caledonia. In Australia there are some remarkable endemic genera, *Candollea* in western, *Adrastea* in eastern, and *Pachynema* in north and western Australia.

Important anatomical characters are the bordered pits of the wood-prosenchyma, the frequent occurrence of broad medullary rays in the xylem, and there is usually no special type of stoma; there are no glandular hairs,

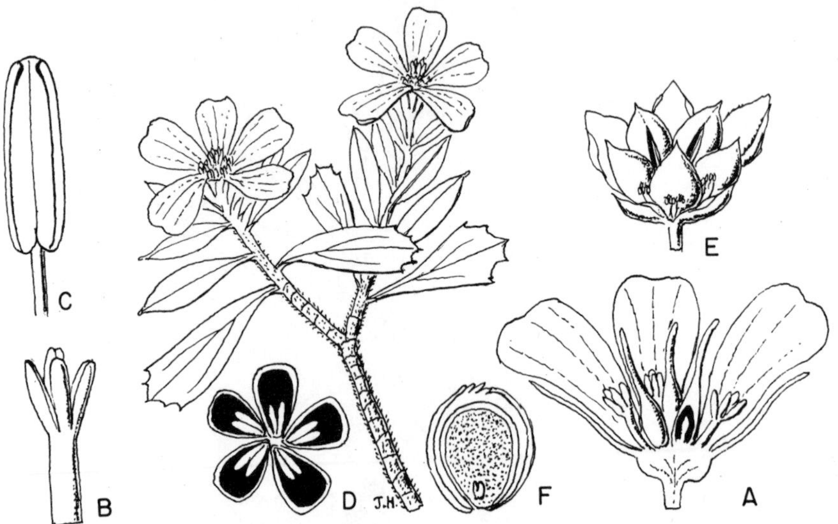

Fig. 37. *Candollea cuneiformis* Labill. (*Dilleniaceae*), Western Australia; the genus was named in honour of the celebrated Augustin Pyramus de Candolle (1778–1841), Professor of botany at Geneva and author of the PRODROMUS. **A**, vertical section of flower. **B**, column of stamens. **C**, anther. **D**, cross-section of carpels. **E**, fruiting carpels. **F**, vertical section of seed showing the minute embryo (orig.).

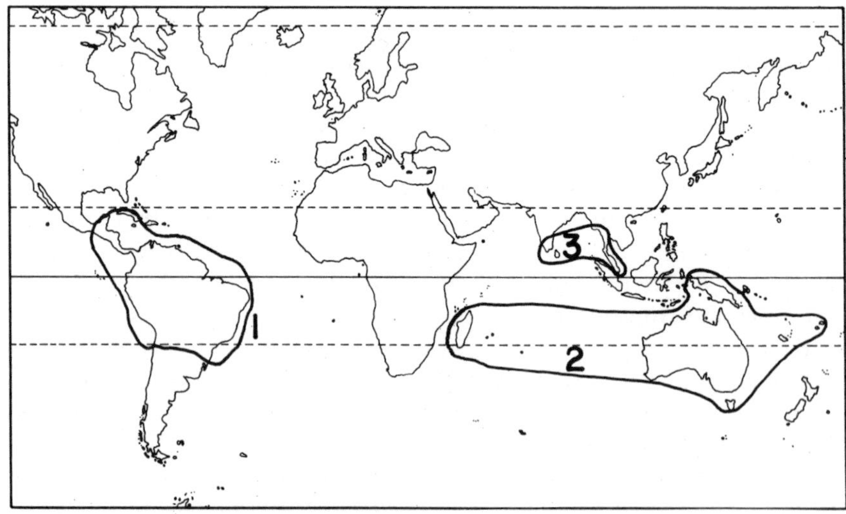

Map 4. Distribution of some genera of *Dilleniaceae*: **1**, *Davilla*. **2**, *Hibbertia*. **3**, *Acrotrema*.

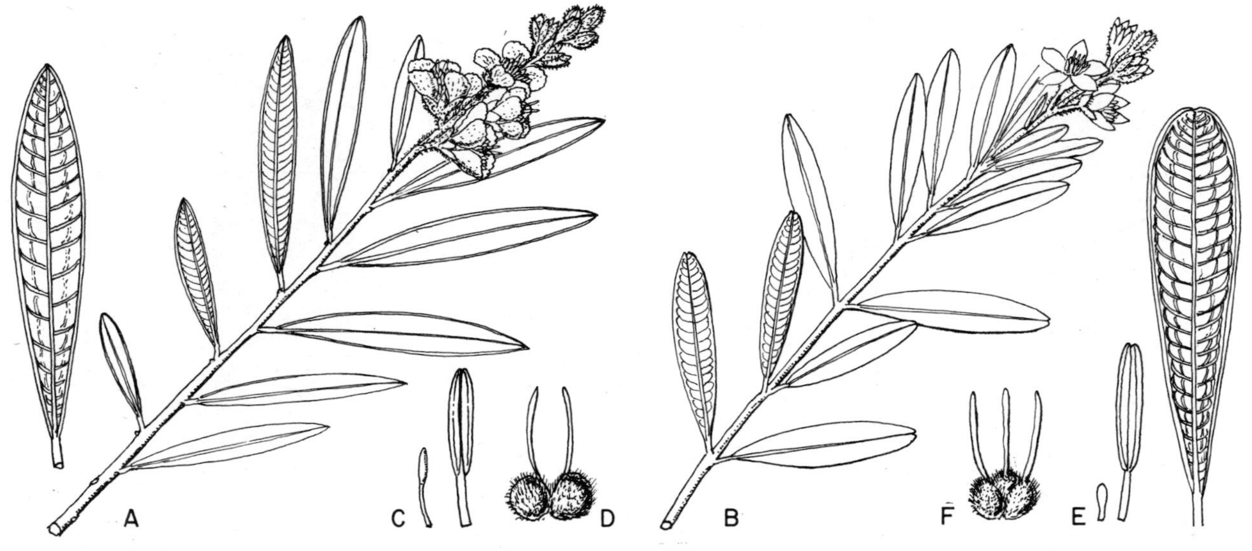

FIG. 38. The occurrence of the natural genus *Hibbertia* in Madagascar and Australasia (see Map 4) is a striking example of discontinuous distribution; similar distributions are noted in the genera *Adansonia* (*Bombacaceae*) and *Nepenthes*. On the left, **A**, *Hibbertia banksii* (R.Br.) Benth., N.E. Australia; on the right, **B**, *Hibbertia aubertii* DC., Madagascar. **C**, stamens and **D**, carpels of **A**. **E**, stamens and **F**, carpels of **B**. (Family *Dilleniaceae*) (orig.).

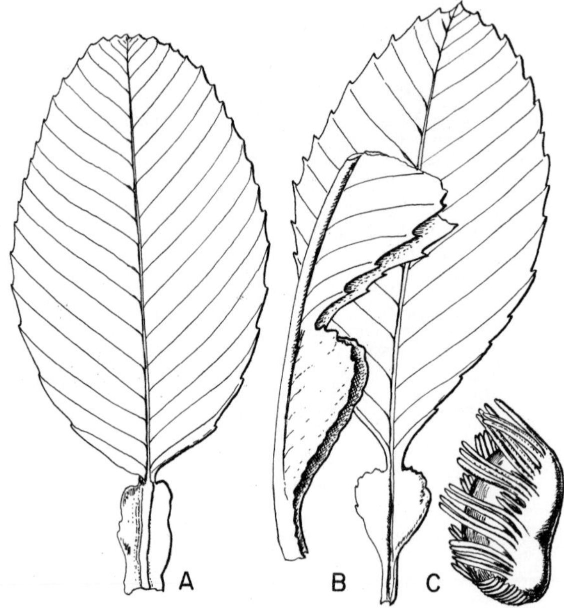

FIG. 39. Leaves of **A**, *Davilla wormiifolia* Baill., tropical South America. **B**, *Reifferscheidia speciosa* Presl, tropical South America, showing the stipules adnate to the petiole. **C**, seed and aril of *Tetracera lasiocarpa* Eichl., Brazil (*Dilleniaceae*).

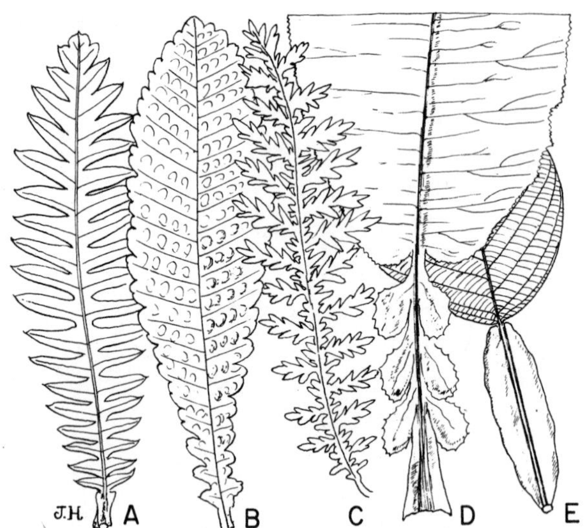

FIG. 40. Various types of leaves in the family *Dilleniaceae*. **A**, *Acrotrema thwaitesii* Hook. f., Ceylon. **B**, *Acrotrema uniflorum* var. *appendiculatum* Thwaites, Ceylon. **C**, *Acrotrema dissectum* Hook. f., Ceylon. **D**, *Acrotrema lyratum* Thwaites, Ceylon. **E**, *Davilla vaginata* Eichl., Brazil.

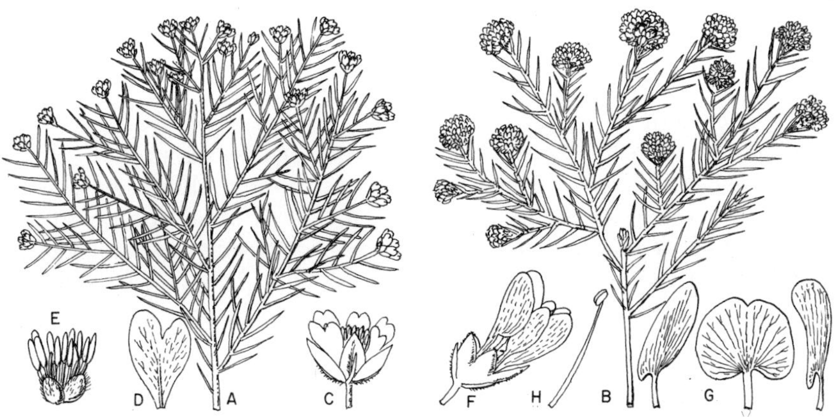

FIG. 41. Several species in the Australian flora bear a remarkable resemblance to each other, especially when not in flower, but are otherwise quite unrelated. Here are two examples; on the left, **A**, *Hibbertia acerosa* Benth. (*Dilleniaceae*)., on the right, **B**, *Pultenaea hibbertioides* Hook. f. (*Fabaceae*), a resemblance observed by Hook. f. when naming the latter. **C–E**, *Hibbertia*: **C**, flower. **D**, petal. **E**, carpels and stamens. **F–H**, *Pultenaea*: **F**, flower. **G**, petals. **H**, stamen (orig.).

and the clothing hairs consist of simple unicellular and stellate hairs, or rarely of peltate hairs (*Hibbertia* spp.).

The family **Connaraceae** is confined to the tropics and subtropics and is one of the most homogeneous (natural), showing little diversity in floral structure. They are woody throughout; a few are small trees, but the majority are shrubs and often scandent or subscandent. Bentham and Hooker f. said that their relationships were very complex, though they considered them to be related to *Anacardiaceae*, "differing from them by the bisexual flowers, pair of orthotropous ovules and superior radicle". I regard them as being more closely related to, though considerably more advanced than, *Dilleniaceae*, with which they share an apocarpous gynoecium and arillate seeds, but differing in their compound or unifoliate leaves.

In my GENERA OF FLOWERING PLANTS **1**, 163 (1964), I placed first those genera with pinnate leaves as being the most primitive, and they have mostly more than one carpel in the flowering stage, though often only one of them develops into fruit. The next reduction of the leaves are those genera with only 3 leaflets, and finally only 1 (unifoliolate). It is significant that in most of the latter there is only 1 carpel. The aestivation of the sepals also seems important, many of the pinnate-leaved genera having imbricate, while the more advanced genera have valvate sepals. Amongst the latter it should be noted that there is one genus, *Pseudellipanthus*, which has unisexual (probably dioecious) flowers with 4 fertile stamens and 4 staminodes, and this genus, therefore, may be considered to be the most highly evolved type in the family.

Connarus, the type genus, embraces about 120 species, in the tropics generally, the type, *C. monocarpus* Linn., in south India and Ceylon (see FAMILIES OF FLOWERING PLANTS, 2nd Ed. **1**, 145, Fig. 20): small trees or scandent shrubs; leaves imparipinnate or trifoliolate, rarely 1-foliolate; inflorescence terminal, paniculate; flowers bisexual; sepals 5 (4), imbricate or subvalvate; petals 5 or 4, often coherent in the middle; stamens 10, sometimes some staminodal and gland-like or bearing sterile anthers; anther-loculi often glandular at the base, connective with a glandular apex; carpel 1, reniform; ovules 2, collateral; fruit often stipitate; seed 1, shining; aril cupular or lateral, crenulate or laciniate, endosperm absent.

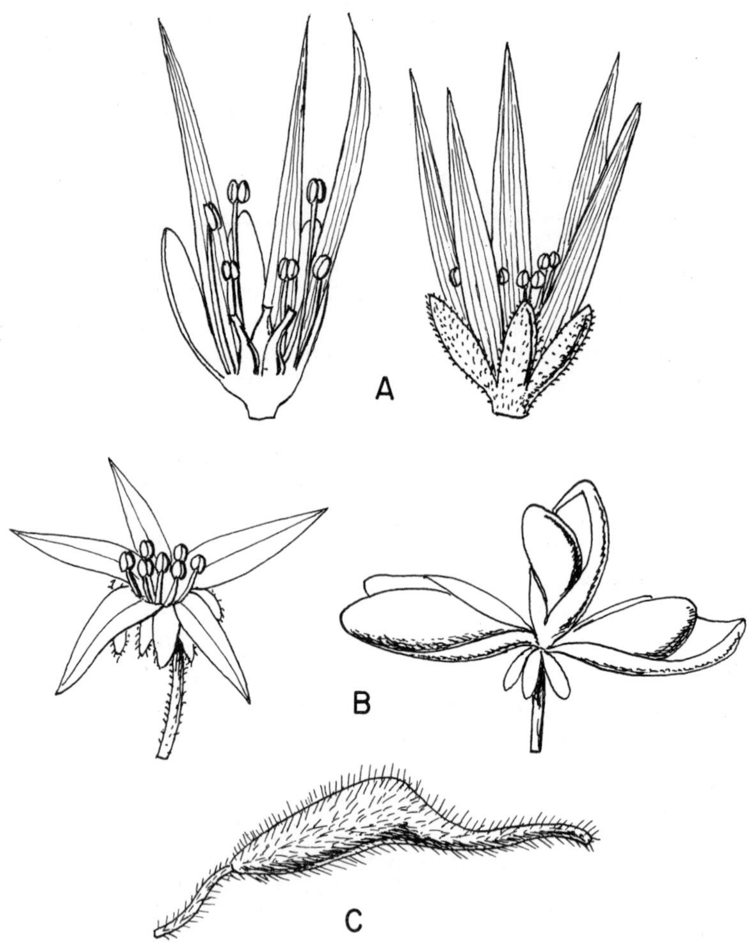

FIG. 42. **A**, Flowers of *Roureopsis thonneri* (De Wild.) Schellenb., tropical Africa. **B**, flower and fruit of *Taeniochlaena griffithii* Hook. f., Malacca. **C**, fruit of *Cnestis corniculata* Lam., west Africa (*Connaraceae*) (orig.).

Outstanding characteristics of other genera are the cauliflorous habit of *Jollydora*, the unisexual flowers of *Pseudellipanthus*, the loriform petals circinate in bud in *Roureopsis* (recalling those of *Hamamelis* (*Hamamelidaceae*)), *Taenichlaena*, *Spiropetalum*, and *Paxia*, stamens 5 fertile and 5 staminodal in *Hemandradenia* and *Ellipanthus*, 4 fertile and 4 staminodal in *Pseudellipanthus*; carpel indehiscent in *Jollydora* and *Hemandradenia*.

Crossosomataceae is a slightly different family with a perigynous type of flower and a short turbinate calyx-tube. Its arillate seed seems to bring it closer to *Dilleniaceae* than to *Rosaceae*, near to which it was placed by Engler.

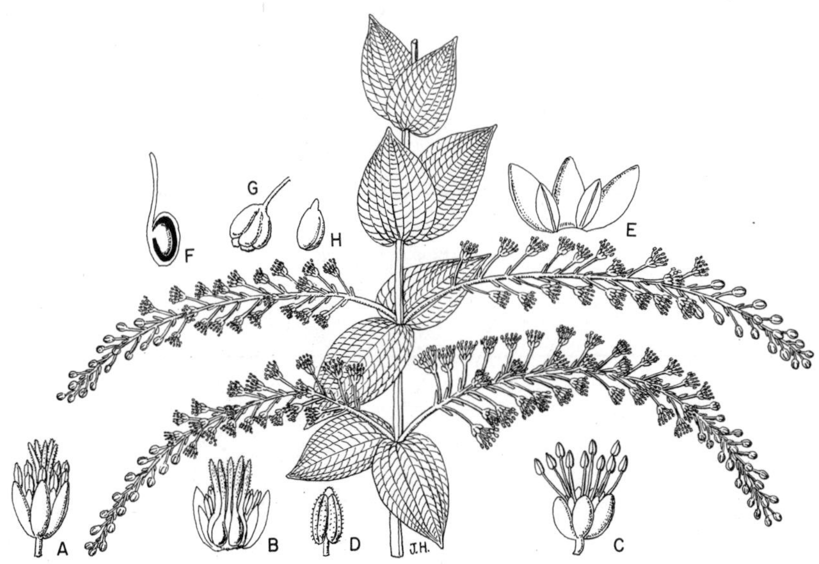

FIG. 43. *Coriaria ruscifolia* Linn. (*Coriariaceae*) has a remarkable distribution (see map). **A**, young flower. **B**, vertical section of same. **C**, older flower. **D**, anther. **E**, sepals and petals. **F**, vertical section of carpel. **G**, fruit. **H**, embryo.

There is also a considerable amount of endosperm in the seed, but there is none in *Rosaceae*. The family is monotypic, *Crossosoma californicum* Nutt., which occurs in California and New Mexico.

The family **Coriariaceae**,[1] also represented by a single genus, is rather a puzzle, and for want of a better position I have placed it near *Dilleniaceae*. The carpels and styles are free, a primitive feature, and the stamens are double the number of the petals, and therefore relatively primitive, but the leaves are opposite or verticillate (advanced character, other things being equal). It is doubtful if there is any affinity with the Order SAPINDALES, where

[1] Including *Sarcoccaceae* Dulac (1867).

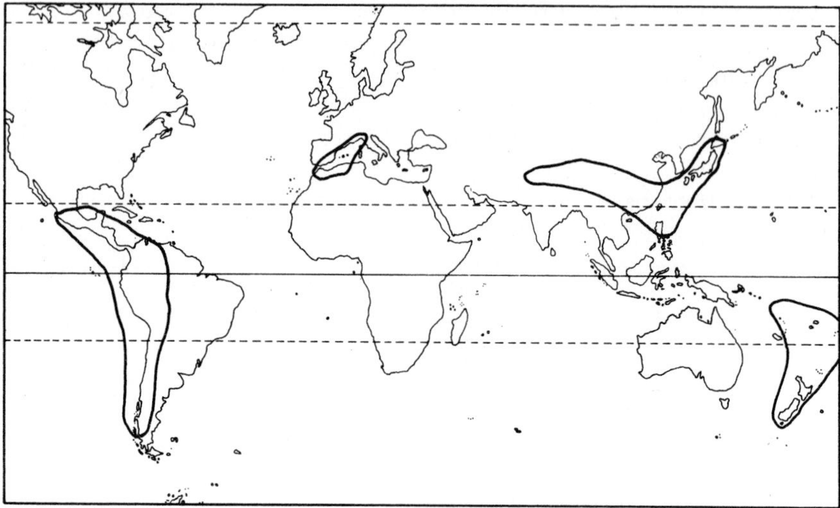

Map 5. The genus *Coriaria* has a remarkable discontinuous distribution, perhaps indication of an ancient group in which the carpels have remained free.

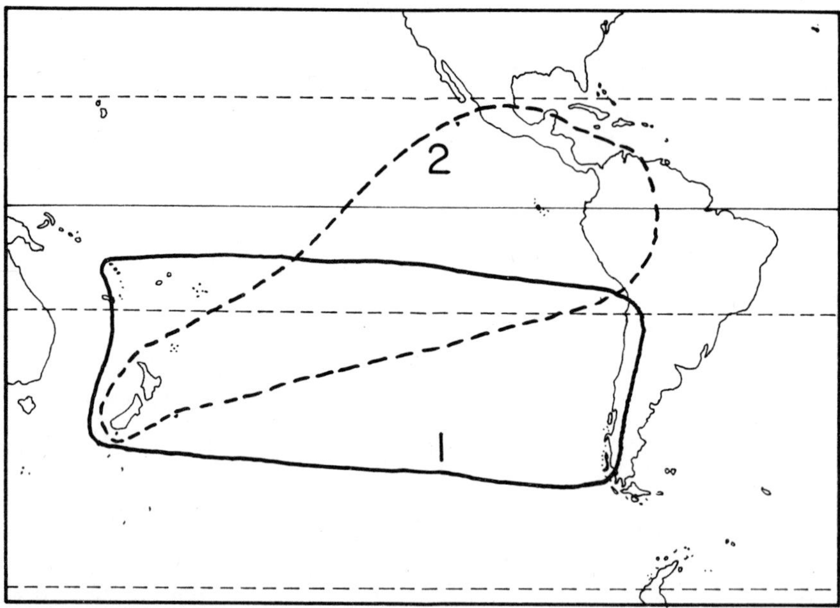

Map 6. Two species of *Coriaria* occur both in New Zealand and far distant South America, pointing to a former land connection. Range of **1**, *Coriaria ruscifolia* Linn.; **2**, *C. thymifolia* Humbl. & Bonpl. (see Fig. 43).

this small family is placed by Engler. Its discontinuous distribution (see Map 5) suggests also a more primitive type than is found in SAPINDALES. Two species of *Coriaria* are common to western America and the Australasian Islands, including New Zealand (see Map 6). Little is to be learned from the anatomical structure regarding affinity.

Coriaria ruscifolia Linn. (Fig. 43) is widely distributed in the Pacific (see Map 6). Cheeseman (ILL. NEW ZEAL. FL. **1**, t. 30 (1914)) wrote of this interesting species (which occurs in New Zealand, Fiji, Samoa, New Hebrides, Solomon Islands, Tahiti, and indeed in far away Chile) as follows:

> Few New Zealand plants are more widely known than *Coriaria ruscifolia* Linn., the Tutu of the Maoris. . . . This is principally due to its remarkable toxic qualities, which in the early days of the colony, and in a smaller degree up to the present time [i.e. 1914], have led to great losses among the flocks and herds of the settlers, and have even caused no small amount of mortality among human beings. . . . The Tutu was originally discovered during Cook's first expedition, and was at once found to have a wide distribution. . . . The poison is present in the young shoots, leaves and seeds of the plant. These are readily eaten by stock, and under certain circumstances, which do not appear to be fully understood, often cause wholesale poisoning. In one case as many as forty-three head of cattle out of a herd of sixty were lost.

Cheeseman goes on to state that in 1909 Dr. F. Fitchett published in the TRANS. NEW ZEAL. INST. **xli**, 287–366, a very full and elaborate account of the physiological action of Tutin, in which he reviews the work of all previous observers, and gives details of numerous experiments by himself showing the behaviour of various animals after the administration of Tutin:

> Notwithstanding the toxic qualities of the plant, a pleasant beverage was obtained by the Maoris from the juicy berries. These were collected in great quantities, and the juice expressed, care being taken to strain out the poisonous seeds through a sieve. . . . The expressed juice was collected in calabashes, and was drunk with avidity. When paying a visit to the island of Mokoia, in Lake Rotorua, seeing almost every available receptacle in the little village was filled with the purplish liquid, the sweet and pleasant taste of which proved most refreshing after our tedious row across the lake.

Order 6. ROSALES

(*Fam. Fl. Pl.* **1**, 148)

Families: **Rosaceae, Dichapetalaceae, Calycanthaceae.**

Path of evolution of **Rosaceae** and groups derived from this basic stock: MAGNOLIALES → DILLENIALES → ROSALES, leading to the following *Caesalpiniaceae*, *Mimosaceae*, *Fabaceae* (*Papilionaceae*) (climax); and in a different line to HAMAMELIDALES, FAGALES, URTICALES (climax) and CASUARINALES (climax).

Rosaceae[1] is a family which may be studied with advantage by those interested in phylogeny. Although fairly advanced in certain characters, they seem to be the basic stock whence several very important groups of plants have been evolved, and important especially from an economic point of view. From this basic stock has been evolved on the one hand the vast assemblage of plants embraced by the Order LEGUMINALES, families *Caesalpiniaceae*, *Mimosaceae* and *Fabaceae* (*Papilionaceae*), and on the other that great and controversial group familiar to older generations of botanists, the "Amentiferae", characterised mainly by having a catkin-like inflorescence. As already pointed out, the idea of regarding this type of inflorescence as representing a primitive type of structure has probably been responsible for clogging the minds of some botanists in the search for a phylogenetic classification. One may even venture to wonder whether the similarity of such catkins to the male strobili of the *Pinaceae* was originally responsible for this idea. It might have been as simple as that!

The difference between *Ranunculaceae* and *Rosaceae* has often been a source of trouble for students of elementary botany. This may be settled at once. The seeds of *Ranunculaceae* are full of endosperm and the embryo is very small; those of *Rosaceae* have no endosperm and the embryo is large and fills the seed. These are very important facts from a biological standpoint, for the *Rosaceae* are thus sufficiently advanced to dispense with the reserve food-material still maintained in the more primitive *Ranunculaceae*. Then there is

---

[1] Including *Fragariaceae* Nestler (1816). *Chrysobalanaceae* R.Br. (1818). *Sanguisorbiaceae* Loiseleur (1819). *Agrimoniaceae* S. F. Gray (1812). *Drupaceae* S. F. Gray (1821). *Pomaceae* S. F. Gray (1821). *Ulmariaceae* S. F. Gray (1821). *Dryadaceae* S. F. Gray (1821). *Amygdalaceae* Bartling (1830). *Spiraeaceae* Bartling (1830). *Quillaiaceae* D. Don (1831). *Mespiliaceae* C. H. Schultz (1832). *Cliffortiaceae* Mart. (1835). *Prunaceae* Burnett (1835). *Pyraceae* Burnett (1835). *Hirtellaceae* Horaninow (1847). *Neilliaceae* Miquel (1855). *Alchemillaceae* J. G. Agardh (1858). *Cercocarpaceae* J. G. Agardh (1858). *Coleogynaceae* J. G. Agardh (1858). *Lindleyaceae* J. G. Agardh (1858). *Neuradaceae* J. G. Agardh (1858). *Potentillaceae* J. G. Agardh (1858). *Rhodotypaceae* J. G. Agardh (1858). *Stylobasiaceae* J. G. Agardh (1858). *Malaceae* Small (1903).

the more easily observed difference in the floral axis or receptacle (hypanthium); in *Ranunculaceae* the axis is more or less conical or convex, the sepals, petals and stamens being below the ovaries in vertical section. In *Rosaceae*, however, the sepals, petals and stamens are mostly around or above the ovaries, the axis or receptacle being more or less concave to tubular in vertical section. In addition *Rosaceae* have usually a very different and more advanced type of inflorescence, frequently racemose or corymbose, as in the bird-cherry, *Padus racemosa* Gilib., and the genus *Crataegus* respectively, to give only two examples.

The flowers of most *Ranunculaceae* are solitary, a primitive character as a rule. It will assist the student, too, if he can realise that the two families are totally different in their origin, their apparent similarity being due to parallel evolution of their floral parts. *Ranunculaceae* have originated from a more primitive herbaceous stock, but the *Rosaceae* are predominantly woody and have descended from woody ancestors, such as, for example, *Dilleniaceae*. To appreciate these points one must become familiar with the tropical representatives and the vast assemblage of *Rosaceae* in the Himalayan and Chinese regions in which many ancient types of flowering plants are preserved. A study only of European examples is not sufficient to allow one even to understand or contradict these speculations!

The type genus of the family is, needless to say, *Rosa*, though amongst the large number of genera its flowers are anything but primitive, the species hybridising freely in nature. The more than 150 species of *Rosa* are found in Europe, Asia, Ethiopia (one only) and North America, but none south of the equator; lectotype *R. canina* Linn., Europe (Fig. 44).

They are much branched, trailing or scandent shrubs or shrublets, mostly heavily armed with prickles; leaves alternate, imparipinnate, rarely 1-foliolate or reduced to connate leaf-like stipules; stipules adnate to the petiole (leaf-rhachis); flowers solitary or corymbose, white, yellow, pink or red; calyx without an epicalyx; tube (receptacle) globose to ventricose, constricted at the mouth; lobes 5 (4), free, more or less foliaceous, often pinnatisect, imbricate in bud; petals 5 (4), free, imbricate; disk lining the calyx-tube, often silky, the mouth annular and almost closing the calyx; stamens numerous, inserted at the mouth of the disk; carpels numerous, free inside the tube; style ventral; ovule solitary, pendulous; achenes numerous, very small, included in the berry-like calyx-tube; seed pendulous.

For our notes about *Rosaceae* we have only space to consider the main groups of the family, mentioning some of the larger genera. Probably the most primitive tribe is *Quillajeae*, the leaves of which are not unlike some *Dilleniaceae*, though the valvate calyx reminds one of some *Tiliaceae*, perhaps due to parallel evolution. In the genus *Quillaja* the carpels are 5 and free from each other, and in fruit they spread in a stellate manner, as in the genus *Sterculia* (*Sterculiaceae*). This tribe is confined to tropical America where

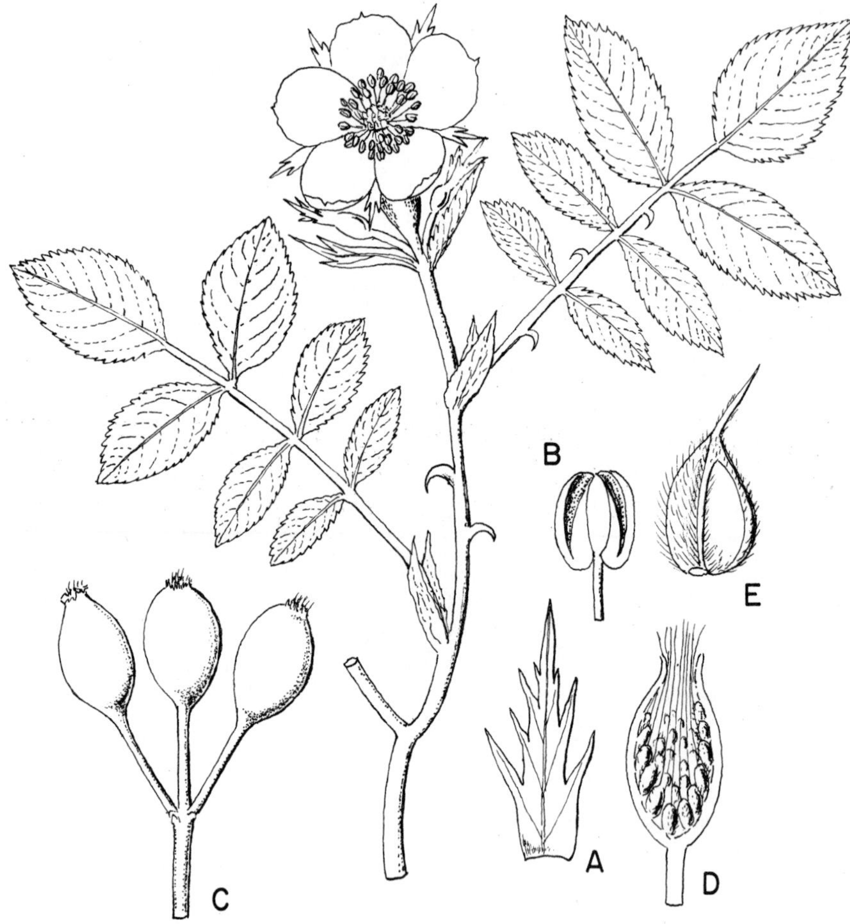

FIG. 44. *Rosa canina* Linn., the type species of the type genus of *Rosaceae*. **A**, calyx-lobe. **B**, anther. **C**, fruits. **D**, vertical section of fruit. **E**, achene (orig.).

there are also numerous species of *Dilleniaceae*. In *Quillaja* the disk is remarkable; it is thick and deeply 5-lobed, the lobes opposite the sepals, each supporting one of the 10 stamens, whilst the other 5 stamens are inserted in the sinus of the disk-lobes opposite the petals; the seeds are winged (see Fig. 45).

The next and more advanced tribe is the *Chrysobalaneae*, more widely distributed than *Quillajeae*, but mainly in the southern tropics. An important feature is the superior ovary composed of 1 carpel with a basal style. The more primitive genera of this tribe are those in which the ovary is inserted at the base of the calyx-tube. This occurs in *Chrysobalanus* (Fig. 46), which is common to both Africa and America (see Map 7). A derived genus is

FIG. 45. *Quillaja saponaria* Moll., Chilean Andes, a primitive genus of *Rosaceae* with free carpels; infusion of bark used as soap. **A**, open flower. **B**, male flower-buds. **C**, floral diagram. **D**, fruits. **E**, seed.

Licania, confined to tropical America, with much reduced or absent petals. Besides the unilateral style, there is a tendency in this group to a unilateral position for the stamens, as in *Hibbertia* (*Dilleniaceae*), especially in some species of *Licania*. This feature is more fully carried out in *Hirtella* (Fig. 47, **A–C**) and *Couepia*, whilst in *Acioa* (*Griffonia*) (Fig. 47, **D**), it is developed to a marked degree; the calyx-tube is long and slender and the stamens are united into a long slender much-exserted ligule-like structure. The most reduced example of the tribe is *Parastemon* (Fig. 48), the polygamous-dioecious flowers of which are very small and racemose and the stamens reduced to 2.

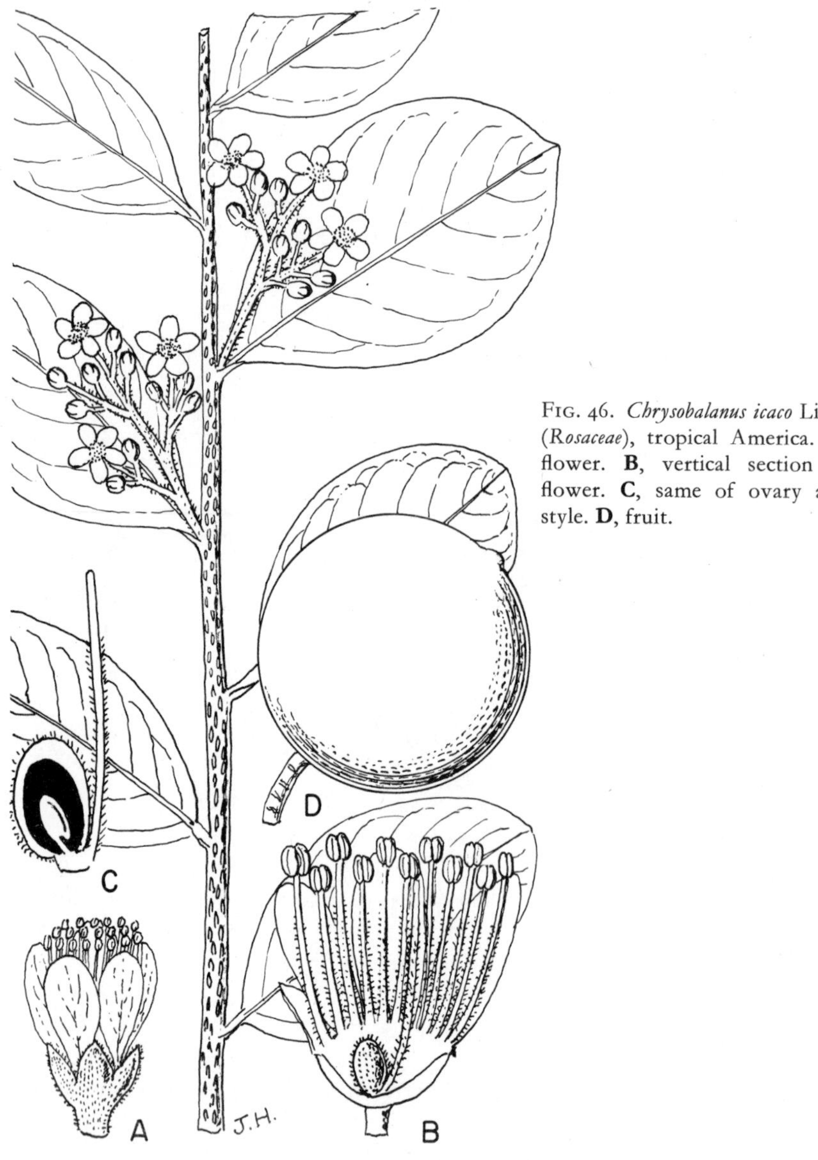

FIG. 46. *Chrysobalanus icaco* Linn. (*Rosaceae*), tropical America. **A**, flower. **B**, vertical section of flower. **C**, same of ovary and style. **D**, fruit.

Undoubtedly the next less primitive group is the tribe containing the cherries, the *Pruneae*. Amongst the genera there is one, *Nuttallia*, which is still apocarpous; the 15 stamens are not inserted at the same level within the cupular receptacle, 10 being at the top along with the petals, whilst 5 are attached some distance below. This floral structure seems to show also a

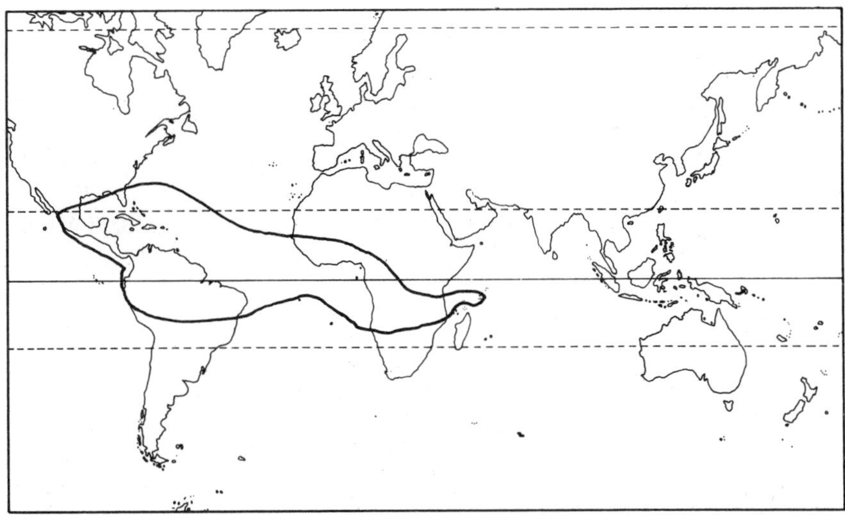

Map. 7. The genus *Chrysobalanus* (*Rosaceae*) closely connects the tropical floras of America and Africa.

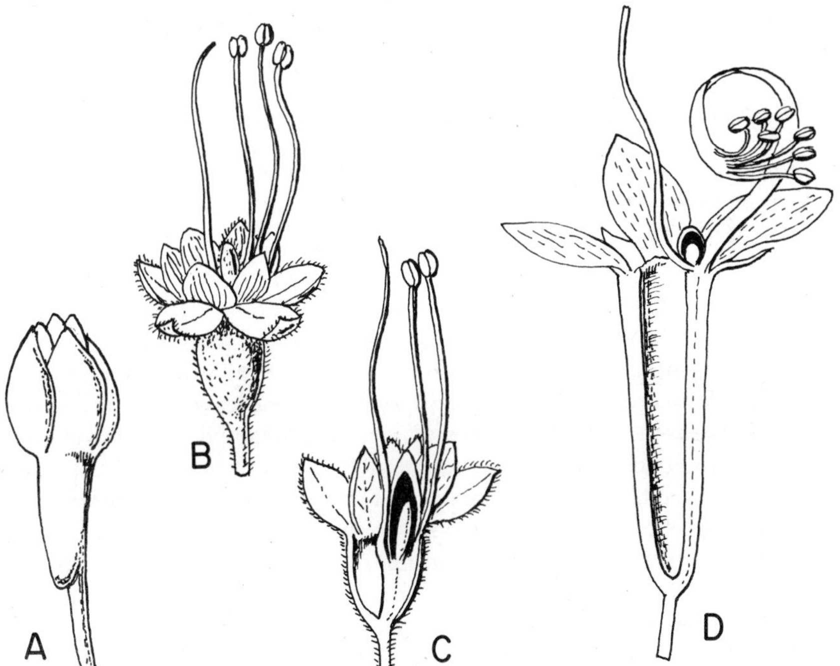

Fig. 47. **A**, bud. **B**, flower. **C**, section of flower of *Hirtella triandra* Swartz (*Rosaceae*, tribe *Chrysobalaneae*), West Indies. **D**, The flower of *Acioa guianensis* Aubl. (*Rosaceae*) is of a very advanced type, a long tubular receptacle ("hypanthium"), a strap-shaped bundle of 9 stamens inserted with the petals and ovary at the mouth of the tube; style basal.

FIG. 48. *Parastemon urophyllus* A.DC. (*Rosaceae*), Indo-Malaya; flowers reduced almost to a minimum with only 2 stamens and a single carpel with a basal style; a striking example of economy in floral structure. **A**, flower. **B**, the same with petals removed. **C**, disk. **D** and **E**, fruits (orig.).

link with the *Dilleniaceae*, in which there are numerous stamens in several whorls or spirals, and the bulk of ROSALES, where the stamens are grouped together in a single ring although perhaps still in several series. In the monotypic Himalayan genus *Maddenia*, the nervation of the leaves is typically that of the *Dilleniaceae*, and there are still 2 carpels retained; the flowers are polygamous-dioecious, and the essentially male flowers have only one carpel. We have here in the separation of the sexes a character more fully carried out in the old group popularly known as the "Amentiferae".

A student with a little imagination might recognise the "germs" of the vast genus *Crataegus* in *Prinsepia*, and of *Cotoneaster* in *Plagiospermum*, while *Prunus* is a large and successful climax genus of this tribe.

Tribe *Pomeae*, which contains the genus *Pyrus* (Apples and Pears), beside *Crataegus* (Hawthorns), and *Cotoneaster* and *Amelanchier*, seems to consist of climax genera derived from tribe *Pruneae*. The ovary or ovaries are united with the receptacle (hypanthium) and the number of carpels varies from 1 to 5, exactly as in *Pruneae*. The stamens, however, are much more uniform,

(continued on p. 62)

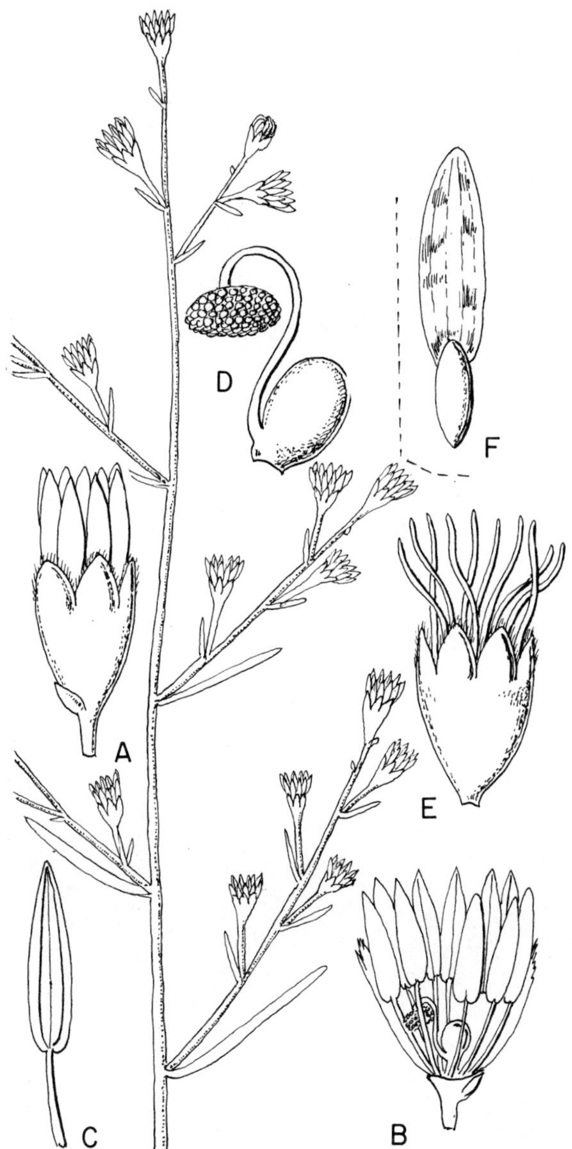

FIG. 49. Aptly named generically, *Stylobasium lineare* Nees (*Rosaceae*), Australia. **A**, flower with calyx and stamens, the latter looking like petals, which are absent. **B**, stamens and gynoecium. **C**, stamen. **D**, gynoecium. **E**, female flower, devoid of anthers. **F**, winged seed of *Kageneckia oblonga* Ruiz & Pavon, Chile (also *Rosaceae*) (orig.).

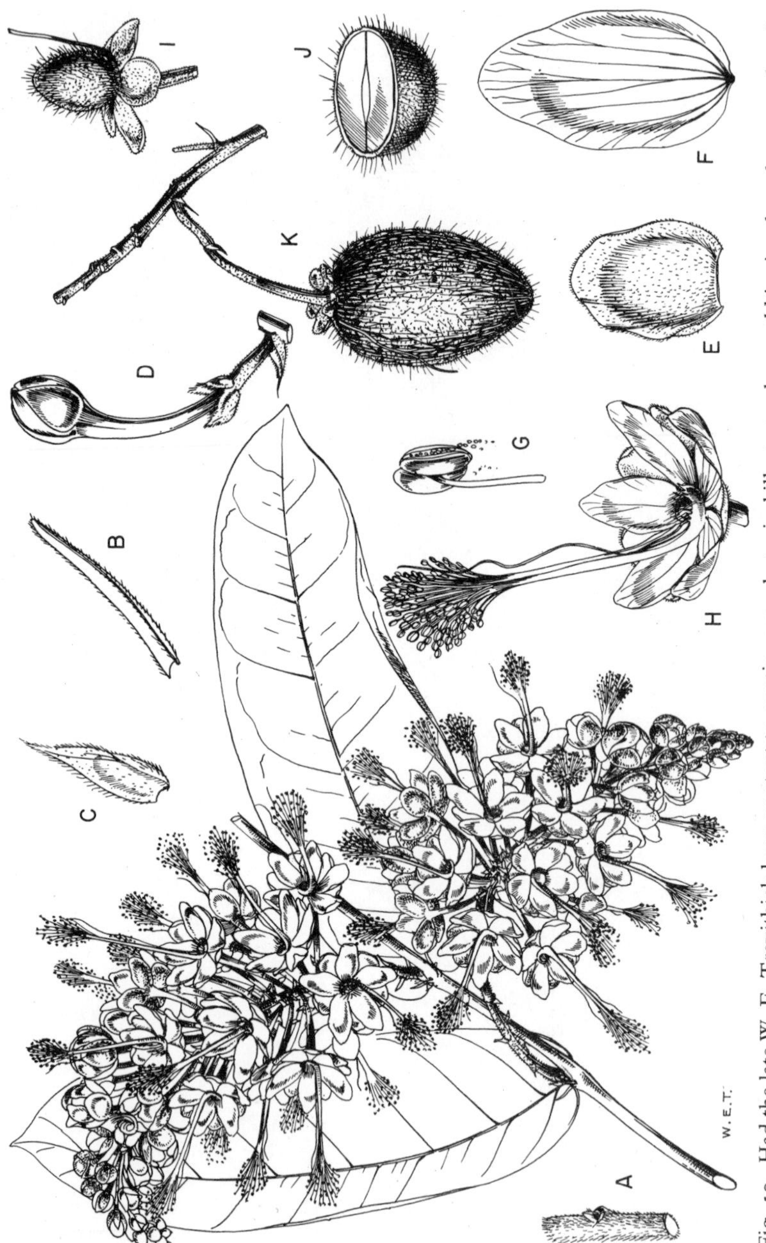

Fig. 50. Had the late W. E. Trevithick been content to continue as a botanical illustrator he would in time have been equal to the great Walter Fitch in Bentham and Hooker's time. This is his drawing of *Acioa pallescens* Baill. (*Rosaceae*), tropical Africa. **A**, portion of peduncle. **B**, stipule. **C**, bract. **D**, flower-bud. **E**, calyx-lobe. **F**, petal. **G**, stamen. **H**, flower showing the remarkable bundle of stamens and ovary. **I**, ovary showing the basal style. **J**, cross-section of seed. **K**, fruit.

FIG. 51. *Parinari excelsa* Sabine (*Rosaceae*), tropical Africa. **A**, petiole and base of leaf. **B**, flowering branchlet. **C**, vertical section of flower showing the unilateral position of the ovary and the insertion of the stamens. **D**, ovary and basal style. **E**, fruit. (From Hutchinson and Dalziel, FLORA OF WEST TROPICAL AFRICA.)

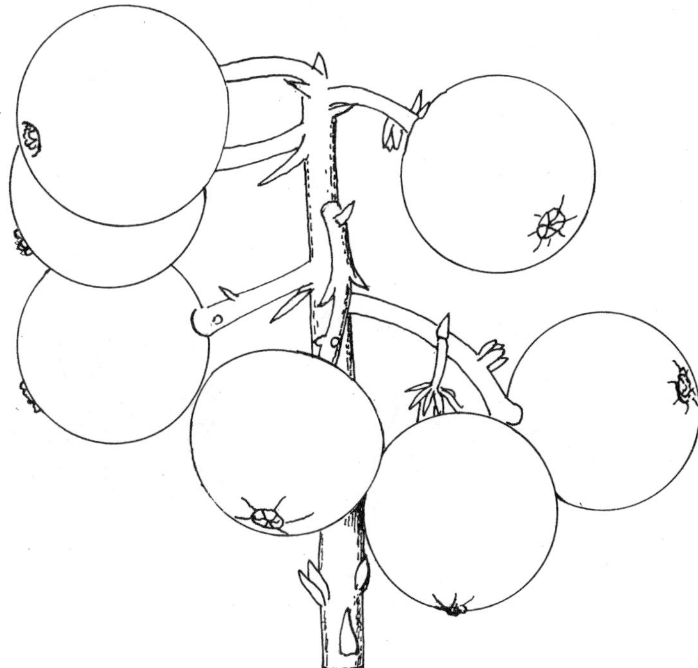

FIG. 52. The Loquat, *Eriobotrya japonica* (Thunb.) Lindl. (*Rosaceae*); a native of China but cultivated in most warm countries; the flesh is slightly acid and not so sweet as most tropical fruits; highly esteemed in the Orient and grown from early days; used fresh and made into jellies, tarts and sauces. Japan produces a large quantity.

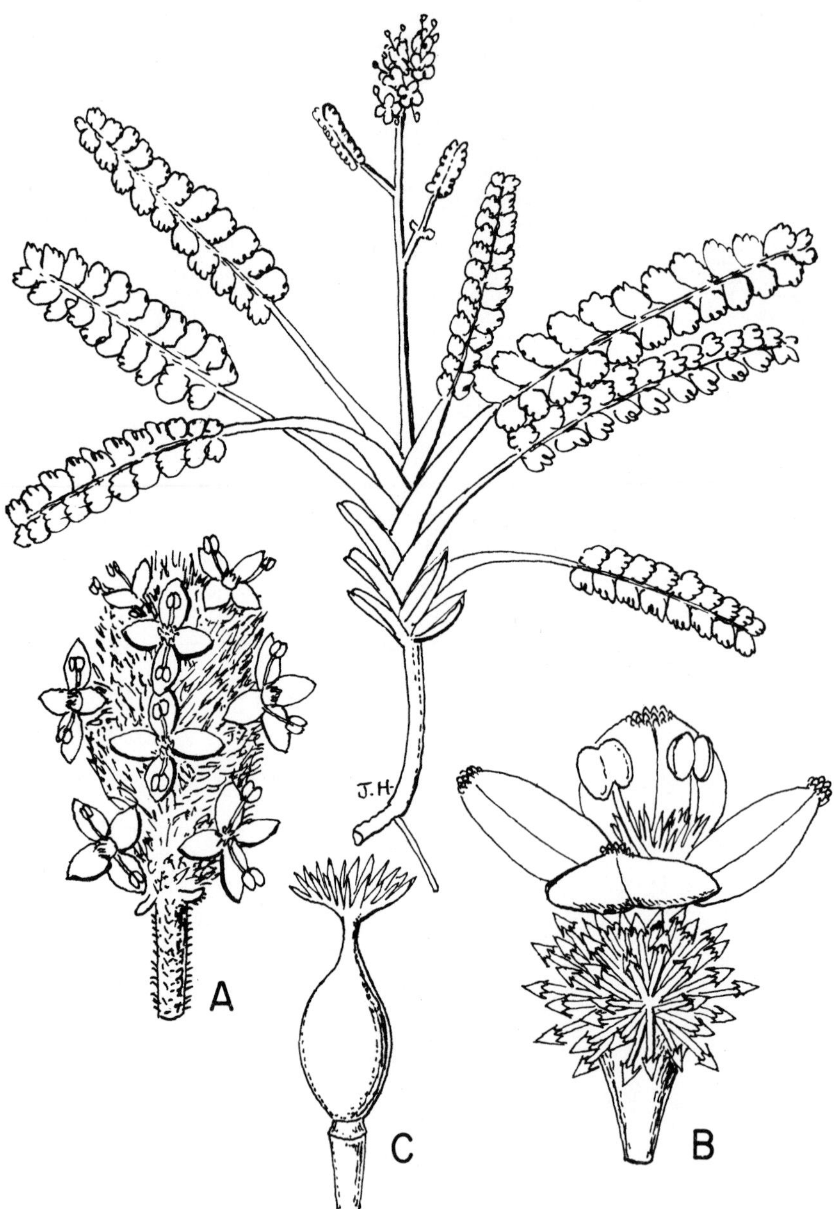

FIG. 53. *Acaena pumila* Vahl (*Rosaceae*), Chile; the distribution of this genus suggests its origin in the Southern Hemisphere, in South Africa, Australia, New Zealand and South America, reaching as far north as California. **A**, inflorescence. **B**, single flower showing the barbed bristles on the ovary (and later on the fruit). **C**, gynoecium.

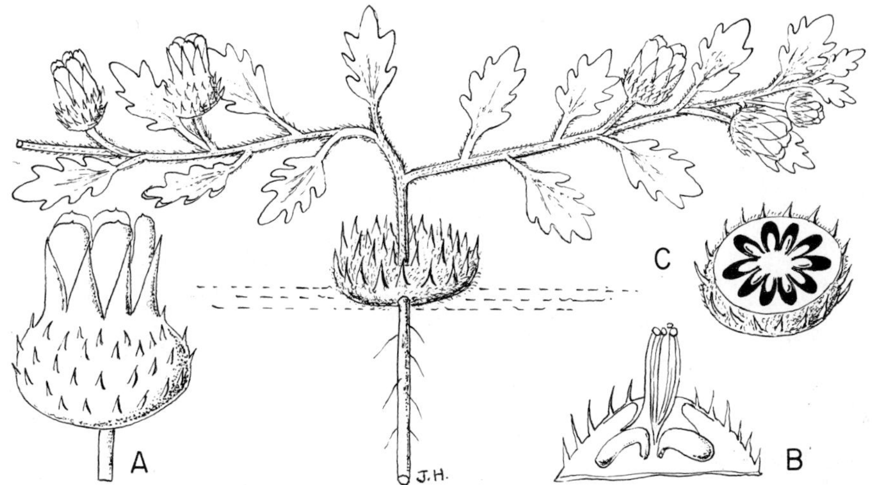

FIG. 54. *Neurada procumbens* Linn. (*Rosaceae*), in which the old receptacle or calyx-tube persists around the root of the seedling. **A**, flower. **B**, vertical section of fruit. **C**, cross-section of ovary (orig.).

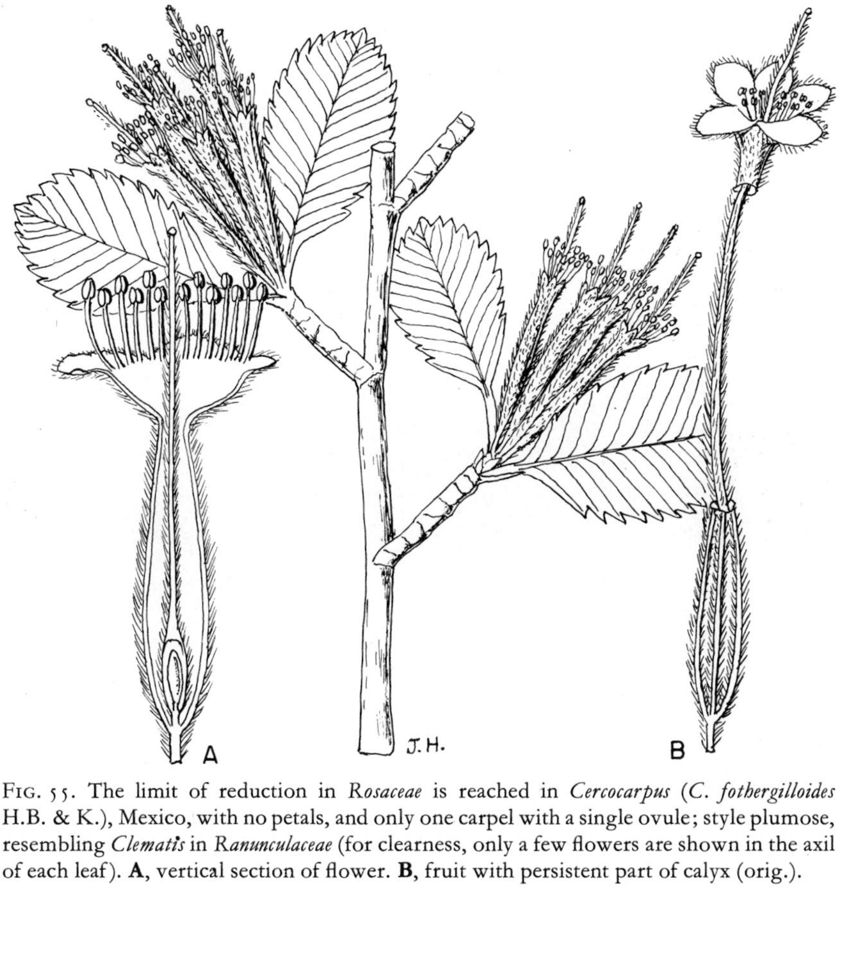

FIG. 55. The limit of reduction in *Rosaceae* is reached in *Cercocarpus* (*C. fothergilloides* H.B. & K.), Mexico, with no petals, and only one carpel with a single ovule; style plumose, resembling *Clematis* in *Ranunculaceae* (for clearness, only a few flowers are shown in the axil of each leaf). **A**, vertical section of flower. **B**, fruit with persistent part of calyx (orig.).

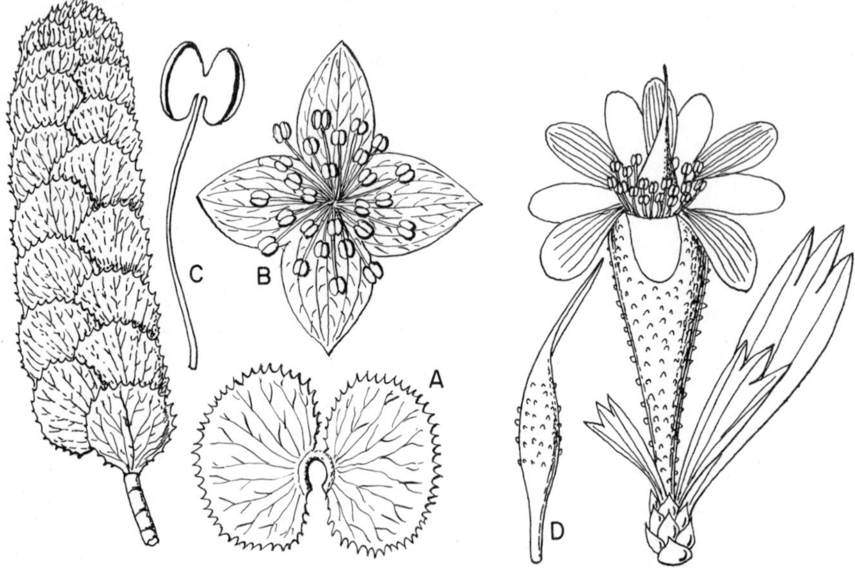

FIG. 56. **A**, bract. **B**, flower. **C**, stamen of *Cliffortia crenata* Linn. f., South Africa. **D**, leaves, flower and carpel of *Purshia tridentata* DC., North America (*Rosaceae*) (orig.).

FIG. 57. *Lindleya mespiloides* H.B. & K. (*Rosaceae*), Mexico, on limestone hills; flowers white and scented. The genus was named in honour of the famous British botanist, John Lindley, of whom the authors stated: "Joannes Lindley, adolescens flagrantissimi in botanicen felicissimique studii, cujus nomen eruditis eximiisque scriptis nobile, huic plantae indidimus". **A**, anthers, back and front. **B**, flower showing sepals and carpels. **C**, gynoecium. **D**, vertical section of carpel showing ovule. **E**, stipule (orig.).

FIG. 58. This fine drawing by Trevithick scarcely needs a legend except to give the specific name, *Rubus apetalus* Poir. (*Rosaceae*). **A**, stipule. **B**, flower. **C**, carpel. **D**, section of same. **E**, fruit. **F**, ripe achene. (From Hutchinson and Dalziel, FLORA OF WEST TROPICAL AFRICA.)

and show far fewer modifications than in that tribe. The separation of *Pomaceae* as a family has not found much favour among taxonomists.

Of the remaining tribes three have retained a superior ovary, *Spiraeae*, *Rubeae* and *Potentilleae*. The last mentioned is probably the most advanced especially on account of the presence of an epicalyx of bracteoles such as we find in some *Malvaceae*, and of the uniovulate carpels; many of the *Potentilleae* are, moreover, herbaceous, and grow predominantly in the Northern Hemisphere. Several genera of *Potentilleae* show a very advanced character in the reduction of the number of the carpels to one, and in some the style is elongated and plumosely hairy just as in *Clematis* and *Anemone* in *Ranunculaceae*, showing parallelism with these genera but not relationship. Nearly all are North American.

Cercocarpus seems to be the climax genus in this small and interesting group, with no petals, the single carpel being enclosed by the calyx which eventually splits off and persists around the style (see Fig. 55).

Rosaceae are very important from an economic standpoint, for they include a great variety of fruits such as the apple, pear, plum, cherry, peach, apricot, strawberry and raspberry. And during the last war wild rose-hips were collected and Rose Hip Syrup was extracted, being very rich in vitamin C. Our gardens, also, would be poor indeed without *Rosaceae*, for example the ornamental flowering Cherries, Apple blossom, Cotoneasters, Mountain Ashes and above all Roses!

Ladies may still be interested in the delicate perfume called Otto or Attar of Rose and Rosewater. The source of the best perfume is the Damask Rose, *Rosa damascena* Mill., widely cultivated in the valleys and on the southern slopes of the Balkan Mountains in Bulgaria.[1] The Otto, or Attar, is obtained by distillation from the fresh flowers, and besides its use in perfumery is employed in lozenges, dentifrices, ointments and toilet preparations. Oil of Rose is distilled from *Rosa centifolia* and other species.

Most garden apples have been derived by crossing and selection from the common Crab Apple, *Malus pumila* L., which grows wild in our hedge-rows, and makes delicious jelly. Those used for making Cider are not far removed from the wild type, and some of the best come from Devonshire as we are reminded in the popular song "Glorious Devon". Other counties, especially Hereford, are also famous for their cider. Garden pears have been derived mostly from the wild pear of Europe and Asia, *Pyrus communis* L.

We cannot take leave of this interesting family *Rosaceae* without mentioning one of our own native and most beautiful trees, the Mountain Ash or Rowan, *Sorbus aucuparia* Linn., whose fruits are so ornamental in autumn; nor should we forget Shakespeare's delightful lines about the Eglantine in A MIDSUMMER NIGHT'S DREAM:

---

[1] See THE ROSE INDUSTRY OF BULGARIA by Christo Christoff, transl. by C. H. Piesse (1890).

I know a bank where the wild Thyme blows,
Where Oxlips and the nodding Violet grows;
Quite over-canopied with luscious Woodbine,
With sweet Musk-Roses and with Eglantine.

The late Canon Ellacombe in THE PLANT-LORE AND GARDEN-CRAFT OF SHAKESPEARE stated that if the poet had not written more than these two passages [only one of which is quoted here], they would have told sufficiently of his love for simple flowers, Eglantine being the Sweet Briar, *Rosa rubiginosa* L.

FIG. 59. A characteristic Trevithick drawing of *Dichapetalum toxicarium* Engl. (*Dichapetalaceae*), tropical Africa. **A**, flower. **B**, longitudinal section of same. **C**, petal. **D**, stamen. **E**, gynoecium. **F**, fruits. **G**, transverse section of fruit. Some species of this genus are poisonous to stock, especially in southern Africa (see also Fig. 60).

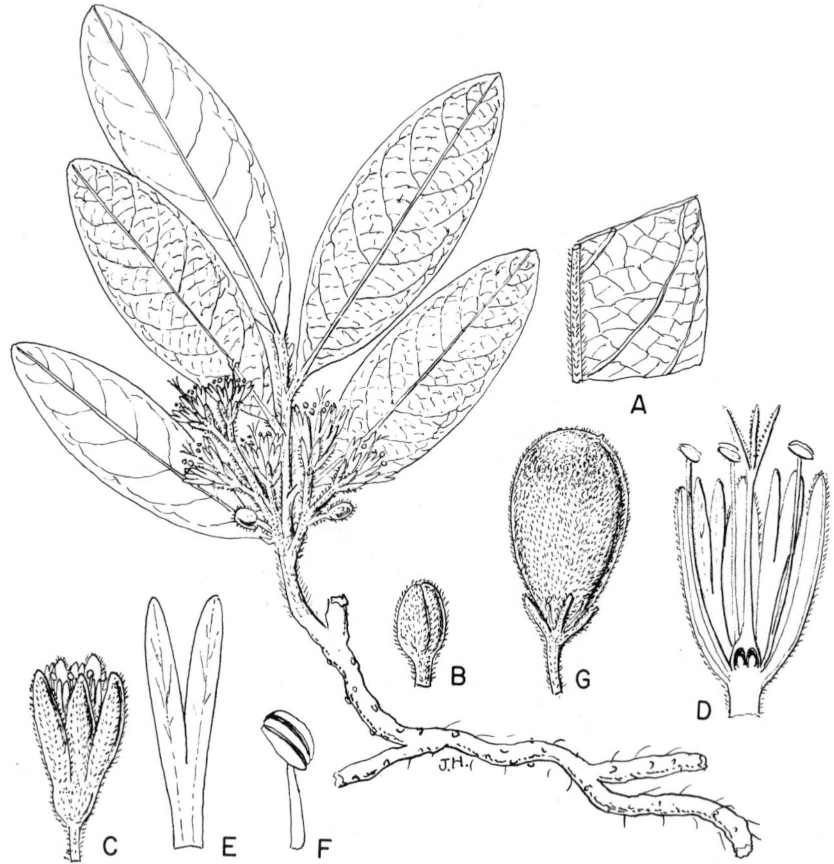

FIG. 60. *Dichapetalum cymosum* (Hook. f.) Engl. (*Dichapetalaceae*), poisonous to stock in southern Africa (see text). **A**, portion of under surface of leaf showing venation. **B**, flower-bud. **C**, flower. **D**, vertical section of flower. **E**, petal. **F**, stamen. **G**, fruit (orig.).

According to Solereder, constant anatomical characters are almost wanting in *Rosaceae*, but some are special to certain tribes. For example the stomata in nearly all the *Chrysobalaneae* are accompanied by two or more subsidiary cells parallel to the pore, whilst in the other groups they are surrounded by ordinary epidermal cells. Another feature of this tribe is the simple perforations of the vessels, and the tendency to palisade-like cells of the leaf-epidermis. Indumentum consists of simple, unicellular hairs, which are occasionally united into tufted and stellate hairs or are 2-armed, or the hairs may be peltate or glandular. Anatomists generally favour this group to be of family status, but if so then several other tribes should be treated in the same way. There should be a limit to declassification, especially on purely anatomic characters.

The family name **Dichapetalaceae** was formerly *Chailletiaceae* R.Br. (1818), after *Chailletia*, now merged with *Dichapetalum*. In adopting the latter name Engler changed the name of the family, a procedure which would not be allowed under the present International Rules.

According to Solereder the family is distinguished by a series of anatomical characters, including subsidiary cells parallel to the pore of the stomata. An interesting morphological feature is the frequent concrescence of the peduncle and petiole (see Fig. 61), the inflorescence then appearing to arise

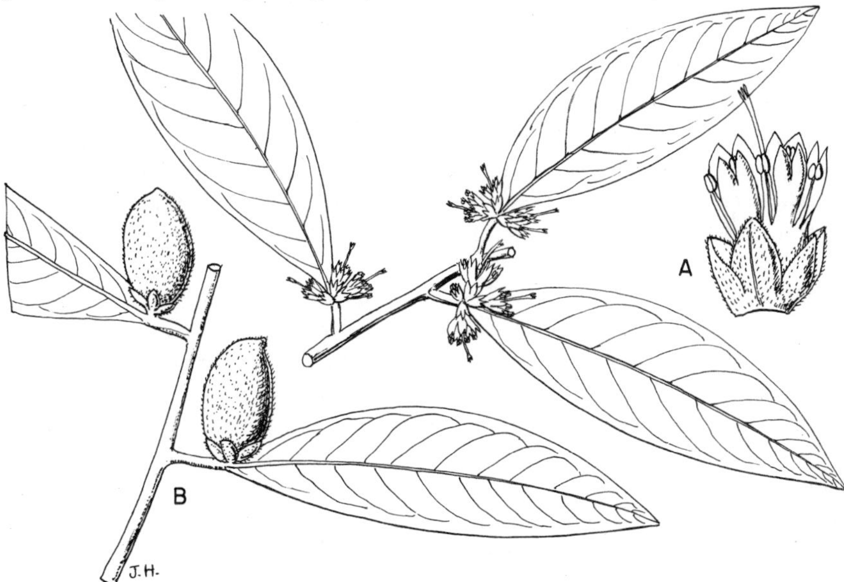

FIG. 61. *Tapura amazonica* Poepp. & Endl. (*Dichapetalaceae*), tropical America. Note the almost epiphyllous flowers due to the adnation of the peduncle to the petiole of the subtending leaf. **A**, flower. **B**, fruits (orig.).

from the base of the leaf-blade, as it does in some *Flacourtiaceae* and one genus of *Araliaceae* (*Helwingia*). Another mark of considerable advancement is the sympetalous corolla of two of the three genera, namely *Stephanopodium* and *Tapura* (Fig. 61), and in the latter the corolla is even somewhat zygomorphic. So we have in this small family "Polypetalae", "Sympetalae" and zygomorphy!

Dichapetalum (Figs 59, 60) is found in most parts of the tropics, extending into S.E. Africa, where *D. cymosum* (Hook. f.) Engl. (Fig. 60) is poisonous and causes (or at one time caused) great loss to farmers. Other species of this genus are also poisonous. The position here allotted to the family may be faulty, though it seems just as good as at the end of the GERANIALES, where it was placed in the two principal systems (Bentham and Hook. f., GENERA PLANTARUM, and Engler and Prantl, DIE NATÜRLICHEN PFLANZENFAMILIEN).

The most suitable position for the small family **Calycanthaceae** requires some discussion. Bentham and Hooker placed it between the *Dilleniaceae* and the *Magnoliaceae*, and Engler also retained it next to the *Magnoliaceae*. There are several reasons why this position should not be maintained. In *Magnoliaceae* and allied families there is always abundant endosperm and a small embryo in the seed. But there is no endosperm in the *Calycanthaceae*, and the embryo is large with foliaceous imbricate cotyledons. The receptacle is also tubular and the outer, so-called sepals are probably bracteoles, a condition not unknown in *Rosaceae*. The stamens are numerous, the inner ones being sterile. These characters are all foreign to the *Magnoliaceae* and allied families. They have much in common, however, with *Rosaceae*, and it is near this group that I consider the family *Calycanthaceae* should be placed. The supposed affinity with *Eupomatiaceae* is probably due to parallelism and to a superficial resemblance because of the hollowed-out receptacle characteristic of both families, *Eupomatiaceae* being an advanced type of *Annonaceae*; just another obvious example of parallel development being mistaken for actual affinity!

According to Solereder *Calycanthaceae* are excellently characterised anatomically by the presence in the stem of four cortical vascular bundles which are inversely orientated as regards the position of their xylem- and phloem-groups, and by the possession of secretory cells. The hairs are simple, unicellular and sclerosed, and with their subsidiary cells are silicified. There are no glandular hairs, and the stomata are accompanied by 2 subsidiary cells parallel to the pore. The vessels are spirally thickened and pitted with simple perforations.

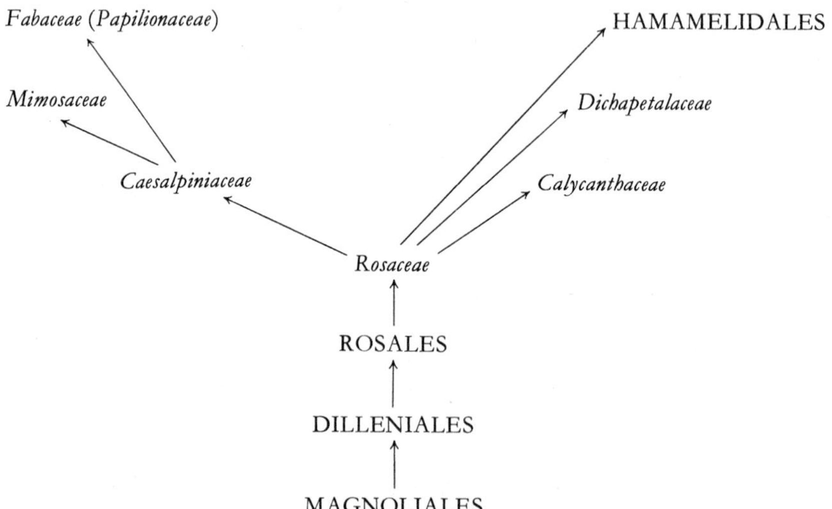

Diagram showing origin and phylogeny of the large family *Rosaceae* and further evolution from this stock, part of which ends in the climax family, *Fabaceae* (*Papilionaceae*); from woody to herbaceous, including annuals.

Order 7. LEGUMINALES

(*Fam. Fl. Pl.* **1**, 152)

Families: **Caesalpiniaceae, Mimosaceae, Fabaceae** (*Papilionaceae*).

Phylogeny: MAGNOLIALES → DILLENIALES → ROSALES → LEGUMINALES, ending in the climax family **Fabaceae** (*Papilionaceae*).

In the present system the Order LEGUMINALES consists of three families, **Caesalpiniaceae, Mimosaceae** and **Fabaceae** (*Papilionaceae*). They were regarded by Bentham as Suborders (i.e. Subfamilies in present-day terminology), although he considered them to be separated by sufficiently definite characters ("in Subordines tres characteribus satis definitis dividitur"). The general tendency amongst taxonomists nowadays, except those who cling to tradition, is to regard them as three separate families, and there is much to be said for this point of view. The fruit, by the way, in spite of the ordinal name, is by no means always a legume. Such a fruit is defined by Jackson (GLOSSARY OF BOTANIC TERMS) as "the seed-vessel of *Leguminosae*, one-celled and two-valved, but various in form". A typical legume is therefore such as that of the common pea, *Pisum sativum* Linn., i.e. one that splits by both sutures into two valves. A great number of fruits in all three families, however, do not open at all (indehiscent), and some are transversely divided (articulated) into several 1-seeded segments which usually fall apart when mature. The accompanying drawings show the great diversity of fruits in the Order.

Of these three families *Caesalpiniaceae* is on the whole the most primitive, and closest to the *Rosaceae*, from the stock of which it seems to have been derived. For example little difference is to be observed in a longitudinal section of a flower of a species of *Parinari* (*Parinarium*) in the *Rosaceae* and that of a *Bauhinia*, such as *B. maximiliana* Benth. This may not be due to parallel evolution. In *Caesalpiniaceae* the petals (rarely absent) are imbricate in bud, the adaxial petal being overlapped on each side by the lateral petals (when present).

In *Mimosaceae* the flowers are actinomorphic, the petals being valvate (very rarely imbricate) in bud, free or connate into a tube (sympetalous), and the anthers often have a deciduous gland at the apex. In *Fabaceae* (*Papilionaceae*), the flowers, with few exceptions, are very zygomorphic and butterfly-like (hence Linnaeus' name for them), the adaxial petal (vexillum or standard) overlapping at the sides the lateral (wing) petals, the latter in turn overlapping the 2 lowermost petals which form the keel; and in this family the stamens are mostly variously united, being either monadelphous or diadelphous, often the adaxial (vexillary) of the 10 stamens being free or partly so, the remainder connate into a usually split sheath. A few of the more primitive tribes, however, have free stamens.

Caesalpiniaceae,[1] mostly tropical and subtropical, are largely composed of trees and shrubs, very rarely herbs, the leaves are chiefly pinnate, either simply pinnate or bipinnate; stipules are present but stipels are very rare

FIG. 62. *Moldenhauera floribunda* Schrad. (*Caesalpiniaceae*), Brazil. Flowers in much-branched panicles. Note the remarkable androecium, of 9 equal short fertile stamens and 1 elongated sterile stamen, **C**. Note also that both simply pinnate, **B**, and bipinnate leaves, **A**, occur on the same branch. **D**, petal. **E**, fertile stamen. **F**, sterile stamen. **G**, gynoecium. **H**, vertical section of ovary and style. **J**, fruit, flat and compressed, few-seeded (orig.).

(frequent in *Fabaceae* (*Papilionaceae*)). A large proportion of the genera have small or rarely petaloid bracteoles, but quite a number have large bracteoles which cover the flower in bud and function like a calyx, which is often then very much reduced or quite rudimentary. I have therefore divided the family into two subfamilies, relying on these characters, the *Eucaesalpinioideae* with the smaller bracteoles or rarely petaloid bracts, and the *Brachystegioideae* with the larger bracteoles. Often, in flowering plants, when one set of organs becomes reduced or disappears, it is replaced by another set,

---

[1] Including *Lomentaceae* R.Br. (1814). *Cassiaceae* Link (1831). *Ceratoniaceae* Link (1831). *Detariaceae* Burnett (1835).

and the take-over for protection of the bud by the bracteoles is a remarkable instance of this. The genus *Anemone* in the *Ranunculaceae* is another familiar example, wherein, in the absence of petals, the sepals have become coloured for attracting insects; and a whorl of leaves functions as a calyx.

Some genera of *Caesalpiniaceae* have only 1 petal, and two, *Polystemonanthus* and *Schizoscyphus*, have numerous stamens, whilst they are reduced to 5 in *Koompassia*, *Didelotia*, *Acrocarpus*, *Duparquetia*, *Zenia*, *Androcalymna*, to

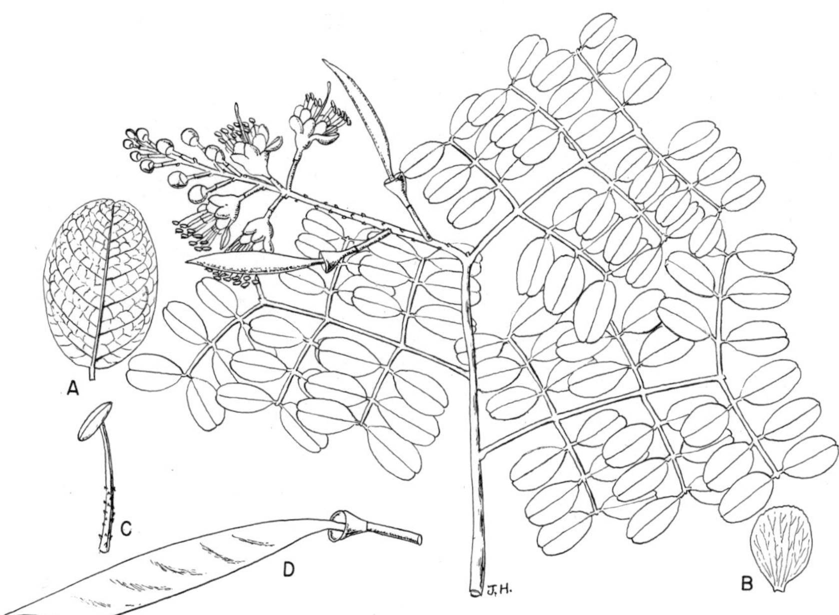

FIG. 63. *Caesalpinia brasiliensis* Linn., the type species of the type genus of *Caesalpiniaceae*, West Indies (Haiti) (but not recorded from Brazil); trunk bears numerous blunt thorns. **A**, leaflet showing venation. **B**, petal. **C**, stamen. **D**, fruit (orig.).

4 in *Tetrapterocarpon*, and even to 3 or 2 in *Distemonanthus*, *Cryptosepalum*, *Dialium*, *Dicorynia*, *Apulia*, *Labichea*, and *Petalostylis*, the last mentioned being unique in having a petaloid style! Anthers, which in *Fabaceae* are frequently dimorphic in the same flower, are of this type only in a single genus, *Moldenhauera* (see Fig. 62). In quite a number of genera the anthers open by terminal pores, as in the best-known and largest genus, *Cassia*, and in several other genera. Only in *Pterolobium* is the fruit 1-seeded at the base and with a terminal wing, a character more common in *Fabaceae*; and in *Melanoxylon* the seeds are winged, a feature frequent in several *Mimosaceae*.

Type genus *Caesalpinia* Linn., about 280 species in the tropics and subtropics: trees, shrubs or tall climbers, unarmed or armed with sharp prickles;

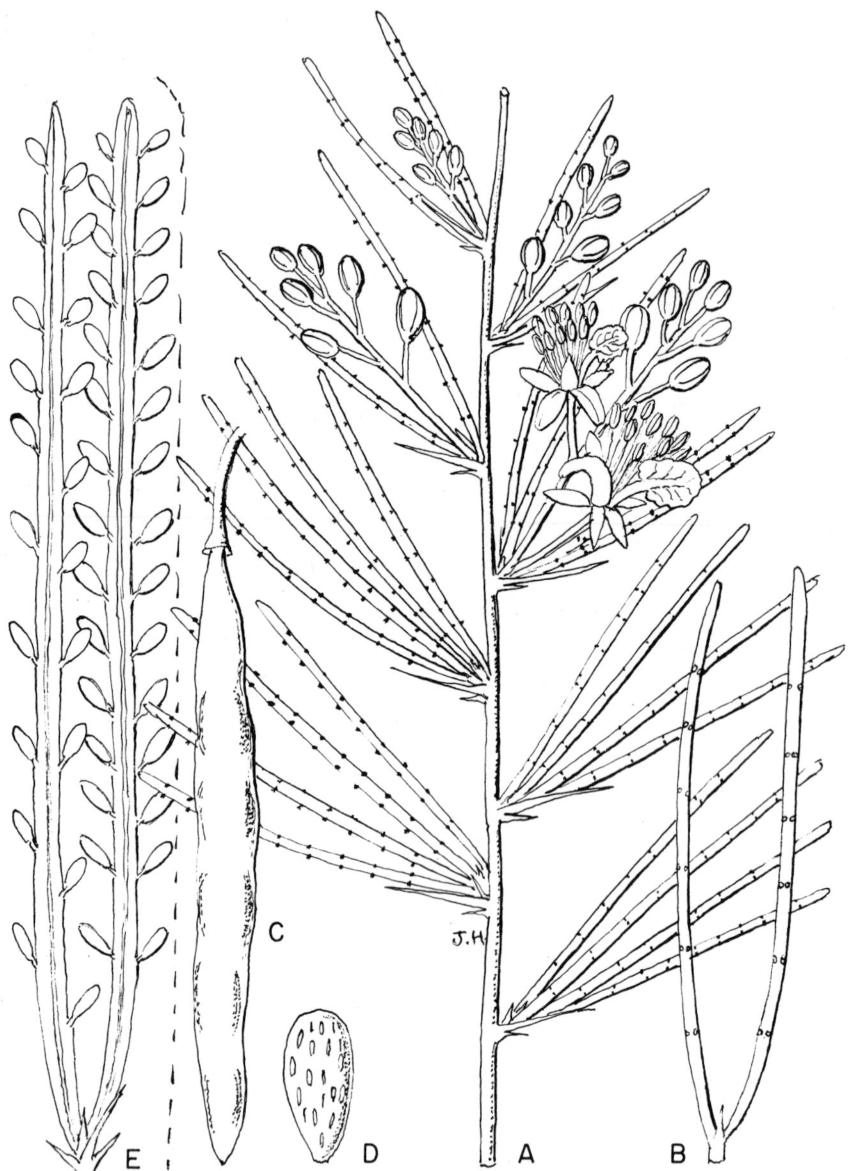

FIG. 64. **A**, *Parkinsonia*[1] *africana* Sond. (*Caesalpiniaceae*), dry regions of S.W. Africa. **B**, showing the spine-tipped rhachis and the twin pinnae with mere traces of leaflets. **C**, fruit. **D**, seed. **E**, trilobed stipule and pair of pinnae with well developed leaflets of *P. aculeata* Plum. ex Linn., tropical and subtropical America, and widely spread in other regions (orig.).

[1] See foot of next page.

leaves bipinnate, leaflets few to many; stipules various; flowers yellow or red, often very showy; racemes paniculate in the upper leaf-axils or terminal; calyx-teeth 5, imbricate, the abaxial outside the others, often large; petals 5, orbicular or oblong, spreading, very imbricate, slightly unequal or the uppermost smaller; stamens 10, free, declinate; filaments often villous or glandular at the base; anthers uniform, opening by a slit lengthwise; ovary sessile, few-ovuled; style filiform, rarely clavate at the apex, stigma terminal, truncate; fruit compressed, ovate to lanceolate or falcate, not winged, sometimes 2-valved or indehiscent, often filled between the seeds; seeds transverse to the fruit, ovate to orbicular or globose, cotyledons flat. Type species *C. brasiliensis* Linn. (pp.), West Indies (not Brazil) (Fig. 63).

A few other genera with exceptional characters may be noted. Leaves both simply pinnate and bipinnate on the same plant in *Moldenhauera* spp., *Gleditsia* and *Haematoxylon*; leaf-rhachis very short and ending in a sharp spine-like point in *Parkinsonia* (Fig. 64); leaves and other parts gland-dotted in *Hoffmanseggia* and *Cordeauxia*; indumentum of stellate hairs in *Cenostigma*; stipules pinnate in *Jacqueshuberia* and *Sclerolobium*; large, long, linear and spirally folded around the apical bud in *Hylodendron* (Fig. 65) and *Daniellia*; peduncles extremely long (up to 2·5 m) and pendulous in *Eperua* spp.; flowers polygamous in *Gleditsia*, *Gymnocladus*, *Arcoa* and *Apuleia* spp.; dioecious in *Tetrapterocarpon*.

The greatest number of genera of *Caesalpiniaceae* occur in the forests of tropical Africa and tropical America, in the former about 56, in the latter about 40 being endemic in each region. Not many genera are common to these two great continents. A small number are found in tropical Asia, but very few in Polynesia and Australia. In less warm countries few occur, *Ceratonia* in the eastern Mediterranean, *Gleditsia* in North and South America, temperate and subtropical Asia and the Malay Archipelago, and *Cladrastis*, like *Magnolia* and a few others, is common to N.E. America and eastern Asia.

Mimosaceae are also trees and shrubs, very rarely herbs. The leaves are bipinnate, except in two genera, *Affonsea* and *Inga*, in which they are simply pinnate. The spikes are condensed into dense globose or clavate heads in *Parkia*, whilst in *Dichrostachys* the flowers are not all the same, those in the

---

[1] Named after John Parkinson by Plumier ex Linn., an apothecary and herbalist; born in 1567 probably in Nottinghamshire; had a garden in Long Acre "well stored with rarities". On publication of his PARADISUS TERRESTRIS in 1629 he obtained from Charles I the title of *Botanicus Regius Primarius*. In 1884 a Mrs. Ewing founded a Parkinson Society, the objects of which were to search out and cultivate garden flowers, to plant waste places with hardy flowers, and to prevent extermination. She was president until her death, and was succeeded by Prof. Daniel Oliver, Keeper of the Herbarium, Kew; eventually the Society was dissolved (DICT. OF NAT. BIOGR.).

FIG. 65. *Hylodendron gabunense* Taub. (*Caesalpiniaceae*), west tropical Africa. Drawn mainly to show the remarkable stipules, **E**, which enclose the terminal bud and are early deciduous, leaving a circular intrapetiolar scar; similar stipules occur in *Irvingiaceae*. **A**, flower-bud. **B**, flower, which is apetalous. **C**, gynoecium. **D**, vertical section of ovary (enlarged). **E**, stipule. **F**, fruit (orig.). Tree about 100 ft, common in forest; flowers in short axillary racemes.

upper part of the spike being bisexual, the lower neutral with long staminodes. A characteristic feature of tribes *Parkieae* and *Adenanthereae* is an apical gland at the tip of the anthers which frequently soon falls off. In tribes *Acacieae* and *Ingeae* the pollen-grains are usually collected into masses in each anther-loculus, whilst the filaments are more or less united into a tube in tribe *Ingeae*. A very advanced monotypic genus is the South African *Xerocladia*, reduced to 1 ovule and 1 seed in the indehiscent fruit, whilst the shoots are well protected by the recurved spinescent stipules; great economy accompanied by adequate protection (see Fig. 78B).

The fruits of *Entada* (sometimes of great size), *Pseudoentada* and *Plathymenia*, split transversely into 1-seeded segments, just as they do in tribes *Hedysareae* and *Desmodieae* in the family *Papilionaceae*. The fruits are subturgid and/or angled or winged in *Stryphnodendron*, *Tetrapleura*, and *Ambylogonocarpus*. In several genera the seeds are winged.

Mimosaceae were the subject of a classical memoir by Bentham,[1] whose views on phylogeny would have been of infinite value had he been of a more

[1] Bentham, Revision of the suborder *Mimoseae*, TRANS. LINN. SOC. **30**, 335 (1875).

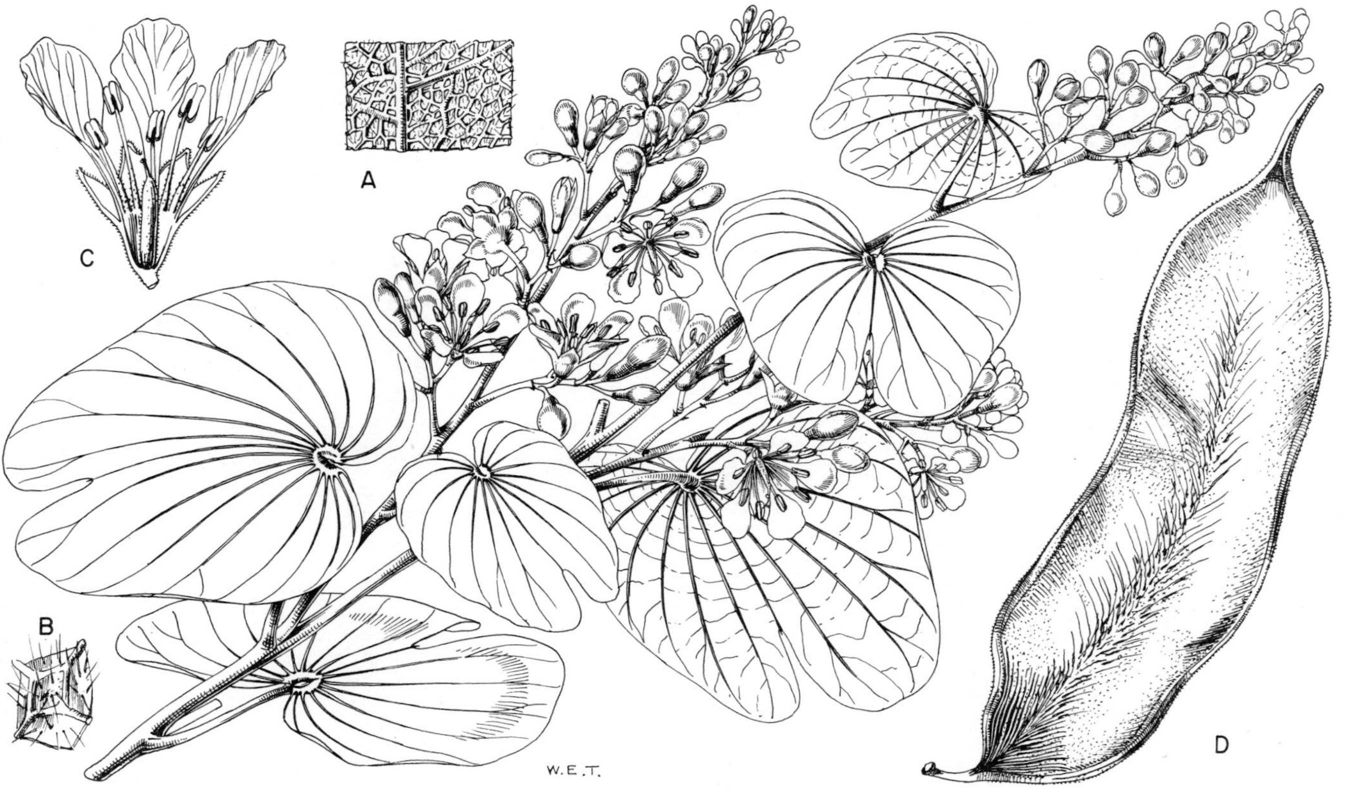

Fig. 66. A bold and detailed drawing by Trevithick of *Bauhinia thonningii* Schumacher (*Caesalpiniaceae*), tropical Africa. **A**, lower surface of leaf. **B**, the same showing hairs. **C**, vertical section of flower. **D**, fruit.

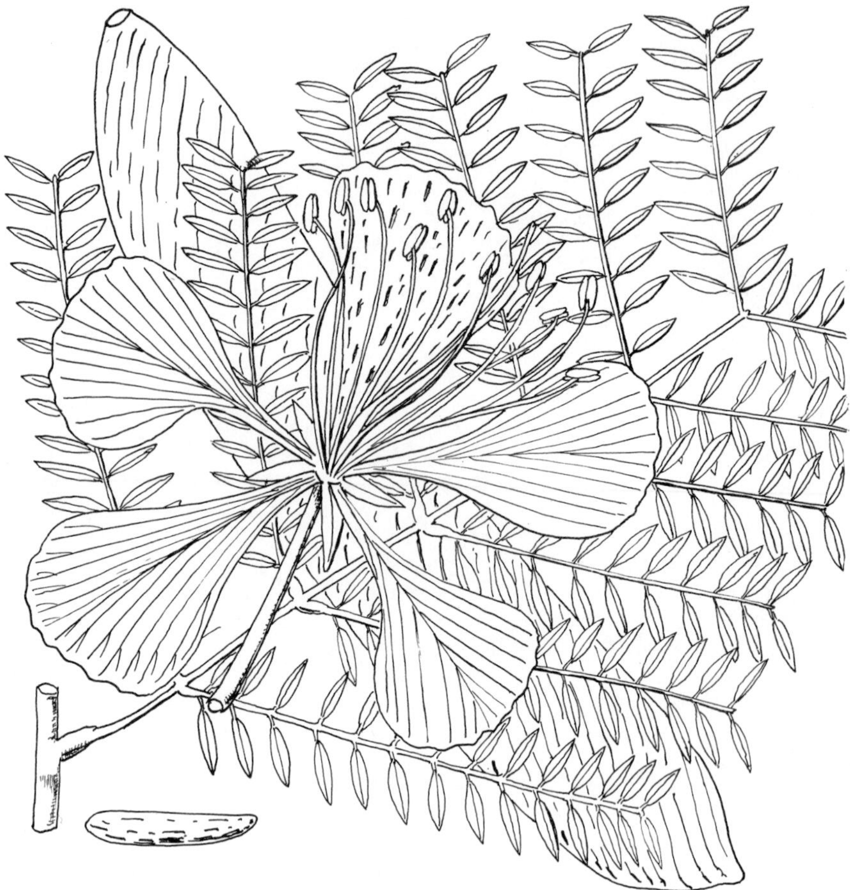

FIG. 67. Flower, leaf, fruit and seed of the Flamboyant, *Delonix regia* Raf. (*Caesalpiniaceae*), a lovely street tree in many parts of the tropics and subtropics; particularly fine in the streets of Durban, South Africa, in December.

speculative mind, the theory of evolution being at that time only in its infancy. The bipinnate type of leaf, predominant in the family, is an advanced character compared with the simply pinnate leaf, and one of the more primitive genera is *Inga*, which is exceptional, together with *Affonsea* (already mentioned), in having simply pinnate leaves, both genera in tropical America. As a rule the genera with racemose or spicate inflorescence should be regarded as being more primitive than those with a capitate inflorescence, though both kinds may occur in the same genus as in *Acacia* and to a lesser extent in *Albizia*. *Affonsea* and a nearly related and aptly named genus, *Archidendron* (see Fig. 75), are remarkable in the family in

FIG. 68. *Amherstia nobilis* Wall. (*Caesalpiniaceae*), south Burma; named after Lady Amherst; a moderate-sized tree; leaf, flower, fruit and seed (orig.).

having more than one carpel, 2–5 in *Affonsea*, and 5–15 in *Archidendron*, maybe a relict character retained from a far distant Rosaceous ancestor!

Tribal characters may be mentioned: the calyx-lobes or sepals are imbricate in *Mimozygantherae* and *Parkieae*, in the other tribes they are valvate; the filaments are free or nearly so in *Acacieae* and *Mimoseae*, in the former the stamens being numerous (more than 10), and the pollen-grains are usually collected into 2–6 masses in each anther-loculus; in the latter the stamens are 10 or fewer, the pollen grains numerous and separate in each loculus. Of these, *Mimoseae* are without a gland at the apex of the anthers, this being present in *Adenanthereae*. Finally the filaments are more or less united into a

FIG. 69. *Cassia acutifolia* Del. (*Caesalpiniaceae*), Egypt. **A**, petals. **B**, stamens and gynoecium. **C**, anthers unequal in size and opening by terminal pores. **D**, one half of fruit.

tube in *Ingeae*, in which the pollen-grains are also usually collected into 2–6 masses.

The type genus is *Mimosa* Linn.; about 600 species in the tropics and subtropics: trees, shrubs (sometimes climbing) or herbs, mostly armed with prickles; leaves bipinnate, often sensitive to the touch, rarely absent and reduced to phyllodes; petiolar glands rarely present; secondary rhachides

FIG. 70. The Mora tree, *Mora excelsa* Benth. (*Caesalpiniaceae*), thrives in poor soil in tropical America; flowers very fragrant; wood light brown, hard, heavy, strong, tough and clos-grained, very durable in water; suitable for railway-sleepers and waggons, boards, scantlings and large beams. Woodcutters recognise two varieties, red and white, the former the superior. **A**, flower. **B**, petals and stamens spread out. **C**, fruit. **D**, seed. **E**, ovary (orig.). The genus *Mora* belongs to the family *Caesalpiniaceae*, and may be distinguished among its congeners by its alternate paripinnate leaves, its dense spikes of snow-white flowers, its 5 subequal shortly clawed petals, opposite to which are 5 fertile stamens whose anthers are provided with a comb of slender white hairs (a most unusual feature), with 5 alternate glabrous club-like staminodes, fruit dehiscent, thin, and with very large kidney-shaped seeds.

FIG. 71. *Hymenaea courbaril* Linn. (*Caesalpiniaceae*), tropical America. **A**, stamen. **B**, calyx and gynoecium. **C**, fruit. **D**, seed (orig.).

mostly 2-stipellate; flowers small, in cylindric spikes or globose heads, bisexual or polygamous, or some neutral in a few species with filiform staminodes subpetaloid at the apex; peduncles axillary, solitary or fasciculate, upper ones sometimes in a raceme; calyx usually minute, papillous or pappus-like; corolla more or less sympetalous, 6–3-merous; stamens double the number or equal to the corolla-lobes, free, exserted; anthers small, not glandular; ovary usually sessile, 2- or more-ovuled; fruit oblong to linear, usually plano-compressed, membranous or coriaceous, valves 2, separating from the persistent margins, entire or divided transversely into segments,

FIG. 72. *Humboldtia laurifolia* Vahl (*Caesalpiniaceae*), India and Ceylon; genus named by Vahl in honour of Alexander von Humboldt, who is also commemorated by the Current of that name which flows northwards along the west coast of South America; born in 1769 and died in 1859. Prior to the travels of Humboldt and his French botanical friend Aimé Bonpland (1773–1858), the botany of the South American continent was little known to Europeans, except Spaniards. Their collections formed the basis for our knowledge of the floras of the then almost unknown lands visited during their voyage. **A**, flower bud. **B**, open flower. **C**, stamen. **D**, gynoecium. **E**, vertical section of ovary (orig.).

continuous or subseptate within; seeds ovate or orbicular, flat. Type species *M. pudica* Linn. (Fig. 76), tropics and subtropics.

A few additional exceptions may be mentioned: staminodes present in *Pentaclethra*; seeds winged in *Newtonia*, *Parapiptadenia* spp., *Piptadeniastrum*, *Monoschisma*, *Indopiptadenia*, *Cylicodiscus* and *Fillaeopsis*.

In **Fabaceae**[1] (*Papilionaceae* R.Br. (1814)) we find the culmination of the advanced line of development derived from the rosaceous stock, resulting in a homogeneous and highly successful group, providing several important food crops for animals and man. Considering the distribution of its more primitive genera, one may reasonably conclude that the *Fabaceae*, with a fair proportion of herbs and herbaceous climbers, have spread from the tropics into temperate regions of the world.

An important anatomical feature of *Fabaceae* is the widely distributed tannin-sacs which have broad lumina filled with brown albuminous contents, and which are also met with in *Mimosaceae*, but not in *Caesalpiniaceae*,

[1] Including *Swartziaceae* Bartling (1830). *Lathyraceae* Burnett (1835). *Lotaceae* Burnett (1835). *Viciaceae* Dostal (1848). *Robiniaceae* Welw. (1858). *Hedysaraceae* J. G. Agardh (1858).

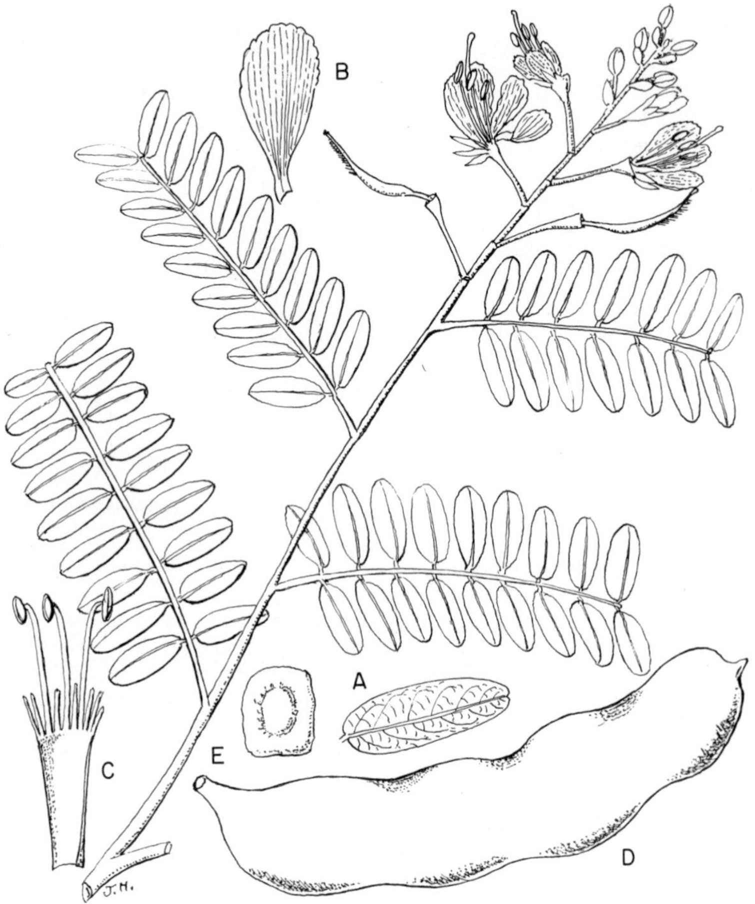

FIG. 73. Tamarind, *Tamarindus indica* Linn. (*Caesalpiniaceae*). **A**, leaflet. **B**, petal. **C**, stamens. **D**, fruit. **E**, seed (orig.).

or only in a very rudimentary form (Solereder). The ordinary clothing hairs consist of simple uniseriate hairs which are made up of one or several short basal cells and a long terminal cell. Hairs like these have not been observed in either *Caesalpiniaceae* or *Mimosaceae*.

Since Bentham published his account of *Fabaceae* (*Papilionaceae*) in the GENERA PLANTARUM in 1865, the number of genera has nearly doubled and the number of so-called "anomalous" or "ambiguous" genera correspondingly increased. In consequence, when writing up the family for my GENERA OF FLOWERING PLANTS I found it quite impossible to key out many genera satisfactorily in the comparatively few tribes as defined by Bentham and later by Taubert (Engler and Prantl, DIE NATÜRLICHEN PFLANZEN-

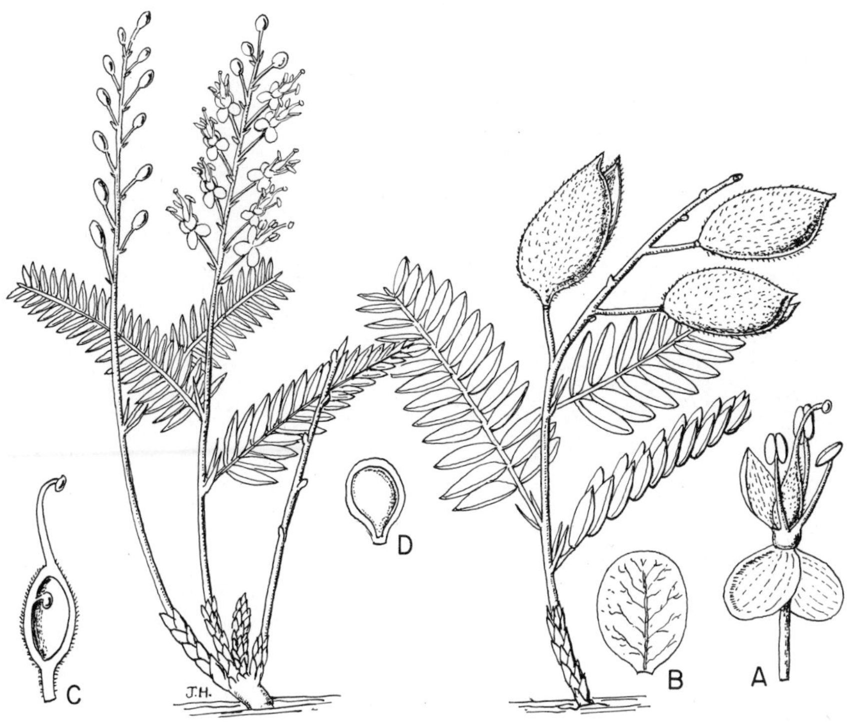

Fig. 74. *Cryptosepalum maraviense* Olive. (*Caesalpiniaceae*). The general trend of evolution from trees to shrubs and then to herbs is well demonstrated in this genus, that shown being a herb with a woody rootstock, native of the Congo region of tropical Africa; related species are trees and shrubs. **A**, flower. **B**, petal. **C**, vertical section of ovary. **D**, seed (orig.).

FAMILIEN). There were too many "exceptions" to the tribes as so constituted, and I found it expedient to elevate Bentham's subtribes into tribes. These are more easy to define and are less encumbered with exceptions.

In classifying these smaller concepts, the three main types of leaves were considered to be important, often characteristic of whole tribes. These types are 1, those primitively simple, 2, pinnately and 3, digitately compound. A fact worth pointing out is that there are no bipinnate leaves in *Fabaceae*, in contrast with their common occurrence in *Caesalpiniaceae* and more especially in *Mimosaceae*. Next, the form of the anthers, either uniform or dimorphic, seems of great taxonomic value, concerned as it may well be with pollination. When the anthers are dimorphic in the same flower, they are alternately basifixed and dorsifixed (versatile) and usually very different in size. The dehiscence or indehiscence of fruits is also of great importance, though liable in some cases to produce a measure of artificiality. Then,

FIG. 75. *Archidendron solomonense* Hemsl. (*Mimosaceae*), Solomon Islands. Although the name chosen for this genus suggests primitiveness, the only claim for this lies in the several free carpels, the other characters being relatively advanced, such as the valvate, sympetalous corolla. The free carpels, therefore, may be regarded as a relict feature retained through the Rosaceous ancestry of the whole family *Mimosaceae*. **A**, flower. **B**, stamens. **C**, free carpels surrounded by the staminal sheath. **D**, fruits. **E**, seed. (Adapted mainly from Hook. IC. PL.)

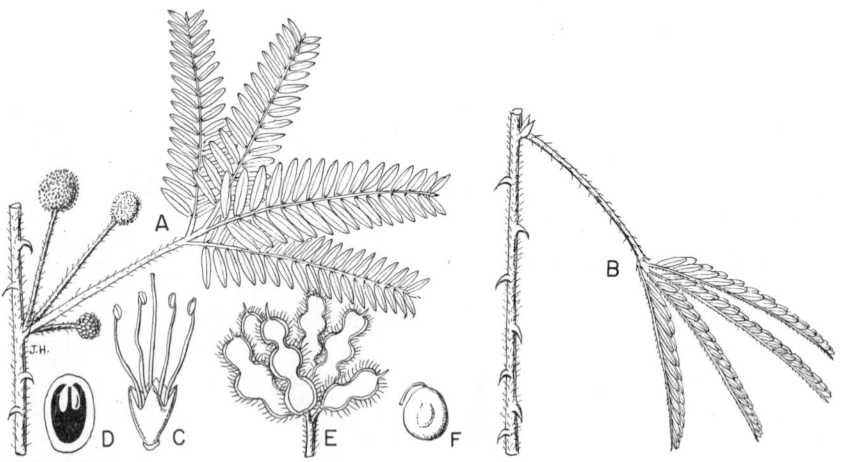

FIG. 76. *Mimosa pudica* Linn., tropics; type of the genus and of the family *Mimosaceae* (orig.). **A**, flowering shoot with leaflets spread out. **B**, shoot after being touched. **C**, flower. **D**, cross-section of ovary. **E**, fruits. **F**, seed (orig.).

FIG. 77. *Enterolobium cyclocarpum* (Jacq.) Griseb. (*Mimosaceae*), Cuba. **A**, leaflet. **B**, flower. **C**, stamen. **D**, fruit. **E**, seed (orig.).

especially in this family, some of the tribes or part of them have gland-dotted or pellucid-glandular leaves, and many have stipels (secondary stipules) which are largely non-existent in both *Caesalpiniaceae* and *Mimosaceae*. Another character of great taxonomic value is the transverse jointing of the fruits so characteristic of tribes *Coronilleae*, *Hedysareae*, *Aeschynomeneae*, *Adesmieae*, *Stylosantheae* and *Desmodieae*. I consider these to be the climax of fruit evolution within the family.

It would be futile for me to try and trace for the student the multitude of different combinations of characters which serve to distinguish the 480 or so genera, and hence their phylogeny. This may be obvious if the list of characters occurring in relatively few genera and species is studied (repeated from my GENERA OF FLOWERING PLANTS, Vol. I), compared with the description of the type genus *Vicia*, which follows.

The type genus of *Fabaceae* (*Papilionaceae*) is *Vicia* Linn. (the family is here called *Fabaceae*, from the Broad Bean, *Vicia faba* L.), with about 120 species in the north temperate hemisphere and in South America; herbs climbing by tendrils or rarely low or erect; leaves pinnate, the rhachis at the top only, or completely transformed into a simple or branched tendril, rarely imparipinnate; stipules semi-sagittate; flowers blue, violet or yellow, axillary, fasciculate or racemose; bracts often very caducous; bracteoles absent; calyx-teeth subequal or unequal; vexillum emarginate; wings obliquely oblong, adherent in the middle to the keel; keel shorter than the

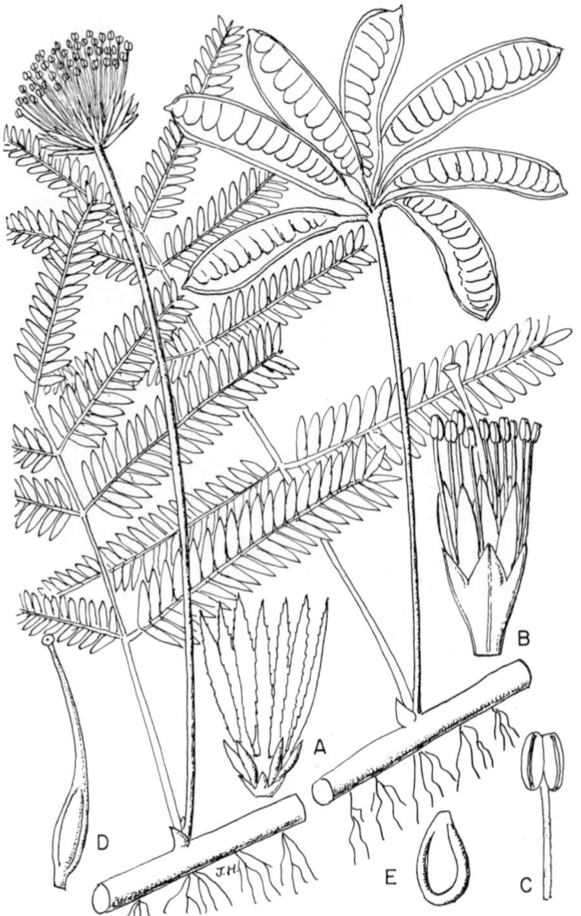

FIG. 78A. *Neptunia oleracea* Lour., one of the very few aquatic members of the *Mimosaceae*. **A**, sterile flower with staminodes. **B**, bisexual fertile flower. **C**, stamen. **D**, gynoecium. **E**, seed (orig.).

wings; vexillary stamen free or more or less connate with the remainder, the sheath of the latter with an oblique mouth; anthers uniform; ovary with numerous or rarely 2 ovules; style compressed, bearded with a bunch of hairs on the back at the apex, rarely glabrous, stigma terminal; fruit compressed, 2-valved; seeds globose or rarely compressed, funicle dilated into a slender aril; cotyledons thick.

CHARACTERS OCCURRING IN RELATIVELY FEW GENERA AND SPECIES OF *Fabaceae*: Aquatic or semi-aquatic habit in *Sesbania* spp.; branches flattened in *Templetonia sulcata* and leaves reduced to scales in *Brachysema* and *Jacksonia*; densely spiny cushion plants in *Erinacea*; shrubs with spiny branches

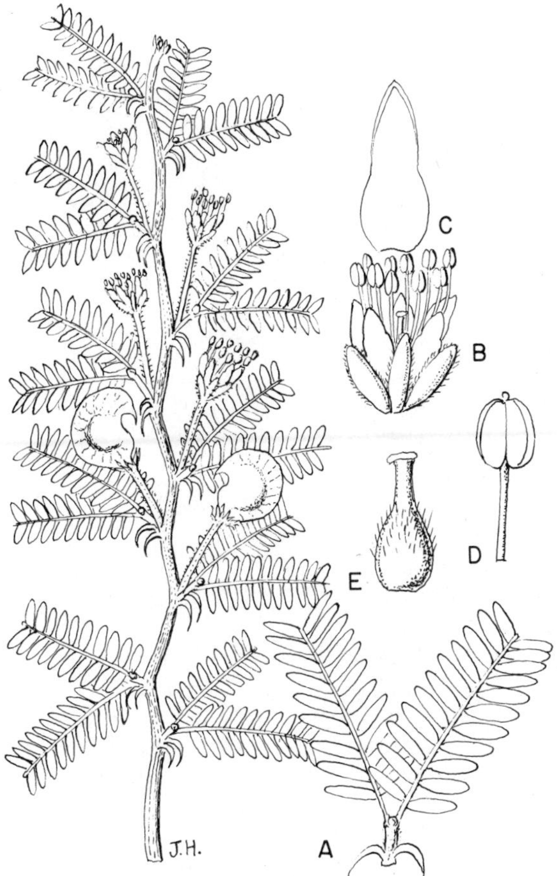

FIG. 78B. *Xerocladia viridiramis* (Burch.) Taub. (*Mimosaceae*), South Africa. **A**, pair of leaves showing the spiny stipules. **B**, flower. **C**, petal. **D**, stamen. **E**, gynoecium (orig.).

in *Gourliea*, *Genista* spp., *Ulex*, *Ononis* spp., and in *Nepa and Ecinospartum*; leaves reduced to leaf-like phyllodes in *Papilionopsis*; leaf-rhachis ending in a bristle in tribe *Abreae*, in *Ammodendron*, *Notodon*, *Bembicidium* and *Halimodendron*; in a tendril or barren point in most of tribe *Vicieae*; perfoliate leaves in *Pericaulon perfoliatum* Raf., peltate, unifoliolate leaves in *Indigofera peltata* Gillett; stipules spiny in *Belairia*; partially united and leaf-opposed in *Anagyris*, *Astrolobium* and *Piptanthus*; large and foliaceous in *Brogniartia* spp.; united at the base with the leaf into a whorl or sheath in *Anarthrophyllum*; bracts enlarged, membranous and enclosing the flower and fruit in *Phylacium*, hooked in *Mecopus*; bracteoles large and enclosing the flower-bud in *Dalhousieae* (as in many *Caesalpiniaceae*); cleistogamous flowers occur in

Fig. 79. *Lupiniphyllum lupinifolium* (DC.) Hutch. (*Fabaceae*), South Africa and tropical Africa. Note the normal flowers **A**, and the cleistogamous flowers **B**, the latter penetrating the soil. Note also the pair of stipels **H**, subtending only the outer pair of leaflets of the digitate leaf. **C**, calyx. **D**, petals of normal flowers. **E**, stamens. **F**, gynoecium. **G**, fruit. (orig.).

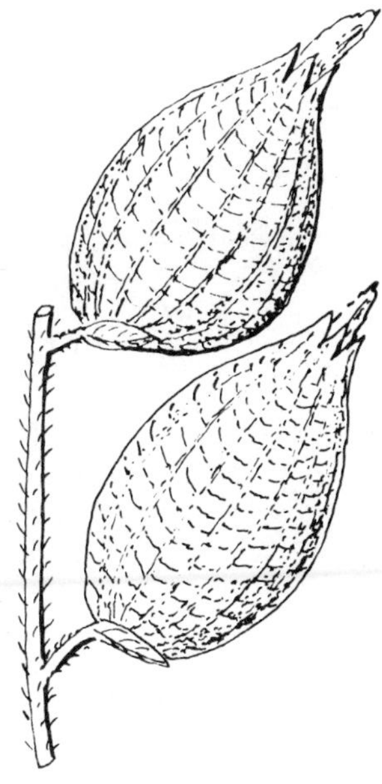

FIG. 80. *Astragalus physocalyx* Fisch. (*Fabaceae*), Greece, has bladdery calyx in fruit.

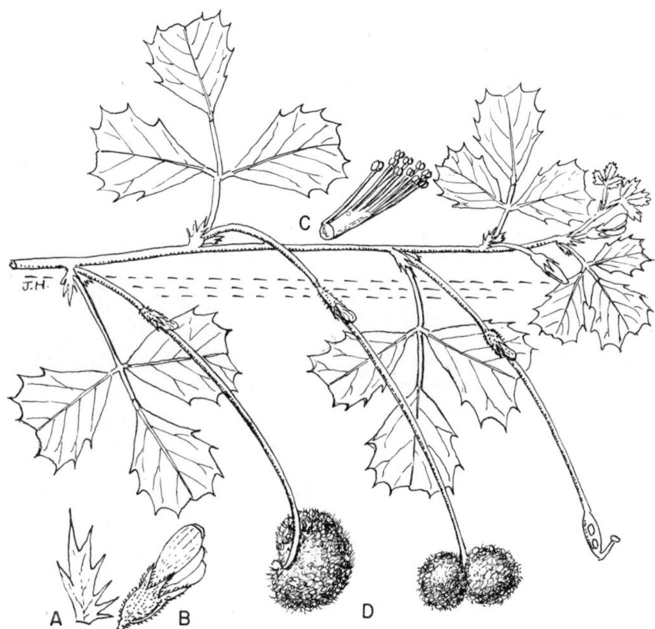

FIG. 81. *Factorovskya aschersoniana* (Urb.) Eig (*Fabaceae*), Orient. **A**, stipule. **B**, flower. **C**, stamens. **D**, fruits which bury themselves in the soil (orig.).

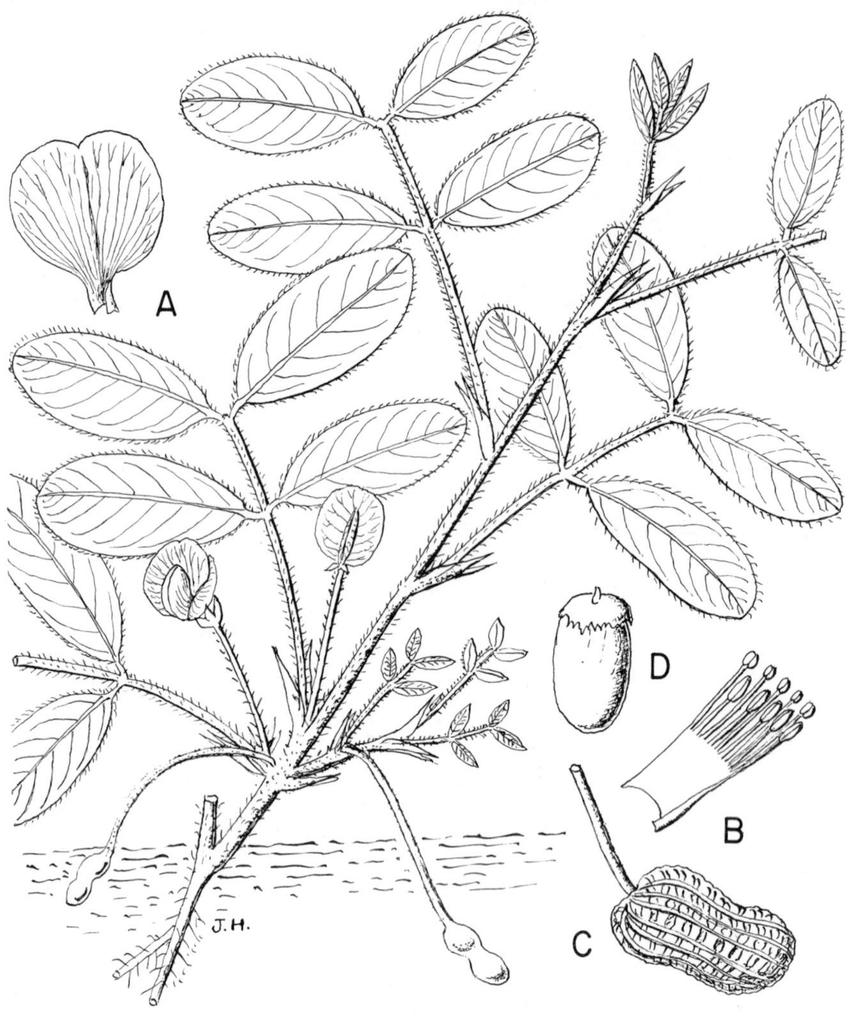

FIG. 82. The Pea-nut or Ground-nut, *Arachis hypogaea* Linn. (*Fabaceae*); native of tropical South America, cultivated extensively in eastern tropics; chief crop in Gambia, west Africa. **A**, standard petal. **B**, stamens (note the unequal-sized anthers). **C**, fruit which buries itself in the ground. **D**, seed (orig.).

Neocracca, *Lupiniphyllum* (Fig. 79), and *Robinia* sp.; calyx remarkable in *Monopteryx*, 2-lobed, the upper lobe large and enclosing the petals and genitalia, lower very small and pointed; enlarged and striate in fruit resembling a Dipterocarp in *Apoplanasia*; inflated in fruit in *Erinacea* and *Astragalus* spp. (Fig. 80); spathaceous in *Fissicalyx* and *Spartium*; upper margin of wing-petals fringed with stipitate glands in *Petaladenium*; stamens numerous in many of tribe *Swartzieae*; reduced to 9 (adaxial missing) in

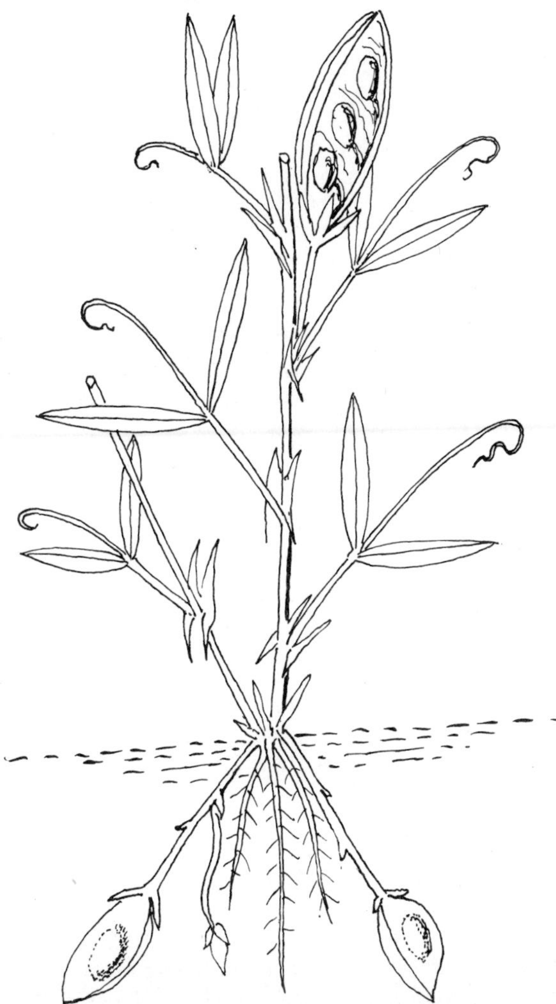

FIG. 83. *Lathyrus blepharicarpus* Boiss. (*Fabaceae*), Cyprus and Mediterranean region, bears cleistogamous flowers which bury their fruits in the ground.

Abrus and a few *Psoraleae*; anther-connective with a gland at the base of alternate anthers in *Haydonia*; anthers opening by terminal pores in *Fissicalyx*; ovary and fruit divided longitudinally by a false septum in *Mirbelia* (*Podalyrieae*), and in part of tribe *Astragaleae*; style circinately coiled in bud in *Lennea*; fruits maturing below the soil in *Neocollettia*, *Factorovskya* (Fig. 81), *Kerstingiella*, *Voandzeia*, *Arachis* (Fig. 82), *Lathyrus* sp. (Fig. 83), *Trifolium* sp. (Fig. 84), *Vicia* sp. (Fig. 85) and *Galactia canescens* Benth.; also those of cleistogamous flowers in *Lupiniphyllum*; transversely septate and

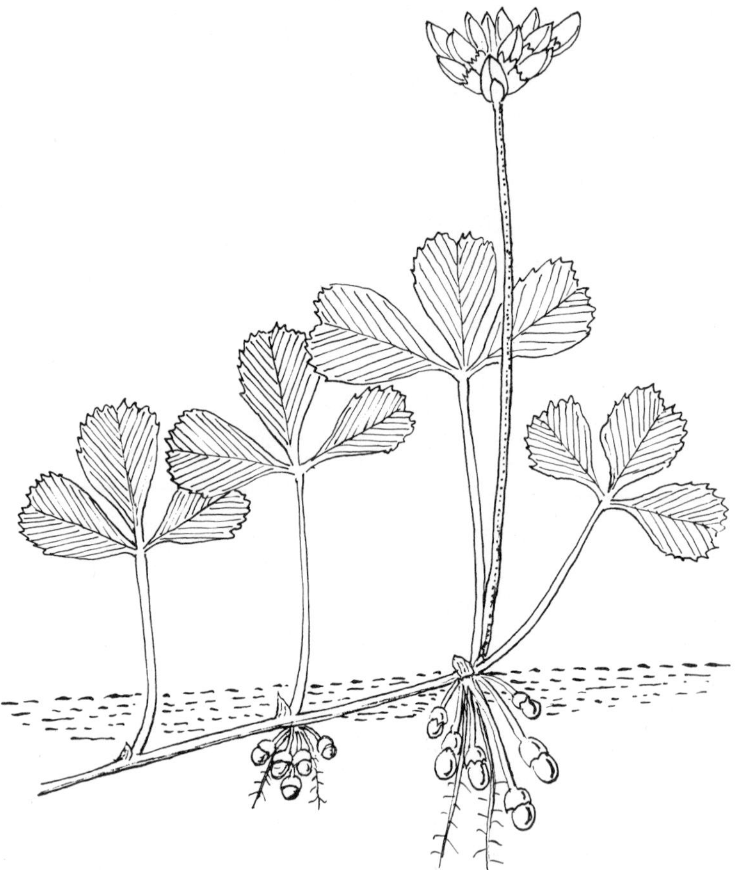

FIG. 84. *Trifolium polymorphum* Poir., Magellan Region, bears cleistogamous flowers which bury their seeds in the ground (*Fabaceae*).

breaking into 1-seeded segments in tribes *Coronilleae*, *Hedysareae*, *Aeschynomeneae*, *Adesmieae*, *Stylosantheae* and *Desmodieae*; old fruit persistent around the seedling in *Onobrychis caputgalli* Lamk.; fruits enclosed by the calyx in tribe *Daleae*; bladder-like in tribes *Coluteae*, *Diphyseae*, drupaceous in tribe *Geoffreeae*; divided into superposed disks in *Medicago* and *Discolobium*; very deeply indented in *Hippocrepis*[1]; circinate-involute in *Scorpiurus*; densely

[1] Linnaeus in his CRITICA BOTANICA (English translation) says of *Hippocrepis*, or "Horseshoe", "Who that has ever seen an iron horseshoe would not, at his first sight of the plant in fruit, cry out at the marvellous resemblance of the fruit to a horseshoe? Who that has ever seen the plant can wonder why it is so called? Such names hold out their right hand to the plant, these plants offer the names their right hand. Such names I decide to be best of all, if they suit all the species in the genus". See Fig. 100, **A**.

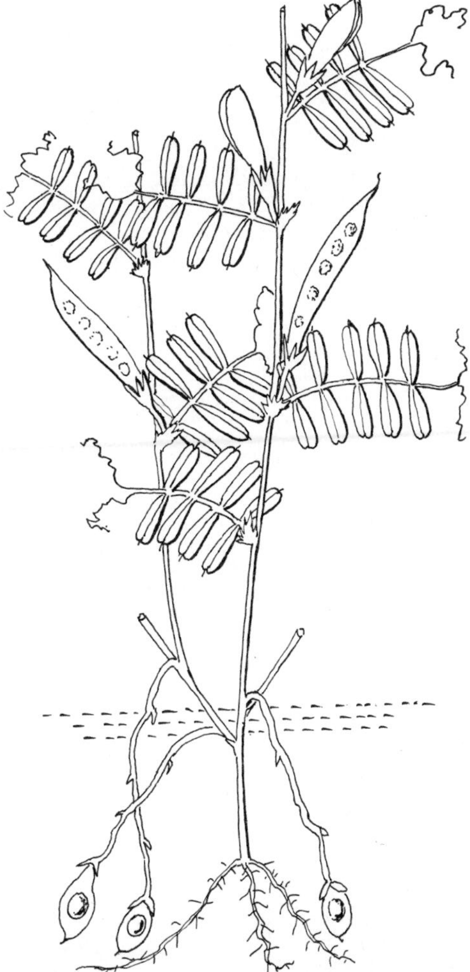

FIG. 85. *Vicia amphicarpa* Dorthes (*Fabaceae*), Europe, with dimorphic fruits, the lowermost from cleistogamous flowers and buried in the soil (orig.).

glandular in *Adenocarpus*; 4-winged in *Phosocarpus*, winged in several other genera; top of the fruit extended into a wing in *Nissolia*; along the upper suture in *Platylobium*. (The above notes are slightly shortened from my GENERA OF FLOWERING PLANTS, Vol. I, 298 (1964).) (Many fruits are illustrated in Figs 89–102, see pp. 94–106.)

In connection with the theory of the evolution of some herbaceous groups from a woody stock, as noted under *Malvaceae* later on, it is interesting that several of the herbaceous genera of *Fabaceae* are fibrous, such as

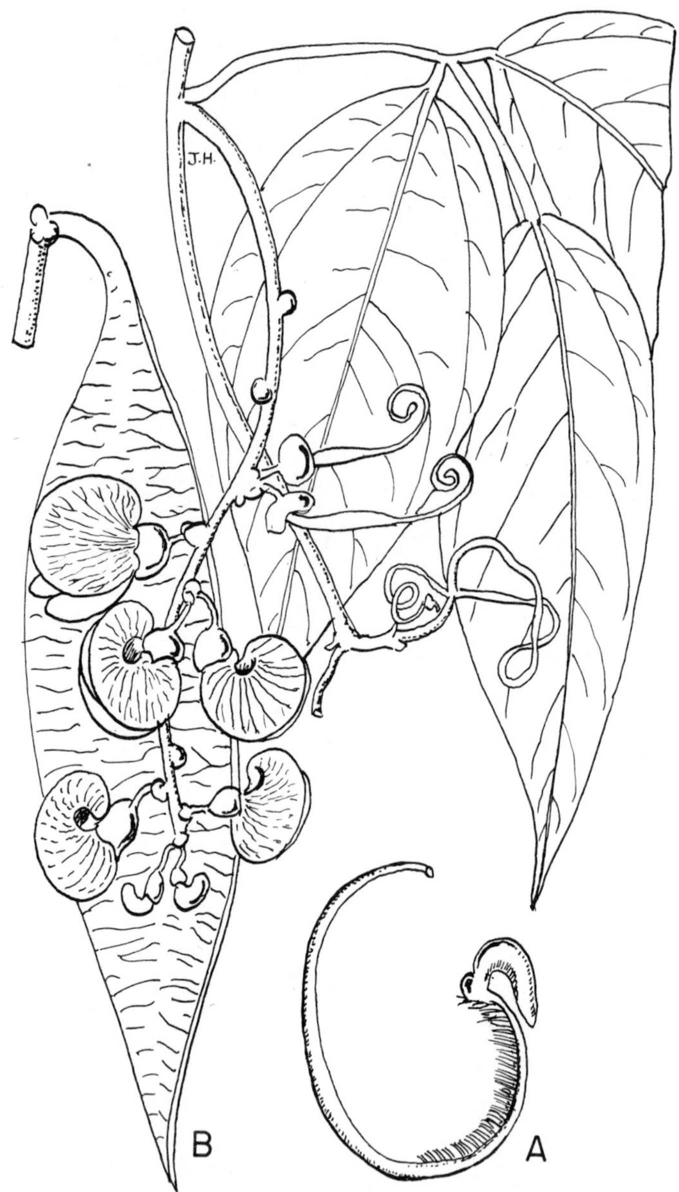

FIG. 86. The Calabar Bean, *Physostigma venenosum* Balf. f. (*Fabaceae*), tropical Africa. **A**, ovary with curled hairy style and curved stigma. **B**, fruit (orig.). "The poisonous effect of eating the bean is caused by the action of the alkaloid as a powerful sedative on the spinal cord, resulting in paralysis of the lower limbs and death by asphyxia, and in the larger doses by paralysis of the heart" (Dalziel USEFUL PLANTS OF WEST TROPICAL AFRICA 256 (1937)).

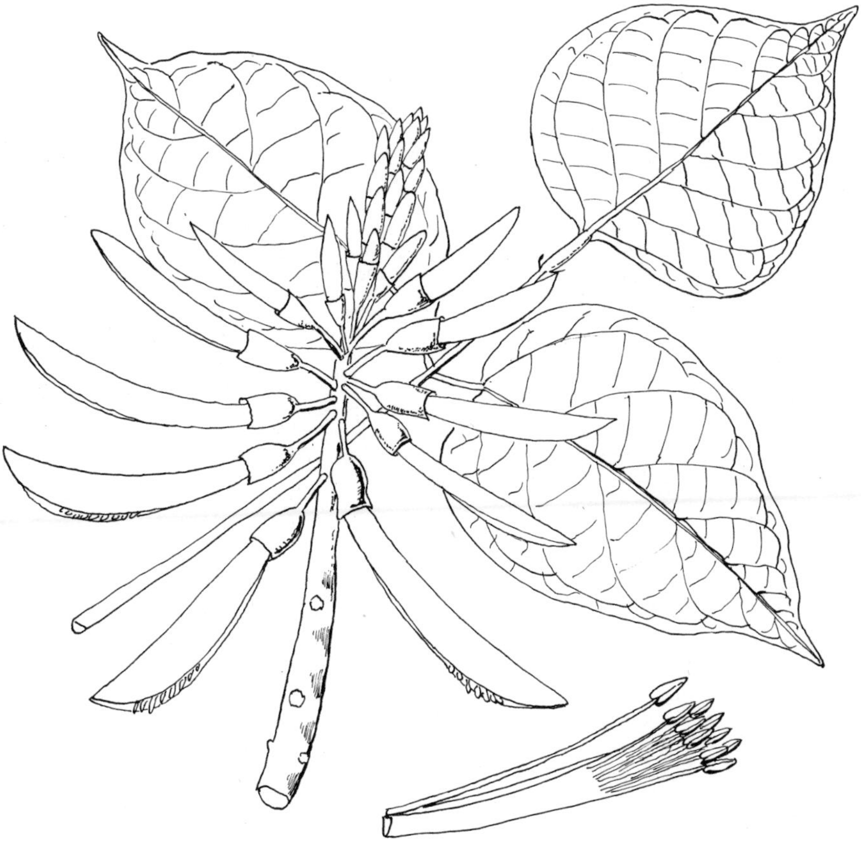

FIG. 87. *Erythrina corallodendron* Linn. (*Fabaceae*), ornamental shrub in the southern United States of America and in the West Indies, and cult.; leaf, flowers and stamens (orig.).

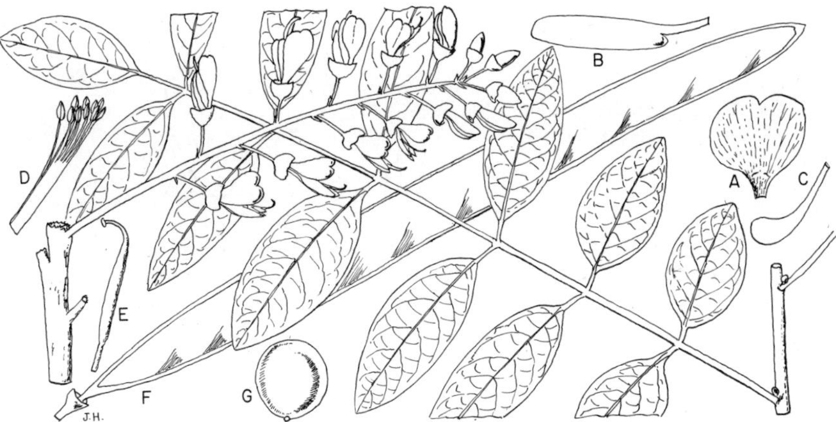

FIG. 88. Bala, *Gliricidia sepium* (Jacq.) Steud. (*Fabaceae*), often planted as a hedge, but more especially as a shade plant for cacao and coffee plants in the tropics, especially Central America. **A**, standard petal. **B**, wing. **C**, keel petal. **D**, stamens. **E**, gynoecium. **F**, fruit. **G**, seed (orig.).

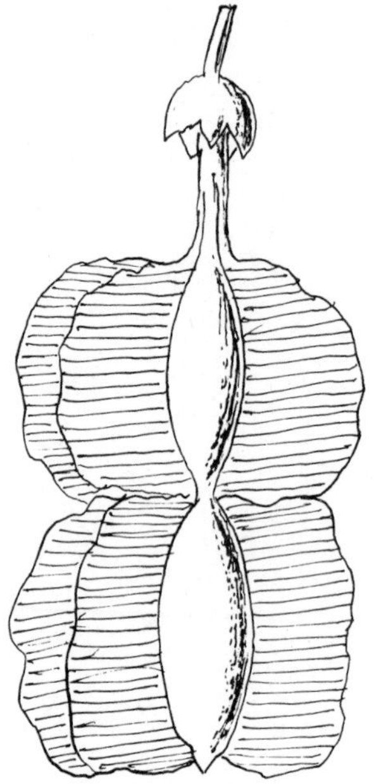

FIG. 89. Fruit of *Piscidia acuminata* (Blake) I. M. Johnston (*Fabaceae*), Central America, West Indies.

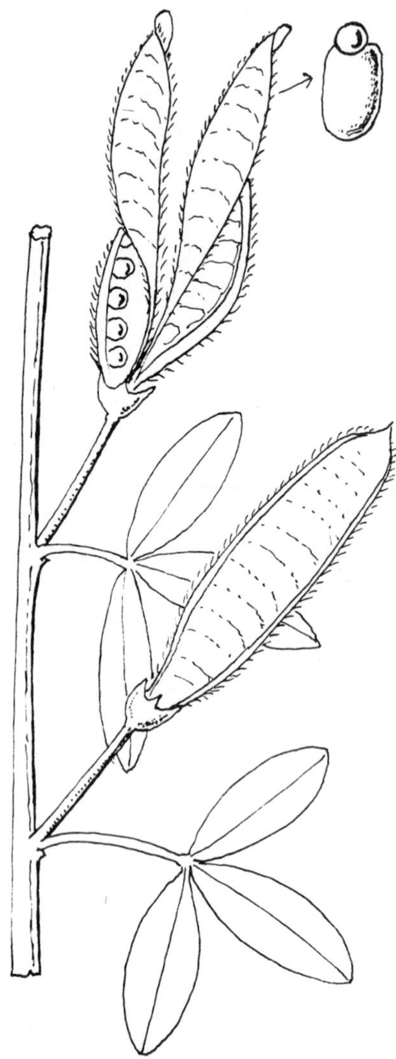

FIG. 90. *Cytisus scoparius* Linn. (*Fabaceae*), Europe, showing the fruit which by twisting throws out the seeds (all enlarged).

Crotalaria, bundles of twine and rope being made in India from *Crotalaria juncea* Linn. Even the stems of Sweet Peas, *Lathyrus odoratus* Linn., contain a fibre, and at one time lace was made from it in Eire. Pretty little baskets are made in Madeira from the shoots of the common Broom, *Cytisus scoparius* Linn.

The financial loss due to the ravages of insect pests on the world's cultivated crops probably amounts to hundreds of millions annually. Consequently for several years much research has been carried out with insecticide

(continued on p. 100)

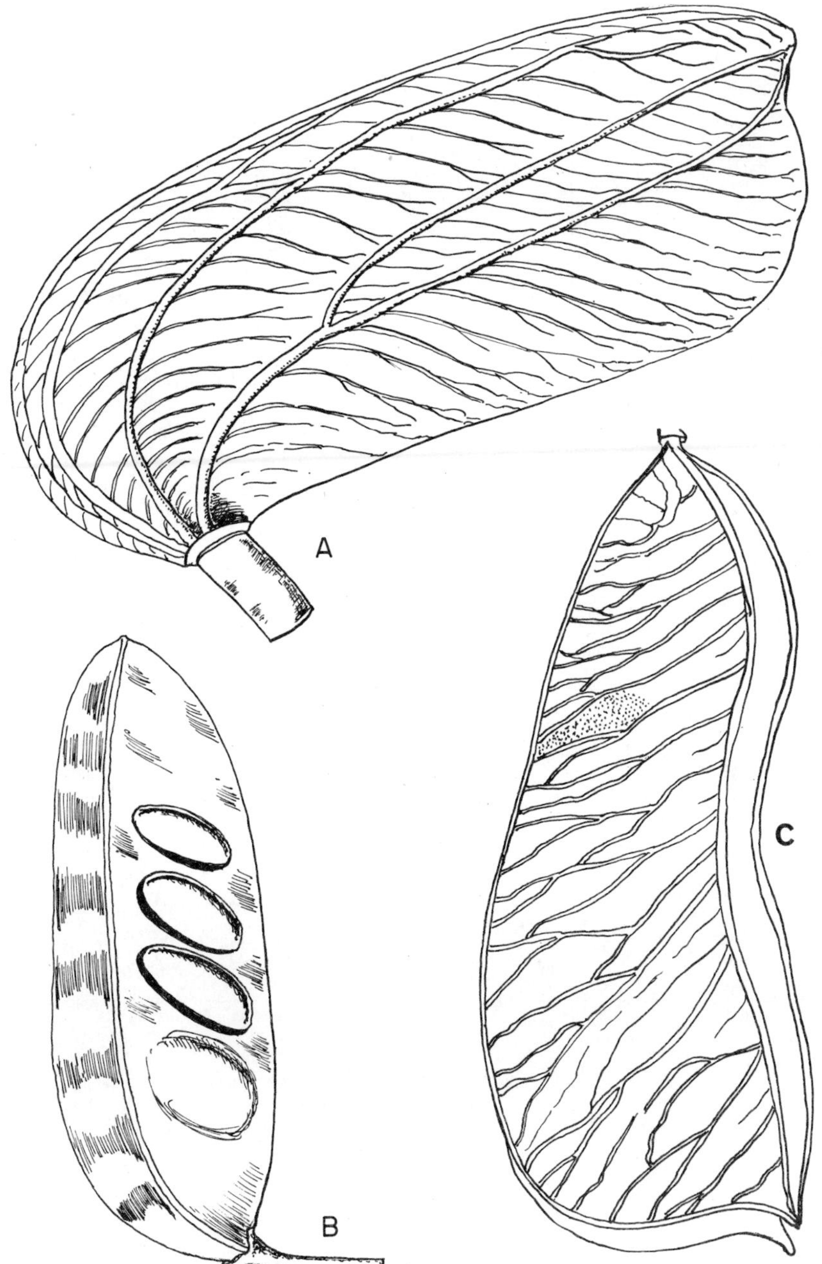

FIG. 91. Fruits of the Order LEGUMINALES: **A**, *Gilbertiodendeon bilineatum* (Hutch. & Dalz.) J. Léonard, tropical Africa. **B**, *Mezoneuron furfuraceum* Prain, India. **C**, *Macrolobium dewevrei* De Wild., tropical Africa.—*Caesalpiniaceae*.

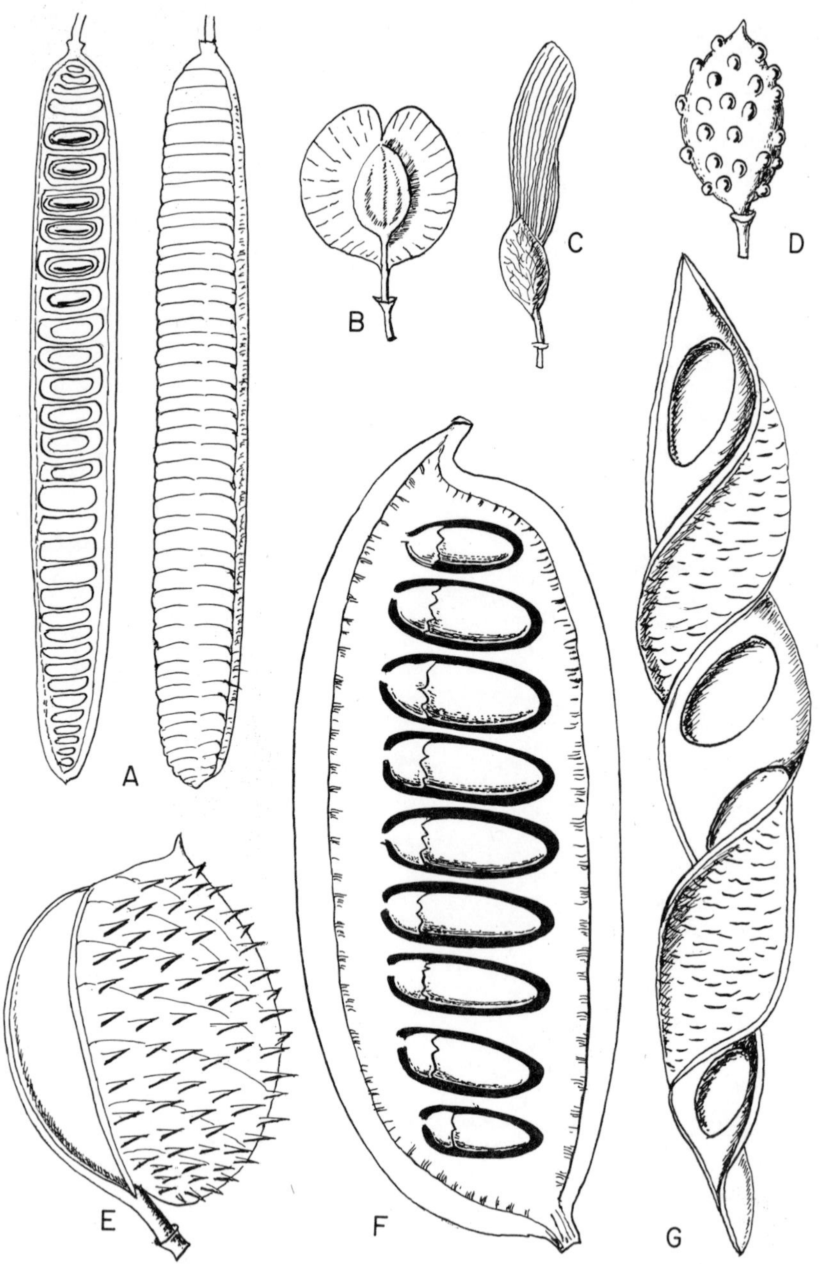

Fig. 92. Fruits of the Order LEGUMINALES: **A**, *Cassia fistula* Linn., tropical Asia. **B**, *Tetrapterocarpon geayi* Humbert, Madagascar. **C**, *Pterogyne nitens* Tul., Brazil. **D**, *Trachylobium verrucosum* Oliv., Madagascar. **E**, *Sindora wallichii* Grah. ex Benth., tropical Asia, Malaya. **F**, *Afzelia africana* Smith, tropical Africa. **G**, *Chidlowia sanguinea* Hoyle, tropical Africa.—All *Caesalpiniaceae*.

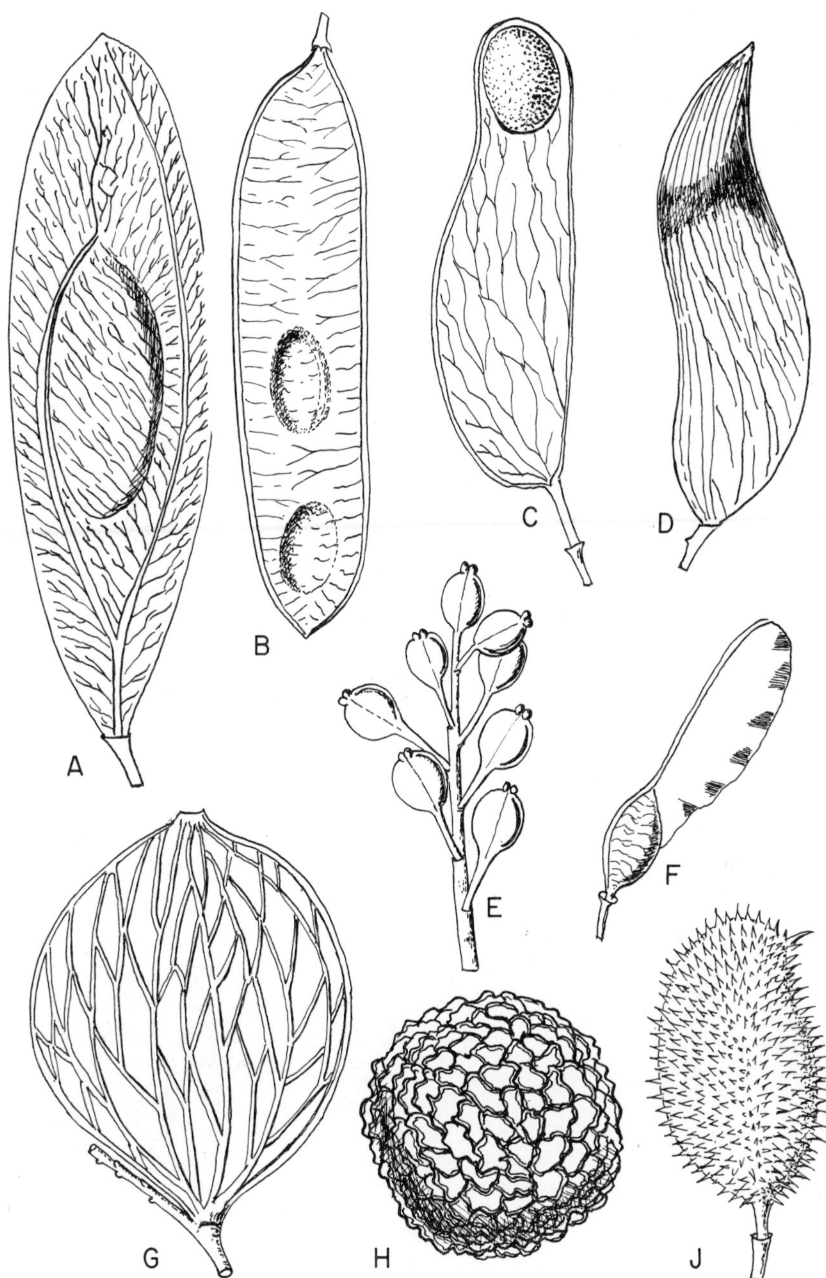

FIG. 93. Fruits of the Order LEGUMINALES: **A**, *Martiodendron macrocarpum* Gleason, Brazil. **B**, *Hylodendron gabunense* Taub., tropical Africa. **C**, *Gossweilerodendron balsamiferum* Harms, tropical Africa. **D**, *Oxystigma oxyphyllum* (Harms) J. Léonard, tropical Africa. **E**, *Polystemonanthus dinklagei* Harms, tropical Africa. **F**, *Pterolobium stellatum* (Forssk.) Pich.-Sermoli, tropical Africa and Arabia. **G**, *Prioria copaifera* Griseb., West Indies and Central America. **H**, *Detarium senegalense* Gmel., tropical Africa. **J**, *Caesalpinia bonducella* Linn., tropics generally.—All *Caesalpiniaceae*.

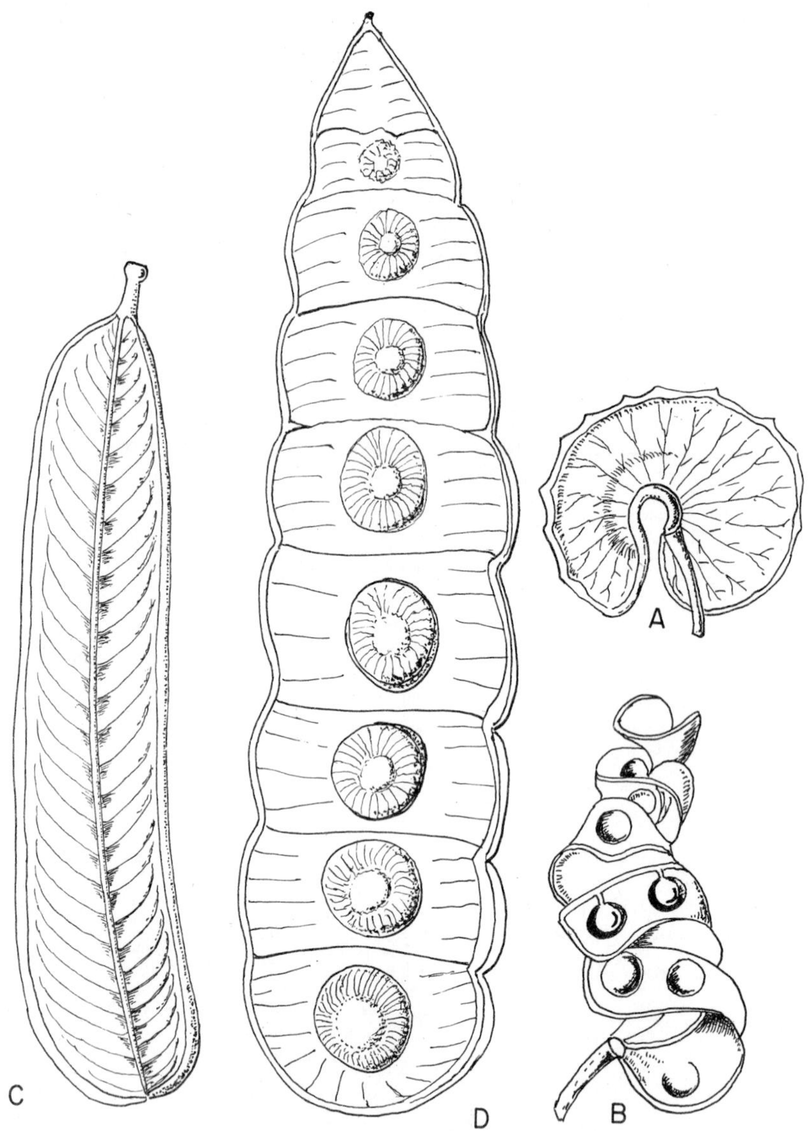

FIG. 94. Fruits of the Order LEGUMINALES: **A**, *Enterolobium ellipticum* Benth., Brazil. **B**, *Pithecellobium auaremotemo* Mart., Brazil. **C**, *Tetrapleura tetraptera* Taub., tropical Africa. **D**, *Entada africana* Guill. & Perr., tropical Africa.—All *Mimosaceae*.

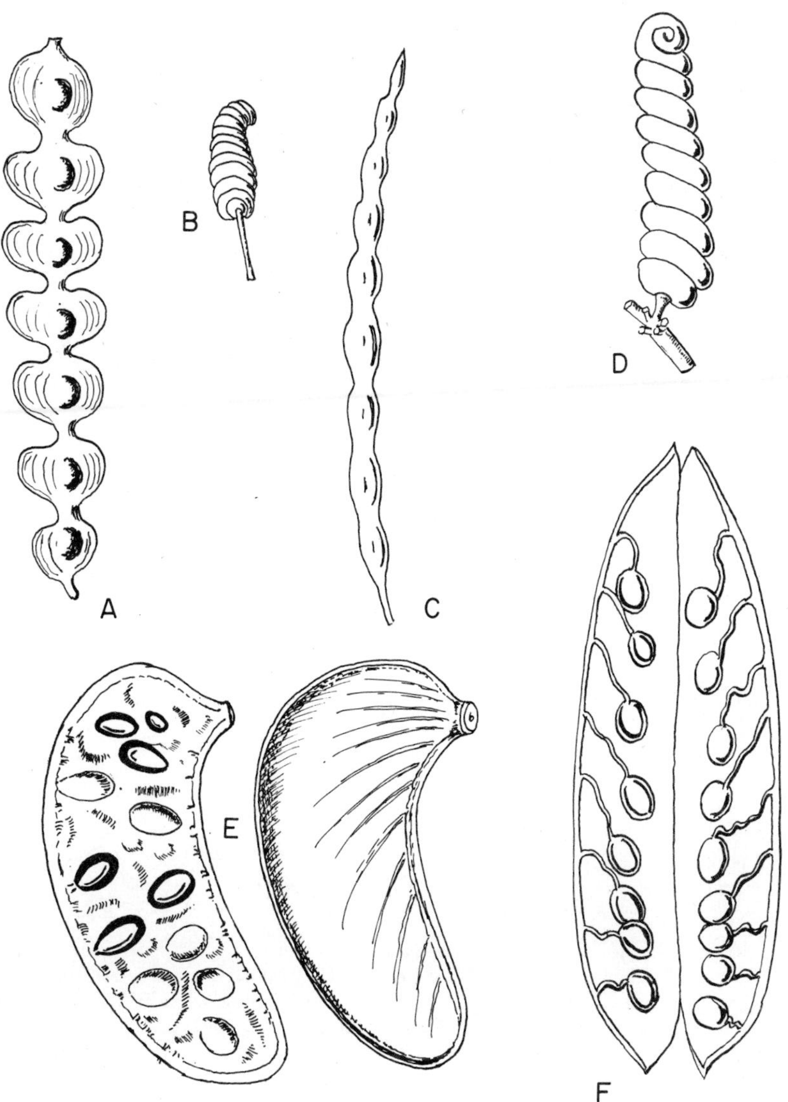

FIG. 95. Fruits of the Order LEGUMINALES: **A**, *Acacia arabica* Del., tropical Africa, Orient. **B**, *Acacia obliqua* A. Cunn., Australia. **C**, *Acacia constricta* Benth., New Mexico. **D**, *Prosopis strombulifera* Benth., South America. **E**, *Acacia giraffae* Burch., South Africa. **F**, *Acacia stolonifera* Burch., South Africa.—All *Mimosaceae*.

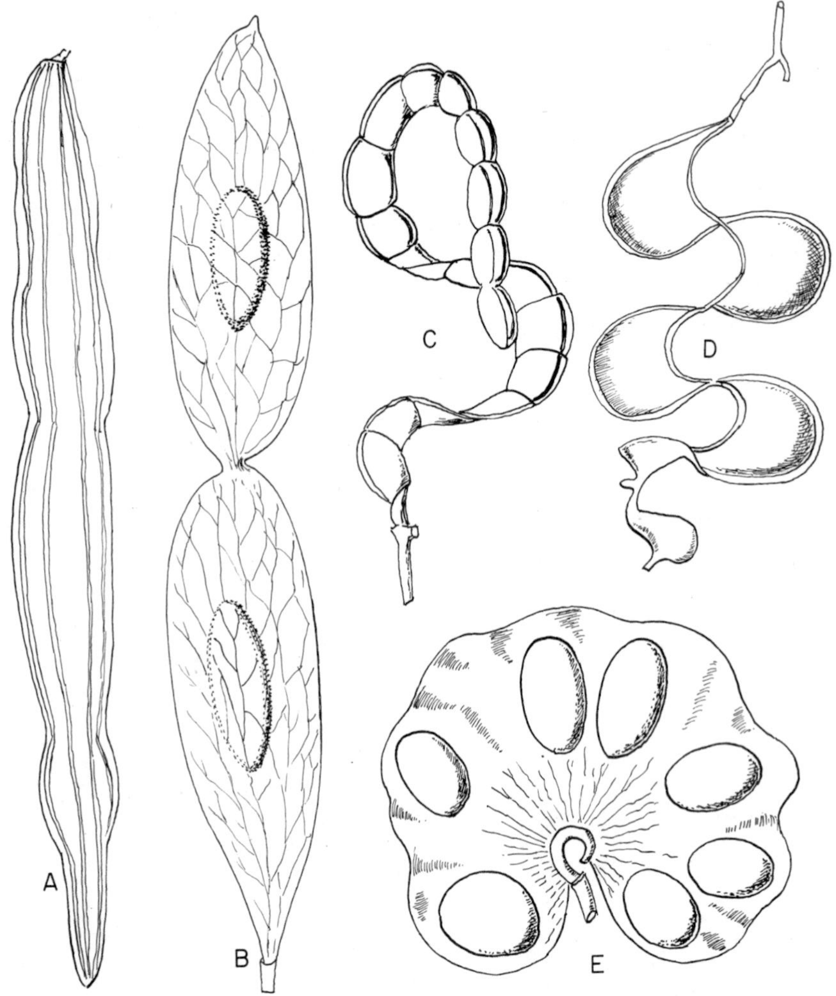

FIG. 96. Fruits of the Order LEGUMINALES: **A**, *Inga edulis* Mart., Brazil. **B**, *Cedrelingia cateniformis* Ducke, Brazil. **C**, *Cathormion altissimum* Hutch. & Dandy, tropical Africa. **D**, *Pithecellobium lobatum* Benth., tropical Asia. **E**, *Enterolobium cyclocarpum* Griseb., West Indies.—All *Mimosaceae*.

materials of plant origin, and in particular those plants used for centuries as fish-poisons by local natives. A handbook devoted to these plants contains much information on the subject. (A SURVEY OF INSECTICIDE MATERIALS OF VEGETABLE ORIGIN, Ed. H. J. Holman (1940).)

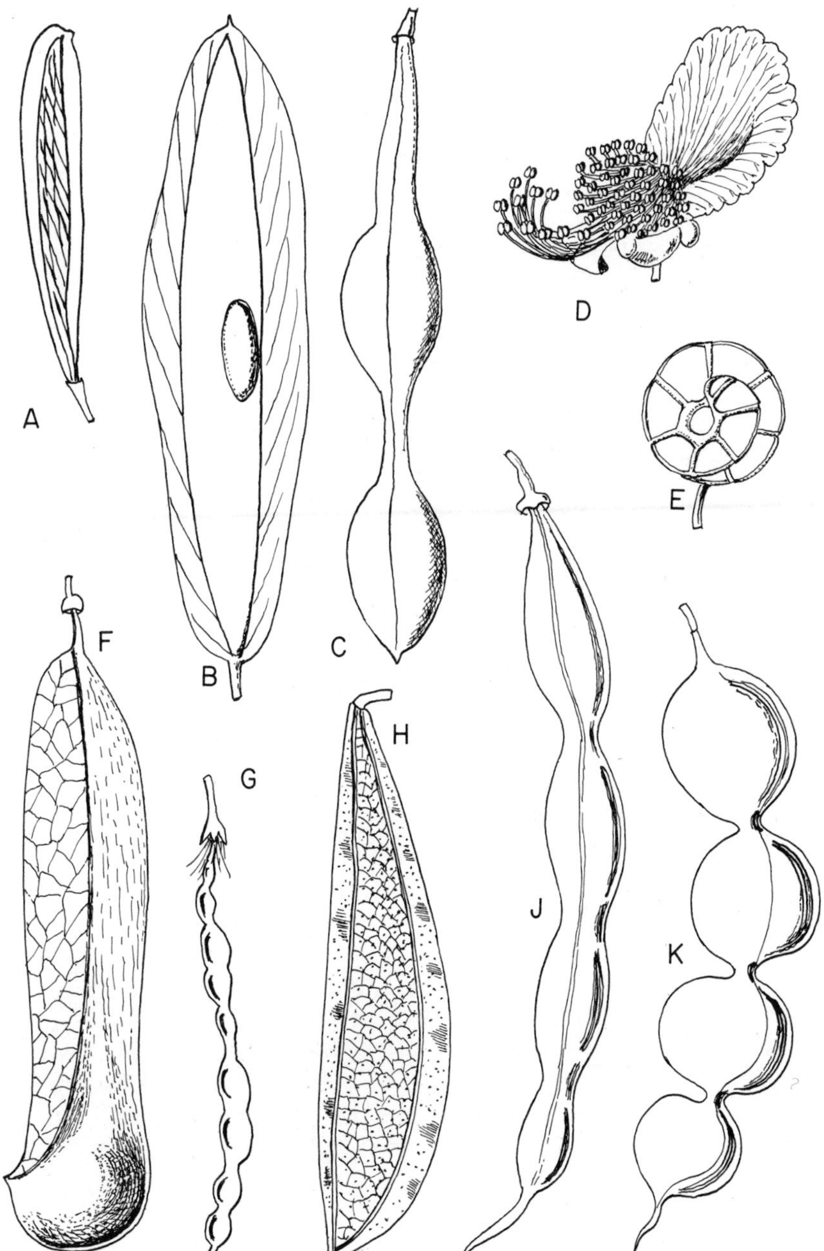

FIG. 97. Fruits of the Order LEGUMINALES: **A**, *Myrocarpus frondosus* Allem., Brazil. **B**, *Amphimas pterocarpoides* Harms, tropical Africa. **C**, *Swartzia pinnata* Wild., tropical South America. **D**, flower of *Swartzia tomentosa* DC., tropical South America. **E**, *Cyclocarpa stellaris* Afz., tropical Africa. **F**, *Myroxylon toluiferum* Kunth, tropical America. **G**, *Sophora japonica* Linn., E. Asia. **H**, *Ostryoderris chevalieri* Dunn, tropical Africa. **J**, *Angylocalyx vermeulenii* De Wild., tropical Africa. **K**, *Muellera frutescens* (Aubl.) Standl., tropical America.—All *Fabaceae*.

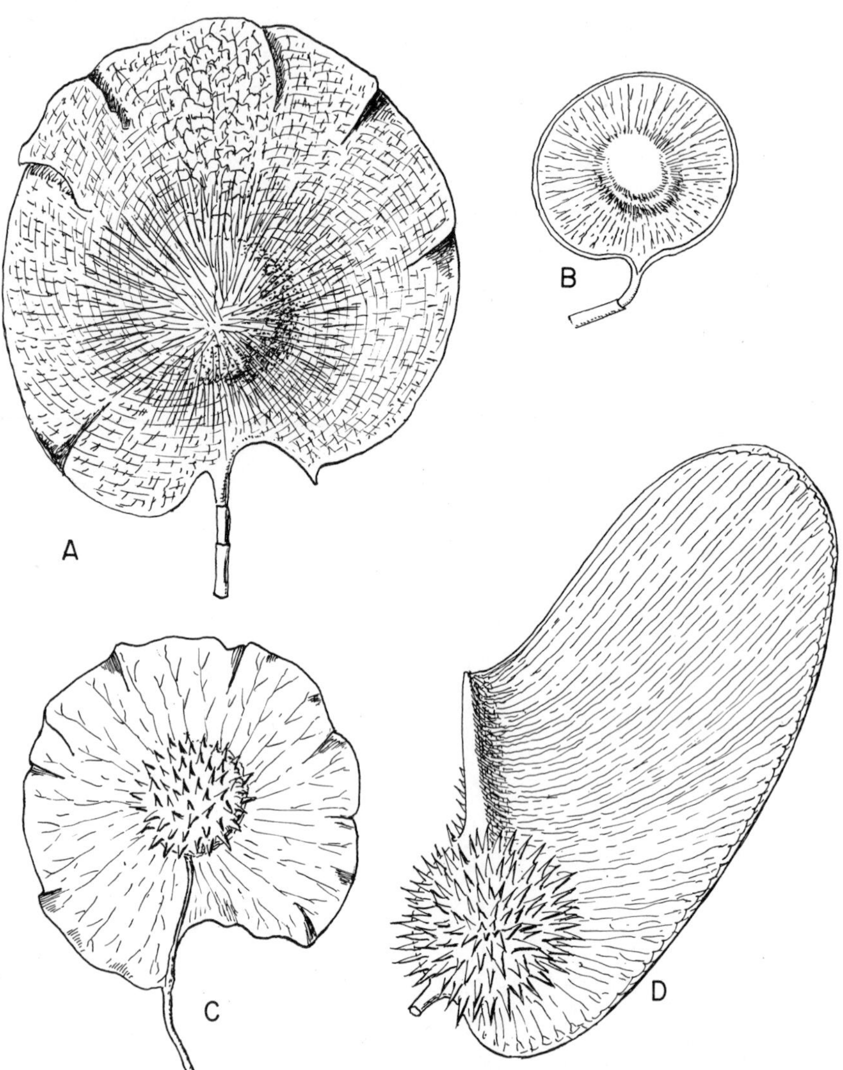

FIG. 98. Fruits of the Order LEGUMINALES: **A**, *Pterocarpus angolensis* DC., tropical Africa. **B**, *Dalbergia monetaria* Linn. f., tropical America. **C**, *Pterocarpus osun* Craib, tropical Africa. **D**, *Centrolobium tomentosum* Guill., Brazil.—All *Fabaceae*.

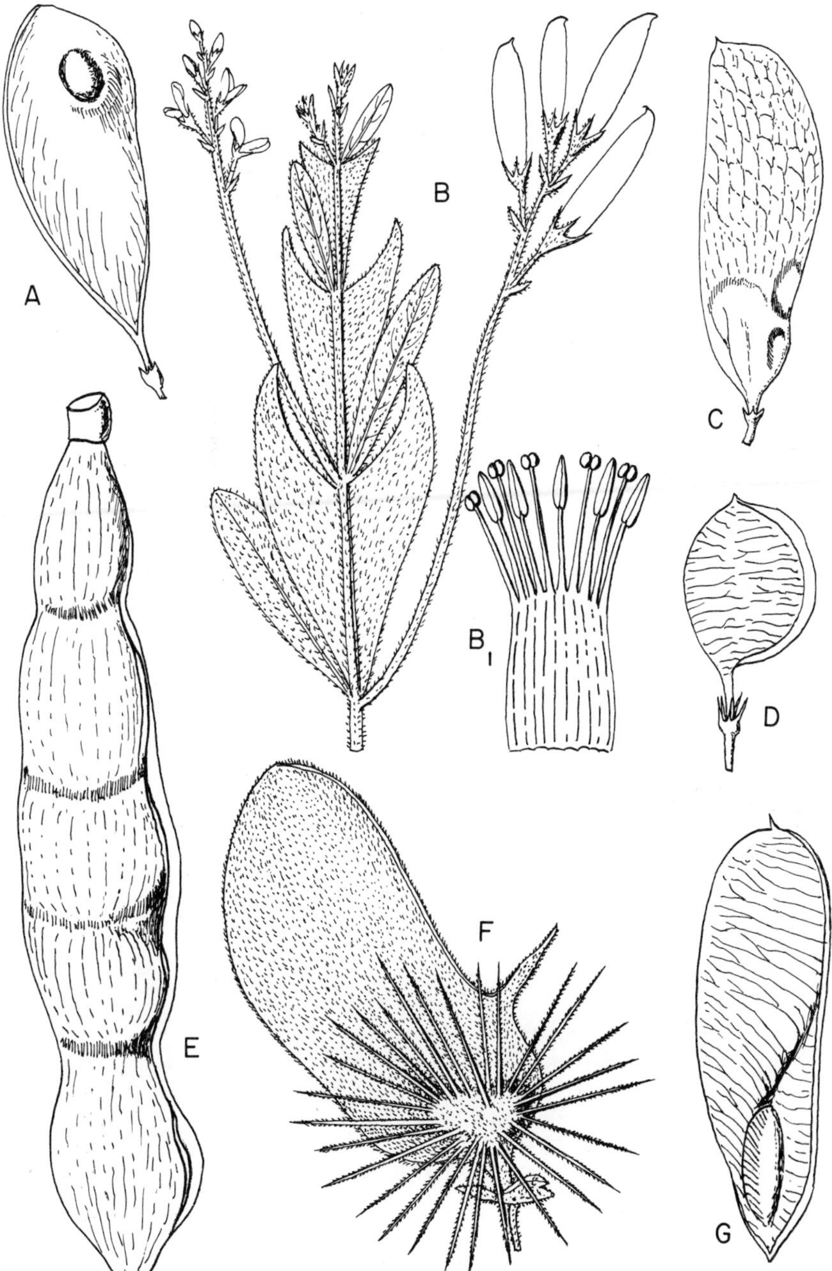

FIG. 99. Fruits of the Order LEGUMINALES: **A**, *Platypodium elegans* Vog., Brazil. **B**, *Crotalaria stipularia* Desv., tropical America, West Indies (showing the large stipules and **B**$_1$ the dimorphic anthers). **C**, *Machaerium mucronulatum* Mart., Brazil. **D**, *Cyclolobium claussenii* Benth, Brazil. **E**, *Millettia australis* Benth., Norfolk Island. **F**, *Centrolobium robustum* Mart., Brazil. **G**, *Vataireopsis speciosa* Ducke, Brazil.—All *Fabaceae*.

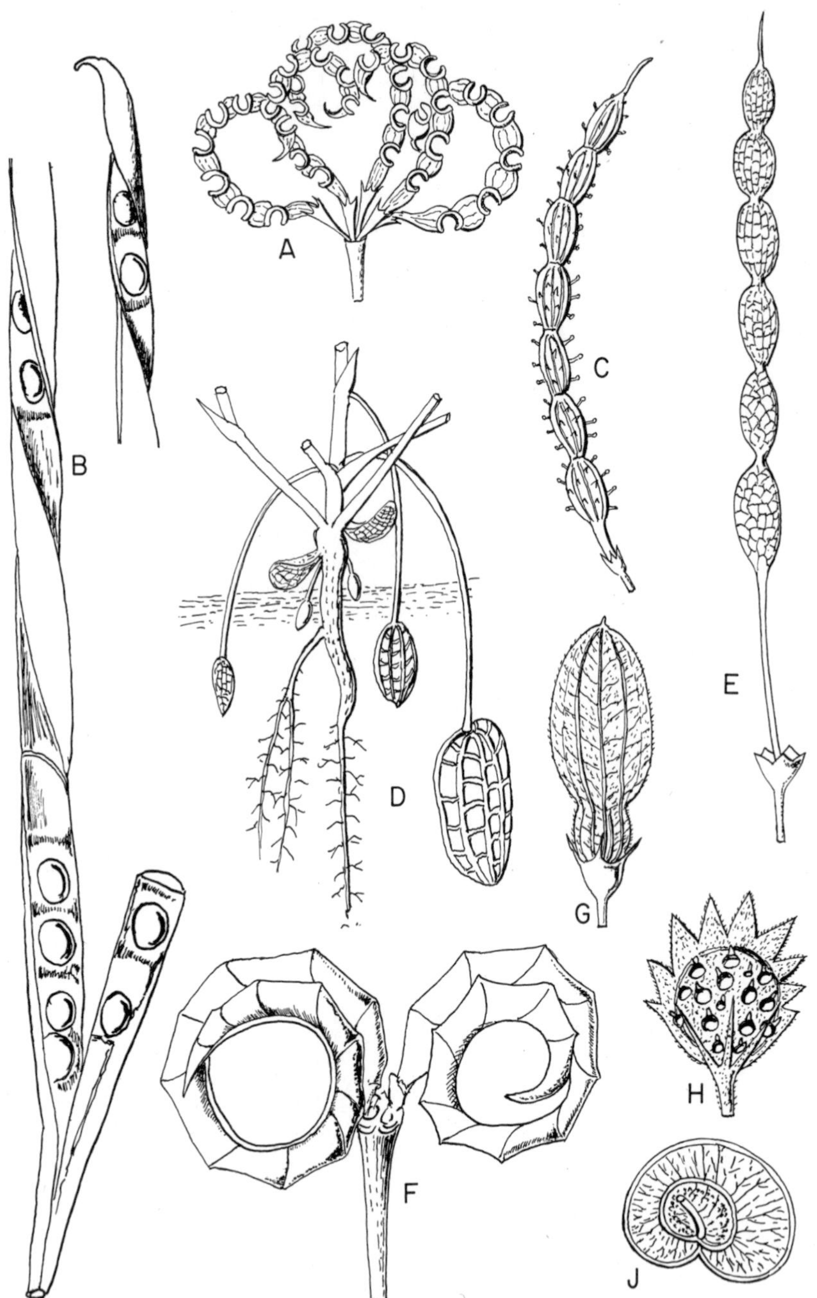

FIG. 100. Fruits of the Order LEGUMINALES: **A**, *Hippocrepis multisiliquosa* Linn., Mediterranean region. **B**, *Sphenostylis stenocarpa* Harms, tropical Africa. **C**, *Ormocarpum megalophyllum* Harms, tropical Africa. **D**, *Arachis hypogaea* Linn., tropical regions, cult. **E**, *Arthroclianthus andersonii* (Seem.) Schindl., New Caledonia. **F**, *Dolichos bicontortus* Dur., N.E. Asia. **G**, *Nissolia hintonii* Sandwith, Mexico. **H**, *Onobrychis cretica* Desv., S. Europe, Persia. **J**, *Discolobium psoralifolium* Benth., Brazil.—All *Fabaceae*.

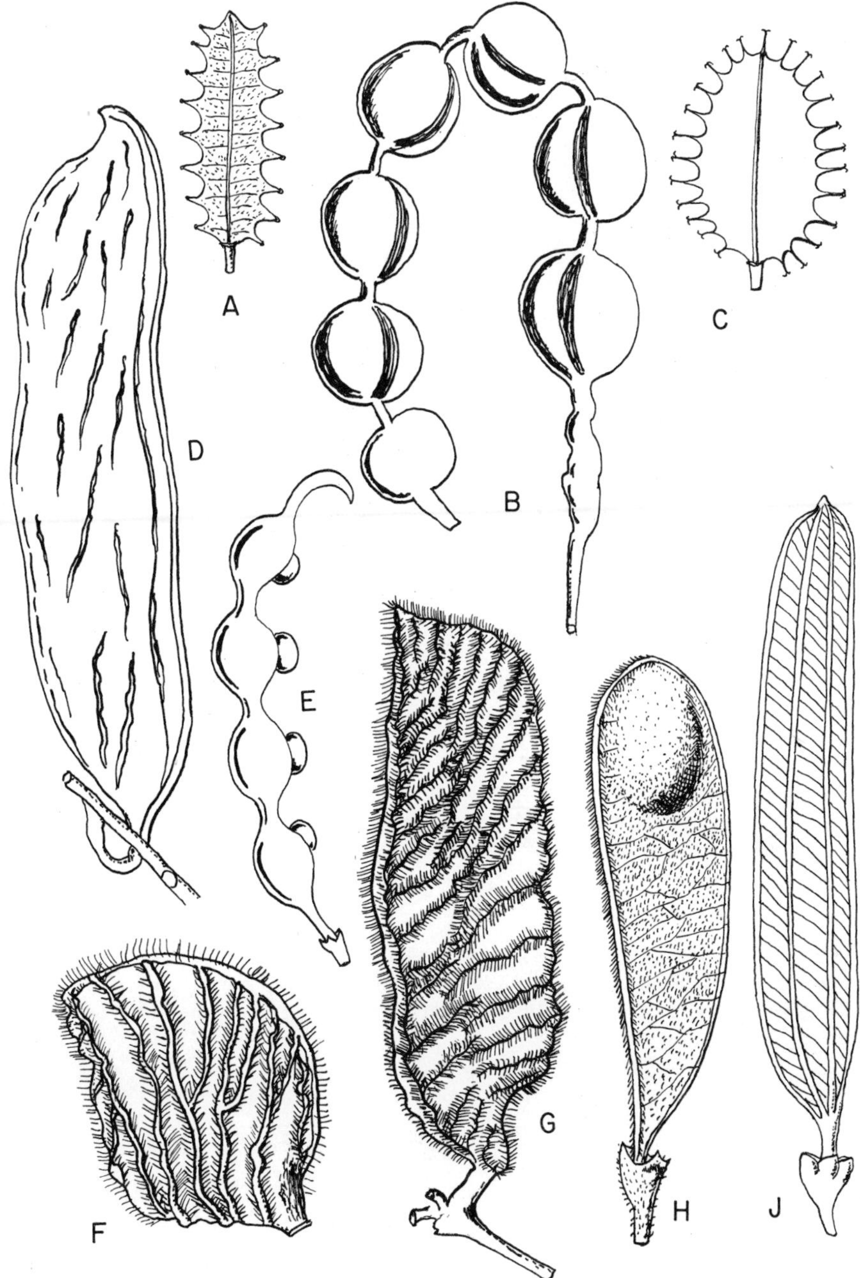

FIG. 101. Fruits of the Order LEGUMINALES: **A**, *Biserrula pelecinus* Linn., Atlantic Isls., Mediterranean region. **B**, *Erythrina addisoniae*, tropical Africa. **C**, *Sewerzowia turkestanica* Regel & Schmalh, Turkestan. **D**, *Canavalia gladiata* DC., tropics generally. **E**, *Erythrina caffra* Thunb., South Africa. **F**, *Mucuna monosperma* DC., India. **G**, *Mucuna urens* Medik., South America. **H**, *Spatholobus roxburghii* Benth., tropical Asia. **J**, *Wenderothia acuminata* Piper, Mexico.—All *Fabaceae*.

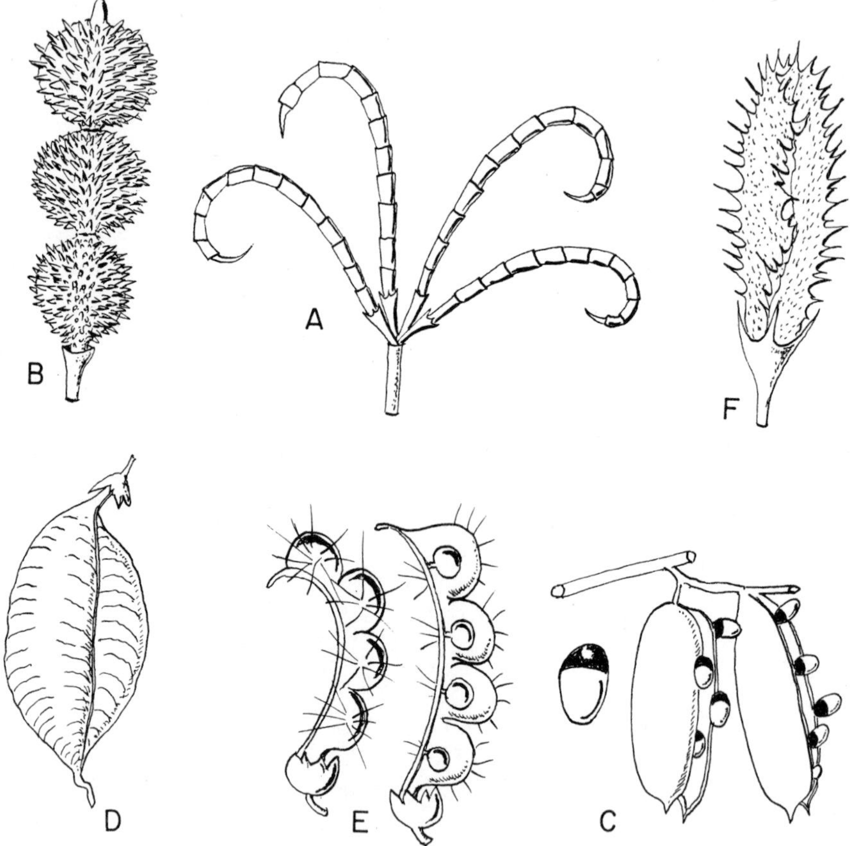

FIG. 102. Fruits of the Order LEGUMINALES: **A**, *Arthrolobium scorpioides* Desv., Mediterranean region to Persia. **B**, *Hedysarum coronarium* Linn., S. Europe. **C**, *Abrus precatorius* Linn., tropics generally. **D**, *Colutea arborescens* Linn., Europe, Orient (cult). **E**, *Adesmia microphylla* Hook. & Arm., Chile. **F**, *Stracheya tibetica* Benth., Himalayas.—All *Fabaceae*.

ORDER 8. **CUNONIALES**

(*Fam. Fl. Pl.* **1**, 156)

Families: **Pterostemonaceae, Cunoniaceae, Philadelphaceae, Hydrangaceae, Grossulariaceae, Oliniaceae, Greyiaceae, Escalloniaceae, Baueraceae, Crypteroniaceae.**

The Order CUNONIALES is mostly composed of woody families, rarely herbs, and is considered in the present system to be something of a side-branch and rather a "mixed bag" derived mainly from the Rosaceous stock, evolved more or less parallel with the *Hamamelidaceae* and its related families; it embraces rather small families of little economic importance, except for a number of ornamental garden plants. Its probable path of evolution may be shown as follows:

MAGNOLIACEAE → ROSACEAE → CUNONIALES, something of a climax group formerly generally included in *Saxifragaceae*.

The genus *Pterostemon* Schauer was raised to family rank, **Pterostemonaceae**, by J. K. Small (N. AMER. FL. **22**, 183 (1905)). It was formerly included in that taxonomic conglomeration "Saxifragaceae". It differs fundamentally from the *Philadelphaceae* (also formerly in *Saxifragaceae*) by the alternate leaves with small stipules and the absence of endosperm from the seeds. From the inferior-ovaried *Rosaceae* it differs by the dehiscent inferior fruits and toothed stamens. This type of stamen is also met with in some *Philadelphaceae* (i.e. *Fendlera* and *Deutzia* spp.).

Cunoniaceae[1] are nearly confined to the Southern Hemisphere, being especially abundant in Australasia. In *Pancheria* we find the very rare combination of a capitate inflorescence associated with an apocarpous gynoecium! The catkin-like inflorescence of apetalous flowers of *Geissois*, a small genus extending from Australia into New Caledonia and Fiji, reminds one very forcibly of those of the "Amentiferae", especially some *Juglandaceae*, and it is possible that we have in this stock the genesis of part of that group. It is significant that it is found in New Caledonia, which harbours some very ancient relics of plant life. The styles of the genus *Callicoma*, for example, are circinate in bud, an ancient character which is rarely found in any group above the *Pteridophyta*, though it also occurs in the petals of *Hamamelis* (*Hamamelidaceae*). Perhaps it is a so-called "relict" character. From a phylogenetic standpoint the family *Cunoniaceae* deserves study, especially with reference to its geographical distribution.

The view that *Cunonia*, the type genus, for example, is relatively ancient seems to be supported by its discontinuous distribution, being found now only in South Africa (one species), and in the island of New Caledonia (about 20 species) (see Map 8). The largest genus is *Weinmannia*, with about 150 spp. in the tropics, but absent from India and Africa. The genus *Pancheria* is confined to New Caledonia, where there are about 28 species. Most of the genera occur in New Guinea, where one might expect even more to be discovered.

---

[1] Including *Belangeraceae* J. G. Agardh (1858). *Callicomaceae* J. G. Agardh (1858). *Codiaceae* van Tieghem (1900). *Davidsoniaceae* Bange (1852).

Cunonia is a very natural association of about 20 species of forest trees and shrubs with opposite 3-foliolate or imparipinnate leaves, the leaflets glandular-serrate; stipules large, soon falling off; flowers bisexual, small, in dense spike-like axillary racemes; calyx of 5 imbricate segments; petals 5, free, imbricate; stamens 10, free, with elongated filaments; ovary superior, 2-locular; styles 2, elongated, persistent; ovules numerous, 2-seriate, pendulous; capsule septicidally 2-valved, valves gaping above on the inside; seeds numerous and narrowly winged. The type species is *Cunonia capensis* Linn. (see Fig. 103A).

Divergence from the type genus may be noted: Leaves simple in *Pancheria*, *Spiranthemum*, *Stollea* and *Caldcluvia*; alternate in *Gumillea* and with large and leafy stipules; rhachis winged in *Weinmannia* spp. and *Davidsonia*; stipules serrate in *Caldcluvia*. Flowers capitate in *Callicoma*, *Codia* and *Pancheria* (Fig. 103B); capitate and involucrate with bracts in *Callicoma* and *Codia*; calyx-segments accrescent in *Ceratopetalum* and *Aphanopetalum*. Ovary of free carpels in *Pancheria*, *Spiraeantheum* and *Aistopetalum*. Fruit winged in *Gillbeea* and *Platylophus*. Seeds often hairy in *Weinmannia* and *Ackamia*; winged in several genera. The general phylogeny and morphology is dealt with in my GENERA OF FLOWERING PLANTS, Vol. 2, 5 (1967).

Suggestive of relative antiquity, and perhaps showing derivation from the general Rosaceous stock, are three genera with free carpels placed at the beginning of the key to genera in my GENERA OF FLOWERING PLANTS.

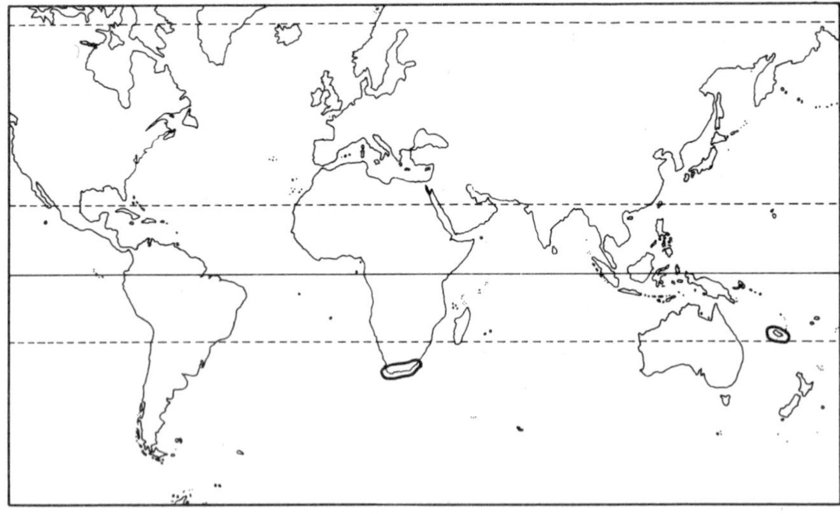

MAP 8. *Cunonia* (*Cunoniaceae*), a genus of very closely related species, several in New Caledonia but only one in far distant South Africa; a very remarkable example of discontinuous distribution. (Repeated from FAMILIES OF FLOWERING PLANTS, 2nd Ed.)

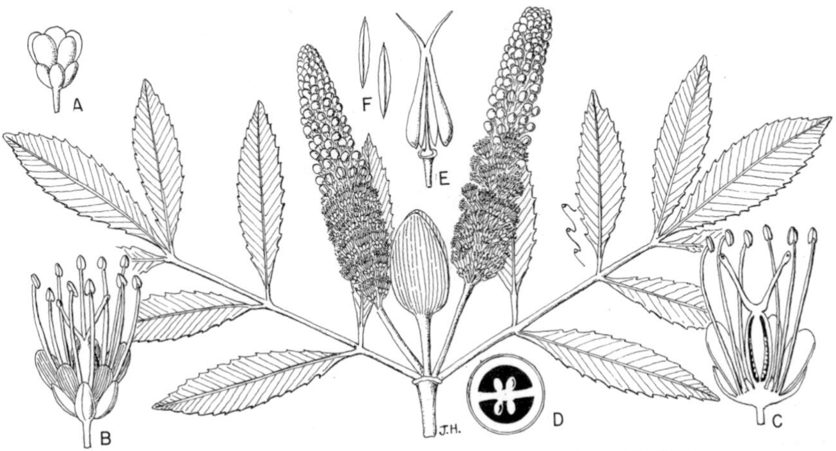

FIG. 103A. *Cunonia capensis* Linn., the type species of the type genus of *Cunoniaceae*; the only species in South Africa, the remainder in the far away island of New Caledonia (see map). **A**, flower-bud. **B**, flower. **C**, vertical section of same. **D**, cross-section of ovary. **E**, fruit. **F**, seeds (orig.).

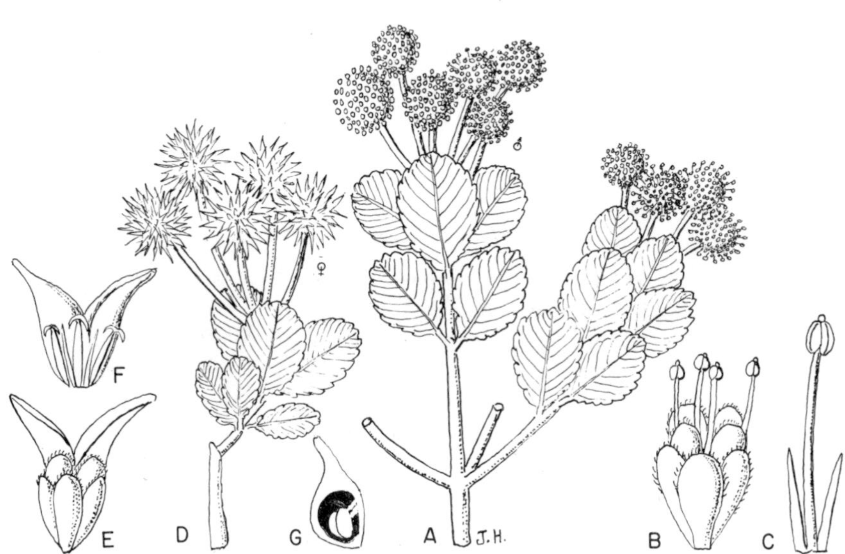

FIG. 103B. *Pancheria engleriana* Schltr. (*Cunoniaceae*), New Caledonia. **A**, male flowering shoot. **B**, male flower. **C**, stamen with disk-segment. **D**, female flowering shoot. **E**, female flower. **F**, carpels, staminodes and disk. **G**, vertical section of ovary (dissections after Schlechter).

These are *Pancheria*, *Spiraeanthеum* and *Aistopetalum*. The remainder have united carpels such as also occur in many *Rosaceae*. Those genera with imbricate sepals and flowers never capitate come next. These are *Aphanopetalum*, *Cunonia*, *Vesselowskya*, *Weinmannia* and *Pullea*, and in the last mentioned the ovary is 2-locular and there are no petals. The remainder of the genera have valvate sepals and one of these, *Lamanonia*, has numerous (more than 20) stamens, also without petals. The flowers are capitate in *Callicoma* and *Codia*, and the fruits indehiscent in *Anodopetalum*, *Opocunonia*, *Schizomeria*, *Ceratopetalum* and *Davidsonia*. In *Ceratopetalum* the calyx-lobes are accrescent in fruit.

In **Philadelphaceae** the principal genera are the "Mock Oranges", *Philadelphus* and *Deutzia*, and these at any rate seem to have had a different origin from *Hydrangea*, with which they have usually been classified. The similarity of their floral diagrams may therefore be due more to convergent evolution than to actual relationship.

The affinity of the more primitive members of this family is clearly with *Rosaceae*, and perhaps the origin of both these groups, as already pointed out, is to be found in the DILLENIALES, which have the primitive free carpels. The genus *Carpenteria*, for example, is not far removed from *Crossosoma*, a close relation of the *Dilleniaceae*, and formerly included in that family. On the other hand genera such as *Dichroa* and *Broussaisia* show great resemblance to *Viburnum* (*Caprifoliaceae*) and even to some *Araliaceae*. These two genera seem to be the most advanced because their ovaries are inferior and their fruit is a berry, whilst the second mentioned genus has polygamo-dioecious flowers. Stellate hairs are common in *Philadelphus* and *Deutzia*, as in many *Araliaceae*.

When treated as a separate family the type genus is *Philadelphus*; shrubs with terete opposite branches; leaves opposite, deciduous, indumentum often stellate-tomentose; flowers axillary, solitary or corymbose, white or yellowish, scented; calyx-tube adnate to the ovary, lobes 4, rarely 5, valvate; petals 4, rarely 5, free, imbricate; stamens 40–20, inserted below the margin of the epigynous disk; anthers short, subglobose; ovary inferior, 5–3-locular; styles 5–3, filiform, free or slightly connate; ovules numerous, pendulous; capsule inferior, turbinate, 5–3-locular, tardily loculicidally dehiscent into as many valves, these entire or 2-fid; seeds oblong, reticulate, with a fimbriate umbilicus; embryo in the middle of fleshy endosperm. The type species is *P. coronarius* Linn., well known in cultivation.

The indumentum is also stellate in *Neodeutzia*; the inflorescence is subcapitate in *Whipplea* and *Fendlerella*; flowers polygamo-dioecious in *Broussaisia*; petals valvate in *Platycrater*, *Deutzia* spp., *Dichroa* and *Broussaisia*; stamens numerous in *Carpenteria*, *Neodeutzia* and *Platycrater*; filaments divided at the apex into 2 long arms overtopping the anther in *Fendlera*, with 2 lateral lobes in *Deutzia* spp.; fruit a berry in *Dichroa* and *Broussaisia*.

The type genus of **Hydrangeaceae**,[1] *Hydrangea*, embraces about 75 species which occur in the Northern Hemisphere from India to Japan, Malay Archipelago, North America, and in the Southern Hemisphere in western South America. Some are very popular in gardens, greenhouses and windows. They are trees and shrubs, sometimes climbing; leaves opposite, often glandular-punctate; corymbs terminal; outer flowers often sterile, without petals but with 4–5 petaloid veiny sepals; calyx of bisexual flowers at most toothed; petals 5–4, valvate; stamens double the number of the petals; ovary inferior, 5–2-locular; styles 5–2; ovules very numerous, on introflexed axile placentas; capsule opening at the top between the styles. The type species is *H. arborescens* Linn.

Tribe *Kirengeshomeae* (*Kirengeshoma*, *Cardiandra*, *Deinanthe*) differs in being herbaceous, with simple stems arising from a creeping rhizome, with petals contorted or imbricate. In tribe *Hydrangeae* the remaining three genera, *Decumaria*, *Pileostegia* and *Schizophragma*, differ from *Hydrangea* in having only one style and by the absence of sterile flowers, or if these are present then with only 1 enlarged ovate sepal, the capsule opening at the sides between the ribs.

There is only one genus of **Grossulariaceae**,[2] the family name being derived from *Grossularia*, a synonym of *Ribes*. There is a very wide gulf between *Ribes* and *Saxifragaceae*, the latter in the restricted sense.

Ribes provides us with the Gooseberry (*Ribes uva-crispa* L.), Black Currant, Red Currant and White Currant (forms of *Ribes rubrum* Linn., the type species), and several lovely early-flowering shrubs; leaves alternate or fasciculate, plicate or convolute in bud; stipules absent or present; petals 5–4, mostly small and scale-like; stamens 5–4; no disk; ovary inferior, 1-locular with 2 parietal placentas; styles 2, free to completely connate; ovules 2- or more-seriate; fruit a pulpy berry; seed with endosperm and rather small embryo.

Ribes is a natural genus of about 50 species spread over the temperate Northern Hemisphere, and down south along the whole of the Andes of South America, but entirely absent from Africa south of the Sahara and from Malaya and Australasia. *Ribes* is therefore probably of comparatively recent origin (see map in my FAMILIES OF FLOWERING PLANTS, 2nd Ed. **1**, 163).

The small family **Oliniaceae** is interesting and perhaps misplaced in the present system, for they may be also related to the *Thymelaeaceae*. The single genus *Olinia* Linn. occurs in east tropical and South Africa. Affinity with *Lythraceae* is also a possibility, due to the presence of intra-xylary phloem.

---

[1] Including *Kirengeshomaceae* Nakai (1943).

[2] Including *Ribesiaceae* A. Rich (1823). *Pulpaceae* Dulac (1867).

The small family **Greyiaceae**, found only in South Africa, was formerly included in the *Sapindaceae* and *Melianthaceae*, but I placed it in more close relationship with *Escalloniaceae*. *Greyia*, the only genus, with three species, has current-like leaves, the petiole sheathing at the base, a remarkable corona-like disk crowned by 10 gland-like spoon-shaped processes, and 10 free stamens.

Here are the chief differences between *Melianthaceae* (*sensu stricto*), and *Greyia*:

	Greyia	*Melianthaceae*
Leaves:	simple	pinnate
Stipules:	absent	present (intrapetiolar)
Flowers:	actinomorphic	zygomorphic
Sepals:	free	partly united
Petals:	equal	unequal
Disk:	cupular within the petals, crowned by 10 gland-like processes	unilateral, lining the calyx
Stamens:	10	stamens 4
Ovules:	numerous on the intrusive parietal placentas	1–4 on axile placentas
Capsule:	septicidal, without a central axis	loculicidal, with central axis

The separation of *Greyia* from *Melianthaceae* is also supported on anatomical grounds. C. R. Metcalfe reported as follows: "*Greyia* does not agree with *Melianthus* or *Bersama*. The latter two hang together quite well. *Greyia* could, broadly speaking, be fitted into CUNONIALES, although plants with similar glands seem to be uncommon in the Order. Somewhat similar glands have been recorded in *Abrophyllum* (*Escalloniaceae*)." In spite of this evidence, which I pointed out in my FAMILIES OF FLOWERING PLANTS, *Greyia* is still included in *Melianthaceae* in the latest SYLLABUS of the Englerian System (12th Ed., 1964).

The family **Escalloniaceae**[1] shows rather mixed relationships, such as with *Pittosporaceae*, *Celastraceae* and *Rhamnaceae*, the genus *Carpodetus*, New Zealand, being quite rhamnaceous in appearance and may be even in affinity; or perhaps due to parallelism.

---

[1] Including *Brexiaceae* Lindley (1830). *Rousseaceae* J. E. Smith (1839). *Carpodetaceae* Fenzl (1841). *Polyosmaceae* Blume (1850). *Iteaceae* J. G. Agardh (1858). *Dulongiaceae* J. G. Agardh (1858). *Phyllonomaceae* Rusby (1905). *Abrophyllaceae* Nakai (1943). *Montiniaceae* Nakai (1943). *Tetracarpaceae* Nakai (1943). *Tribelaceae* Airy Shaw (1965).

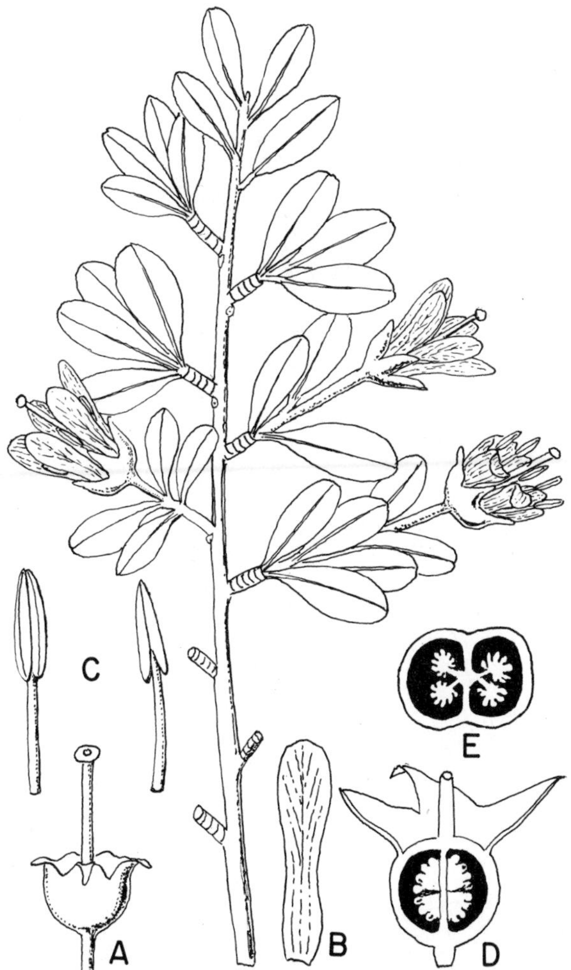

FIG. 104. *Escallonia myrtilloides* Linn. f., South America, the type species of the type genus of *Escalloniaceae*. **A**, calyx and style. **B**, petal. **C**, stamens. **D**, vertical section of ovary. **E**, cross-section of ovary (orig.).

The type genus *Escallonia* consists of about 50 species of trees and shrubs, often glandular-pubescent or resinous; leaves alternate, evergreen, entire or serrate; flowers mostly in terminal racemes or panicles, rarely axillary; calyx adnate to the ovary, lobes 5; petals 5, free, linear-spathulate, claw erect, limb spreading, imbricate at the apex; stamens 5, inserted below the margin of the epigynous disk; ovary inferior, 3–2-locular; style simple, stigma capitate; ovules numerous on axile subglobose placentas; capsule dry, 3–2-locular, septicidally 3–2-valved at the base; seeds numerous,

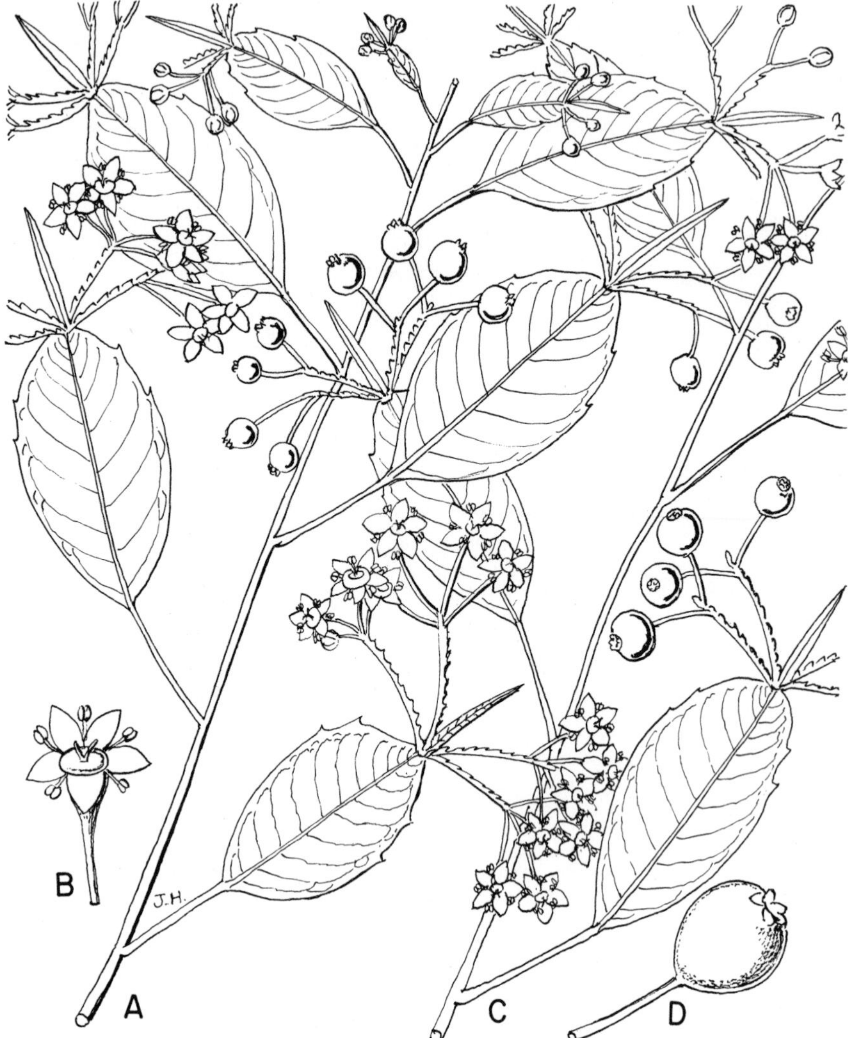

FIG. 105. *Phyllonoma laticuspis* (Turcz.) Engl., a very peculiar member of the family *Escalloniaceae*, its flowers borne apparently towards the top of the leaf; actually the peduncle of the inflorescence is merged with the midrib of the leaf; Mexico and Colombia. **A**, flowering shoot. **B**, flower. **C**, fruiting shoot. **D**, fruit (orig.).

linear-oblong, testa often fimbriate at the base; embryo in the middle of fleshy endosperm. The type species is *E. myrtilloides* Linn. f., western South America (Fig. 104).

The most divergent and outstanding genus is *Phyllonoma*, in which the peduncle is adnate to the midrib, the flowers appearing to be borne on the

Fig. 106a. Variability in the leaves of *Brexia madagascariensis* Thouars (*Escalloniaceae*), Madagascar.

Fig. 106b. The natural genus *Itea* (*Escalloniaceae*) occurs in two widely separated regions, one species, **A**, *Itea virginica* Linn., in the Atlantic states of North America, the others in eastern Asia. **B**, *Itea ilicifolia* Oliv., China. *Itea virginica*: **C**, flower. **D**, vertical section of flower. **E**, spray in fruit. **F**, fruit. **G**, dehiscing fruit. **H**, seed. **J**, vertical section of seed. *Itea ilicifolia*: **K**, flower. **L**, stamen. **M**, calyx and fruit (orig.).

leaf-blade (Fig. 105). The leaves are opposite or verticillate in *Roussea* and *Anopterys*; prominently gland-dotted below in *Dedea* and *Quintinia*; under-surface densely silky-tomentose in *Argophyllum*; leaves very polymorphic in *Brexia* (Fig. 106A) (juvenile linear and sharply toothed, mature elliptic and entire; flowers dioecious in *Montinia*; corolla sympetalous in *Roussea*; carpels free in *Tetracarpaea*; calyx-lobes deciduous in *Carpodetus*, *Brexia*, *Abrophyllum*; seeds winged in *Anopterus*, *Montinia*; ovary quite superior in *Brexia*, *Ixerba*, *Tribeles*, *Anopterus*, *Cuttsia*, *Abrophyllum* and *Roussea*; altogether a considerable range of characters in so small a family!

Most of the genera are confined to the Southern Hemisphere, several being endemic in Australia. The largest genus, *Escallonia*, with about 50 species, occurs only in South America. *Phyllonoma* is found from Mexico south to Bolivia, and in the extreme south are *Tribeles* and *Valdivia*. The genera with the widest range are *Itea* (Fig. 106B), in the N.W. Himalayas to Japan and in the eastern United States of North America, and *Polyosma* from the eastern Himalayas to eastern Australia.

The family is very rare in Africa, only three genera being found in that vast continent, *Grevea* and *Choristylis* in east tropical Africa, and *Montinia* in South Africa. *Grevea* also occurs in Madagascar. Three genera, *Carpodetus*, *Ixerba* and *Quintinia*, are found in New Zealand, the last ranging as far north as the Philippines. *Neocolmeiroa* is confined to Lord Howe's Island, and *Argyrocalymma* to New Guinea. Tasmania claims *Tetracarpaea* exclusively, *Dedea* "jumps" from the Philippines into Caledonia, Burma has *Pottingeria*, and the Mascarene Islands *Brexia*, *Roussea*, and *Fargesia*, with *Brexia* also in the Seychelles.

The family **Baueraceae** was founded by that famous botanist Lindley (NIXUS PLANTARUM 14 (1833)), for the genus *Bauera* Banks ex Andr., with three species native of eastern Australia and Tasmania. By Bentham and Hook. f. it was assigned to *Saxifragaceae* as an "anomalous" genus, and retained by Engler as a subfamily of the same. It seems to have no very close relatives, but in my arrangement it finds at least temporary sanctuary near *Cunoniaceae*, some of which have also pinnate or trifoliolate leaves.

The leaves of *Bauera* appear to be fasciculate but they are in reality sessile and trifoliolate, without stipules; flowers axillary, solitary; there is a remarkable range in the number of sepals and petals, 10–4 each, the petals free and inserted at the base of the calyx around a thin disk; stamens numerous to 4, free, anthers didymous, opening by pore-like slits; ovary superior, 2-locular; styles 2, free; ovules numerous on axile placentas; fruit a 2-valved capsule; seeds with terete embryo in the middle of fleshy endosperm. *Bauera* was named in honour of Francis Bauer (1758–1840), a talented artist employed by Banks, who came to England in 1788; born at Feldsberg in Austria; died and buried at Kew.

Crypteroniaceae[1] (*Crypteronia*) is a small Indo-Malayan family which is perhaps more nearly related to *Escalloniaceae* than to *Lythraceae*, with which it has been associated. They are trees with 4-angled branches, opposite leaves and the stamens occupy the place of the absent petals in the polygamo-dioecious flowers, which are very small and in panicles. Here we have to deal, no doubt, with a very advanced type of plant, one perhaps showing a tendency to an amentiferous condition. Another possibility is that these plants are related to *Rhamnaceae* and *Heteropyxidaceae*, but that might be attributing too much importance to the position of the stamens.

ORDER 9. STYRACALES

(*Fam. Fl. Pl.* **1**, 167)

Families: **Lissocarpaceae, Styracaceae, Symplocaceae.**

This is a small Order not easily placed in any system, though some of my armchair critics will no doubt know where it should go. Corolla mostly sympetalous and ovary superior to inferior; probably nearer to CUNONIALES than to any other more advanced families with more general sympetaly; the seeds have retained their endosperm and the embryo is straight; stellate hairs occur as in many *Hamamelidaceae*.

Lissocarpaceae, single genus *Lissocarpa*, is a segregate from *Styracaceae* and established as a family by Engler and Gilg; it differs in its contorted corolla-lobes and imbricate calyx; small tree of tropical South America, with alternate exstipulate leaves, corolla sympetalous, 4-lobed; stamens 8, inserted towards the base of the tube, anthers apiculate; ovary inferior, 4-locular; ovules 2 in each loculus, pendulous; fruit indehiscent; seeds with copious endosperm and straight embryo.

Nearly half of the 12 genera of **Styracaceae**[2] have a superior or nearly superior ovary; in the others it is from two-thirds to completely inferior. The largest is the type genus *Styrax*, with about 160 species in tropical and temperate regions but absent from Africa; trees and shrubs, all parts except the upper leaf-surface usually more or less lepidote or stellate-tomentose; flowers bisexual, in axillary and terminal racemes; petals 5, free or united, imbricate or valvate; stamens 10, partly adnate to the corolla; ovary

---

[1] Including *Henslowiaceae* Lindl. (1836).

[2] Including *Halesiaceae* Link (1829).

3-locular when young, at length 1-locular with parietal placentas; fruit indehiscent or 3-valved.

Outstanding genera are *Bruinsmia* with polygamo-dioecious flowers, and *Pamphila* with only 5 stamens. The sole representative in Africa is *Afrostyrax* (Fig. 107), found only in the Cameroons, west Africa. Another isolated genus is *Pamphila* in Brazil, whilst *Halesia* occurs in eastern North America and in eastern Asia.

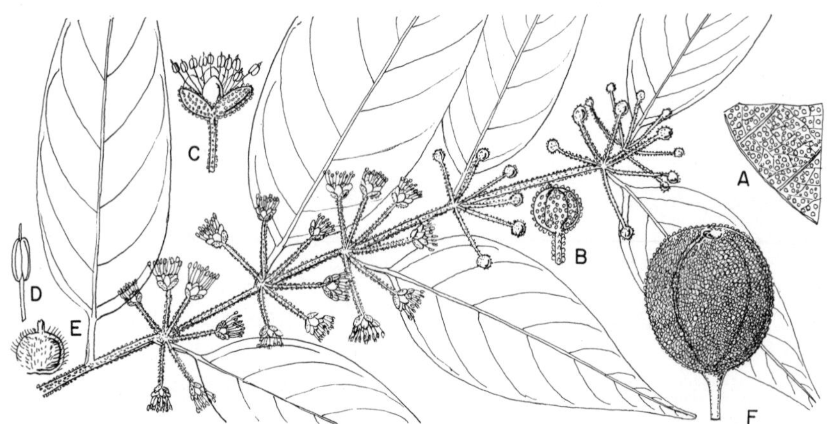

FIG. 107. *Afrostyrax lepidophyllus* Mildbr. (*Styracaceae*). A genus of two species in west Africa, remote geographically from the remainder of the family. **A**, lower surface of leaf showing scales. **B**, flower-bud. **C**, flower. **D**, stamen. **E**, ovary. **F**, fruit (orig.).

The wood contains vessels with perforations, which are usually exclusively scalariform, and wood-fibres with bordered pits. Glandular hairs are absent, but in addition to simple uniseriate hairs, stellate hairs or peltate scales are common, the latter being due to the complete union of the rays of the stellate hairs.

Mostly the flowers are arranged in racemes or panicles, but in *Melliodendron* and *Halesia* they are fasciculate or solitary at the nodes of the older shoots. The flowers of *Bruinsmia* are polygamo-dioecious.

Benzoin or Gum Benzoin is a balsamic resin from *Styrax benzoin* Dryand., one of the chief ingredients in the well-known Friars Balsam. Siam Benzoin is obtained from *Styrax tonkinensis* Craib.

Symplocaceae, a single genus, *Symplocos*, of about three hundred species, is distributed throughout the tropics and subtropics, except Africa; regarded by Don as a distinct family, it was subsequently included in the *Styracaceae* by Bentham and Hook. f., though maintained separate by Engler. It differs mainly by its short ovoid or subglobose anthers, and by the indumentum being non-stellate; the stamens are mostly numerous in 1–4 series, but sometimes as few as 4. The stomata have special subsidiary cells placed parallel to the pore. The type species is *S. martinicensis* Jacq., West Indies.

Lodh Bark is that of *Symplocos racemosa* Roxb., an Indian tree or shrub; leaves and bark used in India for dyeing, giving red and yellow tints, and the bark is employed in Hindu medicine, a few other species being employed in a similar way. The genus *Symplocos* is encumbered with as many as 27 synonyms!

ORDER 10. **ARALIALES**

(*Fam. Fl. Pl.* **1**, 171)

Families: **Cornaceae, Alangiaceae, Garryaceae, Nyssaceae, Araliaceae, Caprifoliaceae.**

From a phylogenetic point of view this is a most interesting and important group, with complete epigyny, the basic and most primitive family being *Cornaceae*; the most advanced, *Araliaceae* (with generally an umbellate inflorescence); and the small climax family *Caprifoliaceae*, the last a parallel rather than a direct relative of *Rubiaceae*, next to which it is usually placed. The family *Nyssaceae* approaches very closely to *Hamamelidaceae*, the next and more advanced Order; derivation may have been more or less as follows:

MAGNOLIACEAE → DILLENIACEAE → ROSACEAE → CUNONIALES → ARALIALES → **Caprifoliaceae** (climax).

The type genus of **Cornaceae**[1] is *Cornus*, though not that genus as it has been usually understood until comparatively recently. According to International Rules, *Cornus* Linn. was founded on *Cornus mas* Linn. (see Fig. 108), a species which with three others subsequently constituted the subgenus *Macrocarpium* of Spach, and eventually became the genus *Macrocarpium* Nakai. If segregated, therefore, the oldest generic name for the 35 or so other species formerly included in *Cornus* (and later known as *Thelycrania*) is **Swida** Opiz; unfortunate, of course, but the Rules have to be followed. Thus *Cornus*, in the restricted sense, consists of only four species of trees

---

[1] Including *Aucubaceae* J. G. Agardh (1858). *Mastixiaceae* Calestani (1905). *Toricelliaceae* Hu (1934).

and shrubs with opposite leaves; flowers precocious, bisexual, capitate-umbellate, yellow, surrounded by a small involucre of imbricate, scaly, yellow bracts; calyx entire; petals 4, valvate; stamens 4; disk pulvinate; ovary 2-locular; ovule solitary in each loculus; fruit a drupe with a bony stone.

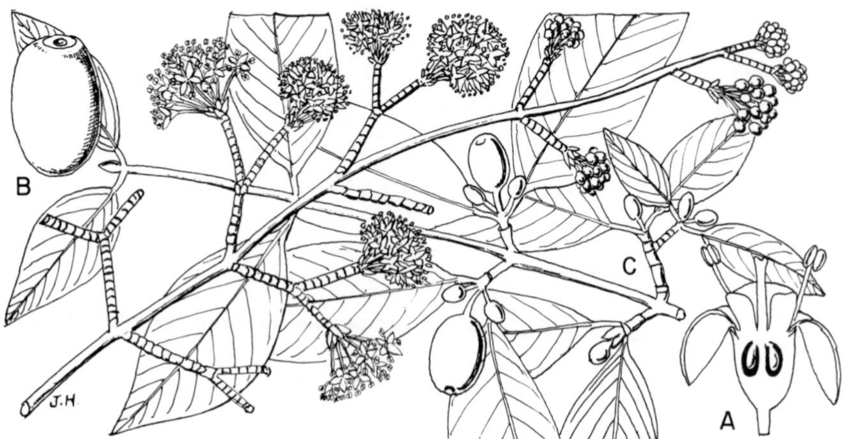

FIG. 108. *Cornus mas* Linn., Europe, Asia Minor, the type species of the type genus of *Cornaceae*. **A**, vertical section of flower. **B**, fruit. **C**, shoot with fruits (orig.).

Melanophylla and *Griselinia* stand out from the remainder of the genera in having imbricate petals and in the latter the flowers are unisexual and dioecious. The flowers are also dioecious in *Afrocrania* (Fig. 109), a monotypic genus found only on the high mountains of east tropical Africa, and entirely isolated from the other members of the family.

Divergent genera are *Chamaepericlymenum*, herbs with annual stems from a perennial rhizome, and T-shaped hairs as in *Indigofera* (*Fabaceae*); the leaves are constantly alternate or fasciculate in *Corokia*, *Mastixia*, *Toricellia*, *Kaliphora*, *Melanophylla* and *Griselinia*; palmately nerved in *Toricellia*; bracts petaloid in *Chamaepericlymenum*, *Cynoxylon* and *Dendrobenthamia*; flowers unisexual in *Griselinia*, *Toricellia*, *Kaliphora*, *Aucuba* and *Afrocrania*. The highest type of inflorescence occurs in *Dendrobenthamia* (FAMILIES OF FLOWERING PLANTS **1**, 127, Fig. 43), the ovaries and fruits of which become united into a fleshy syncarp recalling the tribe *Naucleae* of the family *Rubiaceae*.

Some genera of *Cornaceae* show interesting points in distribution. Isolated in the Southern Hemisphere are *Melanophylla* (9 spp.) and *Kaliphora* (1 sp.), only in Madagascar. The monotypic *Curtisia* is also a southern type confined to the coast forests of South Africa and S.E. tropical Africa. *Griselinia* is common to New Zealand, Chile and south Brazil (see Map 9).

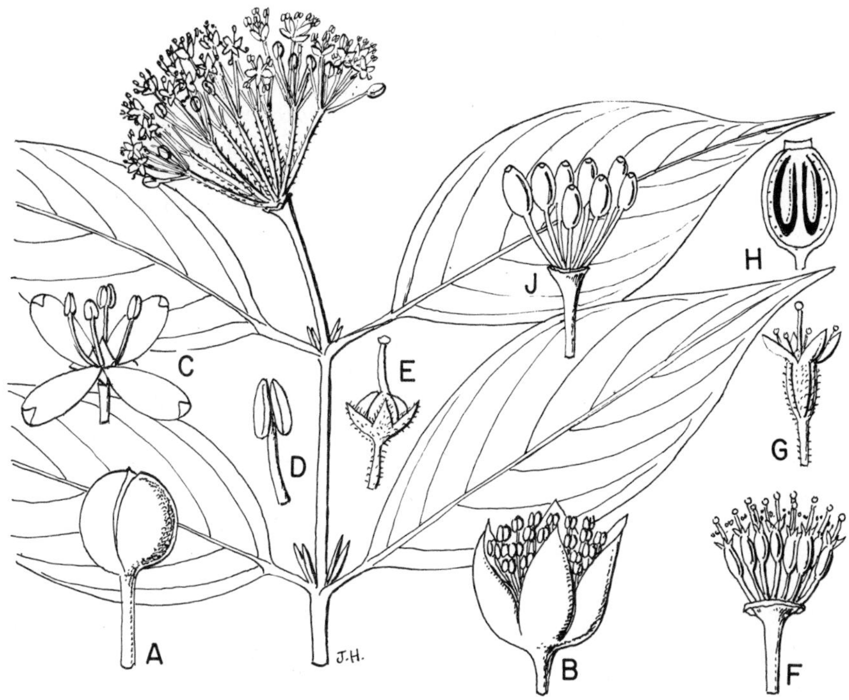

FIG. 109. *Afrocrania volkensii* (Harms) Hutch. (*Cornaceae*), tropical Africa, a genus with dioecious flowers, isolated geographically from the remainder of the family in the mountains of Uganda, Kenya, Malawi, and the Congo. **A**, male flower-bud. **B**, male inflorescence. **C**, male flower. **D**, stamen. **E**, male calyx and rudimentary gynoecium. **F**, female inflorescence. **G**, female flower. **H**, vertical section of ovary. **J**, young fruits (orig.).

The only herbaceous genus, *Chamaepericlymenum* (Fig. 110), is as circumpolar in the Northern Hemisphere as the length of its name, descending in Britain as far as the hills in Derbyshire, and in North America as far south as the mountains of Colorado and north California; its fruits are eaten by Eskimos. *Cynoxylon* is confined to North America, one species on the Atlantic, *C. floridum* (Linn.) Raf., another on the Pacific side, *C. nuttallii* (Andob.) Hutch., and there are two species in Central America.

Economic products are mostly timber: the Pagoda Dogwood of North America is *Swida alternifolia* (Linn. f.) Small; wood hard, heavy, and adapted for turnery. Flowering Dogwood of eastern North America is *Cynoxylon floridum* (Linn.) Raf., wood hard and heavy, used for hubs of wheels, tool-handles, turnery, and engraving blocks; the root contains Cornin, a bitter principle. The Western Flowering Dogwood is *Cynoxylon nuttallii* And., wood hard, heavy, used for tool-handles and cabinet work; bark a local remedy in place of quinine. The edible fruits of *Cornus mas* Linn. are the source of Vin de Cornoulle (France).

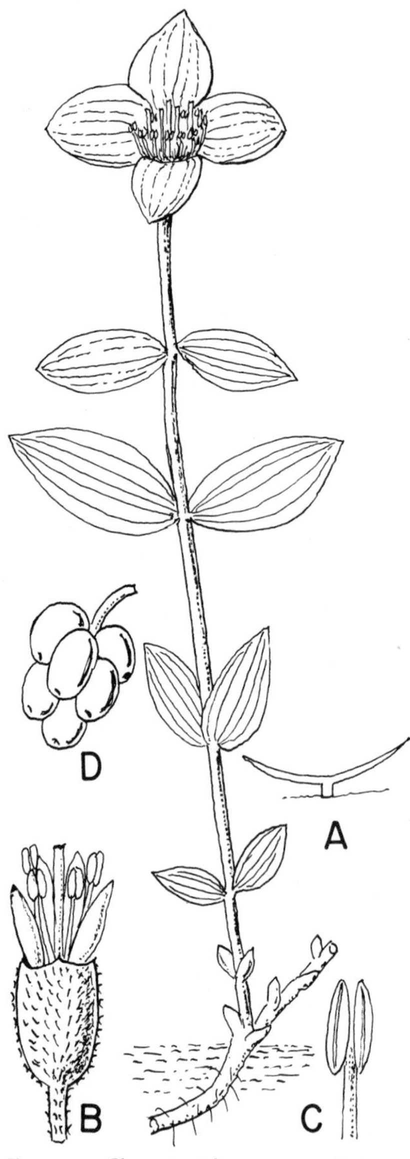

FIG. 110. *Chamaepericlymenum suecicum* (Linn.) Aschers. & Graebn., the only herbaceous genus of the family *Cornaceae*; circumpolar in the Northern Hemisphere. **A**, medifixed hair. **B**, flower. **C**, anther. **D**, fruits (orig.).

The small families *Alangiaceae* and *Nyssaceae* were both formerly included in the more comprehensive concept of *Cornaceae*. **Alangiaceae**, single genus *Alangium*, differs mainly from *Cornaceae* in having two integuments to the ovule, and **Nyssaceae**,[1] with imbricate petals; the latter embraces three genera, *Davidia*, *Nyssa* and *Camptotheca* (Fig. 111), the flower-heads of the first being subtended by large petaloid bracts (well-known "Handkerchief tree"). Further segregation of *Davidia* as a separate family seems undesirable. *Alangium* extends from tropical Africa through Indo-Malaya, China and Japan to N.E. Australia (for map see FAMILIES OF FLOWERING PLANTS, 2nd Ed. **1**, 173).

The family **Garryaceae** is peculiar and therefore not very easy to place in its true affinity, though it seems to be not far removed from *Hamamelidaceae*. It contains only one genus of trees and shrubs, native of North America and the West Indies. The leaves are opposite, without stipules, the flowers are dioecious in pendulous catkins, the male flowers have valvate sepals, no petals, there are 4 stamens; the ovary is inferior and composed of 2 united carpels, whilst the fruit is a berry and the seed has copious endosperm with a minute embryo. Except for the seed, all these characters are highly advanced. In some species there are 4 or 2 very small calyx-lobes below the base of the styles showing the

[1] Including *Davidiaceae* Takhtajan (1952).

ovary to be inferior (compare notes in my FAMILIES OF FLOWERING PLANTS, 2nd Ed. **1**, 174).

It was the late Miss Alice Eastwood who described the female flowers of several species as having minute calyx-teeth at the top of the ovary, proving the latter to be inferior, a fact not obvious when the calyx is completely reduced as it is in some species (see my GENERA OF FLOWERING PLANTS, Vol. 2, 49 (1947)).

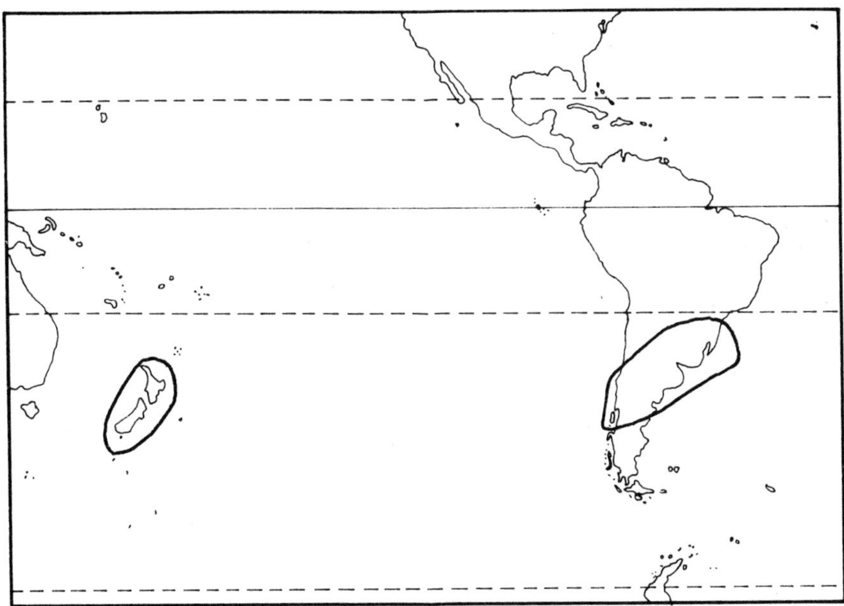

MAP 9. The genus *Griselinia* (*Cornaceae*) is found in New Zealand, Chile and south Brazil; perhaps indicating that New Zealand was at one time much nearer to South America.

Araliaceae[1] can scarcely be the basal stock for *Apiaceae* (*Umbelliferae*), even if only the aestivation of the petals be considered. For in *Araliaceae* it is already mostly valvate, while in *Apiaceae* it is mostly imbricate. Evolution with regard to aestivation of petals usually takes place in the reverse order, i.e. from imbricate to valvate. Again it seems very unlikely that *Araliaceae* are woody representatives derived from *Apiaceae*, because there are nearly always more carpels in *Araliaceae* than in *Apiaceae*, in which there are constantly 2, and the peculiar mericarpic fruit of *Apiaceae* could scarcely give place to the berry or drupe characteristic of *Araliaceae*.

---

[1] Including *Hederaceae* Bartling (1830). *Helwingiaceae* Decaisne (1836). *Botryodendraceae* J. G. Agardh (1858).

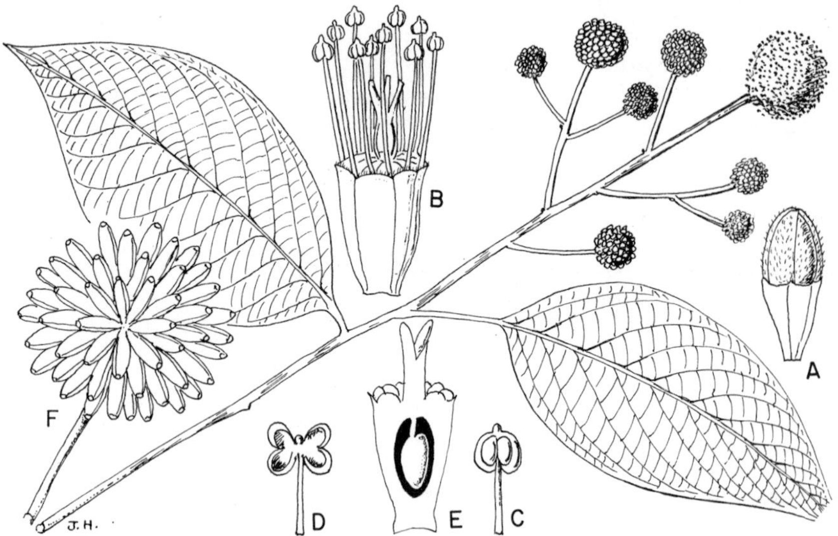

Fig. 111. *Camptotheca acuminata* Decne. (*Nyssaceae*), Tibet. **A**, flower-bud. **B**, flower with petals removed. **C**, stamen. **D**, stamen with anther open. **E**, vertical section of ovary. **F**, fruits (orig.).

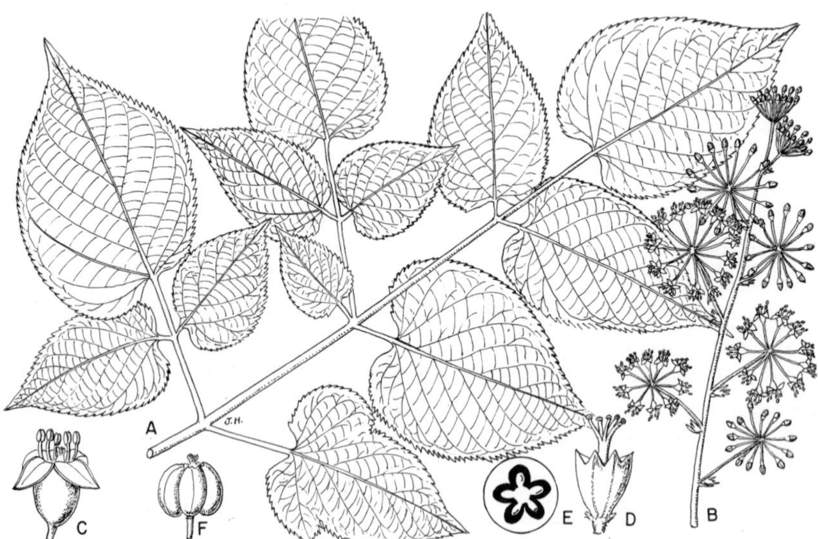

Fig. 112. *Aralia racemosa* Linn. (*Araliaceae*), North America. **A**, typical leaf. **B**, inflorescence. **C**, flower. **D**, calyx and styles. **E**, cross-section of ovary. **F**, fruit.

FIG. 113. The remarkable and probably ancient *Tupidanthus calyptratus* Hook. f. & T. Thoms. (*Araliaceae*), Himalayan region. **A**, flower-bud. **B**, stamen. **C**, fruit. **D**, vertical section (partly after Hook. IC. PL.).

The nomenclatural type of the family is, of course, *Aralia*, a large and fairly natural genus of about 40 species in temperate and tropical America and Asia. The type species of *Aralia* is *A. racemosa* Linn., a common woodland plant of eastern North America, with large bipinnate leaves, the rhachis constricted at the nodes, large narrow panicles of small minutely bracteate umbels of often polygamo-monoecious flowers, jointed pedicels, 5 imbricate petals, 5 stamens, 5–2-locular ovary, small drupaceous fruit and seeds with quite smooth endosperm. A few species are herbaceous from a thick tuber-like rootstock, and in some the leaves are digitately compound.

To many European students the name *Araliaceae* will perhaps call to mind little more than the common Ivy, *Hedera helix* Linn., and maybe one or two other members of the family to be met with in suburban gardens or in cottage windows in company with *Aspidistra*, such as the so-called "Aralia", *Fatsia japonica* (Thunb.) Decne. & Planch. They would be surprised to learn, no doubt, that one genus at least has an ovary composed of nearly 160 carpels accompanied by numerous stamens. This is *Tupidanthus* (Fig. 113), a monotypic, found only in that "Garden of Eden" for primitive plants, the eastern Himalayas (Khasia Hills). This, then, must surely be the most primitive genus of living *Araliaceae*. It is worth noting, too, that the most primitive species of *Magnolia* (*M. pterocarpa* Roxb.) grows not very far away.

The family *Araliaceae* has in most systems been associated in the same group as the *Apiaceae* (*Umbelliferae*), and originally I followed this in my own arrangement. But later I formed a different opinion, and I shall try and justify it as well as possible.

In short, I believe the supposed affinity of *Araliaceae* and *Apiaceae* to be based on superficial resemblances, especially the umbelliform inflorescences, and that the two families may have had quite different origins. To illustrate this point by very familiar examples, I would enquire of the student whether there is any real affinity between the familiar Ivy (*Hedera*) and the common Hemlock (*Conium maculatum*). Both families are no doubt climax groups from the basal stocks of which little further evolution can have proceeded. So I now regard *Araliaceae* as having been derived from the CUNONIALES stock, i.e. from the woody branch of our phylogenetic "tree", especially *Cornaceae*, and the *Apiaceae* from the herbaceous stock, perhaps rather remotely from the *Saxifragaceae* (no doubt rank heresy to many botanists!).

The following table shows the principal characters supporting this view:

Araliaceae	**Apiaceae** (*Umbelliferae*)
Woody; leaves stipulate, stipules often intrapetiolar (as in *Cunoniaceae*); flowers in simple umbels (or even in spikes, racemes or panicles); ovary usually of more than 2 carpels (in *Tupidanthus* nearly 160); fruit a berry or drupe; endosperm often ruminate; no oil or resin.	Herbaceous; leaves exstipulate; flowers often in compound umbels; ovary consistently of 2 carpels, in fruit separating into two 1-seeded mericarps with longitudinal vittae filled with oil or resin; endosperm never ruminate.

Here is the way in which the separate origin of the two families may be shown:

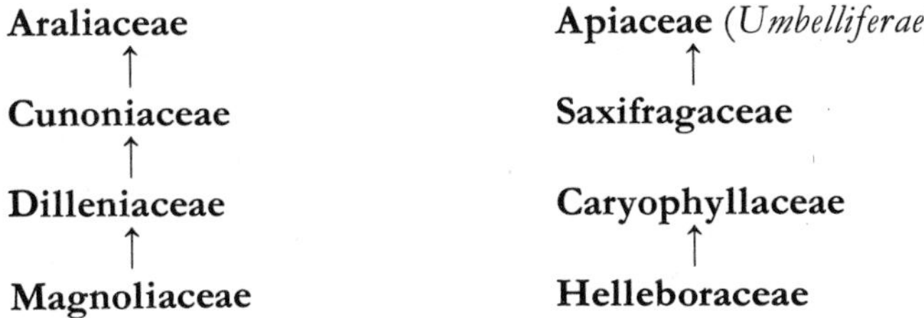

Generic differences within the family are sometimes very slight and are chiefly concerned with the aestivation of the petals, in the majority of which they are valvate; whether the pedicels are jointed or not below the flower, the number of stamens, the free or variously connate styles, the number of carpels, and whether the endosperm is ruminate (as in tribe *Hedereae*) or not.

Outstanding characteristics of some genera are as follows: Stem herbaceous in *Panax* and *Stilbocarpa*; leaves opposite in *Arthrophyllum*, peltate in *Harmsiopanax*; leaflets Poplar-like in *Cheirodendron*; indumentum stellate in *Dipanax* and *Astrotricha*; stipules free from the petiole and hair-like or branched in *Helwingia*; flowers minute in much-branched panicles in *Aralidium*; in umbels on the leaves in *Helwingia*; male and female of very different form in *Meryta*; heads or umbels involucrate in *Horsfieldia*; females subconnate into a capitulum in *Meryta*; petals contracted into a claw in tribe *Mackinlayeae*; closely pressed together into a calyptra in *Tupidanthus*; stamens numerous in *Plerandra*, *Tetraplasandra* and *Tupidanthus*; ovary superior to semi-inferior in *Dipanax*; carpels nearly 160 in *Tupidanthus*; fruit broadly winged downwards in *Myodocarpus* and some species of *Asterotricha*; fruits concrescent into a mass in *Meryta* spp.

The genus *Tupidanthus* mentioned above belongs to the tribe *Plerandreae*, perhaps the oldest group of the family. Related genera are *Tetraplasandra* (Pacific Islands and New Guinea), *Plerandra* (Fiji Islands), and the monotypic *Indokingia* (Seychelles); all of them have numerous stamens.

Surveying these remarkable genera, with their numerous stamens and carpels, makes one wonder whence they may have originated. Such numerous carpels are found only in *Annonaceae*, which are very far removed in other respects. But even in several genera of *Araliaceae*, for example in the common ivy, we find the endosperm of the seeds is ruminate, just as in *Annonaceae*. This is probably due to parallelism, though it might be a survival character.

Another very remarkable genus is *Helwingia* (Himalaya to Japan) (Fig. 114), whose clusters of dioecious flowers are inserted on the middle of the leaf-blade, due to the peduncle being adnate to the midrib of the leaf, recalling a parallel development in some *Flacourtiaceae*. From an anatomical

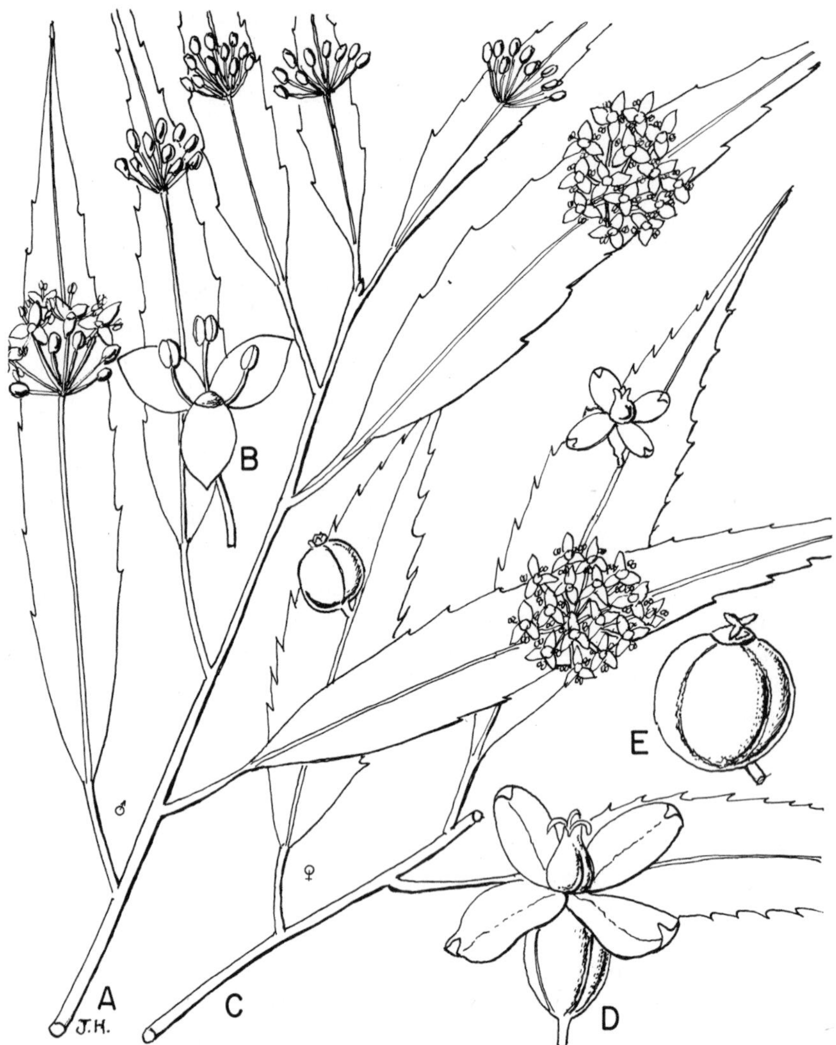

Fig. 114. In the genus *Helwingia* (*Araliaceae*) the umbels of flowers are borne on the leaf-blades, i.e. the peduncle is adnate to the petiole and midrib from which it emerges about half way up. *Helwingia chinensis* Batalin, China. **A**, branch with male flowers. **B**, male flower, enlarged. **C**, branch with single female flower and fruit. **D**, enlarged female flower. **E**, fruit (orig.).

standpoint this genus has been referred to *Cornaceae*, but it does not seem to be related to any genus in that family, and I have retained it in *Araliaceae* where it was included by Bentham and Hooker. When in doubt I usually follow them!

Whilst examining the whole of the family for my GENERA OF FLOWERING PLANTS (Vol. 2), I was struck by the presence of a few genera which had not the ordinary umbellate inflorescence so characteristic of the family as a whole. I described for the first time the tribe *Cussonieae*, distinguished by its inflorescence being racemose or spicate, the racemes or spikes sometimes paniculate, with or without a terminal umbel. This tribe shows very clearly the evolution of the umbel from a raceme. Of particular interest is the genus *Cuphocarpus*, in which the racemose flowers of the inflorescence are male

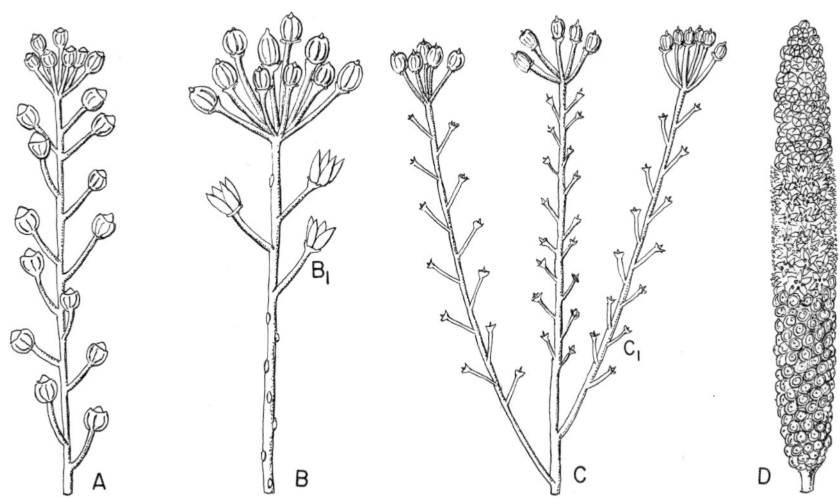

FIG. 115. Inflorescences of primitive genera of *Araliaceae*: **A**, *Reynoldsia sandwichensis* A. Gray, Polynesia, a raceme with a terminal umbel. **B**, *Dipanax gymnocarpa* A. A. Heller, Polynesia, a raceme with the lower flowers male ($\mathbf{B}_1$), and a terminal umbel of bisexual flowers. **C**, *Cuphocarpus aculeatus* Decne & Planch., Madagascar, the racemose portion ($\mathbf{C}_1$) with abortive flowers and a terminal umbel of fertile flowers. **D**, *Cussonia spicata* Thunb., South Africa, with a spicate inflorescence. (The umbels are shown in fruit.)

and infertile, only the terminal umbellate flowers producing fruits (see Fig. 115). I feel sure that if this remarkable inflorescence were known only in a fossil state, it would have excited the interest of palaeobotanists, showing clearly as it does a transition from a racemose to an umbellate type of inflorescence. Thus it may be regarded as a living fossil! I also established another tribe, *Anomopanaceae*, characterised by the inflorescence, which is a panicle of cymules and without umbels!

Very few of the 84 genera are of economic importance. Rice Paper of China and Formosa is made from the pith of the stem of *Tetrapanax papyriferus* (Benth. & Hook. f.) C. Koch. Sarsaparilla (Wild or Virginian) is obtained from the roots of *Aralia nudicaulis* Linn., and used as a substitute for the "Official Sarsaparilla", *Smilax ornata* Lem. (*Smilacaceae*). Ginseng is the root of *Panax ginseng* Nees, north China and Korea. According to Hill (ECONOMIC BOTANY, 2nd Ed., 245), Ginseng is one of the most important drugs in China, where it is considered to be a cure for a great variety of diseases. Quantities of American Ginseng, *Panax quinquefolius* Linn., have been used in recent years in the United States of America as a stimulant and stomachic. Hari-giri, the wood of *Acanthopanax ricinifolius* Seem., Japan, is cut into strips and used for making hats, etc.

The family **Caprifoliaceae**[1] has usually been placed near *Rubiaceae*, but the two more primitive genera forming the tribe *Sambuceae*, i.e. *Viburnum* and *Sambucus*, show more ancient characters than are found in any Rubiaceous genus. Comparison between the two families is scarcely possible owing to the very great disparity in their size.

In *Viburnum* and *Sambucus* the style is very short and divided, and the corolla is actinomorphic, bearing close resemblance to that of some *Cornaceae* and *Araliaceae*. The genus *Viburnum*, section *Opulus*, shows a similar sterilisation of the outer flowers as in *Hydrangea*. This is perhaps not due merely to parallelism but to actual affinity, for other groups of these genera show considerable resemblance, and *Hydrangeaceae* occupy a high position in the CUNONIALES. The difference between *Viburnum* and *Sambucus* lies mainly in the leaves, the pinnately partite example of the latter genus representing the more advanced type.

The more primitive genera of the second and more advanced tribe *Lonicereae* are found in New Zealand and New Caledonia. *Alseuosmia* is a striking genus with a perfectly actinomorphic corolla and alternate leaves and bears a superficial resemblance to certain *Vacciniaceae*. The capsular fruit of *Diervilla* seems to mark that genus as relatively primitive, whilst a basic type for *Lonicera* seems to be *Leycesteria*, with its subregular corolla-limb and 5-locular ovary. *Triosteum* is probably little more than a reduced *Lonicera*, with annual stems from a woody perennial rhizome, and the connate leaf-bases similar to those of the more advanced species of *Lonicera*.

The unequal number of ovules in each of the loculi of certain genera is of considerable interest, as showing an intermediate stage in the reduction of ovules from several to one. This is perhaps a development parallel with a similar feature which is so characteristic of the family *Valerianaceae*, in the herbaceous phylum. It can scarcely be considered to be an indication of direct relationship.

The type genus of *Caprifoliaceae* is *Lonicera* (type species *L. caprifolium* Linn. (Fig. 116)), composed of erect or scandent shrubs with opposite en-

---

[1] Including *Viburnaceae* Dumort. (1829). *Sambucaceae* Link (1829). *Loniceraceae* Endlich. (1841). *Baccataceae* Dulac (1867). *Alseuosmiaceae* Airy Shaw (1965). *Carlemanniaceae* Airy Shaw (1965).

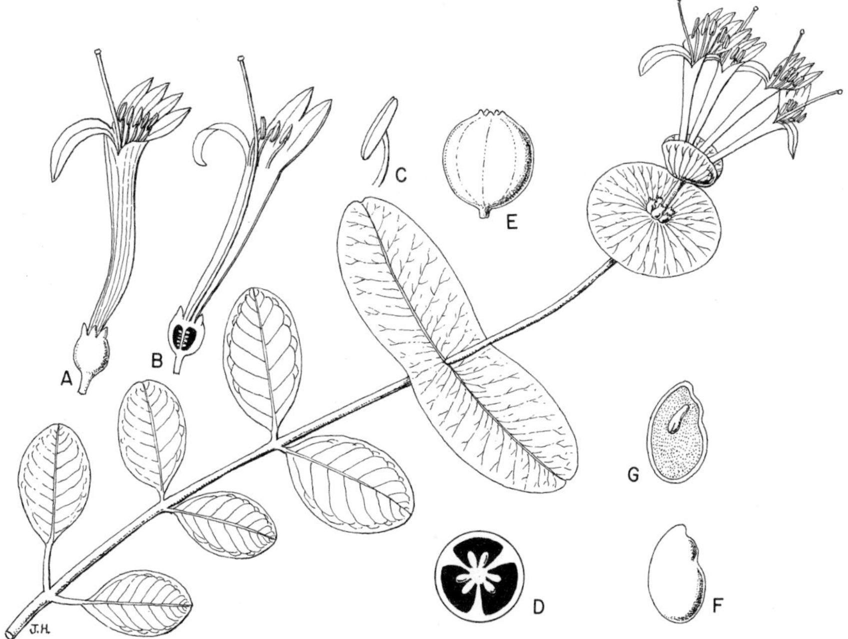

FIG. 116. *Lonicera caprifolium* Linn., the type species of the type genus of the family *Caprifoliaceae*. **A**, single flower. **B**, the same in vertical section. **C**, anther. **D**, cross-section of ovary. **E**, fruit. **F**, seed. **G**, vertical section of seed.

tire leaves sometimes connate at the base, in bud covered by scales, zygomorphic flowers in cymes or heads, sometimes connate in pairs with united bracteoles, corolla with an oblique or 2-lipped limb with 5 imbricate lobes, 5 stamens inserted on the corolla-tube, a pulvinate disk, and a 3–2-locular ovary with filiform style and capitate stigma, numerous ovules, and the fruit a fleshy berry.

Outstanding genera or species are *Triosteum* and *Sambucus ebulus*, which are herbs; *Alseuosmia*, *Memecylanthus* and *Pachydiscus*, with alternate leaves; pinnately compound in *Sambucus*; stipulate in *Viburnum* spp. and *Leycesteria* spp.; outer flowers sterile in *Viburnum* sect. *Opulus*; corolla-lobes valvate in *Sambucus* spp., *Memecylanthus* and *Pachydiscus*; corolla actinomorphic in *Sambucus*, *Viburnum*, *Alseuosmia*, *Memecylanthus* and *Pachydiscus*; stamens 4 in *Linnaea*; ovaries connate in pairs in several species of *Lonicera*; fruit a capsule in *Diervilla* and *Weigela*; bracteoles wing-like and persistent in *Dipelta*.

In my GENERA OF FLOWERING PLANTS (Vol. 2, p. 86), I included in *Caprifoliaceae* two genera, *Silvianthus* Hook. f. and *Carlemannia* Benth., previously classified as anomalous in *Rubiaceae*. I agree with Kern and van Steenis (in

FL. MALESIANA **4**, 175 (1951)) as to the disposition of these two genera, and not as a separate family as treated by Airy Shaw.

ORDER 11. HAMAMELIDALES

(*Fam. Fl. Pl.* **1**, 179)

Families: **Tetracentraceae, Hamamelidaceae, Myrothamnaceae, Platanaceae, Stachyuraceae, Buxaceae, Daphniphyllaceae, Bruniaceae.**

Probable derivation of this group of families: MAGNOLIACEAE → DILLENIACEAE → ROSACEAE → **HAMAMELIDALES.**

Having dealt with the important side branches of ROSALES which are shown to end in *Mimosaceae* and *Fabaceae* (*Papilionaceae*) on the one hand, and in *Araliaceae* and *Caprifoliaceae* on the other, we can now discuss other groups probably derived from the same stock.

The intermediate stage between the ROSALES and part of the so-called "Amentiferae" seems to be the HAMAMELIDALES, the principal family of which is *Hamamelidaceae*. It has been suggested by some writers that this family is related to the MAGNOLIALES. I cannot subscribe to this view, for it seems doubtful that any actual close affinity can be detected between the groups, except through some more intermediate stock. Nowhere in MAGNOLIALES do we find the coarsely parallel flabellately nerved and toothed leaves of the *Hamamelidaceae*. We do find, however, the same nervation (and vernation) in *Dilleniaceae* and *Rosaceae* through which stocks they have very probably descended, for they show strong tendencies to reduction of the flowers, which are often crowded into heads (*Liquidambar*, *Exbucklandia*) or catkins (*Corylopsis*, *Fothergilla*). If there is any group of plants from which the "Amentiferae" have descended then *Rosaceae* and *Hamamelidaceae* are undoubtedly the groups.

Because of the importance of this group as evidence of the origin of the much discussed "Amentiferae", it is dealt with here in some detail.

Tetracentraceae, single genus *Tetracentron*, has received considerable attention as to its morphology and anatomy in reference to its taxonomic position.[1] I give it the premier place in the Order because of its quite superior ovary together with the presence of stipules; the genus is monotypic

---

[1] See especially A. C. Smith, Taxonomic Review of *Trochodendron* and *Tetracentron*, J. ARN. ARB. **26**, 135 (1945), with map and bibliography.

(*T. sinense* Oliv.) and is found in western China and Upper Burma, a region which, like the eastern Himalayas, shelters many primitive types of woody plants. The growth-form is interesting, there being long and short shoots, the latter producing each year a single leaf and a slender catkin-like inflorescence, the short shoot terminated by a bud enclosed by a single stipule adnate to the petiole; flowers bisexual, with 4 sepals but no petals, 4 stamens opposite the sepals; ovary of 4 united carpels, each carpel unilocular with 2 placentas; the 4 styles are at first connivent, then they become sharply recurved and subbasal by lateral growth of the ventral surface; seeds with oily endosperm and minute embryo.

The type genus of **Hamamelidaceae**[1] is, of course, *Hamamelis*, "Witch Hazels", familiar in British gardens and flowering in late winter or early spring; shrubs or small trees; with alternate deciduous rounded pinnately nerved crenate-dentate leaves, precocious often polygamous flowers, 4-partite persistent calyx adnate to the base of the ovary, 4 petals circinate in bud, persistent, sometime absent from female flowers, 4 stamens alternating with 4 scales, anthers muticous, 1-valved, valves opening from the outer side, ovary 2-locular, styles 2, ovule 1, pendulous; capsule superior or semisuperior, loculicidally 2-valved at the apex; seed shining.

Not many visitors to Kew see these weird plants in flower because some of them are in bloom in January, the best being *Hamamelis mollis* Oliv. from China and *H. virginiana* Linn. from the United States. The geographical range of this genus *Hamamelis* is of very great interest and is a striking example of discontinuous distribution, about which a very important paper was published over a century ago. This was written by E. Forbes, who called attention to the great similarity of the flora of the eastern United States and that of eastern Asia, particularly China.

Hamamelis virginiana Linn., the type species (see Fig. 117), is a large shrub throughout the greater part of its range, but on the slopes of the Alleghany Mountains it becomes a tree 30–40 ft high. According to Hough's splendid book on the trees of the northern States and Canada (1907), this Witch Hazel produces its flowers in the autumn, often whilst the leaves have put on their autumnal tints, and the first snows of winter sometimes find it bearing its singular golden and delicately fragrant flowers. The leaves and bark are used medicinally, and the seeds are edible.

A very beautiful tree to be seen in large European gardens and some parks is *Liquidambar styraciflua* Linn.,[2] which grows naturally in the S.E. United States. Few trees of the American forests equal the Sweet Gum, as it is called, in ornamental value, owing to its grand habit of growth and its

---

[1] Including *Fothergillaceae* Link (1831). *Parrotiaceae* Horaninow (1834). *Balsamaceae* Lindley (1836). *Altingiaceae* Lindley (1846). *Bucklandiaceae* J. G. Agardh (1858). *Liquidambaraceae* L. Pfeiffer (1870). *Disanthaceae* Nakai (1943). *Rhodoleiaceae* Nakai (1943).

[2] Hough HANDBOOK OF THE TREES OF THE NORTHERN STATES AND CANADA 227 (1907).

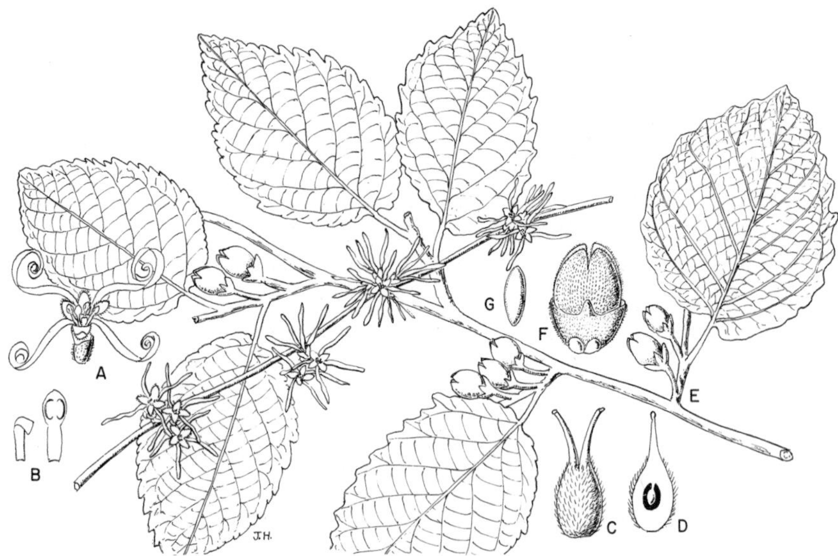

FIG. 117. *Hamamelis virginiana* Linn., eastern United States of America, the type species of the type genus of *Hamamelidaceae*. **A**, flower, showing the circinate petals. **B**, stamens. **C**, gynoecium. **D**, vertical section of carpel. **E**, leaves and fruits. **F**, fruit. **G**, seed (orig.).

beautiful star-shaped leaves, of a rich green in summer and conspicuous in autumn on account of their crimson and purple tints. The tuber-like roots are peculiar.

The wood of this tree has been extensively used for furniture-making in this country under the name of Satin Walnut, but according to Hough "the timber, except for appearance, possesses almost every bad quality which can be found in any wood; it is of a light reddish-brown colour with dark streaks and a lustrous surface; the grain is hard and close, but in seasoning it shrinks unevenly, and after seasoning is completed, continues to expand and contract with variations of the climate, to a greater degree than any other timber". Storax is a balsam obtained from the trunk of *L. orientalis* Mill., a tree which forms forests in S.W. Asiatic Turkey. It is used in the treatment of scabies.

Characters outstanding from those of the type genus are the palmately nerved leaves of *Myrtilaria*, *Exbucklandia*, *Liquidambar* and *Disanthus*; stipules connate face-to-face and enclosing the young shoot in *Exbucklandia*; pectinate or laciniate in *Tetrathyrium* and *Embolanthera*; filaments thickened upwards and very conspicuous in flower in *Fothergilla*; styles with strikingly coloured stigmas in *Eustigma*; flowers unisexual or dioecious in heads or head-like spikes in *Trichocladus*; male heads racemose, female solitary in *Altingia*.

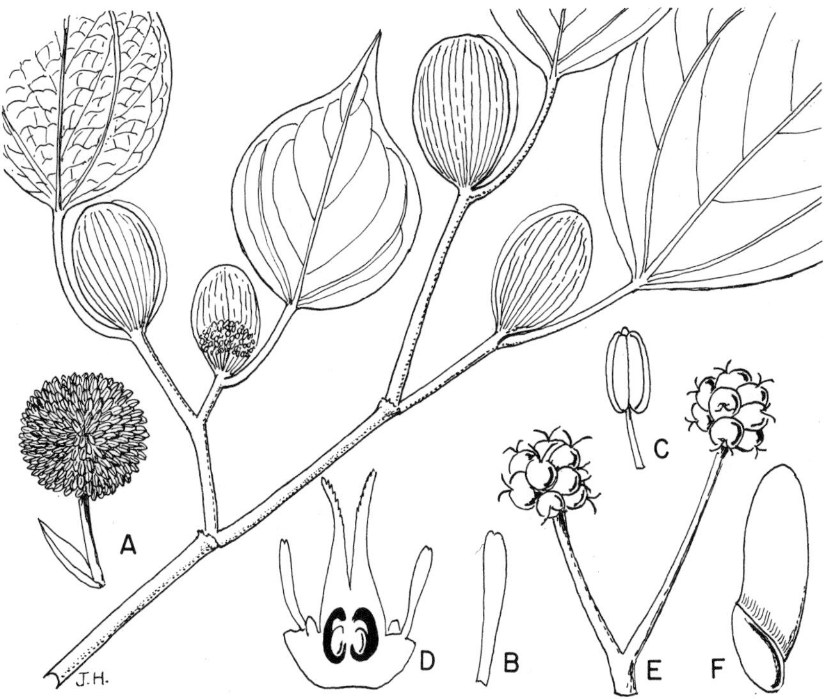

FIG. 118. *Exbucklandia populnea* (R.Br.) R. W. Brown, subtropical eastern Asia, a very advanced genus of the *Hamamelidaceae* with stipules greatly resembling those of *Liriodendron* in *Magnoliaceae*. **A**, male flower. **B**, petal. **C**, stamen. **D**, vertical section of bisexual flower. **E**, fruits. **F**, seed (orig.).

The growth-forms of some genera of *Hamamelidaceae* remind us of *Magnoliaceae*. *Exbucklandia* (Fig. 118), for example, is Magnoliaceous in appearance, especially its evergreen leaves and large leathery stipules very like those of the Tulip Tree (*Liriodendron*). The stipules, as in that genus, enclose the young growths, and on falling leave a circular scar on the shoot. There, however, the resemblance to *Magnoliaceae* more or less ceases, for the flowers are polygamous and in a capitate inflorescence with confluent calyx-tubes, and the fruit is a 2-locular capsule. These facts seem to show, therefore, that the bulk of HAMAMELIDALES have descended, not directly from the MAGNOLIALES, but through the intermediate stock of the ROSALES,[1]

[1] In a paper on "Chromosome numbers in the *Hamamelidaceae* and their Phylogenetic Significance", E. Anderson and K. Sax (J. ARN. ARB. **16**, 212 (1935)) confirm this position for the *Hamamelidaceae*. They say "Before going into details it may be said that on the whole the cytological evidence favours Hutchinson's interpretation of the phylogenetic position of the *Hamamelidaceae*."

where a similar type of flower prevails. An undoubtedly ancient feature is retained in *Hamamelis*, which has circinate petals (see also styles of some *Cunoniaceae*). Even a superficial examination of a genus like *Corylopsis* or of *Fothergilla* suggests a strong affinity with the *Corylaceae* of the so-called "Amentiferae". And it is not a far cry from *Distylium* to the same group.

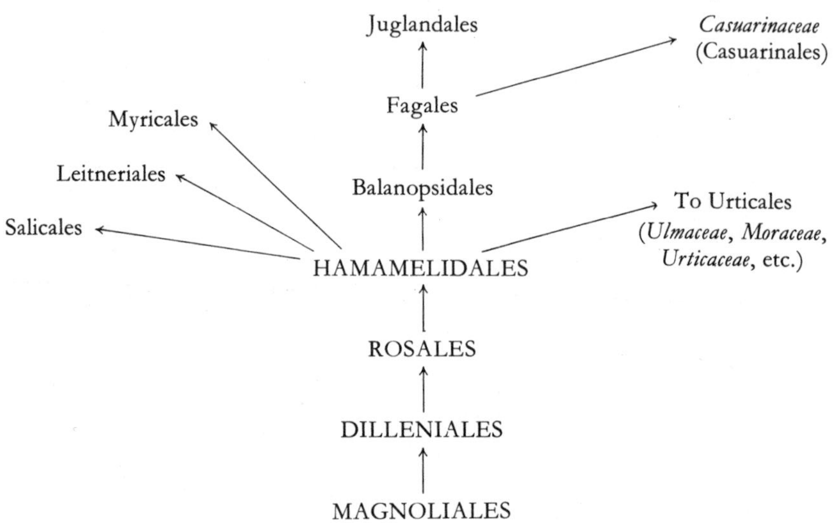

Diagram showing the probable path of evolution of the Order HAMAMELIDALES and further evolution from this stock, ending in the completely climax family *Casuarinaceae* (refer also to general text).

One of the most remarkable genera of *Hamamelidaceae* is *Rhodoleia* (Fig. 119), in which the flowers are crowded into a head with an involucre of bracts after the manner of a Composite. Only the outer flowers have petals, which are arranged on the outer side, and the head therefore looks exactly like a single flower with numerous petals and stamens. There are four species, ranging from Yunnan and Hong-kong to Java, mainly at high elevations.

The distribution of *Hamamelidaceae* repeats in a marked degree that of *Magnoliaceae* and supports the idea of a general, though rather distant, relationship between the two groups. The majority are found in the eastern Himalayan—Chinese—Indo-Malayan region, mainly as isolated and very distinct genera. There are also several in Japan. The only genus of the family which occurs both in eastern Asia and in the eastern United States of America is *Hamamelis*. *Parrotia*, a small tree which enriches the autumn tints in our gardens, is found in Persia, and the closely related *Parrotiopsis* in

N.W. India, whilst *Trichocladus* occurs only in eastern and southern Africa, and *Dicoryphe* in Madagascar, the last represented by about 15 endemic species in this one island. One might conjecture that whilst east Africa and Madagascar were still connected with or a part of the Indo-Malayan region, *Hamamelidaceae* were at the zenith of their development, and that we possess now only a remnant of this formerly large family. If there were representatives of the group in Australia, New Zealand or South America, then separate evolution of these African genera from a southern continental stock might have been surmised, such as is the case in the family *Proteaceae*. But there are no *Hamamelidaceae* in the countries mentioned, apart from a little known genus *Ostrearia*, in northern Queensland, obviously an outlier from the boreal basic stock.

The family is well characterised from the anatomical point of view, as follows: medullary rays narrow; relatively small lumina of the vessels which have scalariform perforations with many bars, and bear large simple pits, where they are in contact with the parenchyma of the medullary rays; wood-prosenchyma with typical bordered pits. The stomata are in the whole family accompanied by two or more subsidiary cells parallel to the pore. The hairs are usually tufted, but there are no glandular hairs.

Myrothamnaceae, a very small family with the aspect of some *Rosaceae*, was formerly included in the *Hamamelidaceae*. It has flowers very nearly approaching in general structure the next and clearly allied family *Buxaceae*.

Solereder says that anatomically *Myrothamnus* differs from *Hamamelidaceae* by the occurrence of spherical resin-cells in the epidermis on both sides of the leaf, by the stomata which are surrounded by ordinary epidermal cells, by the bordered pitting of the vessel-wall in contact with the parenchyma of the medullary rays, and by the compound pollen-grains, which consist of four cells arranged tetrahedrally. There are no clothing hairs.

The single genus *Myrothamnus* occurs in south tropical Africa and northern South Africa and Madagascar, where *Hamamelidaceae* (*Trichocladus*) and *Buxaceae* (*Buxus*) also occur. In the spicate dioecious flowers quite devoid of calyx and corolla, we have here no doubt another forerunner or at any rate a relative of the "Amentiferae". *Myrothamnus* is found only on granite outcrops from the Macalisberg (Transvaal) north to Lake Tanganyika and west to Angola, and in Madagascar. In the Transvaal it is called the "Resurrection plant" because the flabellately nerved leaves spread out fanwise when moistened after being dried.

The small family **Platanaceae** completes the list of the more immediate HAMAMELIDALES alliance. It is represented by the single genus *Platanus*, which provides one of our most successful street trees, *P. acerifolia* Willd. (London Plane), being planted in great numbers in London, where it withstands the smoke-laden atmosphere to a remarkable degree. It is a natural hybrid between *P. orientalis* Linn. and *P. occidentalis* Linn., the former a

Middle East species, the latter from North America. "East is East and West is West and never the twain shall meet" is a very old saying, but it has happened to great advantage in this case and produced London's best street tree.

A peculiar feature of the family is the sheathing petiole, which entirely covers the young bud. This is due to the base of the petiole having an internal conical cavity which encloses the axillary bud. There is considerable resemblance to the genus *Liquidambar* in the *Hamamelidaceae*, and the affinity with that family is undoubted. In distribution also, the genus mentioned is in every way similar, both genera having representatives in the Orient (near East) and in North America.

The several free carpels of *Platanaceae* seem to indicate a relict character of considerable antiquity, but the inflorescence is of a very advanced type, the flowers being collected into unisexual heads arranged on separate peduncles. The presence or absence of sepals and petals has been a disputed point, and I have confirmed their presence by dissection. As Bentham and Hooker regarded them as having neither, they placed the family next to *Urticaceae*, but it seems to find a much closer relationship amongst the HAMAMELIDALES. A whole series of anatomical features characterise the family and one of them, the wide medullary rays, gives the radially cut wood a very beautiful "figure" and is called "Lace Wood". It has been much used in turnery, panelling, etc. A useful feature in an atmosphere like that of London is the deciduous bark of the London Plane, which falls off every year and thus gets rid of the accumulated dirt and soot.

The small family **Stachyuraceae** is but little removed from the more basic family *Hamamelidaceae*. In the single genus *Stachyurus* there are no stipules, the ovary is superior, and petals 4.

The systematic position of the family **Buxaceae**[1] has varied according to different botanists. Bentham and Hooker placed them as a tribe in the *Euphorbiaceae*, whilst Engler included them in his Reihe SAPINDALES. They seem to be more clearly related to *Hamamelidaceae*, resembling them especially in fruit characters. That they are a comparatively decadent group seems clear from their distribution, which is very discontinuous. *Pachysandra*, perhaps the most advanced genus in the family, for it is subherbaceous, occurs in the S.E. United States of America (one species) and in China and Japan (three species), recalling the distribution of *Magnolia* and *Liriodendron* in *Magnoliaceae*, and of *Illicium* in *Illiciaceae*. The largest genus, *Buxus*, is the most widespread but is absent from Australasia. The type species, *Buxus sempervirens* Linn., is widely scattered from chalk districts in southern England, the Azores and Morocco to Asia Minor, with very closely related species in China and Japan.

---

[1] Including *Pachysandraceae* (1858). *Stylocerataceae* Baill. *Simmondsiaceae* van Tieghem (1898).

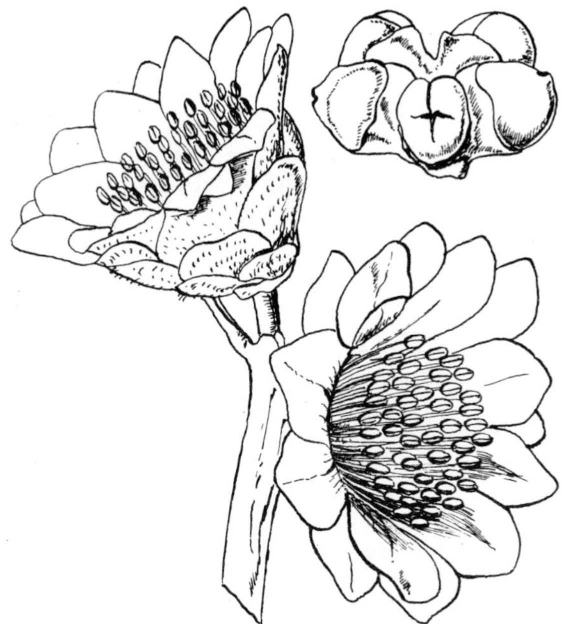

FIG. 119. Flowers and fruits of *Rhodoleia championii* Hook. (*Hamamelidaceae*); the flowers are not the simple things they appear to be, each being an inflorescence of several flowers, as in *Asteraceae* (*Compositae*).

The type genus is *Buxus*, much-branched shrubs or small trees; leaves opposite, entire; flowers monoecious, in short dense axillary racemes, the terminal flower female, the remainder male, bracteate; males with 4 sepals, 2-seriate; stamens 4, opposite the sepals, anthers dorsifixed near the base, introrse; rudimentary ovary in the male truncate or 3-lobed; female with 6 sepals, no stamens, 3-locular ovary, usually widely separated styles, 2 pendulous ovules, and ovoid 3-horned loculicidally dehiscent capsule, and black shining seeds.

Styloceras and *Simmondsia* have numerous stamens, the former with alternate leaves, as in *Sarcococca*. *Pachysandra* (Fig. 120) is outstanding because of its herbaceous procumbent stems and alternate often coarsely toothed leaves with spicate inflorescence, the female flower being either at the base or top.

The common Box, *Buxus sempervirens* Linn., familiar as a garden path edging in western Europe, grows wild in England only on Box Hill in Surrey, and in the Chilterns. Formerly its wood was much used for engraving blocks, rulers, etc., and for many other purposes. At one time large quantities were imported from the countries around the Black Sea. Howard

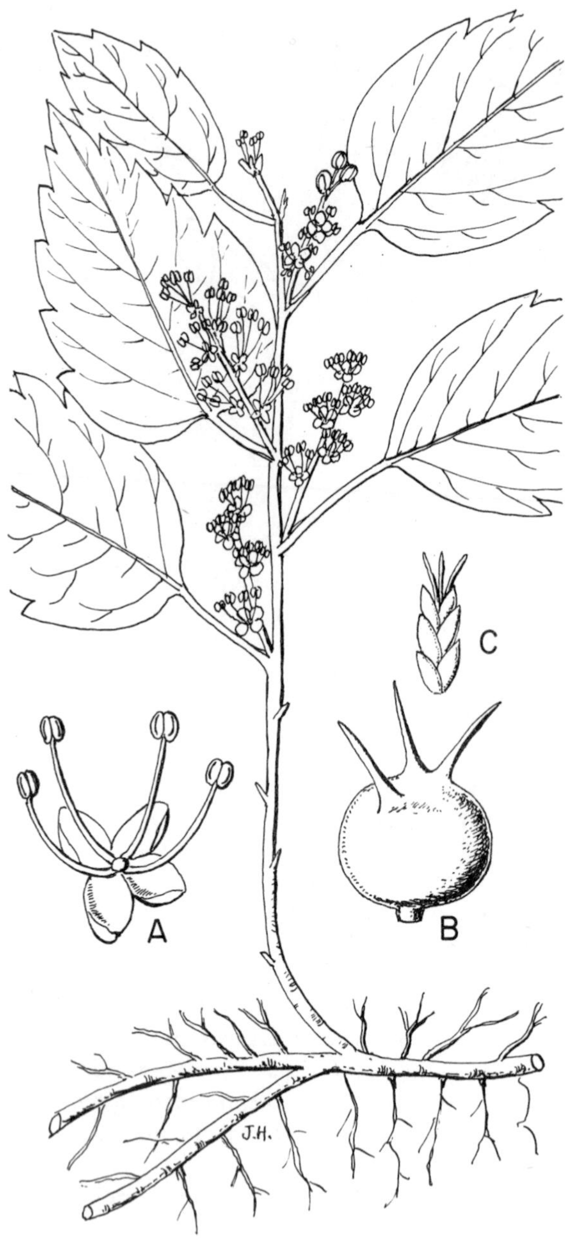

FIG. 120. *Pachysandra axillaris* Franch., a Chinese species; this genus of *Buxaceae* has a discontinuous distribution, S.E. United States of America and eastern Asia. **A**, male flower. **B**, fruit. **C**, female flower (orig.).

(TIMBERS OF THE WORLD) states that during the 1914–18 war boxwood alone was found capable of resisting the great strain of hammering the load into shells in the form known as "punners" or "stemming rods", circular rods $1\frac{1}{4}$ in. in diameter and varying in length from 14 in. to about 3 ft. The wood of a S.E. African species, *Buxus macowanii* Oliv., compares favourably with our native kind.

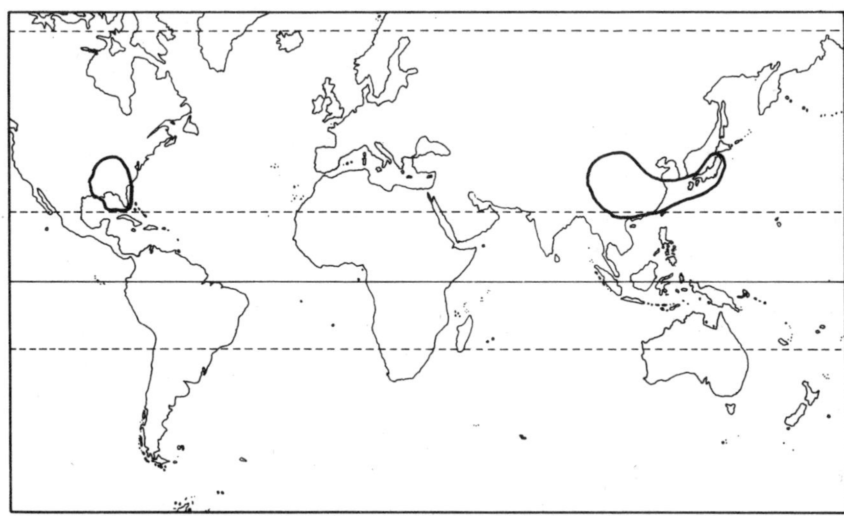

MAP 10. The natural genus *Pachysandra* (*Buxaceae*) is found in two widely separated regions.

Daphniphyllaceae embraces only one genus, *Daphniphyllum* (about 25 spp.), formerly also included in the *Euphorbiaceae*. Mueller, the monographer of the latter family in De Candolle's PRODROMUS, regarded it as a separate family, however, and it has also been treated as such in Engler's PFLANZENREICH, though not in the first edition of the PFLANZENFAMILIEN. It differs from *Euphorbiaceae* in the absence of stipules, and in the abundant endosperm with minute embryo. It seems more closely related to *Buxaceae*. The genus ranges from the Himalayas to Japan and south-east to Timor. It should be noted that Solereder considered that there were no special anatomical characters separating the genus from *Euphorbiaceae*. This is not surprising, for there is a vast range of morphological and anatomical characters in that family.

The family **Bruniaceae**[1] belongs entirely to the Southern Hemisphere, occurring only in South Africa. Although the petals are mostly free, there

[1] Including *Berzeliaceae* Nakai (1943).

is some tendency here towards a sympetalous type of corolla (*Lonchostoma*) and towards epipetalous stamens. The flowers are mainly collected into heads and are small and inconspicuous.

The type genus is *Brunia*, polymorphic undershrubs with subverticillate branches, ericoid or flattened laxly or densely imbricate leaves, small capitate or paniculate flowers, calyx-tube adnate to the base of the ovary, 5 clawed ovate or spathulate gland-crested petals, didymous or oblong versatile anthers, semi-inferior 2-locular ovary, one of the loculi sometimes empty, 2 divergent styles or only 1 and bifid, ovules 1–2 in each loculus, fruit 1-locular and indehiscent or rarely septicidally dehiscent, 1-seeded, seeds ovate, compressed, smooth.

The most divergent genera from this type are *Lonchostoma* with the petals united at the base into a short tube, the subsessile stamens inserted on the corolla; *Audouinia* with a 3-locular ovary and a spike-like inflorescence; and *Mniothamnus*, with solitary axillary or terminal flowers.

One of the most striking features of this and some other South African families is mimicry by certain species with others which are not otherwise related. For example the genus *Audouinia* closely resembles a species of *Erica* (*Erica margaritacea* Ait.), and *Staavia* is very similar to some species of *Phylica* (*Rhamnaceae*). *Lonchostoma*, mentioned above, is very like certain *Thymelaeaceae*; *Thamnea thesioides* Dümmer is well named, whilst *Nebelia* even resembles a *Lycopodium*.

Bruniaceae are almost confined to a particular geological formation in South Africa, namely, the Table Mountain Sandstone. The family is of no economic importance except as cut flowers in their own country.

The stomata are surrounded by several unspecialised epidermal cells. The vessels have scalariform perforations in their end-walls, and bordered pits on the walls in contact with the parenchyma of the medullary rays, and the wood-prosenchyma has distinct bordered pits. The indumentum consists of simple unicellular hairs; glandular hairs and internal glands are absent.

Order 12. **SALICALES**

(*Fam. Fl. Pl.* **1**, 187)

Family: **Salicaceae.**

From these highly interesting HAMAMELIDALES, about which alone a book on phylogeny might very well be written, we pass on to the much discussed willow-family, the **Salicaceae**,[1] composed of the two genera, *Salix* and *Populus*. In the Engler system it is regarded as a primitive type and given a very lowly position as the third series (Reihe) in his sequence of families. On the contrary, according to our view, it is really very advanced, for the following reasons: the flowers are dioecious, borne in highly specialised catkins, the perianth is entirely reduced, the stamens often reduced to 2, and the ovary is composed of 2 united carpels with parietal placentas. Not one of these characters can be considered primitive. The supposed affinity with

FIG. 121. No one could mistake this fine drawing by Trevithick (for the FLORA OF WEST TROPICAL AFRICA) for anything but a willow, *Salix ledermannii* Seeman (reproduced by courtesy of the Crown Agents). **A**, male flowering shoot. **B**, male flower. **B**$_1$, stamens. **C**, female flowering shoot. **D**, female flower. **E**, vertical section of ovary. **F**, cross-section of ovary. **G**, fruiting branchlet. **H**, fruit. **I**, seed.

Tamaricaceae seems to be entirely superficial, not only from a morphological but also ecological standpoint. The species of *Salix*, like those of *Rubus*, *Rosa*, and many other advanced genera, appear to be still in a state of flux, hybridising freely, a condition usually the reverse of primitive. The late H. H. Haines made a very important discovery when he observed bisexual flowers with a rudimentary perianth in *Populus glauca* Haines. It should be noted that *Populus* is anemophilous and has deteriorated, or at any rate has

[1] Including *Amentaceae* Dulac (1867).

not evolved into many species or forms, whilst *Salix* has remained entomophilous and perhaps in consequence has become much the larger and more successful genus.

Solereder gives several anatomical characters common to the family. We need only note the stomata which tend towards the Rubiaceous type, i.e. with subsidiary cells parallel to the pore. There are no glandular hairs, and internal secretory organs are also absent.

The wood of no hitherto known tree is equal to that of *Salix alba* Linn. var. *caerulea* Syme for the manufacture of cricket-bats. It is known as the cricket-bat willow, and is supposed to be a natural hybrid between *Salix alba* and *Salix fragilis*. It is common in the eastern counties of England, and the young growths of several other species have been much used in the basket industry.

The wood of Aspen, *Populus tremula* Linn., is widely used in the British Isles for making match-sticks and match-boxes, and for chip-baskets to carry fruit and flowers. Floor-boards are also made from various species, for, like Sweet Chestnut, it does not readily burn.

ORDER 13. **LEITNERIALES** ORDER 14. **MYRICALES**
ORDER 15. **BALANOPSIDALES**

(*Fam. Fl. Pl.* **1**, 188)

We have now to consider the origin and affinities of a number of small families, most of them woody, with much-reduced flowers, though it may need a better eye and a more vivid imagination than mine for this task. I may, however, venture some suggestions on broad lines.

For the Birch trees, etc., *Betulaceae*, the Nuts, *Corylaceae*, and the Oaks and Beeches, *Fagaceae*, it is indicated by their position in my linear sequence that they may in general have arisen from the Rosaceous stock, their descent being traced through the family *Hamamelidaceae*. On the whole their present-day distribution follows closely that of the basic stock.

Leitneriaceae (genus *Leitneria*) are shrubs with much reduced dioecious flowers arranged in catkin-like erect spikes, each flower subtended by a bract. The male flowers consist only of a few stamens, but the female has still the vestiges of a calyx, and the ovary is apparently composed of one carpel with an undivided style. This family may have been derived directly from an apocarpus family, possibly *Rosaceae*, and not through the intermediate stock of the HAMAMELIDALES, wherein syncarpy with reduction is the general rule. Considerable reduction occurs even in some *Rosaceae*, for example in that family the genus *Margyricarpus* has no petals, only 2 stamens and a single carpel! That genus has no affinity, of course, with *Leitneria*, but it is mentioned as an example in order to show that very nearly as great a reduction is possible directly within the general basic stock of *Rosaceae*. *Leitneria* is confined to the S.E. United States, occurring in muddy saline swamps from southern Missouri to Texas and Florida. The S.E. region of the United States still retains a ligneous flora of considerable antiquity. Solereder says that the wood, which is exceptionally light, in its anatomical features recalls that of the *Dipterocarpaceae*; but there, in my opinion, the resemblance ends entirely; also of the *Hamamelidaceae*, especially *Liquidambar*. It cannot be near both families, however, for they are very far apart in their relationship, and the development of a similar type of wood-structure may well be due to parallelism, as *Liquidambar* is related, along with other members of its family, to the *Rosaceae*.

Order **MYRICALES**. Family **Myricaceae**

Our next family, **Myricaceae**,[1] Bog-myrtles, is more familiar to European botanists and also those in South Africa. It is distinguished by the aromatic, glandular leaves and dense spikes of small, unisexual flowers, the males with two or more stamens, the females with two style-arms and a solitary, erect, basal ovule. The family is widely distributed, with numerous and variable species in southern Africa, some of these[2] colonising the shifting coastal sand-dunes, in contrast with our European species, *Myrica gale* Linn., which favours boggy places on acid soils.

There are only two genera, *Myrica* (type genus) and *Comptonia*. In the former there are no stipules and the leaves are entire or at most only coarsely toothed, the ovary subtended by 4–2 bracteoles, soon falling off; in the latter there are foliaceous stipules, deeply pinnatifid leaves, the ovary subtended by 8 linear persistent bracteoles which become subulate and fur-like and longer than the light brown glossy nut.

Myrica faya Ait. is a small tree and an important constituent of the moist forest belt of the Canary Islands and Madeira. The genus is thus very remarkable in its great range of habitat, which is perhaps evidence of its advanced nature.

Anatomical features are large peltate glands, simple unicellular hairs, vertical transcurrence of the smaller veins of the leaf, tendency to form scalariform perforations in the vessels, and the wood prosenchyma with

---

[1] Including *Galeaceae* Bubani (1897).

[2] For example *Myrica cordifolia* Linn.

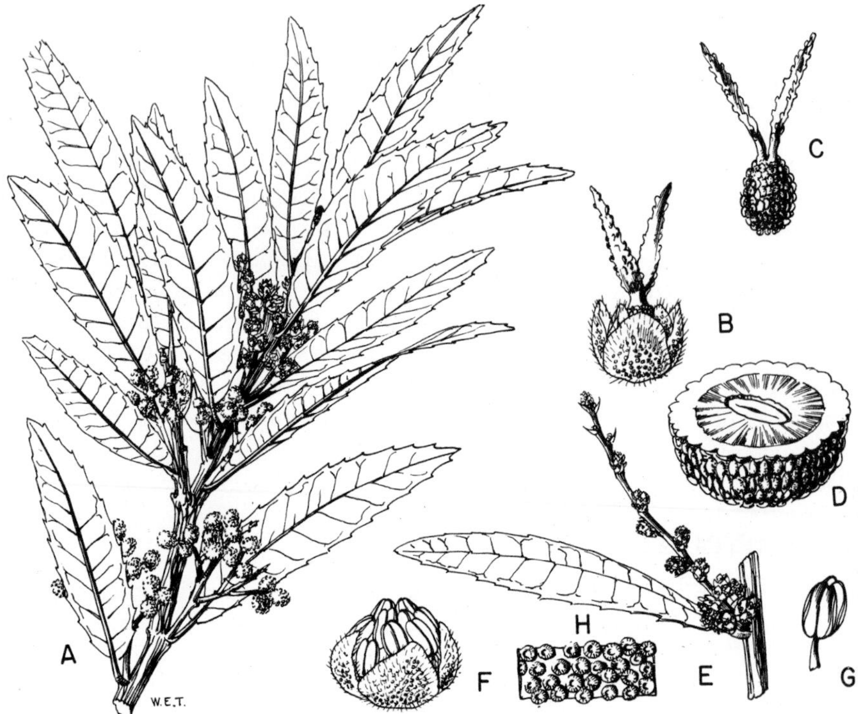

FIG. 122. *Myrica arborea* Hutch. (*Myricaceae*), a tree in the Cameroons region of west Africa. **A**, female shoot. **B**, female flower. **C**, gynoecium. **D**, cross-section of fruit. **E**, male shoot. **F**, male flower. **G**, stamen. **H**, glands on the leaf. (From Hutchinson and Dalziel, FLORA OF WEST TROPICAL AFRICA.)

bordered pits. The peltate glands consist of a uniseriate or biseriate stalk, and a shield in which some of the ray-cells often do not reach the centre.

Order **BALANOPSIDALES**

In this small family, **Balanopsidaceae**, there are two genera of trees and shrubs: *Trilocularia* Schltr., three species in New Caledonia; ovary 3-locular; styles 3, each deeply partite; ovules 2 in each loculus, superposed; and *Balanops* Baill., 12 species in New Caledonia and N.E. Australia: ovary imperfectly 2-locular; styles 2, bipartite nearly to the base; ovules 2 in each loculus, collateral.

ORDER 16. FAGALES

(*Fam. Fl. Pl.* **1**, 190)

Families: **Betulaceae, Fagaceae, Corylaceae.**

Phylogenetic path of FAGALES: MAGNOLIACEAE → DILLENIALES → ROSALES → HAMAMELIDALES → **FAGALES**.

The families composing the Order FAGALES have such reduced flowers that their true relationships can be only a matter of speculation. The above families, forming the bulk of the so-called "Amentiferae", have as a general rule catkin-like inflorescences, their gynoecia being composed of 2 or more united carpels, which are seen to be inferior when accompanied by a definite perianth. It is important to note the structure of the ovary when considering the phylogeny of the group, for an ovary composed of united carpels cannot possibly be primitive, according to our reasoning, accompanied, as it is, by a complicated catkin-like inflorescence of reduced flowers. The catkins of an undoubted primitive group such as Gymnosperms are entirely different structures from the catkins of a birch, nut-tree or oak, and it was probably due to the failure to recognise this that led to the assumption that amentiferous Angiosperms were primitive, the anemophilous pollination, which in this case is a secondary condition, completing the delusion.

As Arber and Parkin wrote in their classical paper on the Origin of Angiosperms[1]:

> Apetalous orders without perianth, such as PIPERALES, Amentiferous families, and PANDANALES, cannot be regarded as primitive Angiosperms. We thus dissent entirely from the current view, advocated especially by Engler. Engler's theory is criticised on three grounds. Firstly it presupposes that the perianth must arise *de novo*, and be an organ *sui generis*. On the contrary, we surmise that the perianth is an ancient structure, present in the fructification of the immediate ancestors of the Angiosperms. In the second place, the so-called primitive flowers of the above orders are invariably accompanied by a complicated and highly evolved inflorescence, which we are unable to regard as a primitive character. Thirdly such a theory is phylogenetically sterile, for while it has the merit of simplicity, it does not afford any clue to the ancestry of the group, nor does it tend to bring the living Angiosperms into line with the fossil plants of the past.

The family formerly known as "Cupuliferae" has for a long time been regarded as a group of families, the Order FAGALES, and is divided into three, *Betulaceae*, *Corylaceae* and *Fagaceae*.

---

[1] J. LINN. SOC. LOND. BOT. **38**, 75 (1907).

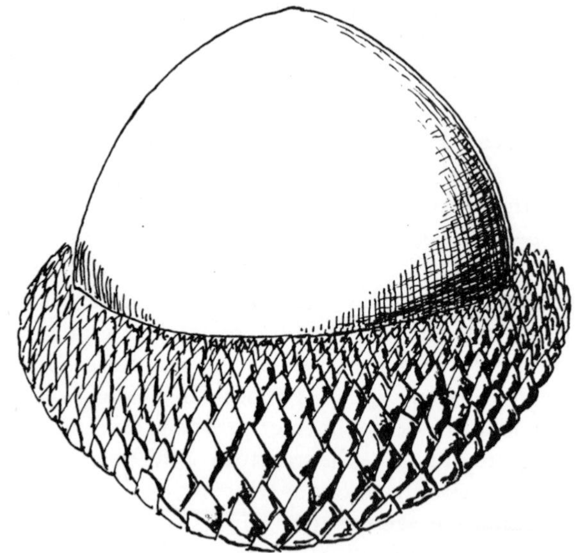

FIG. 123. An Oak with a very large acorn, *Quercus corrugata* Hook. (*Fagaceae*), Central America.

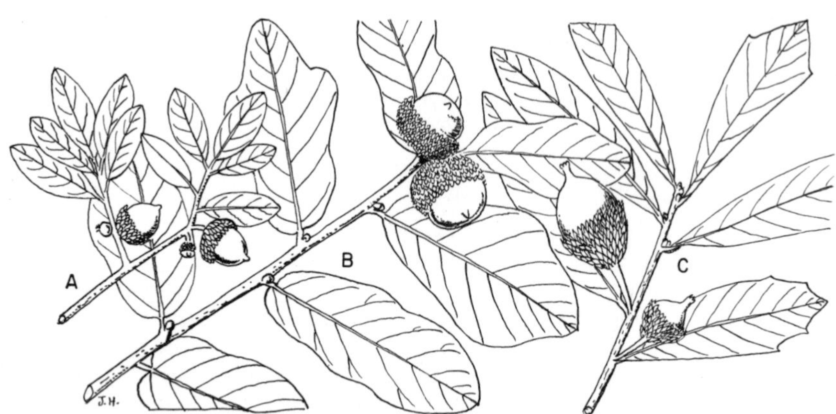

FIG. 124. Dwarf Oak trees of the Florida Keys (*Fagaceae*). **A**, *Quercus myrtifolia* Willd. **B**, *Q. chapmanii* Sargent. **C**, *Q. virginiana* Miller, var. *maritima* Sargent (orig.).

Betulaceae,[1] genera *Betula* and *Alnus*, are trees with prominently pinnately nerved leaves as in many *Rosaceae* and *Hamamelidaceae*, and are mainly found in the north temperate regions, *Alnus*, like *Fagus* (*Fagaceae*), being also represented in the Andes of South America. The male catkins and the female cone-like inflorescences have only a superficial resemblance to those

[1] Including *Nuculaceae* Dulac (1867).

of *Pinaceae*. Birches are some of the most beautiful trees, and their wood is in great demand for furniture and for plywood. It is also a very good firewood. Much of the wood of the Common Alder, *Alnus glutinosa* Gaertn., grown in the British Isles is made into clog-soles, and young coppice-wood into charcoal for making gunpowder.

Our next family has played a great part especially in the history of the British nation. This is the Beech or Oak family, **Fagaceae**,[1] which among others also embraces the Sweet Chestnut, *Castanea sativa* Mill.

The Oak for furniture, general construction work, and shipbuilding is too well known to occupy much space here. When ships were built almost entirely of wood, Oak was used more than any other. The bark is rich in tannin, and was for a long period the principal substance used for tanning hides. The genus *Quercus* is a very large one and is found chiefly in the temperate regions of the Northern Hemisphere. There are two native species in Britain, the pedunculate Oak, now called *Quercus robur* Linn. (*Q. pedunculata* Ehrh.), and the sessile or Durmast Oak, *Quercus petraea* Lieblein (*Q. sessiliflora* Salisb.). Intermediate forms are fairly common, due to free hybridisation between the two. Pure *Q. robur* is more common at low elevations, and pure *Q. petraea* predominates or occurs alone at higher altitudes. The Holm Oak is *Quercus ilex* Linn., and occurs wild in the Mediterranean region. Besides providing good timber it is an important evergreen ornamental tree which thrives equally well near the sea.

The common Beech, *Fagus sylvatica* Linn., is also one of our most useful and beautiful forest trees. It is usually the dominant feature on chalky soils in Britain, especially in the Chiltern Hills, and there are some venerable examples at Burnham Beeches, near Slough. Several towns in or near the Chilterns owe their prosperity to the beech woods, the timber being used for making chairs and many other things. Like Oak, Beech makes excellent firewood and splits very easily. The beeches found in the Southern Hemisphere are regarded as a separate genus, *Nothofagus*, and are grown for ornament in the British Isles.

The timber of the Sweet Chestnut, *Castanea sativa* Mill., is almost equal to Oak in strength and durability, and the one is often substituted for the other. It is, however, useless as firewood. Coppiced Chestnut is in great demand for fencing, which lasts for very many years even when not creosoted.

Fagaceae, composed of the genera *Quercus*, *Castanopsis*, *Castanea*, *Trigonobalanus*, *Fagus* and *Nothofagus*, represent the culmination of development, both in respect to the reduction of their flowers and to their great woody stature. Many of them are large trees producing hard and valuable timber.

---

[1] Including *Quercaceae* A. L. de Juss (1816). *Nothofagaceae* Kuprinova (1962).

Thus the ROSALES and the groups derived from them provide some of the most useful commodities in the plant kingdom.

Corylaceae[1] have a good deal in common in general appearance with *Hamamelidaceae*, but are much reduced and more advanced.

The Hornbeam, *Carpinus betulus* Linn., belongs here, and the Common Hazel, *Corylus avellana* Linn., the nuts (Filberts and Barcelona) of which are too well known to need more than passing mention. Turkey Filberts are those of *C. colurna* Linn.

ORDER 17. **JUGLANDALES**

(*Fam. Fl. Pl.* **1**, 194)

Families: **Rhoipteleaceae, Juglandaceae, Picrodendraceae.**

Phylogeny: MAGNOLIALES → DILLENIALES → ROSALES → HAMAMELIDALES → FAGALES → **JUGLANDALES.**

In my original linear arrangement I was in error in placing the JUGLANDALES after the SAPINDALES, and I now regard the supposed affinity of these two Orders with the *Anacardiaceae* to be superficial. The ovary in both *Corylaceae* and *Juglandaceae* is inferior, a characteristic already partly developed in the HAMAMELIDALES, but not in SAPINDALES. The absence of stipules from *Juglandaceae* is somewhat disconcerting, for most of the immediate family stocks from which they seem to have been derived have stipulate leaves. But stipules are not constant even in *Rosaceae*, and in *Caesalpiniaceae*, for example, which are little removed from *Rosaceae*, stipules are very rarely present. It seems likely that in this advanced family *Juglandaceae* they have been suppressed. So I now regard *Juglandaceae* to be pinnate-leaved derivatives of the *Corylaceae*, or at any rate to be from the same common stock as that family.

Rhoipteleaceae, a single genus *Rhoiptelea*, one species in Indo-China, *R. chilantha* Diels & Hand.-Mazzet., is an interesting monotype probably representing a primitive stock leading up to the more advanced *Juglandaceae* (for figure see FAMILIES OF FLOWERING PLANTS, 2nd Ed. **1**, 195).

Juglandaceae[2] embraces eight genera, *Carya*, *Juglans*, *Pterocarya*, *Cyclocarya*, *Engelhardtia*, *Oreomunnea*, *Platycarya* and *Alfaroa*. They are mostly confined to the Northern Hemisphere, with only a few in South America. The

---

[1] Including *Carpinaceae* Kuprianora (1963).

[2] Including *Pterocaryaceae* Nakai (1930). *Platycaryaceae* Nakai (1943).

FIG. 125. *Juglans regia* Linn., the Walnut, the type species of the type genus of *Juglandaceae*. **A**, shoot with young male inflorescence. **B**, male inflorescence. **C**, male flowers. **D**, female flower. **E**, vertical section of female flower. **F**, young fruits. **G**, seed.

wood of *Carya ovata* Koch is strong and elastic and used for axe-handles in North America. Hickory Nuts are the seeds of the same species, and are edible, and Peccan or Pecan Nuts of *Carya peccan* Engl. & Graebn., a native of the southern United States. These and the Walnuts belong to the family.

Edible walnuts are the seeds of *Juglans regia* Linn. (Fig. 125). One of the most valuable woods in the world is produced by the Burrs or excrescences which are found on some trees, rarely in England, but more commonly in its native habitats. Sometimes they are very large, measuring 2 to 3 ft in diameter, but usually smaller, and are sold at high prices. They are called *Loupes* in France and are cut into very thin sheets (veneers) to cover the finest pianoforte-cases, and for cabinet-making.

Until mahogany became common in England about the middle of the eighteenth century, walnut was considered the most valuable wood for furniture, carving and inside work. On the continent of Europe most of the best old furniture was made of it. Later it became very valuable for gun-stocks. Loudon states that during the long wars at the beginning of the nineteenth century, in France, no less than 12 000 trees were cut annually for gunstocks, which caused it to become very scarce, and in England as much as £600 was paid for the wood of one tree. *J. regia* has a very wide distribution, occurring wild in Europe in Greece, Bosnia, Haerzegovina, Albania, Bulgaria and Armenia, extending eastwards through Asia Minor,

FIG. 126. *Picrodendron baccatum* (Linn.) Krug & Urban (*Picrodendraceae*), West Indies; note the remarkable difference between the male inflorescence, **A**, and the female, **E**, the latter reduced to a single flower (orig.). **B**, male flower from the side. **C**, the same from below. **D**, stamen. **F**, gynoecium. **G**, vertical section of ovary. **H**, fruit. **J**, seed. (Repeated from FAMILIES OF FLOWERING PLANTS.)

the Caucasus, Persia, and the Himalayas to Burma and north China and Japan. For panelling, walnut comes second only to Oak.

The figure (Fig. 126) of *Picrodendron* is repeated here from my FAMILIES OF FLOWERING PLANTS. It is the sole member of **Picrodendraceae**, a genus confined to the West Indies. It may be observed that there is a remarkable difference between the male and female inflorescences, as there is also in some *Euphorbiaceae*; the males are in slender interrupted simple or slightly branched catkins borne in the axils of the leaves of the previous season's growth, while the female flowers are solitary and axillary on slender pedicels on the new shoots; the ovary is 2-locular and there are 2 ovules pendulous from a hemispherical placenta at the top of the loculi.

ORDER 18. **CASUARINALES**

(*Fam. Fl. Pl.* **1**, 197)

Family: **Casuarinaceae.**

Hypothetical phylogenetic path of evolution of "Amentiferous" families: MAGNOLIALES → DILLENIALES → ROSALES → HAMAMELIDALES: → **Salicales**, **Myricales**, **Balanopsidales**, **Fagales**, **Juglandales**, culminating in the most reduced and advanced of dicotyledonous families, **Casuarinaceae.**

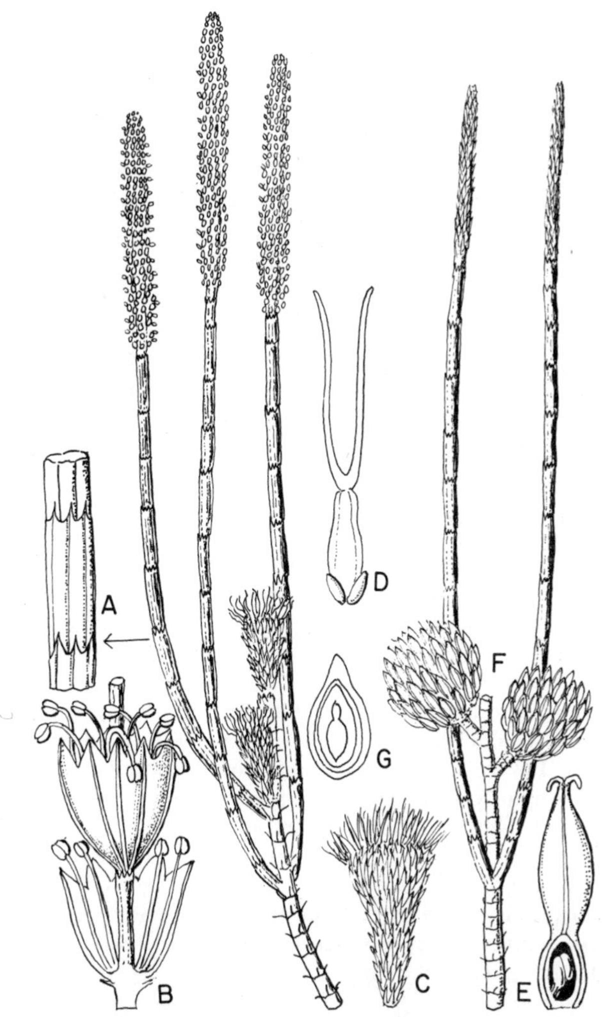

FIG. 127. *Casuarina equisetifolia* Linn., the type species of the genus, Malaya and Pacific Islands (*Casuarinaceae*). **A**, part shoot. **B**, flowers, the lower half in vertical section. **C**, female inflorescence. **D**, female flower. **E**, vertical section of ovary. **F**, fruits. **G**, vertical section of seed (orig.).

The family **Casuarinaceae**, single genus *Casuarina* (Fig. 127), is so much reduced both in its vegetative and floral characters that its true affinity is difficult to ascertain. It occurs mainly around the shores of the Indian Ocean eastwards to New Caledonia and Australia, and is composed of trees or shrubs with jointed branches and whorls of much reduced scale-like leaves united in the lower part into a sheath after the manner of an *Equisetum*. The male flowers are spicate, the females in heads; there is only 1 stamen and the ovary is 1-locular with 2 long style-arms and 2 ascending ovules. *Casuarinaceae* is here regarded as an extreme reduction adapted mostly to dry climatic conditions, but with no very near relations still living. The cone-like infructescence resembles that of the *Pandanaceae* in the Monocotyledons, but should not be regarded as more than a parallelism, nor has it anything to do with the cones of the *Pinaceae*, the resemblance being entirely superficial. Maybe it was due to this that *Casuarinaceae* occupies a very lowly position in the Englerian system. Species of *Casuarina* flourish mostly near the sea, and they possess very hard and heavy wood with wide medullary rays, which is put to a variety of uses. In Fiji wooden "pillows" were made of this wood, and formerly formidable war-clubs.

M. F. Moseley, in a paper entitled "Comparative Anatomy and Phylogeny of *Casuarinaceae*" (BOT. GAZ. **110**, 231 (1948)) has dealt very ably with the question of the position of the *Casuarinaceae*, part of which I have quoted in my GENERA OF FLOWERING PLANTS (Vol. 2, 143 (1967)):

A family, consisting of one genus (*Casuarina*), that has proved to be one of the most perplexing groups of angiosperms to place in a natural system. . . . It has been considered to be among the primitive groups of angiosperms by Engler and Prantl, by Rendle, and others; and it has occupied a key position as the most primitive of angiosperms in the phylogenetic systems of Engler and Prantl, Engler and Diels, Johnson, and Wettstein. On the contrary, the family has been considered extremely reduced, yet always assigned a position tentatively, in the systems of Hallier, Bessey, Hutchinson and others. Indeed, *Casuarina* has been described as the "amphioxus" of the plant kingdom.

Over a long period of years, taxonomists and systematists have established that there are apparently certain trends in the evolution of the external morphology of angiosperms, especially of the flower. Similarly, during the last 30–40 years (i.e. 1900–48), plant anatomists have worked out the lines of phylogenetic specialisation of the stele, particularly of the secondary xylem. These trends of phylogenetic specialisation may be stated in the form of dicta. . . .

This important contribution by Moseley should be read in detail, especially by those who continue to follow the Engler and Prantl system! I need only quote a little further from it (p. 276):

The phylogenetic conclusions based on anatomical evidence are as follows: *Casuarinaceae* is a specialised family of the *Angiospermae*, and are not a primitive group. . . . Floral morphology indicates that the *Casuarinaceae* have been derived from the *Hamamelidaceae*-like ancestors. The lines of floral reduction seen in the *Hamamelidaceae* seem to have been carried to extremes in the *Casuarinaceae*. A study of the correlation between anatomy and flower-structure of the *Casuarinaceae* precludes the retention of the family as a primitive (or the primitive group) of the *Angiospermae*. In addition, the anatomical evidence supports, or at least is not inconsistent with, the derivation of the *Casuarinaceae* from hamamelidaceous ancestors as suggested by morphology.

Moseley also gives a very valuable and comprehensive bibliography dealing with this highly interesting subject.

ORDER 19. **URTICALES**

(*Fam. Fl. Pl.* **1**, 199)

Families: **Ulmaceae, Cannabiaceae, Moraceae, Urticaceae, Barbeyaceae, Eucommiaceae.**

The above families, which include the Elms, Mulberries, Nettles, etc., have quite a lengthy pedigree, maybe as follows:

MAGNOLIALES → DILLENIALES → ROSALES → HAMAMELIDALES → FAGALES → URTICALES → climax family **Urticaceae** (mostly herbaceous).

The Order URTICALES completes the large group of families supposed to have been derived from the Rosaceous-Hamamelidaceous stock. It should be noted that the stems of many herbaceous *Urticaceae* are fibrous, which may tend to support the view that they have been derived from a ligneous stock, similar to the MALVALES as a climax from the more woody TILIALES.

Ulmaceae,[1] composed of the genera *Ulmus*, *Planera*, *Zelkova*, *Celtis* (Fig. 128), *Trema*, *Hemiptelea* (Fig. 129) and a few others are, as a rule, large trees with small and mostly unisexual flowers and the fruits often adapted for wind-dispersal. The family is widespread over a great part of the world, *Ulmus* being the principal genus in the North Temperate Zone, and *Celtis* and *Trema* being mainly in the tropics.

Some genera have cystoliths in their leaves, showing in this respect their affinity with the more advanced *Urticaceae*, in which they are such a common feature. The stomata are mostly confined to the lower surface and there are no special subsidiary cells accompanying them.

The wood of various species of Elm (*Ulmus*) is noted for being tough, strong, and durable, especially under water, and it is put to many uses. Of historical interest, it may be recalled that the Duke of Wellington stood

[1] Including *Celtidaceae* Link (1831). *Samaraceae* Dulac (1867).

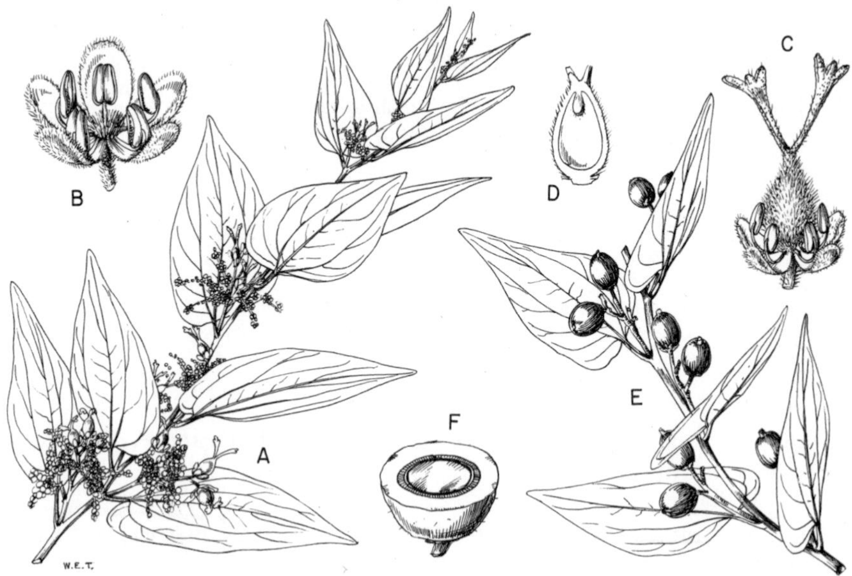

FIG. 128. *Celtis integrifolia* Lam. (*Ulmaceae*), tropical Africa and Arabia. (From Hutchinson and Dalziel, FLORA OF WEST TROPICAL AFRICA.) **A**, flowering shoot. **B**, male flower. **C**, female flower. **D**, vertical section of ovary. **E**, fruiting shoot. **F**, cross-section of fruit.

under an Elm during the battle of Waterloo, and a portion of the tree is preserved in the Kew Museum. The murderous tomahawks of the Indians of North America were largely made of Elm wood. The wood of *Zelkova serrata* Makino has been extensively used in Japan for making beautifully carved boxes. Slippery Elm Bark, derived from *Ulmus fulva* Michaux, a small tree in the centre and north of the United States of America, is employed in medicine because of its high mucilage content. Elms in Britain, and no doubt elsewhere, are somewhat notorious for accidents due to the branches suddenly breaking off without warning.

Cannabiaceae[1] (as it is now spelled by the purists, and not *Cannabinaceae*) contains only two genera, *Cannabis* and *Humulus*. It differs from *Urticaceae* mainly in its erect anthers in bud (not inflexed). Hemp is obtained from *Cannabis sativa* Linn., an annual herb, much cultivated since ancient times. The stem provides Hemp Fibre, used for twine, cordage, and for many other purposes. The seeds are the source of Hemp Seed Oil, used for paints, etc., and as food for birds. The dried flower-tops of the female plant are used medicinally, being sedative and narcotic; also the source of *Marihuana*, used for smoking but prohibited in many countries except in parts of Asia and Africa. Excessive smoking is physically and mentally injurious, producing

[1] Including *Lupulaceae* Link (1831). *Strobilaceae* Dulac (1867).

FIG. 129. *Hemiptelea davidii* Planch. (*Ulmaceae*), north China and Korea; a small much-branched tree or shrub, used as a hedge plant. **A**, barren spiny shoot. **B**, leaf with minute bulbous-based hairs on the upper surface, on older leaves appearing like gland-dots. **C**, flowering shoot. **D**, flower. **E**, shoot with fruits. **F**, fruit (orig.).

moral weakness and depravity. The Hop, *Humulus lupulus* Linn., is much cultivated (in Britain mainly in Kent and Surrey), for the bitter substance present in the glandular hairs of the female strobilus and used for flavouring beer; also in medicine. The stems are the source of a fibre. Oil of Hops is employed in certain perfumes.

Moraceae[1] is a large and interesting family met with mostly in the tropics and warm temperate regions. To the layman the best known examples are the common Fig, *Ficus carica* Linn., and the Breadfruit, *Artocarpus altilis* (Park.) Fosb. (Fig. 137), of "Bounty" fame in the island of Tahiti, in the Pacific. Most people are familiar with the story of Captain Bligh's attempt to introduce it into the West Indies to provide food for the negro slaves imported from tropical Africa. Amongst those who perished during the voyage was a young gardener, David Nelson, from the Royal garden at Kew, who

[1] Including *Artocarpaceae* R.Br. (1818). *Ficaceae* Dumort. (1829). *Sycoideae* Link (1829).

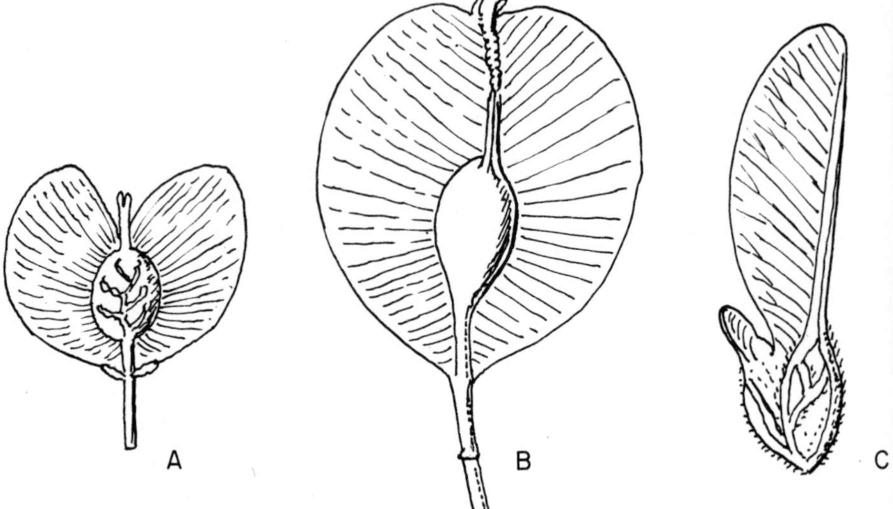

FIG. 130. Some fruits of *Ulmaceae*: **A**, *Pteroceltis tatarinowii* Maxim., Mongolia. **B**, *Holoptelea grandis* (Hutch.) Mildbraed, tropical Africa—which, alas, the present author in his younger days mistook for a species of *Hymenocardia* (*Euphorbiaceae*—see Fig. 242). **C**, *Phyllostylon brasiliensis* Capan, Brazil.

was employed to look after the young plants on their long journey around Cape Horn.

There are other genera of economic importance. Several kinds of paper and other articles, including some beautiful fans, are made from the bark of *Broussonetia papyrifera* Vent., a small tree widely distributed in China, Japan, Polynesia, etc. For commercial purposes it is often cultivated on the coppice system in order to obtain long, clean, annual shoots, from which the bark is stripped in ribbons. Skeletonised leaves of this tree are sold as a souvenir in Pitcairn Island, where the mutineers from the Bounty made their home. Other edible fruits are the Jack fruit, *Artocarpus heterophyllus* Lamk., and the Black Mulberry, *Morus nigra* Linn.

The most widely known of Moraceous timbers are "Iroko", *Chlorophora excelsa* Benth. & Hook. f., a large tree in tropical Africa; "Snakewood" or Letterwood", *Brosimum guianense* Huber ex Ducke, in Guyana, South America; and "Satine", *Brosimum paraense* Huber, in Brazil. The coffins used by the ancient Egyptians were made of *Ficus sycomorus* Linn.

The leaves of *Morus alba* Linn., a common Asiatic tree, have long been used for feeding the larvae of the silk moth, and also those of the North American Osage Orange, *Maclura pomifera* (Raf.) Schneider. The latex of *Ficus elastica* Roxb., India and Malaya, and *Castilloa elastica* Cerv., Mexico and Honduras, is no longer of importance as a source of rubber, compared

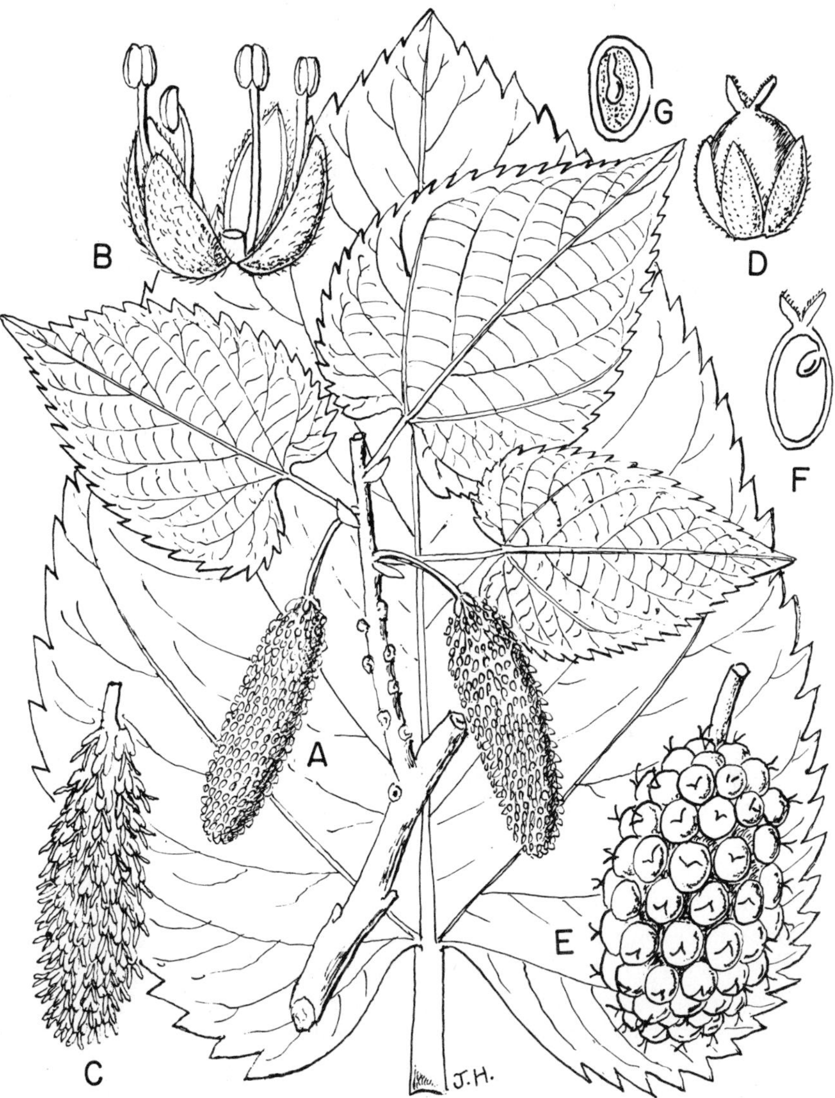

FIG. 131. *Morus nigra* Linn., the type species of the type genus of *Moraceae*, temperate Asia. **A**, male catkin. **B**, male flower. **C**, female catkin. **D**, female flower. **E**, fruits. **F**, vertical section of ovary. **G**, vertical section of seed (orig.).

with that of the Para Rubber tree, *Hevea brasiliensis* Muell.—Arg. (*Euphorbiaceae*). The leaves of some *Moraceae* are so rough, due to the large number of cystoliths, that they are used locally as sand-paper.

The type genus is *Morus* Linn. Latex bearing trees and shrubs; leaves alternate, undivided or 3-lobed, 3-nerved at the base; stipules caducous; flowers monoecious or dioecious, densely spicate; spikes axillary, pedunculate, male catkin-like, female long or short; male flowers: calyx 4-partite, imbricate; stamens 4, filaments inflexed in bud: ovary vestigial; female flowers: calyx as in the male but becoming succulent in fruit; ovary ovoid or subglobose; style central, 2-partite, branches linear, equal; ovule 1, pendulous; fruits enclosed by the enlarged succulent calyces, densely clustered; seeds subglobose, with fleshy endosperm; embryo with oblong equal cotyledons. Type species *M. nigra* Linn. (Fig. 131), temperate Asia. Most of the genera of this family are in need of revision (see my GENERA OF FLOWERING PLANTS Vol. 2, 153 (1967)).

We have space here only for a few notes about the classification of the 3 subfamilies and tribes. In subfamily *Moroideae* the stamens of the male flowers are inflexed in bud and the ovules in the female are always inserted at the top of the ovary; leaves mostly with small stipules which leave little or no scar.

In the second subfamily, *Artocarpoideae*, the stamens are erect in bud, the ovules also at or near the top of the ovary (pendulous), and the leaves are spirally folded in bud with the stipules leaving an amplexicaul scar after falling off. To this tribe belongs the huge genus *Ficus* (see Figs 132–136), the "fruit" of which is a modified inflorescence, the so-called Fig, which encloses a number (often very many) of small unisexual or bisexual flowers which produce the "pips" (fruitlets).

In subfamily *Conocephaloideae* the stamens are also erect in bud, but the ovules are usually erect at or near the base of the ovary, and the leaves are spirally folded in bud, the stipules leaving an amplexicaul scar.

The family **Urticaceae**[1] differs very little from the more tropical *Moraceae* except by the erect ovule. Many are herbs or more rarely soft-wooded trees, and the leaf-epidermis is mostly marked with prominent cystoliths. Tribe *Urereae*, which contains the common Nettle, *Urtica dioica* Linn. (Fig. 146), is distinguished by the presence of stinging hairs. *Laportea gigas* Wedd. (*Dendrocnide*) is a large tree in Polynesia up to 40 ft, with large cordate leaves which sting severely, the irritation lasting for a considerable time. Two or three species of this genus occur in Australia.

Tribe *Procrideae* has the stigma brush-like, and the calyx of the female flowers mostly 3-partite. In the remainder of the tribes the stigma is never brush-like, and the calyx of the female mostly tubular, rarely reduced. In tribe *Forsskohleeae* the male flowers have usually only a single stamen, something of a parallel but not related to *Euphorbia*.

The common Nettle contains a small amount of silky fibre, when well prepared. The leaves have been used for the extraction of chlorophyll. It is

---

[1] Including *Nemelataceae* Dulac (1867).

unnecessary to say, of course, that this species is also a noxious weed to farmers and gardeners. Ramie Fibre, China Grass, is *Boehmeria nivea* Gaudich., and its var. *tenacissima*, the chief sources being China, Japan and Taiwania (Formosa), and cultivated elsewhere. Olona, *Touchardia latifolia* Gaudich., Hawaiian Islands, was at one time cultivated for its fibre.

Barbeyaceae, genus *Barbeya*, represented by a single species, *B. oleoides* Schweinf., native of Arabia and N.E. tropical Africa, seems to have no very

(continued on p. 166)

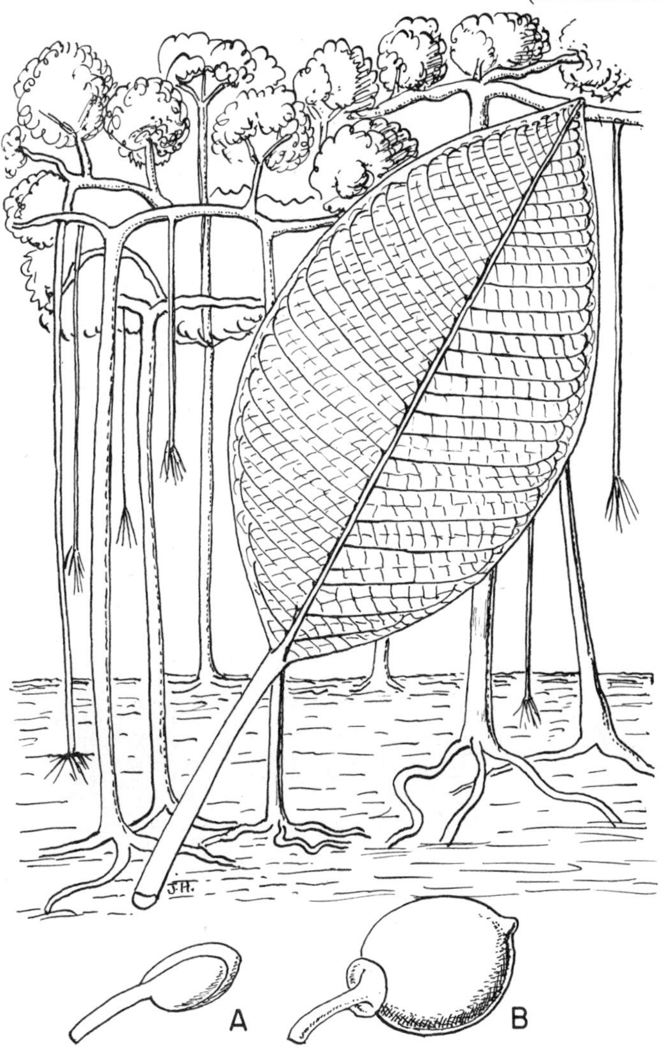

FIG. 132. *Ficus macrophylla* Desf. ex Pers. (*Moraceae*), the Moreton Bay Fig tree on Lord Howe's Island. **A**, bud of receptacle. **B**, fig (orig.).

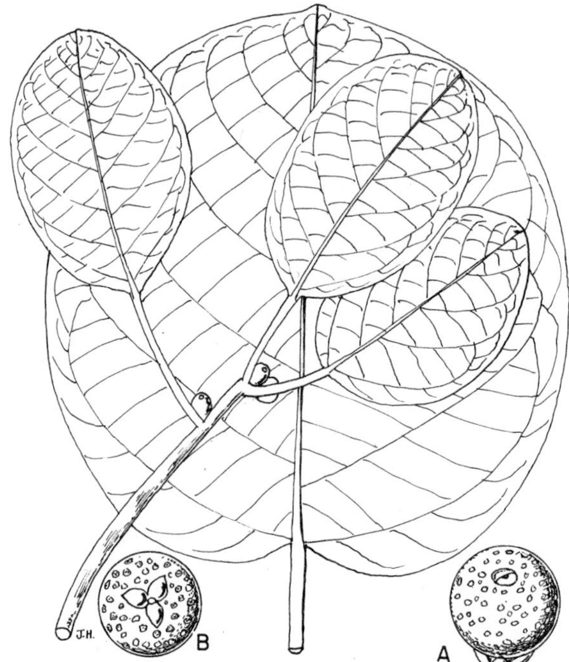

FIG. 133. *Ficus cotinifolia* H. B. & K. (*Moraceae*), the largest tree on Socorro Island in the Revillagigedo Archipelago, off the west coast of Mexico. **A**, fig. **B**, the same from below (orig.).

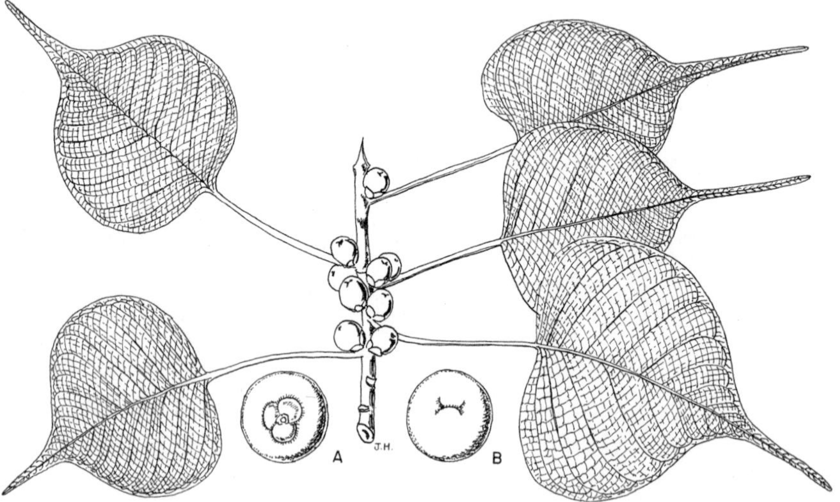

FIG. 134. *Ficus religiosa* Linn. (*Moraceae*), the sacred tree of Hindustan; grown in many tropical countries. **A**, a fig from below showing involucre of bracts. **B**, the same from above, showing the ostiole (orig.).

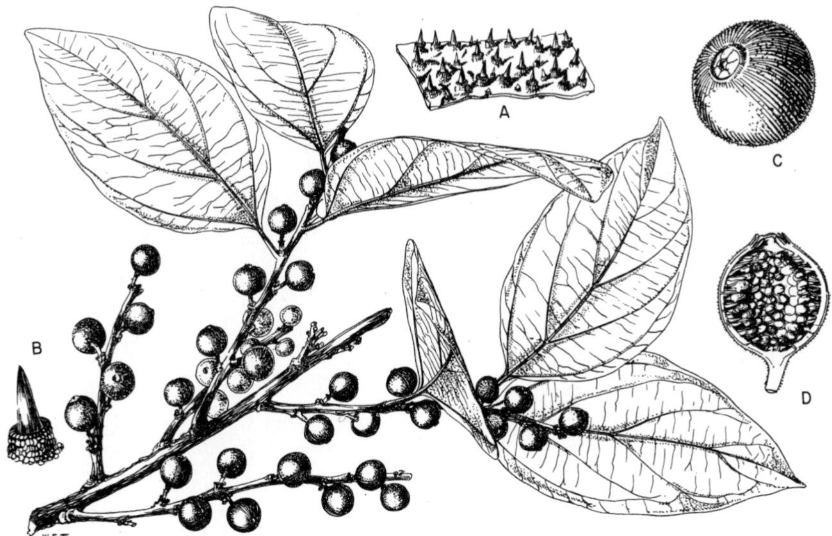

FIG. 135. *Ficus exasperata* Vahl (*Moraceae*). **A**, showing the rough surface of leaf. **B**, enlarged of the same. **C**, fig. **D**, vertical section of fig. (From Hutchinson and Dalziel, FLORA OF WEST TROPICAL AFRICA.)

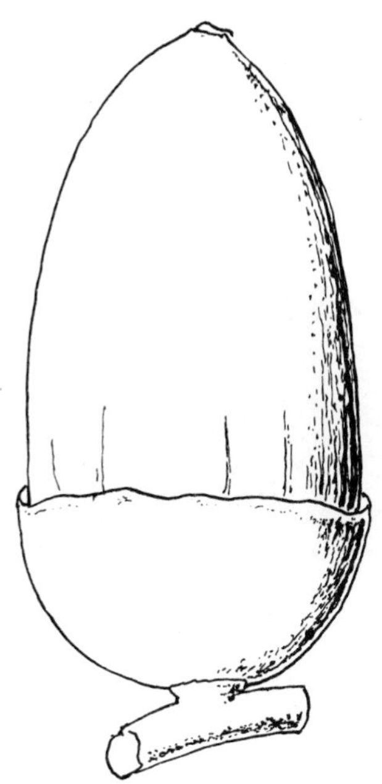

FIG. 136. This is not an acorn but the fruit of a fig, *Ficus glandifera* Summerhayes (*Moraceae*), native of the New Hebrides, Pacific region; involucre of bracts large and cup-shaped (orig.).

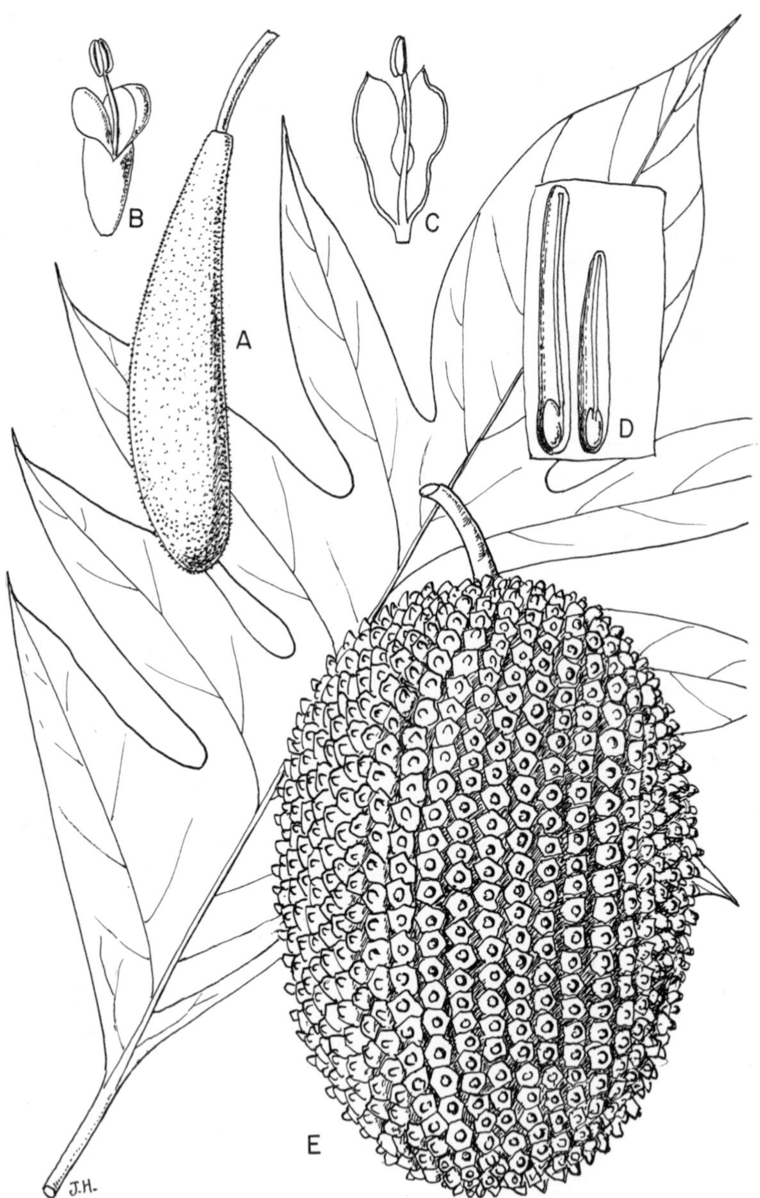

FIG. 137. The Bread-fruit, *Artocarpus altilis* (Park.) Fosb. (*Moraceae*). **A**, male inflorescence. **B**, male flower. **C**, vertical section of same. **D**, female flowers. **E**, fruit (orig.).

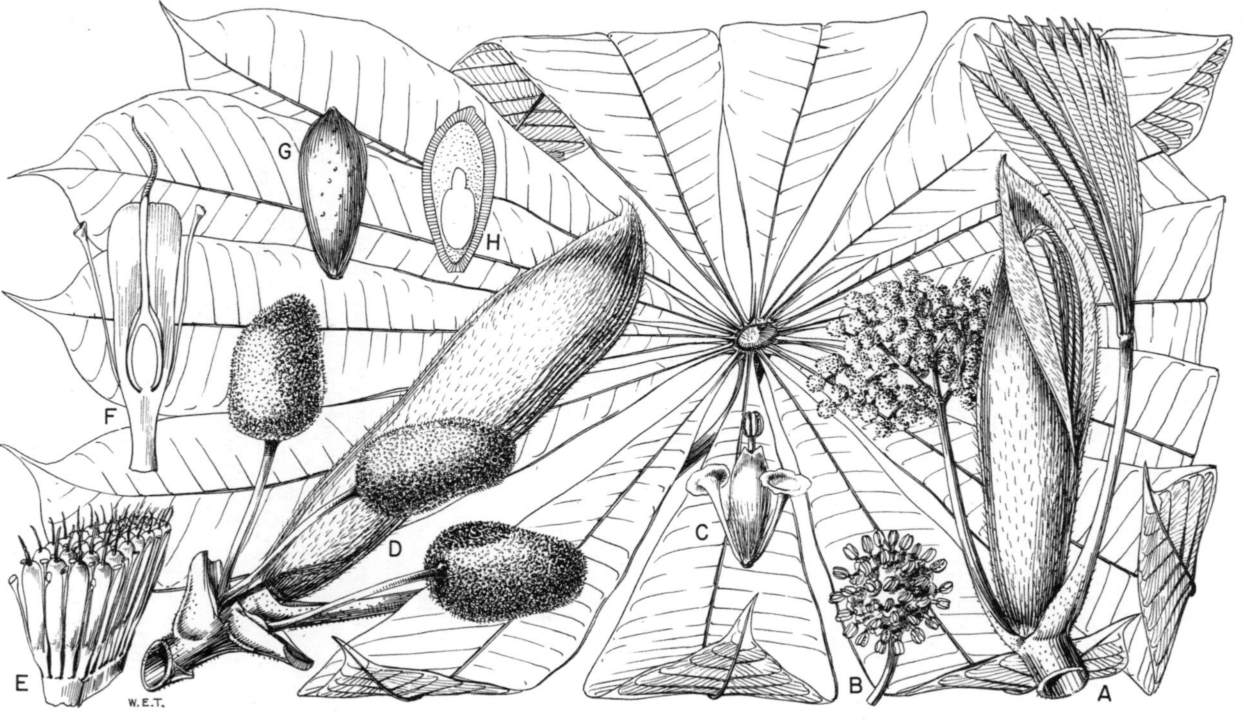

FIG. 138. *Musanga cecropioides* R.Br. (*M. smithii* R.Br.) (*Moraceae*). **A**, male shoot, with terminal bud and young leaf. **B**, head of male flowers. **C**, male flower. **D**, female inflorescence and terminal bud. **E**, female flower. **F**, section of female flower. **G**, fruit. **H**, vertical section of fruit. A magnificent drawing by Trevithick; rarely has a botanical artist so skilfully shown so many generic and specific features in so small a space. (From Hutchinson and Dalziel, FLORA OF WEST TROPICAL AFRICA.)

near relations. It is a tree with opposite exstipulate leaves, small, cymose, apetalous flowers, the calyx of the female enlarging in fruit and becoming membranous rather like some species of *Dipterocarpaceae*.

The family **Eucommiaceae** is monotypic, genus *Eucommia* Oliv., and was originally placed by its author in *Magnoliaceae*. Its dioecious, naked flowers, bicarpellary, syncarpous ovary and 2 collateral ovules and samaroid fruits remove it very far from that family. It seems to be quite a near relative of *Ulmaceae*. It is a remarkable fact that like the ancient *Ginkgo biloba*, the Maiden-hair tree, this *Eucommia ulmoides* Oliv. has never been found in a wild state, but owes its preservation to Chinese cultivation. The bark furnishes a drug valued by the Chinese and used by them from very early times. The tree also produces an inferior rubber (see FAMILIES OF FLOWERING PLANTS, 2nd Ed. **1**, 204, Fig. 73).

ORDER 20. **BIXALES**

(*Fam. Fl. Pl.* **1**, 204)

Families: **Bixaceae, Cistaceae, Flacourtiaceae, Cochlospermaceae, Hoplostigmataceae, Achatocarpaceae, Lacistemataceae, Peridiscaceae.**

The largest family is *Flacourtiaceae* (including the *Samydaceae* of Bentham and Hooker), and the Order seems phylogenetically to occupy more or less of a half way place between the more primitive DILLENIALES and the more advanced TILIALES; the ovary has become syncarpous but with the carpels united only by their margins (parietal placentation), an earlier condition than axile placentation, which is characteristic of the more advanced TILIALES and other higher families. The Order is but a short step from the MAGNOLIALES and shown as follows:

MAGNOLIALES → DILLENIALES → **BIXALES**, branching off into at least three subphyla, such as TILIALES (*Tiliaceae*, *Sterculiaceae*, *Bombabaceae*, *Malvaceae*), and especially PASSIFLORALES (*Passifloraceae*, etc.) and THYMELAEALES (*Thymelaeaceae*, etc.).

The Order BIXALES comprises a group of plants whose relationships have been the subject of much divergence of opinion and very different treatment. It was included in the unwieldy and unnatural group PARIETALES in both the

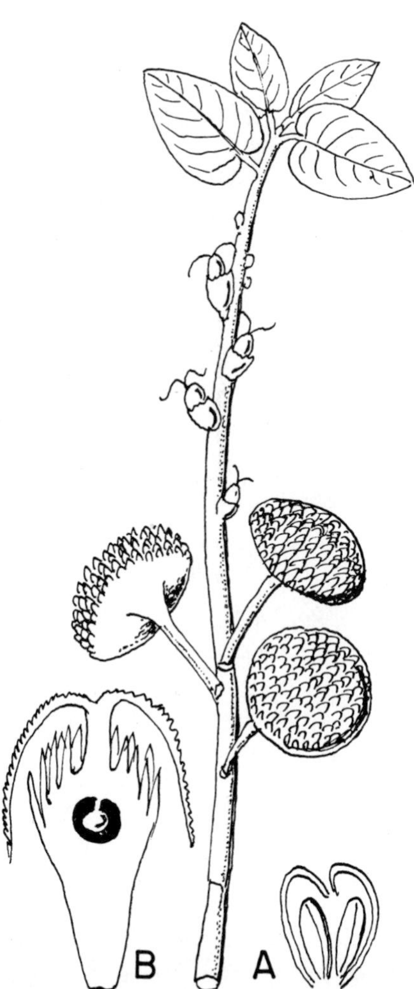

FIG. 139. *Antiaris toxicaria* Lesch. (*Moraceae*), Indo-Malaya; a genus pointing to the evolution of a fig (*Ficus*). **A**, male flower. **B**, vertical section of female flower.

Bentham and Hooker and the Englerian systems, unnatural because it was held together mainly by a single character, the parietal placentation of the ovules.

The family **Bixaceae** is now generally restricted to the single genus *Bixa*, which seems to have a more or less affinity with *Dilleniaceae*. The stamens are peculiar in being somewhat horseshoe-shaped, the anther-loculi being bent around on themselves but with the dehiscence at the top. We meet with this feature again in the genus *Gonystylus*, suggesting affinity of this family which is regarded as being an intermediary towards the THYMELAEALES and PROTEALES. *Bixa* is a genus of shrubs or small trees belonging to a single species, *Bixa orellana* Linn., found generally in the tropics, from the seeds of which the well known Annatto dye is obtained; leaves alternate, simple and palminerved, stipulate; the flowers are bisexual, paniculate, the pedicels with 5 glands below the calyx; sepals 5, imbricate, deciduous; petals 5, large, free, imbricate; no disk; stamens numerous, hypogynous, free; anthers horseshoe-shaped; ovary superior, 1-locular, with 2 parietal placentas; ovules numerous; style recurved in bud, 2-lobed; fruit a densely echinate-setose or smooth capsule, 2-valved, the placentas in the middle of the valves; seeds red, endosperm copious, embryo large, with broad cotyledons.

The well-known family **Cistaceae**,[1] Rock Roses, etc. of our gardens, is in this woody phylum something of a parallel to the *Papaveraceae* in the

[1] Including *Duotriaceae* Dulac (1867).

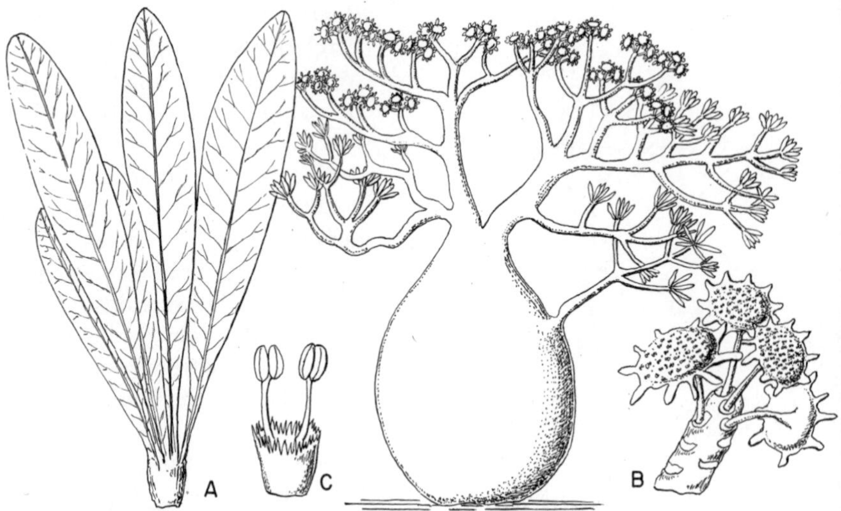

FIG. 140. *Dorstenia gigas* Schweinfurth, Socotra (*Moraceae*), a species with unique habit. **A**, bunch of leaves. **B**, inflorescences. **C**, male flower.

herbaceous phylum. Not only the general appearance of the flowers of *Cistus*, for example, but also the extremely fugitive petals are suggestive of *Papaveraceae*, while the intrusive placentas of the ovary lend further colour to this view.

The number of genera of *Cistaceae* varies greatly according to different authors. Bentham and Hooker recognised only four, *Cistus* and *Helianthemum*, with numerous ovules on each placenta, and *Hudsonia* and *Lechea*, with the ovules on each placenta reduced to 2. In the second edition of the PFLANZENREICH, however, eight genera are recognised, *Halimium* Spach, separated from *Cistus*, and *Fumana*, *Crocoanthemum* and *Tuberaria* from *Helianthemum*. *Hudsonia* and *Lechea* are found only in North America.

The type genus, *Cistus*, about 50 species, shrubs or undershrubs with opposite evergreen or half-evergreen leaves; no stipules, but petioles connate at the base; flowers usually very handsome, bisexual, in terminal cymes or panicles; sepals 5 or 3; petals 5, spreading, sometimes with a large darker blotch at the base; stamens numerous, all fertile; ovary 10- or 5-locular; stigma 10- or 5-lobed; ovules numerous; capsule loculicidally 10- or 5-valved; embryo circinate. Type species *C. crispus* Linn., W. Mediterranean.

In *Lechea* there are only 3 petals, which persist, and the upper leaves are alternate; in all genera except *Cistus* the capsule is 3-valved, whilst in *Fumana* the outer stamens are sterile.

FIG. 141. A species of a genus tending towards the evolution of a fig; *Dorstenia elata* Hook. (*Moraceae*), Native of Brazil (orig.).

Flacourtiaceae,[1] as here understood, represents most of the *Bixaceae* of the Bentham and Hooker system, and includes also the *Samydaceae*. These two families were placed by them far apart in the *Thalamiflorae* and *Calyciflorae* respectively. They are essentially a somewhat indeterminate and intermediate group of plants, but even so they hang together fairly well especially

[1] Including *Samydaceae* Ventenat (1807). *Homaliaceae* R.Br. (1818). *Kiggelariaceae* Link (1831). *Blackwelliaceae* C. H. Schultz (1832). *Patrisiaceae* Mart. (1835). *Pangiaceae* Blume ex Endlich. (1850). *Neumanniaceae* van Tieghem (1889). *Erythrospermaceae* van Tieghem (1900). *Dioncophyllaceae* Airy Shaw (1951). *Plagiospermaceae* Airy Shaw (1965). *Triphyophyllaceae* Emberger (1960). *Emblingiaceae* Airy Shaw (1965).

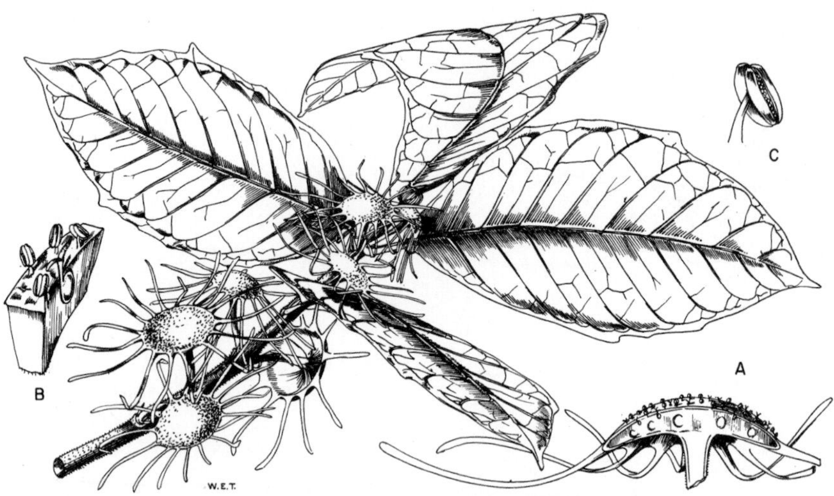

FIG. 142. Another fine drawing by Trevithick of the west African *Dorstenia mannii* Hook. f. (*Moraceae*), a remarkable genus, a vegetable "octopus", related to and tending towards the evolution of the figs (*Ficus*), but with open receptacles. **A**, cross-section of receptacle. **B**, showing male flowers. **C**, stamen. (From Hutchinson and Dalziel, FLORA OF WEST TROPICAL AFRICA.)

by the parietal placentation of the ovules. The same can hardly be said of them, however, as delimited in the latest edition of the Engler and Prantl system, wherein Gilg, following the lead of Warburg in the first edition, included a large part of *Passifloraceae* and a portion (*Prockieae*) of *Tiliaceae*. The addition of these causes the family to be less definitely circumscribed and difficult to separate from either of these families. To my mind *Paropsia* and allied genera are better associated with *Passifloraceae*, and *Prockieae* combine better with *Tiliaceae*. The presence or absence of mucilage is stressed in the German system, but this does not seem to me to outweigh in importance the characters derived from the floral structure, which in a system based on comparative morphology should take precedence over anatomical or chemical characters.

A very interesting point about a few of the genera with hypogynous flowers (*Berberidopsis* (Fig. 149), etc.), is that the sepals and petals are scarcely distinguishable from each other and on this account they should perhaps be regarded as representing the more primitive types, just as in *Annonaceae*. Then there is a second group leading on from them in which the petals are more numerous than the sepals and are not arranged symmetrically with them, as if the parts of these flowers had not quite settled into their orthodox whorls, as they have in the more advanced genera.

The marked difference in the anthers of the more primitive family *Dilleniaceae* is repeated in the *Flacourtiaceae*, some genera having very short and

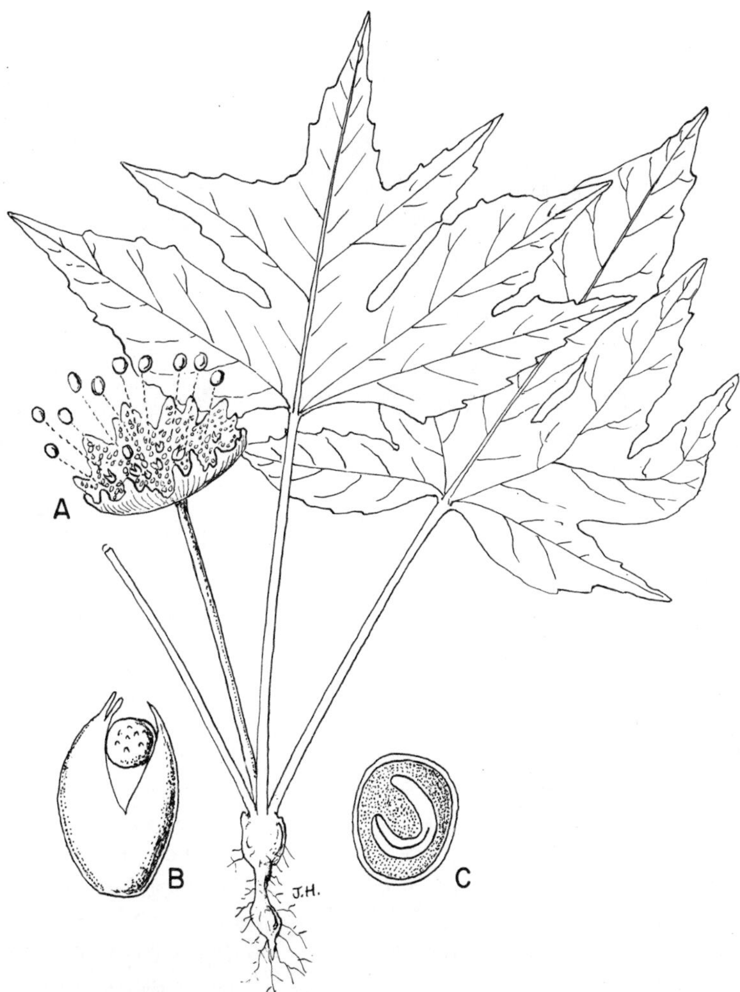

FIG. 143. *Dorstenia contrayerva* Linn. (*Moraceae*); Mexico through Central America and the West Indies south to Venezuela and Peru. The fruits are thrown out with force from the fleshy receptacle to as far as 3–4 metres. **A**, receptacle and fruit. **B**, calyx and fruit. **C**, vertical section of seed showing the horseshoe-shaped embryo.

rounded and others linear anthers. These two types are also found in the higher family, *Tiliaceae*. Then it is in some *Flacourtiaceae* that we meet with for the first time the development of a basal scale on the inside of the petals, a feature found also in some *Tiliaceae*, such as *Grewia* and allied genera.

Some *Flacourtiaceae* have lost their petals and it is amongst these that the

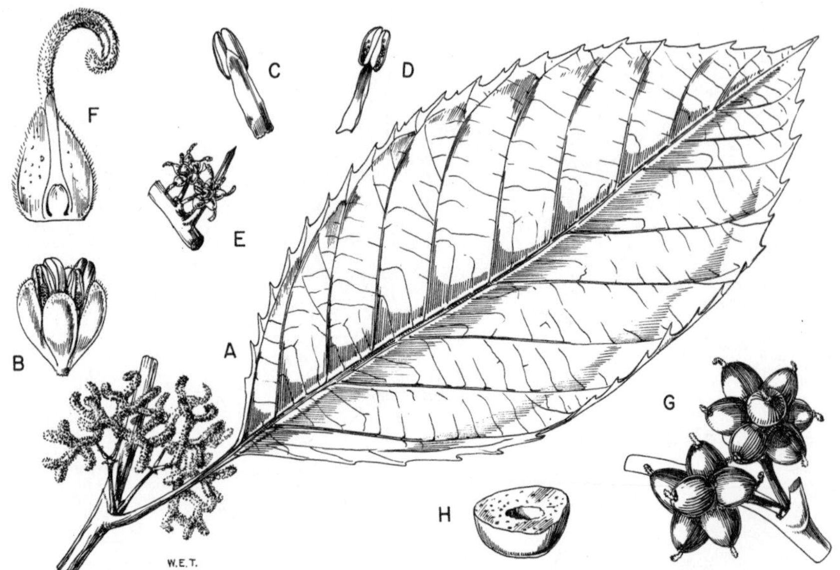

FIG. 144. *Myrianthus serratus* (Trecul) Benth. (*Moraceae*), tropical Africa. **A**, male inflorescence and leaf. **B**, male flower. **C** and **D**, stamens. **E**, female flowers. **F**, vertical section of female flower. **G**, fruits. **H**, cross-section of fruit. (From Hutchinson and Dalziel, FLORA OF WEST TROPICAL AFRICA.)

placentas of the ovary tend to meet in the middle of the cavity, thus approaching more closely the axile placentation so fixed a feature of *Euphorbiaceae*. Probably a small part of *Euphorbiaceae* has been derived from the same stock as the *Flacourtiaceae*. This might be illustrated by the genus *Kiggelaria* (Fig. 150), in which the anthers open by pores as they do in a few *Euphorbiaceae*, and the indumentum is composed of stellate hairs as in *Croton*, etc. (*Euphorbiaceae*).

The type genus is *Flacourtia* (type species *F. indica* Burm. f., see Figs 151, 152), trees and shrubs, often spiny, and with dentate leaves; flowers dioecious, in short racemes or clusters; sepals 5–4, in the females very small or reduced to subdistant bracteoles; no petals; stamens numerous, sometimes surrounded by glands; anthers versatile, short; ovary 6–2-locular, ovules mostly 2 in each loculus and inserted on the dividing walls; styles numerous to 2; fruit a drupe with a hard endocarp, seeds with orbicular cotyledons.

A peculiar development within the family is the adnation of the axis of the inflorescence to the midrib of the leaf in *Phyllobotryum*, *Phylloclinium* and *Mocquerysia* (Fig. 153). This is repeated in another form in *Tiliaceae*, in the

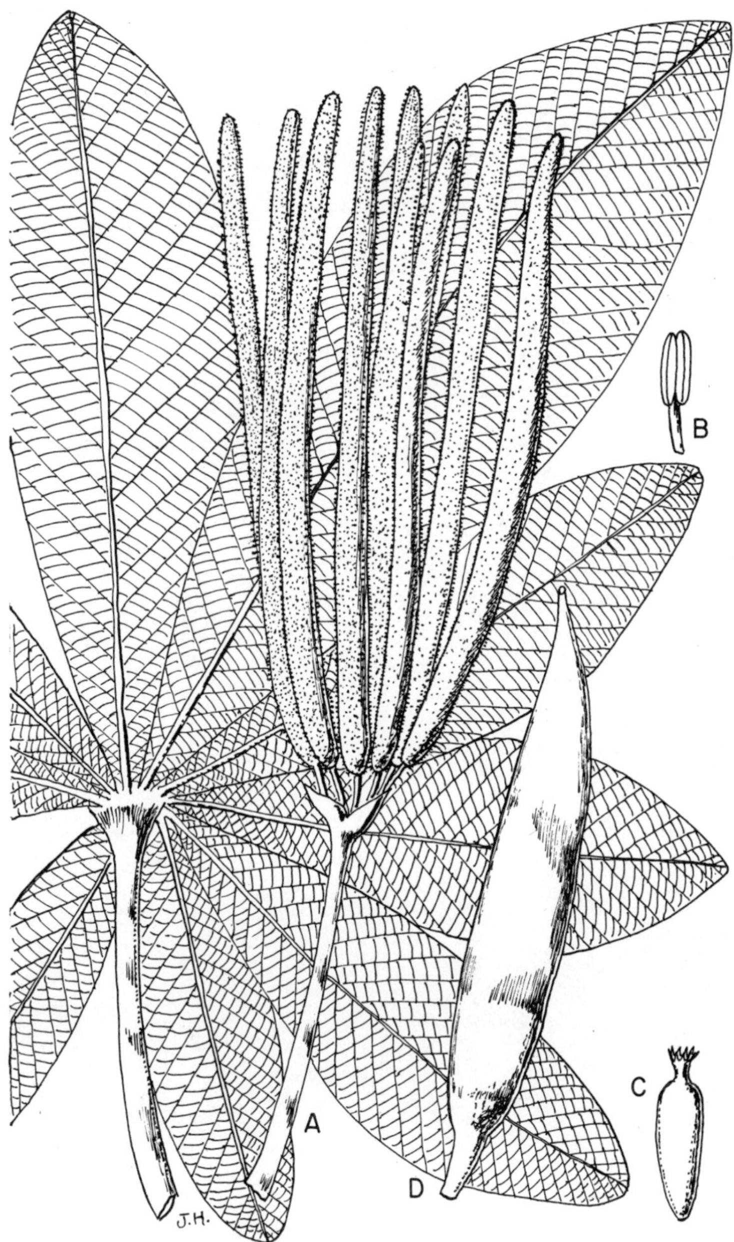

FIG. 145. *Cecropia mexicana* Hemsl. (*Moraceae*), a large tree in Central America. **A**, male inflorescence. **B**, stamen. **C**, gynoecium. **D**, fruit (adapted from drawing by W. Fitch).

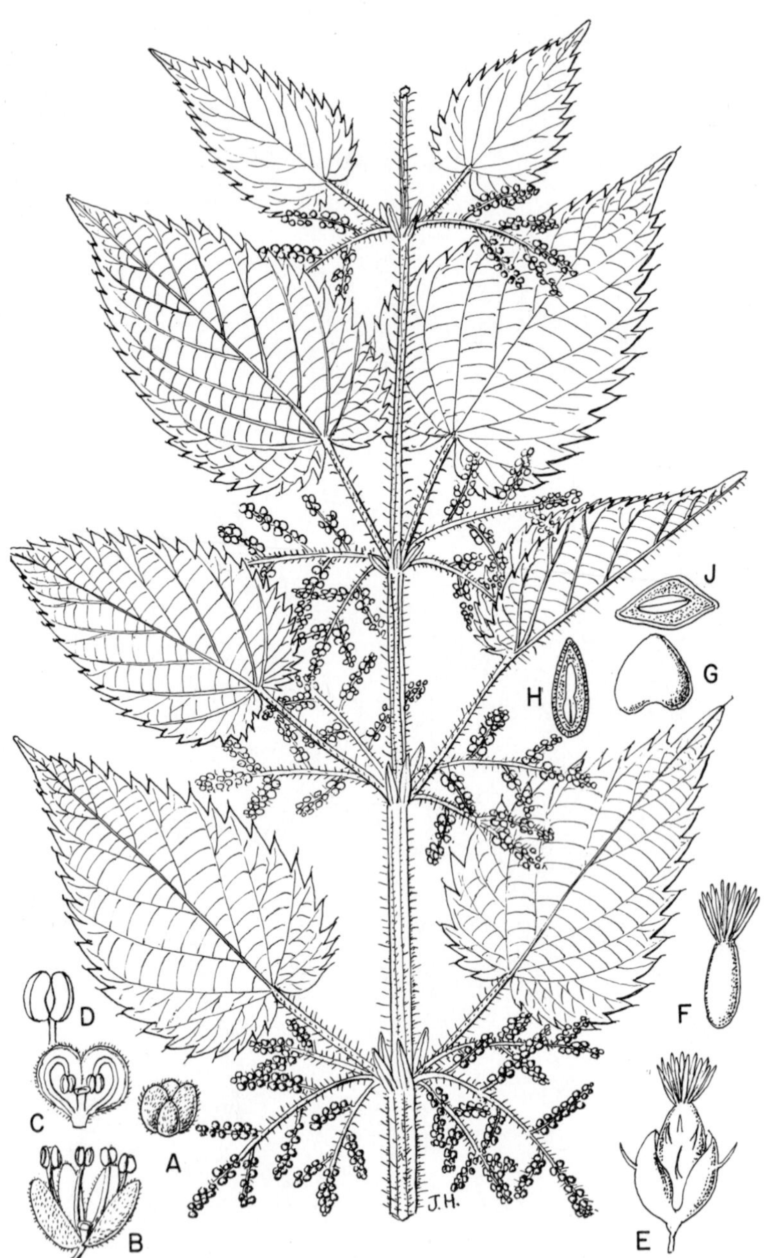

FIG. 146. The common Nettle, *Urtica dioica* Linn., is the type of the genus and family *Urticaceae*. Although it is a noxious weed, the stems have a small amount of silky fibre, and the leaves have been used for the extraction of chlorophyll. **A**, male flower-bud. **B**, male flower. **C**, vertical section of male flower. **D**, anther. **E**, female flower. **F**, ovary. **G**, seed. **H**, vertical section of same. **J**, cross-section of seed (orig.).

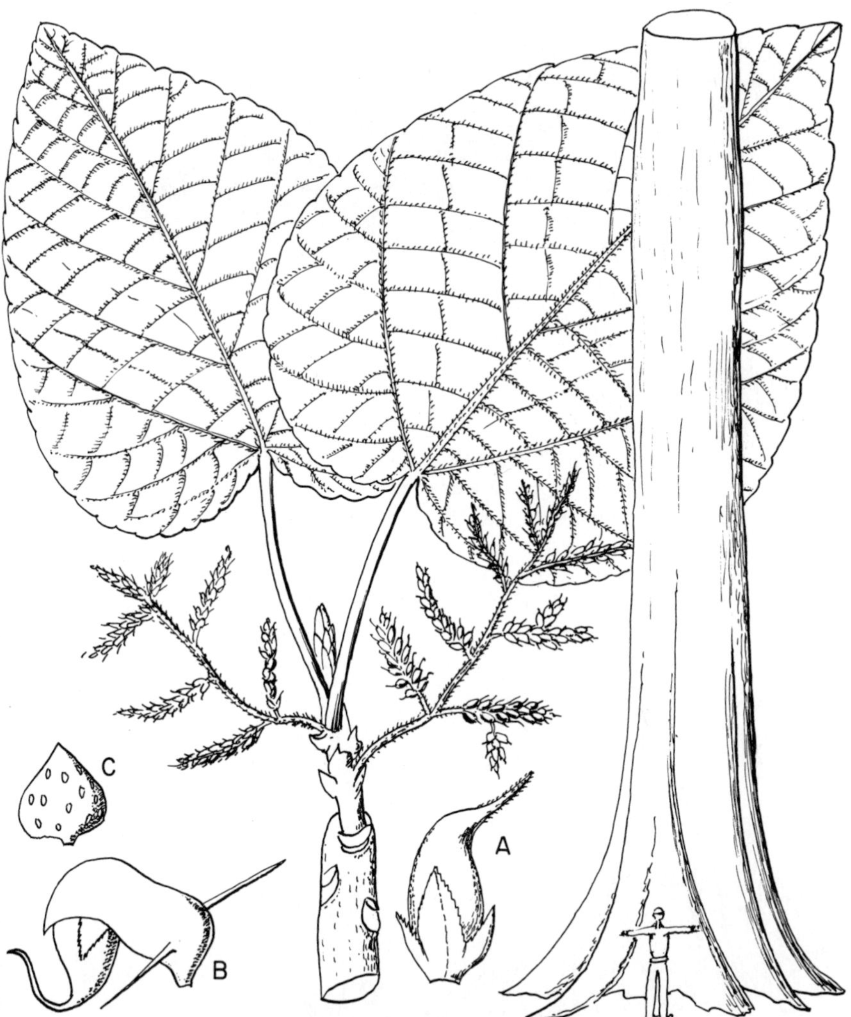

FIG. 147. The Erowa tree of Tahiti, *Laportea gigas* Wedd. (*Urticaceae*), a gigantic "Nettle", the bark used for making native fishing lines; also occurs in Australia. **A**, female flower. **B**, fruit. **C**, seed (orig.).

familiar Lime trees, though in that case the subtending leaf is considerably modified into a large bract.

It would carry me too far to go into further details of these interesting families, which I have studied very thoroughly, except that I must mention the genus *Bembicia* (Fig. 154) which has a completely inferior ovary, and the

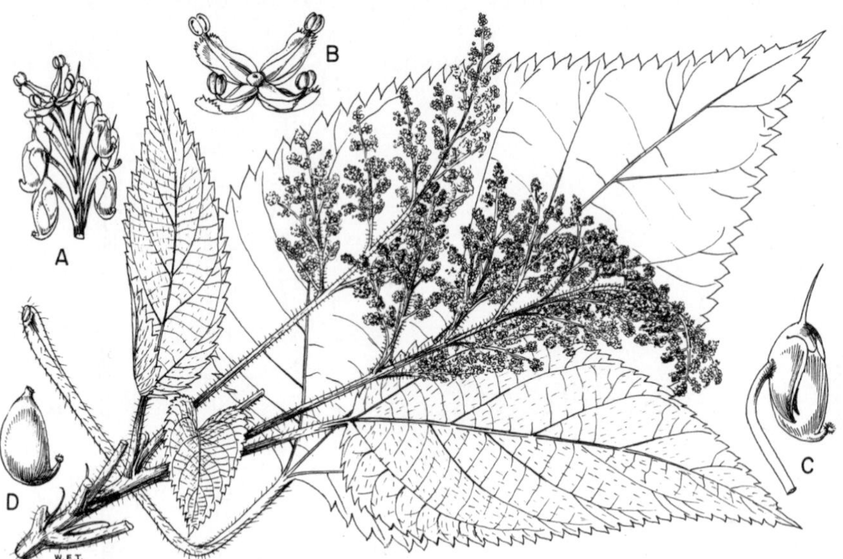

FIG. 148. *Fleurya aestuans* (Linn.) Gaudich., a fine drawing by Trevithick of a member of the Nettle family, *Urticaceae*. **A**, female and one male flower. **B**, male flower. **C**, fruit and calyx. **D**, fruit. (From Hutchinson and Dalziel, FLORA OF WEST TROPICAL AFRICA.)

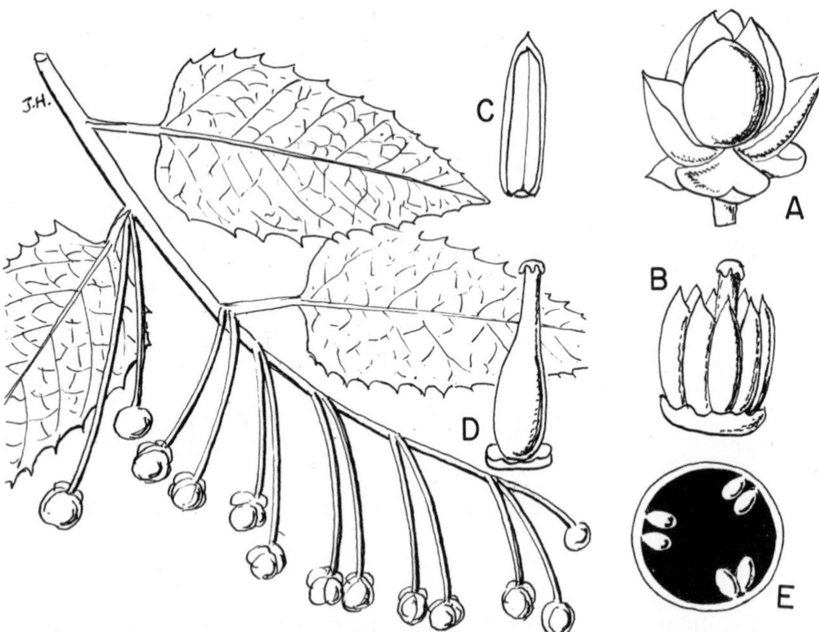

FIG. 149. This well named genus and species, *Berberidopsis corallina* Hook. f., shows a striking resemblance to *Berberis* (*Berberidaceae*), but the structure of its flowers reveals quite a different affinity, i.e. in the family *Flacourtiaceae*, with which it shares the longitudinal dehiscence of the anthers and the parietal placentation of the ovules. **A**, flower. **B**, stamens and part of the style. **C**, stamen. **D**, gynoecium. **E**, cross-section of ovary (orig.).

FIG. 150 and MAP 11. *Kiggelaria africana* Linn., a very distinct monotypic genus of the family *Flacourtiaceae*, with inset map showing the very wide range of this tree. **A**, male flowering shoot. **B**, fruiting shoot. **C**, male flower. **D**, petal of male flower showing the scale. **E**, stamen. **F**, female flower. **G**, petal of female flower. **H**, gynoecium. **J**, cross-section of ovary. **K**, seed (orig.).

FIG. 151. *Flacourtia indica* (Burm. f.) Merr. (*F. ramontchi* L'Herit.), tropics, type of the genus and family *Flacourtiaceae*; flowers unisexual. **A**, male flowering shoot. **B**, male flower. **C**, female shoot. **D**, female flower. **E**, fruits. **F**, cross-section of fruit. **G**, embryo (orig.).

flowers aggregated into short axillary cone-like heads surrounded by imbricate bracts. Finally the resemblance of certain genera to those of other families is very striking. For example *Prockiopsis* and *Buchnerodendron* are

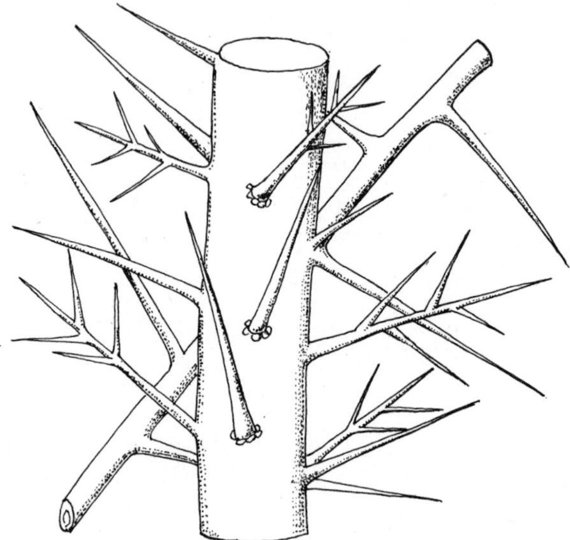

FIG. 152. Stem and branch of *Flacourtia indica* (Burm. f.) Merr. (*F. ramontchi* L'Herit.) (*Flacourtiaceae*), tropics, showing the formidable spines.

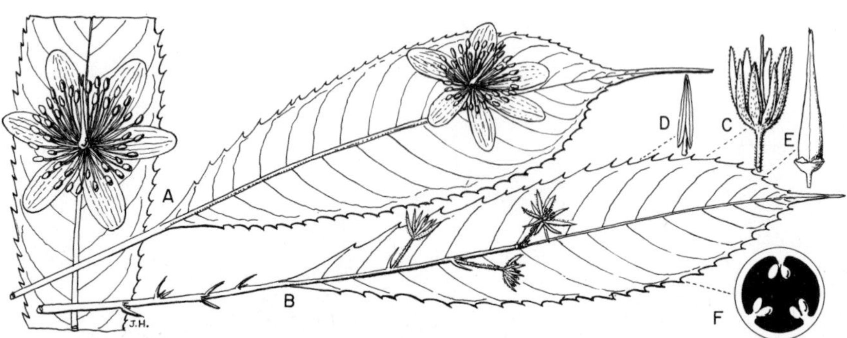

FIG. 153. The flowers of **A**, *Phylloclinium paradoxum* Baill., and **B**, *Mocquerysia multiflora* Hua (*Flacourtiaceae*), tropical Africa, are borne on the upper surface of the leaves, due to the adnation of the peduncle to the midrib. **C**, calyx, **D**, anther, **E**, gynoecium, and **F**, cross-section of ovary of *Mocquerysia* (orig.).

definitely Tiliaceous in general aspect, as are also *Ahernia* and *Zuelania*. Certain genera of tribe *Scolopieae* recall some *Rosaceae*, *Gerrardina* is like some *Celastraceae*, and catkin-like inflorescences are found in *Osmelia*, *Lunania*, *Ophiobotrys*, *Abatia*, *Aphaerema*, and *Ryparosa*.

In the small family **Cochlospermaceae** the anthers open by short apical pore-like slits, and the seeds of *Cochlospermum* are densely covered with

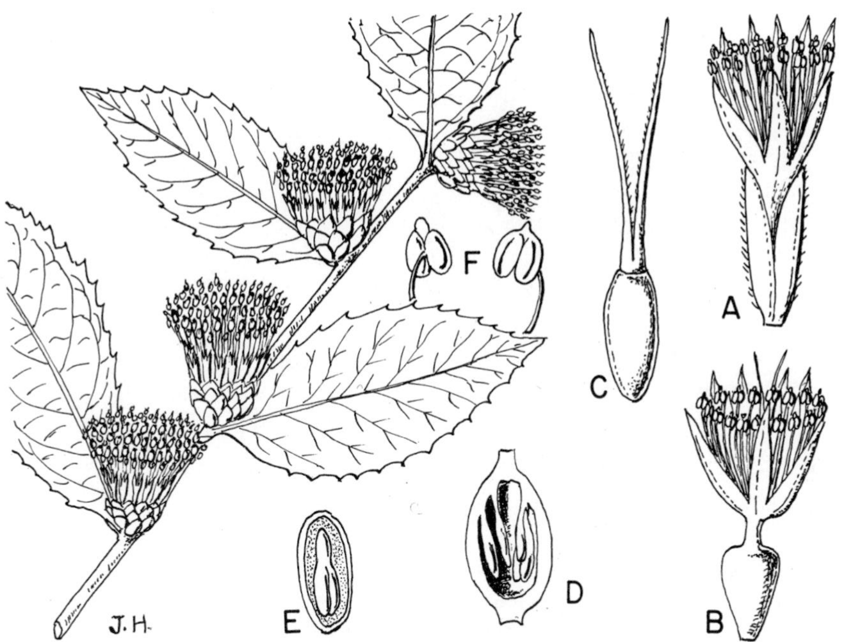

FIG. 154. *Bembicia axillaris* Oliv. (*Flacourtiaceae*); a beautiful but deceptive plant, for the seemingly solitary axillary flowers are actually inflorescences consisting of several flowers. **A** and **B**, single flowers. **C**, gynoecium. **D**, vertical section of ovary. **E**, vertical section of seed. **F**, stamens.

woolly hairs. Probably we have here a similar development to that which has become so marked a feature in some *Malvaceae*, namely the cotton genus, *Gossypium*. The digitately nerved leaves of *Cochlospermum* add to this impression. The family is confined to the tropics.

Cochlospermum, the type genus, has a 1-locular ovary, but sometimes the placentas meet in the middle or at the base or apex, and the seeds are covered with woolly hairs. In habit they vary from trees or shrubs to herbs with a tuber-like rhizome, and a coloured juice; leaves palmate or digitate; flowers showy, yellow, sepals and petals 5, numerous free stamens, anthers opening by pore-like slits at the apex; ovules numerous, capsule 5–3-valved.

The second genus, *Amoreuxia*, has a completely 3-locular ovary with axile placentas and glabrous or slightly pilose seeds.

Hoplestigmataceae, single genus *Hoplestigma*, with only two species endemic to west tropical Africa, ranging from the Cameroons south to Gabon. Pierre, who first described the genus, assigned it to the *Bixaceae* (*sensu lato*), but Gilg, when establishing the family, considered it to be related to *Sapotaceae* (FAMILIES OF FLOWERING PLANTS, 2nd Ed. **1**, 209, Fig. 78).

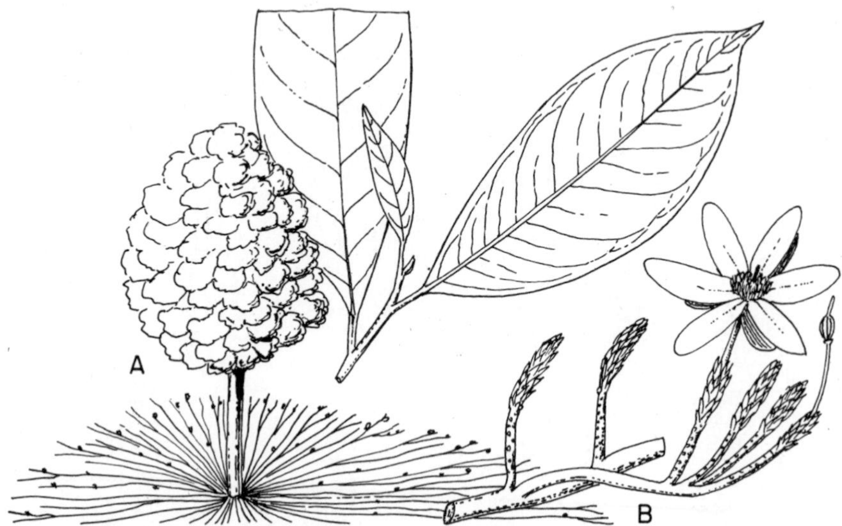

FIG. 155. **A**, showing the remarkable habit of *Caloncoba flagelliflora* (Mildbr.) Gilg ex Pellegr. (*Flacourtiaceae*), forest region of south Cameroons, west Africa; a tree 10 m high, with the flowering branches radiating from the base of the stem; **B**, flowering shoot (adapted from Engler and Prantl DIE NATÜRLICHEN PFLANZENFAMILIEN, 2nd Ed.).

The family **Achatocarpaceae** embraces two genera from Central America to temperate South America, *Achatocarpus*, with a 5-partite calyx and the pedicels furnished with bracteoles, and *Phaulothamnus*, with a 4-partite calyx or only that of the terminal flower 5-partite, and the pedicels without bracteoles. The seeds are rich in endosperm around which the embryo forms almost a complete circle (some of these characters are shown in the drawing in my FAMILIES OF FLOWERING PLANTS, 2nd Ed. **1**, 210, Fig. 79).

The small family **Lacistemataceae** was placed near *Piperaceae* by Bentham and Hooker, and I left it in the same position in my first arrangement. But German botanists found the true affinity of the family when they placed it near *Flacourtiaceae*. It agrees with that family in its unilocular ovary with 3 or 2 parietal placentas, but the stamens are reduced to 1. There are two genera, in America, *Lacistema* Swartz, with about 16 species, and *Monandrodendron* Mansfeld, one species in Colombia.

Peridiscaceae: Bentham described the sepals of *Peridiscus* as subvalvate, and made no mention of stipules, but he saw very poor specimens. Together with the peculiar apical placentation, this induced me to place the family *Peridiscaceae*, described by Kuhlman, in TILIALES "for want of a better place". Since then however, Kuhlman has shown, and also my late colleague N.Y. Sandwith, when describing a second genus, *Whittonia*, that the sepals

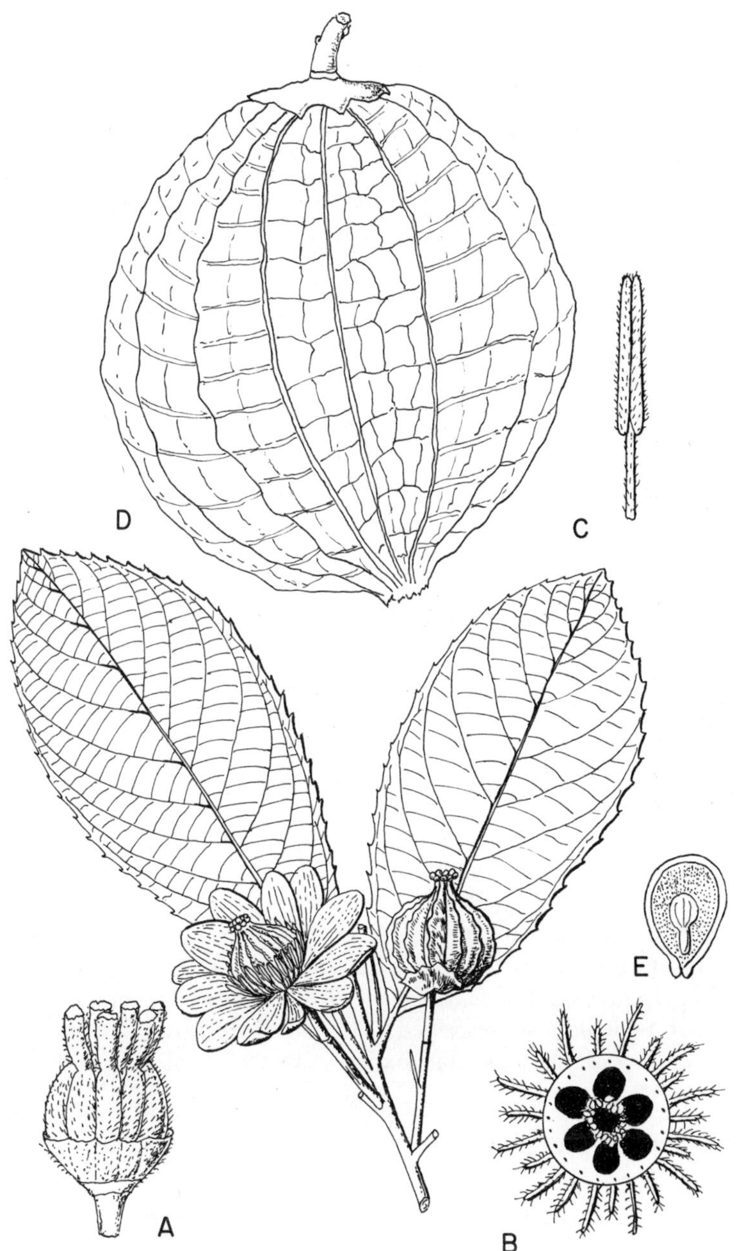

Fig. 156. *Carpotroche brasiliensis* Endl. (*Flacourtiaceae*), South America; note the general similarity to some genera of *Dilleniaceae*, considered in the present system to be the basic stock for *Flacourtiaceae*, the gap between the two families being not very wide. **A**, gynoecium and disk. **B**, cross-section of ovary. **C**, stamen. **D**, fruit. **E**, vertical section of seed (orig.).

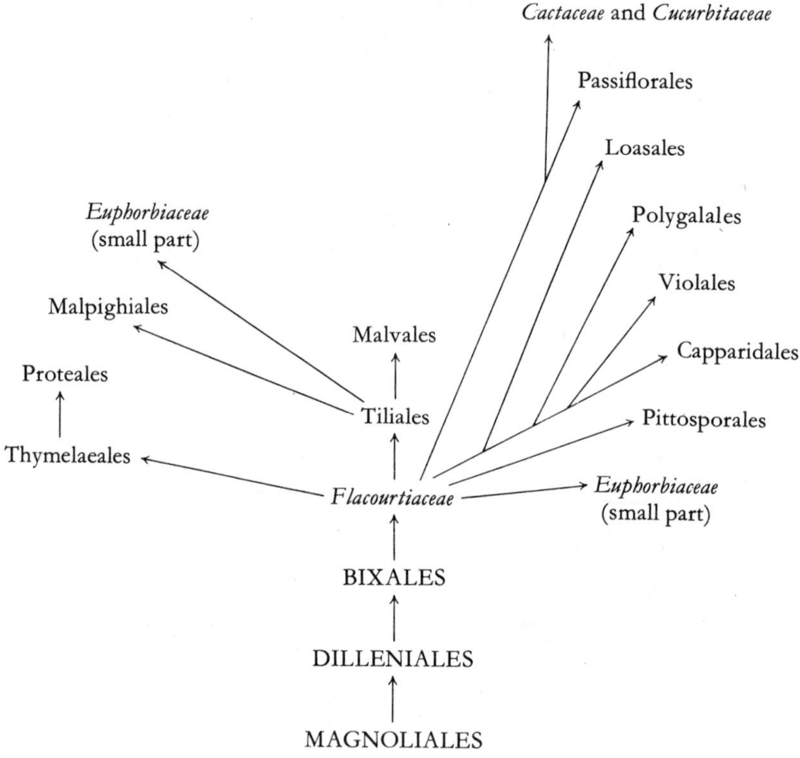

Diagram showing the probable phylogeny of the Order BIXALES (especially *Flacourtiaceae*) and further development as high as *Cactaceae* and even a small part of *Euphorbiaceae*.

are imbricate, and that the seeds have endosperm. The family is therefore perhaps nearer *Flacourtiaceae*, and differs from it especially by the free central apical placentation. I have found the anthers of both genera to be 2-locular, and not 1-locular, as described. The latter are rare outside the families *Bombacaceae* and *Malvaceae*, due in these cases to the splitting of the filaments.

ORDER 21. THYMELAEALES

(*Fam. Fl. Pl.* **1**, 212)

Families: **Gonystylaceae, Aquilariaceae, Geissolomataceae, Penaeaceae, Thymelaeaceae, Nyctaginaceae.**

Phylogeny: The rather long pedigree of this group of largely apetalous families seems to run as follows: MAGNOLIALES → DILLENIALES → BIXALES → **Gonystylaceae** → **THYMELAEALES**.

In the Order THYMELAEALES we appear to have apetalous representatives of the *Flacourtiaceae*. They mostly occur in South Africa where advanced woody or xerophytic types of many families are found, such as *Proteaceae*, *Restionaceae*, *Ericaceae*, etc. The connecting link between *Flacourtiaceae* and *Thymelaeaceae* seems to be **Gonystylaceae**, a small tropical family.

So far there are only three genera of this family known, and our knowledge of them is still far from complete. The fruit is a capsule, as in most *Flacourtiaceae* and in the related family *Aquilariaceae*. That it represents a transitional group to a more fixed and advanced type, which is clearly attained in *Thymelaeaceae*, seems obvious by the instability of the floral parts. The petals vary from many to about 8, and they are free or united in a ring; the stamens are many to 8, and the carpels vary from 8 to 2.

Wherever *Thymelaeaceae* are placed I am convinced that *Proteaceae* should follow, because they seem to be closely related. They were near each other in the Bentham and Hooker system, but in Engler and Prantl widely separated, *Proteaceae* being inserted early on near the "Amentiferae", and *Thymelaeaceae* quite high up in the system in the *Myrtiflorae*. In the first edition of my own system I put the two families near *Lythraceae*, being misled, I am rather sorry to say, by the similarity of the position of the stamens in the calyx-tube in that family and *Thymelaeaceae*. "To err is human" and there are many such examples in the history of taxonomic botany!

A more ancient family than *Thymelaeaceae* is **Aquilariaceae**,[1] mostly included as a tribe of *Thymelaeaceae*, but considered to be a separate family by R. Brown, Lindley, De Candolle, Endlicher, and others. It differs from *Thymelaeaceae* by the capsular fruit and the absence of a disk.

The variability in the number of the floral parts parallels that of *Gonystylaceae*. The calyx-tube is absent or present, petals are absent or scale-like, the stamens many to 5, the filaments free or united, disk mostly absent, and the carpels vary from as many as 12 to 2. The seeds have mostly a distinct chalaza with a funicular appendage, and endosperm may be present or absent.

There are five genera of this small family, which helps to link up the *Flacourtiaceae* with *Thymelaeaceae*, namely, *Gyrinops*, *Aquilaria* (*Gyrinopsis*), *Lethedon*, *Solmsia*, *Deltaria* and *Octolepis*.

Aquilariaceae have a wide range from tropical Africa through the eastern tropics to New Caledonia. *Aquilaria*, the type genus, embraces six species from India to China and the Malay Archipelago; trees; leaves with closely

[1] *Aquilariaceae* (R.Br.) Lindl. NAT. SYST., 2nd Ed., 196 (1836).

parallel nerves; flowers bisexual, in axillary and terminal subsessile umbels; calyx campanulate; petals scale-like, 5 in the throat, shortly connate; stamens 10; ovary perfectly or imperfectly 2-locular; capsule compressed contrary to the septum. The stamens are numerous in *Lethedon* and there are no petals in *Solmsia*, besides the flowers in the latter being dioecious.

Associated around the *Thymelaeaceae* are two small families, **Geissolomataceae**, monotypic, *Geissoloma marginatum* A. Juss., native of South Africa, which differs from the *Penaeaceae*, the other small family, by its imbricate calyx-lobes and double the number of stamens, versatile anthers, and the endospermic seeds.

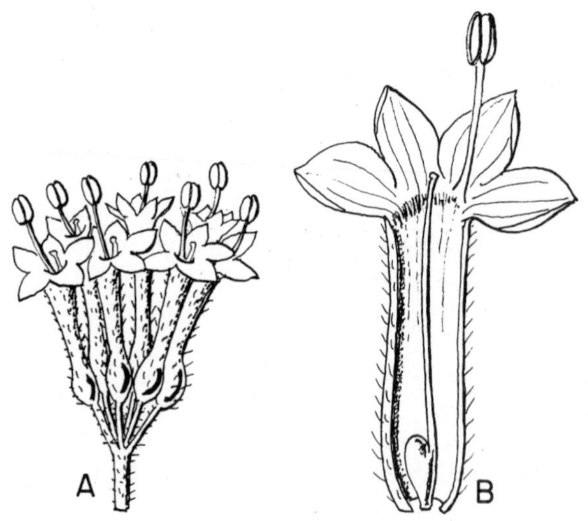

FIG. 157. The climax of evolutionary floral reduction in the family *Thymelaeaceae* is reached in the genus *Pimelea*, some species of which manage to survive and reproduce themselves with only one stamen which is admirably placed to ensure cross-pollination; this is *P. filiformis* Hook. f., Tasmania. **A**, inflorescence. **B**, flower opened out (orig.).

Penaeaceae are distinguished from *Thymelaeaceae* mainly by their more advanced aestivation (valvate), and they are also endemic in S.W. Africa. There are five genera, all small shrubs of ericoid habit, differentiated by rather trivial characters.

The more primitive genera of the family **Thymelaeaceae**[1] are found in the eastern tropics. Tribe *Phalerieae*, a very homogeneous and natural group, is mainly eastern; they have a 2-locular ovary and drupaceous fruit. A few considerably advanced genera occur in tropical America, some of which,

[1] Including *Daphnaceae* Ventenat (1799). *Phaleriaceae* Meisn. (1836–43). *Distretaceae* Dulac (1867).

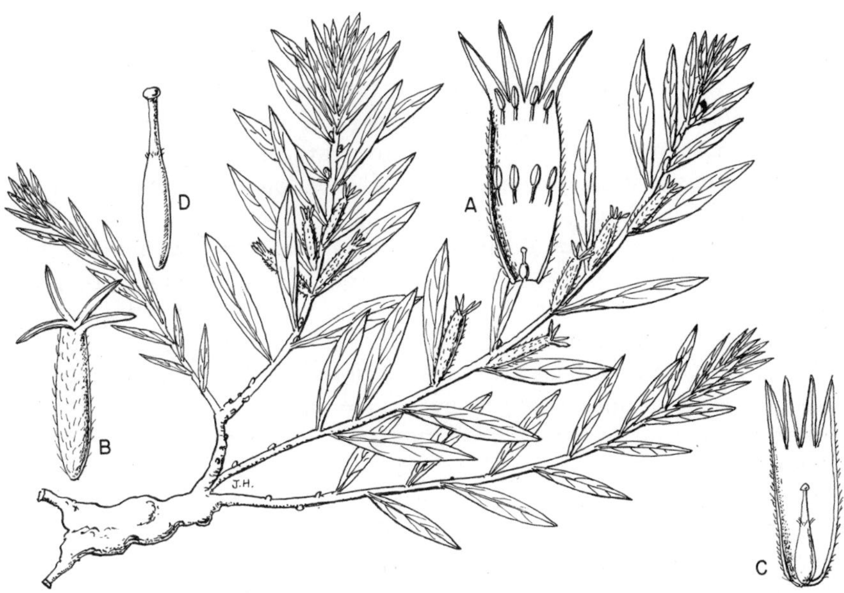

FIG. 158. *Thymelaea salamunda* All., the type species of the type genus of *Thymelaeaceae*, native of Europe. **A**, male flower, showing stamens and rudimentary ovary. **B**, female flower. **C**, female flower opened out. **D**, gynoecium (orig.).

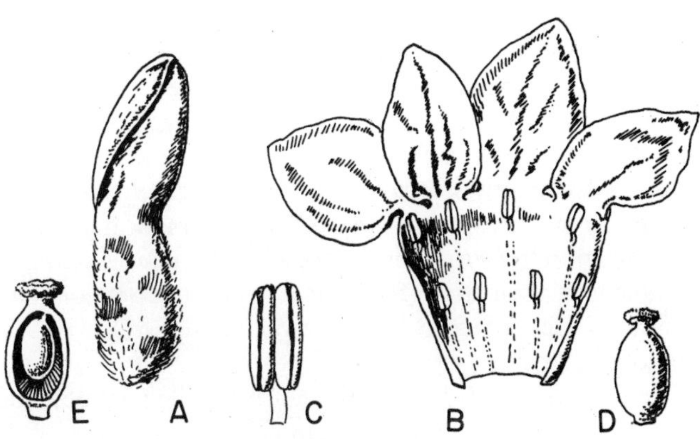

FIG. 159. *Daphne mezereum* Linn. (*Thymelaeaceae*). **A**, calyx (perianth) in bud. **B**, calyx opened out, showing the two rows of stamens. **C**, anther. **D**, gynoecium. **E**, vertical section of gynoecium (orig.).

Daphnopsis and *Lasiadenia*, have dioecious or polygamous flowers, indicating a tendency more fully carried out in the more highly evolved *Proteaceae*.

The South African members of the family are the most advanced, the flowers being mainly capitate and surrounded by an involucre of bracts, as in many South African *Proteaceae*. Some, such as *Passerina*, have become so much evolved and reduced as to have reverted to wind-pollination; on the other hand the Australian genus *Pimelea* (Fig. 157) is so reduced in its androecium as to have only 1 or 2 stamens left for it to carry on its pollination functions. Further economy would no doubt prove fatal to the existence of this genus!

The type genus is *Thymelaea* P. Mill., perennial or rarely annual herbs or shrublets with scattered leaves, the flowers are either bisexual or polygamous, small, sessile, fasciculate or solitary in the leaf-axils, and the stamens are 8 arranged in 2 series (see Fig. 158 of type species *T. salamunda* All., Europe), and the fruit is dry and enclosed by the persistent calyx or rarely the latter deciduous. A few genera are easily spotted by exceptional characters. Among these are *Dirca* with a truncate indistinct calyx-limb, and *Stephanodaphne* in which the petals are connate into a fimbriate annulus.

It is not easy to give a very clear word-picture of the next family, **Nyctaginaceae**,[1] which is mainly tropical. Familiar examples in greenhouses and subtropical gardens, such as in Madeira, the West Indies and other tropical countries, are *Bougainvillea* and *Mirabilis*. The latter is not only the "Marvel of Peru", but is also a puzzle to the novice; for how is he to know that the apparent calyx is not a calyx, but is an involucre of bracts, and that the apparent corolla is not a corolla, but a calyx? More experienced botanists know this because the calyx-like structure of *Mirabilis multiflora* A. Gray contains several flowers which proves the calyx-like structure of other species of the genus to be an involucre.

It is noteworthy that in many genera with a reduced or absent part of the flower another part takes on the function of the reduced or absent member. Thus the calyx of *Mirabilis* (Fig. 160) has become more attractive and coloured and looks exactly like a corolla, whilst the involucre of bracts exactly simulates a calyx, a very wonderful transformation indeed! We find a similar phenomenon in *Hepatica* in *Ranunculaceae*. In *Bougainvillea* however, there is a double transformation, for the calyx, though petaloid, is not very attractive, and its lack of colour is compensated for by the large and brilliantly coloured bracts.

The type genus is *Mirabilis* Linn. (*Nyctago* Juss., illeg. name). Herbs with elongated or tuberous roots; leaves opposite; involucres of bracts in branched often dense cymes; flowers showy, the involucre calyx-like, 1–many-flowered, 5-lobed, lobes plicate; calyx-tube elongated, limb expanded, 5-lobed, lobes plicate; stamens 6 or 5, exserted, filaments connate at the base into a fleshy cup; anthers didymous; ovary ellipsoid or ovoid;

---

[1] *Allioniaceae* Horaninow (1834). *Bougainvilleaceae* J. G. Agardh (1858). *Pisoniaceae* J. G. Agardh (1858). *Mirabilidaceae* W. R. B. Oliver (1936).

FIG. 160. One of the most deceptive of flowering plants, *Mirabilis jalapa* Linn. (*Nyctaginaceae*), tropical America, in which the involucre of partly united bracts greatly resembles a calyx, and the petaloid tubular calyx is indistinguishable from a sympetalous corolla. *M. jalapa* is the type species of the type genus of the family (orig.).

style filiform, exserted, stigma capitellate; anthocarp ribbed; nut obovoid; seed-testa adherent to the pericarp; embryo hooked, cotyledons folded around the mealy endosperm.

Here are some genera and species with rather outstanding characters. Tall tree with thick trunk in *Andradaea*. Roots tuberous in *Collignonia*; spiny shrub, *Tricycla*; lateral shoots spine-tipped in *Phaeoptilum*; leaves anisophyllous in *Okenia* and *Neea* spp.; indumentum stellate in *Leucaster* and *Ramisia* (Fig. 163); with a nude gland at the apex in *Reichenbachia*. Cauliflorous in *Neea* spp.; flowers dioecious in *Cephalotomandra*; unisexual in *Phaeoptilum* and *Neea*; bracts petaloid in *Bougainvillea* and *Collignonia*; pedicels much elongated in fruit and penetrating the soil in *Okenia* (Fig. 161), filiform in *Boerhaavia elegans* Choisy; calyx (anthocarp) with numerous hooked hairs in *Boldoa*; sticky with stipitate glands in *Boerhaavia*, *Pisonia* spp. (Fig. 162) and *Pisoniella*; broadly winged in *Phaeoptilum*, *Ammocodon*, *Selinocarpus*, *Abronia* spp., *Tripterocalyx* and *Collignonia* spp.

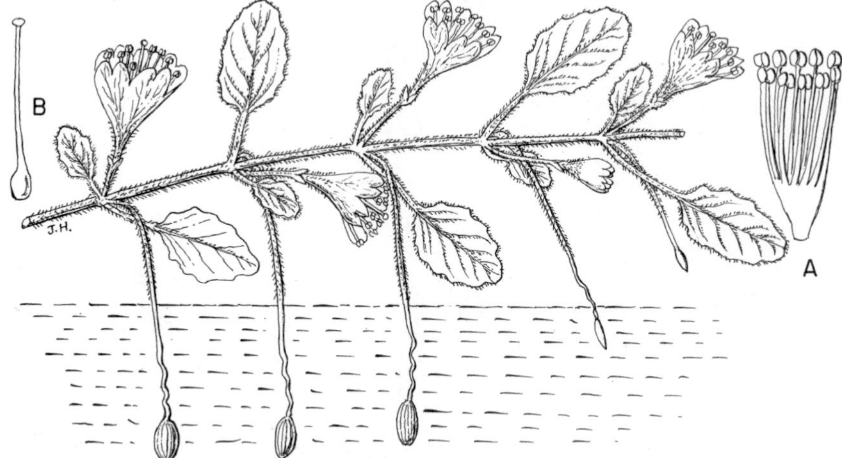

FIG. 161. *Okenia hypogaea* Cham. & Schlecht. (*Nyctaginaceae*); grows in sand along the beach in Florida and buries its fruits in the ground, the peduncles elongating up to a depth of 11 in. **A**, stamens. **B**, gynoecium (orig.).

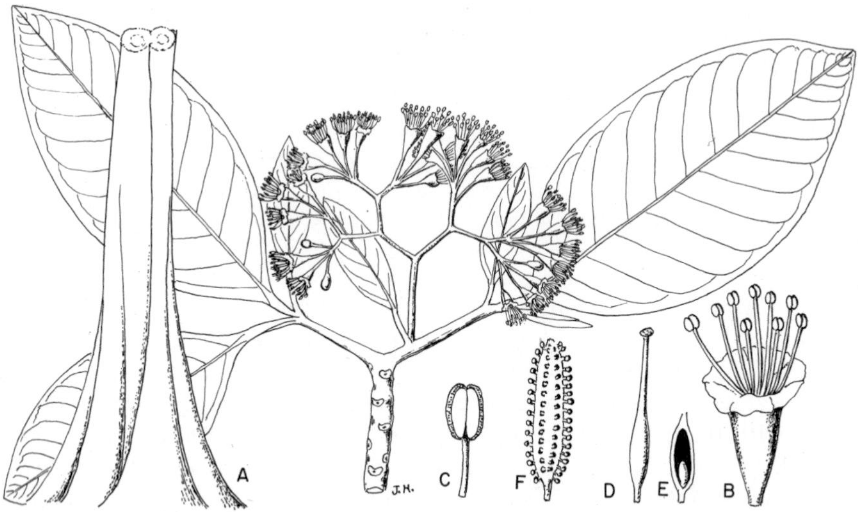

FIG. 162. *Pisonia grandis* R.Br. (*Nyctaginaceae*), widely distributed by far-ranging sea birds on account of the fruit being sticky and adhering to the feathers (orig.). **A**, showing the base of the tree. **B**, flower. **C**, stamen. **D**, gynoecium. **E**, vertical section of ovary. **F**, fruit (orig.).

The genus *Okenia* (3–4 spp.) is especially interesting on account of its geocarpic fruits. In *O. hypogaea* Cham. & Schlecht. (Fig. 161) the peduncle elongates up to as much as 11 in. and digs deep into the sand after which the

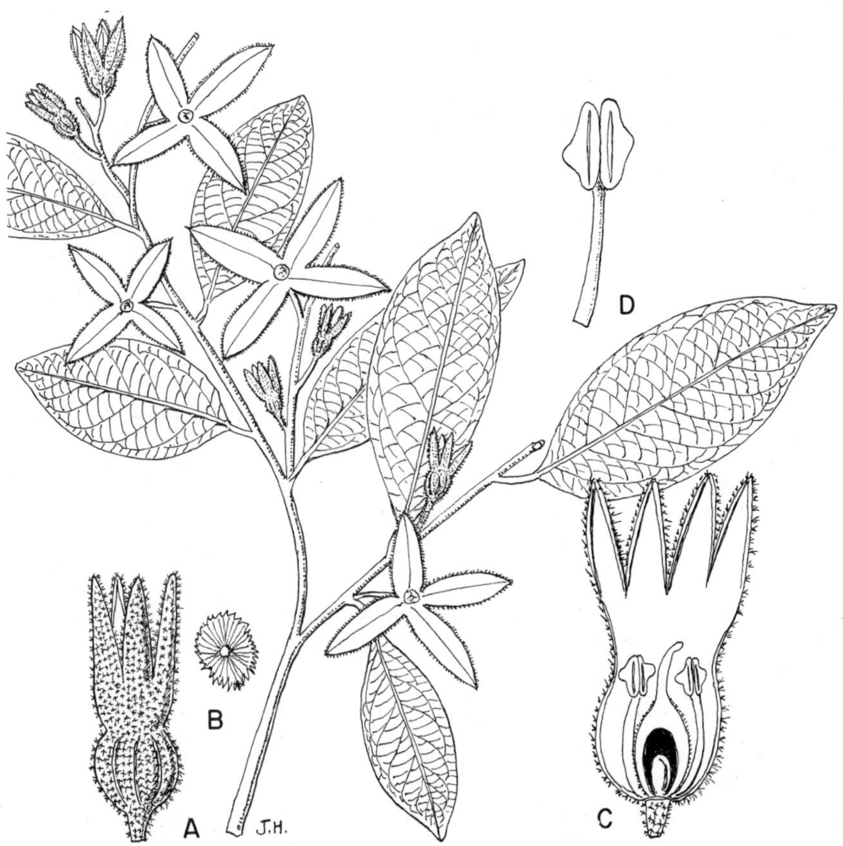

Fig. 163. *Ramisia brasiliensis* Oliv. (*Nyctaginaceae*), in which the calyx enlarges in fruit and spreads out. **A**, calyx. **B**, stellate hairs from the same. **C**, vertical section of the flower. **D**, stamen (orig.).

fruit matures. The species occurs in maritime sands from Florida through Mexico to Central America. "Although the plant appears to be a perennial, it is really an annual and when its season is past and the leaves have disappeared, there remains a tangled mat of brown branches and branchlets in place of the former beautiful ground cover of green leaves. . . . A young plant arises from each fruit as a tuft of leaves with a large deep rose-purple or nearly blue flower. Branches arise from the tuft of leaves, often a dozen or sometimes more" (J. K. Small in ADDISONIA **4**, t. 126 (1919)). Whether the flowers which produce the fruits are cleistogamous, I am unable to say. In addition the plant is markedly anisophyllous, alternate leaves in each pair being larger and smaller.

Commenting on the origin of generic names, Linnaeus in his CRITICA BOTANICA said of the genus *Pisonia* (see Fig. 162): "*Pisonia* is a tree of sinister

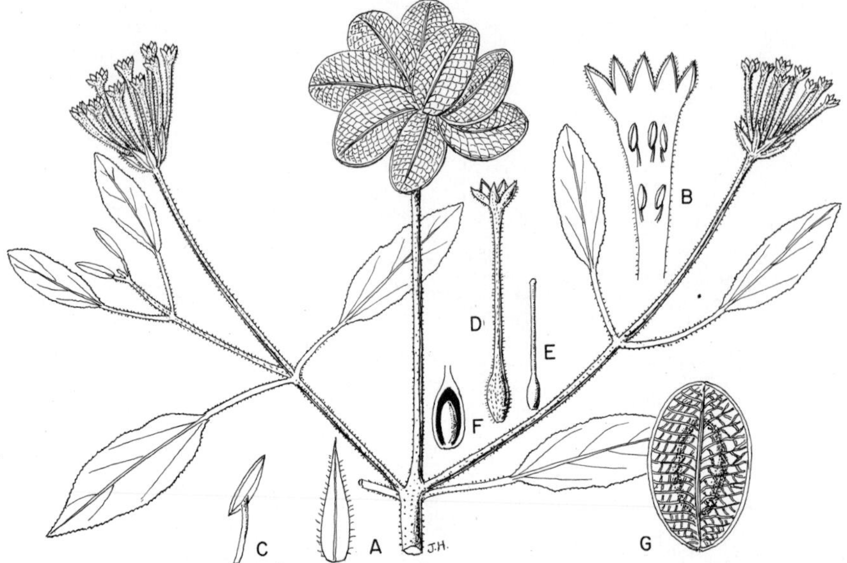

FIG. 164. *Tripterocalyx cyclopterus* (A. Gray) Standley (*Nyctaginaceae*), Mexico and southern United States; plant in flower and fruit at the same time; the base of the calyx-tube persists and forms three wings to the fruit. **A**, bract of involucre. **B**, calyx opened out. **C**, stamen. **D**, flower. **E**, gynoecium. **F**, vertical section of ovary. **G**, one wing of fruit (orig.).

appearance for its thorns—from a tradition about Piso which is assuredly sinister, if that is true which a relative of Marcgraf charges against him, namely that he obtained all his knowledge from Marcgraf after the latter's death and so forth" (translation from Hort).

ORDER 22. **PROTEALES**

(*Fam. Fl. Pl.* **1**, 217)

The family **Proteaceae**[1] is of very considerable interest both from a phylogenetic and phytogeographical standpoint. It is concentrated mainly in southern Africa and in Australia. In its inflorescence it often mimics both *Asteraceae* (*Compositae*) and *Pinaceae*, in *Protea* and *Leucadendron* respectively, whilst the superficial resemblance of its fruits with those of some *Fabaceae* (*Papilionaceae*) has even caused some authors to suggest an affinity with the

[1] Including *Lepidocarpaceae* C. H. Schultz (1830).

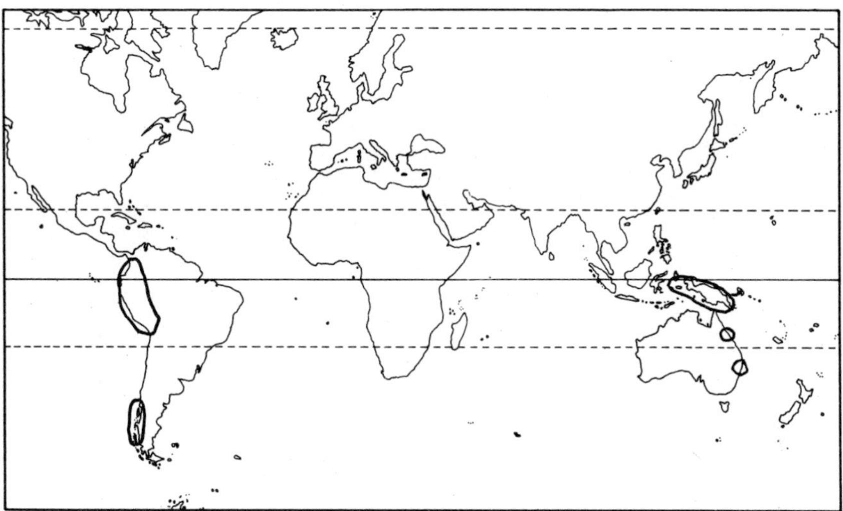

MAP 12. Remarkable discontinuous range of the small natural genus *Embothrium* (*Proteaceae*).

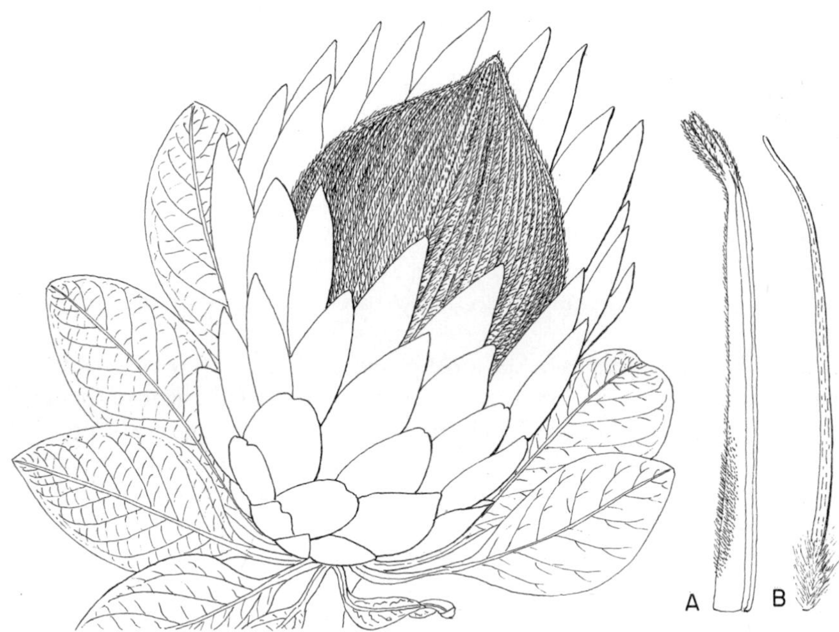

FIG. 165. *Protea cynaroides* (Linn.) Thunb., the lectotype species of the type genus of *Proteaceae* (South Africa). **A**, flower, **B**, gynoecium.

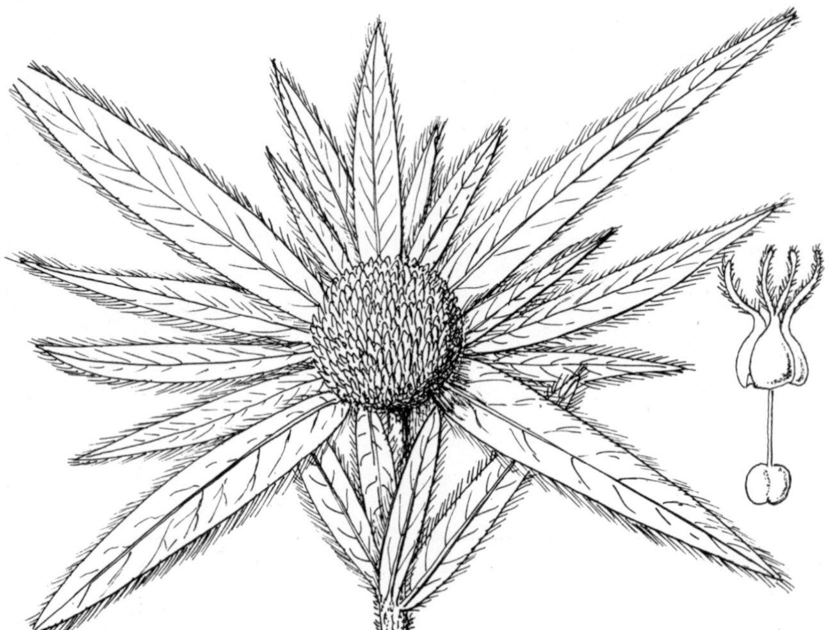

FIG. 166. Leaves and male flower-head of the Silver tree, *Leucadendron argenteum* Linn. (*Proteaceae*), a very rare tree with attractive foliage found only on the Cape Peninsula, South Africa; note the dry perianth forming a parachute with the fruit hanging by the tip of the persistent style (orig.).

last mentioned family. A comparison of the floral structure of these two groups shows the impossibility of any such relationship.

Structurally the Australian representatives are the most ancient. Most of them have dehiscent follicular fruits, and the inflorescences, on the whole, are not so specialised as those found in South Africa. And it is noteworthy, also, that no genus is common to the two areas, which suggests long isolation.

The *Grevilleeae* seem to be the most primitive Australian tribe, with often racemose exinvolucrate inflorescences such as are characteristic of the large genera *Grevilleea* and *Hakea*. They are large trees. Tribe *Banksieae* is perhaps the most advanced in Australia, with densely capitate or spicate inflorescences often surrounded by an involucre of bracts and sometimes even strobiliform. A very similar development is observable in South Africa, the genera *Protea* (Fig. 165) and *Leucadendron* (Fig. 166) being almost replicas of these types, and *Aulax*, like *Leucadendron*, has dioecious flowers in cone-like inflorescences. It should be noted that in *Aulax* the female inflorescence is of a much more advanced type than that of the male, just as it is in *Uapaca* (*Euphorbiaceae*) (see p. 275).

Proteaceae form a considerable proportion of the vegetation in the S.W. region of South Africa, with a few outliers along the higher plateaux and mountains northwards to Ethiopia in the east, and to Upper Guinea in the west.

ORDER 23. PITTOSPORALES

(*Fam. Fl. Pl.* **1**, 219)

Families: **Pittosporaceae, Byblidaceae, Stegnospermataceae, Vivianiaceae, Tremandraceae.**

The Order PITTOSPORALES seems to be most closely related to and derived from DILLENIALES. Their seeds retain abundant endosperm with a minute embryo, and the placentation of the ovules remains mostly parietal, which, as shown in the family *Annonaceae* (p. 15), is sometimes associated with the first stage of syncarpy.

The largest family is **Pittosporaceae.** I cannot trace any direct relationship of this family with *Escalloniaceae*, near which they are placed in the Engler and Prantl system. It is true there is superficial resemblance between the most primitive genus *Pittosporum* and some *Escalloniaceae*, but other genera of the family such as *Marianthus*, *Billardiera*, *Sollya* and *Cheiranthera* show no similarity.

Pittosporaceae are most abundant in Australasia, eight of the nine genera being endemic in that part of the world. They are absent from the American continent. The type genus, *Pittosporum* (type species R. *tenuifolium* Banks & Soland., New Zealand), consists of small trees and shrubs, and some are of decorative value for their foliage; leaves very often evergreen, sometimes subverticillate at the tops of the branches; flowers terminal, axillary or lateral; sepals free to connate at the base, rarely calyx spathaceous (as shown in Fig. 169); petals connivent or coherent up to or beyond the middle; anthers opening by slits lengthwise; ovary imperfectly or subperfectly 5–2-locular, with the ovules on the walls or intruded placentas; capsule thick; seeds erect, not winged.

Pittosporum is the most widely distributed genus, with about 140 species, a remarkable outlier, *P. coriaceum* Ait. (Fig. 170), occurring in the island of Madeira at 2400–4000 ft altitude, and in a single locality in Tenerife (Canary Islands). The nearest related species, as might be expected, are found in tropical Africa. Most of the species of *Pittosporum* are strikingly restricted in distribution, many of the Malayan being confined to single islands. In

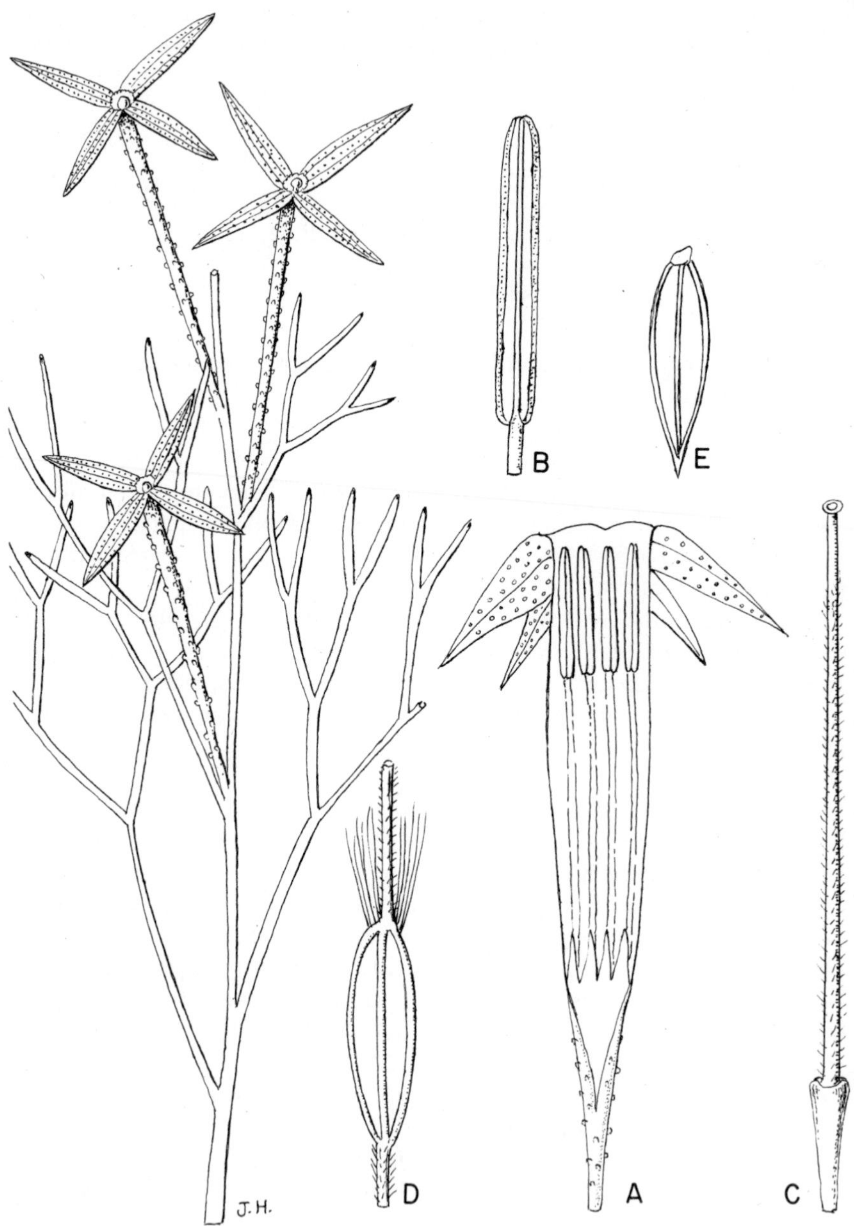

FIG. 167. *Franklandia fucifolia* R. Br. (*Proteaceae*), Australia. **A**, flower opened out. **B**, anther. **C**, gynoecium. **D**, fruit. **E**, seed (orig.).

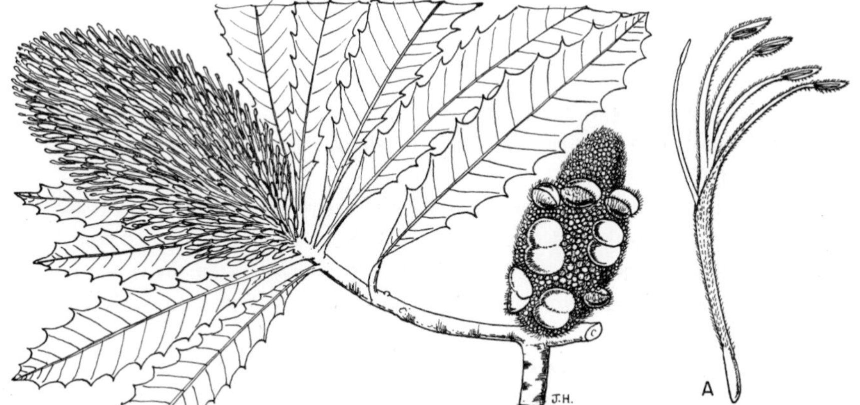

FIG. 168. *Banksia dentata* Linn. f. (*Proteaceae*), the type of the genus named after Sir Joseph Banks, President of the Royal Society for very many years and botanist on Captain Cook's first voyage around the world. **A**, flower (orig.). The shoots often bear both flowers and fruits at the same time.

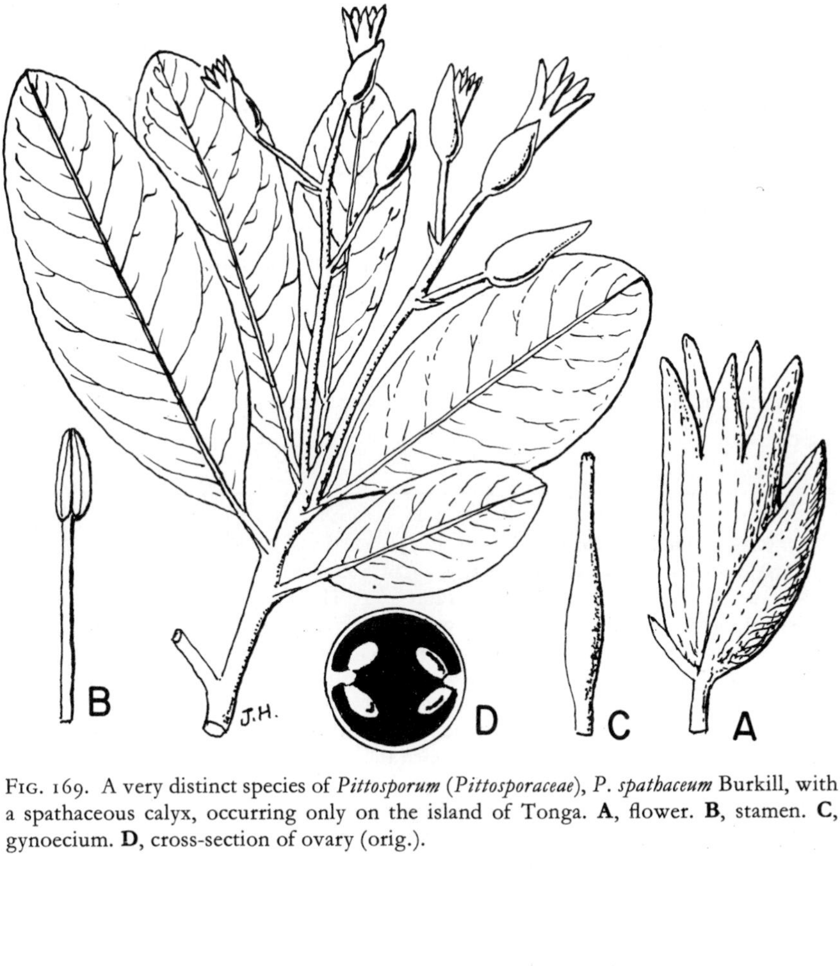

FIG. 169. A very distinct species of *Pittosporum* (*Pittosporaceae*), *P. spathaceum* Burkill, with a spathaceous calyx, occurring only on the island of Tonga. **A**, flower. **B**, stamen. **C**, gynoecium. **D**, cross-section of ovary (orig.).

New Caledonia, the home of numerous other endemics, there are no less than about 30 endemic species, and this is probably a record for one genus in a single island of comparatively small dimensions. A very distinct species, *P. spathaceum* Burkhill (Fig. 169) is endemic in the remote island of Tonga, in the Pacific.

As in many families there are two main types of fruits; in the more primitive tribe *Pittosporeae* it is a capsule, and they are mostly erect trees and shrubs; whilst in the more advanced tribe *Billardiereae* the fruit is a berry, and they are mainly twiners or rarely spiny shrubs. In *Sollya* the anthers open by terminal pores.

Byblidaceae[1] (*Roridulaceae* Engl. & Gilg. (1924)) were formerly classed with *Droseraceae*, and that renowned botanist, Engler, even placed them as a subfamily of *Lentibulariaceae*, a position which today seems little short of a taxonomic absurdity. However, Domin eventually pointed out their affinity with *Pittosporaceae*, and they are also near *Tremandraceae*. Melchior, in the latest edition of Engler's SYLLABUS, has put them, as we have them, next to *Pittosporaceae*.

The dense covering of gland-tipped hairs no doubt formerly gave the impression of *Droseraceae*, but that is only superficial, especially since Marloth[2] demonstrated that *Byblidaceae* are not really insectivorous. The anthers of *Byblidaceae* open by terminal pores, a character already developed in *Pittosporaceae* (*Sollya*). There are only two genera, *Roridula* (2 spp.) in South Africa, and *Byblis* (2 spp.) in Australia.

In the latest (12th) edition of the SYLLABUS of the Engler and Prantl system, I was surprised to find *Byblis* and *Roridula* maintained as separate families. Here is how they were "separated":

Antheren mit kurzen apikalen Spalten oder Poren. Karp. (2). Gestielte Drüsenhaare *Byblidaceae*

Antheren mit apikalen Poren. Karp. (3). Langgestielte Drüsenhaare *Roridulaceae*

---

[1] *Byblidaceae* Domin, ACT. BOT. BOHEM. **1**, 3 (1922).

[2] Marloth FLORA OF SOUTH AFRICA **2**, **1**, 29, pl. 10 (1925).

Marloth states about *Roridula dentata* Linn. . . . "The plants do not digest the insects, which, by incidentally coming into contact with the leaves, persist on the bushes, but while no advantage accrues from them to the plant, they are used as food by a spider of the genus *Synaema* (crab-spiders). This spider has become adapted to a life on the *Roridula* by being immune against the viscid nature of the secretion of the glands, and thus able to run about freely over leaves and glands without the slightest hindrance. The spiders generally hide between the dry leaves or in their nests which they build between the dead leaves, but as soon as the vibration of a twig betrays the presence of an insect, the spider pounces upon and kills it. At the Tulbagh locality we have not observed any other kind of spider on the *Roridula*, but on the plants in the Cedar Mts a large green spider is also to be seen."

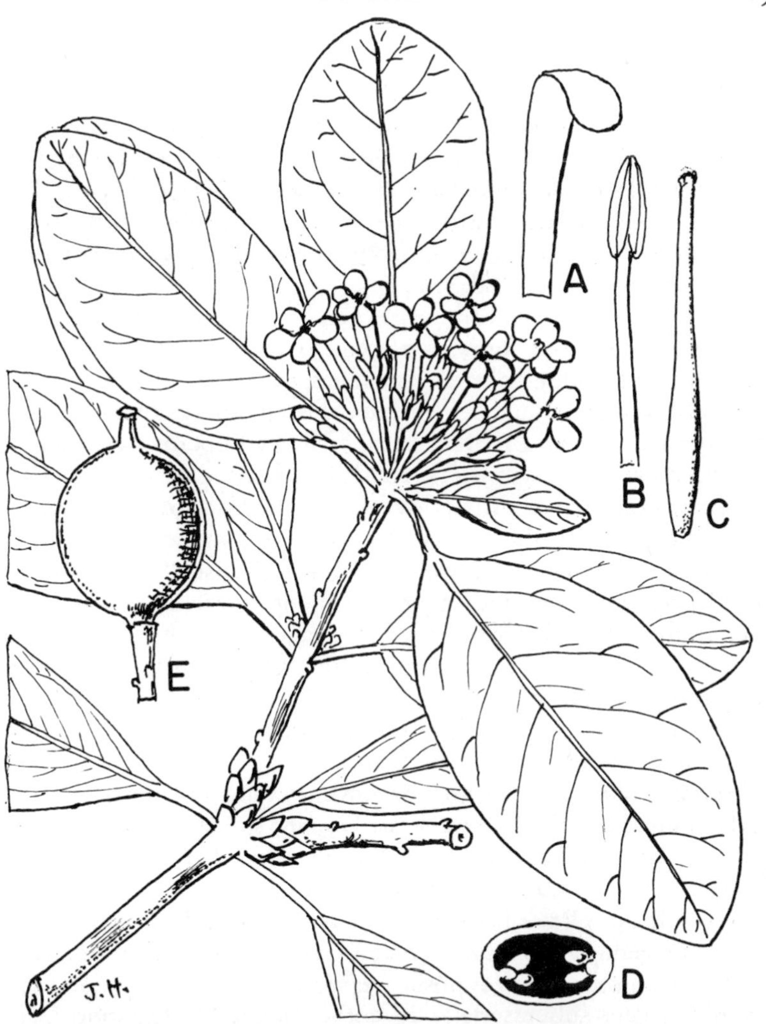

Fig. 170. Another species of *Pittosporum* (*Pittosporaceae*), *P. coriaceum* Ait., endemic in Madeira and Tenerife. **A**, petal. **B**, stamen. **C**, gynoecium. **D**, section of ovary. **E**, fruit (orig.).

One may well ask what is the difference other than generic? One with stalked glandular hairs, the other with long-stalked glandular hairs?

In my FAMILIES I distinguished the two genera as follows:

Ovary 3-locular; ovules 2 or 1, pendulous; shrublets; anthers opening by terminal pores; leaves short and crowded on short lateral branchlets; South Africa *Roridula*

Ovary 2-locular; ovules numerous, axile; herbs; anthers opening by pore-like slits; leaves elongated; Australia *Byblis*

The generically monotypic family **Stegnospermataceae** was established by Nakai (J. JAP. BOT. **18**, 108 (1942)) for the genus *Stegnosperma* Benth., two or three species in Mexico, Central America and the West Indies. It was formerly placed in *Phytolaccaceae*, but is probably more closely related to *Pittosporaceae* or even *Tamaricaceae*. Distinguishing features are the 1-locular ovary with a central column, basal erect ovules, 5-valved capsule, the seeds partly covered by a large fleshy white aril, and the embryo bent around the mealy endosperm (for figure showing these details see my FAMILIES OF FLOWERING PLANTS, 2nd Ed. **1**, 222).

Vivianiaceae consists of a single genus, *Viviania*, about 30 species in Chile and south Brazil, formerly placed in *Geraniaceae*, has opposite simple leaves but no stipules, valvate calyx-lobes and free contorted petals, 3- or 2-locular ovary, and ovules 2 in each loculus superposed on the inner angle; embryo much curved or circinate in fleshy endosperm (see figure in my FAMILIES OF FLOWERING PLANTS, 2nd Ed. **1**, 223).

Tremandraceae are a fairly advanced group, as shown by their valvate sepals and petals. In this respect they occupy a higher plane than *Pittosporaceae*, and an associated advanced feature is the usually opposite or verticillate leaves, whilst the anthers open at the apex by a single pore, which is also a feature of *Byblis* (*Byblidaceae*). The family is confined entirely to the continent of Australia, and mainly in the western district. *Spartium*-like growth-forms occur in *Tetratheca*, *T. aphylla* F. Muell., *T. efoliata* F. Muell., *T. nuda* Lindl., etc., whilst the branches are broadly winged in *T. affinis* Endl., var. *platycaula*, in western Australia.

The leaves of many species have a tendency to roll their margins; they are bristle-pointed in *Platytheca juniperina* Domin; stomata are present only on the lower side, the guard-cells being surrounded by several irregularly arranged epidermal cells; the hairy covering consists of three forms of hairs, simple unicellular hairs, stellate hairs and glandular hairs.

The type genus, *Tremandra*, contains only 2 species; shrubs more or less stellate-tomentose; leaves opposite; sepals 5, valvate; petals 5, induplicate-valvate; stamens subuniseriate, the anthers jointed to the short filaments, 2-locular and opening by a 2-valved apical pore; disk conspicuous, 5-lobulate; style entire; ovules paired in each loculus; seeds strophiolate.

As noted by Chodat, the east Australian and Tasmanian *Tremandraceae* have mostly tetramerous flowers and short anther-loculi, whilst the west Australian have usually pentamerous flowers and long anther-loculi. Perhaps these characters hark back as far as *Dilleniaceae* where a similar difference in the stamens is found.

ORDER 24. CAPPARIDALES

(*Fam. Fl. Pl.* **1**, 224 (partly))

Families: **Capparidaceae, Moringaceae.**

Phylogeny: MAGNOLIALES → DILLENIALES → BIXALES → *Flacourtiaceae* → **Capparidales.**

Since I published the second edition of my FAMILIES OF FLOWERING PLANTS in 1959, I have made a more intensive study of the family **Capparidaceae** as understood at that time, and I came to the conclusion that, morphologically at any rate, it consists of two distinct groups which are not really phylogenetically related.

The true Capparids, with *Capparis* as its generic type (see Fig. 172), are woody plants and have indehiscent fruits without a replum, and are closely related to *Flacourtiaceae* (BIXALES), whilst the subfamily *Cleomoideae*, type genus *Cleome*, are related to *Brassicaceae* (*Cruciferae*), all being herbs with dehiscent fruits provided with a replum, just as in many Crucifers. So in my latest work THE GENERA OF FLOWERING PLANTS, Vol. 2, 303 (1967), I have limited the family *Capparidaceae* to tribes *Cappareae*, *Cadabeae* and *Apophylleae*.

In connection with the above it may be recalled as a matter of interest (not criticism!) that a great German botanist described *Cleomodendron*, believing it to be *Capparidaceae*, but which proved to be *Farsetia somalensis* Engl. in *Brassicaceae* (*Cruciferae*). Again *Dipterygium* Decne., originally placed in *Capparidaceae*, also eventually found a better home in *Brassicaceae*; and furthermore *Stephaninia* Chiov. proved to be a *Reseda* (*Resedaceae*). These examples go to show that even the most celebrated of systematists sometimes mistake superficial resemblance for actual relationship (see note about the present author, p. 158, and also under *Campanulaceae*).

A few outstanding genera or species may be mentioned. *Apophyllum*, Australia, are *Spartium*-like leafless shrubs. There are long shoots and short shoots in *Atamisquea*, Mexico to Argentina. The 1-foliolate leaflets of *Steriphoma peruviana* Spruce, Peru, are peltate at the base. Inflorescence adnate to the branchlet and appearing as comb-like outgrowths in *Capparis multiflora* Hook. f., India, and to a lesser extent in *C. viminea* Hook. f. & Thoms., Sikkim to Burma, in *C. disticha* Kurz, Burma, and *C. pyrifolia* Lamk, Indo-China. The flowers are borne on the old wood in *Bachmannia*, South Africa; dioecious in *Apophyllum*, Australia. Petals connate and reduced to 2 in *Emblingia*, west Australia. Stamens dimorphic, the fertile ones irregularly inserted at the top of the long androgynophore, the sterile ones in a bundle

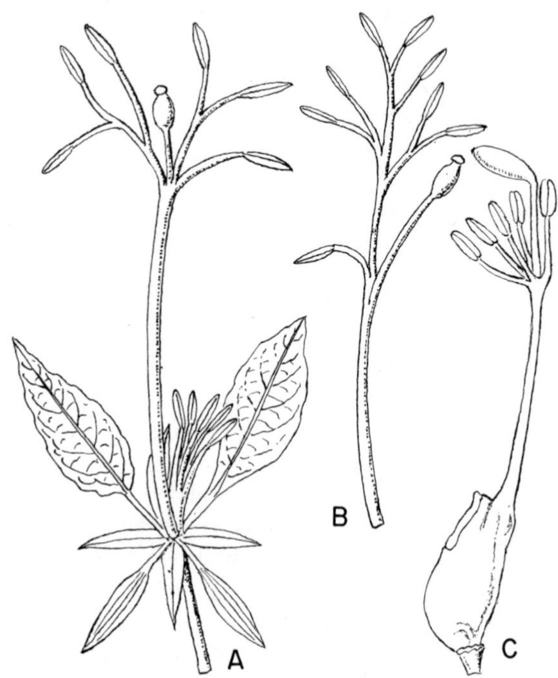

FIG. 171. A unique development of an androgynophore is present in *Cladostemon paradoxus* A.Br. & Vatke; note the different position of the gynoecium in separate flowers, one terminal, **A**, the other lateral, **B** (after Engler). **C**, androecium and gynoecium of *Cadaba termitaria* N.E.Br., tropical East Africa, showing the large nectary at the base of the androgynophore.

FIG. 172. *Capparis spinosa* Linn., type species of the type genus of *Capparidaceae*. **A**, anther. **B**, cross-section of ovary. **C**, fruit. **D**, seed. **E**, vertical section of seed (orig.).

at its base in *Cladostemon*, Africa (Fig. 171). Fruits transversely locellate in *Maerua* spp., tropics of the Old World.

Capers are the pickled flower-buds of the Caper Bush, *Capparis spinosa* Linn. (Fig. 172), a spiny shrub in the Mediterranean region, and are an important commercial product, especially in south Europe.

The family is named from *Capparis* (type sp. *C. spinosa* Linn., Mediterranean region) (see Fig. 172), with about 350 species distributed in the tropics and warm temperate regions; trees and shrubs, sometimes armed with spiny stipules; leaves simple, rarely completely reduced; flowers often bracteate; sepals 2-seriate, free or rarely connate and irregularly split, sometimes with a ligule inside, imbricate; petals usually 4, imbricate; stamens mostly numerous, free; ovary 4–1-locular, with 7–2 placentas; ovules numerous; stigma sessile; fruit a stipitate berry, sometimes elongated, embryo convolute in thin endosperm.

Moringaceae,[1] single genus *Moringa* Adans., includes about 12 species in the tropics of the Old World, and cultivated elsewhere. The Horse-radish tree is *M. oleifera* Lam. (*M. pterygosperma* Gaertn.), the presence of myrosin giving the roots the flavour of horse-radish; fruit edible, and the seeds yield an oil used for lubricating delicate machinery. This family is difficult to place in any system. According to Erdtman, the pollen grains similar to those of *Moringa* occur in several families such as *Capparidaceae* and *Resedaceae*, but certainly there is no relationship with the latter family.

Order 25. **TAMARICALES**

(*Fam. Fl. Pl.* **1**, 227)

Families: **Frankeniaceae, Tamaricaceae, Fouquieriaceae.**

TAMARICALES have not a very long evolutionary history, as follows: MAGNOLIALES → DILLENIALES → BIXALES → **TAMARICALES.**

Frankeniaceae is a small family of shrublets adapted to a special maritime habitat, with small opposite ericoid leaves. Their petals have, like some *Flacourtiaceae*, a scale-like appendage on their inner face. They are more advanced in their calyx, which is tubular, with induplicate-valvate lobes.

[1] Including *Hyperantheraceae* Link (1831).

Frankenia (lectotype *F. laevis* Linn.) embraces about 70 species of low shrublets of ericoid habit; leaves opposite, very small; flowers often rose-coloured, bisexual; calyx 5–4-lobed, lobes induplicate-valvate; petals 5–4, imbricate, clawed, the claw with an adnate scale within; stamens 6–4, alternate with the petals; ovary with 5–3 parietal placentas; stigmas 3–2; capsule 1-locular, 3-angled.

There are four other genera, *Hypericopsis*, one species in south Persia, with numerous stamens; *Beatsonia*, a shrub with rounded fleshy leaves endemic in St. Helena; *Anthobryum*, five species at high altitudes in western South America, the claws of the petals connivent; and *Niederleinia*, also only one species, *N. juniperoides* Hieron., endemic in Patagonia, differing from the others by its dioecious or polygamo-monoecious flowers and fruits with 1-seeded placentas. The family occurs mainly on maritime shores, and is especially abundant around the Mediterranean and the Atlantic seaboard. There is also a considerable concentration of endemic species in west and S.W. Australia.

Tamaricaceae[1] is an especially interesting family to students because of its suggested affinity with *Salicaceae*, as in the Engler system. It is perhaps understandable, but nevertheless surprising that superficial resemblances have sometimes been mistaken for real relationship. These two families are examples of such, though there is really very little in common between them except that in some *Tamaricaceae* (*Tamarix* and *Myricaria*) there are slender catkin-like inflorescences, and seeds with a turf of hairs at the apex. But there the resemblance between the two families ends. For in *Tamaricaceae* we have a bisexual flower with a normal calyx of imbricate sepals and the same number of free petals. In *Salix*, however, the flowers are unisexual, dioecious, and arranged in real catkins, i.e. inflorescences in which the bracts take the place of the very much reduced or absent calyx, whilst there are no petals. There is no resemblance whatever in the vegetative parts. Bentham and Hooker[2] said in regard to the supposed affinity between these two families: "Affinitas ab auctoribus nonnullis laudata cum *Salice* nobis omnino effugit. Semina enim comosa sunt in generibus numerosis nullo alio vinculo junctis."

Tamaricaceae are of little economic importance, but owing to their partiality for sandy soil they are extensively grown in temperate and warmer regions as wind breaks and hedges, especially near the sea.

The type genus of this family is *Tamarix*; about 80 species ranging from western Europe to N.E. China, and in Africa; shrubs, sometimes small trees; leaves minute and scale-like; flowers spicate or densely racemose, sometimes the spikes in panicles; sepals 5–4, rarely 6, free; petals free or

---

[1] Including *Reaumuriaceae* Ehrenberg (1827). *Comaceae* Dulac (1867).

[2] GENERA PLANTARUM I, 100 (1862).

FIG. 173. *Crateva tapia* Linn. (*Capparidaceae*), tropical South America (adapted from Martius FLORA BRAS.). **A**, leaves and fruit. **B**, flower. **C**, sepal. **D**, petal. **E**, anther. **F**, the same after opening. **G**, gynophore and ovary. **H**, ovary and stigma. **J**, cross-section of ovary. **K**, seed. **L**, vertical section of seed.

slightly connate, below the disk; styles 4–3, rarely 5 or 2; placentas very short at the base of the ovary, many-ovuled; seeds produced at the apex into a coma of hairs, the axis of the coma setiform and plumose with long hairs; no endosperm.

Myricaria shares the seed characters of *Tamarix*, but has monadelphous stamens, whilst the remaining two genera, *Reaumuria* and *Hololachne*, have seeds long-pilose all over and they have endosperm.

The family **Fouquieriaceae** consists of two genera in Mexico and the southern United States of America. *Fouquieria* was named after Pierre Ed. Fouquier, at one time professor of medicine in Paris; shrubs or trees with branched stems and red flowers, and *Idria*, a stout columnar tree and normally undivided stem, and yellow flowers. The family was formerly included in the *Tamaricaceae*, and even placed in the *Metachlamydeae* (*Gamopetalae*), but there is no good reason on account of their anatomy for amalgamating them with *Tamaricaceae* (according to Metcalfe and Chalk ANAT. DICOT. 1, 59).

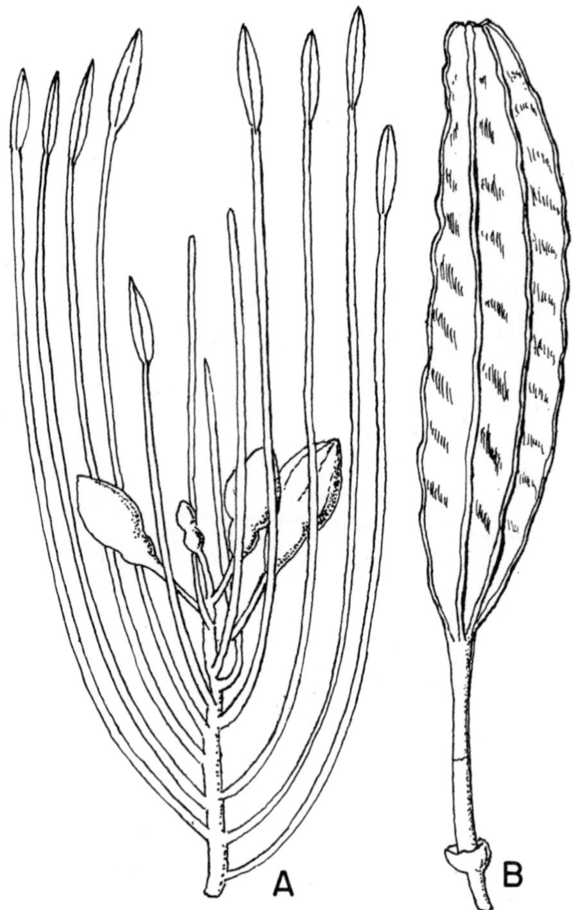

FIG. 174. A very distinctive genus of *Capparidaceae*, *Thylachium paradoxum* Gilg; note the remarkable long petioles and reduced leaf-blades; tropical Africa. **A**, leaves and flower-buds. **B**, fruit. (After Engler.)

ORDER 26. VIOLALES

(*Fam. Fl. Pl.* **1**, 230)

Family: **Violaceae.**

Violaceae[1] seems to be a climax family, the more primitive members of which are woody and the more advanced have become herbaceous, accom-

[1] Including *Leoniaceae* A. de Candolle (1844). *Alsodeiaceae* J. G. Agardh (1858). *Retrosepalaceae* Dulac (1867).

panied by zygomorphy of the flowers, so well shown in the large genus *Viola*. Its ancestral line of descent may have been as follows: MAGNOLIALES → DILLENIALES → BIXALES (*Flacourtiaceae*) → **VIOLALES.**

The two orders VIOLALES and POLYGALALES have mostly zygomorphic ("irregular") flowers. *Violaceae* are rather distantly related to *Flacourtiaceae*, although the produced connective of the anthers characteristic of most members of the family is not evident in *Flacourtiaceae*.

FIG. 175. *Corynostylis arborea* (Linn.) S. F. Blake (*Violaceae*), Mexico to Brazil and Peru, also St. Vincent Island, West Indies; described by a collector as a magnificent vine growing on banks by creeks and rivers in open places; flowers white, pollinated by humming birds. **A**, stamens. **B**, cross-section of ovary. **C**, fruit. **D**, seed (orig.).

The more primitive members of **Violaceae** have actinomorphic ("regular") flowers and are woody (*Rinorea*, etc.), whilst the more advanced, such as the familiar genus *Viola* and also *Hybanthus*, have zygomorphic ("irregular") flowers. The greatest development of species occurs in *Viola*, and the majority of them are herbaceous. It seems clear that in this case there are herbs which have been derived from shrubs or trees. If that

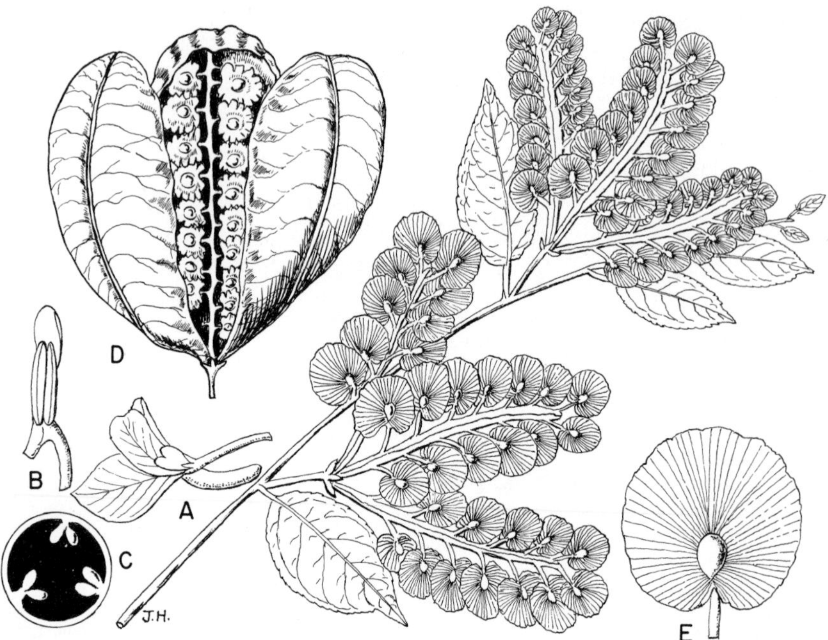

Fig. 176. Fruiting shoot of *Anchietia salutaris* A. St. Hil., var. *hilariana* (*Violaceae*), Brazil. **A**, flower. **B**, stamen. **C**, cross-section of ovary. **D**, fruit. **E**, seed. Note that the valves of the fruit fall away and the three placentas grow out and enlarge, bearing the winged seeds (orig.).

be so, then the proper place for *Violaceae* in this system is amongst the predominantly arboreal group, LIGNOSAE. *Violaceae* show both primitive and advanced characters in a very marked degree. Their seeds are usually provided with abundant endosperm and with a straight embryo (primitive), whilst often both the calyx and corolla are remarkably zygomorphic, the abaxial petal being saccate or spurred. This feature is more especially developed in certain tropical South American climbers, whose flowers with their long spurs more resemble Balsams than Violets. These are *Corynostylis* (Fig. 175), *Noisettia*, *Anchietia* (Fig. 176), and *Schweiggeria*. According to Solereder there seems little to specially mark the family anatomically, and only a few possess medicinal properties. Bentham and Hooker's tribe *Sauvagesieae* is now referred to *Ochnaceae*.

Viola, the type genus (type species *V. odorata* Linn.), has probably about 300 species, several of them being endemic in the Atlantic Islands (Madeira and the Canaries); a number of species are common to N.E. Asia and North America, there are some shrubby species in the Pacific Islands, and some remarkable examples (see Fig. 177) in the Andes of South America; leaves alternate; stipules persistent, often foliaceous and divided; many species

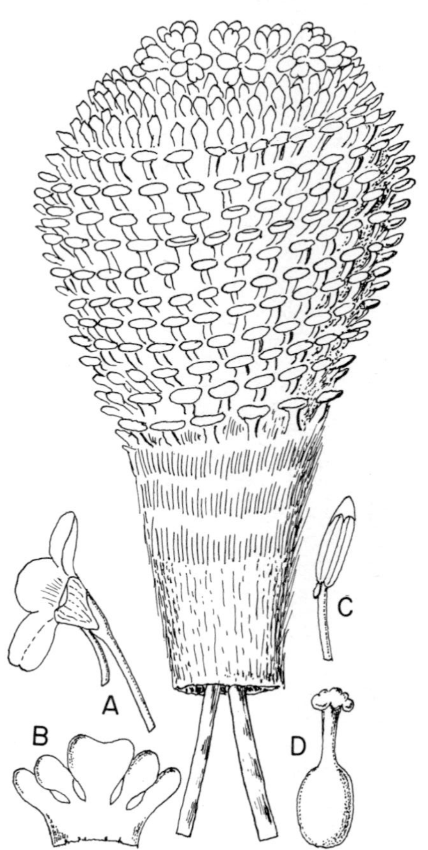

FIG. 177. A violet with a remarkable habit, *Viola coronifera* W. Becker (*Violaceae*), Andes of Argentina, 840–2250 m. **A**, flower. **B**, corolla laid open. **C**, stamen. **D**, gynoecium.

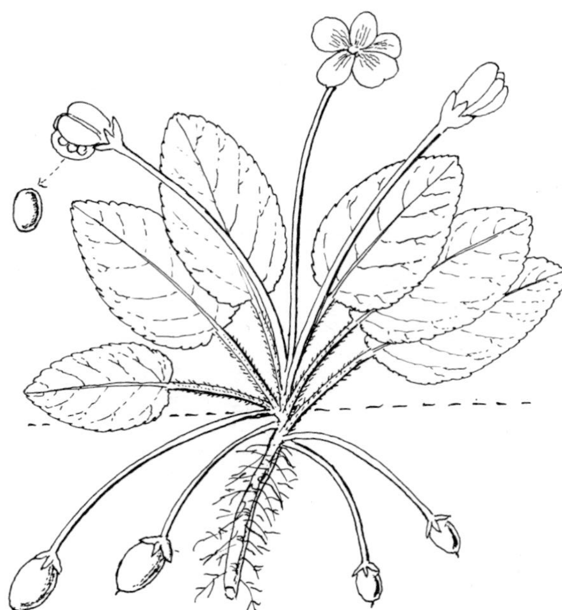

FIG. 178. *Viola hirta* Linn. (*Violaceae*), Europe and north Asia, buries some of its fruits in the soil.

have dimorphic flowers; petals often unequal, lower often larger and spurred or saccate at the base; connective produced at the apex into a membrane; lower 2 stamens often spurred; capsule elastically 3-valved; seeds ovoid-globose.

Here are a few of the outstanding characters of genera or species which diverge more or less from the type genus: Roots tuberous in *Viola arborescens* Linn.; spiny shrubs: *Hybanthus havanensis* Jacq. (Cuba), and *Hymenanthera dentata* R.Br. (Australia, New Zealand); climbers: *Corynostylis, Anchietia, Agatea*. Leaves opposite in some *Hybanthus* (*Ionidium*) and *Rinorea* (*Alsodeia*) spp.; oak-like in New Caledonia spp. of *Rinorea* (*Alsodeia*), closely pellucid-punctate in *Leonia*. Corolla usually very zygomorphic in Tribe *Violeae*; lower petal much larger and longer-clawed in *Hybanthus* (*Ionidium*). Lower two or four stamens with long basal appendages within the spurred petal in *Corynostylis*, *Noisettia*, *Anchietia*, *Schweiggeria*, *Viola* spp., and *Hybanthus* (*Ionidium*) spp. Flowers dioecious in *Melicytus*, *Hymenanthera* spp., subspicate in *Paypayrola*; borne on the main trunk in *Leonia glycycarpa* Ruiz & Pavon and *Allexis cauliflora* Pierre. Fruits penetrating the soil in *Viola hirta* Linn. (Fig. 178); bladder-like and opening early in *Anchietia*; opening very early and exposing the unripe seeds in *Decorsella*; capsule woody in *Agatea*; densely echinate in *Rinorea echinocarpa* Burkill (Malay Peninsula); fruit a berry in *Melicytus*, *Hymenanthera*, *Leonia* and *Gloispermum*. Seeds winged in *Anchietia* and *Agatea*, compressed and finely mottled in *Corynostylis*; arillate in *Allexis*. Endosperm scanty in *Corynostylis* and *Allexis*.

ORDER 27. **POLYGALALES**

(*Fam. Fl. Pl.* **1**, 231)

Families: **Polygalaceae, Krameriaceae, Trigoniaceae, Vochysiaceae.**

Path of evolution of the Order POLYGALALES: MAGNOLIALES → DILLENIALES → BIXALES → **POLYGALALES**, ending with the small climax family *Vochysiaceae*.

Of the Order POLYGALALES, the family **Polygalaceae**[1] is the most interesting to the student, because of the general resemblance of *Polygala* to some members of the *Fabaceae* (*Papilionaceae*). Indeed many beginners will recollect having actually at first mistaken a *Polygala* for a papilionaceous plant. But the resemblance, such as it is, is due to parallelism, for the ovary of

[1] Including *Moutabeaceae* Endlich. (1841). *Disantheraceae* Dulac (1867). *Xanthophyllaceae* Gagnep. (1909).

Polygala is formed by the union of 2 carpels, whilst that of *Fabaceae* is composed of only 1 carpel. The stamens connate into a sheath split on the upper side are liable to complete the downfall of the novice in his diagnosis. In the more advanced members of this family there is also a kind of unilateral sympetaly, as in some *Fabaceae*. The tropical genera are mainly trees and shrubs.

Polygala, the type genus (type species *P. vulgaris* Linn., Europe and north Asia), is very large and consists of shrubs, shrublets and herbs; flowers in racemes or spikes, sometimes crowded into heads, rarely paniculate; sepals unequal, the inner 2 petaloid and wing-like; petals 3, united into a sympetalous corolla split above; upper petals absent or very minute; stamens 8, united into a sheath split above and adnate at the base to the petals; anthers 2–1-locular, usually opening by a transverse slit; ovary 2-locular; style dilated at the apex; capsule often membranous, compressed, obovate to orbicular, emarginate or didymous, dehiscing at the margins into the loculi; seeds pilose or glabrous.

The genera which diverge most from this type genus are, especially, *Securidaca*, with samaroid fruits (Fig. 179, **C**) resembling those of some *Malpighiaceae*, while the fruits in a few other genera are drupaceous, such as those of *Monnina*, *Atroxima*, *Carpolobia*, *Nylandtia* and *Xanthophyllum*, etc.

The most primitive and large genus *Xanthophyllum* is almost wholly tropical and confined to eastern Asia; they are trees and shrubs with more or less free stamens and with a 1-locular ovary with parietal placentas, the latter character probably retained from its flacourtiaceous ancestry. In the most advanced genera belonging to the tribe *Moutabeae* the calyx is united with the petals into a tube.

The genus *Krameria*, **Krameriaceae**, was formerly included in the *Polygalaceae*, but in the Engler and Prantl system it was placed as the sole member of a tribe of *Caesalpiniaceae*! It seems to be quite misplaced in the latter position, and I agree with Kung (BEIHEFT BOT. CENTRABL. **30**, 412 (1913)) and B. L. Turner (RHODORA **60**, 101 (1958)) that it should be regarded as a separate family and quite near to *Polygalaceae*, in which family it was placed by Bentham and Hooker f.

The species of *Krameria* (Fig. 180, reproduced from my FAMILIES OF FLOWERING PLANTS) are shrublets or tough herbs, often prostrate and silky-tomentose; leaves entire or 3-foliate; flowers resupinate (i.e. turned upside down), in terminal racemes; sepals 5–4, free; petals 5, 3 of them long-clawed, claws connate or rarely free, 2 thick and orbicular, much shorter and sessile on the staminal tube; stamens 4, connate below; anthers opening by an oblique pore; ovary 1-locular or semi-locular by the intrusion of the placenta; ovules 2, collateral, pendulous; fruit globose, spinous or muricate, indehiscent, 1-seeded; seed without endosperm, with straight embryo and with thick cotyledons.

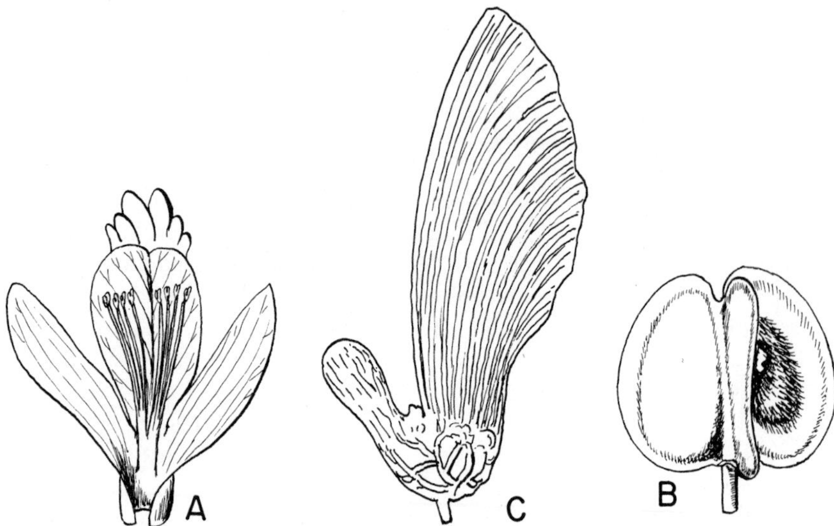

FIG. 179. **A** and **B**, open flower and capsule of *Polygala cabrae* Chod. **C**, fruit of *Securidaca longipedunculata* Fres. (*Polygalaceae*); tropical Africa.

FIG. 180. *Krameria tomentosa* A. St. Hil. (*Krameriaceae*). **A**, open flower. **B**, 3 upper petals with stamens. **C**, anther. **D**, fruit. **E**, section of fruit. **F** and **G**, seeds. (Repeated from FAMILIES OF FLOWERING PLANTS, see text.)

FIG. 181. *Erismadelphus exsul* Mildbraed, the only genus and species of *Vochysiaceae* in Africa, the remainder of the family being in America; note the resemblance of the fruit to those of some *Dipterocarpaceae*. **A**, cluster of flowers. **B**, flower. **C**, vertical section of flower. **D** and **E**, stamens. **F**, fruit (orig.). (For map of distribution of family see FAMILIES OF FLOWERING PLANTS, 2nd Ed. **1**, 235.)

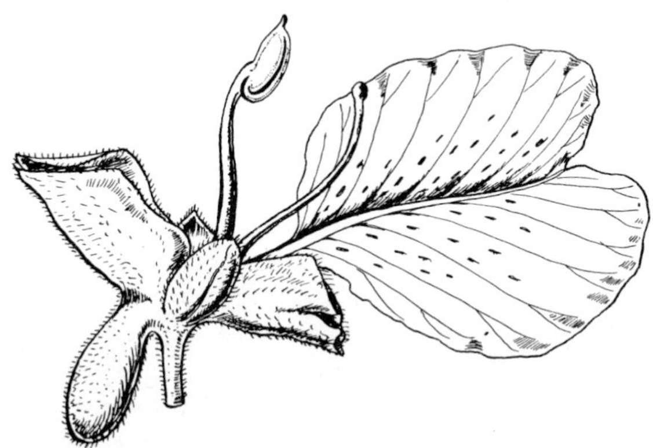

FIG. 182. Flower of *Qualea multiflora* Mart. (*Vochysiaceae*), Brazil. (After Martius FLORA BRAS.)

The remaining two families of this order are **Trigoniaceae** and **Vochysiaceae**, in both of which the flowers are zygomorphic, the stamens united or much reduced in number (sometimes only one), and the seeds are either enveloped in cottony hairs or they are winged. The flowers of many bear some superficial resemblance to those of *Impatiens* (*Balsaminaceae*).

For a long time *Trigoniaceae* and *Vochysiaceae* were thought to be confined to the American tropics, but an additional genus, *Erismadelphus* (Fig. 181), belonging to *Vochysiaceae*, was eventually discovered in primaeval forests in the Cameroons. It is an old saying that the African continent may always be relied upon to produce something new, though on the whole it is very deficient in primitive types of plants, excepting, of course, *Cycadaceae*, *Welwitschia* and *Podocarpaceae*.

Malaya can now also claim a genus by the transference of *Trigoniastrum* (formerly in *Polygalaceae*) to *Trigoniaceae*.

ORDER 28. **LOASALES**

(*Fam. Fl. Pl.* **1**, 236)

Families: **Turneraceae, Loasaceae.**

This Order, having retained parietal placentation, may be a climax rather remote from the BIXALES, as follows: MAGNOLIALES → DILLENIALES → BIXALES → **LOASALES**.

The families **Turneraceae** and *Loasaceae* will not be familiar to many students, for they mostly occur in the American tropics and very few are in cultivation in the Old World. *Turneraceae*, superficially, might seem to be intermediate between *Papaveraceae* and *Brassicaceae* (*Cruciferae*), differing from both of these families in having a more advanced feature, a tubular calyx. Instead of the usual two valves in the fruit such as in *Brassicaceae*, however, there are three valves in that of *Turneraceae*. It is more likely that this resemblance is due to parallelism, and that *Turneraceae* especially are perhaps more nearly related to *Passifloraceae* in the woody subphylum. In general facies certain *Turneraceae* also recall some *Cistaceae* and *Malvaceae*, for stellate hairs occur in *Piriqueta* spp. Some species of *Turnera* are like *Corchorus* (*Tiliaceae*), some resemble certain *Polemoniaceae*, while others recall *Sida* (*Malvaceae*). *Turnera subnuda* Urb. (Brazil) and *T. guianensis* Aubl. (Guyana and Trinidad) are sometimes leafless or nearly so, and *Turnera genistoides* Cambess. (Brazil) is specifically aptly named.

The type genus, *Turnera* (type species *T. ulmifolia* Linn., trop. South America, see Fig. 183), is mainly in America with one or two species in Africa and Asia. It embraces shrubs, undershrubs and herbs; leaves often 2-glandular at the base and usually clothed with stellate hairs; flowers yellow and without a corona; calyx 5-partite; petals inserted at the throat of the calyx, clawed; stamens sometimes quite hypogynous; styles 3, free,

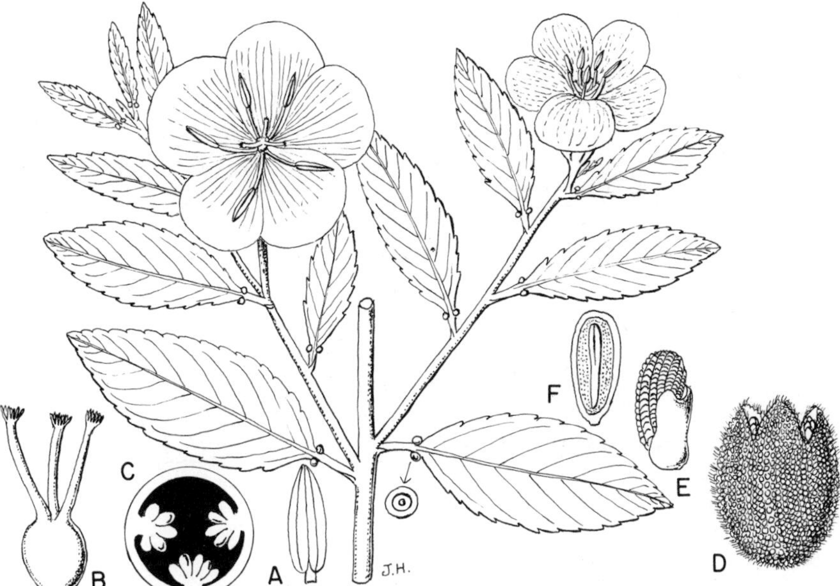

Fig. 183. *Turnera ulmifolia* Linn., tropical America, the type species of the type genus of the family *Turneraceae*. **A**, anther. **B**, gynoecium. **C**, cross-section of ovary. **D**, fruit. **E**, seed. **F**, vertical section of seed (orig.).

stigmas mostly flabellately lobed; capsule ovoid or oblong, valves with usually numerous seeds in the middle; seeds curved, sulcate, pitted or rough, with a linear submembranous aril.

The genera *Erblichia* and *Piriqueta* have a corona as in some *Passifloraceae*, whilst *Mathurina* Balf. f. (see Fig. 184), in the island of Rodrigues (Mascarenes), has a peduncle bearing a pair of large leafy bracts about the middle, and the aril of the seed is clothed with long thread-like hairs. The African genus *Wormskioldia* bears a striking resemblance to some *Brassicaceae* (*Cruciferae*), with its yellow clawed petals and its siliqua-like, torulose (but 3-valved!) capsule (Fig. 185).

Loasaceae[1] are very numerous in the S.W. United States of North America and Mexico. They have always an inferior or semi-inferior ovary, very often numerous stamens, which are mostly gathered together into bundles; and in some genera, such as *Klaprothia* and *Sclerothrix*, the bundles opposite the sepals are sterile. The twisted capsules of certain genera such as *Sclerothrix* (Fig. 186, **E**), *Caiophora* and *Blumenbachia*, recall a similar tendency in the *Papaveraceae* (genus *Meconella*), whilst in a physical sense only

[1] Including *Gronoviaceae* Endlich. (1841). *Cavalliaceae* Griseb. (1854).

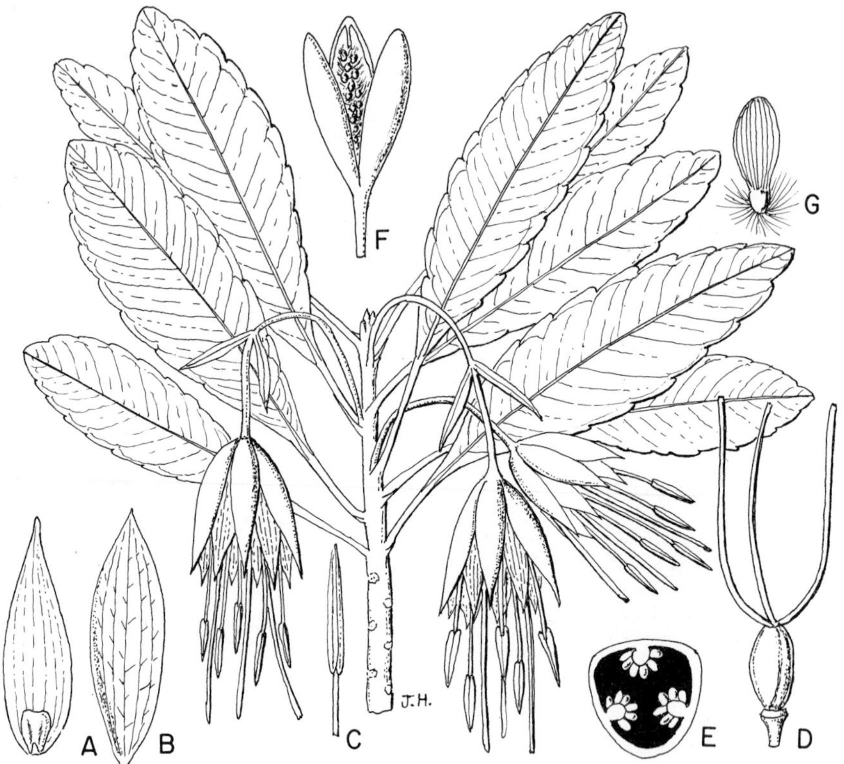

FIG. 184. *Mathurina penduliflora* Balf. f. (*Turneraceae*), Rodrigues Island. **A**, sepal. **B**, petal. **C**, stamen. **D**, gynoecium. **E**, cross-section of ovary. **F**, fruit. **G**, seed (orig.).

the stinging hairs are apt to remind us rather sharply of the common nettle (*Urticaceae*) in temperate regions, or of *Mucuna* (*Fabaceae*) in the tropics.

Loasaceae have a remarkable distribution, nearly the whole family being found in America, only one genus occurring outside that continent. This is *Kissenia*, a genus of two species in Africa and Arabia; *K. capensis* R.Br. (see Fig. 186) in S.W. Africa (opposite South America!), the other, *K. spathulata* R.Br., completely isolated in southern Arabia and in Somaliland (for map see FAMILIES OF FLOWERING PLANTS, 2nd Ed. I, 238).

There are nearly a hundred known species of *Loasa*, the name-type genus of the family (type species *L. acanthifolia* Desr., Chile); they occur in America from southern Mexico and the West Indies south to Patagonia; many of them have to be handled with great care because of the bristly stinging hairs; erect or climbing herbs; leaves from entire to compound; flowers yellow to brick-red; calyx-lobes 5, equal; petals 5, hooded, connivent, usually valvate; stamens usually numerous in bundles opposite the petals; staminodes

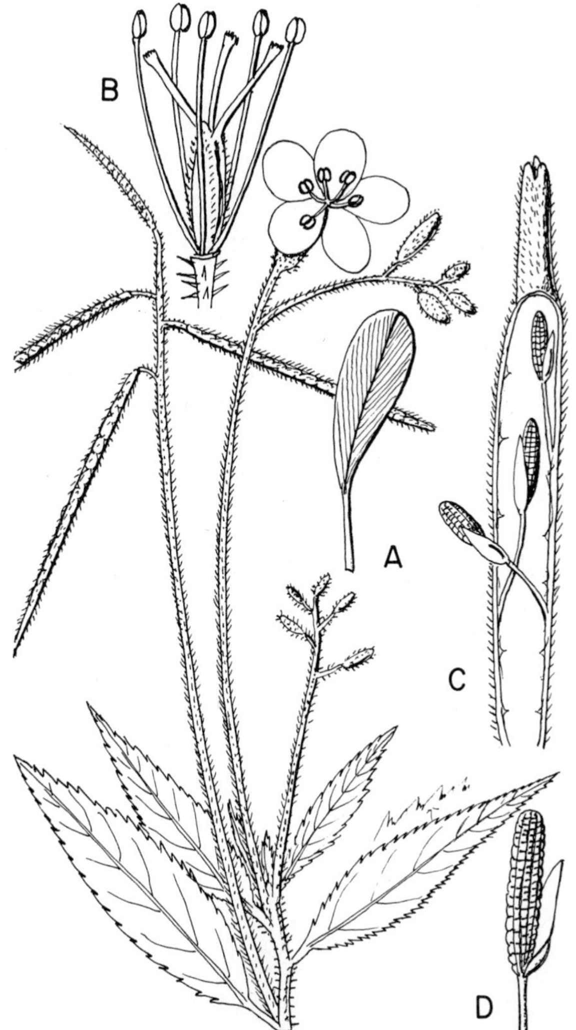

FIG. 185. *Wormskioldia glandulifera* Klotzsch (*Turneraceae*), tropical Africa, has fruits remarkably like those of some *Brassicaceae* (*Cruciferae*). **A**, petal. **B**, stamens and gynoecium. **C**, part of fruit laid open. **D**, seed (orig.).

10; ovules numerous on 3 parietal placentas; capsule linear, straight, 3-valved, valves bearing the seeds on the margins; seeds minute, angular.

My former colleague, J. E. Dandy, who described this family in my GENERA OF FLOWERING PLANTS (Vol. 2, p. 353), noted the following outstanding characters: Habit arborescent in *Mentzelia arborescens* Urban &

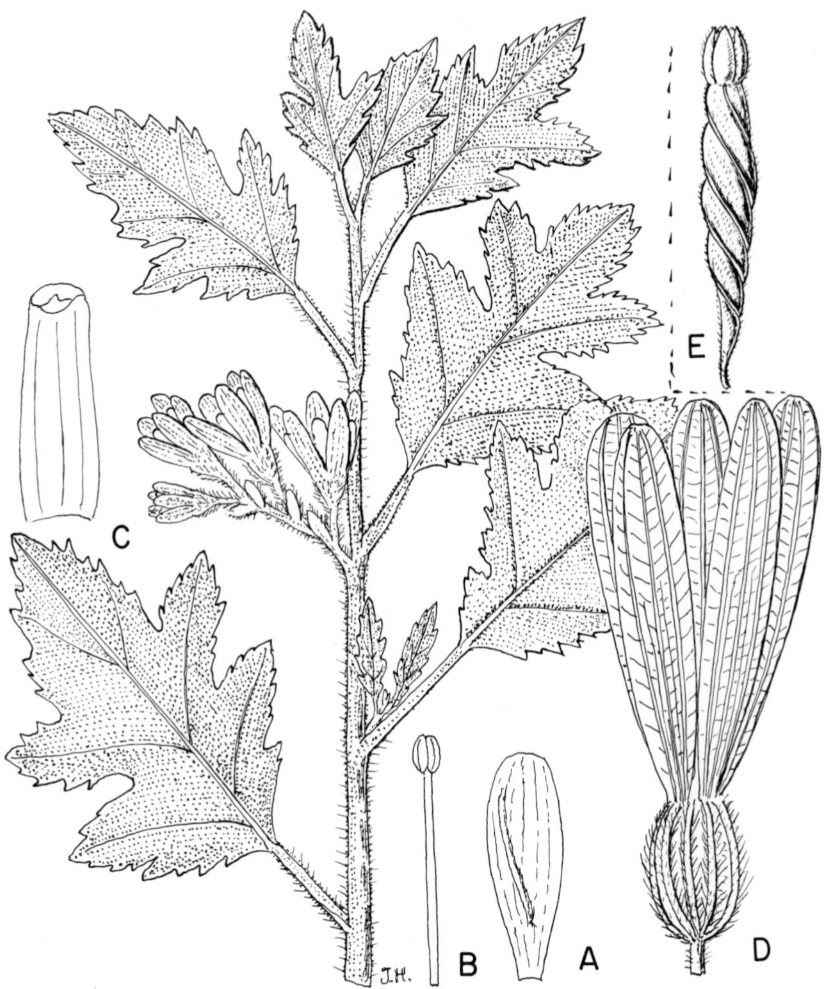

FIG. 186. *Kissenia capensis* R.Br. (*Loasaceae*), S.W. Africa. **A**, petal. **B**, stamen. **C**, staminode. **D**, fruit. **E**, the spirally twisted fruit of *Sclerothrix fasciculata* Presl (*Loasaceae*), Mexico. The genus has a remarkable discontinuous distribution in Africa. (For map see FAMILIES OF FLOWERING PLANTS, 2nd Ed. **1**, 238) (orig.).

Gilg, woody and climbing in *Fuertesia*. Flowers capitate in *Cevallia* (sometimes subcapitate in *Petalonyx*); 4-merous in *Klaprothia*, *Sclerothrix*, and rarely in *Pentalonyx*, 6–7-merous in *Loasa* spp. and *Caiophora* spp. Sepals accrescent and wing-like in fruit in *Kissenia* and *Fuertesia*. Petals 3-lobed and laciniate in *Fuertesia*; connate into an elongated tube in *Sympetaleia* spp.; connate along the claws above the base in *Petalonyx* spp. Only 2 fertile stamens in *Petalonyx crenatus* A. Gray; outer 5 staminodial and petaloid in

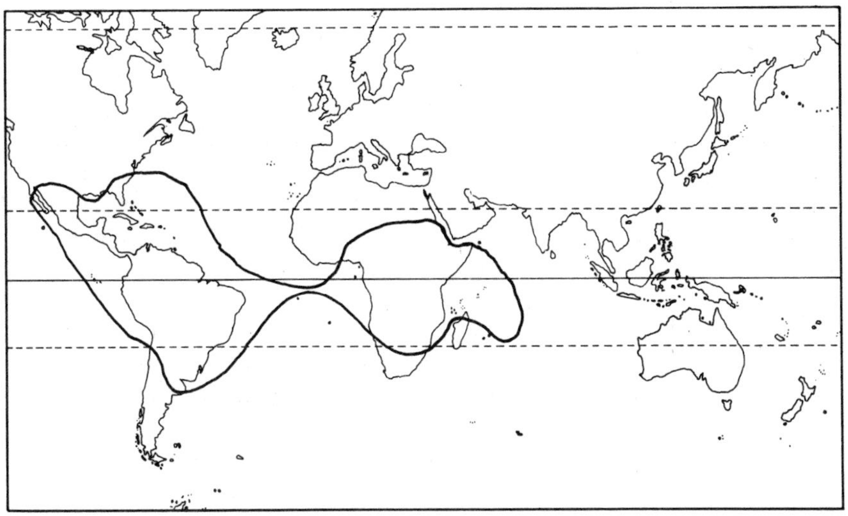

MAP 13. Range of the family *Turneraceae*, an advanced perigynous-flowered mostly woody group. Its distribution emphasises the close connection between the floras of tropical Africa and tropical South America. A few members of the family are introduced into and partly naturalised in Indo-Malaya.

Mentzelia spp.; filaments very short in *Cevallia*, adnate to the corolla-tube in *Sympetaleia*; anthers 1-locular in *Sympetaleia*, sharply 4-locellate in *Petalonyx*; connective produced into an elongated appendage in *Cevallia*. Ovary partly inferior in *Schismocarpus*, *Loasa* spp. and *Caiophora* spp., becoming 2-locular in *Kissenia*.

ORDER 29. **PASSIFLORALES**

(*Fam. Fl. Pl.* **1**, 239)

Families: **Malesherbiaceae, Passifloraceae, Achariaceae.**

The principal family of this group, *Passifloraceae*, is mixed in the Engler and Prantl system with *Flacourtiaceae*, in BIXALES, so the affinity must be obvious; origin perhaps as follows: MAGNOLILALES → DILLENIALES → BIXALES (*Flacourtiaceae*) → **PASSIFLORALES**.

In a linear system it is not always possible to place some groups as near to others as their close affinity warrants. This is well demonstrated by the

PASSIFLORALES which are advanced perigynous-flowered groups probably derived from the BIXALES, and show close relationship especially with *Flacourtiaceae*. Many of them have become herbaceous or have adopted a climbing habit. Their seeds are mainly devoid of endosperm, and within the petals there is usually a more or less well-developed corona. The **Malesherbiaceae** are South American herbs or undershrubs with a long, tubular, ribbed calyx with valvate lobes; the petals are likewise valvate. The seeds have the pitted testa so characteristic of the *Passifloraceae* and of some *Papaveraceae*. Indeed it is possible that we have in this group some descendants of the RHOEADALES as well as of the BIXALES, especially also through the LOASALES. A peculiarity of the *Malesherbiaceae* lies in the styles, which are free from each other and widely separated at the base, sometimes being decurrent on the outside of the ovary (as shown in Fig. 106 of FAMILIES OF FLOWERING PLANTS, 2nd Ed. **1**, 240).

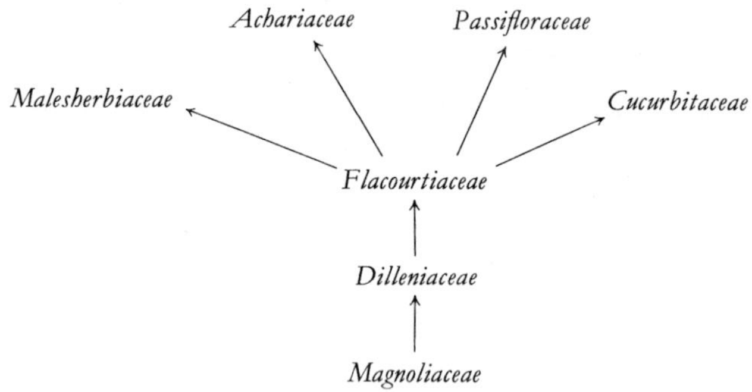

Diagram to show the origin of *Passifloraceae* and *Cucurbitaceae*.

There are only two genera which are endemic in South America, and mostly in Chile and Peru. These are *Malesherbia* and *Gynopleura*, the former with an elongated tubular calyx, the styles arising from the sides of the ovary, the latter with a turbinate or campanulate calyx and the styles arising from near the apex of the ovary.

The typical family of this order is **Passifloraceae**,[1] the best known genus being *Passiflora*. The more primitive genera, however, are like some of the BIXALES; they are erect shrubs and have numerous stamens with a rather poorly developed corona. The more advanced types with conspicuous often brightly coloured corona have also the more recent climbing habit. As in nearly every advanced family of flowering plants there are a certain number of genera with reduced flowers, i.e. unisexual, and with a partial or complete reduction of the petals. These are represented by the tribe

---

[1] Including *Paropsiaceae* Dumortier (1829). *Modeccaceae* J. G. Agardh (1858).

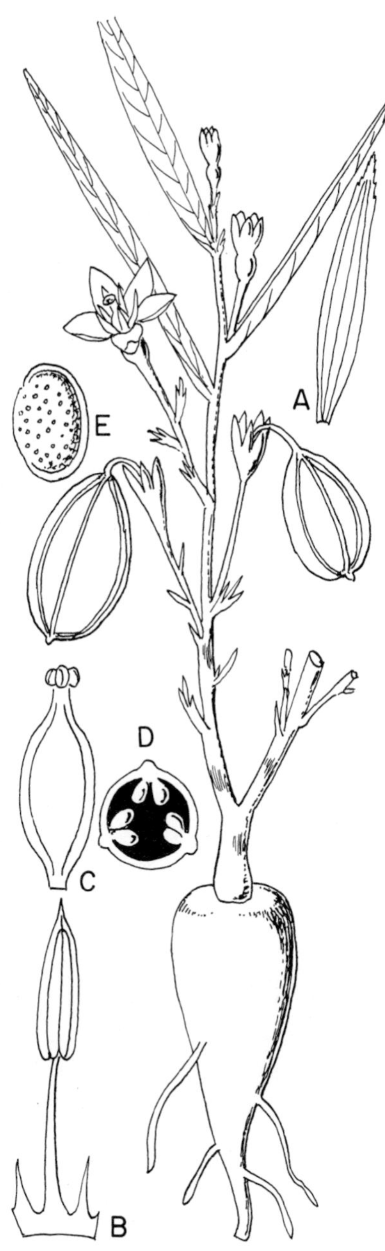

FIG. 187. *Machadoa huillensis* Welw. (*Passifloraceae*), Angola. **A**, petal. **B**, stamen. **C**, gynoecium. **D**, cross-section of ovary. **E**, seed (orig.).

Modecceae. In one of the genera the habit has become reduced, the tropical African *Machadoa* being a herb (Fig. 187).

Passiflora Linn., the type genus, is widely distributed in the tropics and subtropics, but none is native of Africa, and there is only one in Madagascar. They are climbing shrubs or herbs, rarely erect; leaves alternate, rarely opposite, entire, lobed or partite; petiole often glandular; tendrils lateral, undivided; flowers often very handsome, usually bisexual; calyx-lobes often horned on the back below the apex; petals 5–4 or absent; corona simple or double, the outer part of numerous filaments; gynophore elongated; stamens 5–4, filaments adnate to the gynophore; anthers versatile; ovary stipitate; stigmas 3, capitate; fruit dry or pulpy, sometimes a capsule; seeds arillate. Type species *B. rubra* Linn., West Indies (Fig. 188).

More primitive genera in the family have numerous stamens, and they are erect shrubs without tendrils; these are *Smeathmannia* and *Barteria*, both in tropical Africa. The most divergent genus is *Adenia* (Fig. 189), with unisexual flowers without a corona (or this very small), and the leaves are biglandular at the base (hence the name); it is found only in the tropics of the Old World; the type species is *A. venenata* Forssk., from Arabia to Tanganyika, remarkable for its large fleshy rootstock and spiny leafless branches.

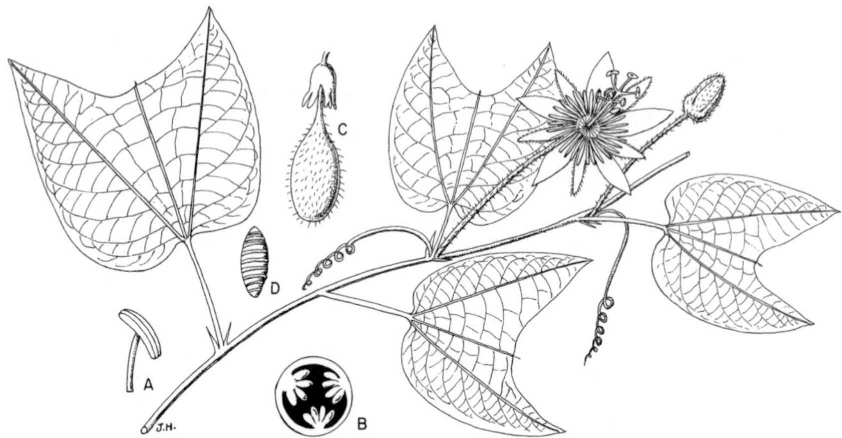

FIG. 188. *Passiflora rubra* Linn., West Indies; the type species of the type genus of *Passifloraceae*. **A**, stamen. **B**, cross-section of ovary. **C**, fruit. **D**, seed (orig.).

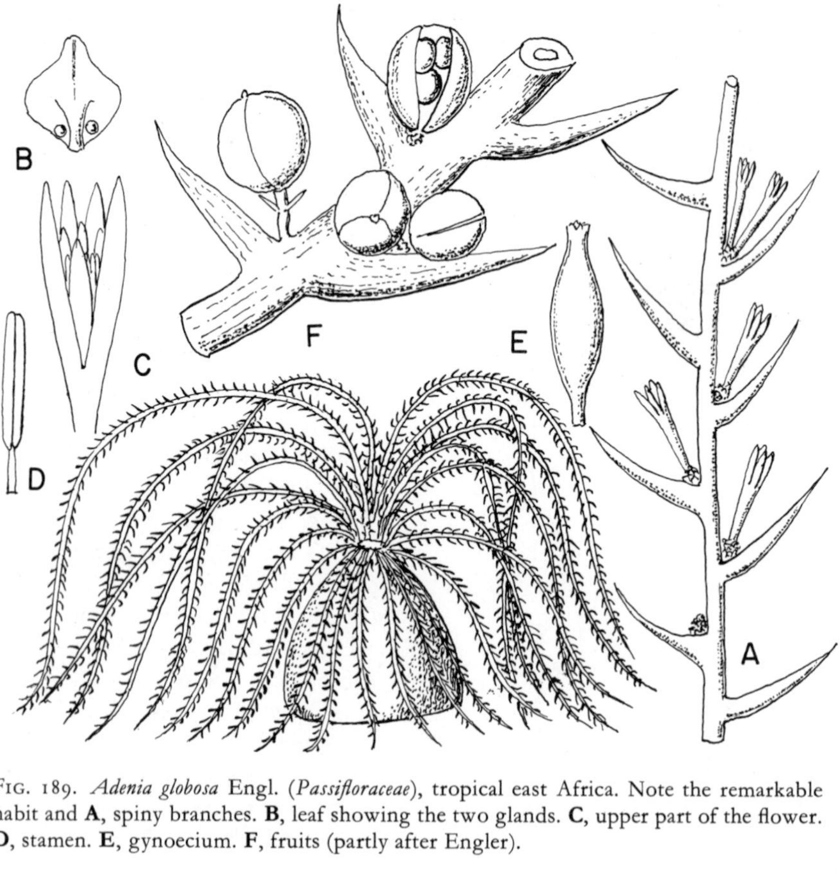

FIG. 189. *Adenia globosa* Engl. (*Passifloraceae*), tropical east Africa. Note the remarkable habit and **A**, spiny branches. **B**, leaf showing the two glands. **C**, upper part of the flower. **D**, stamen. **E**, gynoecium. **F**, fruits (partly after Engler).

Deidamia (Madagascar) and *Efulensia* (west tropical Africa) have compound leaves, the former pinnate, the latter usually trifoliolate or more rarely digitately 5-foliolate.

A further advanced character is to be noted in the small South African family **Achariaceae** in which the corolla is sympetalous, a feature not often associated with a unisexual condition, except in *Cucurbitaceae* and in a few genera of *Euphorbiaceae*. In the genus *Acharia* the stamens are adnate to the corolla-tube, and it is a woody shrublet. *Ceratosicyos* is a slender scandent herb, whilst *Guthriea*, rather like some *Saxifragaceae*, is an acaulescent herb with radical cordate leaves.

ORDER 30. CUCURBITALES

(*Fam. Fl. Pl.* **1**, 242)

Families: **Cucurbitaceae, Begoniaceae, Datiscaceae, Caricaceae.**

This group is very highly evolved and represents a complete climax of the families mostly characterised by having parietal placentation; probably best traced phylogenetically as follows: → MAGNOLIALES → DILLENIALES → BIXALES → PASSIFLORALES → CUCURBITALES.

The family **Cucurbitaceae**[1] is one of the most homogeneous, and shows considerable affinity with *Passifloraceae*. In the Engler and Prantl system, however, it is allotted a very high position in the *Metachlamydeae* (*Sympetalae*; *Gamopetalae*), between the *Rubiaceae* and the *Campanulaceae*. I fail to see any affinity with *Campanulaceae*, emphatically none with *Rubiaceae*, or with any other sympetalous family. Even followers[2] of the Engler system ventured to alter the position of *Cucurbitaceae*, and there is a lot to be said for Bentham and Hooker's note "Ordo valde naturalis, Passifloreis quam maxime affinis".

The flowers of *Cucurbitaceae* are constantly unisexual, the ovary is inferior with one or two exceptions, and the anthers and styles are often flexuous or twisted. There are a few genera with very remarkable and outstanding characters. Such are the Indo-Malayan *Hodgsonia*, which has the ovules and seeds connate in pairs, in the seed stage one being twice the size of the other (see Fig. 190). This union of a pair of ovules is probably a unique feature in

---

[1] Including *Nhandirobaceae* A. St. Hilaire (1822). *Zanoniaceae* Dumort. (1829). *Ventraceae* Dulac (1867). *Fevilleaceae* L. Peiffer (1870).

[2] See Rendle CLASSIFICATION OF FLOWERING PLANTS (Vol. 2, DICOTYLEDONS. 1926).

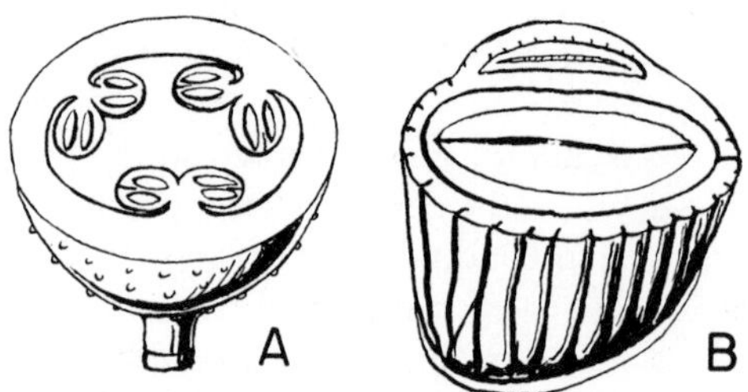

FIG. 190. **A**, transverse section of ovary showing the paired connate ovules of *Hodgsonia heteroclita* Hook. f. & Thoms. (*Cucurbitaceae*), Indo-Malaya, and **B**, the paired connate seeds, perhaps a unique feature in flowering plants.

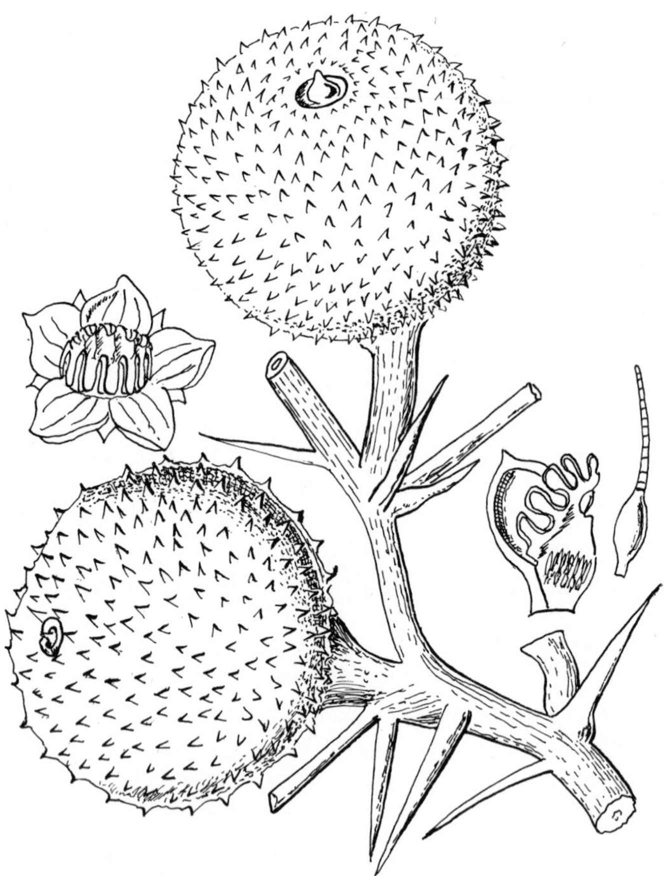

FIG. 191. *Acanthosicyos horrida* Welw. (*Cucurbitaceae*), one of the very few plants that grow in the deserts of S.W. Africa (orig.).

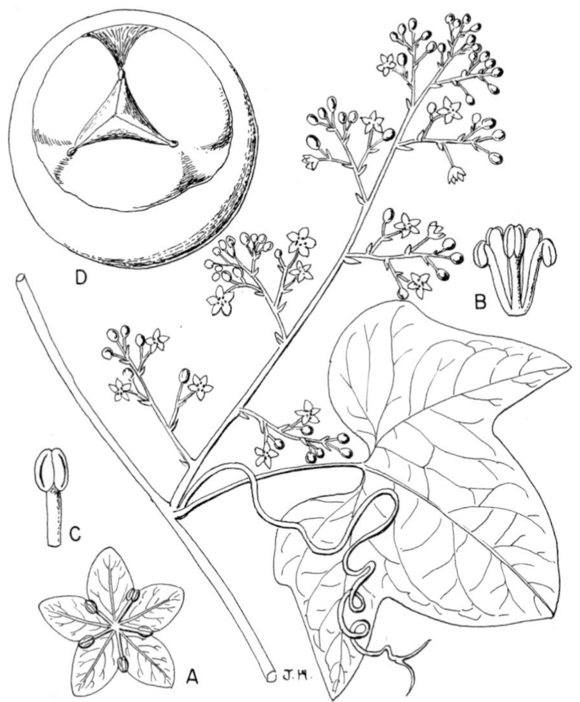

FIG. 192. *Fevillea trilobata* Linn. (*Cucurbitaceae*), tropical America. **A**, male flower. **B** and **C**, stamens. **D**, fruit seen from above (orig.).

the vegetable kingdom. Then in *Cyclanthera* there is only one stamen, the anther of which forms a circle. The usual rather weak climbing habit is sharply departed from in the erect shrubby and very spiny African genus *Acanthosicyos* (Fig. 191), which is found in the barren Namib desert of S.W. Africa along with *Welwitschia*. Evolution within the family has mainly been concerned with the modification of the stamens and fruits, some of the latter considerably modified in the form of the well-known gourds. The genus *Fevillea* (see Fig. 192), in tropical America, is perhaps one of the most primitive and nearest to the Passifloraceous type, with 5 free stamens, 2-locular anthers, and a 3-locular ovary.

The family is named from *Cucurbita* Linn., a comparatively small genus in the tropics and subtropics; annual herbs with the stem often trailing on the ground and rooting at the nodes; leaves cordate at the base, lobed; tendrils multifid; flowers monoecious, large, yellow, solitary; corolla sympetalous; stamens 3; filaments free but the anthers confluent into a head, one 1-locular, the others 2-locular, loculi elongated, sigmoid-flexuous; female flowers with 3 rudimentary stamens at the bottom of the calyx; fruit

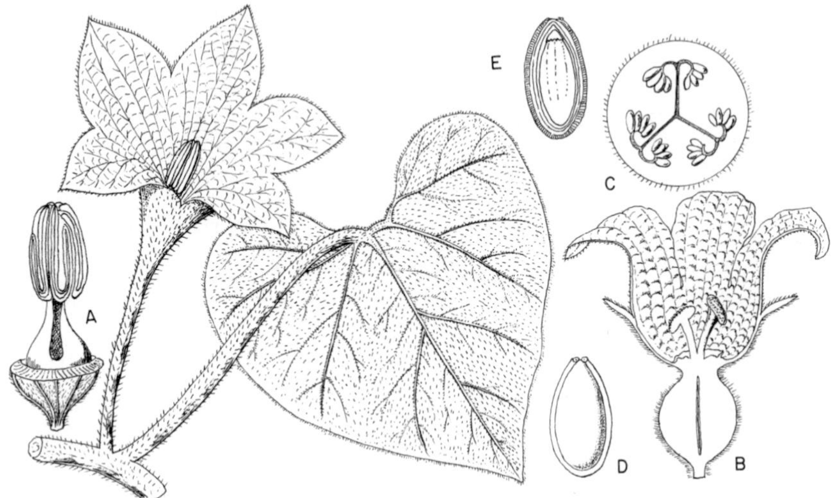

FIG. 193. *Cucurbita pepo* Linn., the type species of the type genus of *Cucurbitaceae*. **A**, male flower with sepals and petals removed showing androecium. **B**, vertical section of female flower. **C**, cross-section of ovary. **D**, seed. **E**, vertical section of seed.

often gigantic, fleshy or corky, with numerous ovate or oblong flattened seeds. Type species *C. pepo* Linn. (Fig. 193).

Cogniaux classified the genera of this family in five tribes, the most advanced, tribe V, differing from the others in having the anther-loculi horizontally arranged into a ring and dehiscing by a continuous slit. From the other four tribes number IV, *Sicyoideae*, differs by the filaments being connate into a column, the more primitive tribes, I, *Fevilleae*, II, *Melothrieae* III, *Cucurbiteae*, having the filaments free or connate only at the base or only the anthers connate. *Fevilleae* have 5 or rarely 4 stamens and the seeds are pendulous; *Melothrieae* and *Cucurbiteae* have 3, rarely 2 or 1 stamens, the former with straight or slightly arcuate loculi, the latter with conduplicate, triplicate or contorted loculi, all forming a pretty phylogenetic pattern.

A group with winged seeds is the subtribe *Zanonineae* of tribe *Fevilleae*, whilst the beautiful wing development of *Alsomitra* in subtribe *Sicydiineae* is very marked (see Fig. 194). In a few genera the so-called "Gourds" (fruits) are very variable in shape.

Another notable exception to the general habit is the genus *Dendrosicyos* (Socotra), an erect tree with a short thick fleshy stem, like a miniature Baobab (*Adansonia*), and it has no tendrils. The genus *Hemsleya* Cogn. (Fig. 195) has very distinctive fruits truncate at the top.

A few of the more outstanding characters are noted in the following: Small trees with large fleshy trunk in *Dendrosicyos* (Socotra); branches with pairs of formidable spines in *Acanthosicyos* (S. W. Africa); petioles with a

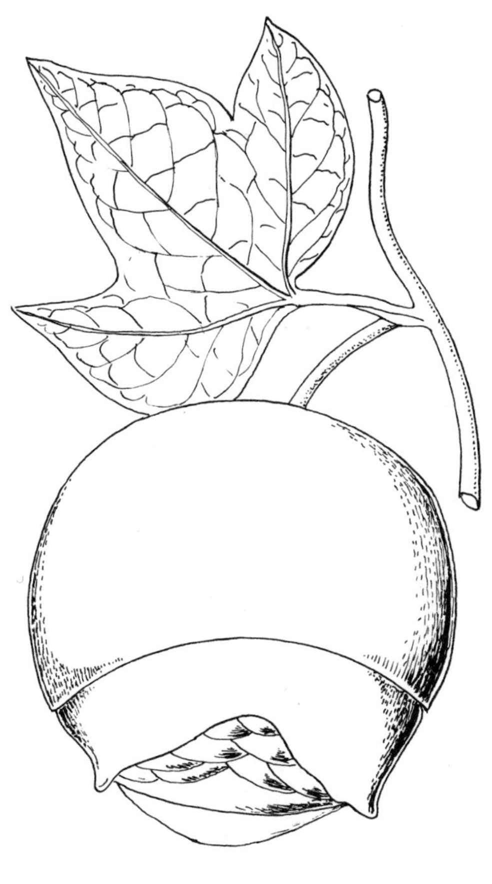

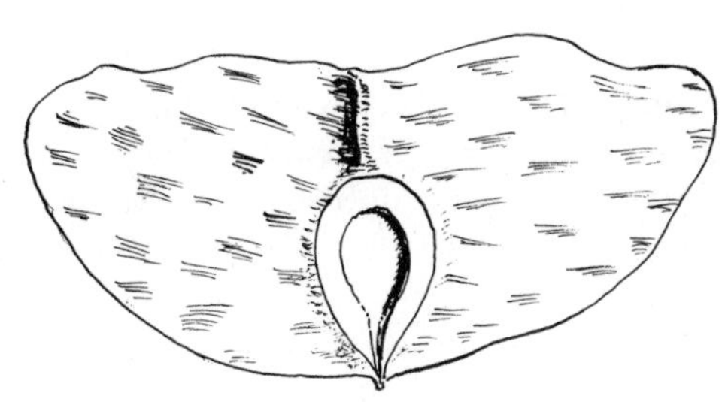

FIG. 194. Fruit and beautifully winged seed of *Alsomitra macrocarpa* M. Roem. (*Cucurbitaceae*), Malaya (orig.).

stipule-like bract at the base in *Ctenolepis*, *Muellerargia*, *Trochomeria* spp. and *Dactyliandra*. Flowers very dissimilar in *Dimorphochlamys*. Calyx-tube closed within by scales in *Thladiantha* and *Momordica*; lobes pectinate in *Raphidiocystis*, serrate in *Telfairia* and *Benincasa*; elongated, persistent and adpressed to the fruit in *Dimorphochlamys*. Stamen 1 and anther 3-locular in *Cucumella*; anthers horizontal in a ring in tribe *Cyclanthereae*; conduplicate,

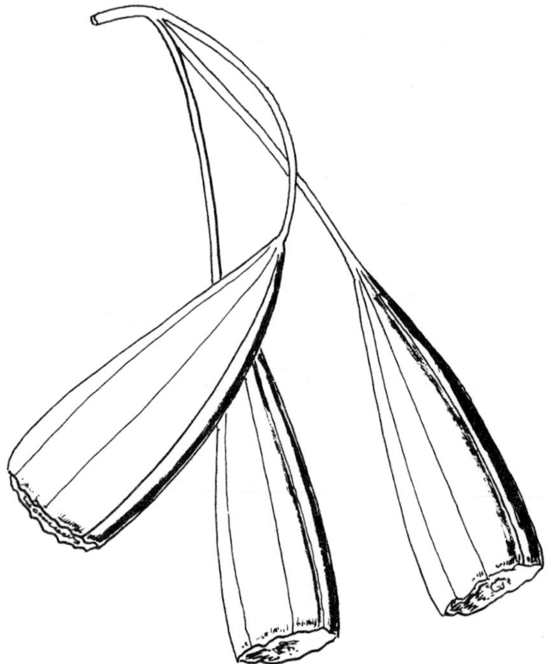

FIG. 195. Distinctive fruits of *Hemsleya chinensis* Cogn. (*Cucurbitaceae*), China (orig.).

triplicate or contorted in tribe *Cucurbiteae*. Styles remote in *Fevillea*; stigma radiately multifid in *Cucurbitella*. Fruits opening by a transverse slit (circumscissile) in *Actinostemma* and *Bolbostemma*; compressed and samara-like and 1-seeded in *Pseudosicydium*, *Cyclantheropsis*, and *Pterosicyos*; 3-winged in *Sechiopsis*. Seeds winged in subtribe *Zanoninae* of tribe *Fevilleae* and in *Anisosperma*; connate in pairs in *Hodgsonia*.

Begoniaceae: There are five genera of this well-known family in our greenhouses and flower gardens. These are *Hillebrandia*, Hawaii Isls; *Begonia* with over 500 species in the tropics and subtropics; *Symbegonia*, 12 species in New Guinea; *Begoniella*, five species in Colombia, South America; and *Semibegoniella*, two or three species in Ecuador.

The family shows some general affinity with *Cucurbitaceae*, but they have become such a homogeneous group that their descent is not very easy to trace. Like those of the latter family, their flowers are always unisexual, the ovary is inferior and often winged, and there are always 2 stipules but never tendrils. The placentation of the ovules is axile, and their number is often very considerable. The anther-loculi are always straight, but the twisted stigmas bring to mind those of many *Cucurbitaceae*. The family is most abundantly represented in tropical America, and the habit is almost without exception herbaceous and many are epiphytic. *Begonia baccata* Hook. f. is exceptional in having a baccate fruit and is endemic in the island of St. Thomas, West Africa.

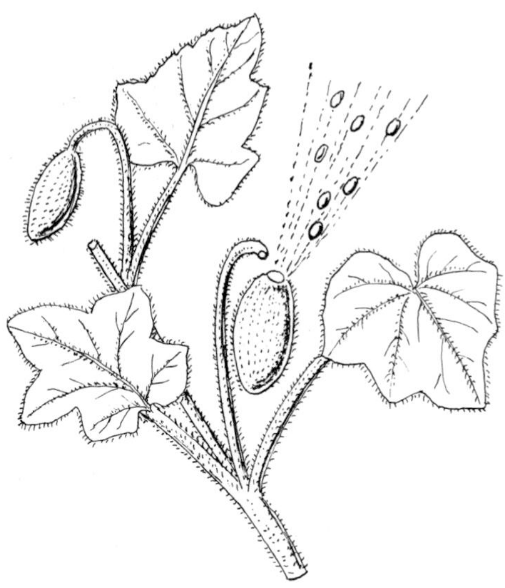

FIG. 196. The Squirting Cucumber, *Ecballium elaterium* A. Rich. (*Cucurbitaceae*), Mediterranean region.

There is a great range in the structure of the hairs when present: ordinary uniseriate hairs, multiseriate shaggy hairs with varied structure, two-armed shaggy hairs, stellate hairs, tufted hairs, small scales, and short- or long-stalked glandular hairs with varied types of structure in the stalk and head.

Datiscaceae[1] is another small family of rather uncertain affinity. There are only three genera, one with petals, *Octomeles*, tree with simple leaves lepidote-mealy below, and *Tetrameles* and *Datisca*, without petals, the former trees with simple leaves and short anthers, the latter herbs with trisected or pinnate leaves. *Datisca* mimics *Cannabiaceae*, and *Octomeles* and *Tetrameles* are superficially very similar to some *Urticaceae*, except in their fruits. The indumentum of *Octomeles* greatly resembles that of *Elaeagnus*, consisting of a quadriseriate stalk and a one-layered circular shield with an entire margin.

Caricaceae[2]: In this small family of five genera, the flowers are mostly unisexual, and the petals are united into a slender tube, the stamens are double the number of the corolla-lobes and inserted in two rows at the mouth of the tube. There is therefore combined in this one small family,

[1] Including *Tetramelaceae* Airy Shaw (1965).

[2] Including *Papayaceae* Blume (1834).

which on account of its affinities belonged to the *Archichlamydeae*, the general characters of the *Metachlamydeae* of the Englerian system, showing the artificiality of the latter group, depending mainly on the union of the petals.

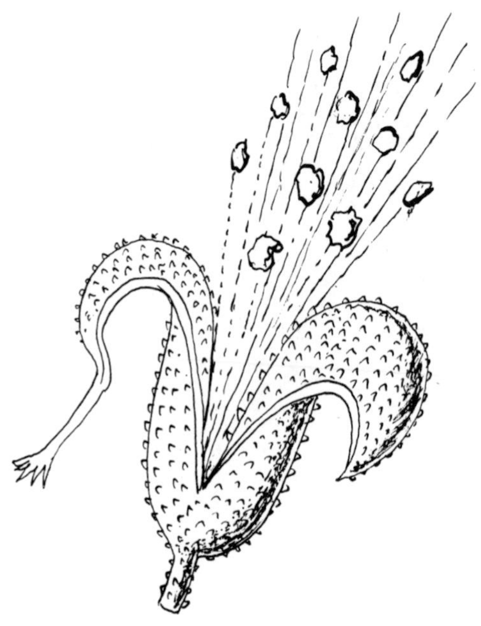

FIG. 197. Explosive fruit of *Cyclanthera explodens* Naud. (*Cucurbitaceae*), tropical South America.

In *Carica* and *Pileus* the filaments are free from one another, in the former the leaves are simple but sometimes deeply lobed or partite, and the fruits not winged at the base; in the latter the leaves are 5–7-foliolate, and the fruits more or less produced at the base into wings. In the other three genera the filaments are partly connate into a tube, leaves simple, trees with prickly erect stems in *Cylicomorpha*, tropical Africa, herbs with smooth prostrate stems in *Jarilla*, American tropics and subtropics; and leaves digitately 5–12-foliolate, often covered with bloom below in *Jacaratia*, tropical America. The Papaw (Pawpaw) is the fruit of *Carica papaya* Linn., a favourite breakfast food in the tropics and subtropics and very appetising. Papain is a drug with digestive properties and is obtained from the latex of the unripe fruits.

ORDER 31. CACTALES[1]

(*Fam. Fl. Pl.* **1**, 247)

This Order is composed of the single family **Cactaceae**,[2] named after the genus *Cactus* Linn., now rejected in favour of *Mamillaria* Haworth. The reason for this is explained in my GENERA OF FLOWERING PLANTS (Vol. 2, 458) by Mr. D. R. Hunt, who kindly undertook the classification of the family for that work.

Nowadays *Cactaceae* are very familiar to many as pot plants, highly specialised, fleshy perennials of very diverse and often weird habit, usually very spiny. The spines and flowers always arise from cushion-like axillary areoles. The ovary is almost invariably inferior with three to many parietal placentas. It is mainly on account of this placentation that the family is placed amongst those with a similar structure, including *Passifloraceae* and *Cucurbitaceae*, though widely different in habit from those two families. Hunt's delimitation and classification of the genera follows closely that of Britton and Rose in their monumental book entitled THE CACTACEAE (1919–23).

The family is mostly of importance from a horticultural point of view, and plants in pots may be seen in many a cottage or suburban window, and special collections in more pretentious greenhouses and botanical gardens. Opuntias are grown for their edible fruits (known as "prickly pears"), as food plants for the cochineal insect, and to arrest and prevent soil erosion. Spineless forms were developed by Luther Burbank and these provide cattle forage in arid regions. Introduced into South Africa, Australia and elsewhere, however, they have in places exceeded their usefulness and become a pest, and vast sums have been spent in their eradication. Some of the more spiny kinds make formidable hedges which need little attention. The medicinal and hallucinogenic properties of *Lophora* and other American genera, which contain a variety of alkaloids, are much used by the Mexican and American Indians.

Cacti occur throughout the Americas from British Columbia and Alberta to as far south as Patagonia, and the genus *Opuntia* ranges from 53° N to 50° S. The greatest number inhabit the drier regions, in Mexico and the S.W. United States, etc., where Cacti are often a characteristic feature of the landscape. Many species in the forest regions of the tropics are epiphytic. The only Old World species (suspected to be introduced) is *Rhipsalis*

---

[1] Condensed from D. R. Hunt's account in Hutchinson GENERA OF FLOWERING PLANTS **2**, 427 (1967).

[2] Including *Opuntiaceae* A. L. de Juss. (1825). *Nopaleaceae* Burnett (1835).

baccifer (Soland. ex Mill.) W. T. Stearn, in tropical Africa and Ceylon, but also in the New World.

The most primitive of the three tribes seems to be *Pereskieae*, composed of only two genera. *Pereskia*, morphologically the least highly modified of the family, are trees, shrubs or scramblers with broad flat leaves and stalked clustered flowers, in one or two species of which the ovary is more or less superior.

ORDER 32. **TILIALES**

(*Fam. Fl. Pl.* **1**, 248)

Families: **Dirachmaceae, Scytopetalaceae, Tiliaceae, Sterculiaceae, Peridiscaceae, Bombacaceae.**

The phylogeny of this important Order is not difficult to trace according to the present system: MAGNOLIALES → DILLENIALES → BIXALES (especially *Flacourtiaceae*) → **TILIALES**.

This is one of the most interesting Orders for the study of phylogenetic relationships. There has been prolific evolution in various directions, and there is clear evidence of reduction in habit from trees to shrubs and then to herbs. The progenitors of the group were probably the Dilleniaceous and Bixaceous stocks. Compared with them, however, there is a great advancement in the gynoecium, the axile placentation in place of parietal having become firmly established as a fixed character. The tendency to cohesion of the stamens into a single bundle is very marked in the more advanced *Malvaceae*, and has been accompanied by the evolution of the herbaceous habit, though usually with fibrous stem structure. Some *Sterculiaceae* show a gradual reduction of the petals together with a separation of the sexes, a condition more completely carried out in part of the *Euphorbiaceae*. The calyx is valvate throughout the Order.

In my FAMILIES OF FLOWERING PLANTS (2nd Ed. **1**, 248) I felt impelled to create a new family, **Dirachmaceae**, for the remarkable genus *Dirachma* Schweinf. ex Balf. f., formerly included in the *Geraniaceae*. There is but one known species, *D. socotrana* Schweinf. ex Balf. f., which grows only in the remote island of Socotra about 100 miles east of the Horn of Africa; a shrub with long and short shoots; epicalyx of 4 bracteoles; sepals 8, valvate; petals 8, free, contorted; stamens 8, free, opposite the petals; ovary 8-locular,

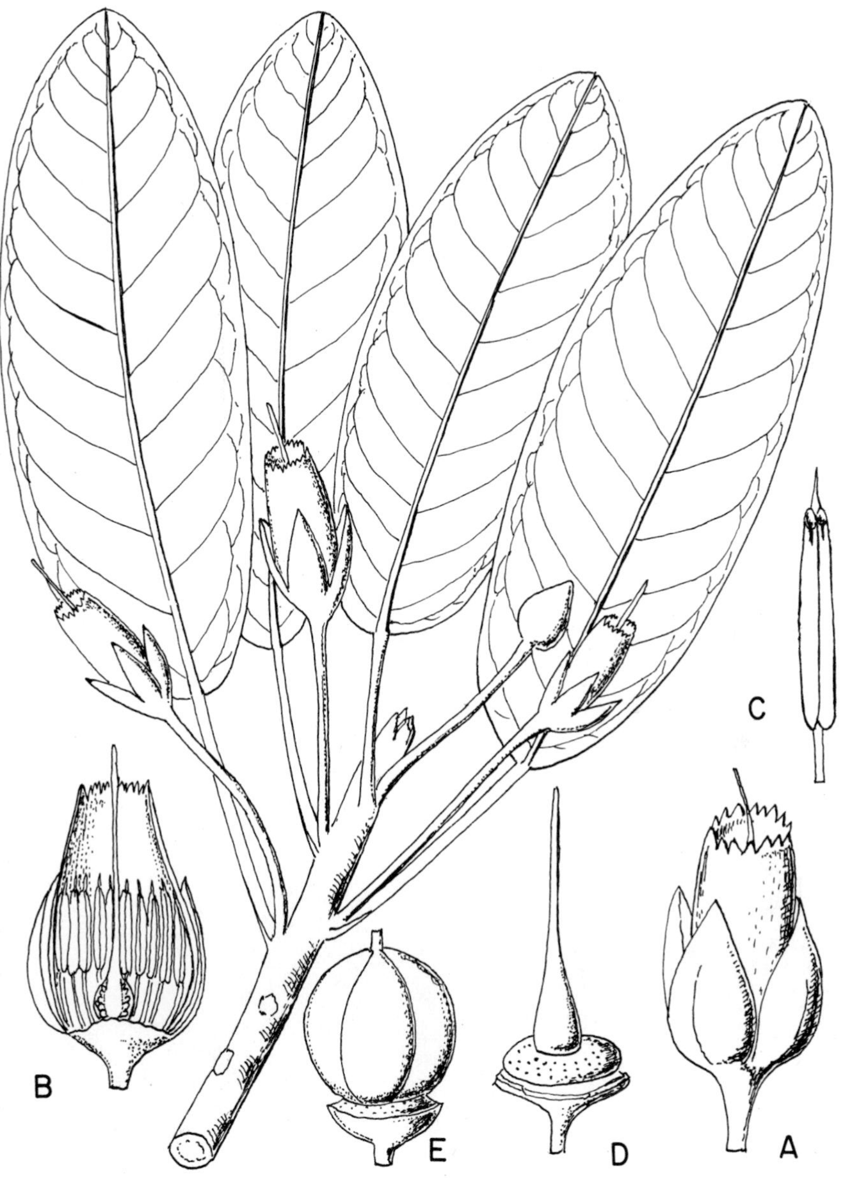

FIG. 198. The genus *Antholoma* (*A. montana* Labill., New Caledonia, shown above) is remarkable in the family *Tiliaceae* in having a sympetalous corolla. **A**, flower. **B**, vertical section of same. **C**, stamen. **D**, gynoecium. **E**, fruit (orig.).

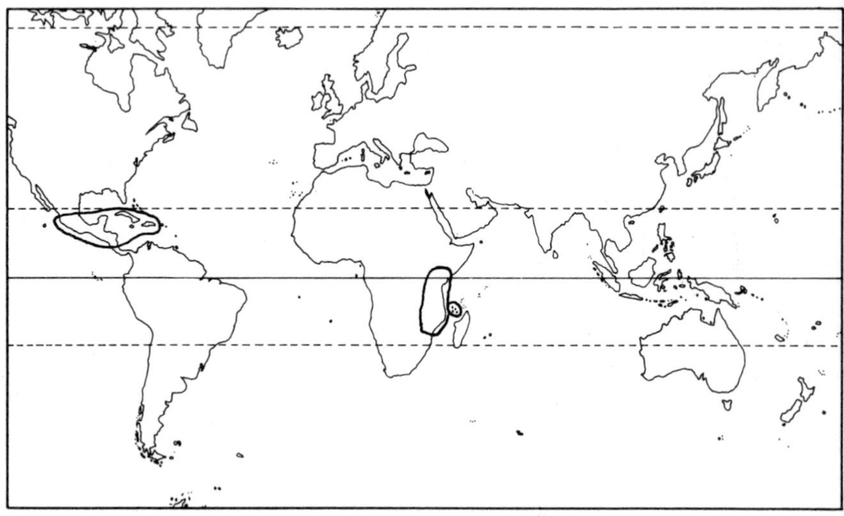

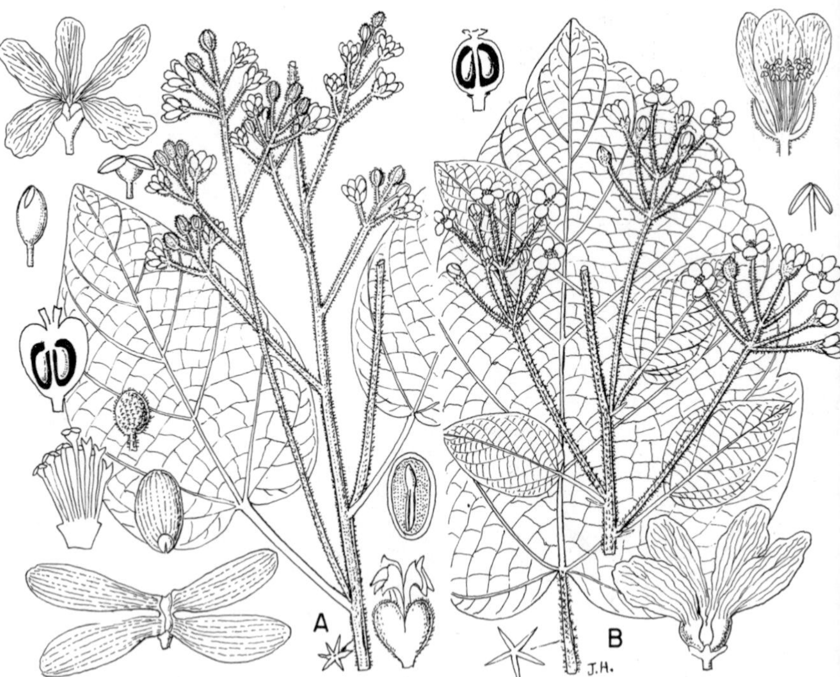

FIG. 199 and MAP 14. Many hundreds of miles of land and ocean separate the few species of the natural genus *Carpodiptera* (*Tiliaceae*); one species, **A**, *C. africana* Mast, in tropical east Africa, one. *C. biovinii* Baill., in the Comoro Islands, one, **B**, *C. ameliae* Lundell, in Mexico and central America, besides two or three in the West Indies.

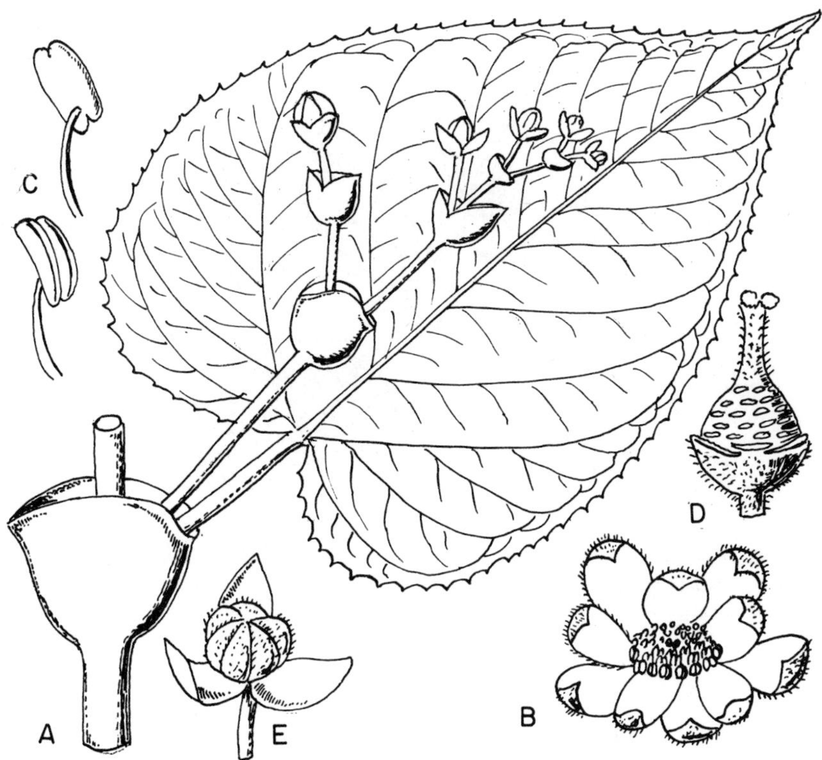

FIG. 200. *Graeffea calyculata* Seem. (*Tiliaceae*), a rare (perhaps extinct) species of the Fiji Islands; note the extrapetiolar cupular sheathing stipules, **A**. **B**, open flower. **C**, stamens. **D**, gynoecium. **E**, fruit.

deeply 8-lobed; stigmas 8; ovule 1 in each loculus, basal; capsule separating into 8 ventrally dehiscent segments woolly inside; seeds compressed, testa shining.—A most curious mixture of characters!

Tiliaceae[1] is undoubtedly the most primitive family of the Order, showing unmistakeable affinity backwards to *Dilleniaceae* and further up the evolutionary scale especially with certain *Flacourtiaceae*. The copious endosperm of the seeds of these two families is here retained, whilst the apocarpous gynoecium so typical of *Dilleniaceae*, has not quite disappeared from the tropical African genus *Christiana* and the Asiatic *Brownlowia*.

The more primitive groups of *Tiliaceae* have the sepals free to the base or

[1] Including *Elaeocarpaceae* DC. (1824). *Prockiaceae* D. Don. (1831). *Maquinae* Martius (1835). *Aristoteliaceae* Dumort. (1829). *Sparrmaniaceae* J. G. Agardh (1858). *Carcerulaceae* Dulac (1867).

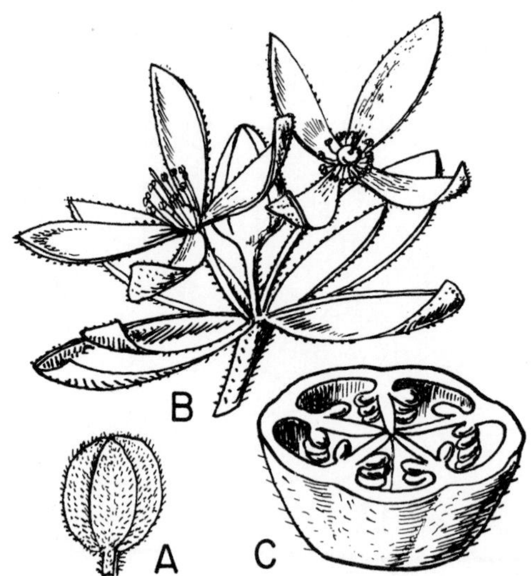

FIG. 201. Flowers, **B**, and transverse section of ovary, **C**, of *Duboscia viridiflora* (A. Chev.) Mildbr. (*Tiliaceae*); the flowers are enclosed by an involucre of bracts which may be mistaken for a calyx. **A**, bud of involucre.

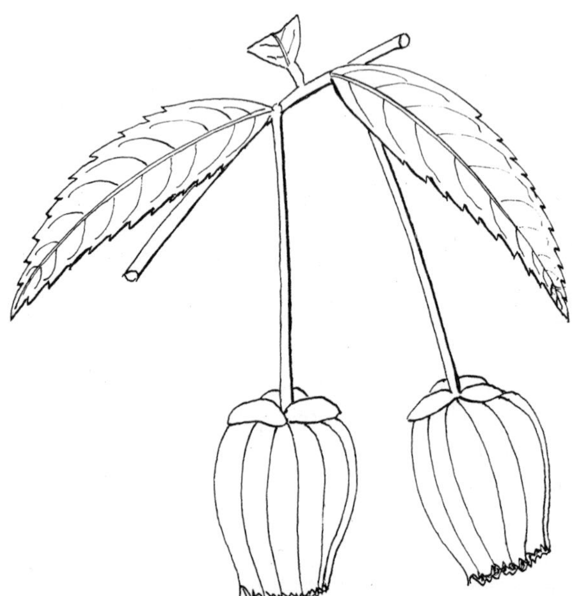

FIG. 202. Flowers of *Crinodendron dependens* C. K. Schneider (*Tiliaceae*), Chile.

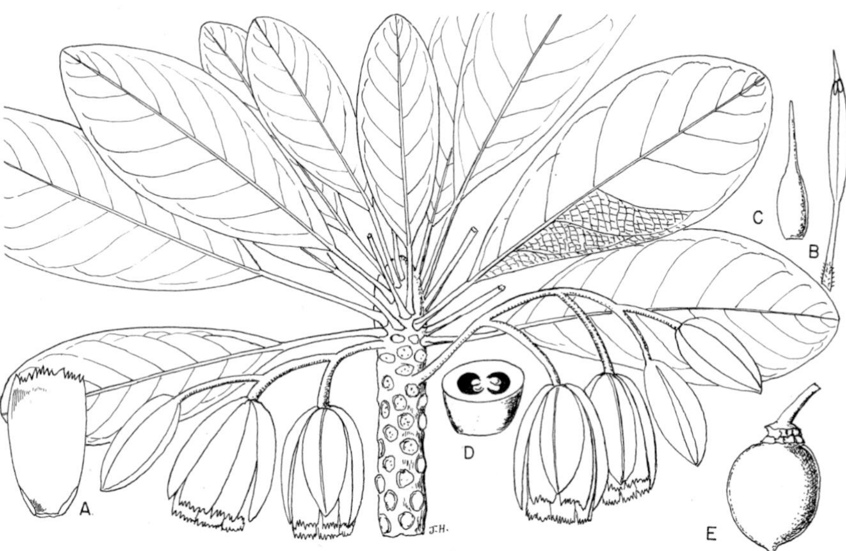

FIG. 203. *Elaeocarpus storkii* Seem. (*Tiliaceae*), a large tree with yellow pink-tinged flowers, endemic in Fiji Islands. **A**, petal. **B**, stamen. **C**, gynoecium. **D**, cross-section of ovary. **E**, fruit; exudes a gum resin, vernacular name "Gaigai".

nearly so. In tribe *Brownlowieae*, however, the sepals are united into a campanulate calyx, and this is accompanied by an advanced type of anther, the loculi of which are at length confluent at the apex. An outstanding development is the sympetalous corolla of the genus *Antholoma* (Fig. 198). Opposite leaves are rare, but occur, associated with another very advanced character, a winged fruit, in *Plagiopteron*, the latter character also in a few other genera, *Pentace*, *Berrya*, *Colona*, *Trichospermum* and *Diplophractum*. The genus *Carpodiptera* Griseb. (Fig. 199) is of especial interest, with three of the five species in the West Indies, one in the coastal zone of east tropical Africa, and the fifth in the Comoro Islands.

Grewieae, the tribe of which the large genus *Grewia* is typical, is considerably advanced; the petals, when present, are foveolate at the base, and thereby show a close affinity with some *Flacourtiaceae* as already mentioned; and the stamens and ovary are supported on an elevated torus (androgynophore).

Sepaloid petals are characteristic of most of the tribe *Prockieae*, and this may be rather an ancient feature, as it occurs in tribe *Miliuseae* of the more primitive family *Annonaceae*, and in some *Flacourtiaceae*.

A very remarkable genus discovered not many years ago in Peru is the monotypic *Neotessmannia* Burret (1), with a completely inferior ovary, a character previously unknown in the family.

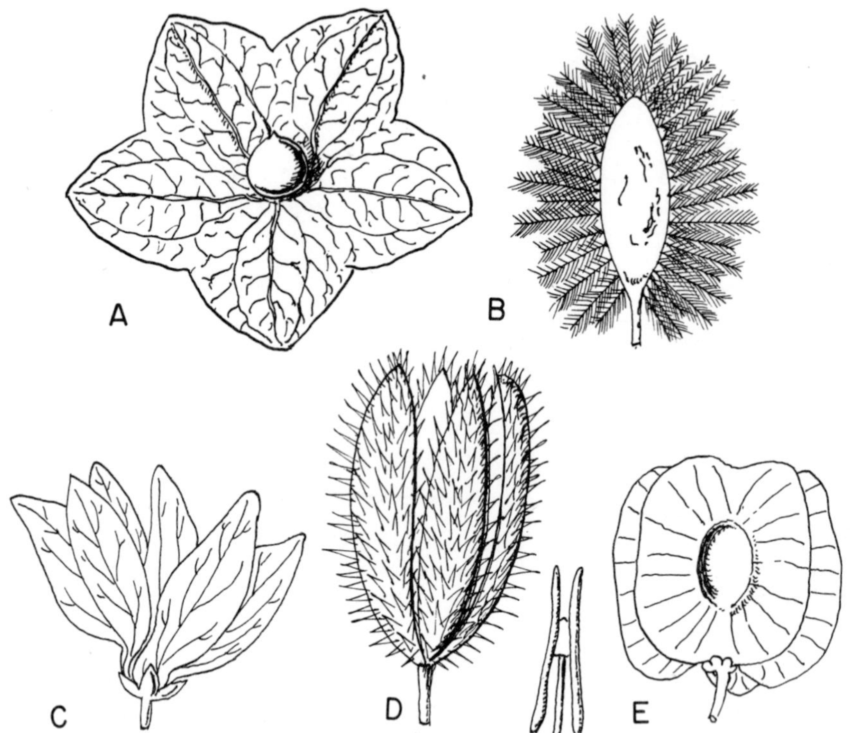

FIG. 204. Fruits of some *Tiliaceae*: **A**, *Schoutenia accrescens* (Maing.) Merrill, Malaya. **B**, *Heliocarpus*[1] *donnell-smithii* Rose, Central America. **C**, *Berrya ammonila* Roxb., Ceylon and India. **D**, *Clappertonia ficifolia* (Willd.) Decne., tropical Africa. **E**, *Pentace burmanica* Kurz, Burma (orig.).

[1] Linnaeus in his "Critica Botanica" (English translation) states:
"It is a distinguishing mark of a very good name that the plant should offer its hand to the name and the name should grasp the plant by the hand; if they are connected so closely that they can hardly be separated, assuredly they ought not to be. For example take *Helianthus*, and *Hippocrepis*, *Heliocarpus* or 'Sunlike fruit'. Who could ever behold an almost round fruit, bordered with a halo of rays, without thinking of the Sun, as conceived by painters? This idea, once associated with the name *Heliocarpus*, unites with it so closely that neither plant nor name can ever come before us without suggesting the idea of the other."

After a close study of the whole group, I do not consider the *Elaeocarpaceae* to be sufficiently distinct for family rank, but this is just a matter of opinion.

The indumentum consists of unicellular or uniseriate simple hairs, of stellate or tufted hairs, the rays of which are usually unicellular, though some-

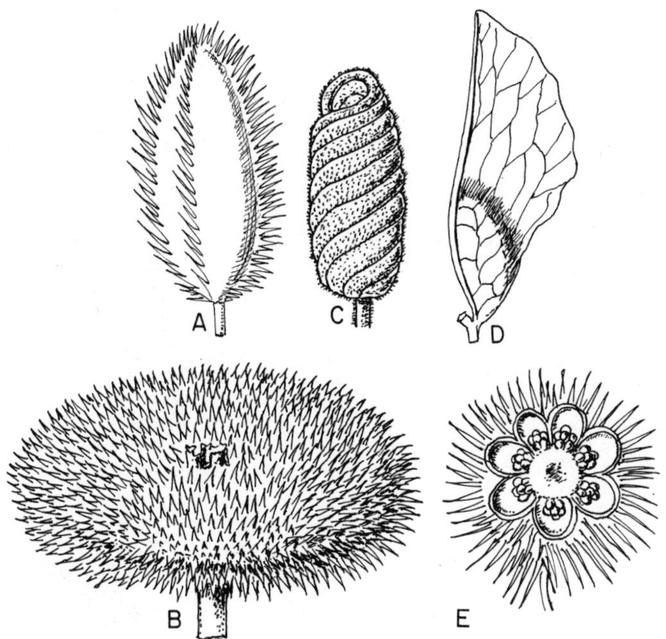

FIG. 205. Fruits of some *Tiliaceae* and *Sterculiaceae*: **A**, *Cephalonema polyandrum* K. Schum., tropical Africa (*Tiliac.*). **B**, *Apeiba echinata* Gaertn., tropical America (*Tiliac.*). **C**, *Helicteres jamaicensis* Jacq., West Indies (*Stercul.*). **D**, *Mansonia dipkae* Purkay, east India (*Stercul.*). **E**, *Entelea arborescens* R.Br., New Zealand (*Tiliac.*) (orig.).

times uniseriate (*Grewieae*), of peltate hairs, and of glandular hairs. The stomata have no special subsidiary cells.

The type genus *Tilia* is familiar to most people throughout the temperate regions of the Northern Hemisphere, through which it is distributed, and represented by about 20 species; they are trees clothed with simple or stellate hairs, and serrate, alternate leaves; cymes axillary or terminal, the peduncles winged up to the middle with the adnate foliaceous or coloured bract; sepals 5, free; petals 5, nude or with a petaloid scale within the base; stamens numerous, free or irregularly united at the base into bundles, all bearing anthers; ovary 5-locular, loculi 2-ovulate; fruit nut-like, indehiscent.

Some valuable fibres are obtained from the phloem of *Corchorus*, especially Jute from *C. capsularis* Linn., *C. olitorius* Linn., and other species. Important timbers are the Linden or European Lime, *Tilia vulgaris* Hayne (actually a hybrid), and the American Basswood, *Tilia americana* Linn., which is put to many uses in the United States of North America. Macqui berries are those of *Aristotelia maqui* L'Herit., Chile and Argentina.

Many years ago when I worked in the Kew Herbarium and was engaged

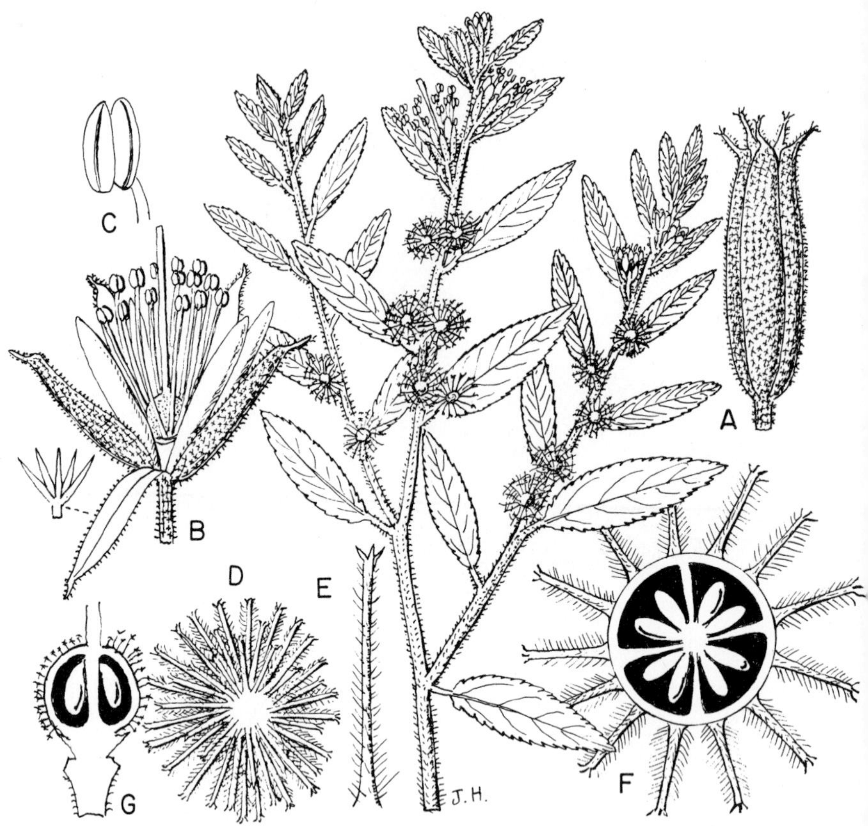

FIG. 206. *Triumfetta setulosa* Masters (*Tiliaceae*), tropical Africa. **A**, calyx in bud showing the horned sepals. **B**, flower and stellate hair. **C**, anther. **D**, fruit. **E**, bristle of fruit. **F**, transverse section of ovary. **G**, vertical section of ovary (orig.).

in sorting collections of dried specimens into families, I was often in doubt as to whether some should be put into *Tiliaceae* or *Sterculiaceae*. So in my recently published GENERA OF FLOWERING PLANTS (Vol. 2, 471) I provided a key to the tribes of these families, using more or less easily observed characters. With the exception of the tribe *Neotessmannieae*, all the tribes of these two families have a superior ovary. The majority have bisexual flowers, but some *Tilieae* and *Triumfetteae* are unisexual, as also in all *Sterculieae* and *Tarrietieae*. The presence or absence of staminodes was also used, nearly equally dividing the combined tribal key into two parts, and a few are characterised by their anthers opening by apical pores, especially tribe *Elaeocarpeae*, often treated as a separate family. Several other characters were used to identify various tribes, such as those which appear to be of

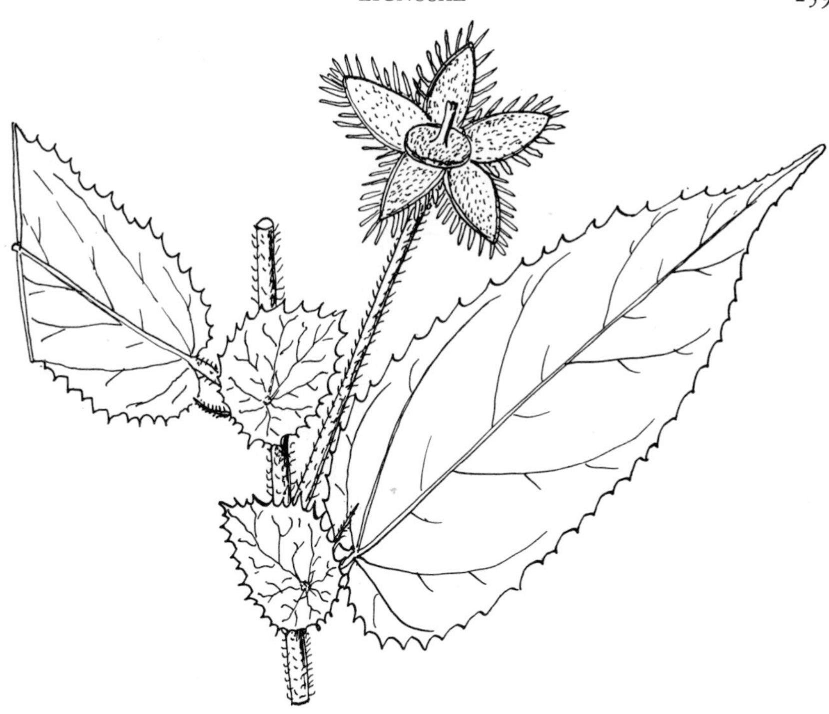

FIG. 207. *Dicraspidia donnell-smithii* Standley (*Tiliaceae*), a remarkable plant of Panama and Costa Rica, with "anisophyllous" stipules; exceptional also in the family in having an inferior ovary, a character it shares with only one other genus in the family, *Neotessmannia* Burret, Peru (orig.).

phylogenetic importance. Thus tribe *Prockieae* (*Tiliaceae*) have petals often more or less similar to the sepals, a feature present as far back as in the much more primitive *Annonaceae*, and in *Berberidopsideae* in the family *Flacourtiaceae*.

To mankind in general the most important thing about the family **Sterculiaceae**[1] is Cocoa, which is specially prepared from the seeds of *Theobroma cacao* Linn. (Fig. 208), a native of the lowlands of tropical America. It is grown in great quantity and exported from several tropical countries, for example Ghana, west Africa, for which it is a principal source of revenue. Cocoa beverage was unknown to Europeans until the voyage of Cortez in 1519, and it was introduced in 1526.

Sterculiaceae are clearly derived from the same stock as the *Tiliaceae*, but are more tropical in their distribution. Although mainly trees and shrubs,

---

[1] Including *Byttneriaceae* R.Br. (1814). *Dombeyaceae* C. H. Schultz (1832). *Hermanniaceae* C. H. Schultz (1832). *Helicteraceae* J. G. Agardh (1858). *Lasiopetalaceae* J. G. Agardh (1858). *Melochiaceae* J. G. Agardh (1858). *Theobromataceae* J. G. Agardh (1858). *Cheiranthodendraceae* A. Gray (1887). *Triplochitonaceae* K. Schum. (1900).

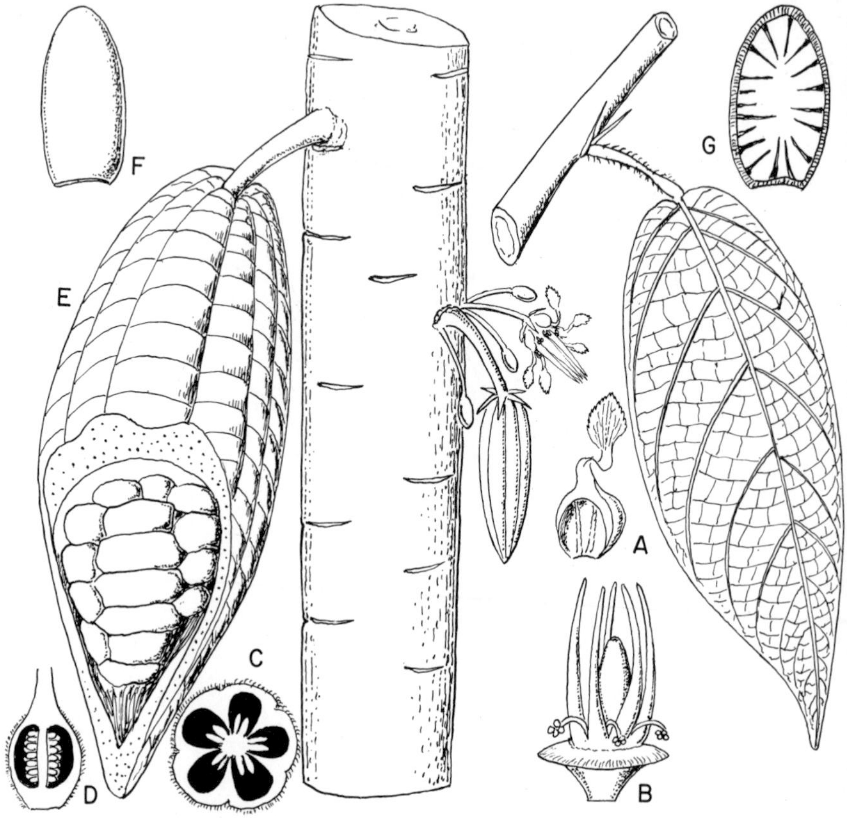

FIG. 208. The Cocoa plant, *Theobroma cacao* Linn. (*Sterculiaceae*), native of lowlands of tropical America, of great economic importance. **A**, petal. **B**, androecium and gynoecium. **C**, cross-section of ovary. **D**, vertical section of ovary. **E**, fruit. **F**, seed. **G**, vertical section of seed.

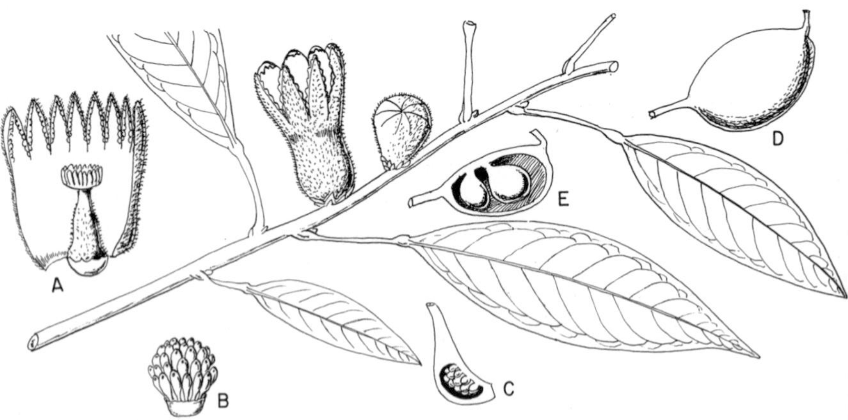

FIG. 209. A very distinct member of the family *Sterculiaceae*, *Octolobus spectabilis* Welw., tropical Africa. **A**, calyx laid open showing the column of stamens which conceal the carpels, **B**. **C**, vertical section of carpel. **D**, carpel in fruit. **E**, section of carpel (orig.).

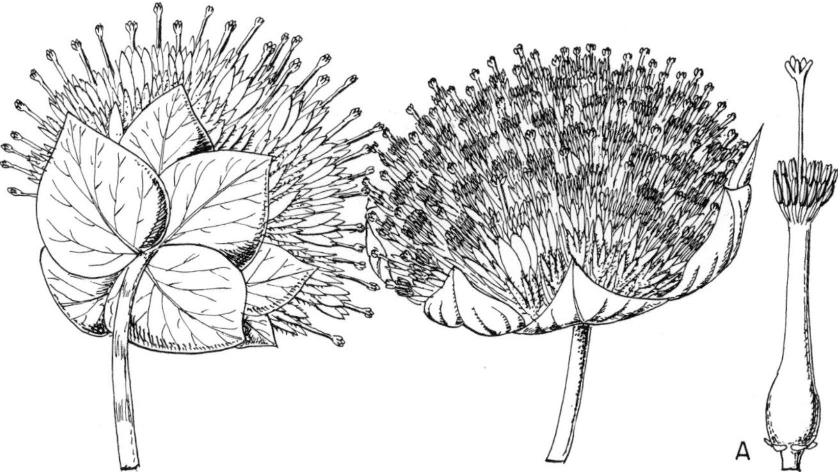

FIG. 210. *Dombeya wallichii* Benth. & Hook. f., India, a highly advanced member of the family *Sterculiaceae*. **A**, stamens and style (orig.).

FIG. 211. *Sterculia foetida* Linn., Old World tropics, the type species of the type genus of *Sterculiaceae*. **A**, leaf. **B**, inflorescence. **C**, androecium. **D**, fruit. **E**, seed and caruncle (orig.).

some herbaceous genera have been evolved such as *Hermannia* and *Mahernia*, which are very numerous in southern Africa; also *Waltheria*, a common weed in the tropics. The last genus is, in addition, one of the most advanced of the family in its floral structure, for the gynoecium is reduced to a single carpel.

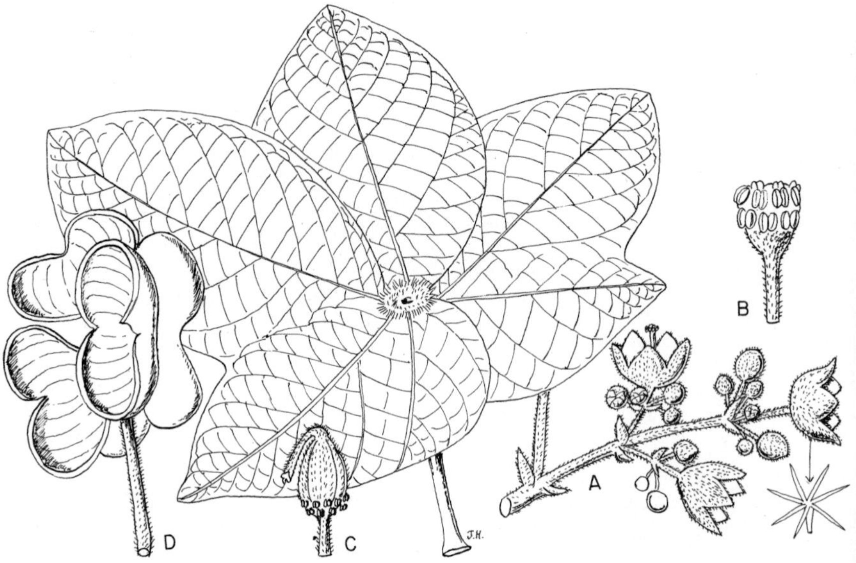

FIG. 212. The Panama Tree, *Sterculia apetala* (Jacq.) Karst., of giant stature, well deserves to be the national tree of Panama, its Indian name, from which the title of the republic is derived. **A**, part of inflorescence. **B**, androecium. **C**, ovary and abortive stamens. **D**, open fruit (orig.).

Some genera of this family show a curious association of characters, with often a mixture of quite primitive and highly advanced type of floral structure. *Octolobus* (Fig. 209), a small genus of low trees in the forests of west Africa, is an example. It possesses only one very primitive feature, a large number of quite free carpels spirally arranged (primitive), but the remainder of the floral characters are highly advanced. The leaves are unifoliolate (by reduction), as shown by the presence of a pulvinus at the top of the petiole; the unisexual flowers are solitary and surrounded at the base by an involucre of bracts, indicating reduction from an inflorescence of several flowers; the calyx is gamosepalous and is coloured to compensate for the absence of petals. Furthermore the stamens are completely united into a column, with the anthers connivent into a ring. The first character, the carpels, therefore, harks back as far as the *Annonaceae* and *Dilleniaceae*, the remainder reaching the standard of evolution as developed in the *Euphorbiaceae*. Indeed, this is quite a disturbing genus, if intensely interesting, to the phylogenist.

Reduction of the petals to scales, or their complete absence, is characteristic of tribe *Lasiopetalae*; and tribe *Dombeyeae* are distinctive because the petals are mostly persistent and often enlarged after flowering. *Dombeya* (Fig. 210) is very highly represented in the Mascarene Islands, where there

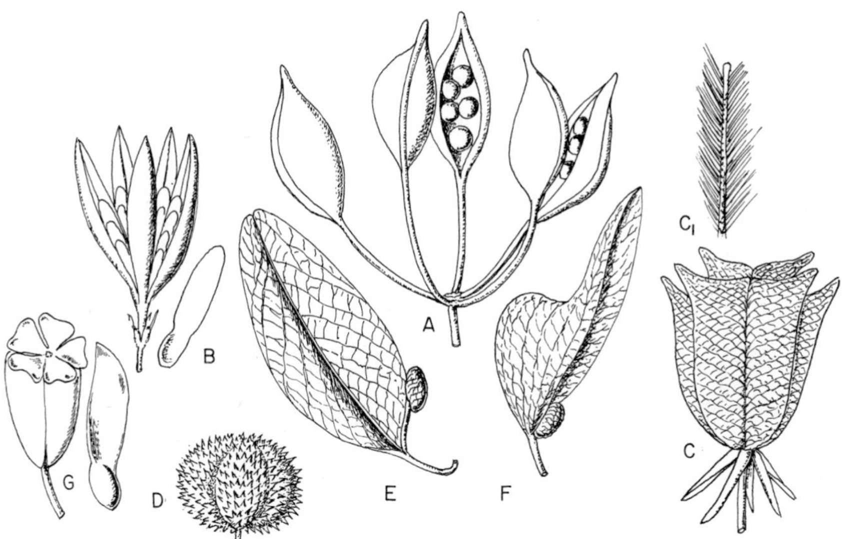

FIG. 213. Fruits of some *Sterculiaceae*. **A**, *Brachychiton populneum* R.Br., Australia. **B**, *Pterospermum grewiifolium* Pierre, and seed. **C**, *Abroma augusta* Linn. f., tropical Asia. **C_1**, placenta of same. **D**, *Guazuma ulmifolia* Lam., tropical America. **E**, *Firmiana odorata* (Roxb.) R.Br., India. **F**, *Pterocymbium javanicum* R.Br., Malaya. **G**, *Nesogordonia papavifera* (A. Chev.) Capuron, and seed, tropical Africa (orig.).

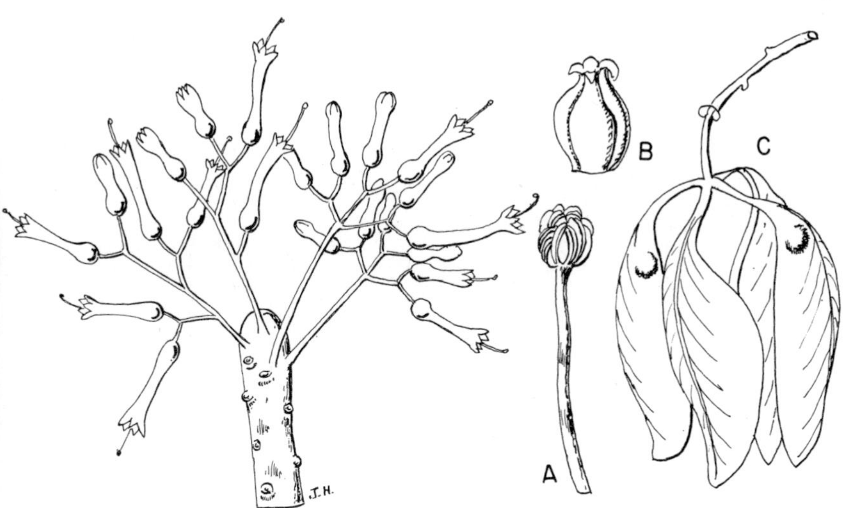

FIG. 214. *Hildegardia barteri* (Mast.) Kosterm. (*Sterculiaceae*), tropical Africa. **A**, androecium. **B**, gynoecium. **C**, fruit.

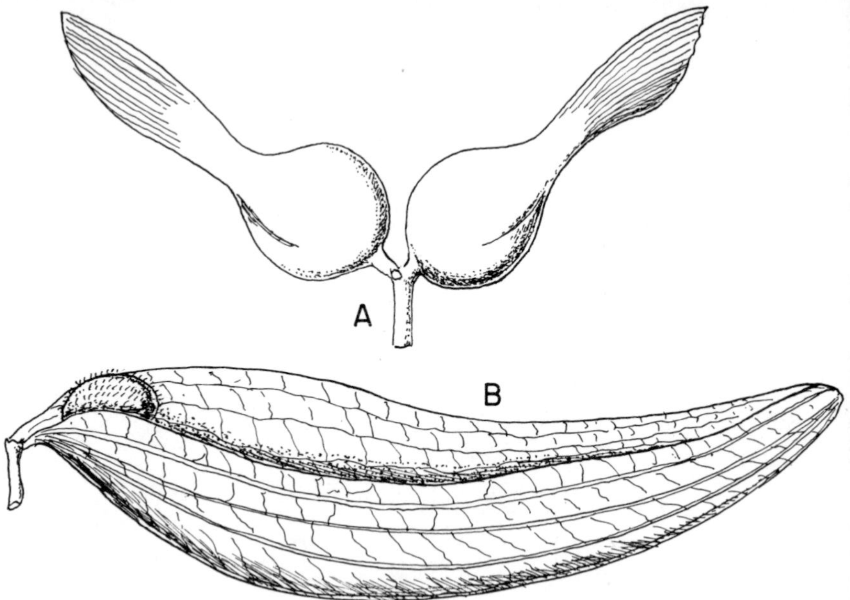

FIG. 215. **A**, fruits of *Heritiera sumatrana* (Miq.) Kosterm., Malay Peninsula. **B**, *Scaphium linearicarpum* (Mast.) Pierre, Malacca (*Sterculiaceae*).

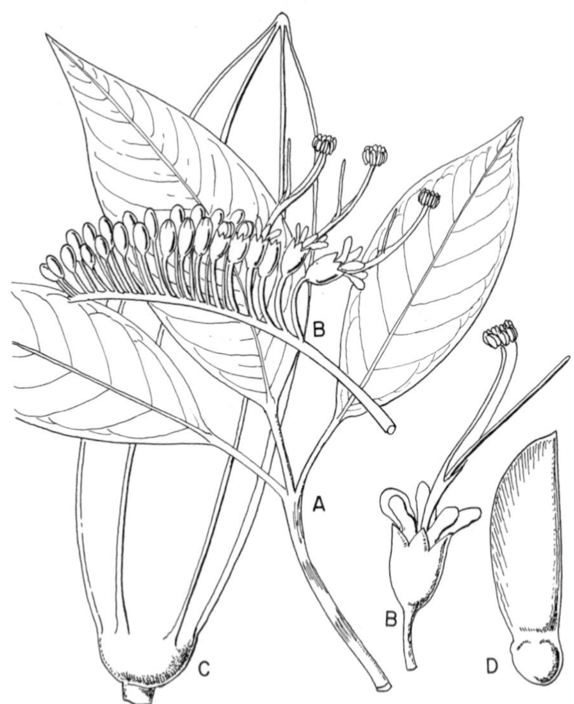

FIG. 216. **A**, leaf, **B**, flowers, **C**, fruit, and **D**, seed of *Bernoullia flammea* Oliv. (*Sterculiaceae*), Central America; note the curious secund inflorescence, and the split staminal tube through which the style emerges (orig.).

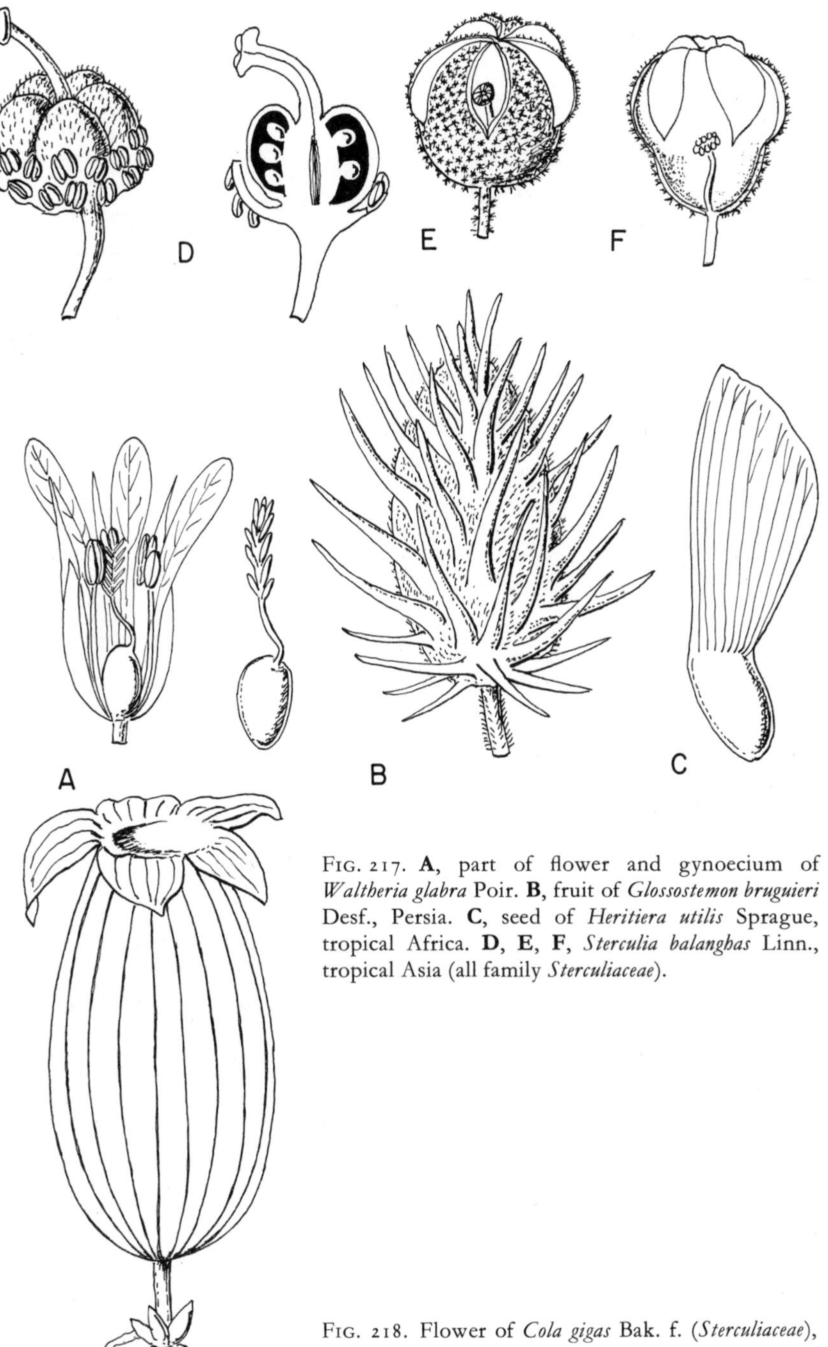

FIG. 217. **A**, part of flower and gynoecium of *Waltheria glabra* Poir. **B**, fruit of *Glossostemon bruguieri* Desf., Persia. **C**, seed of *Heritiera utilis* Sprague, tropical Africa. **D**, **E**, **F**, *Sterculia balanghas* Linn., tropical Asia (all family *Sterculiaceae*).

FIG. 218. Flower of *Cola gigas* Bak. f. (*Sterculiaceae*), west tropical Africa.

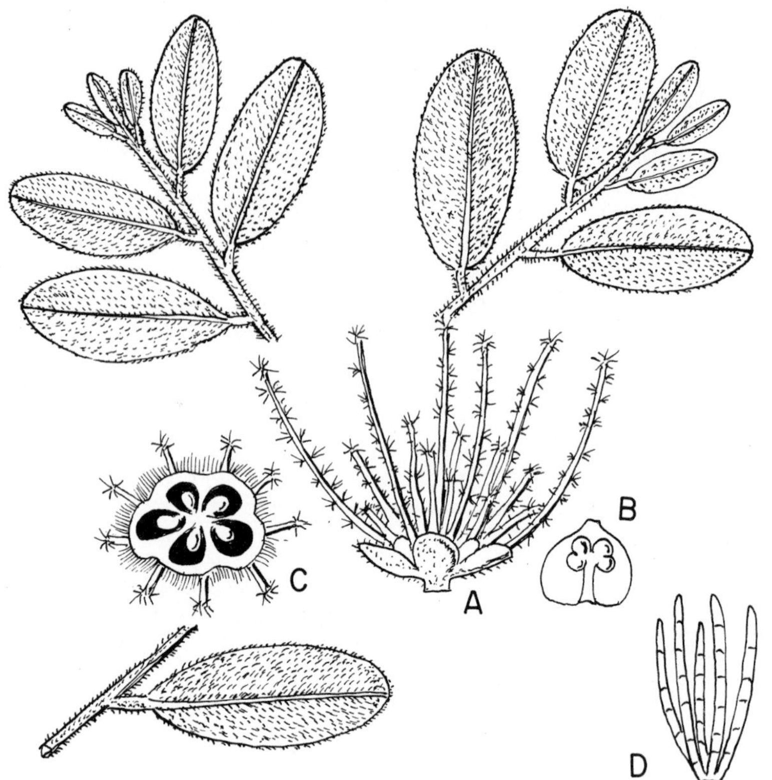

FIG. 219. *Pimia rhamnoides* Seem. (*Sterculiaceae*), a rare tree of Fiji, 40–50 ft high. **A**, flower. **B**, petal and stamen. **C**, cross-section of ovary. **D**, a tuft of hairs (orig.).

are over 180 species, many with handsome heads of flowers. *Sterculia* is burdened with no less than over 20 synonyms!

The type genus, *Sterculia*, contains about 100 spp., confined to the tropics; the type (selected) of the genus is *S. foetida* Linn. (Fig. 211), tropical Asia; trees; characters of this genus are: leaves undivided, lobed or digitately compound; inflorescence paniculate or racemose; flowers unisexual or polygamous, the terminal mostly female and more precocious; calyx 5- rarely 4-fid or partite, often more or less petaloid; petals absent; staminal column irregularly 15–18-anthered at the apex; carpels 5, partly free, 2–more-ovulate; style peltate or lobed at the apex; mature carpels free, spreading stellately in fruit, soon dehiscing; seeds with endosperm often resembling thick cotyledons, the latter flat and thin.

The type genus, as sometimes happens, is not typical of the family as a whole. It belongs to the tribe *Sterculieae*, which differs from the other eight

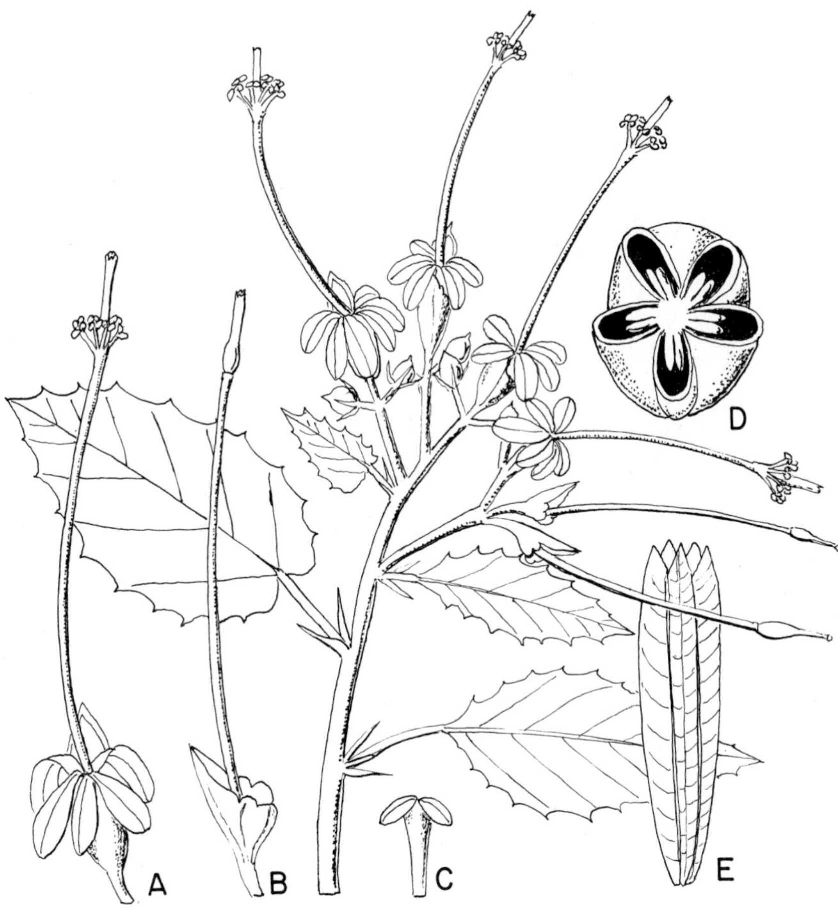

FIG. 220. *Helicteres trapezifolia* La Sagra (*Sterculiaceae*), Cuba (a rare plant only known to me by the drawing in La Sagra FL. CUBANA (1853)). **A**, flower, showing the very long androgynophore. **B**, calyx and gynophore with gynoecium. **C**, stamen. **D**, cross-section of ovary. **E**, fruit.

tribes in having unisexual or polygamous apetalous flowers, with the carpels free, especially in fruit.

The Panama tree, *Sterculia apetala* (Jacq.) Karst. (Fig. 212), is common in the Panama canal zone and often planted for shade. It is of rather giant stature, up to 120 ft high, with a thick trunk and a broad dense crown. The leaves are up to 2 ft wide and with 3 or 5 broad entire lobes and softly tomentose below with star-shaped hairs. The unisexual flowers are borne in large axillary panicles and consist of a bell-shaped 5-lobed calyx reddish and woolly outside and dark red and greenish yellow inside. There are no petals, these having been lost during the course of evolution. The fruit is a

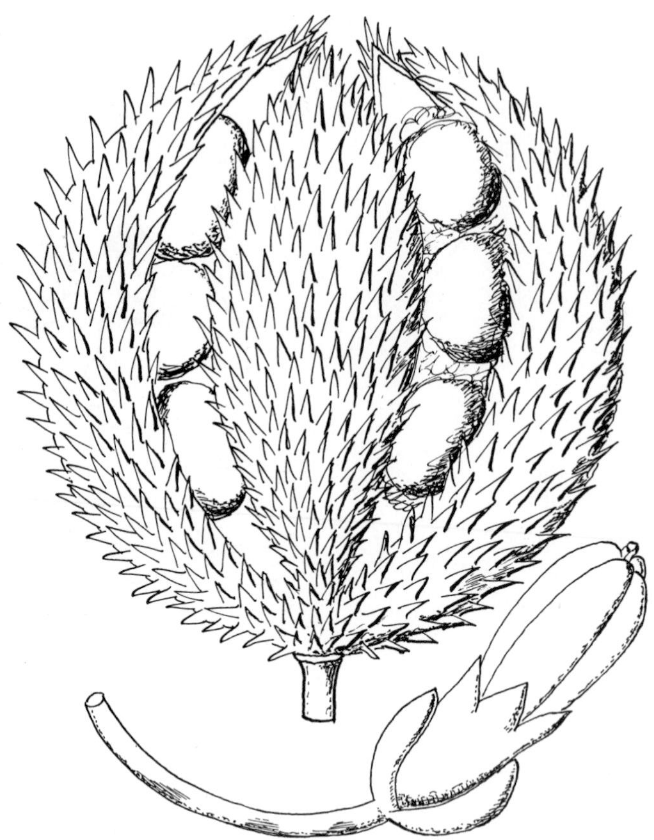

FIG. 221. Flower and fruit of the Durian, *Durio zibethinus* Murr. (*Sterculiaceae*), Malaya.

cluster of 5 carpels about 4 in. long, containing large brown chestnut-like seeds. Beware of the interior of the carpels, which is covered with stiff bristles that pierce the skin and cause intense irritation like the hairs on the *Mucuna* pods in the family *Fabaceae*. The seeds, however, known as castanas, are edible.

This tree well deserves to be the national tree of Panama (*fide* Standley), for it is from its Indian name *Panama* that the title of the republic is derived. The tree ranges from southern Mexico to the West Indies and northern South America. According to Standley, in Guatemala, Salvador and Honduras, the tree is called *castano*, in Tabasco *bellota*, in Columbia *camajon*, in Cuba *camaruca*.

The family **Bombacaceae**[1] is confined to the tropics and most numerous

[1] Including *Fremontiaceae* J. G. Agardh (1858).

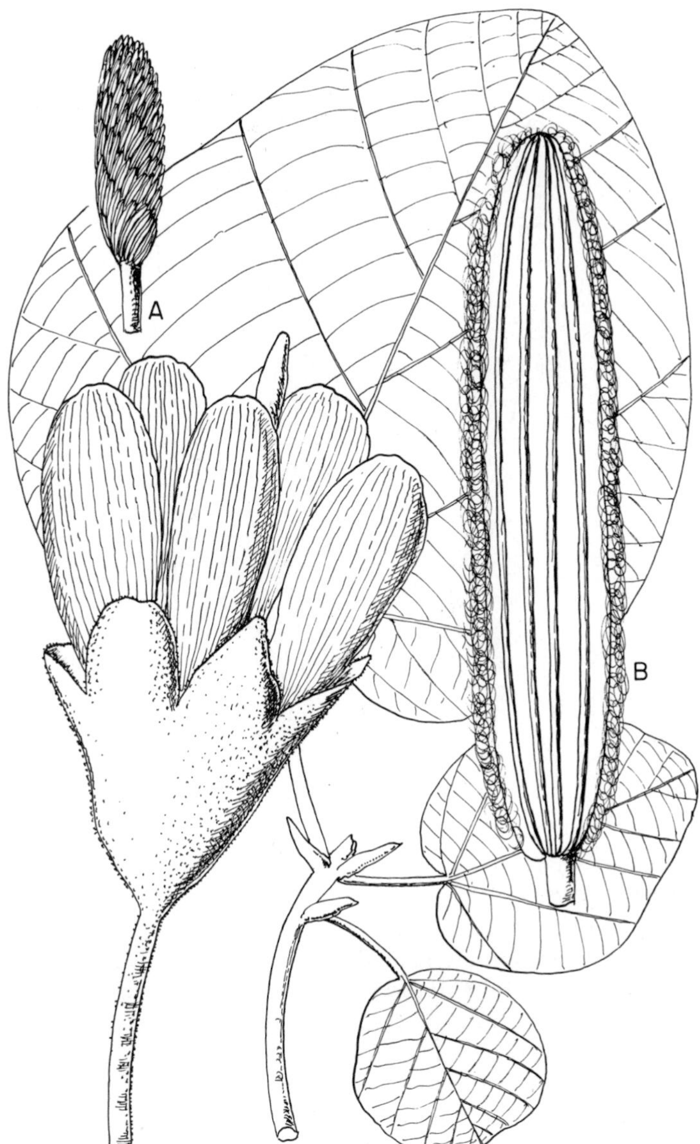

FIG. 222. Balsa tree, *Ochroma pyramidalis* (Cav. ex Lam.) Urban (*Bombacaceae*), better known as *Ochroma lagopus* Sw. The very light wood of this tree was used for the Kon-Tiki raft; the seeds are surrounded by wool inside the capsule, and the wool is used by the people of Ecuador for stuffing pillows. **A**, stamens. **B**, fruit (orig.).

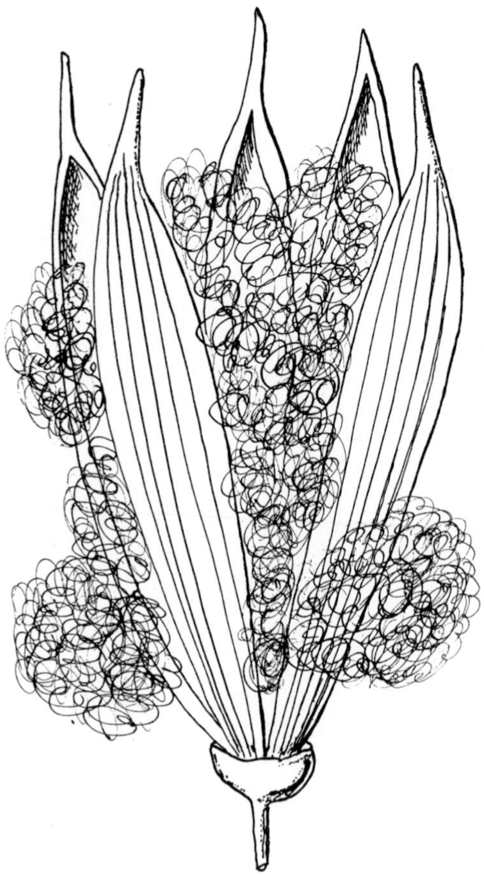

FIG. 223. Fruit and woolly seeds of the Silk Cotton tree, *Ceiba pentandra* Gaertn. (*Bombacaceae*), tropical Africa and Asia.

in America. They are closely related backward to *Sterculiaceae* on the one hand and forward to the *Malvaceae* on the other, but have retained their character. The genus *Ochroma*, *O. pyramidalis* (Cav. ex. Lam.) Urb. (*O. lagopus* Sw.) (Fig. 222), received much publicity a few years ago because the Kon-Tiki and the Seven Little Sisters rafts were made of this lightest and most buoyant of commercial timbers. It is indigenous in the tropical forests from south Mexico to northern Peru, most of it supplied by Ecuador. Kapok, one of the most valuable of stuffing materials, is the floss produced on the inside of the fruits of *Ceiba pentandra* Gaertn. (Fig. 223), originally found only in the American tropics, but now scattered in Africa and Asia. The floss is impervious to water and for this reason it is employed for life-jackets, portable pontoons, etc., and for insulation.

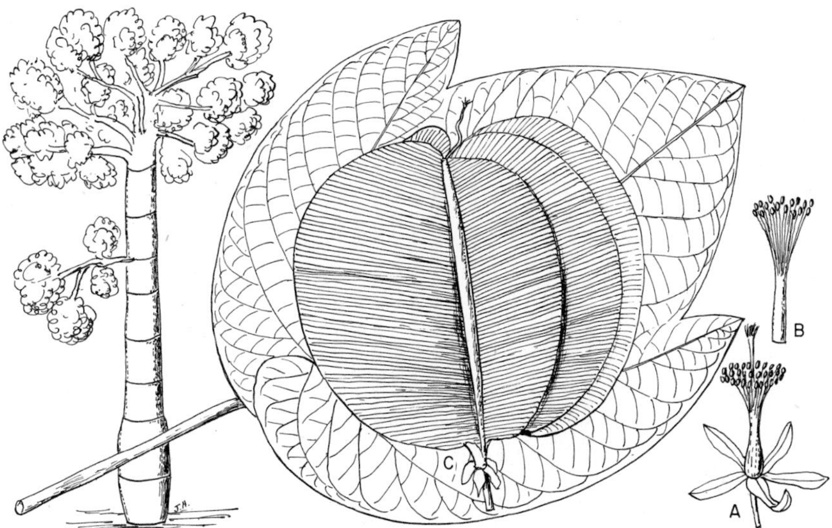

FIG. 224. *Cavanillesia platanifolia* H. B. & K. (*Bombacaceae*), one of the most remarkable trees of the Panama region; trunk marked by transverse scars; wood very soft and pith-like, used for making rafts. **A**, flower. **B**, androecium. **C**, fruit imposed on leaf (orig.).

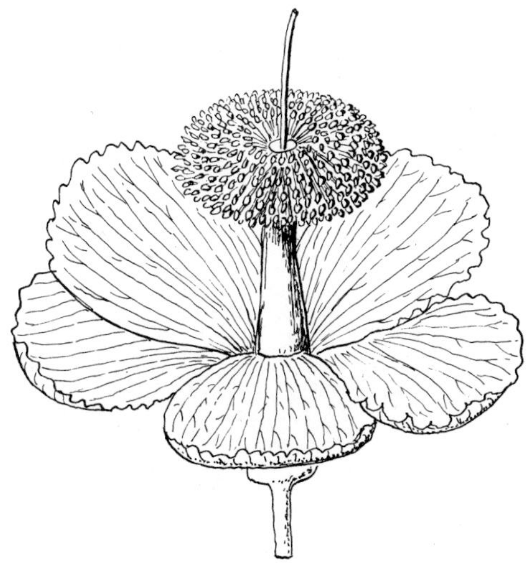

FIG. 225. Flower of the African Baobab, *Adansonia digitata* Linn. (*Bombacaceae*). This very distinct genus of giant trees is found in tropical and subtropical Africa, Madagascar, and N.W. Australia. (For map showing the range of this genus see FAMILIES OF FLOWERING PLANTS, 2nd Ed. **1**, 253.)

Bombax, the type genus, with about 8 species, consists of trees, sometimes very tall; leaves digitately compound; flowers axillary or subterminal,

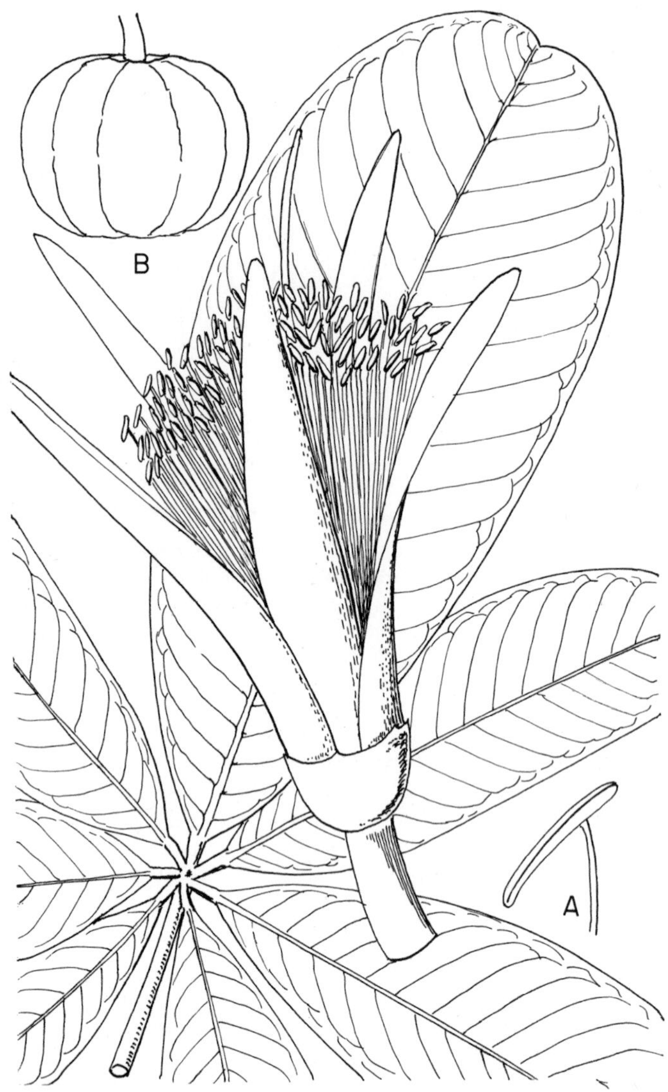

FIG. 226. Leaf and flower of *Pachira insignis* Savign. (*Bombaceaceae*), tropical America. **A**, anther. **B**, fruit (orig.).

often white; calyx cupular; petals narrow to obovate; staminal column divided in the upper part into numerous 1-anthered filaments, sometimes connate in pairs into 5 or more bundles; ovary 5-locular, loculi many-ovuled; capsule woody or coriaceous, loculicidally 5-valved, densely woolly inside; seeds with thin endosperm and cotyledons much contorted–folded and wrapped around the radicle.

ORDER 33. MALVALES

(*Fam. Fl. Pl.* 1, 254)

Single family: **Malvaceae.**

Accorded an Order of its own in the present system to emphasise its completely climax position; clearly derived from the less advanced and woody TILIALES, the habit often reduced to shrubs and herbs.

Phylogeny: MAGNOLIALES → DILLENIALES → BIXALES → TILIALES → **BOMBACACEAE** → **MALVALES.**

Malvaceae[1] is a very homogeneous and well marked family. Though often herbs, they have mainly fibrous stems and are probably derived from the preceding woody groups. The supposed affinity of this family and *Geraniaceae* is due in my opinion to superficial resemblance. Every taxonomist knows that *Malvaceae* are frequently clothed with stellate hairs. There are often bristle-hairs, which are unicellular or uniseriate, and peltate and glandular hairs of varied structure. They also have secretory organs containing mucilage; these are either epidermal cells which have a mucilaginous inner membrane and frequently give rise to transparent dots in the leaf, or cells with mucilaginous walls in the ground-tissue of axis and leaf, or mucilage-cavities of lysigenous origin sometimes differentiated as canals.

Malva, the type genus of over 100 species (type species *M. sylvestris* Linn. (Fig. 227)) consists of glabrous or hairy herbs, leaves toothed, lobed or dissected; flowers solitary or fasciculate in the leaf-axils, rarely in terminal racemes, rose or white (never yellow); bracteoles 3, free; calyx 5-fid; staminal column divided at the apex into numerous filaments; ovary-loculi numerous, 1-ovulate; style-branches filiform, stigmatose along the inner face; carpels arranged in a circle, 1-seeded, beakless, indehiscent, separating from the axis; seed ascending.

Evolution within the family has been slight, and the range of floral structure is therefore not very great. Lines of descent may be traced by certain characters. In some large genera, such as *Hibiscus*, the tracing of the gradual evolution of the involucre of bracteoles (the epicalyx) provides an interesting phylogenetic study.

Tribe *Malopeae* is probably the most primitive group, at least as to the carpels which are numerous and arranged more or less spirally. The remainder of the tribes have the carpels arranged in a single whorl (by reduction). Of these, in *Abutileae*, *Malveae* and *Sideae* the staminal column bears

---

[1] Including *Philippodendraceae* Endlich. (1839). *Hibiscaceae* A. G. Agardh (1858). *Plagianthaceae* J. G. Agardh (1858). *Tubifilaceae* Dulac. (1867).

FIG. 227. *Malva sylvestris* Linn., the type species of the type genus of the family *Malvaceae*. **A**, petal. **B**, androecium. **C**, anther. **D**, cross-section of ovary. **E**, fruit and calyx. **F**, fruiting carpel. **G**, seed (orig.).

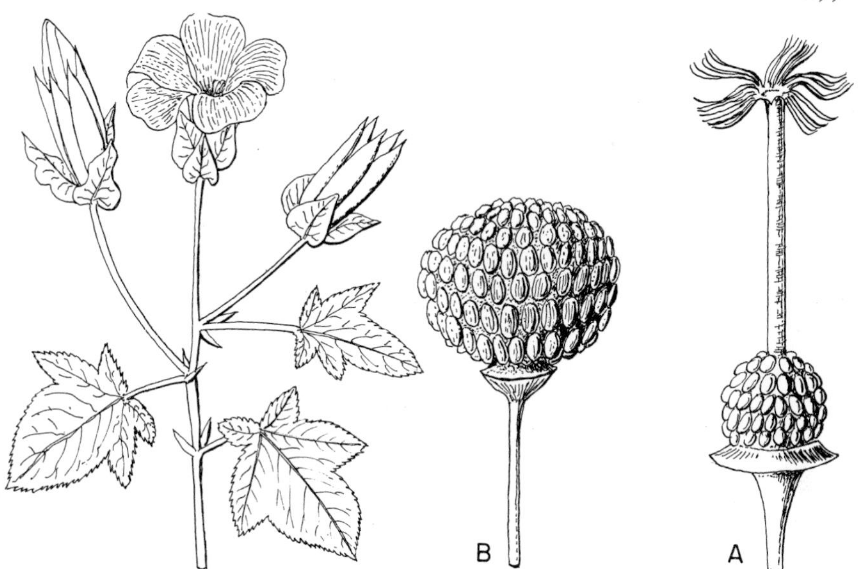

FIG. 228. *Malope trifida* Cav. **A**, flower with perianth removed. **B**, carpels in fruit (adapted from Baillon).

anthers right up to the apex, whilst in *Hibisceae* and *Ureneae*, the staminal column is without anthers at the top and is truncate or 5-toothed, and in the tribe which may be considered the most advanced, the *Ureneae* (incidentally also represented by numerous highly successful weeds), the carpels fall away from the axis in fruit.

The irregularly arranged 1-seeded carpels of *Malope* (Fig. 228) and related genera might lend support to the possibility of that group having been derived more directly from the RANALES. But the remainder of their characters are on the whole considerably more advanced than any of the latter. Another feature of considerable importance is the barren upper part of the staminal column of the *Ureneae*, associated as it is with the reduction of the carpels to 5 in number, both features indicating this tribe to be considerably advanced. In addition the style branches and stigmas are twice the number of the carpels, in contrast to the other tribes in which the styles are the same number as the carpels.

There are very few outstanding genera. In *Abelmoschus* the calyx is spathaceous and deciduous after flowering. In the monotypic *Neobaclea* (*N. crispifolia* (Cav.) Krapov), Argentina, the calyx-lobes are very broad, cordate, pinnately lobulate, appearing to be winged and spirally twisted in bud. In nearly all genera the petals are partly adnate to the base of the staminal column, but in *Humbertianthus* (Madagascar), shrubs or small trees, they are quite free, small and suborbicular.

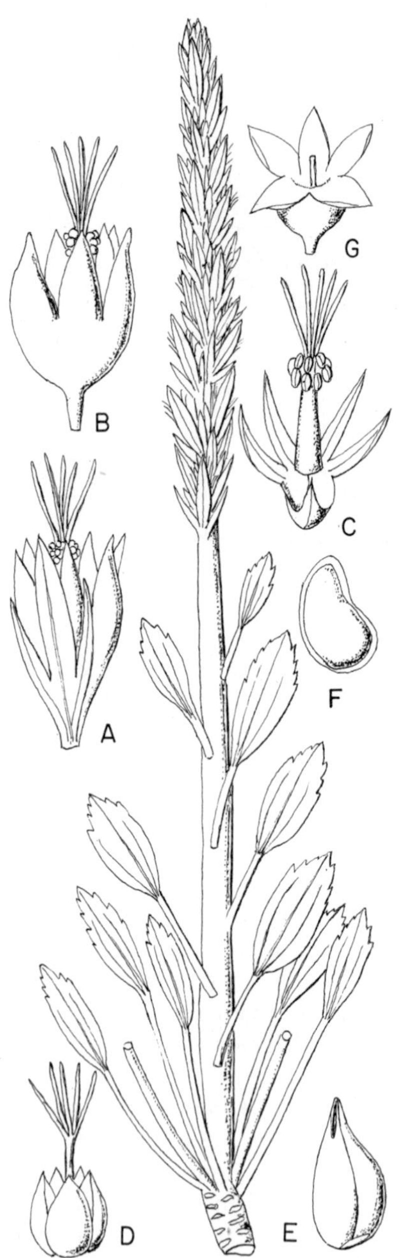

FIG. 229. *Lawrencia spicata* Hook., Australia and Tasmania, a species with a distinct habit in the family *Malvaceae*. **A**, flower showing the deeply lobed bract. **B**, the same without the bract. **C**, petals removed. **D**, carpels and style. **E**, carpel. **F**, seed. **G**, corolla (orig.).

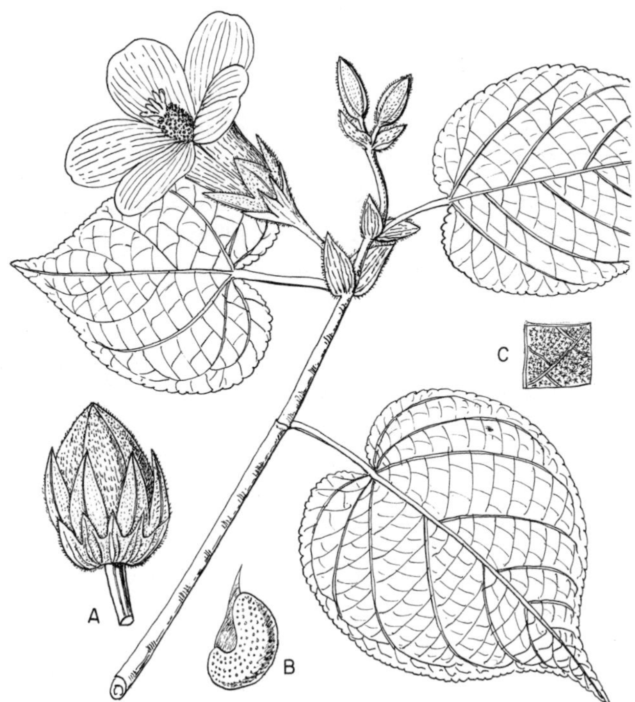

FIG. 230. *Hibiscus tiliaceus* Linn. (*Malvaceae*), a common strand tree in tropical countries; up to 30 ft; flowers yellow; bark used in Pacific Islands for Hula Hula skirts, fishing lines and ropes. **A**, fruit. **B**, seed. **C**, lower portion of leaf showing stellate hairs (orig.).

Malvaceae are found in all regions except very cold ones, but are most numerous in warm temperate and tropical countries, especially in South America. *Malva rotundifolia* Linn. reaches farthest north in Europe, whilst species of *Hoheria* and *Plagianthus* occur farthest south, in New Zealand. In the Andes of South America a large number of species of *Nototriche*, a very advanced genus phylogenetically, are found up to a very high altitude and are mostly acaulescent.

ORDER 34. MALPIGHIALES

(*Fam. Fl. Pl.* **1**, 255)

Families: **Ixonanthaceae, Malpighiaceae, Humiriaceae, Linaceae, Irvingiaceae, Huaceae, Ledocarpaceae, Erythroxylaceae, Ctenolophonaceae, Lepidobotryaceae, Balanitaceae, Zygophyllaceae.**

Except for the family *Malpighiaceae*, which gives to the Order its name, this is a group of mostly very small families which have retained their woody habit, except in the most highly evolved family, *Zygophyllaceae*, in which there are herbs, some of them tropical weeds; pedigree as follows: MAGNOLILAES → DILLENIALES → BIXALES (*Flacourtiaceae*) → TILIALES → **MALPIGHIALES** → climax family *Zygophyllaceae* (some herbs).

The family **Malpighiaceae** is a very natural one and easily recognised. It consists of trees and shrubs, rarely shrublets, often climbers. The indumentum, when present, is usually of medifixed T-shaped hairs, known to taxonomists as Malpighian hairs. This type of hair is probably derived by reduction from the many-rayed stellate hairs so common a feature of the more primitive Order TILIALES. The stomata are of the Rubiaceous type, i.e. they have special subsidiary cells parallel to the pore. Often members of this family may be spotted by the large more or less fleshy glands either on the margin or on the lower side of the leaves, or sometimes on the petiole, but more especially on the calyx where they are often in pairs at the base of the sepals; also by the frequently clawed petals. The seeds have no endosperm.

Usually the habit is climbing and the leaves have become opposite, while there is a corresponding reduction in the number of the carpels and various modifications in the fruit, often of a samaroid type. The headquarters of the family is in tropical and subtropical South America, a few occurring as far north as Texas and southwards to Argentina. The family is relatively poorly represented in the Old World tropics and subtropics.

The type genus[1] is *Malpighia* Linn. (type species *M. glabra* Linn., Texas to Peru, Fig. 231): small trees or shrubs, sometimes with long and short shoots; leaves opposite, some linear, entire or spiny-dentate; hairs of some stinging; flowers bisexual, axillary and terminal, fasciculate or subumbellate-corymbose, rarely solitary; calyx 5-partite, 5–10-glandular; petals clawed, denticulate; stamens 10, all perfect; ovary entire, 3-locular; styles 3, free, stigma truncate; fruit a fleshy drupe of 3 pyrenes, these at length scarcely coherent, crested or ribbed on the back; seeds with straight embryo.

In tribe *Malpighieae*, to which the type genus belongs, the habit is mostly erect, the flowers have a flat or concave torus (floral axis), and the drupaceous fruits are neither winged nor covered with long bristles; and the stamens are usually all fertile; all American. In the other four tribes the torus is pyramidal, usually 3-sided, and the carpels separate when mature; stem mostly climbing. Dimorphic flowers occur in tribe *Gaudichaudieae*. Apart from a few edible fruits, economic properties are not important.

---

[1] Linnaeus named the genus in honour of Marcello Malpighi, born in 1628 at Crevalcoure in Bologna, professor of medicine from 1656 in Bologna, physician to Pope Innocent XII, and died in Rome in 1693. Malpighi published ANATOME PLANTARUM, etc., in London, 1675–79, with a wonderful frontispiece, and OPERA OMNIA, etc., in London in 1686.

FIG. 231. *Malpighia glabra* Linn., Texas to Peru and West Indies, the type species of the type genus of *Malpighiaceae*. **A**, petal. **B**, stamens. **C**, gynoecium.

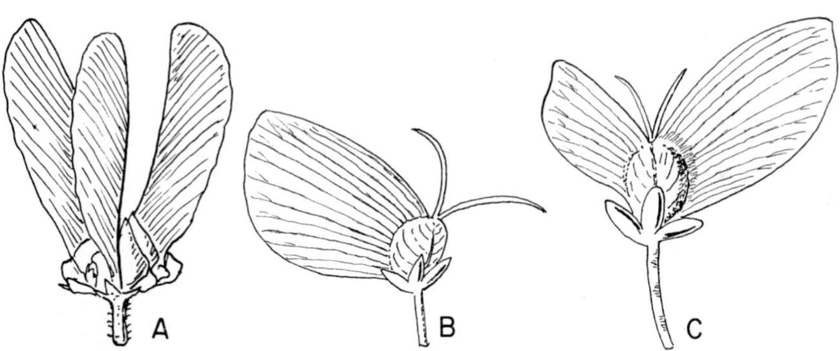

FIG. 232. Fruits of some *Malpighiaceae*: **A**, *Banisteria argentea* Spreng., South America. **B** and **C**, *Acridocarpus orientalis* A. Juss., South Africa (orig.).

The small family **Ixonanthaceae**, established by Exell and Mendonça in 1951, was formerly regarded as a subfamily of *Linaceae* with which it is no doubt closely related. There are now five genera included: 1, *Allantospermum* Forman, described in the same year by a French botanist as *Cleistanthopsis*, the one on a Bornean species and the other on a Madagascar species, a very remarkable distribution as well as coincidence; 2, *Ixonanthes* Jack, the type genus, about 12 species in tropical Asia and New Guinea; 3, *Ochthocosmus* Benth., about five species confined to tropical South America, with winged seeds; 4, *Phyllocosmus* Klotzsch, a close relative, 15 species on the opposite side of the south Atlantic in tropical Africa; and 5, *Cyrillopsis*

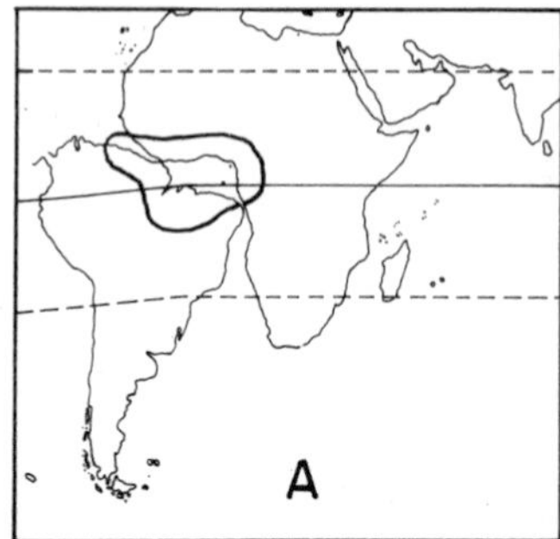

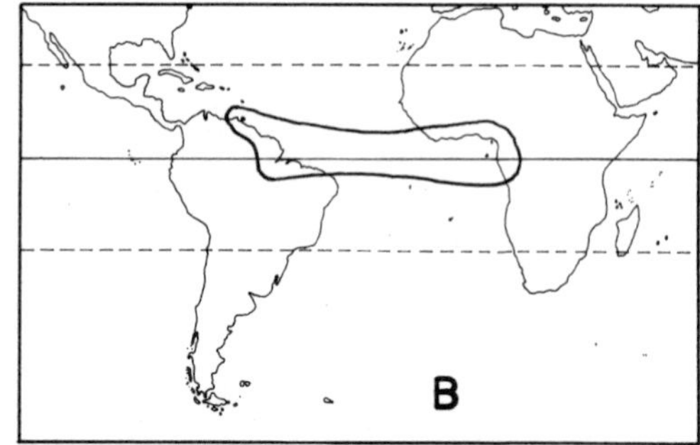

MAP 15. Although the distribution of the very natural (homogeneous) genus *Sacoglottis* (*Humiriaceae*) is at the present day discontinuous as shown in Map **B**, it was continuous before South America drifted apart from Africa as shown in Map **A**; a significant botanical example in favour of the theory of continental drift.

FIG. 233. *Sacoglottis gabonensis* Urban (*Humiriaceae*), west tropical Africa. **A**, flower bud. **B**, vertical section of flower. **C** and **D**, stamens. **E**, cross-section of ovary. **F**, fruits. (From Hutchinson and Dalziel, FLORA OF WEST TROPICAL AFRICA.)

Kuhlmann, one species in Brazil, transferred by Forman from the *Cyrillaceae*.

Ixonanthes is a genus of trees with simple, alternate, pinnately nerved leaves, minute stipules, and small bisexual flowers in axillary cymes; sepals 5, shortly connate; petals 5, contorted, persistent; stamens 20–10, inserted on an annular or cupular disk; ovary 5-locular; ovules 2 in each loculus; style undivided, stigma discoid; capsule septicidally dehiscent, the loculi often spuriously septate; seeds with a wing-like aril. Type species *I. reticulata* Jack, Malaya.

The family **Humiriaceae** was established by Jussieu in 1829. He included only two genera, *Humiria* (*Humirium*) and *Helleria*. The latter name, however, is antedated by *Vantanea* Aubl. (1775). The family was similarly maintained by A. de Jussieu (1829), Lindley (1830), Meisner (1837), Endlicher (1840), Miers (1852), Bentham and Hooker (1862) and also by Reiche in Engler and Prantl DIE NATÜRLICHEN PFLANZENFAMILIEN (1890).

Baillon, who often took a very comprehensive view of families, included them, in 1874, in *Linaceae*, a procedure followed by Hubert Winkler in the second edition of Engler's DIE NATÜRLICHEN PFLANZENFAMILIEN (1931),

As constituted the family is homogeneous. The genera now increased to eight are trees with simple, alternate leaves, and rather small flowers arranged in lateral or terminal cymes or panicles. The most noteworthy features of the family are the peculiar anthers and fruits. The anthers have a large thick broadly conical connective on the sides of which the short loculi are borne like a pair of ear-rings; some have 2, others 4 loculi. The fruit is drupaceous with a woody or bony putamen, and all the genera have a simple style.

Sacoglottis (Fig. 233) is the most interesting genus from a geographical standpoint, for it is found on both sides of the Atlantic, a natural distribution for several other genera in various families and providing additional evidence in support of Wegener's hypothesis of drifting continents (see Map 15).

A comprehensive revision and history of this small and very homogeneous family, a model of its kind, has been published by Jose Cuatrecasas (CONTRIB. UN. ST. NAT. HERB. **35**, pt. 2, 1–214, Figs 1–38 (1961)). I have adopted his classification in my GENERA OF FLOWERING PLANTS, Vol. 2 (1967), in which he recognises eight genera, the most primitive being *Vantanea*, with numerous stamens, the remainder of the genera having 30 or less. Of the latter *Duckesia* and *Endopleura* have 4-locular anthers, the loculi superposed in pairs, the remainder with 2-locular anthers. *Sacoglottis* has the least number of stamens (10) and is no doubt the most advanced genus, besides being most widely distributed.

In the first edition of my FAMILIES OF FLOWERING PLANTS I left the family **Linaceae**[1] in the Order GERANIALES, that is to say amongst an entirely herbaceous group. After further study of the family, however, I have no hesitation in saying that, as here restricted, it clearly belongs to the woody subphylum **LIGNOSAE**, and should stand near to *Erythroxylaceae*, following on the TILIALES alliance of families.

Botanists in the temperate Northern Hemisphere may be apt, as I was

[1] Including *Hugoniaceae* Arnott (1834). *Disandraceae* Dulac (1867).

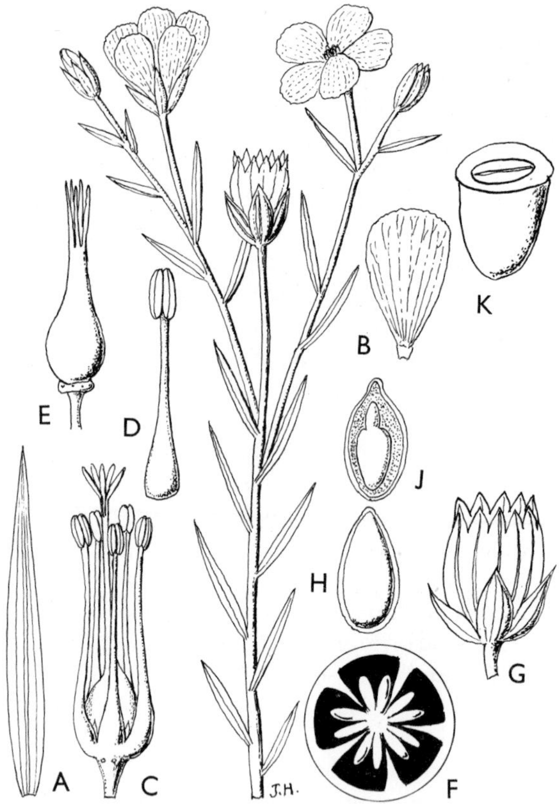

FIG. 234. *Linum usitatissimum* Linn., the type species of the type genus of *Linaceae*. **A**, leaf. **B**, petal. **C**, androecium and gynoecium. **D**, stamen. **E**, gynoecium. **F**, cross-section of ovary. **G**, calyx and fruit. **H**, seed. **J**, vertical section of seed. **K**, cross-section of seed.

myself, to regard *Linaceae* in terms of *Linum*, with which they are most familiar. Although the majority of the species of *Linum* are herbaceous, and some even annuals, there are many which have a woody rootstock, and at least one species, *L. arboreum* Linn. in Crete, is a real shrub with a single woody much branched stem. *Linum*, therefore, is now regarded by me as a partially herbaceous genus derived from more woody ancestors. Parallel cases are *Potentilla* in *Rosaceae*, *Triumfetta* in *Tiliaceae* and many *Fabaceae*.

Flax, *Linum usitatissimum* Linn. (Fig. 234), is one of the most valuable of fibres employed by man from prehistoric times. It is grown in many countries not only for its fibre but also for its seed, from which linseed oil is expressed.

Linum, the type genus, as stated above, varies in habit from undershrubs to herbs; stipules are absent or gland-like; leaves rarely opposite; sepals 5;

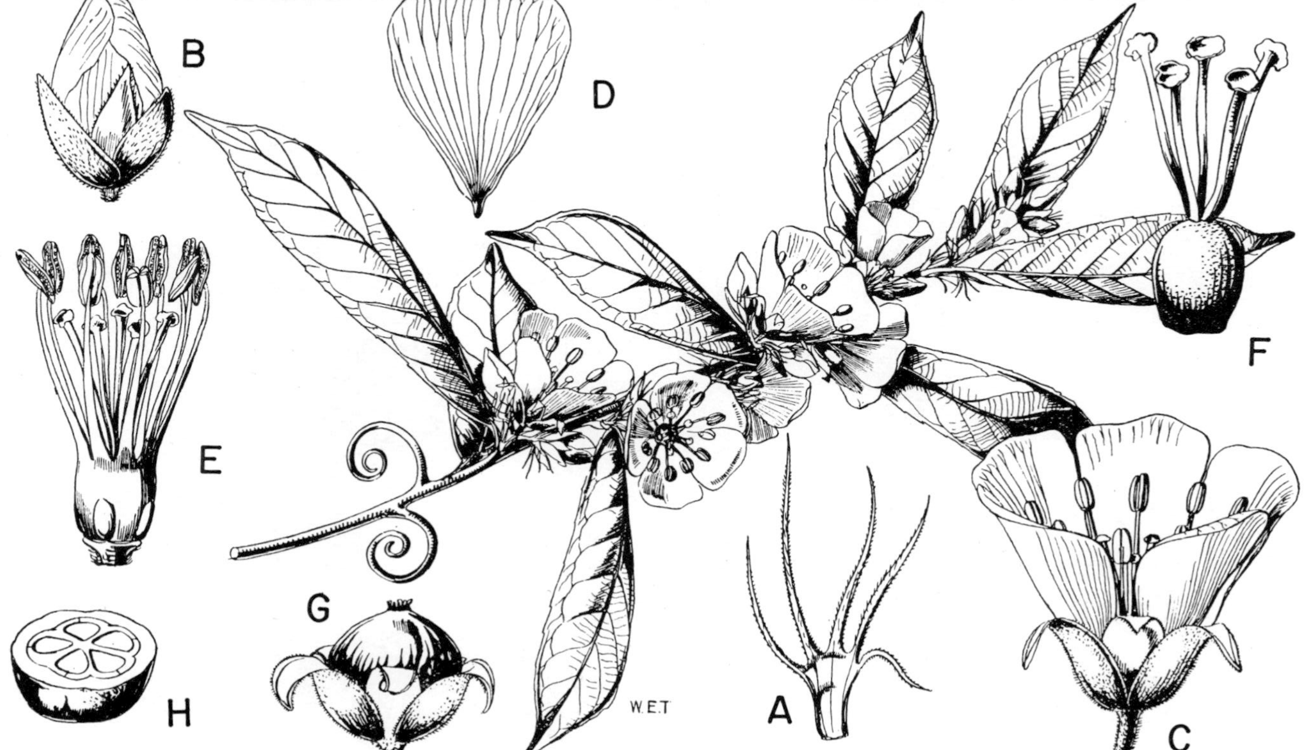

FIG. 235. *Hugonia planchonii* Hook. f. (*Linaceae*). **A**, stipule. **B**, flower-bud. **C**, flower. **D**, petal. **E**, flower after removal of sepals and petals. **F**, ovary with styles. **G**, fruit. **H**, cross-section of fruit. (This fine drawing shows the skill of Trevithick, who prepared it from a dried herbarium specimen!)

FIG. 236. *Anisadenia pubescens* Griff. (*Linaceae*), Himalayas. **A**, stipules. **B**, flower. **C**, stamens and staminodes. **D**, gynoecium. **E**, cross-section of ovary (orig.).

petals 5, contorted, fugaceous; stamens united at the base, 5 with anthers alternate with the petals, 5 minute and setiform; glands 5, adnate to the outside of the staminal tube and opposite the petals; ovary 5-locular, loculi 2-ovuled and spuriously sub-2-locellate; styles 5; capsule septicidally 5-valved, 5-locular, loculi 2-seeded, or these completely separated by septa and 10-coccous; seeds with thin endosperm and straight embryo.

The more primitive tribe is *Hugonieae* (*Hugonia* (Fig. 235), *Durandea*, etc.)

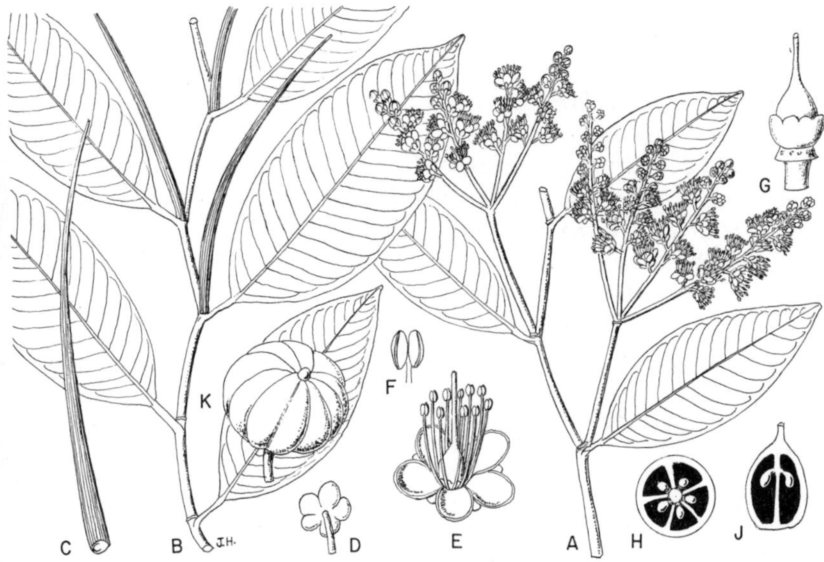

FIG. 237A. *Kleinedoxa gabonensis* Pierre (*Irvingiaceae*), tropical Africa. **A**, flowering shoot. **B**, sterile shoot showing the remarkable stipules **C**, which encircle the terminal bud and which are very caducous, leaving a scar (as in *Ficus*). **D**, calyx from below. **E**, flower. **F**, anther. **G**, disk and gynoecium. **H**, cross-section of ovary. **J**, vertical section of ovary. **K**, fruit (orig.).

with the stamens double the number of the petals and with a drupaceous fruit, all in the tropics.

Anisadenia (Fig. 236) is the sole genus of tribe *Anisadenieae*, a herb with perennial rhizome, and a racemose inflorescence.

The most advanced tribe is *Eulineae*, to which *Linum* belongs, with some annuals, the monotypic *Radiola* being reduced to a tiny annual greatly resembling some *Caryophyllaceae*.

The small family **Irvingiaceae**, established by the French anatomist, van Tieghem, is easily recognised especially by its stipules, which are large and very long, intrapetiolar, and folded around the terminal bud, early caducous and leaving a very distinct scar, as in many *Moraceae*. The style of the 5–4 or 2-locular ovary is undivided and terminal; ovule 1 in each loculus and pendulous from the top of the central axis; fruit a drupe or broadly winged samara. There are only three known genera.

The type genus is *Irvingia* Hook. f, with a 1-locular drupaceous fruit and not winged; about 25 spp. in tropical Africa, Cochinchina and Malaya. *Klainedoxa* Pierre (Fig. 237A), about 20 spp. confined to tropical Africa, has a 5- or 4-locular ovary with a drupaceous fruit, while the third genus *Desbordia* is monotypic in west tropical Africa and has fruits broadly winged all around. (For figure see FAMILIES OF FLOWERING PLANTS, 2nd Ed. 1, Fig. 125.)

The fruit of *Irvingia gabonensis* Baill., a tropical west African tree, is known as Wild Mango, and the seeds are the source of Dika Butter, eaten by Africans; the timber has been used for street paving. Dika Bread, Dika Nut, Gabon Chocolate is derived from *Irvingia barteri* Hook. f.; fruit edible, fat from seeds recommended for manufacture of soap and candles. Seeds of *Irvingia oliveri* Pierre, tropical Asia, source of Cay-Cay Fat, used for candles. The seeds of *Kleinedoxa gabonensis* Pierre, tropical west Africa, are also edible, and the very hard wood is used for the decks of steamers on the Congo, and for poles and boards.

Huaceae, genus *Hua* Pierre, is a remarkable monotypic family which occurs in the Gabon and Congo regions of tropical Africa. The anthers are very distinctive, being 4-locular, peltate, and the clawed petals are remarkable (see Fig. 126 in FAMILIES OF FLOWERING PLANTS).

The family **Ledocarpaceae** Meyen dates from as far back as 1834 and usually has been included in *Geraniaceae*, but not very happily placed in that family according to our system. The three genera, *Balbisia*, *Wendtia* and *Rhynchotheca*, are confined to western South America, mostly in the Andes. The family name is from *Ledocarpon* Desf., a synonym of *Balbisia*, a conserved generic name. There is a figure of this genus in my FAMILIES OF FLOWERING PLANTS (Fig. 127) showing the flowers, which have only a superficial resemblance to some *Geranium* species.

The family **Erythroxylaceae**[1] has been limited by O. E. Schulz in the second edition of Engler and Prantl's PFLANZENFAMILIEN to two genera, *Erythroxylum* P.Br. (*Erythroxylon* Linn.), and *Aneulophus*. In the same work the genus *Nectaropetalum* (*Peglera*) is included by H. Winkler in the *Linaceae*. This is very unfortunate, for wherever *Erythroxylum* goes then *Nectaropetalum* should undoubtedly go with it, for the two are only just separable as genera, so closely are they related.

Bentham and Hooker included the genus *Hebepetalum* in their tribe *Erythroxyleae* in *Linaceae*, but this shows a closer affinity with *Hugonia* in the true *Linaceae*.

Erythroxylaceae are distinguished by the imbricate deciduous appendaged petals and drupaceous fruit, and the intrapetiolar stipules. The type genus, *Erythroxylum* P. Browne, comprises about 200 species confined to the tropics and subtropics, the type species being *E. areolatum* Linn., a native of the West Indies and tropical South America; small trees and shrubs; leaves alternate, involutely folded in bud and entire; stipules intrapetiolar; flowers small, often fasciculate in the leaf-axils; sepals and petals 6–5 each, the latter imbricate, clawed, scaly within the base; filaments connate below;

---

[1] Including *Nectaropetalaceae* Exell & Mendonça (1951).

FIG. 237B. The Cocaine plant, *Erythroxylum coca* Linn. (*Erythroxylaceae*), South America. **A**, flower-bud. **B**, flower. **C**, petal showing scale. **D**, stamens. **E**, gynoecium. **F**, fruit.

ovary 4–3-locular, ovules 2–1; styles 4–3, stigma capitate or clavate; drupe 1-locular and 1-seeded.

The leaves of *Aneulophus* are opposite and the filaments connate at the base, whilst *Nectaropetalum* and *Pinacodium*, both with alternate leaves, have the filaments free except at the very base.

Cocaine is obtained from *Erythroxylum coca* Lam. (Fig. 237B) and *E. truxillense* Rusby in South America. The leaves are a powerful stimulant, and after chewing them people under its influence can go for several days

FIG. 238. *Zygophyllum fabago* Linn., the type species of the type genus of *Zygophyllaceae*. **A**, stamen. **B**, cross-section of ovary. **C**, fruit. **D**, seed. **E**, vertical section of seed (orig.).

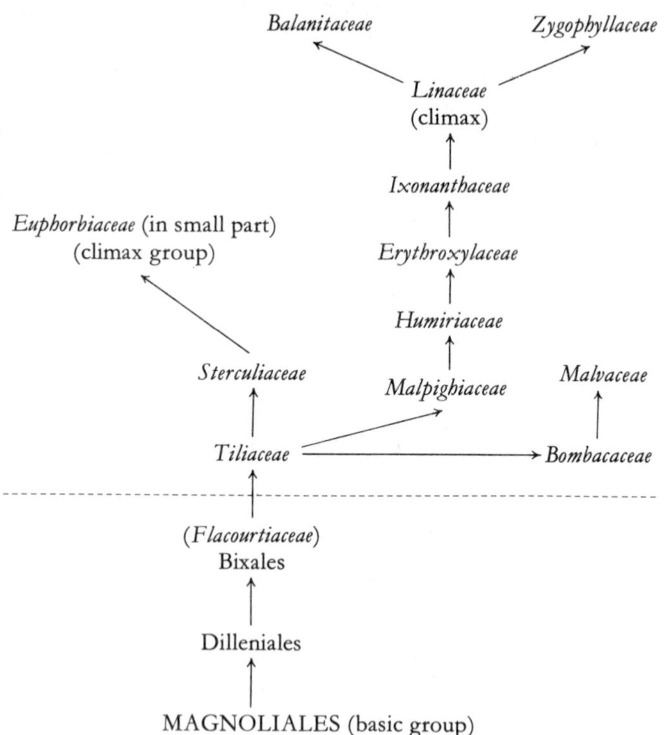

Diagram showing the probable origin of the family *Tiliaceae* and families derived from it; the basic groups are woody or fibrously herbaceous; the higher climax families become increasingly herbaceous but usually remain fibrous (*Linum*, *Hibiscus*, etc.).

FIG. 239. A very fine drawing by the late W. E. Trevithick of the plant known for several generations as *Fluggea microcarpa* Bl., now called *Securinega virosa* (Roxb. ex Willd.) Baill. **A**, male flower. **B** and **C**, sepals. **D**, stamens. **E**, female flower, **F**, fruits. **G**, transverse section of fruit. **H**, vertical section of female flower. (From Hutchinson and Dalziel, FLORA OF WEST TROPICAL AFRICA.)

without food or drink. The habit is widespread in South America and the plant is widely cultivated on the eastern slopes of the Andes as far south as Argentina. As with Opium, the chewing of coca leaves may become a habit with serious consequences if overindulged. Cocaine is exceedingly valuable as a local anaesthetic; it causes dilation of the pupil of the eye.

Ctenolophonaceae is another small family established by Exell and Mendonça; one genus, *Ctenolophon* Oliv., three species in tropical Africa and Malaya; also formerly included in the broader concept of *Linaceae*.

In our FLORA OF WEST TROPICAL AFRICA I suggested that the African genus *Lepidobotrys* Engl. might be regarded as a separate family from *Linaceae*, wherein it was placed by Engler. This was done by J. Léonard in 1950 in the FLORA OF THE CONGO. In my FAMILIES OF FLOWERING PLANTS **I**, 266, I added two genera found in the Malay Archipelago, *Sarcotheca* Blume and *Dapania* Korth. The leaves of all three genera are compound, either 3-foliolate or 1-foliolate (in the latter case the petiole with a distinct pulvinus at the apex), and the seeds are arillate. This brings this small family **Lepidobotryaceae** nearer to *Zygophyllaceae* and *Balanitaceae*.

Balanitaceae[1] was established as a family by Endlicher in 1841, but was

[1] Including *Agialidaceae* van Tieghem (1906).

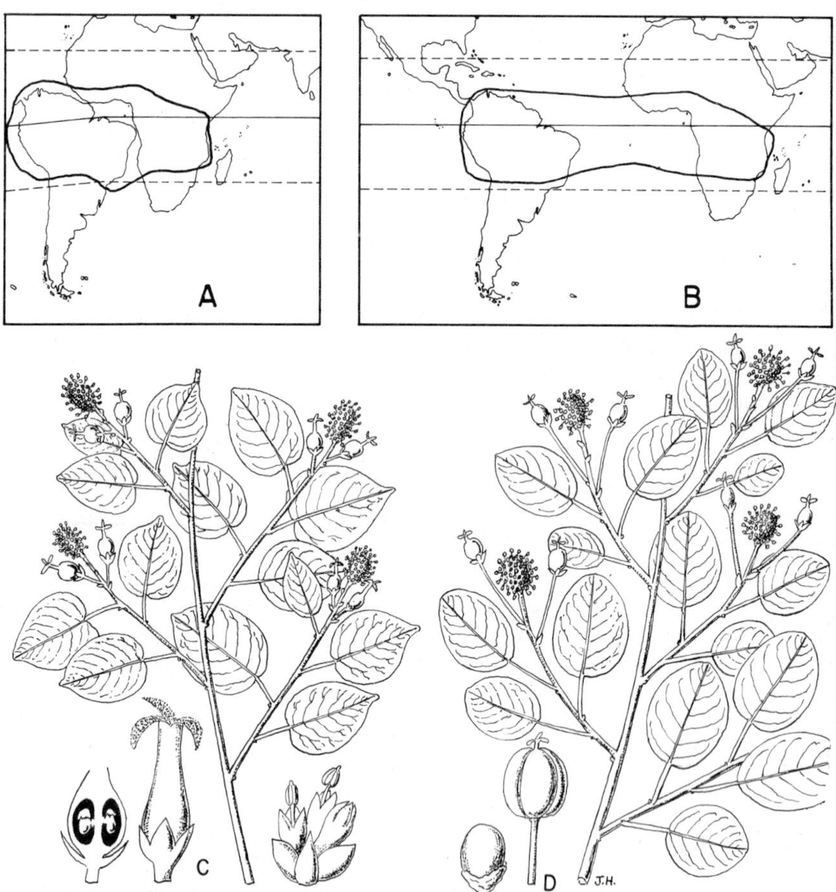

FIG. 240 and MAP 16. Although the distribution of the very natural (homogeneous) Euphorbiaceous genus *Maprounea* is at the present day discontinuous (Map **B**), it was continuous before South America and Africa drifted apart (Map **A**); there are four closely related species in this genus, two in each area. **C** is *M. brasiliensis* Muell. Arg., South America, **D** is *M. africana* Muell. Arg., tropical Africa; a good botanical example in support of the theory of drifting continents.

included in Bentham and Hooker's GENERA PLANTARUM in *Simaroubaceae*, and later by Engler as a subfamily of *Zygophyllaceae*. Divergence of opinion such as this often results in the group in question being regarded at the present day as belonging to neither family! The leaves are bifoliolate, there are no stipules, and the 10 stamens are inserted in the grooves below the outside of a large disk; fruit a fleshy oily drupe, 1-seeded; single genus *Balanites* Del.; species about 25 in the Orient, tropical Africa and Asia. The seeds are the source of Betu oil; fruit edible; wood hard and fine grained, used as clubs, for ploughs, walking sticks, turnery, etc.; bark source of

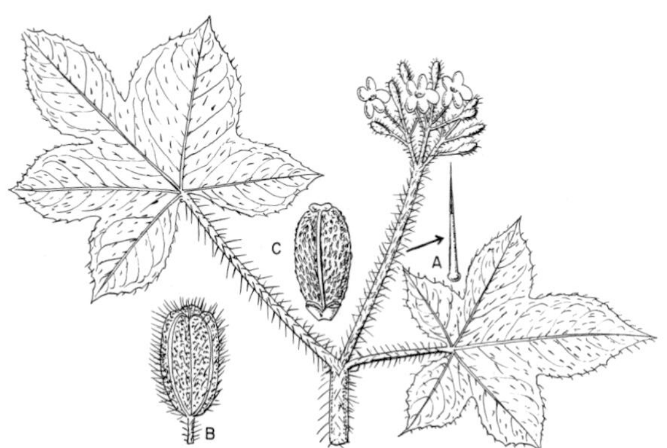

FIG. 241A. *Cnidoscolus urens* (Linn.) Arthur (*Euphorbiaceae*), tropical America; covered with stinging bristles, **A**, which when touched produce itching for a few minutes and afterwards little pustules are formed on the skin. **B**, fruit. **C**, seed (orig.).

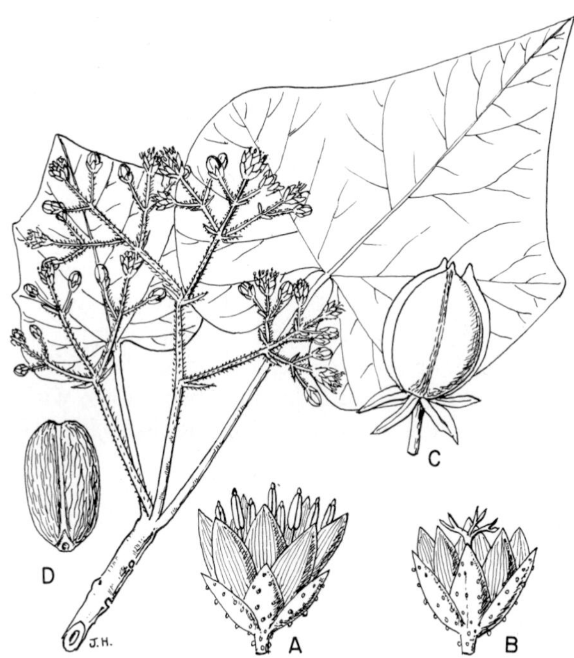

FIG. 241B. *Jatropha curcas* Linn. (*Euphorbiaceae*), Cuba. **A**, male flower. **B**, female flower. **C**, fruit. **D**, seed (orig.).

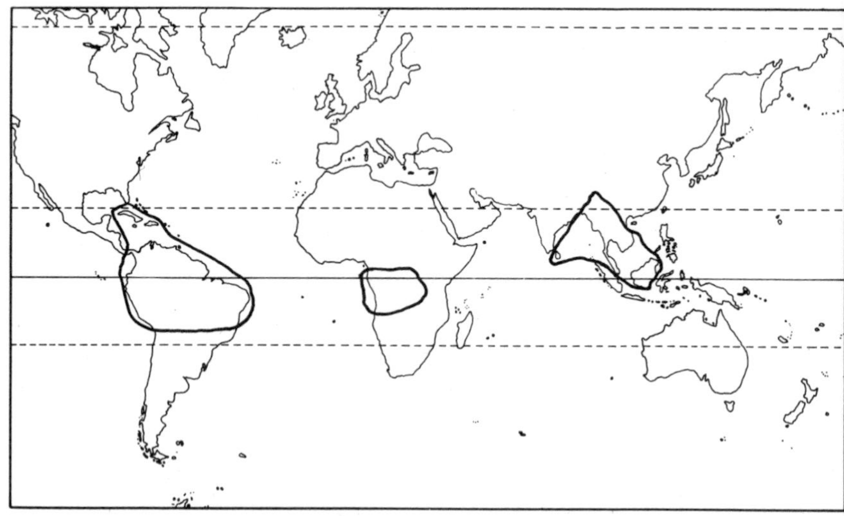

MAP 17. Discontinuous range of the natural genus *Chaetocarpus* (*Euphorbiaceae*).

strong fibre (see FAMILIES OF FLOWERING PLANTS, 2nd Ed. **1**, 268, Fig. 131).

The family **Zygophyllaceae**[1] is based on the genus *Zygophyllum* Linn., with upwards of 80 species, found mostly in the deserts and steppes of the old world. They are low-lying bushlets, rarely annuals, with fleshy branchlets and leaves, the latter opposite, mostly 2-foliolate, more rarely with 2 or more pairs of leaflets, with a pair of sometimes thorny stipules; flowers solitary, terminal, or paired, white or yellow, mostly with a purple or red basal spot; sepals 5–4, imbricate; petals 5–4, free, contorted or imbricate, clawed; stamens 10–8, filaments with or very rarely without a scale within the base; ovary sessile on a disk, 5–4-locular; style simple, stigma minute; ovules 2 or more, superposed, with a free or adnate raphe; fruit 5–4-angled or winged, indehiscent or breaking septicidally into 5 cocci, or loculicidally 5-valved; seeds 1 or more in each loculus, pendulous, with scanty endosperm and oblong cotyledons. The type species is *Z. fabago* Linn. (see Fig. 238), in S.W. Asia.

The genera more divergent from the type genus are *Miltianthus* and *Seetzenia*, which have lost their petals, the former with imbricate sepals and 10 stamens, the latter with valvate sepals and 5 stamens. The remainder of the genera have retained their petals. Some, such as *Peganum*, *Tetradiclis*, *Malacocarpus*, *Nitraria* and *Sericodes*, have simple leaves, many others have compound or unifoliolate leaves. Several have endosperm in their seeds,

[1] Including *Nitrariaceae* Lindley (1830).

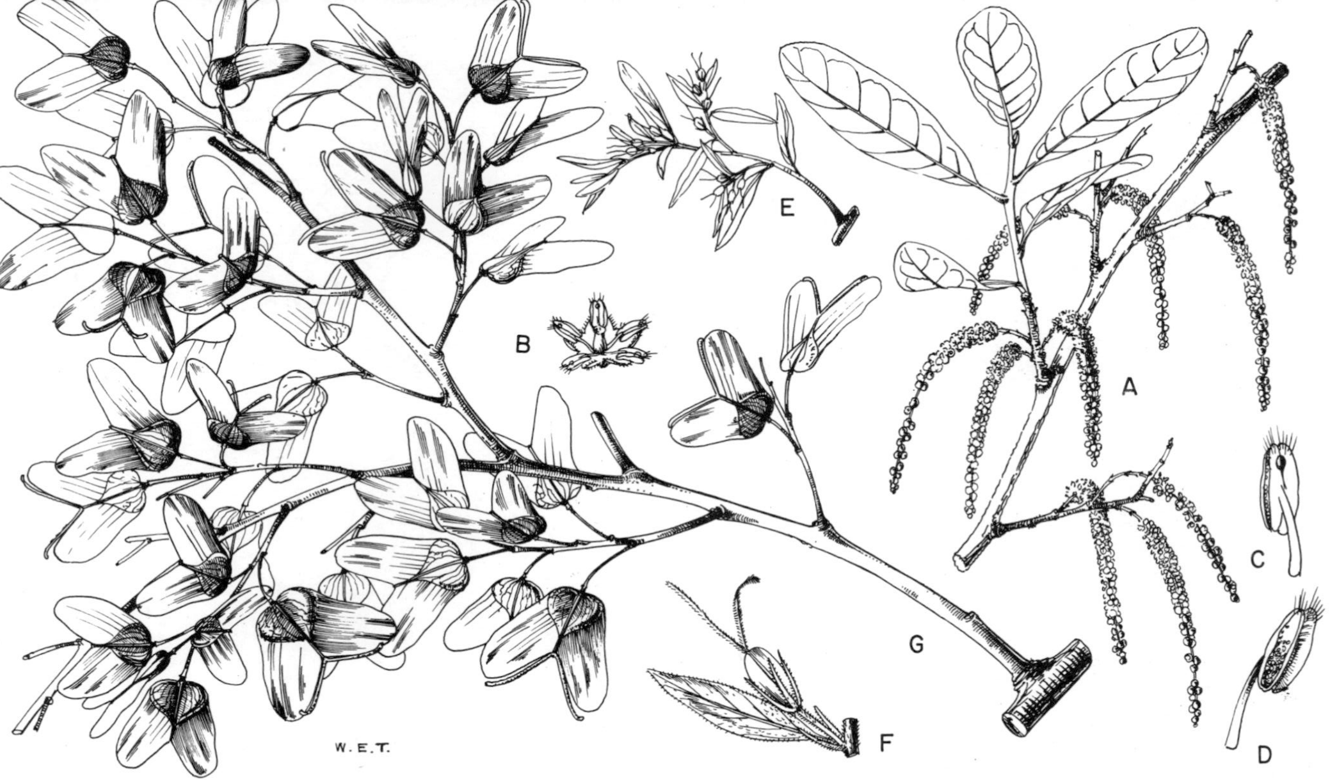

FIG. 242. A fine drawing by Trevithick of *Hymenocardia acida* Tul. (*Euphorbiaceae*) for our FLORA OF WEST TROPICAL AFRICA; the species is widely distributed in Africa. **A**, male catkins. **B**, male flower. **C** and **D**, stamens. **E**, female flowers. **F**, female flower and bract. **G**, fruits.

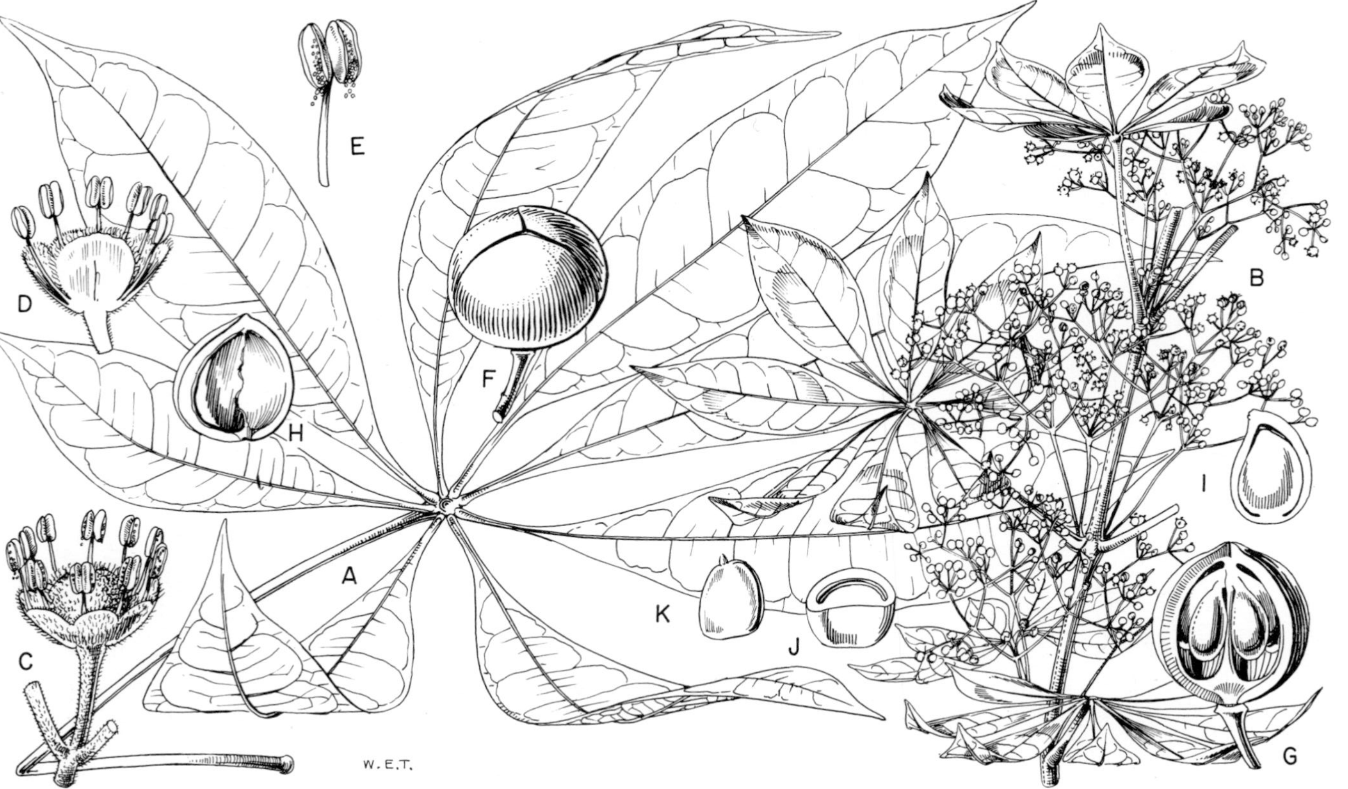

FIG. 243. Another *multum in parvo* drawing by Trevithick: *Oldfieldia africana* Hook. (*Euphorbiaceae*). **A**, leaf. **B**, male flowers. **C**, male flower. **D**, section of male flower. **E**, stamen. **F**, fruit. **G**, vertical section of fruit. **H**, one valve of fruit showing seed. **I**, vertical section of seed. **J**, cross-section of seed. **K**, embryo.

Larrea, *Malacocarpus*, *Metharme*, *Viscainoa*, *Bulnesia*, *Fagonia*, *Morkillia*, *Peganum*, *Pintoa*, *Porlieria* and a few others.

The family is relatively advanced with mainly opposite compound leaves and paired stipules. They occur mostly in dry regions, especially in the Sahara and in South Africa. For example *Augea capensis* Thunb. was the only living plant I met with for hundreds of miles in Bushmanland which I crossed in 1929, when there had been scarcely a drop of rain for four years or so. It was then still juicy and fresh!

ORDER 35. EUPHORBIALES

(*Fam. Fl. Pl.* **1**, 270)

Family: **Euphorbiaceae.**

From here we pass into that large and fascinating family **Euphorbiaceae**,[1] beloved of old by the great botanist Mueller of Argov (Muell.-Arg.), and subsequently by his very worthy successor, the late Professor Pax of Breslau. Compared with these, the present writer's contribution to the taxonomy of the family is small, although he has had for a very long time a general working knowledge of it.[2]

The very great range of structure to be found in this family is not perhaps realised by the ordinary student, and to trace its several affinities it is necessary to carry out a detailed study of some widely separated families. Strange as it may seem the family is rather unfortunately named, for the type genus, *Euphorbia*, is more or less exceptional and possesses a remarkable floral structure not shared by any other genera apart from a few very closely related smaller ones. The student should therefore avoid thinking of the family *Euphorbiaceae* in terms only of *Euphorbia*. He should also remember other familiar but very different genera such as the Castor Oil plant, *Ricinus*

---

[1] Including *Tithymalaceae* Ventenat (1799). *Stilaginaceae* C. A. Agardh (1825). *Treviaceae* Lindley (1836). *Scepaceae* Lindley (1836). *Antidesmataceae* Endlich. (1837). *Putranjivaceae* Endlich. (1841). *Pseudanthaceae* Endlich. (1841). *Bennettiaceae* R.Br. (1852). *Acalyphaceae* J. G. Agardh (1858). *Bertyaceae* J. G. Agardh (1858). *Crotonaceae* J. G. Agardh (1858). *Hippomanaceae* J. G. Agardh (1858). *Micrantheaceae* J. G. Agardh (1858). *Phyllanthaceae* J. G. Agardh (1858). *Peraceae* Klotzsch (1859). *Columellaceae* Dulac (1867). *Porantheraceae* Hurusawa (1954). *Ricinocarpaceae* Hurusawa (1954). *Androstachydaceae* Airy Shaw (1965). *Bischofiaceae* Airy Shaw (1965). *Hymenocardiaceae* Airy Shaw (1965). *Uapacaceae* Airy Shaw (1965).

[2] See my contributions to the FLORA OF TROPICAL AFRICA, FLORA CAPENSIS and FLORA OF WEST TROPICAL AFRICA.

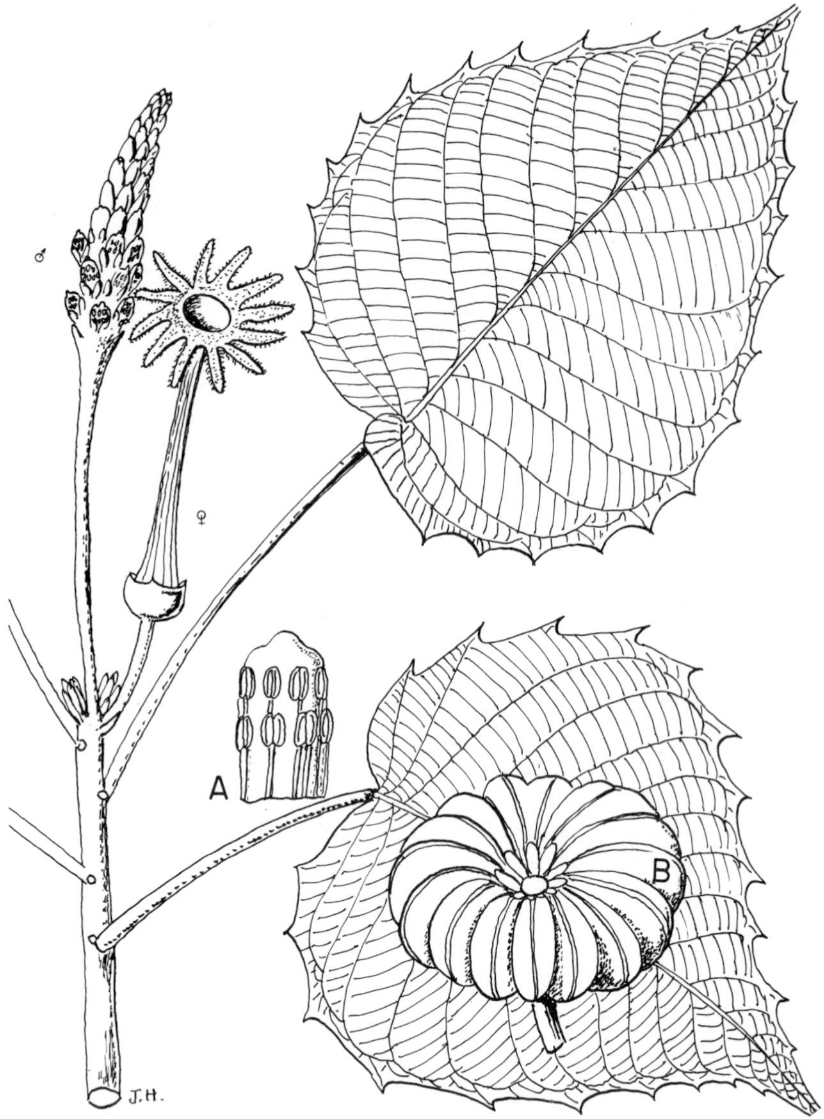

FIG. 244. The Sandbox tree, *Hura crepitans* Linn., family *Euphorbiaceae*, frequent in the Panama Canal zone of Central America and in other parts of the tropics; a very striking example of the separation of and great difference in the sexes, the male flowers **A** in a dense spike (marked ♂), the female solitary and remarkably different (marked ♀). **B**, fruit (orig.).

communis Linn., and the most famous rubber producing plant, *Hevea brasiliensis* Muell.-Arg. (Fig. 247).

In the cyathium or involucre of *Euphorbia* there is a structure which is

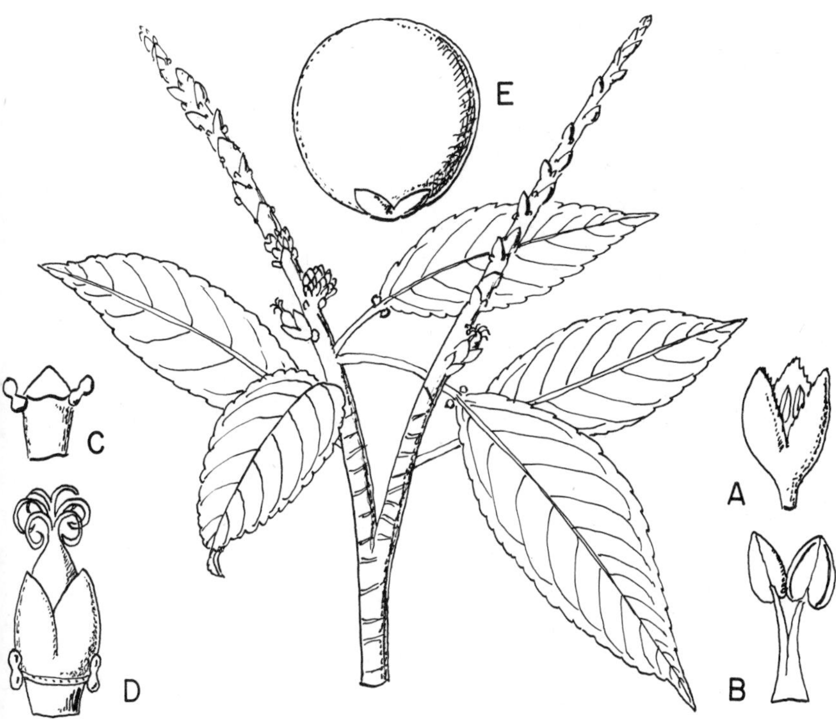

FIG. 245. "Manzanillo", *Hippomane mancinella* Linn. (*Euphorbiaceae*), a virulently poisonous plant of Panama, also in Venezuela, the West Indies and south Florida. **A**, male flower. **B**, stamens. **C**, bract. **D**, calyx and ovary of female flower. **E**, fruit.

quite comparable with the involucre of *Asteraceae* (*Compositae*), and *Euphorbia* may be considered to be even more highly evolved than any Composite, because of the reduction of the male flower to a single stamen and the female flower to a single gynoecium, truly the very acme of reduction, both sexes destitute of a perianth, or this very rudimentary.

It would carry me too far to attempt to indicate more than the general affinities of some of the better known *Euphorbiaceae*. For such as *Bridelia*, *Phyllanthus*, etc., some relationship may be claimed with *Celastraceae* or *Rhamnaceae*; for *Croton*, *Hevea* and other related genera affinities are very strong with some *Sterculiaceae*, such as the genus *Sterculia* and *Cola*. *Antidesma*, *Baccaurea* and related genera find almost their counterparts in *Sapindaceae*, whilst another source of origin for a part of the family may have been the Malvaceous stock.

It seems clear that the family *Euphorbiaceae* is composed of groups of genera which have been derived from various different stocks, partly from those of *Tiliaceae*, *Sterculiaceae* and *Malvaceae*, but more particularly from

FIG. 246. *Acalypha umbrosa* Brandegee (*Euphorbiaceae*), an endemic species in the Revillagigedo Islands; note the unusual mixture of the female and male flowers (orig.).

Bentham and Hooker's *Disciflorae*, such as *Celastraceae*. Though the flowers are constantly unisexual and frequently monoecious or dioecious, no doubt they have been derived from more primitive ones with bisexual flowers, indicated by the presence of a vestigial ovary in the male flowers of many genera. It seems logical to assume, therefore, that those genera in which such an ovary has been retained should be regarded as more primitive than those from which it has disappeared. Again those genera

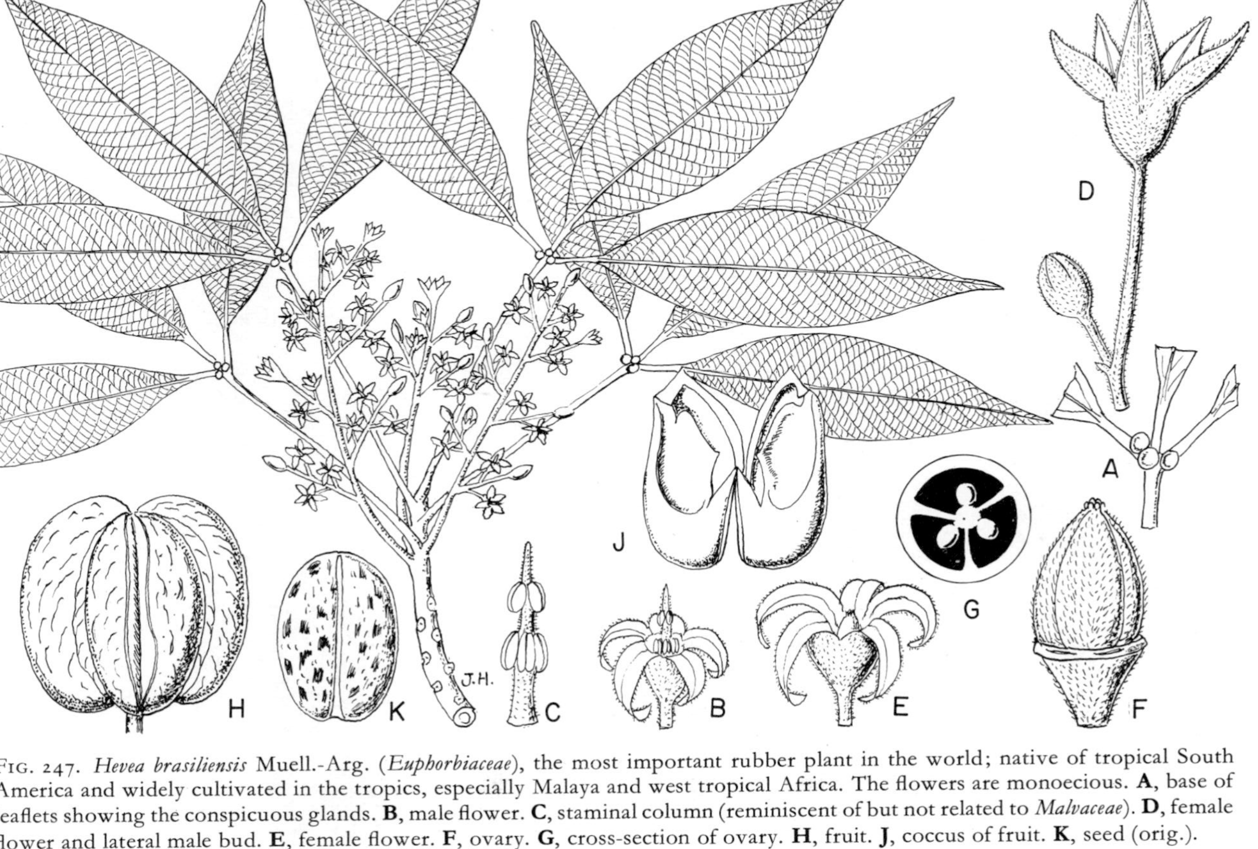

FIG. 247. *Hevea brasiliensis* Muell.-Arg. (*Euphorbiaceae*), the most important rubber plant in the world; native of tropical South America and widely cultivated in the tropics, especially Malaya and west tropical Africa. The flowers are monoecious. **A**, base of leaflets showing the conspicuous glands. **B**, male flower. **C**, staminal column (reminiscent of but not related to *Malvaceae*). **D**, female flower and lateral male bud. **E**, female flower. **F**, ovary. **G**, cross-section of ovary. **H**, fruit. **J**, coccus of fruit. **K**, seed (orig.).

devoid of a disk are perhaps on the whole more primitive than those in which it is present, for discifloral families such as *Celastraceae* are relatively more advanced than those without a disk.

The type genus, *Euphorbia* (named by Linnaeus after Euphorbos, physician to King Juba of Mauretania (about 54 B.C.)), embraces a very large number of species throughout the world except very cold regions; many are adapted to deserts or semi-deserts and are fleshy and spiny; some species are weeds and widespread in cultivation and waste places. The ultimate inflorescence (so-called cyathium) is unique in that it resembles a single flower with numerous stamens surrounding a single ovary; but the stamens are themselves single flowers, without a perianth, or this very rudimentary, and the ovary is also a single flower in the midst of the males. The cyathium, often margined by conspicuous variously shaped glands, is really an involucre of united bracts. These characters raise the genus to the very top of the family and it is a climax from an evolutionary point of view, quite equivalent to the capitulum of the *Asteraceae* (*Compositae*) as stated above.

The Sandbox tree, *Hura crepitans* L. (Fig. 244), is frequently met with in the Panama Canal Zone and is often planted as a shade tree. It is a large or medium-sized tree, its trunk usually densely covered with short sharp spines so as to resemble (according to Standley) a grater. The male flowers are in a dense spike, the female is solitary by the side of the stalk of the male. The capsule (see sketch) is shaped like a small pumpkin and consists of about fifteen 1-seeded woody chambers. When ripe it explodes violently with a loud report, throwing the seeds some distance from the tree. In former days the young capsules were dried and used as containers for the sand employed for drying or blotting ink, hence the name Sandbox. The wood is pale yellow, creamy white or yellowish brown, light and soft, and has many local uses. The milky sap is poisonous and causes inflammation of the skin. In parts of Mexico the sap, mixed with meal, is thrown into the streams to stupefy fish.

ORDER 36. **THEALES**

(*Fam. Fl. Pl.* **1**, 271)

Families: **Bonnetiaceae, Theaceae, Saurauiaceae, Actinidiaceae, Pellicieraceae, Pentaphylacaceae, Tetrameristaceae, Marcgraviaceae, Caryocaraceae, Medusagynaceae.**

This economically important Order, with axile placentation, has a relatively short pedigree, as follows: MAGNOLIALES → DILLENIALES → BIXALES → THEALES.

The Order embraces a most interesting group of families, for amongst other things it provides the very important beverage, Tea, from the leaves of *Camellia sinensis* Linn. (Fig. 248). The Order, as here understood, seems fairly natural and is entirely woody, probably derived mostly from the DILLENIALES and BIXALES. Here, however, syncarpy is complete, and the placentation of the ovules has become axile. The seeds have little or no endosperm.

FIG. 248. The Tea plant, *Camellia sinensis* (Linn.) O. Kuntze (*Theaceae*), native of Assam; much cultivated in Ceylon, India, China and less so in other regions. **A**, gynoecium. **B**, cross-section of ovary. **C**, fruit (orig.)

The family **Theaceae**[1] is named after the genus *Thea*, now merged in the older and better known name *Camellia*. When a generic name becomes a synonym it does not or should not alter the name of the family, in this case to *Camelliaceae*, though that name has been used occasionally.

Although always placed in *Polypetalae* (*Archichlamydeae*), there is a strong tendency to sympetaly, especially marked in *Camellia*, *Ternstroemia* and *Eurya*, and a few other genera, pointing to its relationship with ERICALES, almost bridged over by *Clethraceae* in the latter group. Another interesting feature and perhaps one showing the beginning of a development so fully carried out in the more advanced *Hypericaceae* and *Clusiaceae*, is the 5-bundled

FIG. 249. The genus *Ficalhoa* was formerly included in *Ericaceae*, but in this system is considered to be more happily placed in *Theaceae*, near the genus *Eurya*. **A**, flower. **B**, corolla opened out showing the stamens in groups of three. **C**, anther. **D**, gynoecium and calyx. **E**, seed. **F**, vertical section of seed (orig.).

stamens of *Archytaea* and *Ploiarium*, here included in *Bonnetiaceae*. Other advanced characters in the family are present in the genera *Visnea* and *Anneslea*, the flowers of which are more or less polygamous, and the calyx-tube or torus is enlarged and encloses the fruit. Advanced characters also are the winged seeds of *Gordonia*, *Laplacea*, *Schima*, *Stuartia* and *Hartia*, whilst the fruit of *Pyrenaria* is indehiscent, drupaceous, and the cotyledons are plicate-corrugate or convolute.

The type genus then is *Camellia*,[2] trees and shrubs; leaves evergreen,

---

[1] Including *Ternstroemiaceae* Mirbel (1813). *Camelliaceae* DC. (1824). *Malachodendraceae* J. G. Agardh (1858). *Asteropeiaceae* Takhtadzlyan (1957).

[2] Linnaeus named the genus in honour of Georg Joseph Camellus (or Kamel), a Moravian Jesuit in the seventh century, who travelled in Asia; he wrote among others a history of the plants of the island of Luzon in the Philippines.

FIG. 250. *Franklinia altamaha* Bartram ex Marshall (*Theaceae*) is one of those rare trees which have disappeared in a wild state, for it is not now known to grow anywhere naturally. It was discovered by John Bartram in 1765 during a journey through the southern states of North America, near Fort Barrington on the Altamaha River in Georgia, distributed over an area of only two or three acres. It was such a beautiful tree that he thought it worthy of the name of *Franklinia*, in honour of their distinguished friend and neighbour, Benjamin Franklin, President of the United States.

Dr. Moses Marshall visited the same locality in 1790 and observed the tree, but no botanist since that date has seen it in a wild state, and all efforts to find it in the original locality or elsewhere have been unsuccessful. The tree, however, is still in cultivation in North America and Europe. This drawing is adapted from Sargent SILVA OF NORTH AMERICA. **A**, stamen. **B**, gynoecium. **C**, cross-section of ovary. **D**, fruits.

FIG. 251. The natural genus *Stuartia* (*Theaceae*) occurs in eastern Asia and in far distant S.E. United States of North America. **A**, *Stuartia malacodendron* Linn. (*S. virginica* Cav.), eastern United States and **B**, *Stuartia pseudo-camellia* Maxim., China. Long ago the close relationship between the floras of these two widely separated regions was pointed out in a paper by E. Forbes. **C**, anther of *S. malacodendron*. **D**, calyx and gynoecium. **E**, cross-section of ovary. **F**, fruit. **G**, seed. **H**, vertical section of seed. **J**, anther of *S. pseudo-camellia*. **K**, gynoecium. **L**, cross-section of ovary. **M**, seed. **N**, vertical section of seed.

serrate; flowers solitary or clustered, often very showy; sepals 6–5, rather gradually transformed from bracteoles to petals, the latter shortly united at the base, very imbricate; stamens numerous, the several outer series united sometimes almost to the apex and adherent to the base of the petals, the inner 12–5 stamens free; anthers versatile; ovary 5–3-locular; styles free to partially connate; ovules 5–4 in each loculus, pendulous; capsule woody, loculicidally dehiscent; seeds wingless; no endosperm; embryo straight.

There are two tribes, *Camellieae*, with versatile anthers, and the fruit a loculicidally dehiscent capsule or indehiscent, and *Ternstroemieae*, with basifixed anthers, and the fruit indehiscent.

Tea is derived from the dried leaves of *Camellia sinensis* (Linn.) O. Kuntze (*Thea sinensis* Linn.) (Fig. 248), a native of Assam, India; medically it is an astringent, stimulant and a nervine, and the seeds are the source of an oil. Tea is perhaps the most popular of the caffeine beverages, and is used by

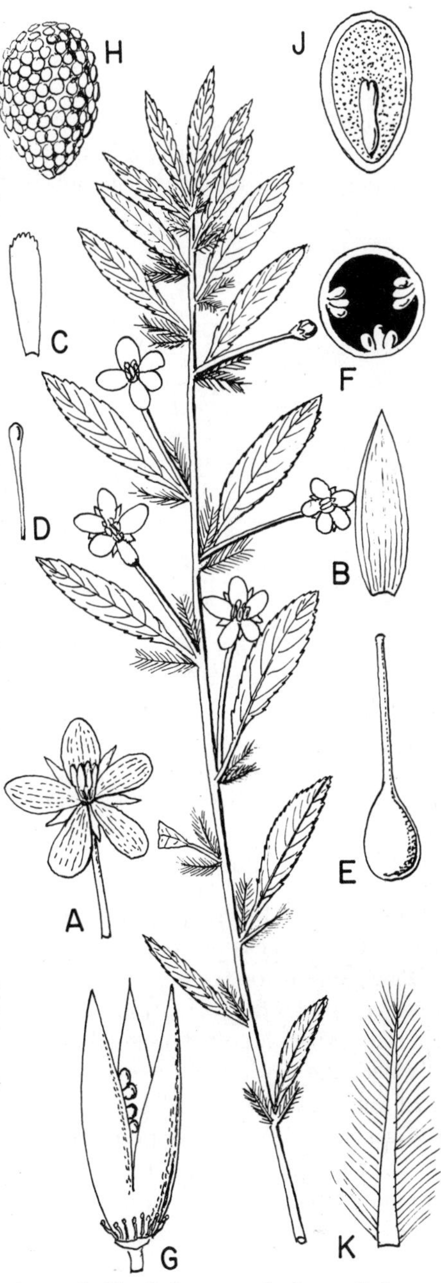

FIG. 252. *Sauvagesia erecta* Linn. (*Ochnaceae*), tropical Africa and America. This and a few related genera were at one time classified in the family *Violaceae*, but now find a more suitable place in *Ochnaceae* of which they seem to be advanced members, some being annuals in an otherwise woody family; a good example of the evolution of herbs from woody ancestors. **A**, flower. **B**, sepal. **C**, staminode. **D**, disk-gland. **E**, gynoecium. **F**, cross-section of ovary. **G**, fruit. **H**, seed. **J**, vertical section of seed. **K**, stipule (orig.).

about half of the population of the world. From a commercial point of view, however, it is considered to rank second to coffee.

At first it was valued only for its medicinal properties, and became known in Europe in the sixteenth century, but was not of any importance until the seventeenth. It has been conjectured that Chinese travellers at a very early period penetrated into Assam and obtained seed for growing in their own land. For a long time India had remained ignorant of the treasure bestowed on her by nature, and actually made a start in its cultivation by reimporting seeds from China. To China, therefore, belongs the credit of teaching the world to drink tea.

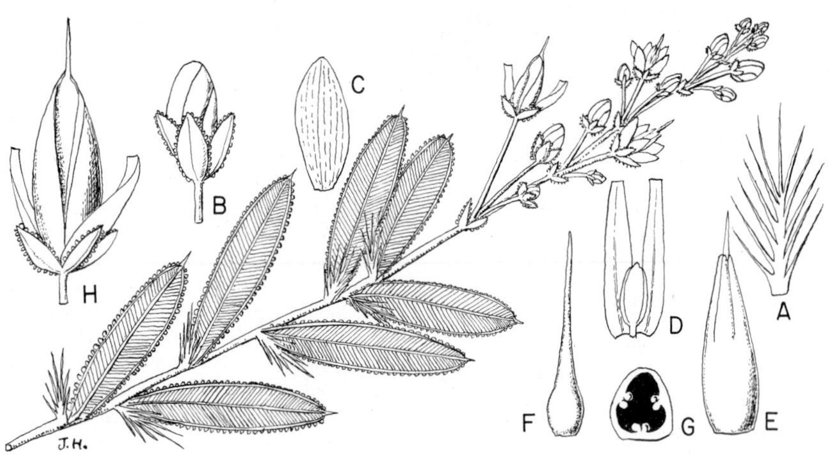

FIG. 253. *Lavradia glandulosa* A. St. Hil. (*Ochnaceae*), Brazil; the outer staminodes, **E**, are united into a tube which encloses the gynoecium, splitting apart in fruit. **A**, stipule. **B**, flower-bud. **C**, petal. **D**, anther and staminodes. **F**, gynoecium. **G**, cross-section of ovary. **H**, fruit (orig.).

When tea first arrived in Britain in 1664, the East India Company sent it as a present to Queen Catherine, wife of Charles II, and thereafter it became fashionable in high society. At first it cost 10 guineas per pound. Later it dropped to 60s., and by 1740 it could be bought for from 7s. to 24s. per pound. The price fell still further, however, when the plantations made in India began to yield crops, and by 1854 Indian tea was obtainable at a reasonable cost in Britain. Today India leads the world in the production of tea, China comes next, Ceylon is third and Japan, Java and parts of east Africa grow it on a smaller scale. Needless to say, millions of people earn a livelihood in the growing, preparing, transporting and sale of tea.

A striking phytogeographical feature is the paucity of *Theaceae* in Africa, *Adinandropsis* Exell being the only representative and confined to the island of San Thomé. A remarkably rare American plant is *Franklinia altamaha* Bartram ex Marshall, which according to Bailey (1) has not been collected in a wild state since 1790. It grew formerly on the low ground along the Altamaha River, near Fort Barrington, Georgia, U.S.A., and like some

FIG. 254. *Diegodendron humbertii* R. Capuron (*Diegodendraceae*), Madagascar; an interesting new family belonging to the Order OCHNALES. The gynoecium is remarkable, with the typical gynobasic style of many *Ochnaceae*; but the leaves are pellucid-punctate (as in *Rutaceae*), and the stipules, **A** and **B** (section), much resemble those of *Irvingiaceae*. **C**, stamen. **D**, section showing style and 2 carpels. **E**, vertical section of carpel.—Adapted from a drawing by D. Godot de Mauroy illustrating Capuron's paper in ADANSONIA.

Chinese trees and shrubs has only been preserved by cultivation. (Further particulars are given at the foot of the drawing on p. 283.) A slight tendency to the Ericaceous type of anther is shown in *Trematanthera*, in which the dehiscence is by apical pores as in *Saurauiaceae*.

There are several small families related to *Theaceae* about which little need be noted. These are **Bonnetiaceae, Actinidiaceae, Pellicieraceae, Pentaphylacaceae, Tetrameristaceae, Marcgraviaceae, Caryocaraceae** and **Medusagynaceae**, and their relationships are shown in the diagram on p. 290. At least one of them, however, is of extraordinary interest. This is **Medusagynaceae**, represented by the single monotypic genus *Medusagyne*, found only in that botanical "museum" of endemics, the Seychelles Islands; a shrub with opposite leaves, no stipules; flowers in terminal panicles, bisexual; sepals and petals 5, imbricate; stamens very numerous; ovary superior, 25–20-locular, the carpels nearly free to the central axis, the styles as many as the loculi and arranged in a ring on the shoulders of the carpels; stigmas capitate; ovules 2, one erect, the other pendulous; fruit capsular, the carpels septicidally dehiscent from the base and diverging like the ribs of an umbrella; seeds winged (the drawing in my FAMILIES OF FLOWERING PLANTS, 2nd Ed. 1, Fig. 281, shows most of these features).

In some respects this seems to be rather an ancient type of plant, with its multilocular ovary, the styles of which are separate and form a ring on the margin of the ovary. There is perhaps here a close connection with the Order MAGNOLIALES, especially such as *Trochodendron*. The two ovules in each loculus of the ovary, one ascending, the other descending, are a very remarkable feature.

The family **Pellicieraceae** (*Pelliciera*) is unique in this Order in inhabiting a special habitat, i.e. the mangrove swamps of Panama and western tropical South America. Its large showy flowers are solitary and axillary and are suggestive of *Magnolia*, having a spread of 8–12 cm. It is interesting to note that this peculiar habitat is almost general in members of the derived and more advanced family *Rhizophoraceae*.

Marcgraviaceae are the "Pitcher Plants" of tropical America, though in no way related to *Nepenthaceae* of the eastern tropics. They resemble the latter in that they develop on some part of their inflorescence curiously formed vessels or receptacles which secrete nectar. These modifications are, however, transformed bracts which serve as landing places for humming birds and insects which assist in pollination. Belt[1] states that the flowers of *Marcgravia nepenthoides* Seem. expand in February and March, when the pitcher-like vessels are filled with a sweetish liquid. This attracts small insects, and the insects in turn attract numerous insectivorous birds, including humming birds. The flowers are so disposed with the stamens hanging downwards, that the birds, to get at the pitchers, must brush against them and thus convey the pollen from one plant to another.

Another curious feature, besides being epiphytes, is that the leaves of the lower parts of the plants are often strikingly different from those at the top

[1] See Belt NATURALIST IN NICARAGUA, p. 129 (1874).

near the inflorescence, after the manner of *Ficus stipulata*,[1] and to a lesser extent of the common ivy (*Hedera helix* L.).

Caryocaraceae[2] of Szyszylowicz in Engler and Prantl DIE NATÜRLICHEN PFLANZENFAMILIEN, comprises only two genera, *Caryocar* and *Anthodiscus*, the former with opposite leaves and free petals, the latter with alternate leaves and the petals connate into a calyptra. They formed the first tribe of *Ternstroemiaceae* (here called *Theaceae*) in Bentham and Hooker's GENERA PLANTARUM, but differ from that family especially by the digitately compound leaves, and the enormous radicle with small inflexed cotyledons in the seed. In *Caryocar amygdaliferum* Cav. there are large pouch-like glands at the base of the leaflets which probably harbour ants.

Actinidiaceae,[3] a small family also formerly associated with *Theaceae*, is based on the genus *Actinidia*; shrubs, often climbing; leaves entire or serrate; stipules minute, very caducous; flowers polygamous or dioecious; petals subcontorted-imbricate; stamens numerous; anthers versatile, opening by slits; ovary several-locular, the carpels sometimes scarcely meeting in the middle; styles as many as carpels, free; placentas on the inner angle, many-ovuled; berry many-locular; seeds immersed in pulp; endosperm copious. The fruits of *A. chinensis* Planch., *A. polygama* Franch. and *A. callosa* Lindl. are edible and greatly esteemed in S.E. Asia; they are called Tara or Kismis and are also baked in bread and pastry. In *Clematoclethra* and *Sladenia* the styles are united to the apex and the fruit is a dry capsule.

The genus *Saurauia*, the sole representative of the family of that name, **Saurauiaceae**, is remarkable in that it contains species with polypetalous and sympetalous corollas and even some flowers without petals, so that we have here in one and the same genus flowers representing the main characters of the old groups *Polypetalae*, *Gamopetalae* and *Apetalae*! In *S. cauliflora* DC., the flowers are borne on the main stem. The terminal flower of *S. roxburghii* Wall. (India) is often female and destitute of a corolla. In *S. conferta* Warb. (New Guinea) the flowers are crowded into dense bracteate heads.

This small family is particularly interesting because it seems to point to the origin of the ERICALES, agreeing with *Clethraceae* and *Ericaceae* in having porous dehiscent anthers, though the stamens are sometimes adnate to the corolla-tube. They are tropical trees and shrubs and the species are very closely related. They are singularly absent from both tropical Africa and from Brazil. On the other hand some islands of the Malay Archipelago have a very large number of endemic species; thus Borneo has as many as 25 or more, Java 15, Sumatra 9, Celebes 4, Philippines 30, and New Guinea 20

---

[1] In this connection it is interesting to note that *Marcgravia polyantha* was actually described by Miquel as *Urostigma infestum*, *Urostigma* now being a section of *Ficus*.

[2] *Rhizobolaceae* de Candolle (1824).

[3] Including *Sladeniaceae* Airy Shaw (1965).

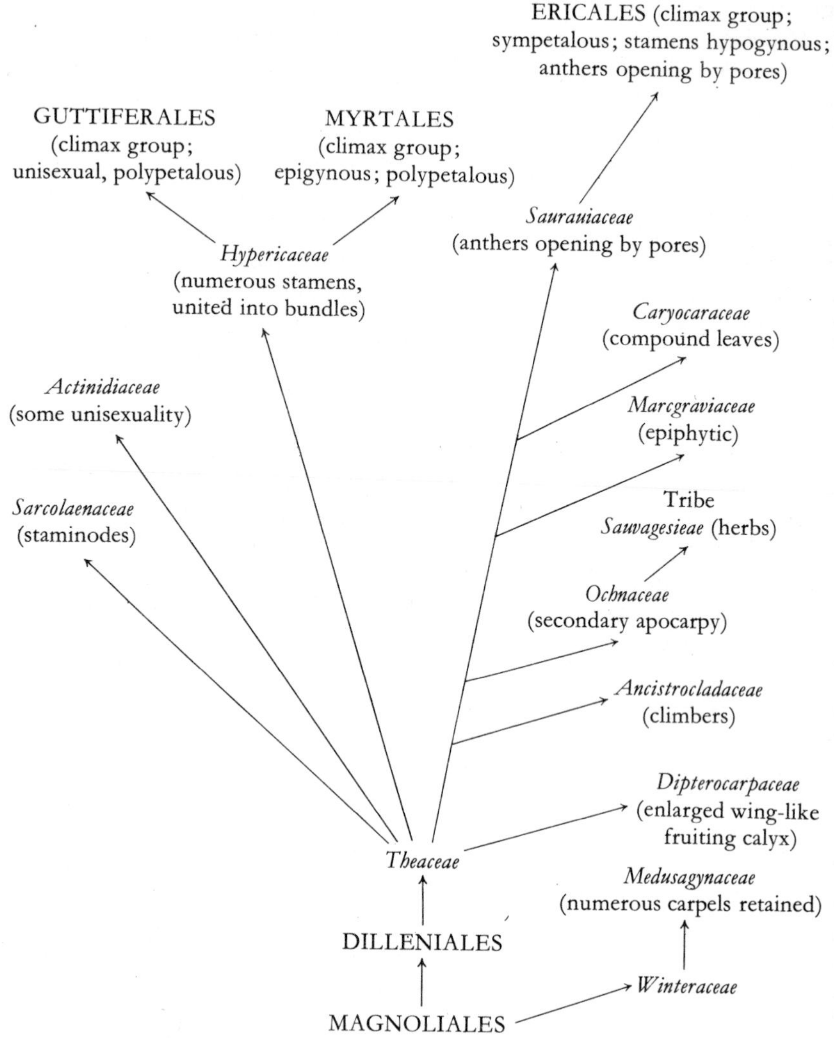

Diagram showing the probable derivation and further development of *Theaceae* and related families.

or more. There is a strong endemic element in Central America, one species of which, *S. subalpina* Donn. Smith, ascends to 3300 m in Guatemala. The fruits of some species in Mexico are eaten raw or cooked by Indians.

To the small family **Bonnetiaceae** should be added the genus *Haploclathra* Benth., four species in Brazil; lectotype *H. paniculata* (Mart.) Benth.; the genus differs from the other six in its opposite leaves, elongate anthers with wavy margins, and 1 ascending ovule in each loculus. The bark of *Kielmeyera coriacea* Mart., known as Pau Campo, is used in Brazil as a source of cork; the seeds yield an oil used locally for skin diseases. The trunk of *Caraipa psidiifolia* Ducke and of other species, is the source of a balsam for healing wounds. The leaves of *Ploiarum alternifolium* (Vahl) Melch., a tree of tropical Asia, are eaten raw or cooked by the inhabitants, and also used as tea.

ORDER 37. **OCHNALES**

(*Fam. Fl. Pl.* **1**, 281)

Families: **Strasburgeriaceae, Ochnaceae, Diegodendraceae, Sarcolaenaceae, Sphaerosepalaceae, Dipterocarpaceae, Ancistrocladaceae.**

Suggested phylogeny: MAGNOLIALES → DILLENIALES → BIXALES → THEALES → OCHNALES.

Evolution within this Order has in some cases been in the direction of special adaptation for fruit dispersal, especially in *Dipterocarpaceae* by enlargement of the sepals which function as wings; in the *Ochnaceae* by berries associated with a secondary form of apocarpy, the floral structure in each of these families being very uniform.

Since my FAMILIES OF FLOWERING PLANTS was published, an interesting new family, **Diegodendraceae**, Madagascar, has been described, and a revised key to the Order is given below.

Revised Key to the Order OCHNALES.

A. Erect trees and shrubs:
  B. Anther-connective not produced at the apex:
    C. Stipules intrapetiolar and wrapped around the terminal bud:
      D. Stamens very numerous; anthers basifixed; disk none: style gynobasic between 2 or 3 carpels *Diegodendraceae*
      DD. Stamens 10; anthers subsagittate, versatile; disk present; style terminal on the 5-locular ovary *Strasburgeriaceae*
    CC. Stipules extrapetiolar:
      E. Stamens free among themselves; ovules axile:
        F. Sepals 10–5, not involucrate by bracts *Ochnaceae*
        FF. Sepals 3, usually involucrate at the base *Sarcolaenaceae*
      EE. Stamens irregularly connate at the base; ovules erect from the base of the loculi *Sphaerosepalaceae*

BB. Anther-connective produced at the apex; calyx-lobes usually enlarged and wing-like in fruit; ovary 3-locular; ovules 2 in each loculus *Dipterocarpaceae*

AA. Climbing shrubs with hooked branches; petals contorted; calyx enlarged and wing-like in fruit; ovary 1-locular; ovule 1, ascending *Ancistrocladaceae*

The family **Ochnaceae**[1] is especially interesting because we have here the somewhat rare occurrence of a secondary kind of apocarpy, i.e. an apocarpous pistil which has been derived from a syncarpous one. The indication or even the proof of this is the single style which serves for all the carpels, similar to but only a parallelism of the gynobasic style of the *Boraginaceae* and *Lamiaceae* (*Labiatae*). In a primitive apocarpous gynoecium each carpel has, of course, a separate style, as in *Magnoliaceae*. The *Ochnaceae* here include the *Sauvagesieae*, a tribe formerly placed with the *Violaceae*. They are a fairly natural and well defined group but scarcely separable as a family. The most advanced genera are *Sauvagesia* (common to tropical Africa and America) and *Vausagesia*, and some species of the former have advanced so far as to become annuals. Otherwise all the genera are woody, although a few adapted to special climatic conditions have become reduced to sub-shrubs with underground rhizomes such as certain African species of *Ochna*. It should be noted that in these more recent types which have become annuals the inner staminodes have become petaloid as in *Sauvagesia* (Fig. 252). In the small genus *Godoya* (tropical America) the leaves may be either simple or pinnate in different species which seem to be otherwise closely related. A parallel example is the genus *Eucryphia* (*Eucryphiaceae*). A further character of note is the transformation of the staminodes in *Lavradia* (Fig. 253) into a tube enclosing the gynoecium.

An enlargement of the torus, on which are seated the apparently separate carpels, is a common mark of this family and especially evident in the fruiting stage. In *Lophira*, African trees which inhabit both the moist high forest and the dry savannah country, we have in the enlarged wing-like calyx-lobes the beginning of a tendency which has become such a marked feature of *Dipterocarpaceae*.

The type genus of *Ochnaceae* is *Ochna*, Old World tropics and subtropics; it embraces about 80 species; trees and shrubs; leaves with close parallel nerves; stipules paired, axillary; panicles mostly from scaly buds arising from below the one-year-old leaves; flowers yellow, pedicels jointed; sepals 5; petals 10–5, deciduous, imbricate; torus thick, lobed or raised on the gynophore; stamens numerous at the base of the disk; anthers opening

---

[1] Including *Sauvagesiaceae* Dumort. (1829). *Lophiraceae* Endlich. (1841). *Luxemburghiaceae* van Tieghem (1901). *Wallaceae* van Tieghem (1904).

lengthwise; ovary deeply 10–3-lobed, the lobes seated obliquely on the torus; styles connate, gynobasic, central; ovule 1 in each loculus, axile; fruit of 10–3 drupes separate on the torus; seeds without endosperm.

In tribe *Ochneae* the seeds are devoid of endosperm, but the other two tribes, *Euthemideae* and *Luxemburgieae*, have endosperm. None of the genera diverges very far from the type genus, though there are a few outstanding characters worth mentioning. In tribe *Blastemantheae*, for example, the sepals are spirally arranged and cone-like in bud; the anthers are connate into a unilateral mass in *Luxemburgia*; and there is only one fertile anther in *Testulea*.

Meni Oil and Niam Fat are obtained from kernels of *Lophira alata* Banks, and the wood is known as African Oak and Dwarf Ironwood, the colour of which is red, resembling Beef-wood (*Mimusops globosa* Gaertn.), with a strong hard interlocked grain, used abroad for railway sleepers, maritime and other heavy constructional work.

Diegodendraceae R. Capuron (ADANSONIA *new series* **3**, 385, Fig. 5 (1963)). 1 sp., *D. humbertii* R. Capuron, Madagascar, mostly in calcereous soil on the plateaux.

Trees or shrubs; leaves simple, alternate, entire, broadly lanceolate, pinnately nerved, pellucid-punctate; stipules intrapetiolar, very long and wrapped around the terminal bud, early caducous (as in most *Irvingiaceae*), leaving an annular scar; inflorescence terminal, cymose-paniculate; bracts and bracteoles soon deciduous; flowers bisexual, actinomorphic; sepals 5 or 6, free, unequal, very imbricate, persistent; petals 5, free, subequal, very imbricate in bud, caducous; stamens hypogynous, very numerous, free; anthers 2-locular, basifixed, loculi latrorsely dehiscent by slits; gynoecium composed of 2 or 3 free carpels on a small elevated receptacle; carpels very warted and with numerous peltate glands; style central, gynobasic, undivided, stigma terminal and punctiform; ovules 2 in each loculus, basal and collateral, ascending, anatropous, micropyle extrorse, inferior; fruit not yet known.

This very interesting new family undoubtedly belongs to the Order OCHNALES. Especially noteworthy are the large intrapetiolar stipules and pellucid-punctate leaves; the illustration (Fig. 254) is adapted from that published by Capuron.

The family **Sarcolaenaceae**[1] (formerly named *Chlaenaceae*) is found only in that wonderful island of endemics, Madagascar, where there are 10 genera embracing about 30 species. The family shows no very close relasionship with any other, except perhaps *Dipterocarpaceae*. A remarkable feature of most of the genera is the metamorphosis of the bracteoles, which

[1] Including *Chlaenaceae* Thouars (1807). *Schizolaenaceae* Wettstein (1935). *Rhodolaenaceae* Bullock (1958).

are united to form a cup or tube (involucel or epicalyx) usually enclosing the fruit. Another characteristic of the family is that the pollen-grains are united into *pollinia* (as is common in the highly evolved *Asclepiadaceae* and *Orchidaceae*), consisting so far as known, of 4 or 16 cells (see C. C. Smith PHYTOLOGIA **1**, 83 (1934)).

The anatomy of *Sarcolaenaceae* helps little in determining the taxonomic position of this peculiar small family. Metcalfe and Chalk say that the presence of mucilage-cells in the cortex and the complex structure of the vascular system of the petiole suggest that it may have affinities with the *Dipterocarpaceae*, differing from them in the absence of resin-canals.

They are trees and shrubs with alternate entire evergreen leaves and caducous stipules; flowers bisexual, actinomorphic; bracteoles often united to form an involucel which often persists and encloses the fruit; sepals 5 or 3, very imbricate; petals 5, contorted, usually free; stamens numerous to 5, inserted within a disk; ovary 3-locular; ovules 2 or more, axile; fruit a loculicidal capsule or indehiscent; seeds with endosperm and straight embryo.

In the type genus, *Sarcolaena*, the involucel is enlarged after flowering and fimbriate or laciniate on the margin. Indeed, most of the generic characters are derived from the involucel. In *Xerochlamys* and *Sarcolaena* it forms a closed tubular calyx-like organ at most denticulate on the margin. *Sarcolaena* is further marked by its leaves which have three parallel lines from the base to apex, no doubt due to folding in the bud stage. Herbaria in Britain are rather deficient in specimens of this family, the chief collections being in Paris.

Sphaerosepalaceae is a small and very interesting monotypic family, which I have tried in vain to fit into some larger established group. *Sphaerosepalum* was originally assigned to the *Clusiaceae* (*Guttiferae*) by Baker, later transferred to *Flacourtiaceae* by Warburgh, and later still to the segregate family *Cochlospermaceae* by Pilger. van Tieghem pointed out, however, that it did not belong to any of these families, and for once at least I have followed him in maintaining it as a separate family near to *Sarcolaenaceae* and *Theaceae*, but more especially to *Ochnaceae*. The basal placenta and the partly connate filaments of the stamens are an unusual combination of characters (see my FAMILIES OF FLOWERING PLANTS, 2nd Ed. **1**, 284, Fig. 147). The name of the single genus is *Rhopalocarpus*, which name takes precedence over *Sphaerosepalum*.

In **Dipterocarpaceae**[1] we have an entirely woody family whose strongly nerved leaves remind us very much of their Dilleniaceous ancestry, far back as it may be. A primitive character which has persisted is the much-contorted petals or corolla-segments, for we find here sometimes a slight

[1] Including *Dipteraceae* Lindley (1836).

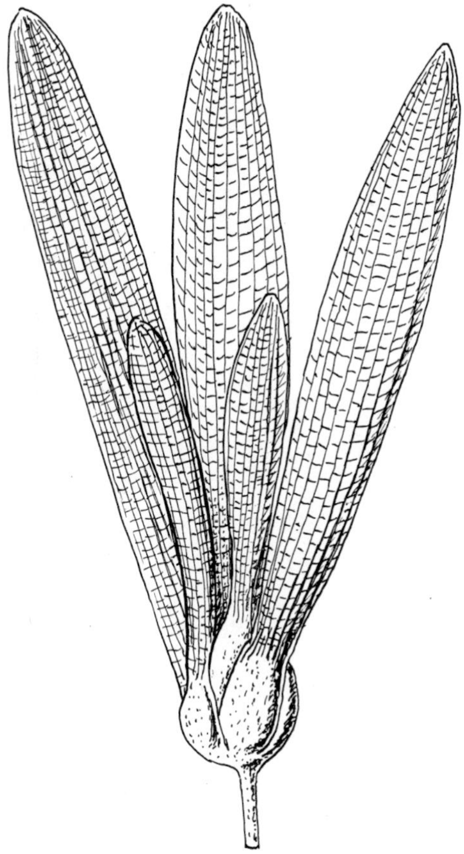

FIG. 255. *Shorea rigida* Durand, Malaya, a typical fruit of the *Dipterocarpaceae*, a family which occurs only in the Old World tropics, mainly in Malaya, very rare in Africa (orig.).

coalescence of the petals. As in *Magnoliaceae* the stipules are caducous and often very large and encircling the young buds.

The greatest evolutionary tendency in this family is the adaptation of the fruits for distribution by the wind. In nearly all the genera the calyx-lobes become unequally enlarged and wing-like in fruit. In spite of this, however, most species are local in distribution and the family is nearly confined to tropical Asia, only two genera, *Monotes* and *Marquesia*, occurring in Africa. There are no *Dipterocarpaceae* in America.

Classifications of the genera of the family *Dipterocarpaceae* show very great divergence of opinion amongst botanists with regard to the number to be recognised. The two classical systematic works, however, agree fairly well in this respect, and I have followed them as closely as possible. As a

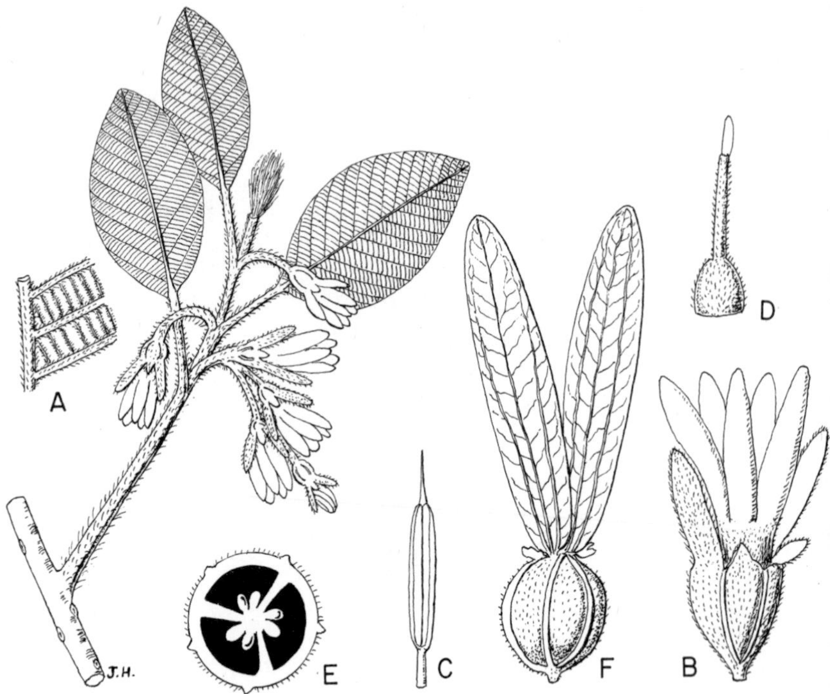

Fig. 256. *Dipterocarpus costatus* Gaertn., the type species of the type genus of *Dipterocarpaceae*. **A**, lower surface of leaf. **B**, flower. **C**, stamen. **D**, gynoecium. **E**, cross-section of ovary. **F**, fruit (orig.).

primary character I have relied on the aestivation of the calyx, the more primitive genera being represented in the imbricate group, and the more advanced in the valvate or subvalvate section. It is significant that the latter character is accompanied by another equally advanced feature, i.e. the re-remarkable adnation of the calyx-tube to the fruit, which imparts almost an epigynous character to the flowers of the two genera in which it occurs, *Anisoptera* and *Pachynocarpus*. The number of enlarged wing-like sepals in the fruiting stage still seems to be the most convenient character for distinguishing certain genera, but at best it is somewhat artificial, though useful for identification purposes.

Contrary to what one might expect, considering their winged fruits, the species of *Dipterocarpaceae* are nearly all very local and of restricted distribution, a fact explained probably by the nature of their habitat, i.e. dense tropical wet forest at low altitudes in Malaya. Sometimes the seeds even germinate before the fruits fall from the trees. A few, however, favour drier country such as *Vatica obscura* Trimen (Ceylon), and most of the species of

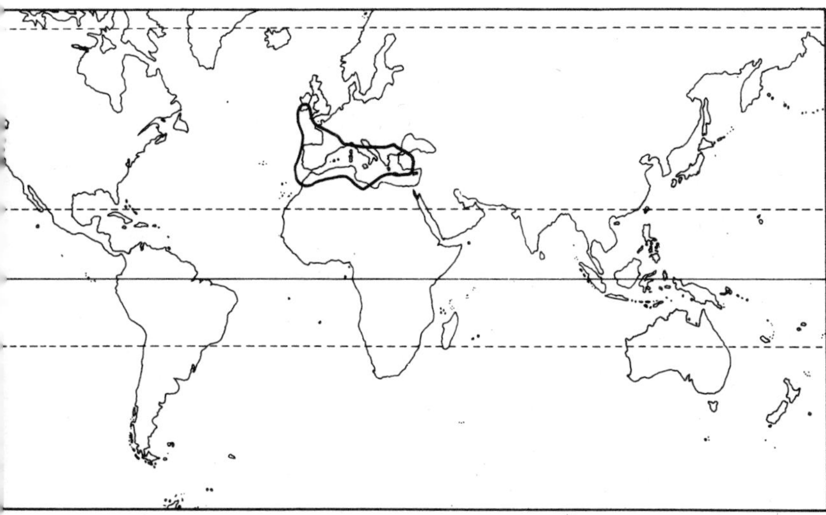

MAP 18. Distribution of *Arbutus unedo* Linn. (*Ericaceae*), probably indicating a former land connexion between S.W. Eire, and France, Portugal and Spain; it extends around the Mediterranean east to Turkey.

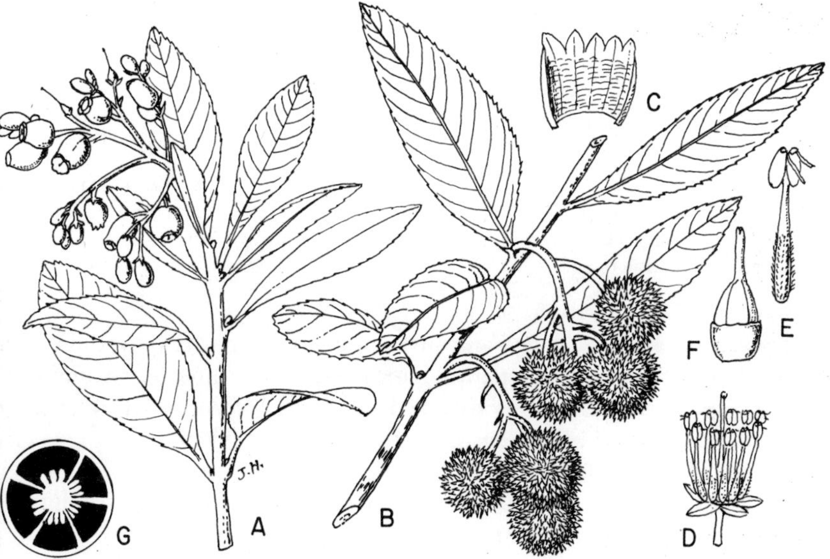

FIG. 257. The Strawberry tree, *Arbutus unedo* Linn., family *Ericaceae*, a Mediterranean species found also wild in S.W. Eire; its presence there supports the supposition that Eire was formerly connected to the Iberian Peninsula. **A**, in flower. **B**, in fruit. **C**, corolla laid open. **D**, calyx and stamens. **E**, stamen. **F**, disk and gynoecium. **G**, cross-section of ovary (orig.).

Monotes and *Marquesia* in Africa, which grow in the light savannah *Brachystegia* forest. There are many valuable timbers in this family.

Dipterocarpus, the type genus, contains over 100 species distributed in Indo-Malaya, Indo-China and the Philippine Islands. In spite of the fact that the fruits are adapted for wind-distribution, however, the species are mostly of very restricted range. *Dipterocarpus* is a genus of tall resinous trees; stipules large at the ends of the shoots, enclosing the bud, valvate, soon deciduous and leaving an annular scar; flowers few, in axillary racemes; calyx-tube in fruit smooth or variously ribbed, winged or transversely

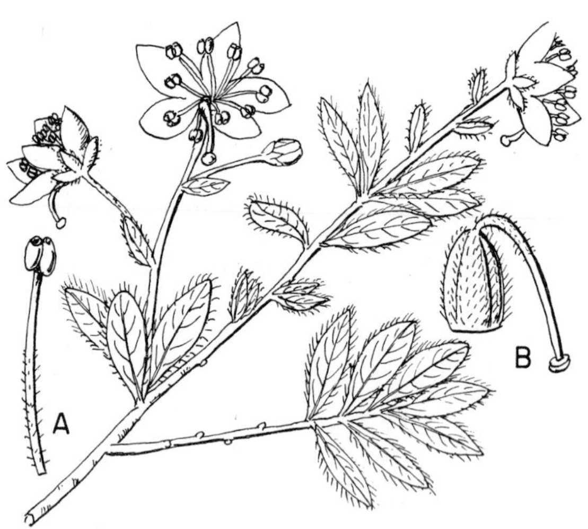

FIG. 258. *Therorhodion redowskianum* (Maxim.) Hutch. (*Ericaceae*), distinguished from *Rhododendron* by the flowers being produced on new annual shoots and the corolla split to the base on one side. **A**, stamen. **B**, gynoecium. Note the sharply reflexed style which prevents self-pollination (orig.).

lamellate, the lobes enlarged and surrounding the fruit, two of them large and wing-like; stamens numerous; anthers linear, connective acuminate; ovary 3-locular, each loculus 2-ovuled; fruit indehiscent; seeds with large fleshy unequal wrinkled-lobate or contortuplicate cotyledons. Type species *D. costatus* Gaertn. (Fig. 256).

A notable feature about the distribution of the family is its complete absence from America and its rarity in Africa. The stamens are reduced to 5 in *Monoporandra* and from 10–5 in *Stemonoporus* and *Balanocarpus*.

The fruit character of *Lophira* is also repeated in the small family **Ancistrocladaceae**, scandent shrubs with hooked branches which occur only in the high forests of west Africa and the Congo and of far distant Indo-Malaya. Considered alone the isolation of this interesting family in these two widely separated areas might not be regarded as of much importance. But taken in conjunction with the distribution of other plants it seems to indicate that a high forest area at one time covered much of the intervening country which has disappeared through subsequent movement and elevation of the earth's surface and has become clothed with the savannah flora, a more recent association in some places which is continually encroaching on the dense primaeval forest.

ORDER 38. **ERICALES**

(*Fam. Fl. Pl.* **1**, 288)

Families: **Clethraceae, Pyrolaceae, Ericaceae, Epacridaceae, Diapensiaceae, Monotropaceae, Lennoaceae, Vacciniaceae.**

Suggested phylogeny of ERICALES: MAGNOLIALES → DILLENIALES → BIXALES → THEALES (*Saurauiaceae*) → **ERICALES**.

This is a very natural group of families not easily placed in a linear system, though they are here considered to be derived from the THEALES stock. They undoubtedly represent a very early stage in sympetaly because of their hypogynous stamens. The premier place is given to the small family **Clethraceae**, the type genus, *Clethra*, having been regarded by Bentham and Hooker as a *genus anomalum* in the *Ericaceae*. The leaves are strongly reminiscent of those of *Eurya* (*Theaceae*), but the flowers are borne in racemes or panicles after the manner of *Styrax*. There is only this single genus *Clethra*, with about 56 species in eastern Asia, the Malay Archipelago, N.E. America, Central and South America, the West Indies, and with one remarkable isolated species, *C. arborea* Ait., in the remote island of Madeira, where it is a dominant tree in the laurel forest between 2000–5000 ft. (See map in my FAMILIES OF FLOWERING PLANTS, 2nd Ed. **1**, 289.) The genus *Schizocardia* formerly placed in this family is now included in *Cyrillaceae*.

The chief points about the family are the free petals (as in many *Theaceae*) and the anthers opening by apical pores (as in *Ericaceae*), thus providing a definite link with the latter family. Indumentum when present is of stellate hairs.

We have here a natural and primitive family of ERICALES, and from this ancestral stock may be traced the path of evolution of such genera of *Ericaceae* as *Pieris*, *Zenobia*, *Agauria*, *Arbutus* and *Arctostaphylos* (*sensu stricto*), etc., and the mainly alpine or epiphytic genera derived from them such as *Pernettya*, *Gaultheria*, *Diplycosia*, *Cassandra*, *Cassiope*, *Epigaea*, *Andromeda*, etc.

Pyrola, the type genus of **Pyrolaceae**,[1] is represented by about 15 species distributed throughout the north temperate zone; perennial herbs; leaves radical or cauline; flowers racemose, nodding, bracteate; calyx 5-partite, persistent; petals 5, free, concave, deciduous; stamens 10, hypogynous; anthers at first retroflexed, at length erect, 4-locular, opening by terminal pores; ovary 5-locular, stigma 5-lobed; ovules numerous, axile; disk 10-crenate or absent; capsule subglobose, 5-locular, 5-valved to the base; seeds very small, testa produced at each end, reticulate; embryo very minute, axile in fleshy endosperm.

There are five genera in this small family. *Moneses* (1 species) has solitary flowers, whilst *Chimaphila* (5–6 species) has the flowers in umbels or corymbs. The leaves of *Pyrola rotundifolia* Linn., Europe and temperate Asia, are used as a substitute for *Chimaphila umbellata* (Linn.) Barton as a home remedy for healing wounds. Those of *Orthila secunda* (Linn.) House, *Herba Pirolae*, northern Europe and north Asia to America, are also used likewise. *Chimaphila umbellata*, *Folia Chimaphilae*, occurs from Europe to Japan and is used in medicine for stones in the bladder and retarding excretion in urine.

The family **Ericaceae**[2] may be regarded as generally one of the most primitive of those which have attained to the sympetalous condition. It is considered to be primitive because throughout the family the ovary is superior and the stamens are hypogynous and not attached to the corolla. Moreover the stamens are often double the number of the corolla-lobes, the general tendency of the *Sympetalae* as a whole to reduce the number to 5 or fewer not being very pronounced, although it is attained in the more advanced section or subgenus *Azalea* of *Rhododendron*, and even in small groups of closely allied species of dwarf Rhododendrons.

In considering the THEALES group of families, the strong tendency towards the evolution of an ericaceous type of flower as exhibited in the small family *Saurauiaceae*, confined to Asia, has been pointed out. It is perhaps more than a coincidence that *Ericaceae* are very abundant in the same part of the world. In the eastern Himalayas, Yunnan and Szechuan, for example, *Ericaceae*, in the shape of the genus *Rhododendron*, entirely dominate the mountain landscape, occurring as trees, shrubs and tiny alpine shrublets in a multitude of species. It is not implied that *Rhododendron* or even any part of it has been evolved from *Saurauia*, but rather that both might have descended

---

[1] Including *Retalaceae* Dulac (1867).

[2] Including *Rhododendraceae* A. L. de Juss. (1789). *Rhodoraceae* Ventenat (1799). *Diplarchaceae* Klotzsch (1857). *Arbutaceae* J. G. Agardh (1858). *Arctostaphylaceae* J. G. Agardh (1858). *Salaxidaceae* J. G. Agardh (1858). *Ceratheraceae* Dulac (1867).

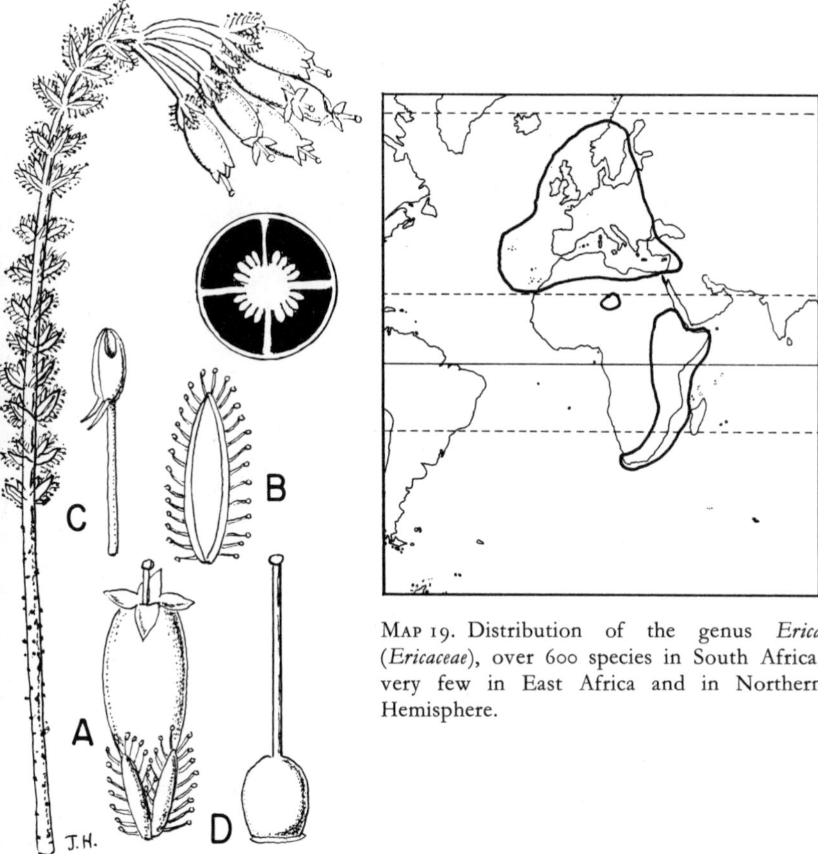

MAP 19. Distribution of the genus *Erica* (*Ericaceae*), over 600 species in South Africa, very few in East Africa and in Northern Hemisphere.

FIG. 259. *Erica tetralix* Linn., the type species of the type genus of *Ericaceae*. **A**, flower. **B**, sepal. **C**, stamen. **D**, gynoecium.

from the same common basal stock. Certain groups of species of *Rhododendron* are more primitive than others. Being an entirely woody genus the arboreal forms are probably the most ancient. Thus in *R. falconeri* Hook. f. we find some very ancient characters. The huge leaves are evergreen, the inflorescence is racemose, the corolla-lobes are numerous (up to 10), and the stamens vary in number from 12 to 20, whilst the ovary-loculi are numerous (up to 20).

There is here, therefore, a type of floral structure not so very far removed from that found in *Theaceae*, for example *Camellia*. More advanced types of *Rhododendron* have a fewer and more definite number of corolla-lobes, stamens and ovary-loculi, whilst the highest evolution is represented by the section *Azalea*, in which the stamens, as already mentioned, are usually reduced to 5, the leaves are deciduous, and the corolla shows a distinct tendency to zygomorphy with a narrow tube hiding the nectaries. With its deciduous leaves, section *Azalea* is therefore better adapted to the more rigorous winter conditions of the north temperate zone, where it mainly grows.

The type genus, *Erica*, comprises over 650 species, ranging from trees (rare) to tiny shrublets; leaves often 3–6 together in whorls, less commonly opposite or scattered, linear with revolute margins, calyx mostly 4-partite; corolla hypogynous, usually deciduous, 4-lobed or 4-fid; stamens hypogynous, usually 8, mostly arising from the base of a free more or less elevated disk; anthers opening by sublateral pores or slits, muticous, crested or aristate at or near the insertion of the filament; ovary sessile or stipitate usually 4- (rarely 8-) locular; ovules 2 or more in each loculus; capsule loculicidally 4-valved, valves separating from the axis; seeds minute, rarely winged. Type species *E. tetralix* Linn., Europe (Fig. 259).

The distribution of *Erica* is shown in Map 19, nearly all the species in S.W. Africa. Especially noteworthy is the range of the natural genus *Arbutus*, which occurs in the Mediterranean basin, the Canary Islands, N.W. and Central America and in Chile. It is of interest that the endemic Canary Island species, *A. canariensis* Veill., which occurs in the forest region of Tenerife and Hierro, is most closely related to certain central American species. In a different direction that of *Pernettya* is also interesting, central and western South America, New Zealand and Tasmania (for map see FAMILIES OF FLOWERING PLANTS, 2nd Ed. 1, 291).

The greatest divergence from the *Erica* combination of characters occurs in tribe *Arbuteae*, in which the fruit is a berry or drupe, and thereby indehiscent. It includes such genera as *Pernettya*, *Arbutus*, *Arctostaphylos*, *Gaultheria*, etc.

Of those tribes with a capsular fruit *Ledeae* has the petals free from one another (*Elliottia*, *Ledothamnus*, *Tripetaleia*, *Ledum*, *Befaria*, etc.), and in the remainder of the tribes the petals are united into a tube. In tribe *Rhododendreae* (*Rhododendron*, etc.) the capsule is septicidally dehiscent, in *Andromedeae* (*Andromeda*, *Pieris*, etc.) loculicidally dehiscent.

Some aberrent or outstanding features of certain genera: Leaves opposite in *Gaultheria* spp., a few spp. of *Erica* and in *Loiseleuria*. Calyx enclosing the capsule and becoming berry-like in *Gaultheria* and *Diplycosia*. Corolla-lobes induplicate-valvate in *Kalmia*. Petals free in *Leiophyllum*, *Ledothamnus*, *Cladothamnus*, *Elliottia*, *Ledum* and *Befaria*. Stamens 5 and filaments adnate to the corolla in *Loiseleuria*; 10 with alternate filaments adnate to the corolla and the others free in *Diplarche*, the flowers crowded into a head; anthers opening by slits lengthwise in *Loiseleuria*, *Macnabia*, *Calluna*, *Oxydendron*, *Epigaea*, and by short slits in *Kalmia* and several small South African genera;

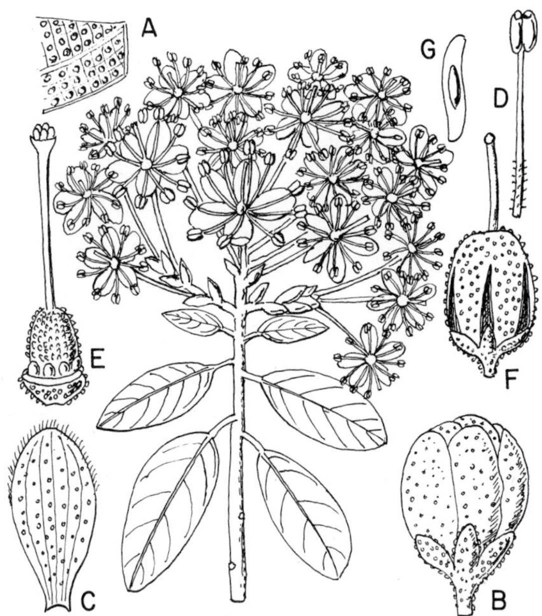

FIG. 260. *Ledum glandulosum* Nutt. (*Ericaceae*), N.W. America, a primitive member of the family and virtually a *Rhododendron* but with free petals. **A**, lower surface of leaf showing glands similar to those in many species of *Rhododendron*. **B**, flower-bud. **C**, petal. **D**, stamen. **E**, gynoecium showing disk-glands. **F**, fruit. **G**, seed (orig.).

in *Kalmia* the filaments are at first recurved with the anthers resting in pits of the corolla from which they are released elastically and scatter the pollen. Ovary 1-locular in spp. of *Simocheilus*, *Scyphogyne* and *Salaxis*.

It would be a very difficult and well nigh impossible task to attempt to follow the path of evolution of the many small and closely allied genera of *Ericaceae*. Some of the broader aspects, however, may be considered. The fruit has developed in various different ways. In *Rhododendreae*, the tribe to which *Rhododendron* belongs, the fruit is a capsule which opens by the septa. An associated character is the early deciduous corolla with imbricate lobes.

The genera *Ledum* and *Befaria* are of great interest on account of their corolla, which consists of free petals, and in which the dehiscence of the anthers is by terminal pores. Of the genera of this group I should say that those with solitary flowers are the most primitive; these are *Cladothamnus* (N.W. America) and *Ledothamnus* (South America). The latter genus might be at once taken for *Rutaceae* by a South African botanist, as also *Leiophyllum* (eastern United States). *Cladothamnus*, with the more or less solitary flowers

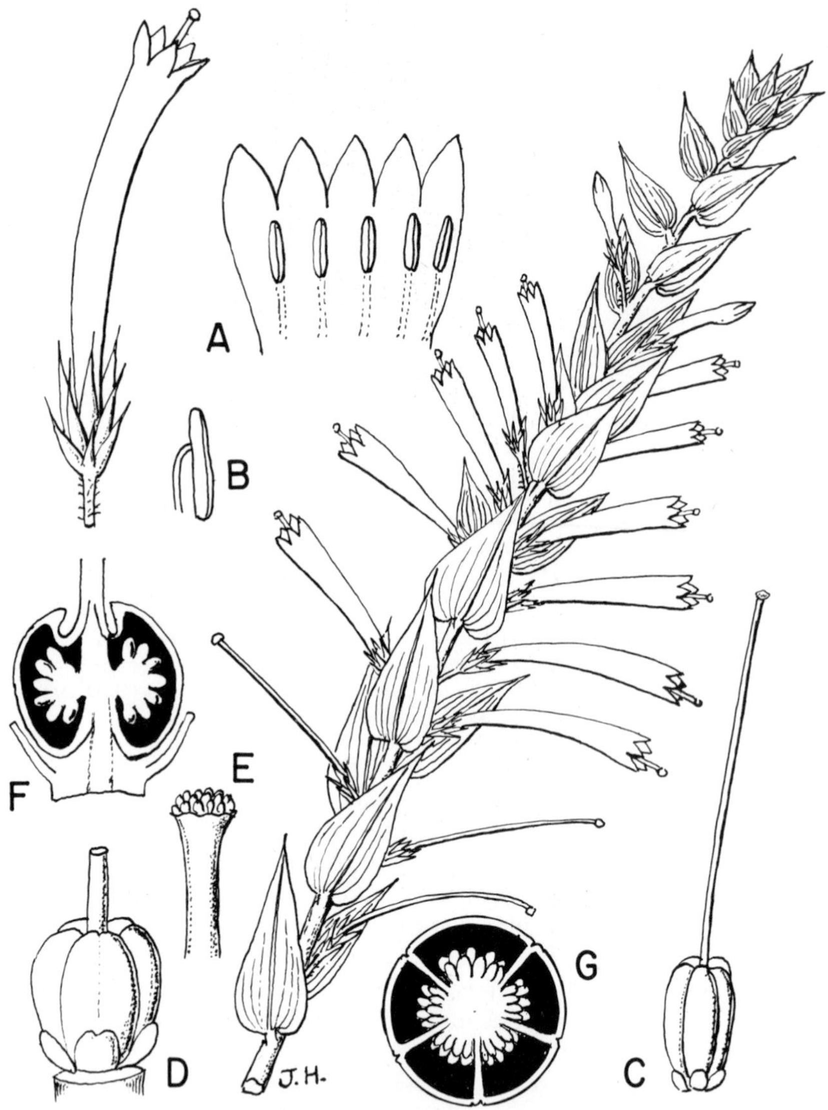

FIG. 261. *Epacris longiflora* Cav., Australia, the type species of the type genus of *Epacridaceae*. **A**, upper part of corolla showing insertion of stamens. **B**, anther. **C**, gynoecium. **D**, ovary and disk-glands. **E**, stigma. **F**, vertical section of ovary. **G**, cross-section of ovary (orig.).

borne on the young leafy shoots, perhaps shows us the origin of *Therorhodion* (Fig. 258), formerly included in *Rhododendron*, with similar growth to *Cladothamnus* but with a sympetalous unilaterally split corolla. *Ledum* especially shows a tendency towards the evolution of the great genus *Rhododendron*, and even then only a small part of it, for I am convinced that it is polyphyletic. There is great similarity between *Rhododendron micranthum* Turcz. and *Ledum glandulosum* Nutt. In *Ledum pacificum* Small (N.E. Asia), at any rate, the leaves have both the glandular undersurface and rough indumentum of many Rhododendrons. In addition the inflorescence and vegetative shoots are perulate, just as in *Rhododendron*. So that *Ledum* (see Fig. 260) is virtually a Rhododendron except for its free petals. Perhaps in some cases we still attach too much importance to the difference between "Polypetalae" and "Gamopetalae" (*Sympetalae*, *Metachlamydeae*).

Just as *Ericaceae* are a dominant family in South Africa, **Epacridaceae**,[1] which they greatly resemble in habit, are equally so in Australia and Tasmania. On the whole the flower-structure is more advanced than in *Ericaceae*, for the stamens are attached to the corolla-tube as in the higher sympetalous families, and the anthers are unilocular, dehiscing by a single slit lengthwise. The pollen-grains may be separate or in tetrads, as in *Ericaceae*, but the anthers are never furnished with appendages or tails which are so common in *Ericaceae*. In about half the genera the fruit is a loculicidal capsule, and in the other half a berry or drupe containing 1–10 pyrenes. In those genera with a capsular fruit the style is deeply set in the middle of the ovary, and in those with dehiscent fruits the style is terminal on the ovary.

Most of the genera and species are confined to Australia, but there are some few, such as *Styphelia*, in New Caledonia and the Pacific Islands.

The so-called anomalous genera *Prionotes* and *Lebetanthus*, together with *Wittsteinia*, are here treated as a separate family, *Prionotaceae*[2] (see p. 306).

The type genus, *Epacris*, contains about 45 species ranging from Australia and New Caledonia to Tasmania and New Zealand; erect or prostrate shrubs or shrublets; leaves jointed at the base, sometimes cordate and pungent-pointed; flowers solitary in the upper leaf-axils, white or rose; bracts many, imbricate, covering the pedicel and overlapping the calyx, passing gradually into sepals and forming an involucre around them; calyx 5-partite; corolla-lobes 5, imbricate; stamens 5, filaments adnate to the corolla-tube; anthers attached above the middle, 1-locular, mostly more or less included; disk of 5 free or rarely connate scales; ovary 5-locular; style inserted in a tubular depression of the ovary; ovules numerous, axile; capsule loculicidally 5-valved, valves separating from the seed-bearing axis. Type species *E. longiflora* Cav., Australia (Fig. 261).

A few exceptional characters may be noted: Leaves sometimes opposite

---

[1] Including *Stypheliaceae* Horaninow (1834).

[2] In my KEY TO THE FAMILIES OF THE FLOWERING PLANTS OF THE WORLD I named the family *Prionotidaceae*, following the incorrect spelling *Prionotis* in the GENERA PLANTARUM of Bentham and Hooker.

in *Needhamia*. Petals free in spp. of *Lysinema* and *Sprengelia*; closed and circumscissile towards the base in *Richea*. Stamens 2 perfect, remainder reduced to staminodes in *Oligarrhena*; anthers deeply split in *Conostephium*; coherent into a cone in *Coleanthera* and *Sprengelia*. Ovary 1-locular in some spp. of *Monoteca* and in a few spp. of *Leucopogon*.

In my KEY TO THE FAMILIES OF FLOWERING PLANTS OF THE WORLD, I proposed the name of a small separate family, **Prionotaceae**, for three genera, *Prionotes* R.Br., *Lebetanthus* Endl., and *Wittsteinia* F. Muell., all from the Southern Hemisphere. My former colleague at Kew, B. L. Burtt (now in Edinburgh) drew attention[1] to *Wittsteinia*, described as an anomalous genus and placed at the end of the *Vacciniaceae* in Bentham and Hooker's GENERA PLANTARUM, because the anthers dehisced by two longitudinal slits and not by pores as in the rest of the family. He recommended its transference to *Epacridaceae* because of its resemblance to two genera in that family, *Prionotes* and *Lebetanthus*, at the same time pointing out that these genera are themselves anomalous in that family, because of their bilocular anthers and stamens free from the corolla, characters at variance with the other members of the family.

Prionotaceae[2] new family, related to *Epacridaceae* and *Ericaceae*, differing from the former by the hypogynous free stamens and bilocular anthers, and from the latter by the 5 stamens and the longitudinally dehiscent anthers. A latin description is given below to conform with *International Rules of Nomenclature*.

Key to genera of PRIONOTACEAE

Ovary superior; anthers oblong; slender shrubs or scandent; fruit a capsule:
  Corolla elongated, cylindric; bracts minute, scattered on the pedicel; Tasmania 1. **Prionotes**

---

[1] B. L. Burtt KEW BULLETIN **3**, 493 (1948).

[2] **Prionotaceae** fam. nov., affinis *Epacridaceae* et *Ericaceae*, ab illis staminibus hypogynis liberis, antheris bilocularibus, ab his staminibus 5, antheris longitudinaliter dehiscentibus differt.

Frutices vel fruticuli, interdum epiphytici et scandentes; folia parva, exstipulata, alterna, parce dentata vel serrata, coriacea; flores coccinei vel albi, bisexuales, axillares, solitarii, longe vel breviter pedicellati, bracteati et bracteolati; sepala 5, fere libera, triangularia; corolla sympetala, tubo cylindrico vel campanulato, lobis 5 parvis latis imbricatis vel induplicatis; stamina 5, hypogyna, filamentis elongatis liberis, antheris bilocularibus, loculis connectivo adnatis rimis longitudinalibus lateralibus dehiscentibus; discus e squamis 5 parvis; ovarium 5–3-loculare; stylus filiformis, elongatus, stigmate discoideo vel truncatulo; ovula numerosa, in placentis axillaribus inserta; capsula 5–3-locularis, loculicide 5-valvis, valvis ab axi placentifero deorsum solutis, vel fructus baccatus; semina parva, fusiformia, testa membranacea utrinque producta et reticulata. Genus typicus *Prionotes* R.Br. PRODR. 552 (1810); species 1, *P. cerinthoides* R.Br., Tasmaniae incola. (Fig. 262A.)

Corolla subcampanulate; bracts lanceolate, crowded on the pedicel; South America 2. **Lebetanthes**

Ovary inferior; anthers didymous; small shrublet, rooting at the nodes; fruit baccate; Victoria, South Australia 3. **Wittsteinia**

1. **Prionotes** R.Br. PRODR. 552 (1810). 1 sp., *P. cerinthoides* R.Br., Tasmania. Described by Coomber (no. 2230) as a beautiful climbing shrub, forming a curtain of flowers around the trunks of trees often 60 ft or more high in the moist forest in the Hantz Mts.

2. **Lebetanthus** Endl. GEN. SUPPL. **1**, 1411 (1841). 1 sp., *L. americanus* (Hook.) Endl., Magellan region, South America.

3. **Wittsteinia** F. Muell. FRAGMENTA PHYTOGR. AUSTRALIAE **2**, *fasc.* 15, 136 (1861). 1 sp., *W. vacciniacea* F. Muell., summits of the Baw Baw and Donna Buang mountains of Victoria, South Australia (see Fig. 262B).

The type genus, *Diapensia*, of the small family **Diapensiaceae**,[1] contains five or six species, in the Arctic regions generally and at high altitudes in Asia; cushion-like shrublets; leaves alternate, spathulate-linear, entire, flowers terminating the branchlets, solitary, white, yellow or purple-rose; peduncles after flowering elongated and scape-like; calyx 2–3-bracteate; corolla 5-lobed, persistent; stamens 5, inserted in the corolla-throat; anthers muticous, loculi oblique, divergent, 2-valved; staminodes absent or very small; ovary 3-locular; ovules numerous; capsule subglobose, 3-locular, loculicidally 3-valved; seeds with abundant endosperm and subcylindric embryo.

Pyxidanthera shares with *Diapensia* the absence of staminodes, but has transversely dehiscent anthers. The remainder of the genera possess staminodes opposite the corolla-lobes, separate or united with the filaments into a ring. In *Shortia* and *Schizocodon* the corolla-lobes are toothed or fringed, and in *Berneuxia* and *Galax* they are entire, the last mentioned being unique in the family in having 1-locular anthers transversely 2-valved.

Diapensiaceae occur only in the colder regions of the Northern Hemisphere. *Diapensia lapponica* Linn. grows all around the Arctic Circle, and there are a number of related species in the mountains of Japan and in the high mountains of central Asia. The genus *Shortia* (Fig. 263) has one representative in the eastern United States of North America, a second in Japan, and a third in southern Yunnan. Judged both from its morphology and geographical distribution, therefore, the family seems to be of considerable antiquity, perhaps in the past having been more widespread, but represented at the present day by only a few relict and well defined species. Not many years ago British botanists were thrilled at the news that *Diapensia lapponica* Linn. had been found in the mountains of Scotland, thus adding another family to the British flora.

[1] Including *Galacaceae* D. Don (1828).

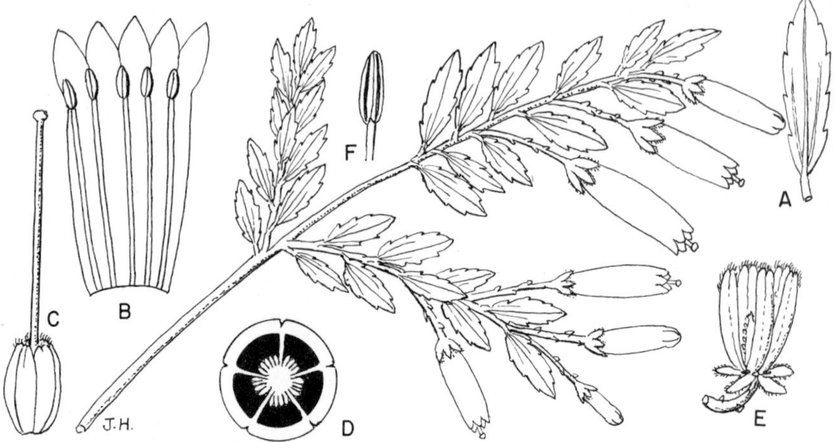

FIG. 262A. *Prionotes cerinthoides* R.Br. (*Prionotaceae*), Tasmania; type species of the type genus. **A**, leaf. **B**, corolla opened out. **C**, gynoecium. **D**, cross-section of ovary. **E**, fruit. **F**, anther (orig.).

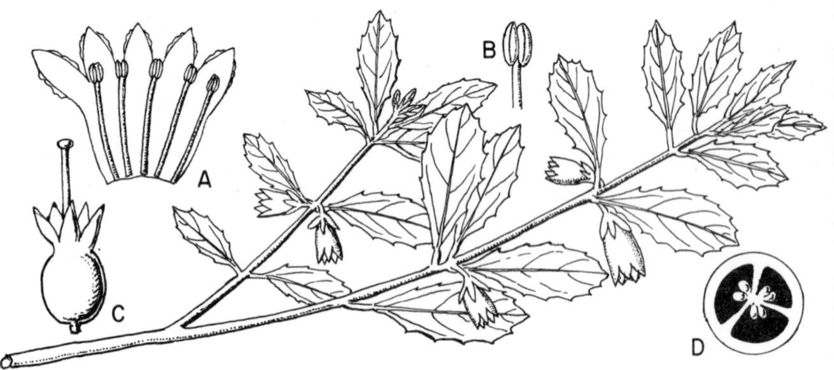

FIG. 262B. *Wittsteinia vacciniacea* F. Muell. (*Prionotaceae*), summits of mountains in Victoria State, south Australia. **A**, corolla laid open showing the almost free stamens. **B**, anther. **C**, fruit and style. **D**, cross-section of ovary (orig.).

The family occupies an advanced position in the ERICALES, and may be derived from somewhat different basic stocks, the *Diapensieae* having more the habit of some *Ericaceae*, whilst the resemblance of the *Galacineae*, especially *Shortia* and *Schizocodon*, to the *Pyrolaceae*, is considerable. The most significant feature of the *Galacineae* is the presence of as many staminodes as stamens, representing an intermediate stage between the typical 10 stamens of the *Ericaceae* and the more advanced sympetalous families with 5 stamens. Accompanying the reduction to 5 stamens is their epipetalous position, which marks a further advancement on the *Ericaceae* in which the stamens are hypogynous.

Monotropa, **Monotropaceae**,[1] a genus of about 10 species, occurs in Asia and in North and Central America; unbranched leafless scaly herbs with slender intricate roots; flowers terminal, solitary, nodding, bracteate; sepals 4, scale-like; petals 6–5, free, oblong; stamens 12 or 10; anthers short, peltate, horizontal, opening by transverse slits; disk 12–10-toothed; ovary 5-locular; style short, thick, tubular, expanded into a funnel-shaped crenulate stigma; ovules very numerous on thick placentas on the inner angle; capsule 5-locular, loculi 5-valved; testa of the minute seeds produced at each end.

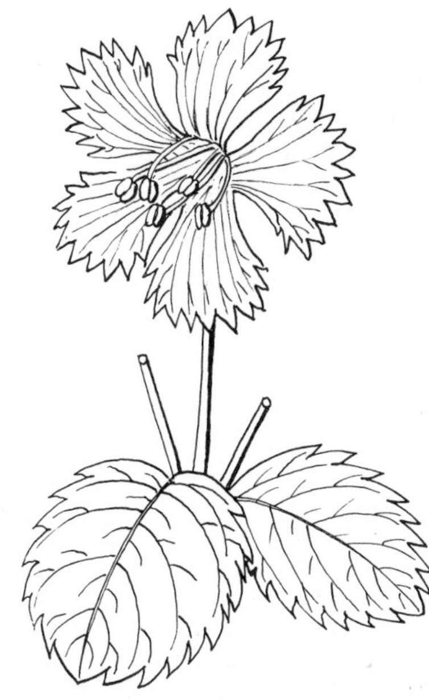

Fig. 263. *Shortia uniflora* Maxim. (*Diapensiaceae*), Japan, only one of several lovely members of this small family related to *Ericaceae*.

About half of the genera share the free petals of *Monotropa* or they may be lacking as in *Allotropa*; the placentas are parietal in *Cheilotheca*, *Pleuricospora*, *Monotropastrum*, *Pityopus* and *Newberrya*. A disk is present in most genera, the exceptions being *Cheilotheca*, *Monotropastrum*, *Pityopus*, *Sarcodes*, *Pterospora* and *Newberrya*.

There are only three genera and four species of the family **Lennoaceae**, endemic in western North America and Mexico. Type genus *Lennoa* (Fig. 264); low-stemmed herbs parasitic on various *Asteraceae* (*Compositae*); stem-scales erect-spreading; cymes dense, subcorymbose; calyx-segments 8, linear or filiform; corolla-tube cylindric, shortly 8–11-lobed; stamens 8, in two rows; anther-loculi divergent; ovary 28–20-locular; stigma subcapitate; fruit subdrupaceous, the upper part splitting off by a horizontal slit and exposing 28–20 cocci in a ring around the very broad axis.

In *Pholisma* and *Ammobroma* the stamens are in a single series and the anther-loculi are parallel, the former with a spicate inflorescence and glandular-hairy calyx-segments, the latter with a saucer-like subcapitate inflorescence and the calyx-segments plumose.

Taxonomists vary greatly in their conception of families, some taking a very broad view, some narrower, and some intermediate. The intermediate

[1] Including *Hypopithydaceae* Link (1831). *Semicirculaceae* Dulac (1867).

course is followed so far as possible in this phylogenetic system; but small groups or even single genera which possess characters at variance with those of the family in which they are placed are usually treated as separate. Compare our restriction of *Saxifragaceae* to a few closely related herbaceous families, to the exclusion of *Cunoniaceae*, *Escalloniaceae*, *Grossulariaceae*, etc., which were classed together probably on account of their sometimes similar floral diagrams. The result is that families are better circumscribed with as few exceptions as possible.

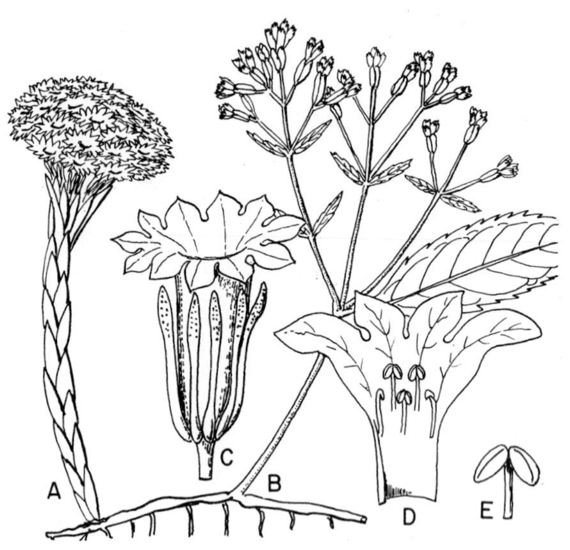

FIG. 264. **A**, *Lennoa madreporoides* Lex. (*Lennoaceae*), Mexico, parasitic on the roots of a species of **B**, *Stevia* (*Asteraceae*). **C**, flower. **D**, part of corolla opened out. **E**, anther (orig.).

In the ERICALES especially *Ericaceae* and *Vacciniaceae* were usually kept apart by most botanists until they were combined in 1889 by Drude in Engler and Prantl's PFLANZENFAMILIEN (Vol. 4, 1), following the same treatment by Endlicher in his GENERA PLANTARUM, the *Vacciniaceae* being sandwiched as a subfamily between the *Rhododendroideae* and the *Arbutoideae* and the *Ericoideae*, and separated by their inferior ovary.

The latest vacillation relating to families in this Order has been carried out by Sleumer in the FLORA MALESIANA, in which he has included in the *Ericaceae*, not only *Vacciniaceae*, but also *Pyrolaceae* and *Monotropaceae*; a retrograde step, in my opinion.

Vacciniaceae[1] are on the whole more advanced than *Ericaceae*, not only by their inferior ovary and baccate fruit, but there is also a difference in their

[1] Including *Siphonandraceae* Klotzsch (1851). *Forotubaceae* Dulac (1867).

FIG. 265. *Vaccinium myrtillus* Linn., the type species of the type genus of *Vacciniaceae*. **A**, corolla opened out. **B**, stamens. **C**, ovary, disk and style. **D**, cross-section of ovary. **E**, fruit. **F**, seed. **G**, vertical section of seed (orig.).

stomata. In *Ericaceae* the stomata in nearly all genera are of the Ranunculaceous type, i.e. the guard-cells are surrounded by several ordinary undifferentiated cells, while in *Vacciniaceae* the guard-cells are accompanied on each side by a special subsidiary cell placed parallel to the pore, i.e. the Rubiaceous type. Critics may twit me about stressing the importance of the inferior ovary in this particular case because I abandoned it in favour of the inflorescence for separating the *Liliaceae* from the *Amaryllidaceae*!

The fruits of several species of *Vacciniaceae* are edible, such as the Cranberry, *Oxycoccus palustris* Pers., the Whortleberry, or Bilberry, *Vaccinium myrtillus* Linn. (see Fig. 265), and the Crowberry, *V. vitis-idaea* Linn. Broussa Tea is brewed from the leaves of *V. arctostaphylos* Linn. There are many beautiful garden plants belonging to this family.

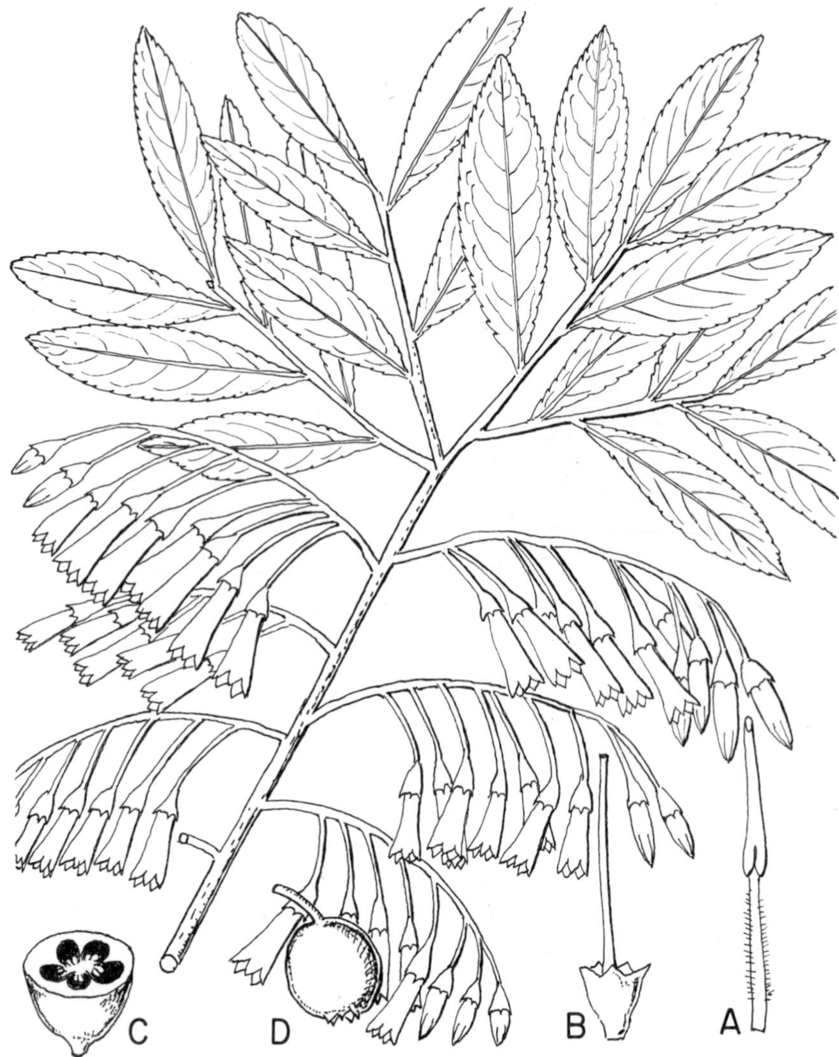

Fig. 266. *Vaccinium cylindraceum* Smith (*Vacciniaceae*), an endemic species in the Azores. **A**, stamen. **B**, calyx and style. **C**, cross-section of ovary. **D**, fruit. (orig.).

Vaccinium,[1] the type genus, covers over 350 species throughout temperate regions and in the mountains of the tropics, but very rare indeed in

[1] Linnaeus states (CRITICA BOTANICA, Hort's translation): "I retain *Vaccinium* as the name of genus, even if a thousand commentators hereafter should prove that the 'Vaccinia' of Virgil were the berries of *Ligustrum* (Privet)." Other authorities consider it to be derived from *Baccinum*, a popular name for a little berry.

FIG. 267. A rare species of *Vacciniaceae*, *Paphia vitiensis* Seem., endemic in Fiji; small tree or shrub, sometimes epiphytic at 4000–4500 ft; corolla white, red or cream, tinged with carmine; calyx dark claret colour; fruit deep red. **A**, flower with corolla removed. **B**, stamens. **C**, gynoecium and calyx. **D**, cross-section of ovary (orig.).

Africa; the type species, *V. myrtillus* Linn. (Fig. 265), extends from northern Europe, through northern Asia to N.W. America: shrubs or rarely trees, rarely epiphytic; buds scaly; leaves entire or serrate; flowers in axillary or terminal racemes or axillary fascicles, rarely solitary; bracts sometimes foliaceous; calyx-lobes 5–4; corolla variously shaped, usually terete, lobes or teeth 5–4; stamens 10 or 8, free from or shortly adherent to the base of the tube, filaments often hairy; anthers awned or muticous at the back, produced into 2 terminal transverse or oblique rounded or elongated pores, rarely by slits; disk pulvinate or convex; ovary 5–4-locular, or 10- or 8-locular by spurious septa arising from the placentas; berry globose; seeds compressed, with fleshy endosperm and straight embryo. There are few exceptions in this family. The calyx is only half superior in *Chiogenes*. Corolla induplicate-valvate in *Hornemannia* and *Semiramisia*. Stamens the same number as the corolla-lobes and attached to the middle of the tube in *Notopora*. Ovule solitary and pendulous in *Gaylussacia*; solitary and attached by the funicle to the ventral angle of the loculi *Rigiolepis*. Fruit drupaceous in *Gaylussacia*.

ORDER 39. **GUTTIFERALES**

(*Fam. Fl. Pl.* **1**, 297)

Families: **Hypericaceae, Clusiaceae (Guttiferae), Eucryphiaceae, Quiinaceae.**

Sometimes taxonomists are doubtful whether a particular genus should be assigned to *Theaceae* or to *Clusiaceae*, which shows that wherever we place *Theaceae*, then the Order GUTTIFERALES should follow as nearly as possible: MAGNOLIALES → DILLENIALES → BIXALES → THEALES → **GUTTIFERALES**.

As in the more advanced Order MYRTALES, the GUTTIFERALES have often gland-dotted leaves, but accompanying the fixed hypogynous type of flower the chief tendency has been the cohesion of the stamens into separate bundles and often the separation of the sexes, both of which characters are most fully developed in the tropical family *Clusiaceae* (*Guttiferae*).

Hypericum, the type genus of **Hypericaceae**[1] (type species *H. perforatum* Linn., Fig. 268), contains about 400 species distributed through temperate regions and mountains of the tropics; a widely distributed species is *H. lanceolatum* Lam., a tree up to 30 ft high, found in Socotra, the mountains of east and west Africa and in the Mascarenes: trees, shrubs or herbs; leaves opposite, mostly punctate-glandular; sepals 5; petals 5, contorted; stamens

[1] Including *Polyadelphaceae* Dulac (1867).

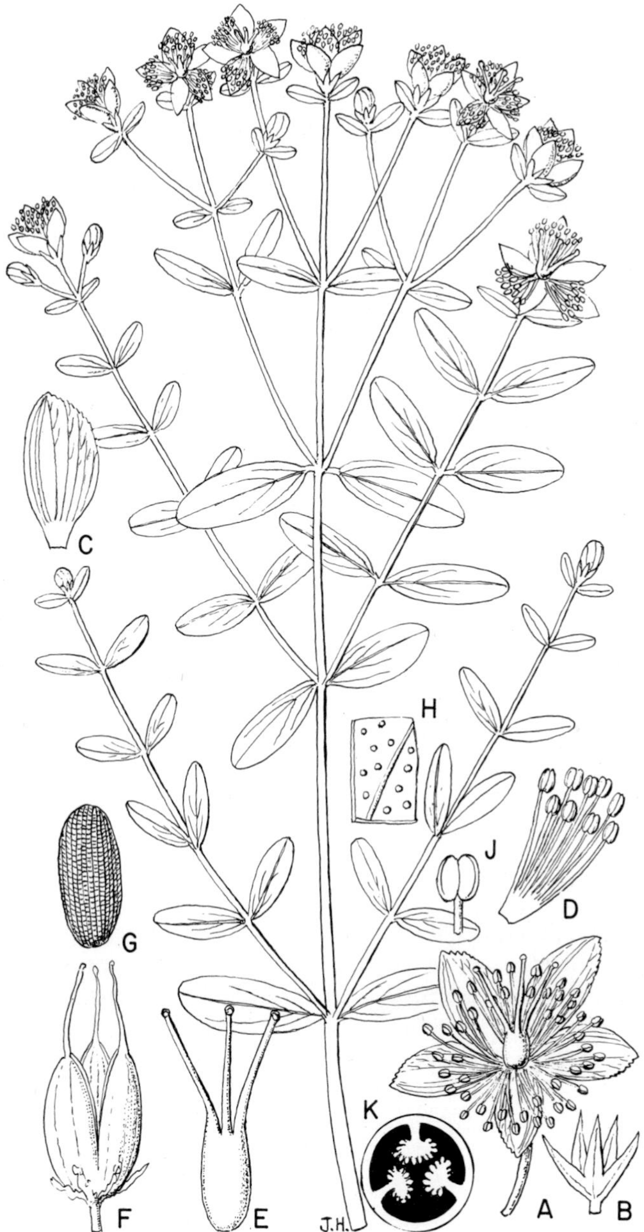

FIG. 268. *Hypericum perforatum* Linn., the type species of the type genus of *Hypericaceae*. **A**, flower. **B**, calyx. **C**, petal. **D**, stamens. **E**, gynoecium. **F**, fruit. **G**, seed. **H**, portion of leaf showing glands. **J**, anther. **K**, cross-section of ovary (orig.).

free to connate into 3–8 bundles, sometimes alternating with hypogynous glands; ovary 1-locular with parietal placentation or 5–3-locular with axile placentation; capsule septicidally dehiscent; seeds with straight, rarely curved embryo.

In South America some very distinct species of *Hypericum* mimic in habit and foliage several other genera belonging to different families, as indicated by their specific names; examples are *H. styphelioides* A. Rich., Cuba; *H. caprifoliatum* Cham. & Schlecht., *H. linoides* A. St. Hil., *H. tamariscinum* Cham. & Schlecht., Brazil. *H. parviflorum* A. St. Hil., Uruguay, has a multitude of tiny flowers.

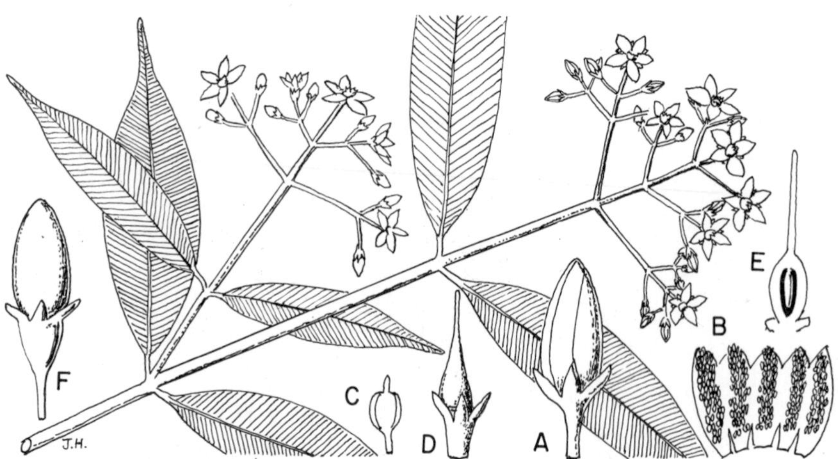

FIG. 269. *Endodesmia calophylloides* Benth. (*Hypericaceae*); the bundles of stamens, **B**, are united into a tube resembling a corolla. **A**, flower-bud. **C**, stamen. **D**, gynoecium. **E**, vertical section of same. **F**, fruit (orig.).

The genus *Eliaea* is confined to Madagascar and is very closely related to *Cratoxylon*, which ranges in tropical Asia from Burma and south Yunnan to the Celebes and Java. *Vismia* is an interesting link between the floras of tropical South America and the forests of west tropical Africa, most largely represented in the former region.

The family is divided into four tribes, *Hypericeae* and *Cratoxyleae*, with a capsular fruit, the former septicidal, the latter loculicidal, and *Vismieae* and *Endodesmieae*, with baccate or drupaceous, the former with the stamens in five bundles, the latter with them united into a tube with numerous apiculate anthers arranged within, and clearly the phylogenetic climax group.

Outstanding characters are the great reduction of the leaves in the genus *Sarothra*; lateral nerves numerous and parallel in *Endodesmia* (see Fig. 269), as in many *Clusiaceae*; indumentum of stellate hairs in *Psorospermum* spp.,

Vismia and *Harungana* (*Haronga*); flowers 4-merous in *Ascyrum*; stamens connate into a tube in *Endodesmia*; carpel solitary in this genus; seeds winged in *Eliaea* and *Cratoxylon*.

Hypericaceae is a fairly well marked family and there seems little to be gained, in these days of smaller family concepts, by including them in *Clusiaceae* (*Guttiferae*), as in the Engler and Prantl system. But taxonomic botanists, especially beginners fresh from college, are sometimes apt to differ from established authority, thereby at times revealing their ignorance or immature judgment. The family differs from *Clusiaceae* by its constantly bisexual flowers and very rarely have the leaves the numerous parallel nerves or the worm-like secretory canals so characteristic of *Clusiaceae*. The secretory cavities of *Hypericaceae* take the form of translucent dots so familiar in the genus *Hypericum*, and in this and other genera sometimes as black dots. In distribution they are mainly temperate or montane tropical, whilst *Clusiaceae* almost invariably inhabit low tropical forests.

A few have medicinal value. *Hypericum connatum* Lam., Uruguay to Argentina, the top of the inflorescence is used as a tonic and vulnerary. *H. laxiusculum* A. St. Hil., a Brazilian shrub, is astringent, aromatic, and excitant antispasmatic, and *H. teretiusculum* A. St. Hil., a herb, used in Brazil as excitant, aromatic and emmenagogue.

There are no resin canals as in *Clusiaceae*, but in their place are often intercellular spaces filled with mucilage which occur in the centre and often also at the periphery of the pith of the axis, and in the pith or parenchyma above the vascular system of the petiole and of the larger nerves. The stomata are accompanied by subsidiary cells parallel to the pore (Solereder ANAT. DICOT., English transl., **1**, 126).

As noted under *Hypericaceae*, the family **Clusiaceae**[1] is almost entirely tropical in distribution, with a few in southern Yunnan (China) and in Natal. Except for the genus *Garcinia* it is rare in Africa, but better represented in Madagascar.

The type genus, *Clusia* Linn.,[2] embraces about 240 species distributed in tropical and subtropical America, the type species being *C. major* Linn., West Indies; trees and shrubs, often epiphytic, rarely climbing, resinous; leaves often nerveless except for the stout midrib; flowers solitary to paniculate; capsule septicidally dehiscent; seeds arillate.

---

[1] Including *Guttiferae* A. L. de Juss. (1789). *Symphoniaceae* Presl (1832). *Camfogiaceae* Horaninow (1834). *Garciniaceae* Burnett (1835). *Moronobeaceae* Miers (1875). *Calophyllaceae* J. G. Agardh (1858).

[2] Linnaeus named this genus in honour of Jules Charles de l'Ecluse (latinised Carolus Clusius), a Belgian born at Arras, France, in 1526; he travelled over almost the whole of Europe, was Curator of the botanic garden in Vienna, then lived in England for a time; later at Frankfurt am Main; professor of botany at Leiden, where he presided for a long time over the Botanic Garden, and died there in 1609.

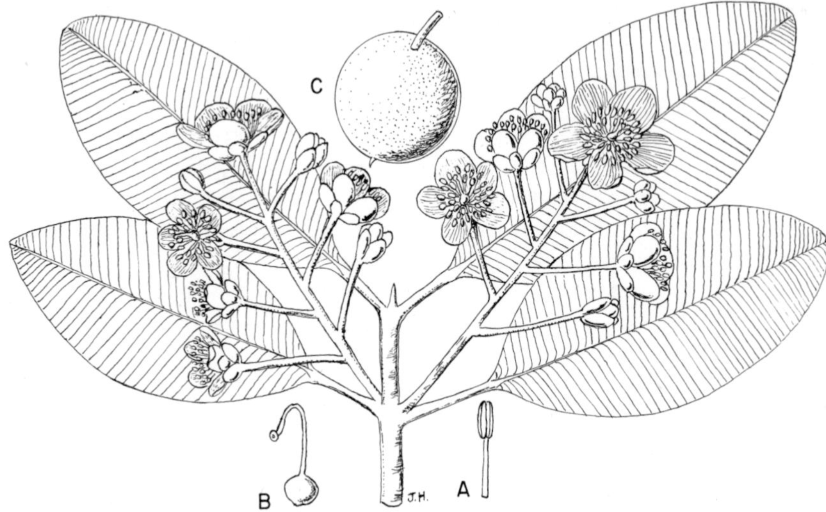

FIG. 270. *Calophyllum inophyllum* Linn., flowers and fruit (*Clusiaceae*); a common coastal tree in the Pacific Islands. **A**, stamen. **B**, gynoecium. **C**, fruit (orig.).

FIG. 271. The Mangosteen, *Garcinia mangostana* Linn. (*Clusiaceae*); native of Malaya, grown in most tropical countries; choicest of all tropical fruits, with a refreshing delicate flavour.

A feature of the family is the entire absence of bud-scales. It is a matter of opinion (see also notes under *Hypericaceae*) as to whether the family should also include *Hypericaceae*, together with a few genera included in the *Theaceae* by Bentham and Hooker as by Engler in the PFLANZENFAMILIEN. In the present writer's opinion these are equally well placed as in the GENERA

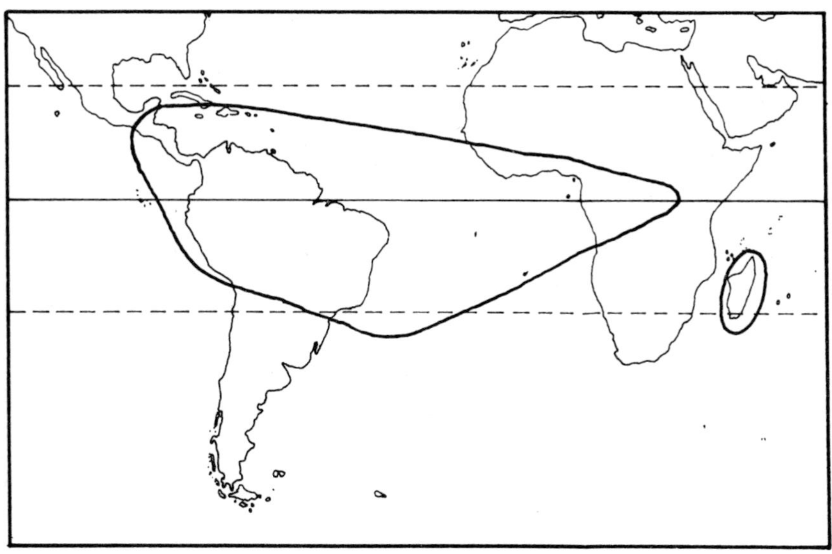

MAP 20. Range of the natural genus *Symphonia* (*Clusiaceae*).

PLANTARUM. The amalgamation of the *Hypericaceae* and *Clusiaceae* results in a cumbersome group of considerable size and is not in accordance with the policy adopted for the present work as stated in the introductory notes.

The opposite leathery exstipulate leaves with variously formed secretory cavities, either in the shape of dots or canals, the actinomorphic flowers with imbricate calyx and usually an indefinite number of stamens, are the characteristics of the family.

The family is divided into five tribes, 1. *Moronobeae*, with bisexual flowers, contorted petals, long style, and a baccate fruit; tribes 2–5 have unisexual or polygamous flowers and mostly absent style, except 2, *Callophylleae*, with a distinct style and rarely dehiscent fruit; 3, *Clusieae*, with dehiscent fruits, the carpels breaking away from the short central axis, and 4 and 5, *Garcineae* and *Allanblackieae*, with baccate (indehiscent) fruits; tribe *Garcinieae* has a 2- or more-locular ovary with axile placentas, tribe *Allanblackieae* a 1-locular ovary with parietal placentas.

In contrast with *Hypericaceae*, the family *Clusiaceae* is quite rich in economic plants. Chief among these are the Mangosteen, *Garcinia mangostana* Linn. (Fig. 271), native of the Moluccas and widely cultivated in the tropics; a delicious dessert fruit, and the pulp is also cooked with rice and called Lempog in Java, or in syrup called Dodol. The fruits of the Mamey tree, *Mammea americana* Linn., of the West Indies and northern South America are edible, 15–20 cm long, the flesh pale yellow, eaten fresh and as preserves and for jam; mature green fruits contain much pectin. The seeds of the

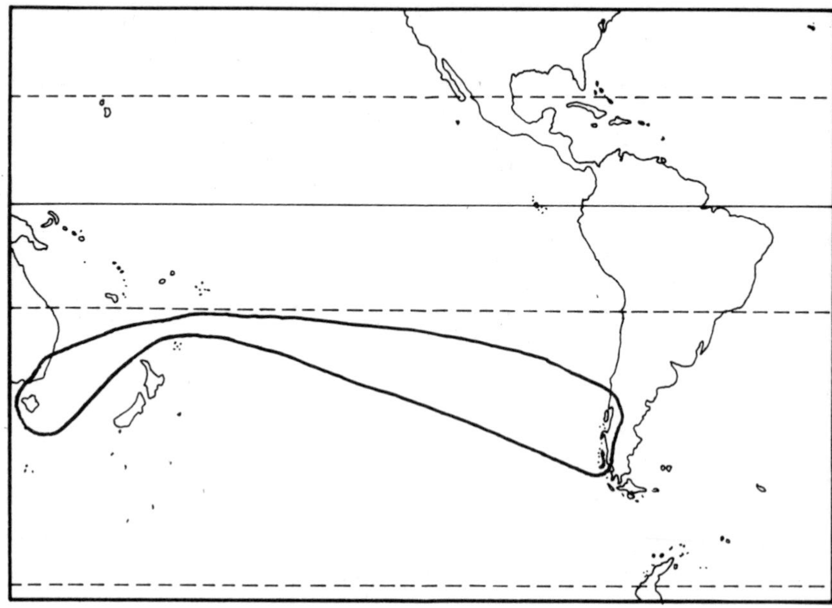

MAP 21. Distribution of *Eucryphia* (*Eucryphiaceae*), S.E. Australia, Tasmania and Chile.

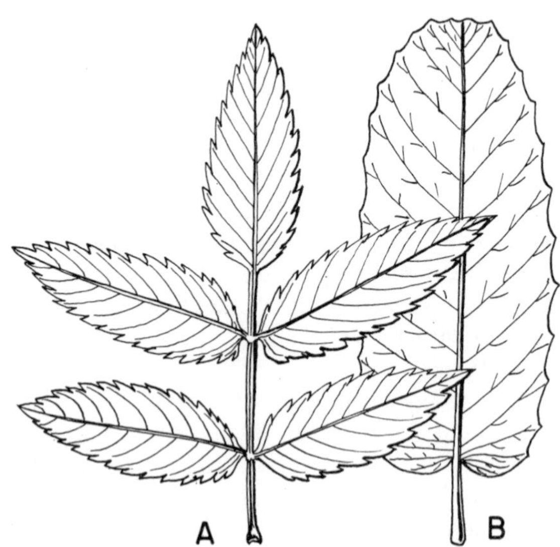

FIG. 272. Simple and compound leaves are sometimes, but not often, found in the same genus. **A**, leaf of *Eucryphia glutinosa* (Poepp. & Endl.) Baill., Chile. **B**, *Eucryphia cordifolia* Cav., Chile (*Eucryphiaceae*).

Butter tree or Tallow tree of tropical Africa, *Pentadesma butyracea* Sabine, are the source of an edible fat used for cooking, called Lamy, Kanga or Sierra Leone Butter, and used for soap, margarine and candles. These are but a few of the useful plants listed in Uphof DICT. ECONOM. PLANTS 165 (1959).

The chief interest of **Eucryphiaceae**, apart from its great ornamental value, lies in its distribution, Tasmania, S.E. Australia and southern Chile (see Map 21), and in the fact that in the single genus *Eucryphia* there are species with both simple and pinnate leaves (Fig. 272). Whether *Eucryphia* really finds its true relationship in this group may be open to question. I consider it to be an advanced opposite-leaved group derived from *Theaceae*, rather than a member of the ROSALES where it was placed by Bentham and Hooker.

Some species are cultivated and are highly ornamental with very showy flowers. *E. cordifolia* Cav., a Chilean tree, has strong hard and close-grained wood employed for flooring, furniture, telegraph poles and parts of vehicles, and by local Indians for canoes; the flowers are a source of excellent honey.

The small family **Quiinaceae** exhibits several interesting features. Here the entire unlobed leaves of the *Clusiaceae* and *Hypericaceae* are occasionally replaced by deeply pinnate segmentation of the blade, pointing to the evolution of a pinnate-leaved group.

ORDER 40. **MYRTALES**

(*Fam. Fl. Pl.* **1**, 302)

Families: **Myrtaceae, Barringtoniaceae, Lecythidaceae, Asteranthaceae, Rhizophoraceae, Sonneratiaceae, Punicaceae, Combretaceae, Lythraceae, Melastomataceae.**

MAGNOLIALES → DILLENIALES → BIXALES → THEALES → HYPERICALES → **MYRTALES** → culminating in *Melastomataceae.*

Even in a system which lays claim to be a natural one there is bound to be a certain amount of artificial grouping on account of the difficulty of showing in a linear sequence that which, in actuality, resembles a much-branched tree, or even as a further example, the main strands of a spider's web with some of the connecting threads missing, the most primitive groups in the centre, the most advanced around the outer strand.

We are confronted with this problem in placing the Orders MYRTALES and GUTTIFERALES. Both are clearly advanced groups descended mainly from the

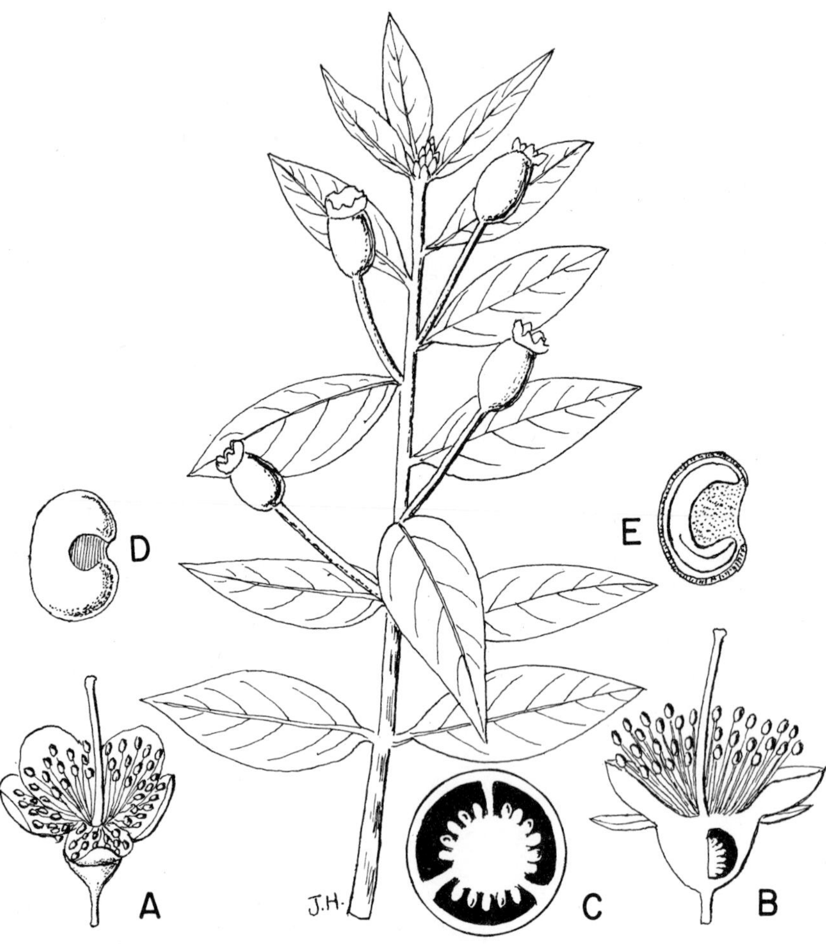

Fig. 273. *Myrtus communis* Linn., the type species of the type genus of the family *Myrtaceae*. **A**, flower. **B**, vertical section of flower. **C**, cross-section of ovary. **D**, seed. **E**, vertical section of seed showing curved embryo (orig.).

THEALES, but each has evolved in a different way. In GUTTIFERALES, on the one hand, the leaves have become opposite, as they are mostly in MYRTALES, but the ovary has remained superior, the stamens have usually become united into separate bundles (as in *Hypericaceae*), and a great tendency towards unisexuality has set in, especially in the most advanced family *Clusiaceae*. In MYRTALES, on the other hand, the ovary has become inferior, but the stamens have as a rule remained numerous and mostly quite free from one another.

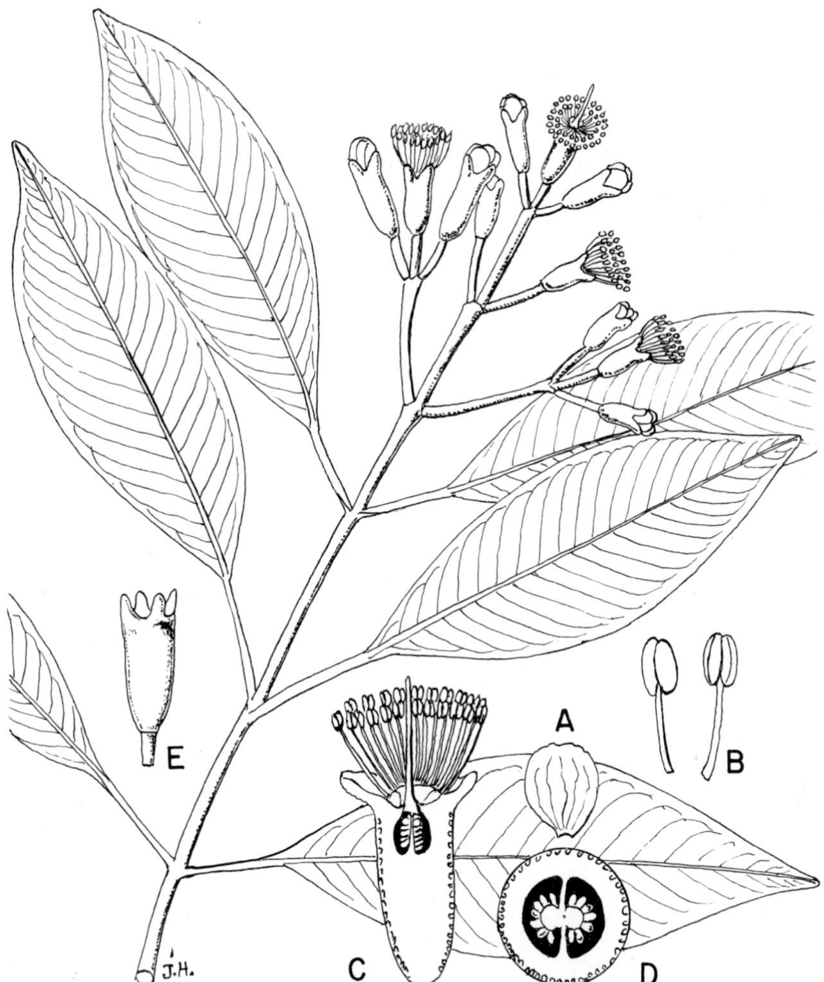

Fig. 274. The Clove plant, *Eugenia caryophyllus* (Spreng.) Bullock & S. G. Harrison, important especially to Zanzibar, east Africa (*Myrtaceae*). **A**, petal. **B**, stamens. **C**, vertical section of flower. **D**, cross-section of ovary. **E**, a clove (orig.).

In the Order MYRTALES the family **Myrtaceae**[1] takes first place mainly because of its indefinite number of stamens. Bentham and Hooker remarked on the close affinity of the family with *Lythraceae*.

---

[1] Including *Melaleucaceae* H. G. Reichenbach (1830–32). *Myrrhiniaceae* Arnott (1839). *Chamaeleuciaceae* Lindley (1846). *Leptospermaceae* Kausel (1957). *Psiloxylonaceae* Croizat (1960).

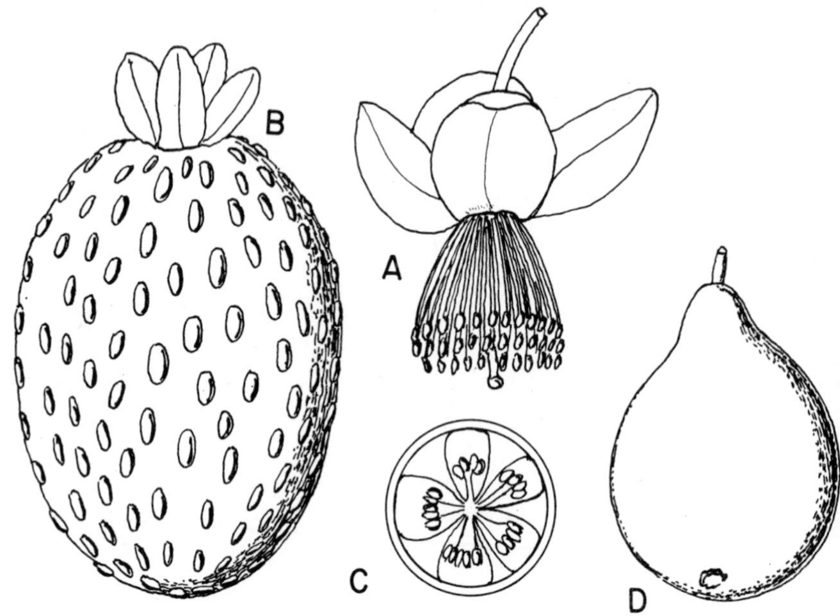

FIG. 275. **A**, flower and **B**, fruit of *Feijoa sellowiana* Berg (*Myrtaceae*), Brazil. **C**, transverse section of ovary, and **D**, fruit of the Guava, *Psidium guajava* Linn., tropical America (orig.).

Of the tribes of *Myrtaceae* recognised by those botanists, the *Leptospermeae*, especially those with free stamens, are probably the most primitive, with typically axile placentation and a loculicidal capsule, and the *Chamaeleucieae*, the more advanced group, with a 1-locular ovary, indehiscent 1–2-seeded fruit, and a more xerophytic ericoid habit. The last mentioned group forms an interesting parallel to that of certain *Rutaceae*, such as tribes *Diosmeae* and *Boronieae*, which are found only in South Africa and Australia respectively.

The type genus of the family is *Myrtus*: shrubs, rarely trees; leaves opposite, pinnately nerved; peduncles axillary, often slender, 1-flowered or centrifugally 3–7-, rarely many-flowered, central flower shortly, lateral long-pedicellate; bracteoles either small or large below the calyx; calyx-tube turbinate, adnate to the ovary, shortly produced above; segments or lobes 4 or 5, slightly imbricate or open in bud; petals 4 or 5, spreading; stamens numerous, many-seriate, free, filaments filiform or flattened; anthers versatile or basifixed, loculi parallel; ovary inferior, perfectly or imperfectly 2- or 3-, or very rarely 4-locular; stigma small or rarely capitate; ovules numerous, inserted on the inner angle, placentas sometimes 2-lamellate; berry enclosed by the calyx-tube, crowned by the limb or rarely the limb deciduous. Type species *Myrtus communis* Linn. (Fig. 273).

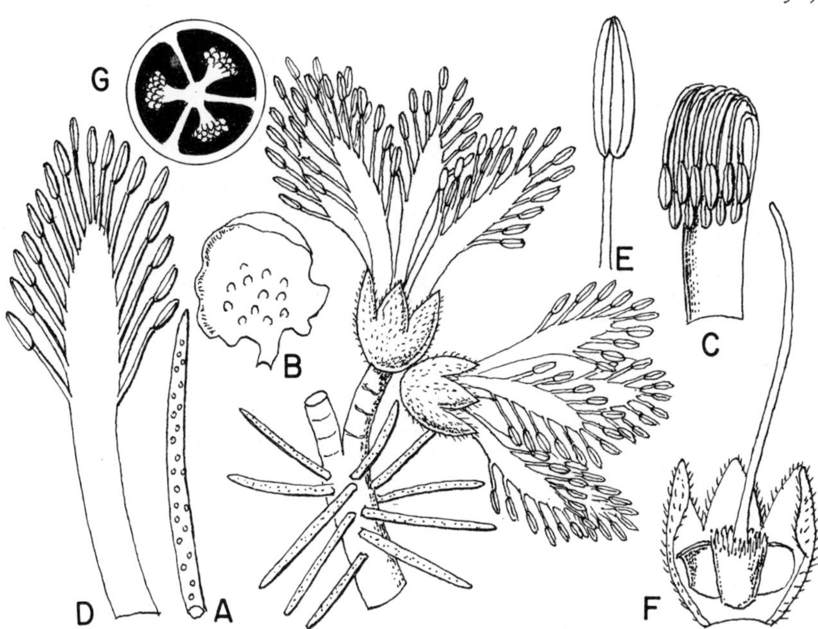

FIG. 276. *Calothamnus rupestris* Schauer (*Myrtaceae*), Australia, in which the bundles of stamens are the attractive feature, the petals, **B**, being inconspicuous. **A**, leaf. **C**, bundle of stamens in the bud stage. **D**, bundle of stamens. **E**, single stamen. **F**, gynoecium and calyx. **G**, cross-section of ovary.

A few outstanding characters may be noted: Stem partly climbing in a few species of *Metrosideros*. Calyx-lobes double the number (10) in *Pileanthus*, spp. of *Verticordia* (Fig. 278), 8 and without petals in *Osbornia*, valvately split or variously ruptured in *Psidium*, connate into a calyptra and deciduous in *Acicalyptus*, spp. of *Syzygium*. Petals connate and calyptrately deciduous in *Eucalyptus* and *Syzygium*, absent from *Osbornia*. Anthers opening by 2 pores in *Actinodium*, *Darwinia*, *Homoranthus*, spp. of *Verticordia*, of *Scholtzia*, and in spp. of *Baeckea*, *Xanthostemon*, *Tristania* spp., and a few others.

The family is fairly rich in economic plants. Chief among them is the Clove, the dried flower-buds of *Eugenia caryophyllus* (Spreng.) Bullock & S. G. Harrison (Fig. 274), native of the Moluccas and much cultivated, especially in Zanzibar and Pemba, east Africa. Oil of Cloves, *Oleum Caryophylli*, is from the same source, used as a flavouring agent, stimulant, aromatic and antiseptic. Oil of Eucalyptus, *Oleum Eucalypti*, an essential oil derived from the fresh leaves of *Eucalyptus globulus* Lab., being antiseptic, expectorant, febrifuge, antiperiodic and diaphoretic. A popular tropical fruit is Guava, *Psidium guajava* Linn. (Fig. 275, **D**), shrub or small tree of the West Indies and tropical America and much cultivated; fruits eaten raw or canned or made into jelly, preserves, etc. For list of many other species

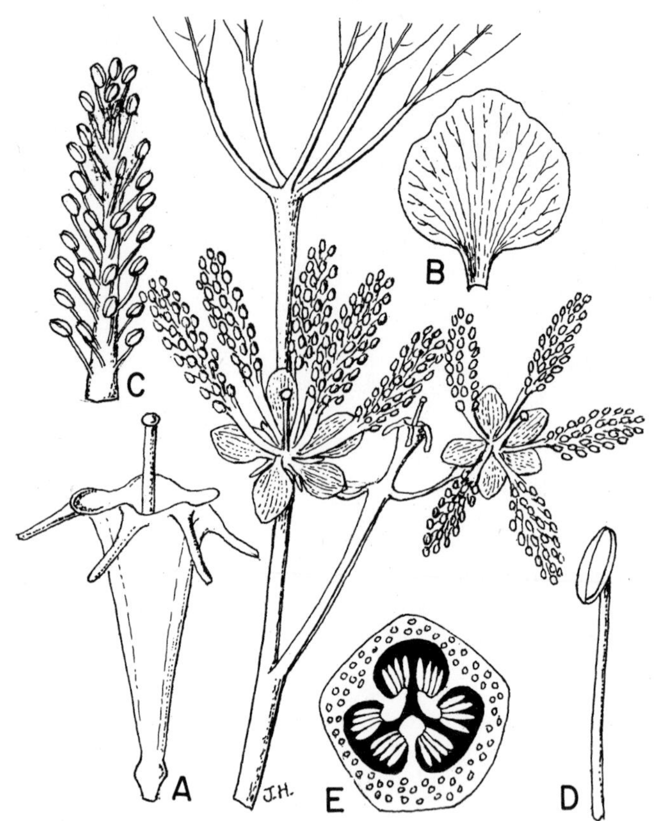

FIG. 277. *Tristania conferta* R.Br. (*Myrtaceae*), Australia; note the attractive bundles of stamens which are more conspicuous than the petals, **B**. **A**, calyx. **C**, staminal column. **D**, stamen. **E**, cross-section of ovary showing the parietal placentas. (Adapted from ICON. SELECT. HORT. THENEN.)

which have medical properties see Uphof DICT. OF ECONOMIC PLANTS 146 (1959).

As I understand the family **Barringtoniaceae**[1] at present (subject to

---

[1] **Barringtoniaceae** Lindl. VEG. KINGD. 754, *emend.* (1847); Knuth in Engler PFLANZENR. 4, 219 (105 Heft), partly, excluding Tribes *Crateranthеae* and *Napoleonaeae* (1939).

Tropical trees or shrubs; leaves alternate, mostly large, elongated and subsessile, crowded, not punctate, entire to serrate; stipules none; inflorescence racemose, axillary or terminal; flowers bisexual, actinomorphic; calyx-tube adnate to the ovary, lobes 4 or 5, subvalvate or imbricate; petals 4, free (rarely absent) (*Foetidia*); stamens epigynous, numerous in several concentric series, filaments more or less connate at the base; anthers basifixed, 2-locular, opening by slits lengthwise; disk intra-staminal; ovary inferior, 2-4-locular; ovules numerous to 1 in each loculus, axile; style simple, mostly very long; stigma capitate or lobulate; fruit drupaceous and fibrous or baccate, crowned by the more or less persistent calyx-lobes, rarely laterally winged; embryo undivided or divided, straight or circinate.

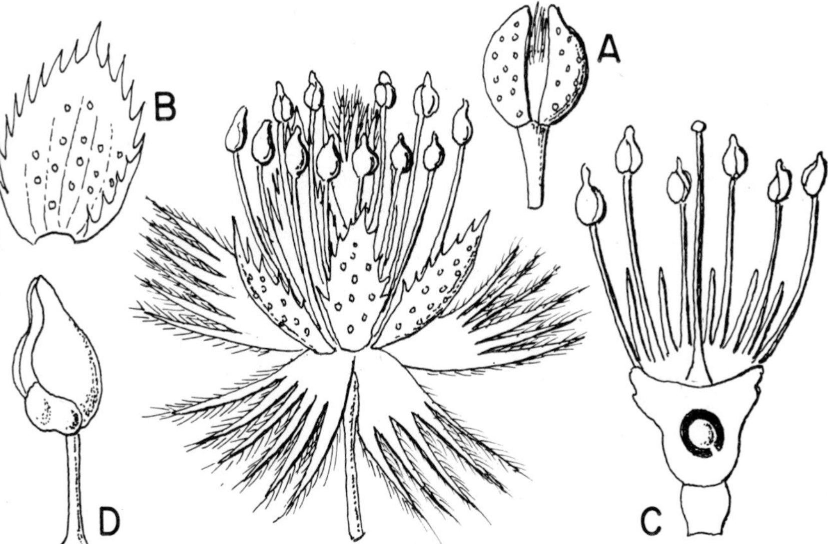

Fig. 278. *Verticordia nitens* Schauer (*Myrtaceae*), Australia, in which the calyx is the attractive feature, the petals being less so. **A**, bud with sepals removed. **B**, petal. **C**, vertical section of flower (sepals and petals removed). **D**, stamen. (Adapted from BOTANICAL MAGAZINE.)

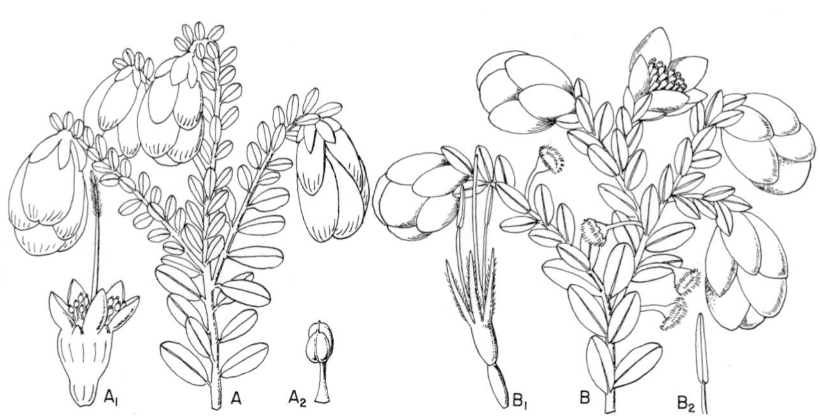

Fig. 279. Examples of parallel development: two Australian plants which look very much alike but belong to quite different and unrelated families. **A**, *Darwinia macrostegia* Benth. (*Myrtaceae*). **B**, *Pimelea physodes* Hook. (*Thymelaeaceae*). $\mathbf{A}_1$ and $\mathbf{B}_1$, petals removed. $\mathbf{A}_2$ and $\mathbf{B}_2$, stamen. The genus *Darwinia* commemorates the name of Britain's most famous evolutionist, Charles Darwin (orig.).

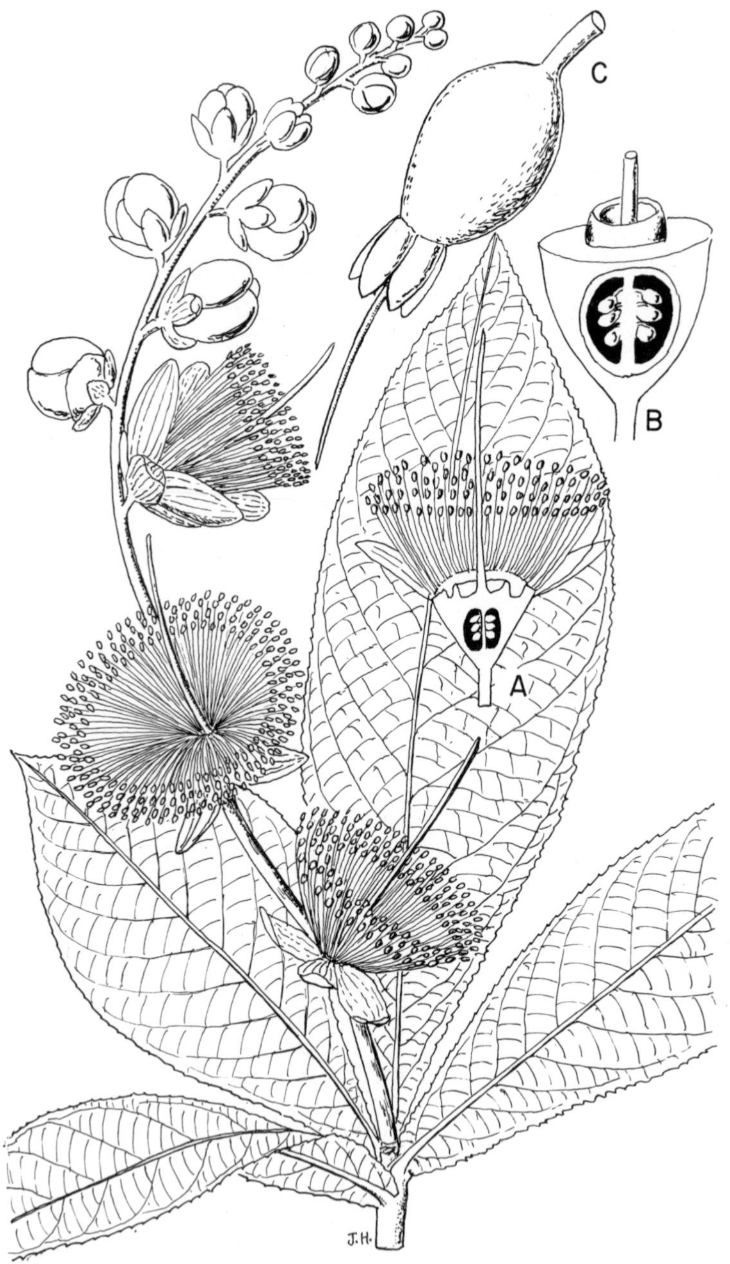

FIG. 280. *Barringtonia racemosa* Bl. ex DC. (*Barringtoniaceae*), tropical Asia. **A**, vertical section of flower. **B**, vertical section of ovary. **C**, fruit (dissections after Baillon).

revision), there are at least six genera which are closely related and which form a very natural group, quite different from *Crateranthus* and *Napoleonaea* (see notes under *Asteranthaceae*, p. 332). In all these genera, except *Foetidia*, there are well developed petals. *Barringtonia*, the type genus (Fig. 280), is the largest with over 80 spp. in the Old World tropics and subtropics, but very rare in Africa. The inflorescence is a long raceme. The ovules are pendulous from near the top of the central axis and the fruits become 1-seeded. In *Careya* and *Planchonia* the ovules spread out from the middle or all over the axis, and in *Chydenanthus* they ascend from near the base of the loculi, and the inflorescence is a panicle. *Combretodendron* stands out with its broadly winged fruits (Fig. 281) and corymbose inflorescence, while the apetalous *Foetidia* occurs only in the Mascarene Islands, the flowers being single and axillary.

A classical paper on the remarkable family **Lecythidaceae**[1] was published by John Miers in 1873. It was included as a tribe of *Myrtaceae* by Bentham and Hooker, but it differs from the remainder of that family by the alternate non-punctate leaves, the remarkable structure of the androecium, and the woody fruits which open by an operculum and have several nut-like or winged seeds. They are confined to tropical America.

The stamens in the more primitive genera, *Grias*, *Gustavia* and *Cariniana*, are "monadelphous", i.e. they are arranged regularly in several concentric series around the intrastaminal disk and ovary, all the filaments bearing fertile anthers. In the remainder of the genera, more advanced, the stamens are "diadelphous", a concentric group of fertile ones around the top of the ovary, and a second bundle, some or all of which may be infertile (staminodial), forming a ligule-like hood over the style and ovary. One of the genera of the latter group is unique in more ways than one; for it was described by Miers from a single flower which he found adhering to the inflorescence of another genus collected by R. Spruce. He named it *Cercophora* (Fig. 282, **B**), but it was later changed to *Strailia* by Durand because the name *Cercophora* had been previously used by Fuckel for a genus of fungi. The dorsal bundle of stamens (see Fig. 282, **B** and $\mathbf{B}_1$) is very remarkable; it is stipitate and tubular (funnel-shaped) with a single whorl of sterile stamens within the tube. So far as I am aware no further specimens of this remarkable plant have yet been collected; when they are found they would be very much desired for the Kew herbarium.

As Miers remarked there is a sufficient degree of uniformity in its general characters to maintain the group as a distinct family in the fullest sense of that term. They are trees of immense growth, rarely of smaller size, with leaves always alternate without stipules, and without the pellucid glands of *Myrtaceae*.

---

[1] Including *Gustaviaceae* Burnett (1835).

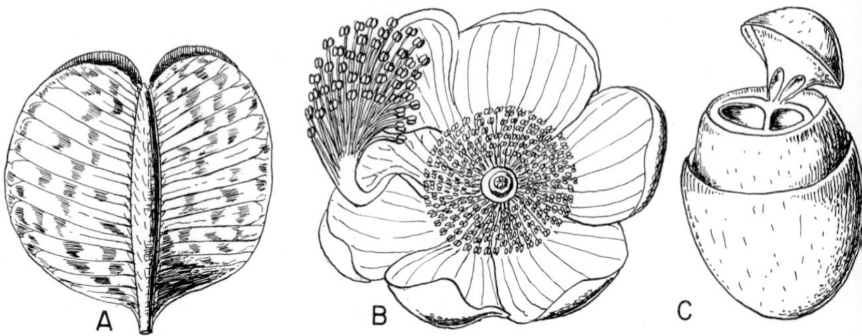

FIG. 281. **A**, winged fruit of *Combretodendron africana* (Welw.) Exell (*Barringtoniaceae*). **B**, flower of *Couroupita guianensis* Aubl. Guianas, and **C**, fruit of *Lecythis ollaria* Linn., tropical America (*Lecythidaceae*).

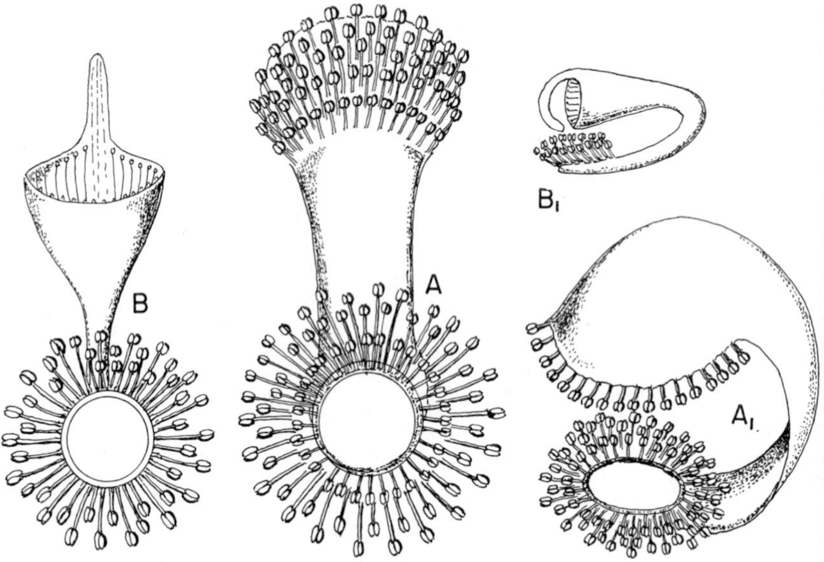

FIG. 282. Remarkable and unique types of androecium in *Lecythidaceae*: **A** and $\mathbf{A}_1$, *Couroupita peruviana* Berg, Peru. **B** and $\mathbf{B}_1$, *Strailia anomala* Durand (*Cercophora anomala* Miers), Brazil (semi-diagrammatic).

CANNON BALL TREE (*Couroupita guianensis* Aubl.): The public parks and the Botanical Gardens in Trinidad and Guyana have many examples of this remarkable tree. W. E. Broadway, writing in the GARDENER'S CHRONICLE many years ago from the island of Trinidad, said of it:

A curious tree often met with in woods and pastures. The large brown bell-shaped fruits, unlike the fragrant flowers, emit a disgusting odour, rivalled only

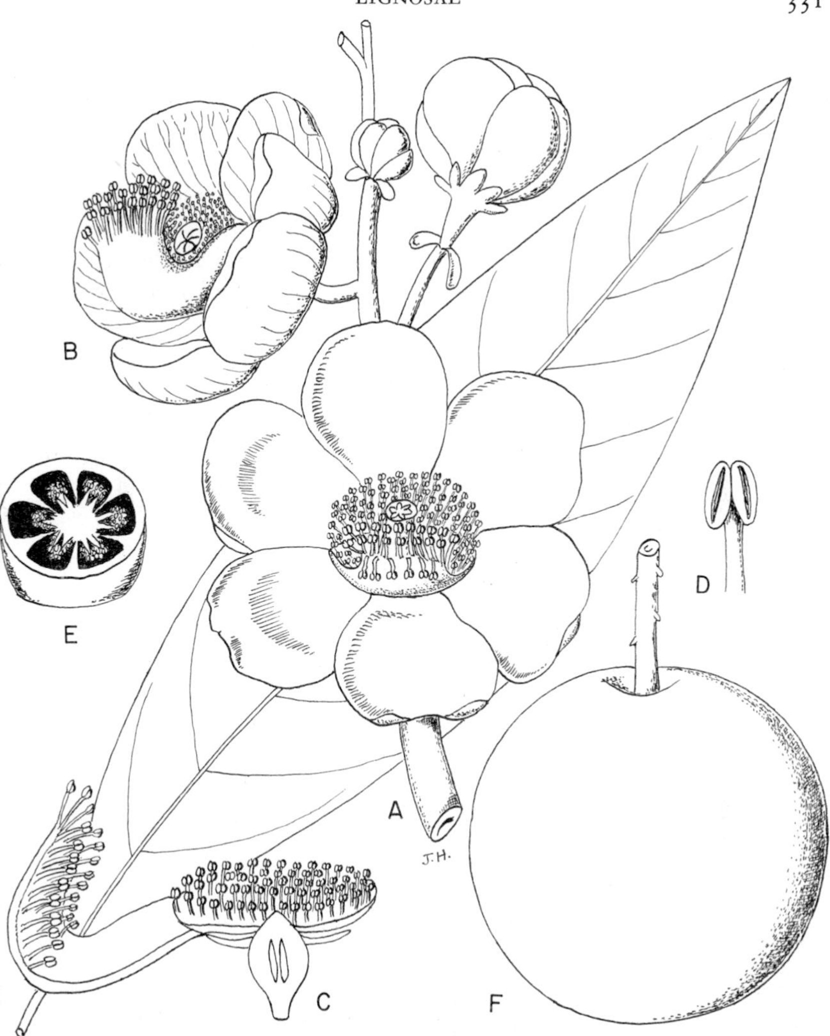

FIG. 283. Cannon Ball tree, *Couroupita guianensis* Aubl. (*Lecythidaceae*), Central America. **A**, front view. **B**, side view of flowers. **C**, vertical section of androecium. **D**, anther. **E**, cross-section of ovary. **F**, fruit (orig.).

by the flowers of *Terminalia belerica*. The latter tree, when in flower, fills the atmosphere throughout the garden in a way which suggests to the uninitiated that the sanitary arrangements of the district are in a very bad condition, and visitors are often deceived and conclude such actually to be the case. The leaves are deciduous and often fall twice and renewed during the year.

The Rev. L. Guilding also wrote of the fruit of this tree (BOTANICAL MAGAZINE tt. 3158, 3159).

In *Couroupita* (Figs 282, **A** and $\mathbf{A}_1$, 283) and *Corythophora* the ligulate stamens are all fertile, in the remainder some or all of the ligulate stamens bear infertile anthers or are merely barren filaments (staminodes). There are no petals in *Foetidia*.

Asteranthaceae, single genus and species, *Asteranthos brasiliensis* Desf., Brazil, Guyana, Venezuela (Fig. 284). A tree with slender branchlets; leaves alternate, subsessile, broadly lanceolate, entire, pinnately nerved, not punctate; flowers axillary, solitary, bisexual, actinomorphic, yellow, fragrant; bracts 2 at the base of the pedicel; calyx-tube shortly and broadly campanulate, partly adnate to the ovary, several-dentate, accrescent and spreading in fruit; no petals; stamens numerous, perigynous, the outer whorl sterile and connate into a corolla- or corona-like many-toothed staminodial structure spreading like an open parasol; fertile stamens very numerous within the "corona", free, filaments filiform; anthers 2-locular, basifixed, opening by slits lengthwise; ovary semi-inferior, 5–8-locular; style simple, stigma lobulate; ovules 4 in each loculus, pendulous from the inner angle; capsule semi-superior, upper free part pyramidal, angular. Benth. and Hook. f. GEN. PLANTARUM **1**, 724 (in *Myrtaceae*); R. Knuth, in Engler, PFLANZENR. **4**, 219b (105 Heft) 1, Figs 1 and 2 (1939).

Although this very remarkable genus is retained here as a separate family, following Knuth in the PFLANZENREICH, it may require a lesser status after further study for my GENERA OF FLOWERING PLANTS. The remarkable corona-like structure (Fig. 284, **A**), interpreted by Knuth as a corolla, is undoubtedly the outermost series of stamens transformed into staminodes. This may be deduced by comparison with the various structures of the androecium in *Lecythidaceae* (see Figs 282, 283) in which family it was included in the PFLANZENFAMILIEN together with *Napoleonaea* Beauv. ("*Napoleona*"); it should also include *Crateranthus* E. G. Baker. In the PFLANZENREICH these genera were included in *Barringtoniaceae* (1939) (see p. 329).

Rhizophoraceae[1] is a family of considerable interest to students, not only for the special habitat (mangrove swamps) favoured by most of them, but also on account of several morphological peculiarities. Although showing certain parallel affinities with the family *Combretaceae*, the origin of *Rhizophoraceae* is perhaps to be looked for in the *Theaceae* or even the *Tiliaceae*.

Anisophyllea is remarkable for its unequal (anisophyllous) leaves, the alternate ones being often quite small and stipule-like. The fringed or laciniate petals of *Cassipourea* are a peculiar feature, whilst the androecium of *Anopyxis* is an obvious parallel with that of *Meliaceae*.

---

[1] Including *Legnotidaceae* Endlicher (1841). *Macarisiaceae* J. G. Agardh (1858). *Anisophyllaceae* Ridley (1922). *Polygonanthaceae* Groizat (1943).

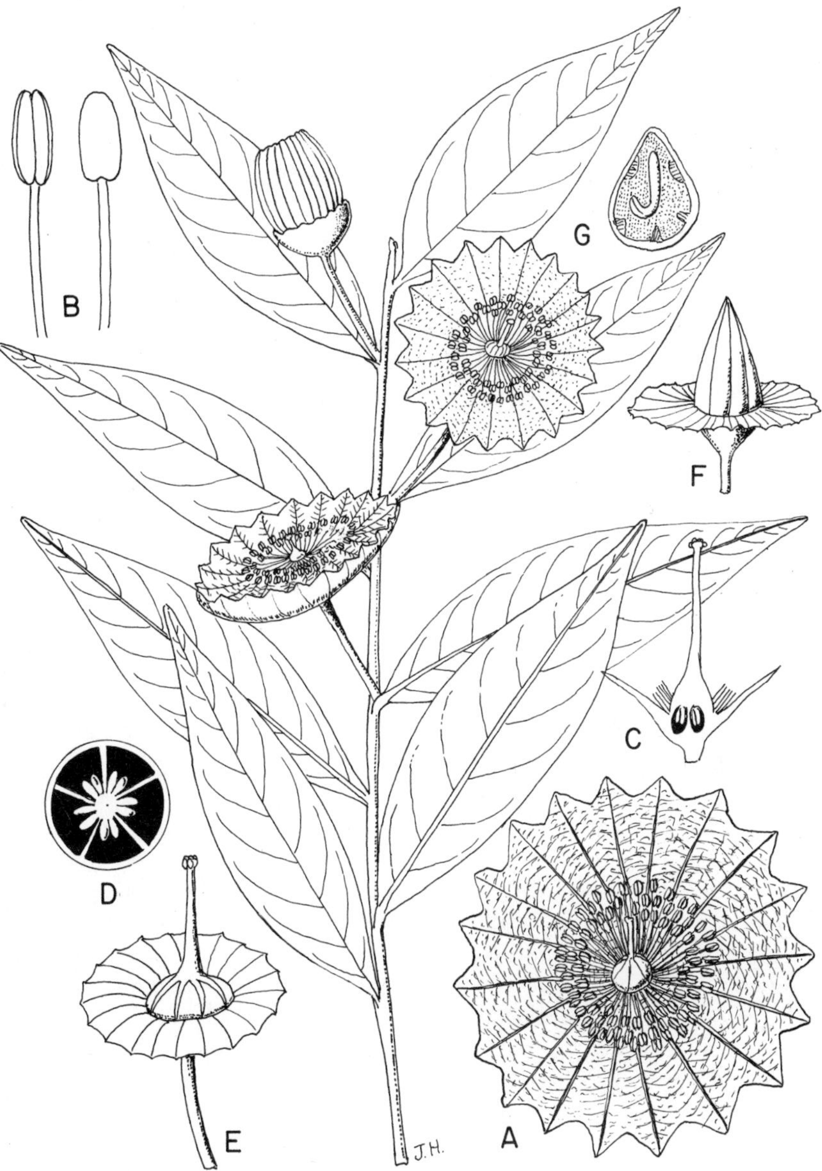

FIG. 284. *Asteranthos brasiliensis* Desf., the type of the family *Asteranthaceae*. **A**, flower from above, showing the remarkable corolla- or corona-like outer staminodes, whorls of fertile stamens and upper part of gynoecium. **B**, stamens. **C**, vertical section of gynoecium. **D**, cross-section of ovary. **E**, calyx and upper part of gynoecium. **F**, fruit. **G**, vertical section of seed.

FIG. 285. *Kandelia candel* (Linn.) Druce (*K. rheedei* Wight & Arn.) (*Rhizophoraceae*). **A**, androecium. **B**, anther. **C**, vertical, and **D**, cross-section of ovary. **E**, fruit.

Rhizophora, a genus of 7–8 species, inhabits the mangrove coasts of tropical and subtropical regions; trees; leaves opposite; stipules long and interpetiolar, wrapped around the terminal bud, caducous; peduncles axillary; calyx 4-partite, lobes valvate; petals 4; stamens 12–8, anthers at first many-locellate, at length 2-valved; ovary semi-inferior, 2-locular, ovules 2 in each loculus; fruit 1-locular, 1-seeded, seed soon germinating; no endosperm; cotyledons folded, radicle elongate-clavate, persistent on the tree for a time and at length falling off and piercing the mud.

Gynotroches, *Cassipourea* and *Anopyxis* stand out from the remainder of the genera in having a superior ovary; in the others the ovary is semi- to completely inferior. In *Blepharistemma* and *Sterigmapetalum* the flowers are polygamo-dioecious or dioecious. In *Carallia* the seeds have endosperm and a small curved embryo, and together with *Rhizophora* the genera *Kandelia*, *Ceriops* and *Bruguiera* share the characters of a large embryo soon germinating (often on the tree), without endosperm, and with large stipules wrapped around the terminal bud but soon falling off. The bracteoles resemble a calyx, the calyx a corolla, and the petals are divided into thread-like segments in *Kandelia* (Fig. 285). The leaves are in whorls of 3 or 5 and the petals are much divided in *Sterigmapetalum*.

Combretaceae[1] is a relatively advanced family, some members of which

[1] Including *Myrobalanaceae* A. L. de Juss. (1804). *Terminaliaceae* J. St. Hiliare (1805).

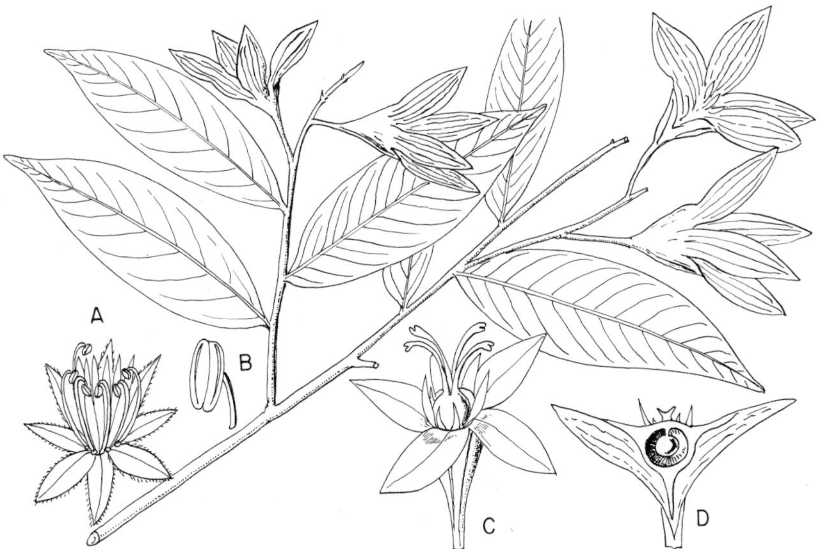

FIG. 286. *Polygonanthus amazonicus* Ducke (*Rhizophoraceae*), tropical South America. **A**, flower. **B**, anther. **C**, with petals removed, showing gynoecium. **D**, vertical section of ovary.

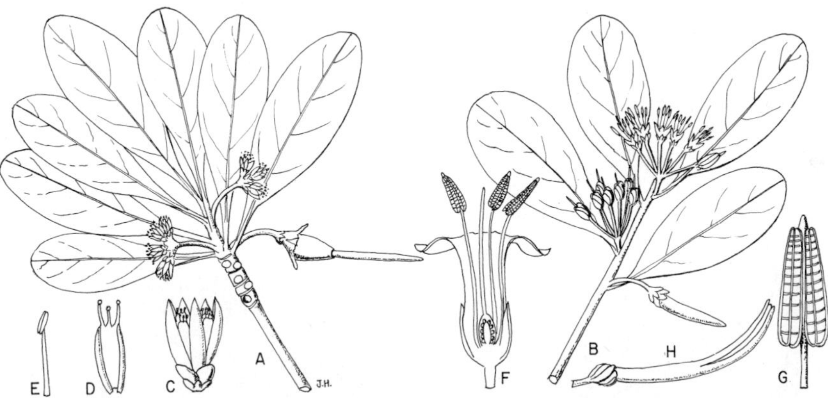

FIG. 287. Some species of plants are so much alike in their habit and foliage that one may be easily mistaken for the other when not in flower or fruit, though belonging to quite different families. **A** is *Ceriops tagal* C. B. Robinson var. *australis* C. T. White (*Rhizophoraceae*): **C**, flower. **D**, petal. **E**, stamen. **B**, *Aegiceras corniculatum* Blanco (*Myrsinaceae*): **F**, vertical section of flower. **G**, stamen. **H**, fruit (orig.).

have taken to special habitats such as mangrove swamps and to drier regions. The tendency to complete reduction of the petals (as in *Terminalia*) is very strongly evident and it is often accompanied by aggregation of the flowers into heads. We may look upon this feature as a parallelism to the

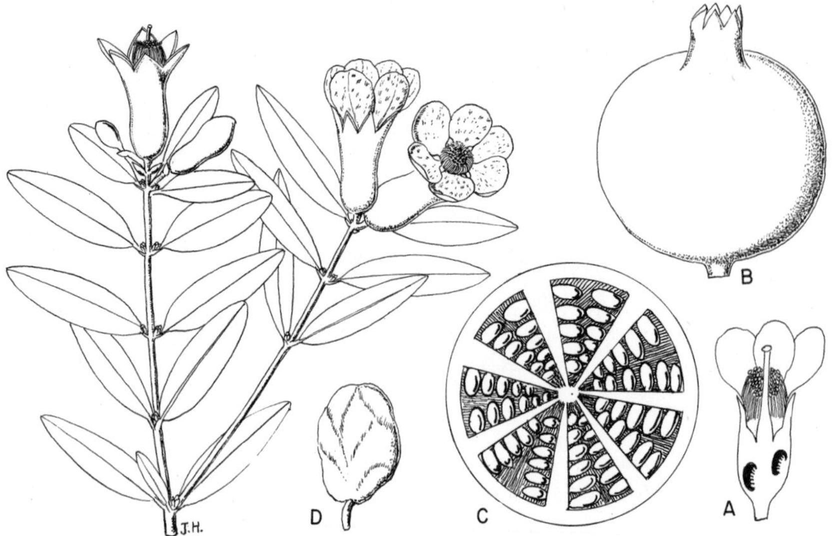

FIG. 288. Pomegranate, *Punica granatum* Linn. (*Punicaceae*), cultivated for its fruits from remote times; probably native of N.W. India, south Persia and Palestine; now spread over warmer countries. **A**, vertical section of flower. **B**, fruit. **C**, cross-section of fruit. **D**, seed.

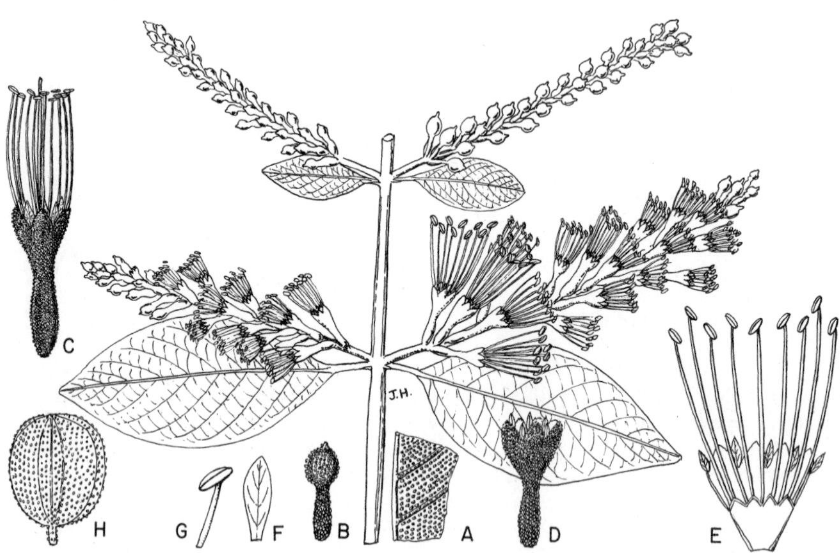

FIG. 289. *Combretum fruticosum* (Loefl.) Stuntz, tropical America, the type species of the type genus of *Combretaceae*. **A**, lower surface of leaf showing glands. **B**, flower-bud covered with glands. **C**, flower. **D**, flower with stamens removed. **E**, flower opened out. **F**, petal. **G**, stamen. **H**, fruit (orig.).

FIG. 290. *Quisqualis indica* Linn. (*Combretaceae*). **A**, vertical section of flower, note the style adnate to the calyx-tube. **B**, stamen. **C**, fruit. **D**, seed (orig.).

catkins of the so-called "Amentiferae", which is shown to have been evolved from the ROSALES. But the chief development in the family is the modification of the fruit for dispersal by the wind. Thus *Combretum* has usually a 4-winged fruit, *Terminalia* a 2-winged fruit. The type of placentation is advanced; the ovules are pendulous from the apex of the unilocular ovary. The family is confined to the tropics and subtropics, where one or at most only a few species are often subdominant in some regions, as in the Bush Veld of the northern Transvaal, South Africa.

FIG. 291. Buttonwood, *Conocarpus erectus* Linn. (*Combretaceae*), one of the first shrubs to establish itself on the newly formed Keys off the Florida coast; wood heavy, hard and close-grained, dark yellow brown. **A**, flower and bract. **B**, fruit (orig.).

Combretum, the type genus, contains about 370 species in the tropics and subtropics (the type species is *C. fruticosum* (Loef.) Stuntz, in tropical America (see Fig. 289)); shrubs, rarely trees, often climbing or scrambling, a few spiny; leaves mostly opposite; flowers spicate to paniculate; petals usually present; calyx-limb and tube deciduous before the fruit ripens; ovary inferior, the style free from the calyx-tube; stamens 10–8; ovules 6–2; fruit angular or more usually 4-winged.

In *Strephonema* the ovary is only semi-inferior, in all other genera completely inferior; the style is adherent to the very long and slender calyx-tube in *Quisqualis* (Fig. 290); filaments not inflexed in bud in *Cacoucia*, a section of *Combretum*; fruits crowded into a mass in *Ramatuela*, *Conocarpus* (Fig. 291), *Anogeissus* and *Finetia*; another outstanding character is the pair of bracteoles adnate to the ovary in *Lumnitzera*, *Laguncularia* (Fig. 292) and *Macropteranthes* (Fig. 293), in the last mentioned becoming enlarged in fruit and forming wings. In *Getonia* the calyx-lobes are very conspicuous, accrescent and persistent in fruit.

Useful products are not of great importance. Some species yield dyes and in some the bark is rich in tannin, and there are some useful timbers. *Terminalia catappa* Linn. is widely grown as a shade tree, and the leaves

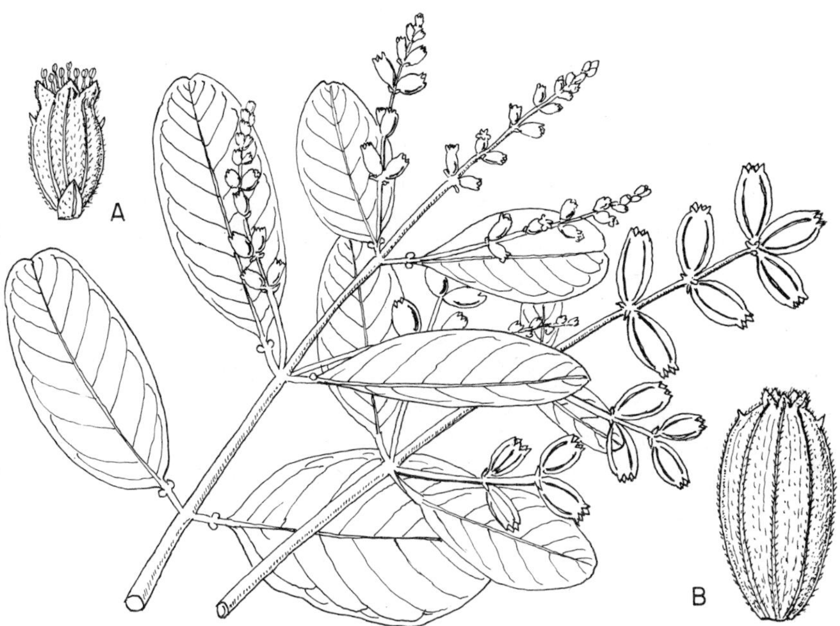

FIG. 292. White Buttonwood, *Laguncularia racemosa* Gaertn. f. (*Combretaceae*); one of the first shrubs to establish itself on the newly formed Florida Keys; the generic name is from *laguncula*, relating to the supposed resemblance of the fruit to a flask; wood hard and heavy, strong and close-grained with a satiny surface, dark yellow-brown. **A**, flower. **B**, fruit (orig.).

provide food for the Tasar Silkworm. *T. superba* Engl. & Diels, the "Afara Terminalia", produces an excellent timber which is put to many uses (for full list of economic plants see Uphof, DICT. OF ECONOMIC PLANTS (1959)).

Lythraceae,[1] according to Bentham and Hooker's GENERA PLANTARUM, perhaps contains more exceptions to the general character than any other family, except *Celastraceae* (see p. 354). But with the so-called *genera anomala* disposed elsewhere, the family is now better defined. There are at least two constant associated characters to mark the remainder, the leaves are exstipulate and the calyx-lobes are valvate.

The type genus, *Lythrum*, is characterised as follows: herbs or shrublets, often pubescent or tomentose; branches 4-sided; leaves opposite, rarely verticillate or alternate, linear to lanceolate and entire; flowers bisexual, axillary and solitary, or in cymes or spike-like racemes, rose, purple or

[1] Including *Salicariaceae* A. L. de Juss. (1789). *Ammanniaceae* Horaninow (1834). *Lagerstroemiaceae* J. G. Agardh (1858). *Lawsoniaceae* J. G. Agardh (1858). *Diplodontaceae* Dulac (1834).

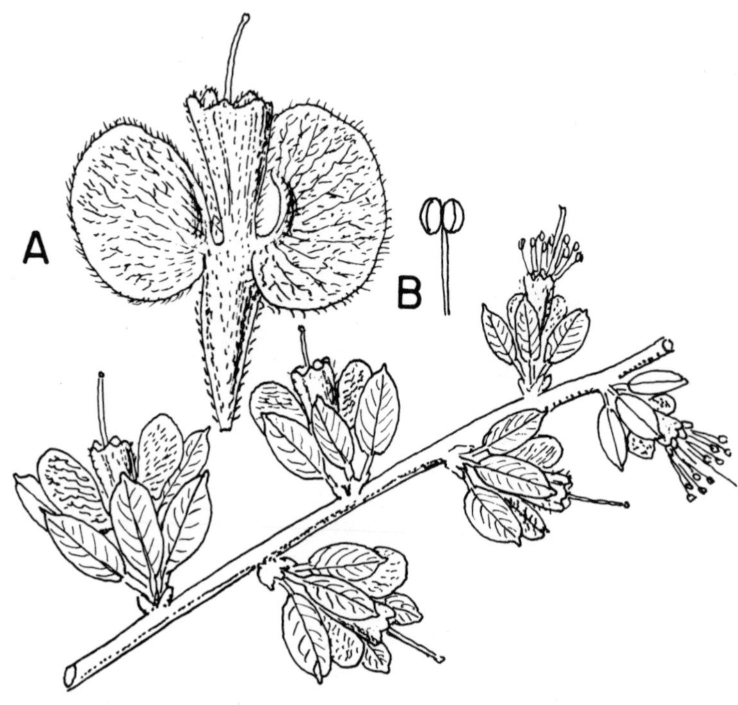

FIG. 293. *Macropteranthes kekwickii* F. Muell. (*Combretaceae*); a small north Australian tree with long and short shoots; remarkable for the bracteoles, **A**, which are enlarged and wing-like in fruit. **B**, stamen (orig.).

rarely white; calyx-tube cylindric, 8–12-ribbed; primary teeth 4–6, with as many more larger and erect or rarely small and spreading; petals 4–6, obovate, rarely absent; stamens 8–12 (rarely fewer), 1- or 2-seriate in the calyx-tube; anthers broadly oblong, sometimes some imperfect; ovary sessile, oblong, 2–1-locular; style filiform, stigma capitate or obtuse; ovules 2- or more-seriate on thick placentas attached to the central axis; capsule enclosed by the calyx, oblong, membranous, 2-locular, or 1-locular with an incomplete septum, septicidally 2-valved or irregularly split, the placentas connate or free, many-seeded; seeds smooth; cotyledons orbicular, auriculate at the base. Type species, *L. salicaria* Linn., in temperate regions (Fig. 294).

It may be noted in the above description that in this type genus of about 25 species, generally distributed, there is a considerable range of characters, even some without petals, and some with 2- or 1-locular ovary.

Darwin investigated very thoroughly the structure and function of the flowers of *Lythrum salicaria* Linn., which are of three forms (trimorphic), differing in the comparative length of the stamens and styles; this arrange-

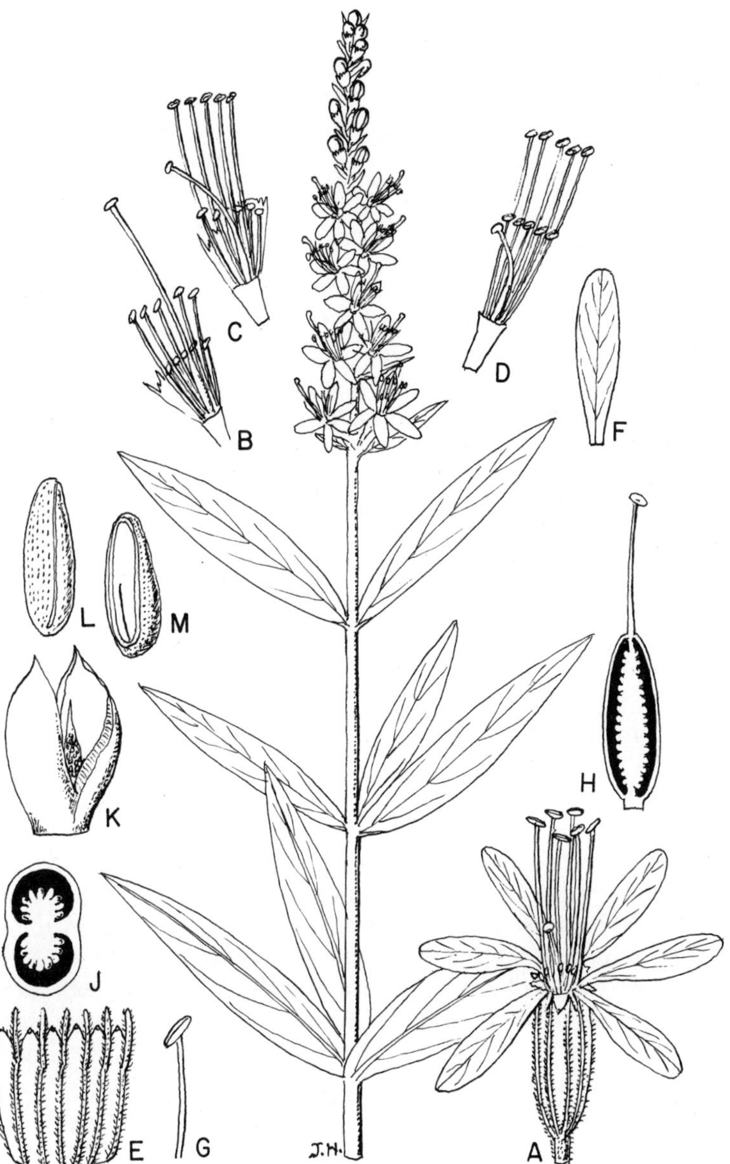

Fig. 294. *Lythrum salicaria* Linn., Europe, lectotype species of the type genus of *Lythraceae*. **A**, flower. **B–D**, flowers showing different lengths of stamens and styles. **E**, calyx opened out showing the outside. **F**, petal. **G**, stamen. **H**, vertical section of ovary. **J**, cross-section of ovary. **K**, fruit. **L**, seed. **M**, vertical section of seed (see text relative to pollination) (orig.).

ment is of benefit to the species, because the reproductive organs, when of different length, behave to one another like different species of the same genus in regard to productiveness and character of the offspring. The drawings show the different lengths of stamens in relation to the styles:

Fig. 294, **B** *long-styled flowers*; style longer than the stamens; half of the latter are of medium length, half short.

Fig. 294, **C** *medium-styled flowers*; style of medium length; half of the stamens longer than the style, half short.

Fig. 294, **D**, *short-styled flowers*; style short; half of the stamens long and the other half of medium length.

The most divergent genus is *Cuphea*, with zygomorphic flowers, the calyx unilaterally saccate or spurred at the base, the dorsal stamen wanting (stamens 11), and the placentas in fruit reflexed and emerging from the calyx by a dorsal split in the tube. There are about 300 species of this genus indigenous in America, West Indies, the Galapagos and Hawaiian Islands.

A few genera may be recognised by their leaves which are clothed with black glands. These are *Pehria* and *Adenaria* in tropical America, and *Woodfordia* in Africa and Arabia to eastern Asia. In *Woodfordia* the stamens are declinate and inserted to one side of the calyx-tube. The calyx is broadly 4-winged in *Tetrataxis*, in Mauritius. Several genera have winged seeds, amongst them the beautiful tree-species of *Lagerstroemia* (Fig. 295), in which the stamens are numerous, and the petals are clawed (as in many *Malpighiaceae*). A recently described genus by Lourteig, *Capuronia*, Madagascar, has dioecious flowers!

Melastomataceae[1] is a large natural family of somewhat obscure origin. They seem to be connected with *Myrtaceae* by the tribe *Memecyleae*, as pointed out by Bentham and Hooker; but except for this one tribe the affinity of the two families is not very obvious. Evolution within the family has chiefly gone in the direction of a modification of the stamens, especially the filaments, the calyx and corolla being more or less uniform throughout. It is perhaps significant from a phylogenetic point of view that in the group showing the more primitive type of placentation, parietal, the *Astronieae*, the stamens are generally uniform in size and are little modified, whereas in those with the more advanced type of placentation, axile, as in the *Melastomeae*, the stamens are mostly unequal and considerably specialised.

The family is almost confined to the tropics of both hemispheres, but very abundant in South America, and like many more tropical families shows little range in structure. The resemblance of a few members of the family to certain *Gentianaceae* (*Exacum* for example) is no doubt quite superficial.

The type genus is *Melastoma* Linn.; about 125 species in tropical and

---

[1] *Memecylaceae* de Candolle (1828). *Mouririaceae* Gardner (1840).

FIG. 295. *Lagerstroemia indica* Linn. (*Lythraceae*), tropical Asia. **A**, vertical section of flower. **B**, small anther. **C**, larger anther. **D**, cross-section of ovary. **E**, fruit (orig.).

eastern Asia, northern Australia, Pacific Isles and the Seychelles: Shrubs or rarely shrublets, mostly strigose-pilose; leaves 3–7-nerved; flowers solitary to fasciculate or paniculate, purple, violet or rose, rarely white; calyx-lobes

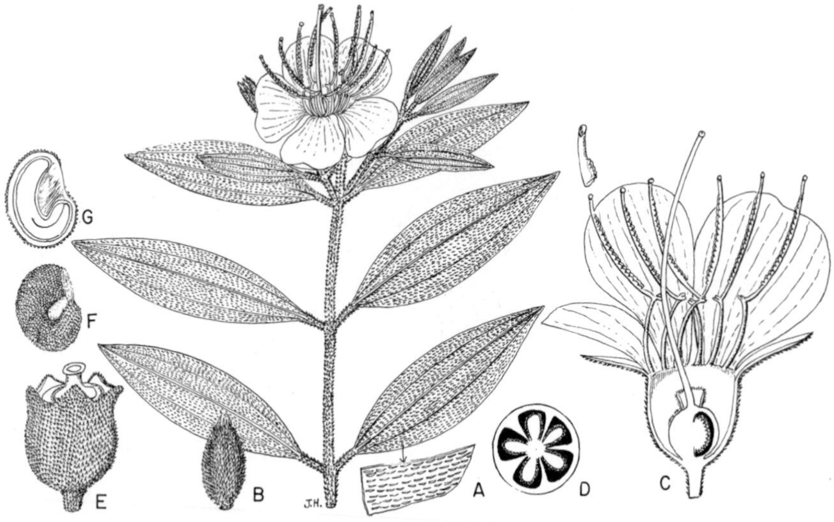

FIG. 296. *Melastoma malabathricum* Linn., India east to N. Australia, the type species of the type genus of *Melastomataceae*. **A**, portion of leaf showing the curious hairs. **B**, flower-bud. **C**, vertical section of flower. **D**, cross-section of ovary. **E**, fruit. **F**, seed. **G**, vertical section of seed (partly after Baillon).

5, rarely 6 or 7, deciduous, alternating with as many teeth; petals mostly 5; stamens 10, rarely 14 or 12, very unequal; anthers opening by a single pore, the connective mostly long-produced, anticously 2-lobed or 2-tuberculate or 2-spurred; smaller stamens yellow and the connective not produced; ovary free or adnate at the base or higher up to the calyx-ribs, usually 5-locular, setose on top; berry irregularly ruptured when ripe; seeds minute, cochleate. Type species *M. malabathricum* Linn., Indo-Malaya, Philippine Isles and New Guinea to northern Australia (Fig. 296).

As I have not yet studied the family in detail, I may borrow a few interesting notes from Rendle's CLASSIFICATION OF FLOWERING PLANTS **2**, 385 (1925): The plants show great diversity of habit, including herbs, shrubs or trees, root-climbers, epiphytes and marsh or water plants. On the roots of some epiphytes, such as species of *Pachycentria*, are developed tuber-like swellings in which ants make a home. The leaves are often large, and in some genera conspicuously spotted or variegated, as in species of *Sonerila* and *Bertolonia*. The leaves of a pair are sometimes unequal (anisophyllous), and this is frequently associated with the development in the larger leaf of sac-like outgrowths on the upper face which also serve as shelters for ants; these *domatia* are entered from the lower leaf-surface. In return for shelter the ants protect the inflorescence from unbidden guests. The small seeds are generally numerous, straight or bent, and contain a very small embryo with

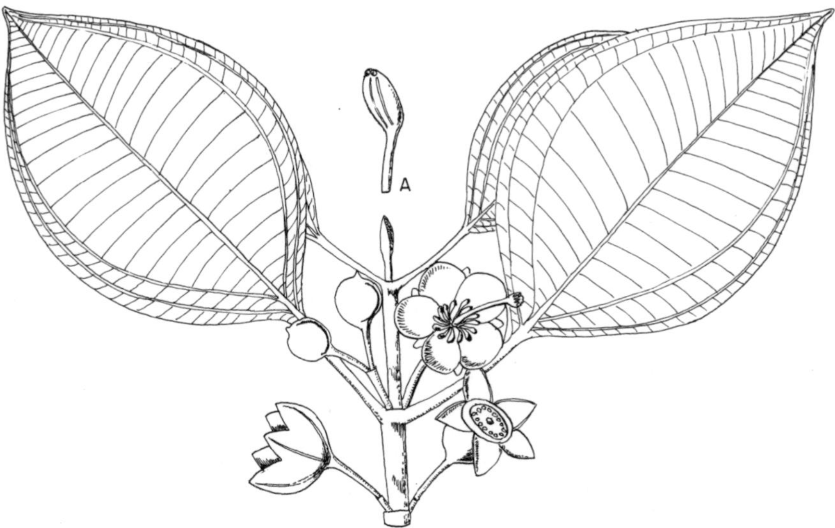

FIG. 297. *Bellucia grossularioides* (Linn.) Triana, the Coronillo or Jambo do Mato of Brazil (*Melastomataceae*); flowers white; fruit a large edible berry. **A**, stamen (orig.).

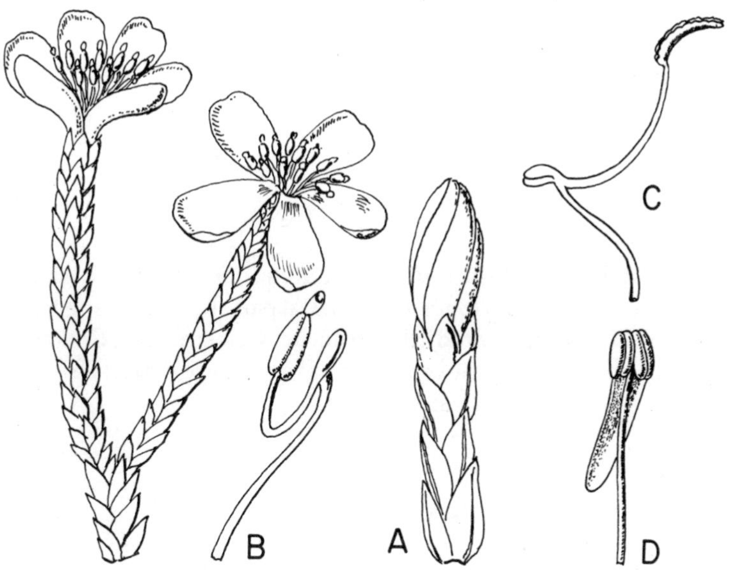

FIG. 298. *Lavoisiera tetragona* DC. (*L. lycopodioides* Gardn.) (*Melastomataceae*), Brazil. **A**, flower-bud and upper leaves. **B**, stamen. **C**, stamen of *Dissotis polyantha* Gilg, tropical Africa. **D**, stamen of *Memecylon talbotii* Keay.

fleshy cotyledons, but no endosperm. Several species are grown in greenhouses in temperate climates, and species of *Gravesia*, *Sonerila* and *Bertolonia* for their variegated leaves.

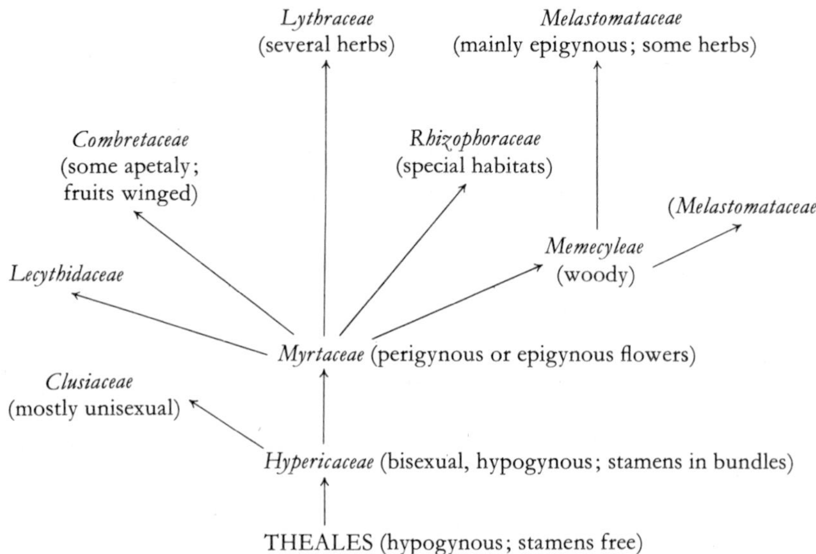

Diagram showing the probable origin and development of *Hypericaceae*, *Myrtaceae*, and allied families.

Order 41. **CELASTRALES**

(*Fam. Fl. Pl.* **1**, 309)

Families: **Pandaceae, Aquifoliaceae, Salvadoraceae, Koeberliniaceae, Cneoraceae, Cardiopteridaceae, Cyrillaceae, Icacinaceae, Empetraceae, Aextoxicaceae, Pentadiplandraceae, Celastraceae, Corynocarpaceae, Stackhousiaceae, Goupiaceae, Hippocrateaceae, Erythropalaceae, Capusiaceae, Scyphostegiaceae.**

This is an association of mostly small families formerly classified as a large part of the de Candolle–Bentham and Hooker system DISCIFLORAE; a distinct disk is usually present, often lining the base of the calyx-tube or receptacle; perhaps mainly descended from the *Flacourtiaceae* stock, but more especially from THEALES; phylogeny perhaps as follows: MAGNOLIALES → DILLENIALES → BIXALES → THEALES → **CELASTRALES** → to a remarkable climax family *Scyphostegiaceae*.

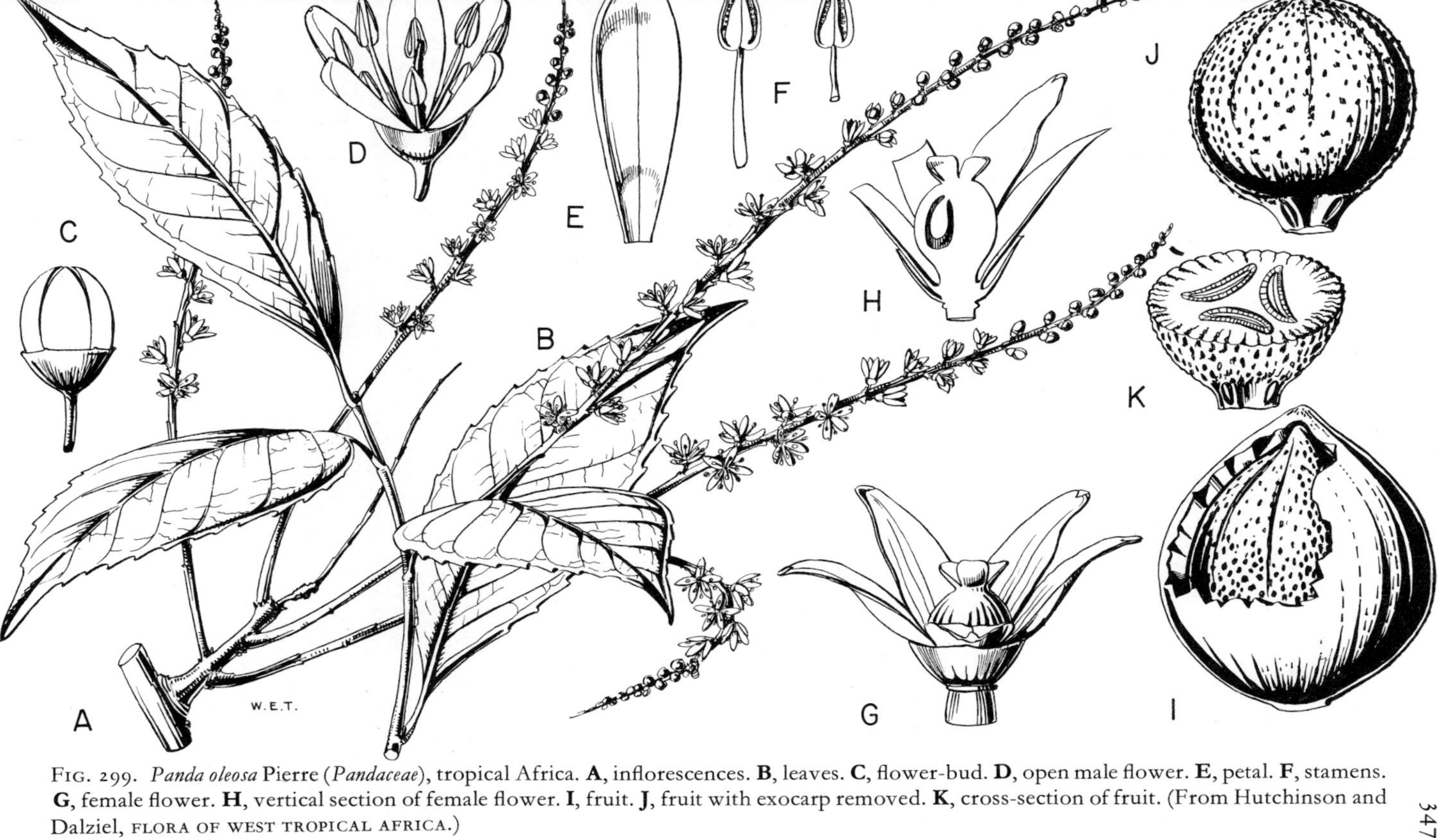

Fig. 299. *Panda oleosa* Pierre (*Pandaceae*), tropical Africa. **A**, inflorescences. **B**, leaves. **C**, flower-bud. **D**, open male flower. **E**, petal. **F**, stamens. **G**, female flower. **H**, vertical section of female flower. **I**, fruit. **J**, fruit with exocarp removed. **K**, cross-section of fruit. (From Hutchinson and Dalziel, FLORA OF WEST TROPICAL AFRICA.)

There are several small families allied to *Celastraceae*, and for the ordinary student it would be somewhat unprofitable to attempt to describe them. Their relationships are not easily traced owing to the reduction of the flowers and fruits to very small dimensions, and their general morphology is much the same throughout. Only the more outstanding need therefore be mentioned.

The genus *Panda* (**Pandaceae**) (Fig. 299) consists of small trees in west tropical Africa, with alternate simple stipulate leaves; flowers dioecious, racemose on the older wood; calyx cupular, open in bud; petals 5, valvate; stamens 10; rudimentary ovary linear-subulate; staminodes and disk absent from the female flowers; ovary 4–3-locular, style-branches reflexed; ovule 1, pendulous from near the top of each loculus, fruit drupaceous; seed with copious oily endosperm and cordate cotyledons.

Until quite recently the family was considered to be represented by this one genus, until a member[1] of the Kew staff discovered that two genera hitherto accepted as belonging to *Euphorbiaceae* should accompany it. These are *Galearia* and *Microdesmis*.

The Holly family, **Aquifoliaceae**,[2] although familiar enough as a Christmas decoration in the fruiting stage, is not in the flowering period so well known to the student. Even after a long experience, the present writer rarely recognises a dried specimen of a species of *Ilex*, especially in tropical collections, apart from the better known kinds with prickly leaves. In many ways it is a relatively advanced family. The small actinomorphic flowers vary from being bisexual through polygamous to completely unisexual[3] and dioecious. The petals may be either free or connate, and the stamens are usually the same number as and alternate with the petals or corolla-lobes. The familiar fruit is of an advanced type, a usually fleshy drupe containing a variable number of 1-seeded pyrenes. The seeds contain copious endosperm and a small straight embryo.

The family is not easy to place near any close affinity. Bentham and Hooker put it between *Olacaceae* (*sensu lato*) and *Celastraceae*, although it lacks the disk characteristic of both those families. I am inclined to regard it as having been derived from the same stock as these families and the *Rhamnaceae*, but lacking their disk, and differing from the *Rhamnaceae* in having retained the staminal whorl alternate with the petals instead of opposite to them. A possible alternative relationship would be with the *Flacourtiaceae*, in which, however, the placentation of the ovules is parietal.

There are over 300 species of the type genus *Ilex* distributed in temperate

---

[1] Mr. L. L. Forman, B.Sc.

[2] Including *Ilicaceae* Brongniart (1827). *Vassulaceae* Dulac (1867).

[3] This explains the absence of berries on many trees of the common Holly, *Ilex aquifolium* Linn., which bear only male flowers.

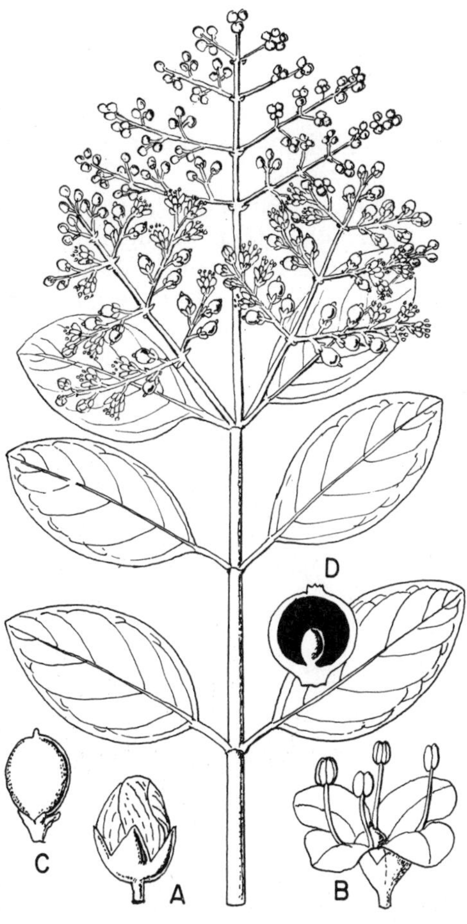

FIG. 300. *Salvadora persica* Linn., the type species of the type genus of the family *Salvadoraceae*. **A**, flower-bud. **B**, flower. **C**, fruit. **D**, vertical section of ovary (orig.).

and tropical regions, the common Holly in the north temperate Old World: trees or shrubs; leaves alternate, evergreen or deciduous, entire or rarely dentate or spinous, mostly with small stipules; flowers bisexual or unisexual, axillary and often cymose; calyx 5–4-fid; corolla sympetalous, rotate, 6–4-partite, lobes imbricate; stamens as many as corolla-lobes, slightly adherent to the corolla-tube; ovary 6–4- (rarely 8–7-) locular; style absent or very short, stigmas as many as loculi; ovules 2–1, collateral on an axile placenta; drupe globose, of 8–4 pyrenes.

In *Nemopanthus* the petals are free, in *Byronia* the stamens are often more numerous than the corolla-lobes, and in *Phelline* the petals are valvate and free.

Salvadoraceae is a small family of three genera in the Old World tropics and subtropics, but absent from Polynesia and Australasia. *Salvadora* embraces 4–5 species from the eastern Mediterranean to India and Ceylon, tropical and subtropical Africa, and the Mascarenes. The corolla in this type-genus is sympetalous with the stamens attached to the base or middle of the tube; in *Asima* and *Dobera* the petals are free, in the former the stamens free, in the latter the stamens monadelphous; rather an unusual mixture of characters in so small a family!

Salvadora persica Linn. (type species of the genus and family, Fig. 300), the Salt Bush, Mustard Tree, Toothbrush Tree; shrub or small tree in the Orient and northern Africa to India; shoots and leaves eaten as a salad, also provide fodder for camels; source of a vegetable salt called Kegr, derived from the ash of the plant; fat from seeds manufactured into candles and for rubbing on the skin; wood also utilised.

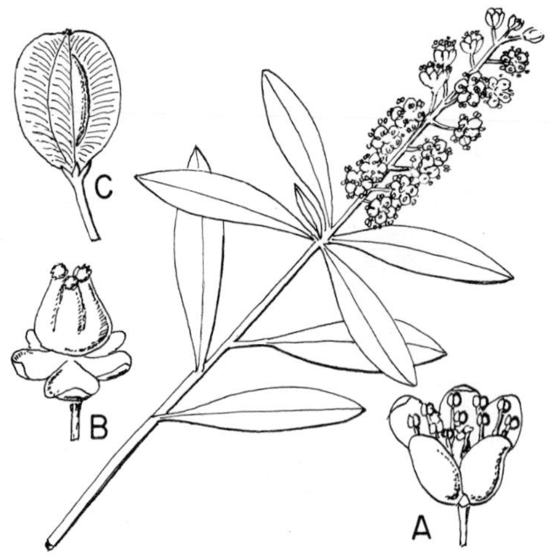

FIG. 301. *Cliftonia monophylla* (Lam.) Sarg. (*Cyrillaceae*), S.E. United States of North America. **A**, flower. **B**, calyx and gynoecium. **C**, fruit.

Cyrilla, the type genus of **Cyrillaceae**, and other three make up this small family of only about fourteen species confined to America. *Cyrilla* has 5 stamens, the filaments shorter than the petals and straight. The other genera have 10 stamens, *Cliftonia* (Fig. 301) with broadly 4–3-winged fruits, and *Purdiaea* with wingless fruits, while *Schizocardia* has a capsular fruit hidden by the hairy laciniate calyx-lobes. *Cyrillopsis*, formerly included in this family, is now placed in the *Ixonanthaceae*.

Icacinaceae[1] were included in the *Olacaceae* by Bentham and Hooker, but

[1] Including *Phytocrenaceae* Arnott ex R.Br. (1852). *Emmotaceae* van Tieghem (1897). *Iodaceae* van Tieghem (1897). *Leptaulaceae* van Tieghem (1897). *Pennantiaceae* J. G. Agardh (1858). *Pleurisanthaceae* van Tieghem (1897). *Sarcostigmataceae* van Tieghem (1897).

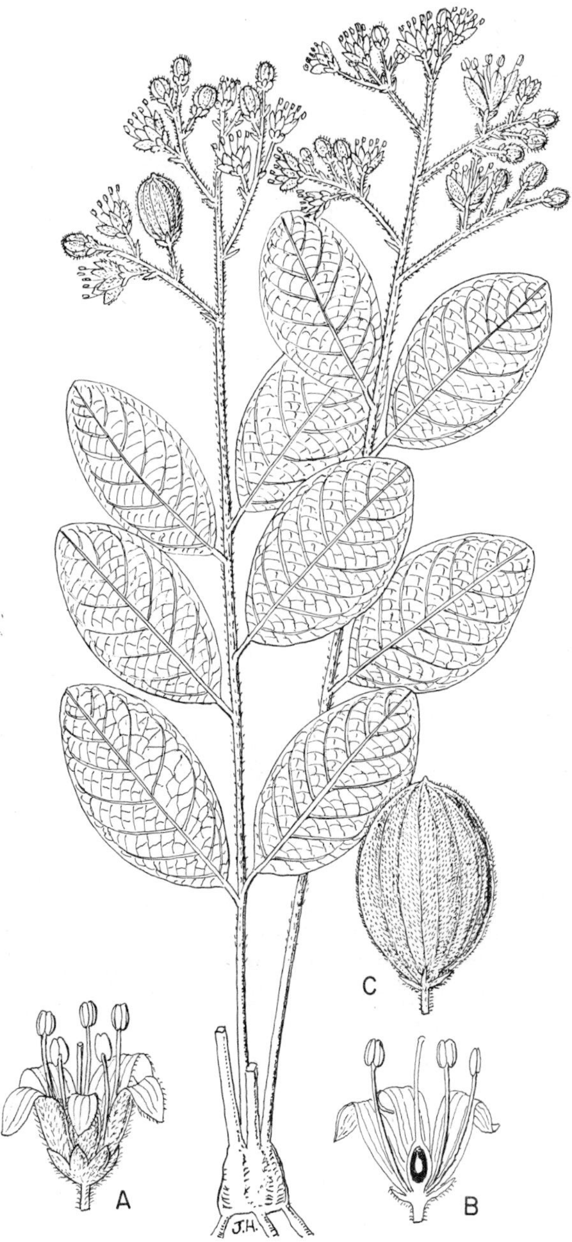

FIG. 302. *Icacina senegalensis* A. Juss., tropical Africa, the type species of the type genus of *Icacinaceae*. **A**, flower. **B**, vertical section of flower. **C**, fruit (orig.).

are now generally regarded as a separate family. Fortunately a fairly recent account of them is available in the second edition of Engler's PFLANZENFAMILIEN, published in 1942. It needs no further recommendation as to its merits than the fact that it was written by Dr. H. Sleumer, of Leiden.

The type genus *Icacina* is African and embraces five species, the type species being *I. senegalensis* A. Juss. (Fig. 302), from Senegal to the Shari; shrubs or tall climbers; leaves entire, conspicuously reticulate-venose; flowers bisexual, villous, paniculate; petals 5, valvate, barbate inside the base; stamens 5, inserted on the hypogynous disk; ovary 1-locular, style elongated, inflexed in bud; ovules 2, pendulous; drupe villous.

FIG. 303. *Polyporandra scandens* Becc. (*Icacinaceae*), Malaya. **A**, unopened flower. **B**, vertical section of same. **C**, vertical section of **D**, ovary (orig.).

It would be beyond the scope of the present work to attempt to give an account of the 60 or so genera which make up the family. It includes trees, shrubs and climbers with mostly alternate entire rarely lobed or toothed leaves and without stipules, small flowers with valvate free or rarely united petals, stamens as many as and alternate with the petals, the anthers opening by slits lengthwise, or very rarely locellate and opening by numerous pores (*Polyporandra*, Fig. 303), usually no disk, and ovary 1-locular with mostly 2 ovules pendulous from the top of the loculus; fruit a drupe, and seed usually with endosperm.

A few of the more outstanding genera, however, may be mentioned: Stems are tuberculate in *Trematosperma cordatum* Urb. and in *Pyrenacantha* spp. Leaves opposite in *Cassinopsis*, *Acrocoelium*, *Tridianisia*, *Iodes*, *Mappianthus* and *Polyporandra*; palmately nerved in *Natsiatum*, *Natsiatopsis*,

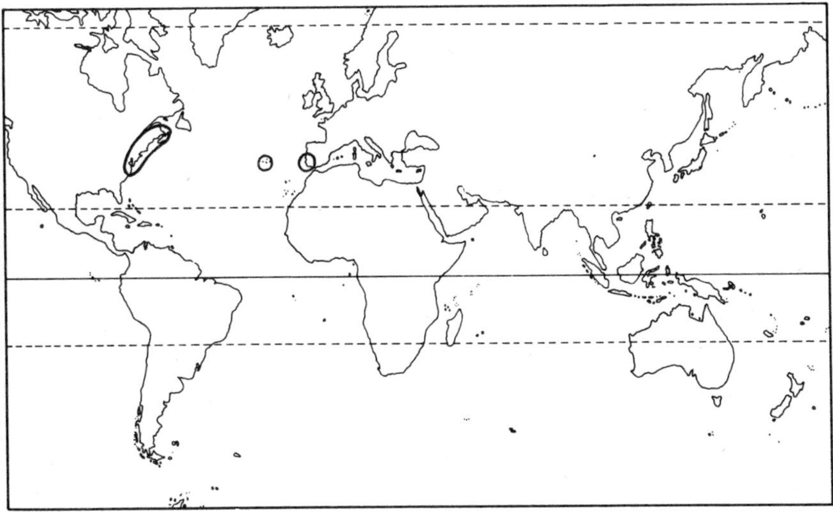

MAP 22. Distribution of the genus *Corema* (*Empetraceae*), in N.E. United States (*C. conradii* Torry), in the Azores, Portugal and Spain (*C. alba* (Linn.) D. Don).

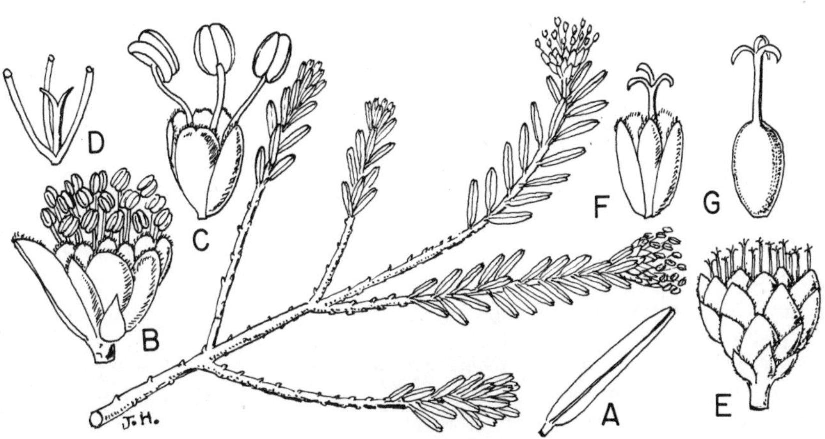

FIG. 304. Broom Crowberry, *Corema conradii* Torrey (*Empetraceae*), a member of a genus of flowering plants both significant and insignificant (see text). **A**, leaf. **B**, male flower-head. **C**, male flower. **D**, the same showing the vestigial gynoecium (anther removed). **E**, female flower-head. **F**, female flower. **G**, gynoecium (orig.).

Phytocrene spp., *Pyrenacantha* spp. and *Polycephalium*; sometimes spinulose-dentate in *Cassinopsis*, toothed in *Villaresia* spp., *Villaresiopsis*, *Pleurisanthes*, *Natsiatum*, *Natsiatopsis* and *Hosiea*; lobed in *Natsiatum* and several *Phytocreneae*. Inflorescence leaf-opposed in *Gomphandra* spp.; interpetiolar in

Cassinopsis ilicifolia (Hochst.) Sleumer; cauliflorous in *Pseudobotrys* and *Lavigeria*; extra-axillary in *Leptaulus*.

The Order CELASTRALES is a somewhat mixed group of families, the true affinities of some being rather doubtful. An example is the **Empetraceae**,[1] assigned to this position by Engler, but placed at the end of that artificial division, *Apetalae*, by Bentham and Hooker. In the latest SYLLABUS of the Englerian system, however, it is included in the ERICALES, another "taxonomic inexactitude" due to superficial resemblance! It is probably a much reduced ancient type, its distribution being very wide and broken, *Empetrum* occurring right through the mountains and cold regions of the Northern Hemisphere, with an isolated very closely related species in the Southern Hemisphere, in the colder parts of South America and adjacent islands. The genus *Corema* (Fig. 304) connects the flora of the N.E. United States of North America with that of the Azores and Portugal; and *Ceratiola* occurs in that ancient piece of land, Florida.

The type genus is *Empetrum*; Erica-like shrublets; leaves crowded, recurved; flowers bisexual or subdioecious, small, axillary; bracts 4, imbricate, like the 3 free sepals; petals 3, free; stamens 4 or 3, free; ovary 9–6-locular; stigmas 9–6; ovule 1 in each loculus, erect; fruit a small black berry-like drupe containing several 1-seeded stones; seeds with a narrow embryo in copious endosperm.

Ceratiola, in the pine woods of the S.E. United States of America, has 3 or 2 flowers in each axil, with only 2 stamens and a 2-locular ovary, and *Corema* (Fig. 304) has the flowers capitate at the ends of the shoots, with 3 or 4 stamens, and the ovary 4–2-locular.

Celastraceae[2] is a family which is very difficult to recognise by any one character or even by a combination of characters. In fact Bentham and Hooker enumerate an exceptionally large number which they rather unfortunately referred to in the GENERA PLANTARUM as *Formae Abnormae*. They give the exceptions to the general characters as follows (translation):

Leaves punctate below in *Kokoona*. Sterile pedicels in *Hippocratea comosa* [*Hippocratea* in this system is referred to a separate family of that name]. Calyx valvate in *Caryospermum*, open in *Perrottetia*. Petals absent from *Alzatea* [In my GENERA OF FLOWERING PLANTS Vol. 2 included in *Flacourtiaceae*] and *Microtropis* spp.; ligulate in *Glossopetalum*; valvate in *Caryopermum*, *Perrottetia*, and some species of *Hippocratea*; induplicate-valvate with long inflexed tips in *Goupia* [see *Goupiaceae*]; hypogynous in *Schaefferia* and a few other genera. Stamens 2 in one species of *Salacia* [see *Hippocrateaceae*]; 10 in *Glossopetalum*; inserted within the disk in *Ptelidium*; sessile on the disk in *Goupia* [see *Goupiaceae*], the anthers being pilose.

---

[1] Including *Ramostigmaceae* Dulac (1867).

[2] Including *Leptolobaceae* Dulac (1867). *Chingithamnaceae* Handel-Mazzetti (1932). *Canotiaceae* Britton (1908). *Lophopyxidaceae* H. Pfeiffer (1951).

Disk absent from *Microtropis*, *Llavea*, and a few others. Ovary stipitate in *Llavea*; semi-inferior in *Mortonia* sp.; 1-locular in *Llavea*, *Glossopetalum* and *Cathastrum*; 5-locular in *Goupia* [see *Goupiaceae*]. Ovules attached to the apex of the central axis in *Microtropis*; solitary and pendulous from the apex of the loculi in *Cassine*; variable in number in *Euonymus*. Embryo minute in *Perrottetia*. Radicle superior in *Cassine*.

To these may be added a few more examples with outstanding characters. Branches spiny in *Gymnosporia* spp., *Forsellesia*, *Acanthothamnus*; leaves *Ilex*-like in *Maytenus ilicifolia* Mart. and *Denhamia*; inflorescence borne on the midrib at the side of the leaf in *Polycardia baroniana* Oliv. (see Fig. 306);

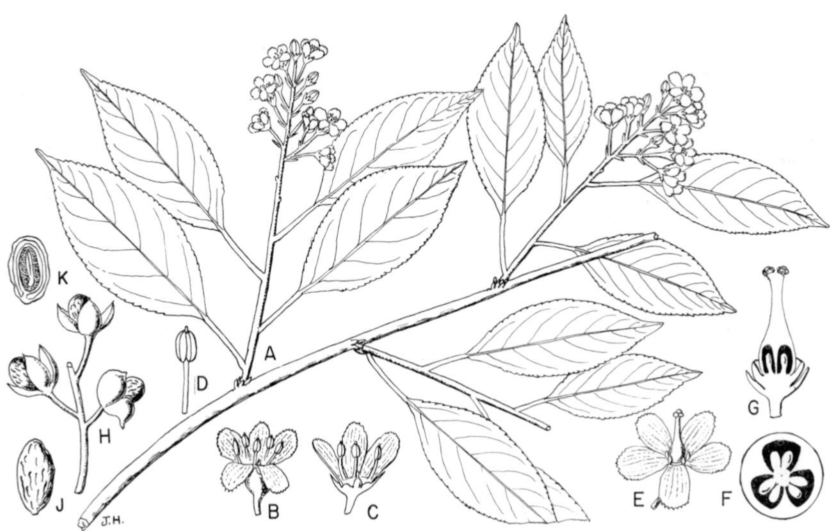

FIG. 305. *Celastrus scandens* Linn., North America, type species of the type genus of *Celastraceae*. **A**, leaves and male flowers. **B**, male flower. **C**, vertical section of male flower. **D**, stamen. **E**, female flower. **F**, cross-section of ovary. **G**, vertical section of female flower. **H**, fruits. **J**, seed. **K**, vertical section of seed (orig.).

petals with processes or crests on the adaxial face in *Lophopetalum*, with longitudinal ribs in *Putterlichia pyracantha* Endl.; anther-connective very thick with the loculi divergent at the top in *Glyptopetalum*; connective produced in *Kokoona*; style becoming lateral in fruit in *Pleurostylia*; fruits winged like a *Combretum* in *Tripterygium*, *Pterocelastrus* and *Wimmeria*; broadly winged in *Ptelidium*, with a long narrow terminal emarginate wing in *Plenckia populnea*; seeds more than half enclosed by a bright red aril in *Glyptopetalum*; completely enclosed by the aril in *Euonymus*; winged from near the base in *Kokoona*; surrounded by a broad wing in *Lophopetalum* and *Peripterygia*; obliquely winged in *Zinowiewia*.

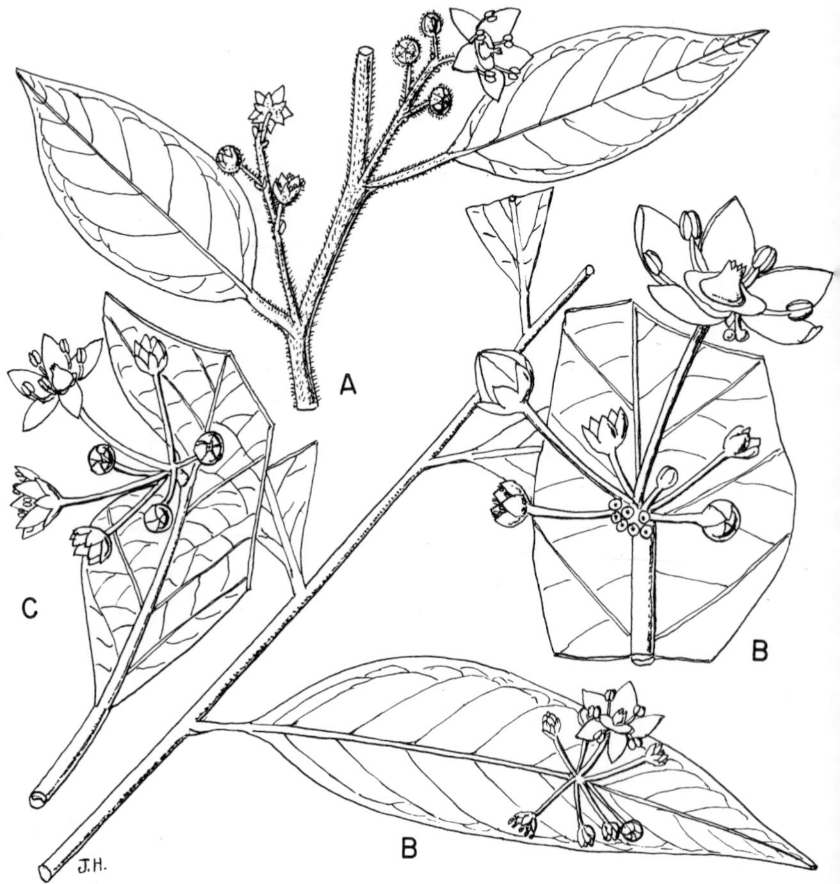

FIG. 306. Remarkable inflorescences in the Mascarene genus *Polycardia* (*Celastraceae*). **A**, *Polycardia libera* O. Hoffm., with a normal axillary inflorescence. **B**, *P. centralis* Baker, with the peduncle united to the midrib. **C**, *P. baroniana* Oliv., similar but the leaf-margin divided or indented to the point of emergence from the midrib (orig.).

This is indeed a formidable array of exceptions in a "natural family", and with all of them included it is not easy to grasp what the family really is. Baillon as usual took a very wide view of *Celastraceae* and included the following treated in the present work as separate families: *Stackhousiaceae*, *Goupiaceae*, *Hippocrateaceae*, *Geissolomataceae*, and even *Buxaceae*! He rather naïvely remarked (NAT. HIST. PL., English translation) that the family thus understood "by concatenation" has *many affinities* (italics mine)!

Celastrus, the type genus, comprises mostly climbing shrubs; leaves alternate, entire or serrate; stipules composed of hairs; flowers dioecious, in axillary and terminal racemes or panicles; petals 5; stamens 5, inserted between the disk-lobes; anthers cordate at the base, introrse; disk cupular or concave, 5-lobed; ovary sessile on the disk, 4–2-locular; stigma 4–2-lobed; ovules 2 in each loculus, erect, collateral, funicle cup-like at the base; capsule globose to oblong, 4–2-locular, loculicidally dehiscent; seeds erect, enclosed by a fleshy aril open at the top; endosperm fleshy; embryo with large leafy cotyledons. Type species *C. scandens* Linn., north America (Fig. 305).

Stackhousia, the type genus of **Stackhousiaceae**, with about 20 species in Australia, New Zealand to New Guinea and the Philippine Islands, are herbs with perennial rhizomes; stems erect; leaves alternate, entire; stipules absent or minute; flowers in terminal spikes or racemes, bisexual; calyx 5-lobed or cleft; petals 5, with elongated connivent claws forming a tube open at the base; disk thin; stamens 5, inserted on the margin of the disk; pollen spiny; ovary 5–2-lobed and locular; style single; ovule 1, erect; fruit with persistent axis and 5–2-globular or angular cocci.

In *Macgregoria* the petals are completely free, the pollen is smooth, and the fruits are provided with hooked hairs. *Tripterococcus*, the third genus of this small family, has petals as in *Stackhousia*, but the cocci of the fruits are winged.

The genus *Goupia*, **Goupiaceae**, has been moved about a bit. Willdenow considered it to belong to the *Araliaceae*; Jussieu placed it in the *Rhamnaceae*, and he was followed by many other botanists. But Endlicher classed it among the dubious genera of *Celastraceae* and he was followed by Lindley and later by Bentham. Loesener retained it in the *Celastraceae* as a subfamily. If only on account of these diverse views it seems better to regard it as a separate family, following Miers (CONTRIB. BOT. **2**, 134, t. 74 (1860–69)). The reader will find a drawing of this genus in my FAMILIES OF FLOWERING PLANTS, 2nd Ed. **1**, 323 (1959). *Goupia glabra* Aubl., tree in Guyana, is the source of Goupi wood, used for furniture, rail-road ties, street paving blocks and boat-building.

The genus *Hippocratea*, **Hippocrateaceae**, with its near relatives, has usually been included as a tribe or subfamily of the larger *Celastraceae*. *Hippocratea* (Fig. 307) embraces about 110 species ranging through tropical America and Florida, tropical Africa, Madagascar, tropical east Asia and Australia; small trees or scandent shrubs; leaves opposite; stipules small, caducous; flowers bisexual, in axillary panicles or cymes; petals 5, imbricate or valvate; stamens 3, anthers extrorse; fruit a discoid 3-lobed capsule or of 3 free mostly vertically or radially, rarely laterally compressed carpels.

Tristemonanthus has introrse anthers, and the remainder of the genera, *Salacicratea*, *Salacighia*, *Thyrsosalacia*, *Salacia* and *Pseudocassine*, differ but slightly from the type genus.

In this Order CELASTRALES a few exceptional characters have been noted already. Another remarkable development occurs in the small family

FIG. 307. *Hippocratea africana* (Willd.) Loes., Old World tropics (*Hippocrateaceae*). **A**, flower. **B**, stamen. **C**, stamen from the back. **D**, cross-section of ovary. **E**, fruit. **F**, seed. (From Hutchinson and Dalziel, FLORA OF WEST TROPICAL AFRICA.)

FIG. 308. *Erythropalum scandens* Blume (*Erythropalaceae*). **A**, flower. **B**, vertical section of flower. **C**, fruit, which is enveloped by the enlarged calyx. **D**, vertical section of fruit. (Repeated from FAMILIES OF FLOWERING PLANTS, 2nd Ed. I, Fig. 185.)

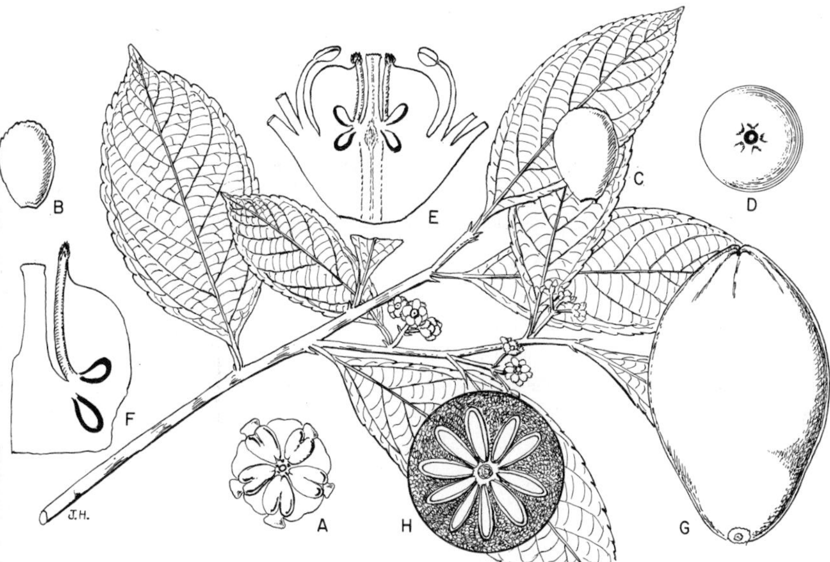

FIG. 309. *Siphonodon celastroides* Griff. (*Capusiaceae*). **A**, view of top of flower without the sepals, showing the anthers appressed to the disk. **B**, sepal. **C**, petal. **D**, view of the disk from above showing the ostiole-like orifice and the 5 stigmas. **E**, vertical section of flower with sepals and petals cut off. **F**, portion of same. **G**, the false fruit composed of the greatly enlarged disk with the little "ostiole" at the top. **H**, cross-section of fruit (orig.). (See notes under *Scyphostegia*, p. 360.)

Erythropalaceae, represented by the single tropical Asiatic genus *Erythropalum*. It is outstanding on account of the remarkable fruit, which is completely enclosed until ripe by the persistent enlarged calyx with its long stipe-like pedicel. This genus of three species shows a curious mixture of characters which are fully described in my FAMILIES OF FLOWERING PLANTS. Most of these are shown in Fig. 308, reproduced from that work for the benefit of the student. Scandent shrubs; leaves alternate, slightly peltate at the base; no stipules; flowers very small in lax axillary dichotomously branched cymes, the peduncles in the lower axils transformed into tendrils; calyx very small in flower, but the tube becoming enlarged and enclosing the fruit and resembling a fig. The stamens are opposite to and adnate to the petals (as in *Rhamnaceae*); ovary half immersed in the disk, 1-locular with 3 or 2 ovules pendulous from the top of the loculus; seed pendulous, with minute embryo near the top of the fleshy endosperm. The drawing may help the student to understand the structure of the flowers in the next two families, *Capusiaceae*, and more especially the very remarkable *Scyphostegiaceae*, about which there is some divergence of opinion.

In **Capusiaceae**,[1] single genus *Siphonodon* (synonym *Capusia*) (Fig. 309), it is the disk that is remarkable. It is very large and fleshy, hemispherical and resembling an ovary, entirely covering the carpels and leaving a small ostiole-like opening at the top through which protrudes the tip of the floral axis and resembling a stigma; the carpels are really separate but completely embedded in the disk, and their styles are adnate to the inner wall of the disk-tube and show as 5 penicillate stigmas around the tip of the floral axis; there is only one pendulous ovule in each carpel; the false fruit **G** is therefore composed of the greatly swollen disk with a minute orifice at the top, pear-shaped to orbicular, crustaceous, in which the bony carpels radiate from the central axis; seeds with rather bony endosperm and large, foliaceous orbicular cotyledons subcordate at the base.

We now come to the most remarkable genus of flowering plants I have ever seen, and the drawings of it are here repeated from my FAMILIES OF FLOWERING PLANTS to enable the student to follow its description. **Scyphostegiaceae** is monotypic, a single genus and species, *Scyphostegia borneensis* Stapf (Fig. 310), found on Mt. Kinabalu, Borneo, at about 2000 ft altitude. In the first edition of my FAMILIES OF FLOWERING PLANTS (1926) there were only female flowers and young fruit known to us at Kew. Of these I made drawings and stated that when the male flowers became known the genus might prove to belong to *Moraceae*. That indeed proved to be a "wild shot", as I pointed out in my second edition (1959) when more complete specimens were available.

In the meantime Swamy[2] had published a more comprehensive account with excellent figures, and on studying this I stated "that I was not happy about his interpretation of the structure of the female flower". He considered the large fleshy globose organ to be a 1-locular ovary containing a large number of ovules on a wide basal placenta. I stated, after careful dissection, that an equally feasible view was that it is a large fleshy disk, as suspected by Stapf (not a fig-like receptacle as I had suggested previously), enclosing a number of free carpels, each with a short stipe to which adhere lobules from the receptacle, with a subterminal stigma, and a solitary erect ovule. I came to this more definite conclusion by comparing the female flower with the flowers of *Siphonodon* (see Fig. 309), related to *Hippocratea* in the CELASTRALES, in which the disk completely encloses the otherwise free carpels and forms a false fruit rather similar to a small fig.

The leaves of *Scyphostegia* are definitely Celastraceous. The flowers are dioecious and apetalous, arranged in axillary and terminal racemes, and composed of tiers of tubular bracts, the males with 3–4 tiers, the females

---

[1] Including *Siphonodonaceae* Gagnep. & Tardieu (1951).

[2] Swamy, On the floral structure of *Scyphostegia*, PROC. NAT. HIST. SCI. INDIA **19**, no. 2, 127 (1953).

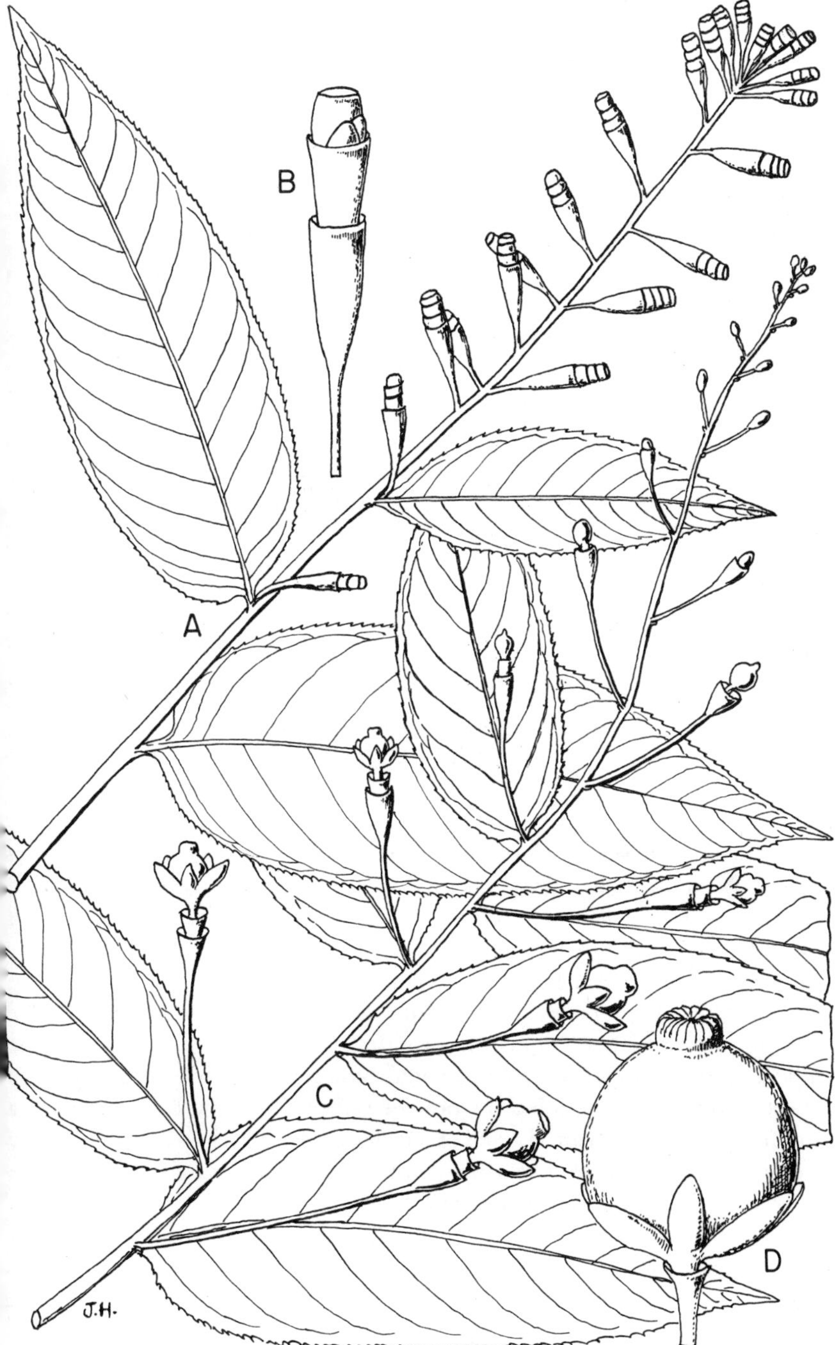

FIG. 310A. *Scyphostegia borneensis* Stapf (*Scyphostegiaceae*). **A**, male flowering shoot. **B**, male raceme. **C**, female flowering shoot. **D**, false fruit (enlarged swollen disk, according to the writer's interpretation) (orig.). (Repeated from FAMILIES OF FLOWERING PLANTS, 2nd Ed. **1**, Fig. 187A) (see notes in text).

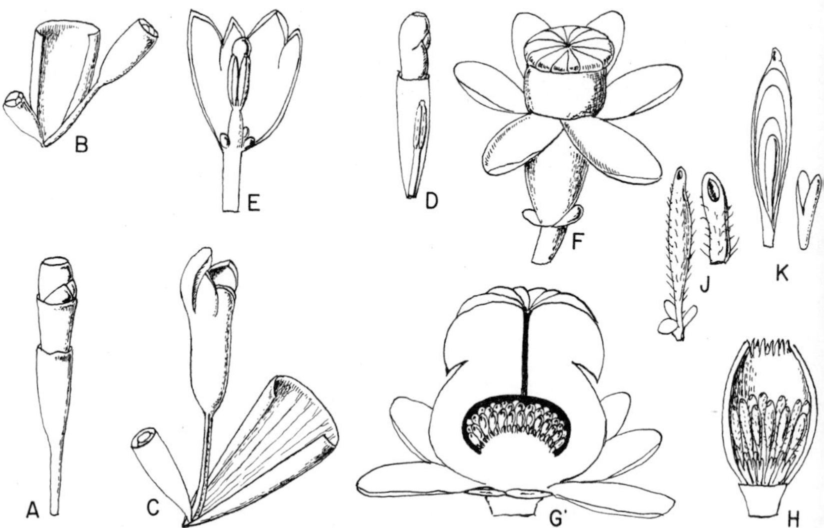

FIG. 310B. *Scyphostegia borneensis* Stapf (*Scyphostegiaceae*). **A**, male raceme. **B**, lower bract opened out. **C**, bracts and male flower. **D**, abortive stamen outside one of the bracts. **E**, vertical section of male flower. **F**, female flower. **G**, vertical section of female flower. **H**, vertical section of disk with free carpels. **J**, fruiting carpel. **K**, vertical section of same with embryo (orig.). (Repeated from FAMILIES OF FLOWERING PLANTS, 2nd Ed. **1**, Fig. 187B) (see text).

with 2 tiers, each bract of the male embracing a single flower; male flowers pedicellate within the bracts, pedicel 2-nerved; calyx tubular, 6-lobed, lobes in 2 series, imbricate; stamens 3, united into a column produced at the apex beyond the 3 extrorse 4-locular anthers (Fig. **E**); at the foot of the staminal column 3 large fleshy disk-glands; female calyx of 6 free segments, within these a large fleshy globular disk with several inflexed stigma-like rays but no apparent stigmas and with an aperture ("ostiole") in the middle; carpels numerous, free on a wide convex receptacle, stipitate, with 3 partly adnate hyaline lobules from the receptacle at the base and with a subterminal stigma; fruit a bunch of narrow achenes enclosed by the greatly enlarged disk (as in *Siphonodon*, Fig. 309), hairy; ovule 1 in each carpel, erect; embryo large, cotyledons ovate, endosperm scanty.

I still consider the above to be a reasonable interpretation of the flowers of this unique plant.

ORDER 42. OLACALES

(*Fam. Fl. Pl.* 1, 329)

Families: **Olacaceae, Opiliaceae, Octoknemaceae, Aptandraceae, Dipentodontaceae, Medusandraceae.**

This Order consists of a small number of families mostly with valvate petals; further advanced than the CELASTRALES; ovules pendulous from the apex of the ovary or from the top of a basal placenta.

Phylogeny: MAGNOLIALES → DILLENIALES → BIXALES → THEALES → CELASTRALES → OLACALES → culminating in the family **Medusandraceae**.

Olax, the type of **Olacaceae**,[1] is a genus of about 50 species in the tropics and subtropics of the Old World; trees, shrubs or shrublets with a woody rootstock, sometimes climbers; leaves alternate, jointed with the branchlets, sometimes small and scale-like; flowers in axillary spikes or racemes; calyx cupular, truncate, in fruit much enlarged and often enclosing the fruit; petals 6, rarely 5, valvate; stamens and staminodes 12–9, the fertile ones

FIG. 311. *Olax ceylanica* Linn., Ceylon, the type species of the type genus of *Olacaceae*. **A**, flower. **B**, stamen. **C**, gynoecium. **D**, fruit (orig.).

[1] Including *Schoeffiaceae* Blume (1850). *Cathedraceae* van Tieghem (1896). *Chamnochitonaceae* van Tieghem (1896). *Coulaceae* van Tieghem (1896). *Heisteriaceae* van Tieghem (1896). *Strombosiaceae* van Tieghem (1896). *Ximeniaceae* van Tieghem (1896). *Tetrastylidaceae* Calestani (1905).

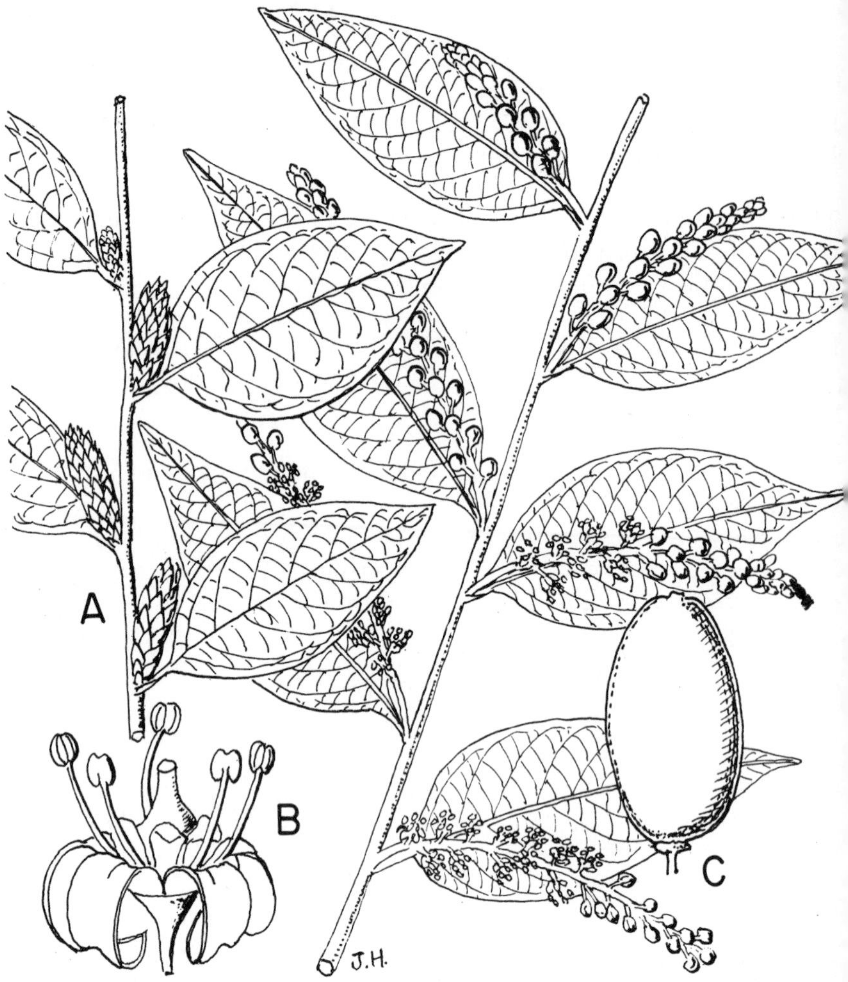

FIG. 312. *Opilia amentacea* Roxb., tropical Asia, type of the genus and family *Opiliaceae*. **A**, leaves and young inflorescences. **B**, flower. **C**, fruit (orig.).

usually in 3 pairs connected to the petals; staminodes often 6, 2-fid or 2-partite; ovary 1-locular, or 3-locular at the base; stigma subcapitate; ovules 3, pendulous from the apex of a central placenta free at the apex, or almost from the base; drupe globose or oblong, more or less enclosed by the enlarged calyx; embryo very small, within the apex of fleshy endosperm. Type species *O. ceylanica* Linn., Ceylon and Madras (Fig. 311).

The type genus of **Opiliaceae**[1] is *Opilia*, with about 25 species distributed

[1] Including *Cansjeraceae* J. G. Agardh (1858). *Harmandiaceae* van Tieghem (1896).

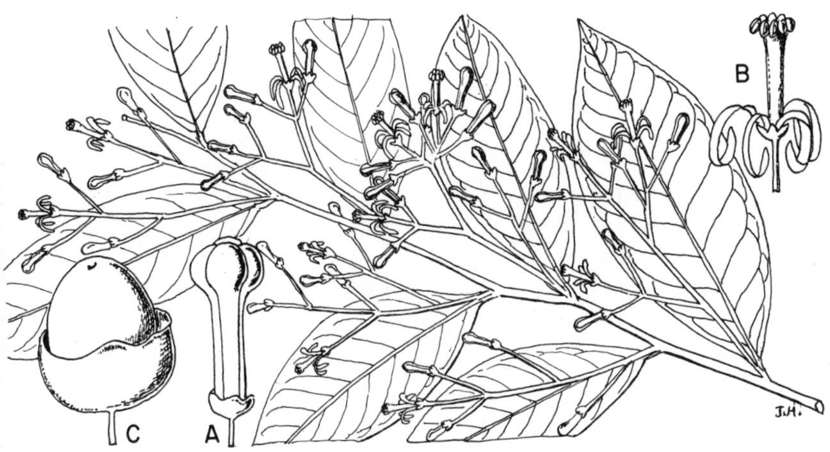

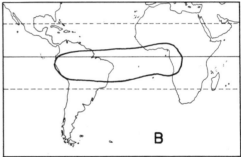

FIG. 313. *Aptandra spruceana* Miers (*Aptandraceae*), Brazil. **A**, flower in bud. **B**, open flower. **C**, fruit and enlarged calyx (orig.).

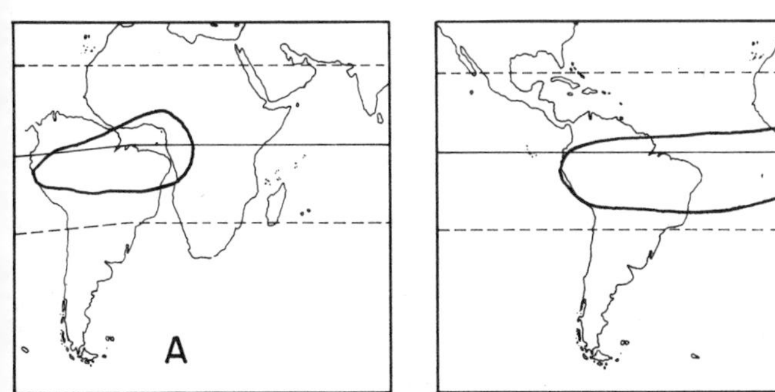

MAP 23. Showing the distribution of the natural genus *Aptandra*, **A**, before America was separated from Africa, and **B**, present range.

in tropical Africa and Asia. The salient features of *Opilia* are the somewhat scandent habit, entire, pinnately nerved, alternate leaves, bisexual flowers in axillary racemes which are catkin-like with imbricate bracts when young, small calyx not enlarged in fruit, valvate 5 or 4 free petals, with as many stamens opposite to them, disk of 5 or 4 scales around the base of the 1-locular ovary with one ovule suspended on a basal placenta from near the top of the loculus; the fruit is a drupe with a crustaceous stone, and the embryo of the spuriously erect seed is short to long in relation to the amount of the fleshy endosperm. Type species *O. amentacea* Roxb., tropical Asia (Fig. 312).

Champereia and *Rhopalopilia* share most of these characters, also *Melientha*,

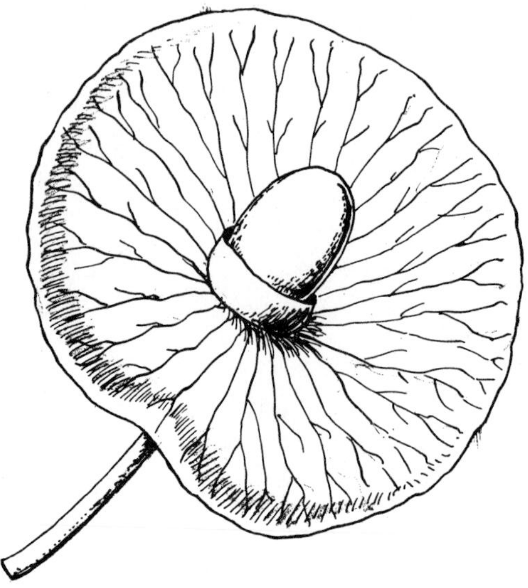

FIG. 314A. Fruit of *Aptandra zenkeri* Engl. (*Aptandraceae*), tropical Africa.

but this diverges in its inflorescence in which the flowers are glomerate. More advanced characters are shown by *Lepionurus* and *Cansjera* in which the petals are united into a short tube.

Aptandra (Fig. 313) is the basic genus for the small family **Aptandraceae**, founded by van Tieghem (BULL. SOC. BOT. FR. **43**, 568 (1896)), and supported by Gagnepain (*loc. cit.* **57**, 377); 4 spp. in tropical America and west tropical Africa; small slender trees; leaves alternate, entire; no stipules; flowers paniculate; calyx minute in flower, much enlarged in fruit; petals 4, valvate; disk-glands 4; stamens within the lobed disk connate into a slender column, the anthers united into a terminal mass perforated by the style; ovary 2-locular, ovules 2, pendulous from a central free placenta; drupe subglobose, enclosed to beyond the middle by the undivided accrescent calyx (Fig. 314A).

In *Ongokea* the calyx splits into 3 segments and the ovary is 1-locular, whilst in *Harmandia* the disk is annular and the stigmas are sessile on the ovary.

The most advanced families in this Order are **Dipentodontaceae** and **Medusandraceae**, which are fully illustrated and described in my FAMILIES OF FLOWERING PLANTS, 2nd Ed., Figs 191 and 192. Both are represented by monotypic genera, *Dipentodon*, S.E. Asia, with flowers in globose umbels, and *Medusandra*, tropical W. Africa, with flowers in paired axillary pendulous racemes, 5 fertile stamens opposite the petals, and 5 spider-leg-like staminodes opposite the sepals.

ORDER 43. SANTALALES

(*Fam. Fl. Pl.* **1**, 337)

Families: **Loranthaceae, Grubbiaceae, Santalaceae, Misodendraceae, Balanophoraceae.**

"Loranthaceae is a family of parasitic or hemiparasitic shrubs having green leaves but deriving a considerable portion of their nourishment from the tissues of the host tree to which they are attached by modified roots (suckers or haustoria)" (Rendle CLASSIF. FL. PL. **2**, 66). Not quite all are of this habit, however, for the monotypic genus *Nuytsia* R.Br. (Fig. 314C) is a terrestrial tree of S.W. Australia. Moreover, it is significant that the flowers of this genus are bisexual, and there is a double perianth of a distinct calyx and a corolla of 6 linear free petals. This seems to be sufficient proof that the so-called perianth of **Loranthaceae**[1] consists of a calyx and corolla, and that the calyx in many cases is much reduced and should not be regarded as an outgrowth from the receptacle, as often described. About 40 genera have usually been recognised, but more recently the genus Loranthus has been much subdivided, and not very satisfactorily.[2]

On a world basis it seems better to stick to the broader concept of the *Loranthus* as described in the GENERA PLANTARUM: *Loranthus* Jacq. (not Linn.), about 500 species in the Old World tropics and subtropics, rare in temperate regions; type *L. europaeus* Jacq. (Fig. 314B), S.E. Europe: shrubs parasitic on trees, rarely (in sect. *Giadendron*) terrestrial; leaves opposite, very rarely alternate or verticillate, entire, often thick and fleshy;

[1] Including *Viscaceae* Miers ex Miquel (1856). *Porosectaceae* Dulac (1867). *Elytranthaceae* van Tieghem (1896). *Arceuthobiaceae* van Tieghem (1897). *Dendrophthoaceae* van Tieghem (1897). *Eremolepidaceae* van Tieghem (1897). *Giadendraceae* van Tieghem (1910). *Ginalloaceae* van Tieghem (1897). *Lepidariaceae* van Tieghem (1910). *Razoumowskiaceae* van Tieghem (1910). *Nuytsiaceae* van Tieghem (1952). *Psittacanthaceae* van Tieghem (1910). *Treubellaceae* van Tieghem (1896), *Bifariaceae* Nakai (1952). *Treubaniaceae* van Tieghem (1910). *Lepidoceraceae* Nakai (1952).

[2] See Danser, New System of the Genera of *Loranthaceae-Loranthoideae*, VERH. AKAD. WETENSCH AMSTERDAM AFD. NATK. **2**, sect. 29, 1–128 (1933). Balle, A propos de la morphologie des "Loranthus" d' Afrique, WEBBIA **11**, 541 (1955), the African species into 22 genera! (mostly Engler and Sprague's sections created into "genera").

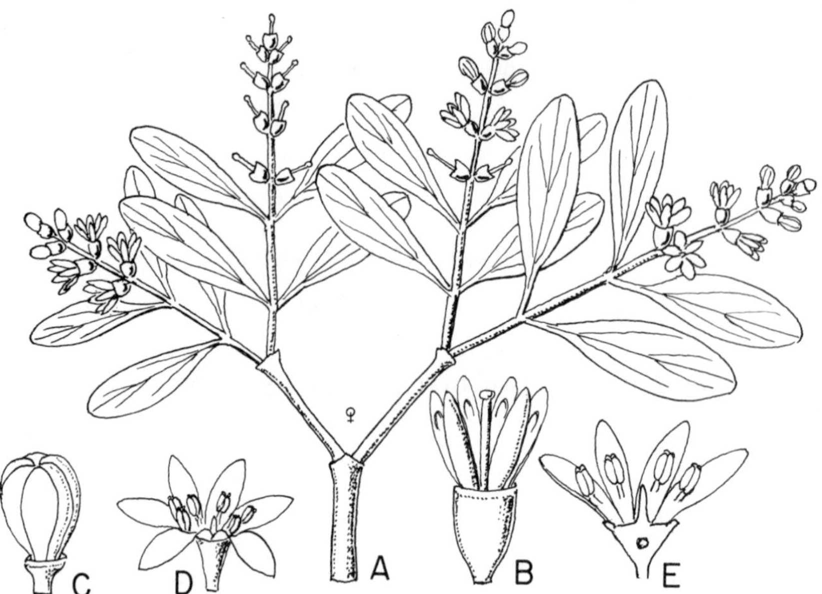

FIG. 314B. **A**, *Loranthus europaeus* Jacq. (*Loranthaceae*). **B**, female flower. **C**, male flower-bud. **D**, male flower. **E**, vertical section of male flower (dissections from Baill.).

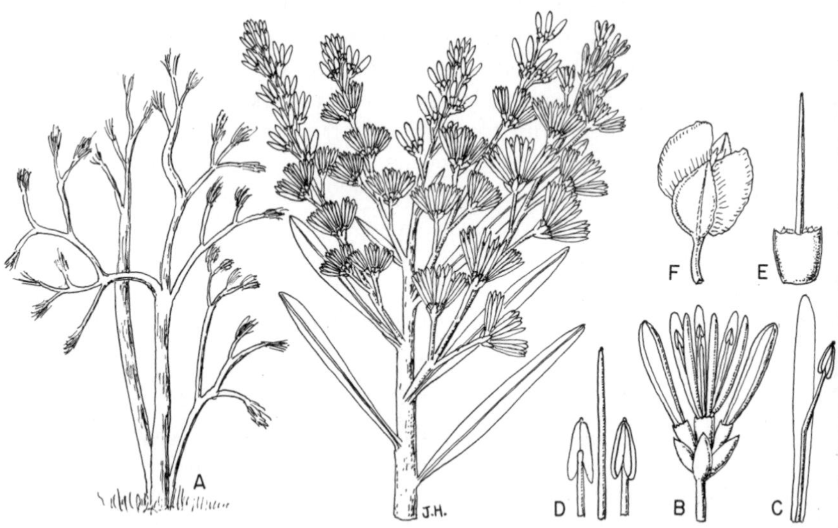

FIG. 314C. *Nuytsia floribunda* R.Br. is a monotypic genus and the most primitive member of the family *Loranthaceae*; endemic in S.W. Australia; primitive because it is the only genus which is completely terrestrial (on its own roots), has alternate leaves, bisexual flowers, a distinct calyx, free valvate petals, and an inferior ovary. This shows that the so-called *calyculus* is not an outgrowth from the receptacle but a real reduced calyx, and that therefore the perianth is a corolla. **A**, habit (after Engler and Drude). **B**, umbel of 3 flowers. **C**, petal and stamen. **D**, stamens and style. **E**, calyx and style. **F**, fruit (orig.).

flowers, bisexual or by abortion dioecious, often beautifully coloured, mostly in axillary spikes, racemes or cymes; bracts and bracteoles often present; calyx-tube adnate to the ovary, limb short, truncate or 4–6-toothed, sometimes reduced to a mere rim; petals 4–6, valvate, free or variously united into a closed or split tube, tube nude within, or rarely with 5 scales above the ovary and opposite the stamens; apex of the petals or lobes of the tube spreading or recurved; stamens opposite the petals or corolla-lobes, often distinctly decurrent to the base of the corolla; anthers ovate-oblong to linear, loculi separate or closely contiguous, sometimes soon confluent, opening by slits lengthwise; no disk; ovary inferior with 1 ovule mostly little differentiated from the ovary; style columnar, filiform or rarely contorted, stigma terminal, obtuse or capitate; fruit a berry or drupe, globose to oblong; seed 1, laterally attached or adherent to the pericarp; no testa; endosperm copious, rarely absent; embryo mostly terete, central and straight, cotyledons 2 or rarely 4.

The family **Grubbiaceae**[1] was formerly included as a tribe (*genus anomalum*) in *Santalaceae*, but is now usually kept separate, even in the latest Englerian SYLLABUS, wherein it is recalled that van Tieghem placed them next to *Bruniaceae*, and Fagerlind in the ERICALES, both suggestions wide of the mark. They remain here next to *Santalaceae*, differing only by their stamens, which are twice the number of the calyx-lobes. The single genus *Grubbia* occurs only in South Africa.

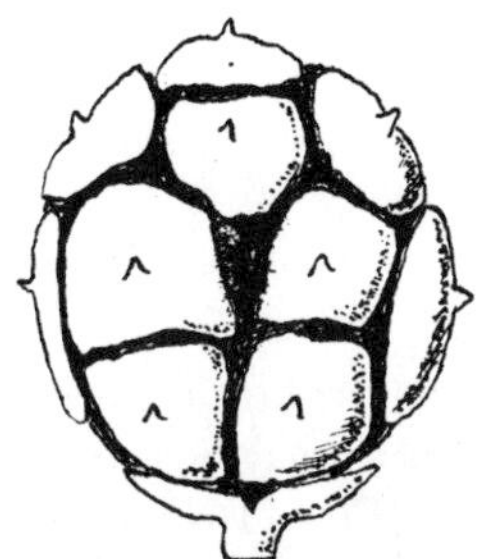

FIG. 315. This is not a drawing of a cone of a *Cupressus*, which it greatly resembles, but of the false syncarp of *Grubbia rosmarinifolia* Berg (*Grubbiaceae*), South Africa.

The family **Santalaceae**[2] consists of hemiparasitic green herbs, shrubs or small trees, and others such as *Thesium* are root-parasites. The leaves may be either alternate or opposite, entire, sometimes reduced to scales; there are no stipules. The flowers are bisexual or unisexual, arranged in spikes, racemes, cymes or heads. The calyx (perianth) is green or petaloid, often fleshy, and usually more or less adnate to the ovary, rendering the latter

[1] Including *Ophiraceae* Arnott (1841).

[2] Including *Osyridaceae* Link (1829). *Canopodaceae* Presl (1851). *Podospermaceae* Dulac (1867). *Arjonaceae* van Tieghem (1896).

inferior or half inferior, or the ovary may be partly immersed in the disk; lobes valvate (or rarely very slightly imbricate); petals absent; stamens the same number as and opposite to the lobes of the calyx; anthers 2-locular, opening lengthwise; usually there is a tuft of hairs just behind each stamen; disk more or less epigynous; ovary 1-locular; ovules 1–3, pendulous from a basal placenta; style more or less simple, or rarely stigmas sessile. Fruit indehiscent, a nut or drupe containing a single seed which has no testa but consists of white fleshy endosperm filling the ovary loculus and within which is embedded the straight embryo.

FIG. 316A. The Sandal Wood, *Santalum album* Linn. (*Santalaceae*), renowned in the history of the Pacific Islands. **A**, calyx-lobe and stamen. **B**, fruit (orig.).

Such is the word picture of this very homogeneous family. The genera are very closely related and not of particular morphological interest, but some are or have been of great historical interest as may be learned from the following. Sandal-wood, *Santalum album* Linn. (Fig. 316A), is renowned in the history of Indo-Malaya and the Pacific Islands. Its use dates as far back as the fifth century B.C., and it is still used in India and China, wherever Buddhism prevails, being employed in funeral rites and religious ceremonies. In India the wood is used in the manufacture of boxes, fans, and other ornamental articles. The Oil, obtained by distilling chips of the wood, is used as a perfume. Oil of Sandal or *Oleum Santali* is obtained by steam distillation from the wood and is used in medicine. The powdered wood is used in cosmetics, and sawdust kept in small bags is used for scenting clothes. Minor products are obtained from various other species of the genus.

The Sandal-wood tree was formerly abundant in the Fiji Islands but was nearly exterminated as a consequence of the busy trade carried on in this valuable commodity between 1804 and 1816. It was mainly the mad rush for Sandal-wood which led to the earlier settlement of white men in the islands. When the supply was exhausted in Fiji the trade was diverted to the southern islands of the New Hebrides. The wood is hard, heavy, and difficult to split, and not attacked by termites.

The red fruits, the size of a cherry, of *Acanthosyris falcata* Griseb., a shrub or small tree in the Argentine, Paraguay and Bolivia, are eaten; they are also used for making liquor and the wood for furniture. The tubers of *Arjona tuberosa* Cav., called Macachi, a herbaceous perennial in Patagonia, are sweet and eaten by the inhabitants.

Misodendraceae[1] (*Myzodendraceae* of auth.) contains the single genus *Misodendron* Soland. ex A. P. de Candolle, MEM. FAM. LORANTH. **12**, t. 11 (1830); type species *M. punctulatum* Soland. ex A. P. de Candolle: green shrublets hemiparasitic on Antarctic beeches (*Nothofagus*); flowers dioecious, minute in small catkins, males nude (neither calyx nor corolla), stamens 2–4 around a small disk, the anthers 1-locular, opening by 2 valves; female flowers with a small calyx on top of the inferior 1-locular ovary crowned by an obscure disk; ovules 3, pendulous from the top of a thick central placenta. (The 11 or 12 species are described by C. Skottsberg in Engler's PFLANZENREICH.)

A full page drawing (Fig. 316B) is given here of a remarkable herbarium specimen at Kew (perhaps unique as such) collected by Mr. H. F. Coomber in Chile. On a small branchlet of *Nothofagus antarctica* he actually found three distinct species of *Misodendron*: **A**. *M. punctulatum* Banks & Soland.; **B**, *M. linearifolium* DC.; and **C**, *M. oblongifolium* DC.

Balanophoraceae[2] is a small family of nevergreen root-parasites, i.e. they are leafless and destitute of chlorophyll and stomata, inhabiting mainly the warmer parts of the world. Although they occupy a lowly position (Reihe 10) in the Englerian system, they are regarded in the present system as being highly advanced, depending as they do on the roots of other plants. How could they be more primitive than their hosts?

The small sessile or shortly stalked flowers are generally crowded into a head or spike, or rarely in a panicle, as in the Cape and east African genus *Sarcophyte*. They are unisexual and monoecious or dioecious, always regarded in this system as very advanced characters. The stamens are equal in number to the lobes of the calyx (perianth), showing that petals have disappeared during the course of evolution; and in the male flowers a

---

[1] J. G. Agardh, THEORIA SYST. PL. FAM. PHAN. 236 (1858).

[2] Including *Latraeophileaceae* Lendro ex A. de St. Hilaire (1837). *Lophophytaceae* Horaninow (1847). *Langsdorffiaceae* van Tieghem (1907). *Hachetteaceae* van Tieghem (1898). *Helondaceae* van Tieghem (1896). *Sarcophytaceae* van Tieghem (1896).

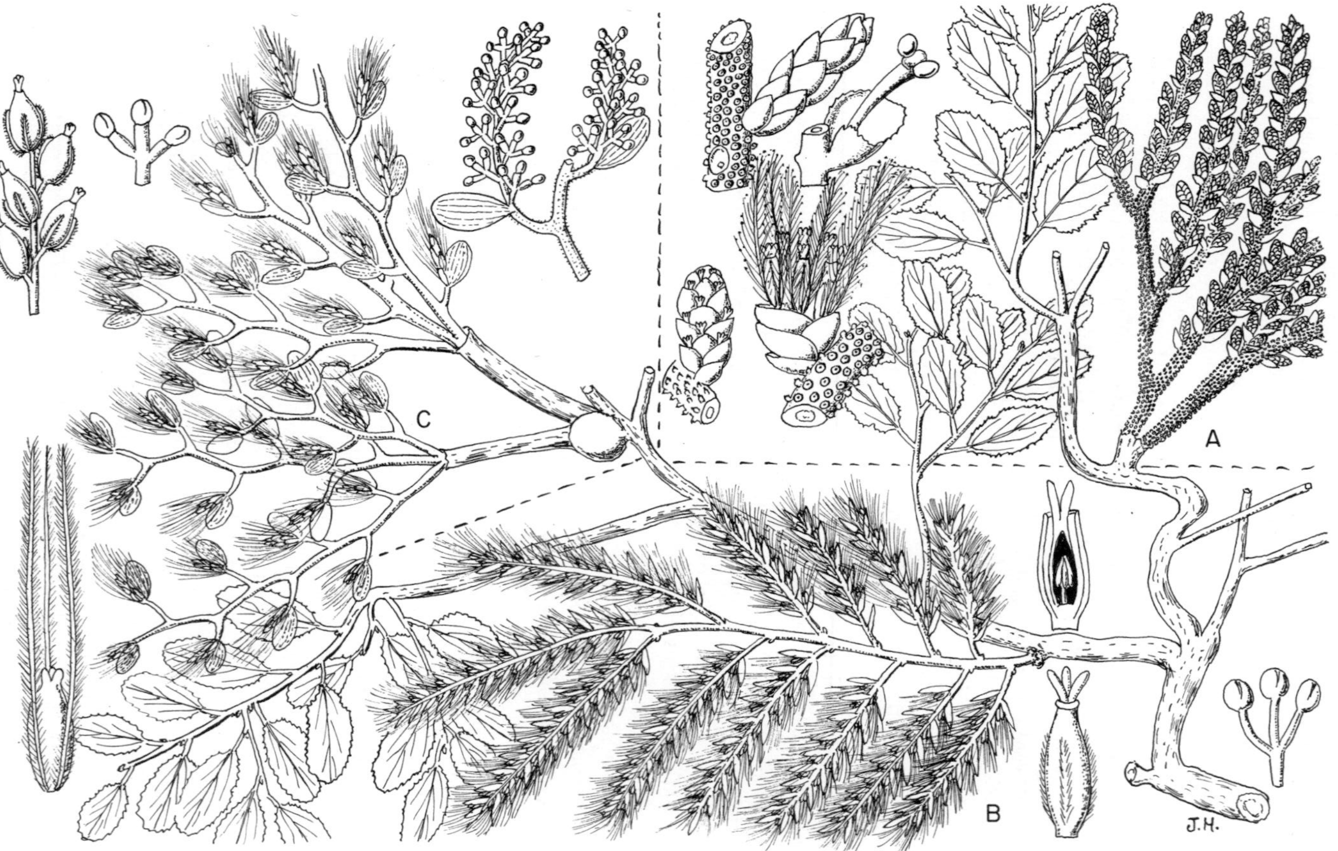

FIG. 316B. On a small branchlet of *Nothofagus antarctica* Oerst., H. F. Coomber found in Chile three distinct species of *Misodendron*. **A**, *M.*

vestigial gynoecium is sometimes present, indicating that the flowers of an ancestral group, such as OLACALES, were most probably bisexual. Further reduction is evident in the female flowers, which are generally naked, though when a calyx is present it is superior (ovary inferior). A good account of the family is given by Rendle (CLASSIF. FL. PL. **2**, 71).

ORDER 44. RHAMNALES

(*Fam. Fl. Pl.* **1**, 341)

Families: **Heteropyxidaceae, Elaeagnaceae, Rhamnaceae, Vitaceae.**

This relatively small Order, of very great economic importance (Grapes, wines, etc.), is something of a parallel of, and closely related to, the CELASTRALES, but with the isomerous stamens opposite to the petals, culminating in the family *Vitaceae*, the latter characterised by having leaf-opposed inflorescences and often tendrils.

Phylogeny: MAGNOLIALES → DILLENIALES → BIXALES → THEALES → CELASTRALES → RHAMNALES.

Rhamnaceae[1] are familiar to most students in the North Temperate Zone, *Rhamnus*, the type genus, being one of the largest. It is one of the most natural and easily recognised families, the spotting characters being the stamens inserted opposite the free petals, the latter usually clawed, and lining the short calyx-tube there is nearly always a well-defined disk in which the ovary is often partially immersed. The 1–2 ovules are erect. The habit is woody and erect, mostly trees or shrubs, rarely climbers, although in the genus *Crumenaria*, in Brazil, there is one very remarkable annual herbaceous species (see Fig. 317); but its congeners are rhizomatous undershrubs with squamiform leaves. Other advanced features of this genus are polygamous flowers, and the quite inferior ovary.

The type genus is *Rhamnus* Linn. (type species R. *catharticus* Linn., Europe and northern Asia); shrubs or trees; leaves deciduous or evergreen, alternate (rarely subopposite), entire or dentate; stipules small, deciduous; flowers axillary, racemose or cymose, bisexual or polygamo-dioecious;

---

[1] Including *Frangulaceae* Lamarck (1805). *Phylicaceae* J. G. Agardh (1858). *Camarandraceae* Dulac (1867).

FIG. 317. *Crumenaria decumbens* Mart., Brazil, the only annual in the otherwise woody family *Rhamnaceae*. **A**, flower. **B**, the same opened out. **C**, stamen. **D**, stigmas. **E**, fruit (orig.).

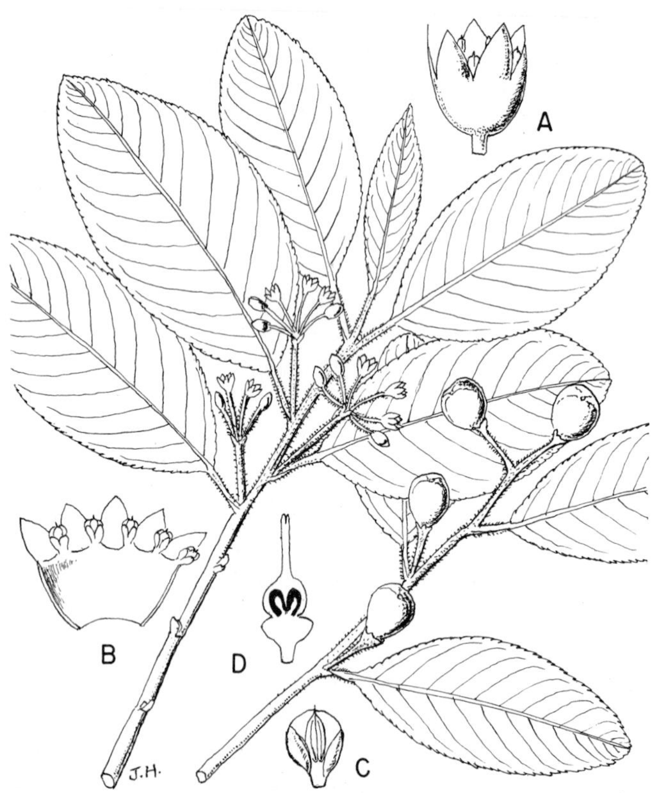

FIG. 318. *Rhamnus purshiana* DC. (*Rhamnaceae*), from the dried bark of which the well-known *Cascara Sagrada* is obtained; native of Pacific States of North America. **A**, flower. **B**, the same opened out. **C**, petal and stamen. **D**, vertical section of ovary (orig.).

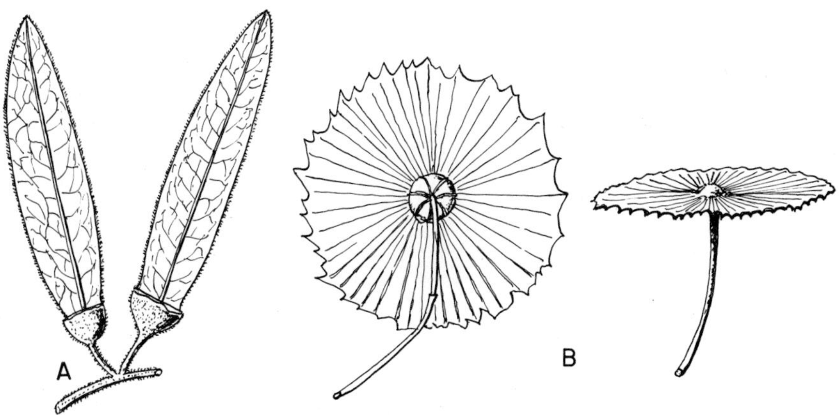

FIG. 319A. Fruits of *Rhamnaceae*: **A**, *Ventilago maderaspatana* Gaertn., India, and **B**, *Paliurus orientalis* Hemsl., China.

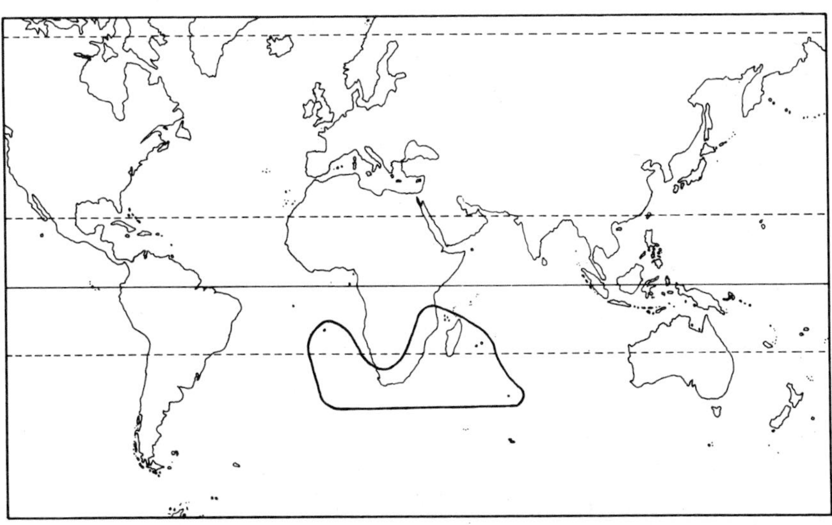

MAP 24. Range of the large and natural genus (over 150 spp.) *Phylica* (*Rhamnaceae*); one sp., *P. ramosissima* DC., in St. Helena, one, *P. arborea* Thouars (see Fig. 319B), in Tristan da Cunha and islands nearby, in far away Gough Island, and in Mauritius; remainder of the species in South Africa with one as far north as south Tanzania (*P. emirensis* (Tul.) Pillans).

calyx 4–5-fid; petals 4 or 5 or absent, inserted on the margin of the disk, hooded or flat; stamens 4 or 5; disk covering the calyx-tube; ovary free, 3- or 4-locular, style 3–4-fid; drupe berry-like, composed of 2–4 pyrenes, pyrenes bony or cartilaginous inside, obscurely dehiscent or indehiscent; seed obovate, endosperm fleshy; cotyledons flat or marginally recurved.

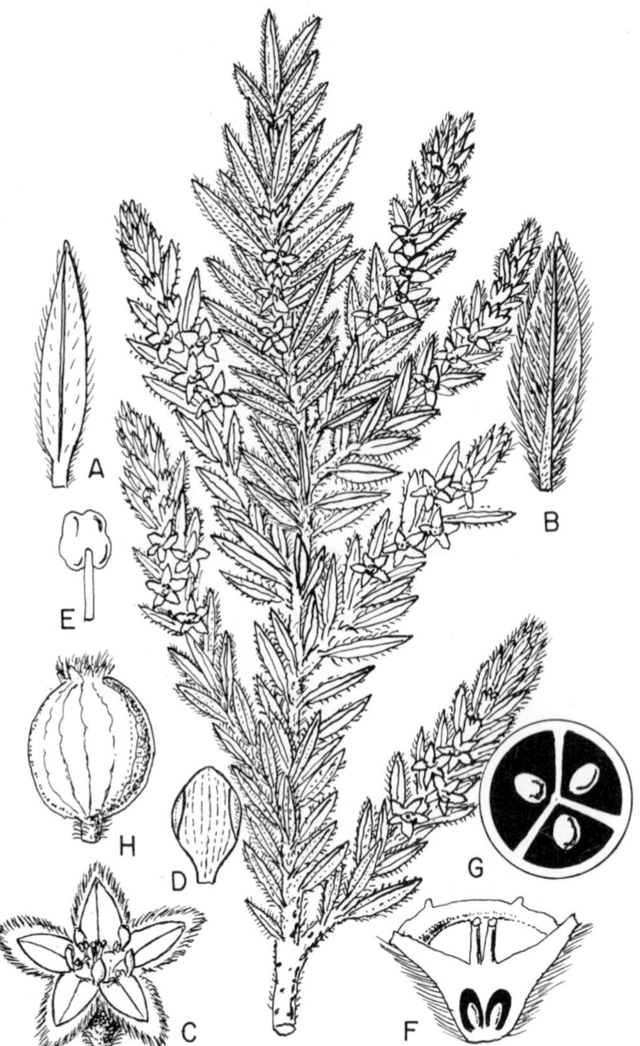

FIG. 319B. *Phylica arborea* Thouars (*Rhamnaceae*), the only shrub or small tree on the island of Tristan da Cunha and nearby islands. **A**, upper surface of leaf. **B**, lower surface. **C**, open flower. **D**, petal. **E**, stamen. **F**, vertical section of ovary. **G**, cross-section of ovary. **H**, fruit (orig.).

The *Rhamnaceae* of the Northern Hemisphere are mostly more or less of the humdrum *Rhamnus*-type, but some of those of the Southern Hemisphere strike a somewhat different note. Young botanists, for example, are usually surprised to find that *Phylica*, a large South African genus, belongs to the family. Its small ericoid exstipulate crowded leaves and its small flowers

FIG. 320. *Cissus palmatifida* Planch., tropical Africa (*Vitaceae*). **A**, flowering shoot, note the leaf-opposed inflorescence. **B**, flower. **C**, vertical section of flower. **D**, cross-section of ovary. **E**, fruit. **F**, tendril. (From Hutchinson and Dalziel, FLORA OF WEST TROPICAL AFRICA.)

usually densely aggregated into heads or spikes render it very distinct. It is also found in the remote island of Tristan da Cunha. In *Cryptandra* the habit is also often ericoid and the tubular calyx looks like a small ericaceous corolla. *Colletia* spp. are strongly xerophytic with reduced leaves and flattened triangular spine-tipped branchlets, being more or less of a parallelism to *Poncirus* (*Aegle*) in *Rutaceae*. *Discaria*, found in New Zealand, Australia and South America, has quite a Rosaceous appearance, *D. crenata* Regel being very like a *Crataegus*. In St. Helena there is an endemic monotypic genus, *Nesiota*, with opposite leaves. Further outstanding genera are *Gouania* (tropics generally) with watch-spring-like tendrils on the inflorescence (Fig. 201 in my FAMILIES OF FLOWERING PLANTS, 2nd Ed. **1**, 343). In *Helinus* (except for *H. ovatus* E. Mey. from Natal), the uppermost peduncles are likewise transformed into tendrils.

The fruits of some *Rhamnaceae* are very distinctive. Those of *Ventilago* (Asia and Africa) are produced at the apex into a long flat wing; and those of *Paliurus* are girt around the middle by a plate-like or parasol-like wing (see Fig. 319A).

Finally the genus *Karwinskia* (S.W. United States and Mexico) stands out from all the remainder by its gland-dotted leaves, and in *Pamaderris* (Australia and New Zealand) the indumentum is often stellate. It does not seem to be a far cry from some *Rhamnaceae* to part of *Euphorbiaceae*, such as tribe *Bridelieae*.

FIG. 321. Fruta de Pava, *Ardisia revoluta* H.B. & K. (*Myrsinaceae*). **A**, flower-bud. **B**, sepal. **C**, Petal from within and stamen. **D**, fruits (orig.).

There are some useful hard woods in this family, and the principal medicinal product is the well-known Cascara Sagrada, a valuable laxative, obtained from the dried bark of *Rhamnus purshiana* DC. (Fig. 321), a native of the Pacific States of North America.

In the next family, **Elaeagnaceae**, familiar to European students in the Sea Buckthorn, *Hippophae rhamnoides* Linn., the stellate indumentum already present in the more primitive *Rhamnaceae* has become almost universally lepidote, scales being a more advanced type of stellate or branched hairs. The distribution of this family is similar to that of the *Rhamnaceae*, but mainly in the Northern Hemisphere. *Elaeagnus* is the largest and most primitive genus, and is moreover the most widespread. In this the flowers are still bisexual, the leaves alternate, and the indumentum may be either stellate or lepidote. The monotypic *Hippophae* is both maritime and continental, but the flowers have become unisexual. The third genus, *Shepherdia*, has opposite leaves and dioecious flowers. The stomata of the leaves of *Elaeagnaceae* are of the ordinary type and are surrounded by a varying number of undifferentiated epidermal cells.

The next family, **Heteropyxidaceae**, is represented by only one genus, *Heteropyxis*, which has been separated from *Lythraceae*, and is a native of south-east and east tropical Africa. It seems to be a more advanced type of *Rhamnaceae* with perigynous stamens and gland-dotted leaves, although it is also distinguished by the numerous ovules on large axile placentas, and there is no endosperm in the seeds, so I am not quite sure whether it is not just as near to *Rutaceae*.

Vitaceae[1] is a small family of 12 genera mainly tropical and subtropical, known to most people by the grape vine, *Vitis vinifera* Linn., the fruits of which, besides the familiar grapes, are the source of Muscatels, Sultanas, Raisins, Currants, Wines, Grape Sugar, etc.; and in temperate countries by the Virginia Creeper, *Parthenocissus tricuspidata* Planch. (*P. quinqefolia* Planch.), native of N.E. North America.

The flowers in the whole family are borne in leaf-opposed spikes, racemes, panicles or cymes, and some peduncles are transformed into tendrils. The stamens are opposite the petals, as in *Rhamnaceae*, and the usually well developed disk is intrastaminal. The genus *Leea*, sometimes regarded as a family, is so obviously related that it seems declassifying to separate it.

Order 45. MYRSINALES

(*Fam. Fl. Pl.* **1**, 345)

Families: **Myrsinaceae, Theophrastaceae** and **Aegicerataceae.**

Phylogeny: THEALES → RHAMNALES → MYRSINALES.

Myrsinaceae[2] have usually been classified next to *Primulaceae*, mainly because they shared with that family and *Plumbaginaceae* the same position of

---

[1] Including *Vitidaceae* A. L. de Juss. (1789). *Ampelidaceae* Kunth (1822). *Leeaceae* Dumort. (1829). *Cissaceae* Horaninow (1847). *Pterisanthaceae* J. G. Agardh (1858).

[2] Including *Ophiospermae* Ventenat (1802). *Ardisiaceae* A. L. de Juss (1810). *Embeliaceae* J. G. Agardh (1858).

the stamens, opposite the corolla-lobes, and the free basal placentation of the ovules. Otherwise the families have nothing in common. Reliance on a floral diagram may be a snare or even a trap! This grouping is still maintained in the latest SYLLABUS of the Engler System. I may also quote from Rendle (CLASSIFICATION OF FLOWERING PLANTS), "*Myrsinaceae* are closely allied to *Primulaceae*, from which they are distinguished by the woody habit, and the one- to few-seeded drupaceous fruit". But Rendle was a confirmed Englerian.

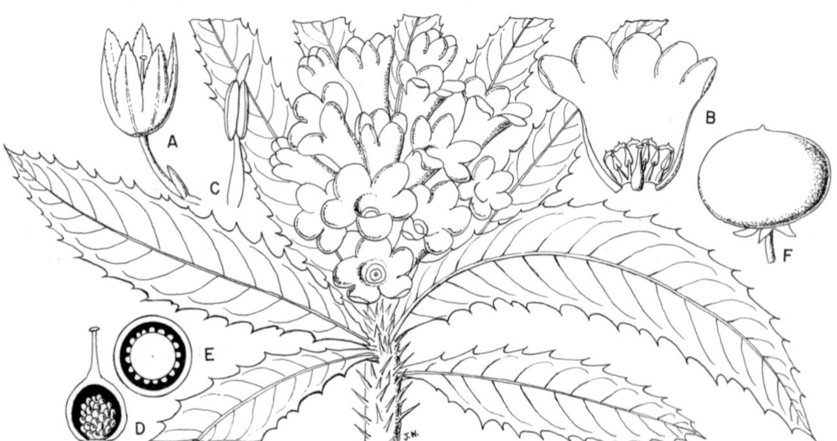

FIG. 322. *Theophrasta jussieui* Lindl. (*Theophrastaceae*), Santa Domingo (West Indies). **A**, calyx. **B**, corolla laid open, showing scales, stamens and gynoecium. **C**, stamen. **D**, vertical section of ovary showing the free basal placenta. **E**, cross-section of ovary. **F**, fruit. The genus is named after the famous Greek, Theophrastus (*circa* 370 B.C.), who has the greatest claim to be called the "father of botany" (see INTRODUCTION).

The type genus is *Myrsine* (type species *M. africana* Linn., very widely spread from the Azores through Africa, including South Africa, Arabia to the Himalayas and Central China); trees to tiny shrubs; leaves scattered, small, mostly serrate or crenate; flowers single or subumbellate, few, axillary or on the previous season's wood, dioecious, 4–5-merous; sepals free or slightly united, imbricate, punctate with glands; corolla short, lobes imbricate, punctate; stamens inserted near the base of the corolla-lobes on a glandular ring; anthers dorsifixed near the base, introrse, opening by slits lengthwise; ovary with a short style and large flat disk-like stigma; placenta with very few ovules in a single whorl; fruit globose, baccate, 1-seeded; seed globose, with bony ruminate endosperm and transverse cylindric embryo.

There are few exceptions in this very natural family. The calyx-tube is

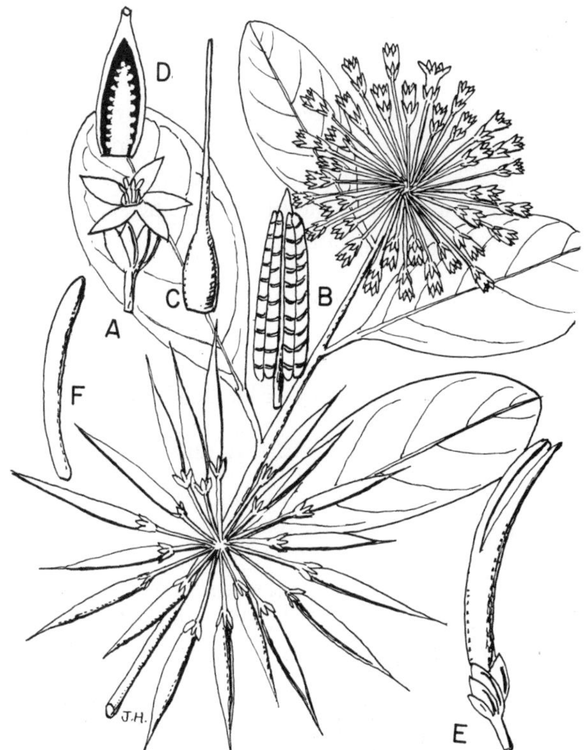

FIG. 323. *Aegiceras corniculatum* (Linn.) Blanco (*Aegicerataceae*), forms mangroves on Lord Howe's Island, in the Pacific; as in several other mangrove plants the seed germinates before leaving the fruit. **A**, flower. **B**, transversely locellate anther. **C**, gynoecium. **D**, vertical section of ovary. **E**, fruit. **F**, seed (orig.).

adnate to the ovary in *Maesa*, and the lobes are often unequal in *Geissanthus*. In *Embelia* the petals are quite free, and also in a few species of *Myrsine*.

The fruits of *Jacquinia pungens* A. Gray, *J. umbellata* A.DC., and *J. seleriana* Urb. in tropical America and especially along the west coast of Mexico and Central America, are used to stupefy fish. The crushed roots of *Maesa tetrandra* A. DC., Malay Archip., are used by the inhabitants for fever. The fruits of *Myrsine capitellata* Wall. a tree of tropical Asia, are eaten by the inhabitants. The wood of *M. grisebachii* Hieron, called Polo Blanco, Langa Marca, and Argentine tree, is of good quality and used for furniture and turnery. The fruit of *Reptonia buxifolia* A.DC., a small tree of eastern India, is sweet and much esteemed and sold in native bazaars.

Theophrastaceae, which occurs only in tropical America and the West Indies, is a small family of four genera with about 70 species, and is distinguished from *Myrsinaceae* by the extrorse anthers and the presence of staminodes alternate with the corolla-lobes; in regard to the latter character it is therefore somewhat more primitive than *Myrsinaceae*, from which staminodes are absent. In *Jacquinia* the staminodes are petaloid, and the flowers (as in *Clavija*) are polygamo-dioecious.

In the small family **Aegicerataceae**, distinguished by de Candolle (PRODR. **8**, 141 (1844)), single genus *Aegiceras* (Fig. 323), and usually included in *Myrsinaceae*, the anthers are transversely locellate, and the cotyledons are connate into a tube and enclose the plumule. The seed germinates before leaving the fruits. Mangrove swamp trees.

ORDER 46. EBENALES

(*Fam. Fl. Pl.* **1**, 348)

Families: **Ebenaceae, Sapotaceae, Sarcospermataceae.**

EBENALES seem to have a long pedigree: MAGNOLIALES → DILLENIALES → BIXALES → THEALES → RHAMNALES → MYRSINALES → **EBENALES** climax family *Sapotaceae*.

In placing the Order EBENALES near MYRSINALES one feels like "drawing a bow at a venture", or as in the war years, "taking a step in the blackout", because the connections between these two groups are not very obvious and the gap is considerable.

Ebenaceae[1] are nearly confined to the tropics with a few in extra-tropical Asia and North America. They are trees or shrubs, many of them with a very hard black wood (Ebony), and there are no stipules. The flowers are bisexual in *Royena*, *Brachynema* and *Rhaphidanthe*, in the last mentioned, found in west tropical Africa, the stamens being reduced to three or two, whilst in *Euclea*, *Diospyros*, *Maba* and *Tetraclis*, the flowers are more or less unisexual. The seeds have copious endosperm, which is sometimes ruminate as in *Annonaceae*. According to Solereder there are no special anatomical characters common to the whole family.

The family is named after the pre-Linnean *Ebenus* of Rumphius, which gave place to *Maba*. Ebony wood is that of *Diospyros ebenum* Koenig, a native of southern India and Ceylon; wood exceptionally hard, closely and evenly grained, used for turnery, keys of pianos, rulers, backs of brushes, stands for ornaments, etc.; some species have edible fruits.

---

[1] Including *Guaicanaceae* A. L. de Juss. (1789). *Diospyraceae* Novak (1954). *Oncothecaceae* Kobuski ex Airy Shaw (1965).

Fig. 324. The Kaki Plum, *Diospyros kaki* Linn. f. (*Ebenaceae*).

In *Maba* Forst., the type genus, the leaves are alternate, flowers often dioecious, axillary and solitary or shortly cymose, the calyx campanulate and sometimes accrescent, usually 3-fid, the corolla campanulate or tubular with usually 3 (rarely 6 or 4) contorted lobes, stamens numerous to 3, often 9, ovary either 3-locular with the loculi 2-ovulate, or 6-locular and the loculi 1-ovulate, with 3 styles or style-arms, and the fruit globose or ovoid, baccate or dry, the calyx much enlarged. Type species *M. elliptica* Forst., Friendly Islands, Pacific.

The genus *Tetraclis*, in Madagascar, stands out from the rest in having valvate corolla-lobes.

Sapotaceae[1] are usually placed next to *Ebenaceae*, and they seem to be a climax tropical forest group from the stock of which no further family types have been evolved. There are between thirty and forty genera, and many of them are very imperfectly known. Botanists travelling in tropical forest regions, therefore, can still do good service to taxonomic botany by making good collections of this family. Fruits and seeds are particularly important, accompanied, of course, by leaves and, whenever possible, flowers.

Owing to recent indiscriminate creation of a large number of so-called genera, the family in that respect is in considerable confusion. Perhaps some courageous experienced orthodox taxonomist will one day provide a reasonable treatment, though his task will be especially difficult owing to incomplete material in herbaria. Consequently only an illustration of the type species of the type genus is given here (Fig. 325).

Sarcospermataceae[2] (note the correct spelling) is a small family repre-

[1] Including *Hilospermae* Ventenat (1799). *Bumeliaceae* Barnhardt (1895). *Boerlagellaceae* Lam. (1925). *Achraceae* Roberty (1953).

[2] Including *Peroniaceae* Dostál (1957)

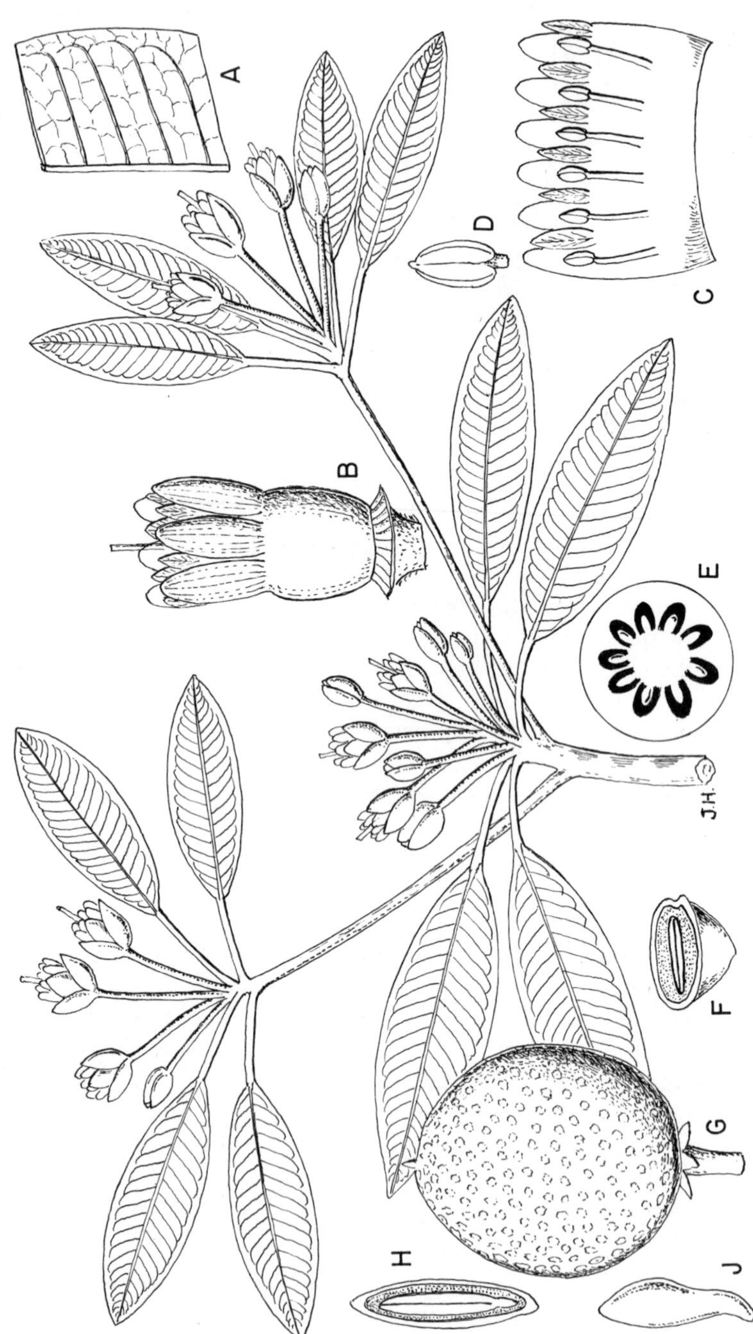

FIG. 325. Sapodilla, Nispero, *Achras zapota* Linn., now called *Manilkara zapota* (Linn.) van Royen, the type species of the type genus of the family *Sapotaceae*; fruit globose to ovoid, with sweet soft flesh, highly esteemed throughout Central America. **A**, part of leaf. **B**, flower with calyx removed. **C**, corolla opened out. **D**, anther. **E**, cross-section of ovary. **F**, cross-section of seed. **G**, fruit. **H**, vertical section of seed. **J**, embryo (orig.).

sented by a single genus of about six species in S.E. Asia, from India and southern China to the Malay Archipelago. As noted in my FAMILIES OF FLOWERING PLANTS it provides a link between the *Myrsinaceae* and the *Sapotaceae*, in the latter of which it was formerly included.

ORDER 47. RUTALES

(*Fam. Fl. Pl.* **1**, 353)

Families: **Rutaceae, Simaroubaceae, Burseraceae, Averrhoaceae.**

Phylogeny: MAGNOLIALES → DILLENIALES → BIXALES → THEALES → CELASTRALES → **RUTALES**.

Mention of the family **Rutaceae**[1] may recall the scent of Citrus groves to those who have visited the warmer regions of the world, for oranges, lemons and grape-fruit are its most important fruits. The name of Engler is most closely linked with it, for he not only wrote several important papers but also elaborated it for both editions of his great work, DIE NATÜRLICHEN PFLANZENFAMILIEN.

The type genus is *Ruta*, with about 60 species distributed from the Atlantic Islands through the Mediterranean region to eastern Siberia, the type species being *Ruta graveolens* L. (see Fig. 326), an odorous herb of southern Europe; generic characters are: undershrubs or perennial herbs, glandular-punctate and strong-smelling; leaves alternate, simple, 3-foliolate or compound; cymes or panicles terminal, with leafy bracts; calyx persistent; petals 5–4, imbricate; disk thick, urceolate, of 10–8 glands or 10–8 pits; filaments dilated at the base; ovary sessile, deeply lobed; ovules numerous; fruit 5–4-lobed, lobes indehiscent or dehiscent at the apex; seeds coarsely punctate.

Genera or species more or less divergent from the type may be noted: Stem herbaceous in *Monnieria*, *Boenninghausenia* and *Dictamnus*; leaves simple in tribe *Diosmeae*, *Boronia* spp., *Leptothyrsa*, *Pitavia*, *Phelline*, *Skimmia*,

---

[1] Including *Aurantiaceae* A. L. de Juss. (1789). *Diosmaceae* R.Br. (1814). *Amyridaceae* R.Br. (1818). *Xanthoxylaceae* Nees & Mart. (1823). *Fraxinellaceae* Nees & Mart. (1823). *Zanthoxylaceae* Nees & Mart. (1823). *Pteleaceae* Kunth (1824). *Boroniaceae* J. G. Agardh (1858). *Correaceae* J. G. Agardh (1858). *Cuspariaceae* J. G. Agardh (1858). *Dictamnaceae* J. G. Agardh (1858). *Diplolaenaceae* A. G. Agardh (1858). *Pilocarpaceae* J. G. Agardh (1958). *Sarcodiscaceae* Dulac (1867).

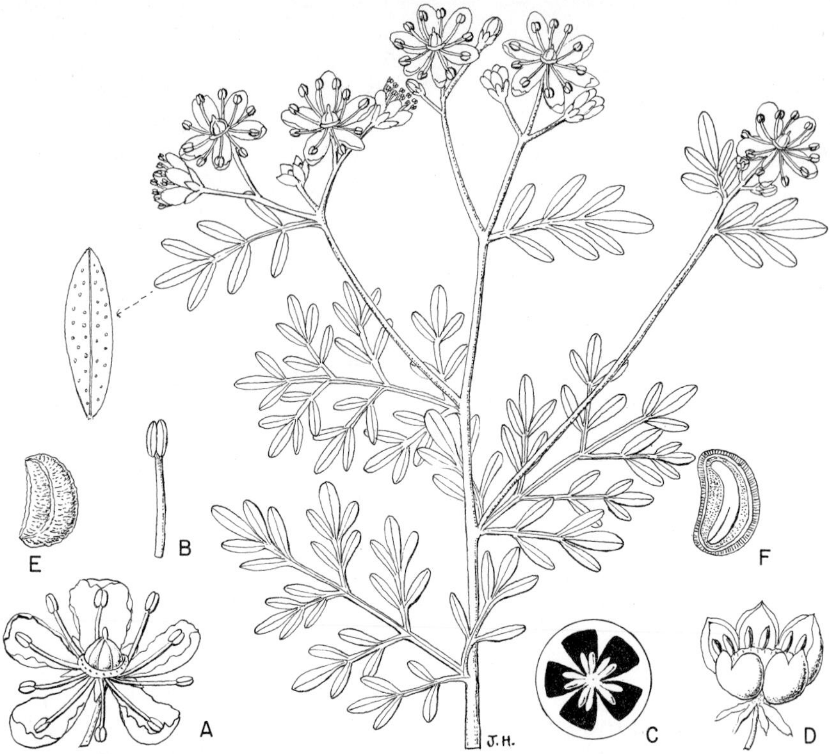

FIG. 326. *Ruta graveolens* Linn., type species of the type genus of *Rutaceae*. **A**, flower. **B**, stamen. **C**, cross-section of ovary. **D**, fruit after dehiscence. **E**, seed. **F**, vertical section of seed (partly after Baillon).

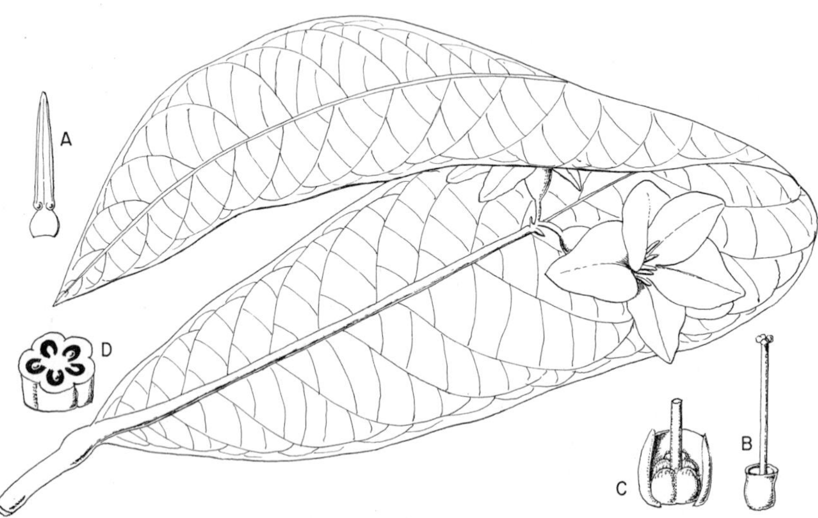

FIG. 327. Epiphyllous flowers occur in a few quite unrelated families; this is *Erythrochiton hypophyllanthus* Planch. & Linden, Colombia, South America, a member of the family *Rutaceae* (compare similar examples in *Flacourtiaceae* and *Araliaceae*). **A**, stamen. **B**, style. **C**, gynoecium and disk. **D**, cross-section of ovary.

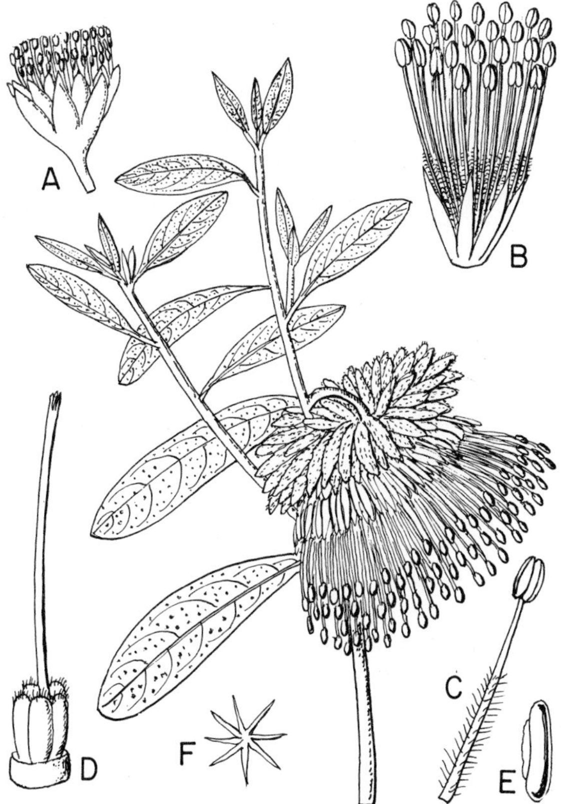

FIG. 328. *Diplolaena dampieri* Desf. (*Rutaceae*), west Australia; named after the famous navigator, Captain Dampier; a single flower with numerous stamens? no, really an inflorescence of several flowers! **A**, single flower. **B**, the same with calyx removed. **C**, stamen. **D**, gynoecium and disk. **E**, seed. **F**, stellate hair from lower surface of leaf (orig.).

Galipea spp.; not glandular-punctate in *Leptothyrsa* and *Phellodendron*; verticillate in *Melicope* spp.; inflorescence united with the midrib in *Erythrochiton hypophyllanthus* Planch. & Linden (Fig. 327); in *Diplolaena* (Fig. 328) it resembles a single flower with many stamens; sepals very unequal in *Monnieria*; obsolete in *Asterolasia*; calyx cupular in *Correa* and *Empleurum*; petals absent from *Empleurum*; connate in *Correa* (Fig. 329), *Phelline*, *Nematolepis*, *Erythrochiton*, *Galipea*, *Ticorea*, *Ravenia*, *Monnieria*; limb 2-lipped in *Monnieria*; stamens numerous in *Peltostigma*, *Citrus*, *Aegle*, *Asterolasia* spp.; declinate in *Dictamnus*; inserted above the disk in *Zieria*; with a hairy scale at the base in *Nematolepis* and *Chorilaena*; monadelphous in *Philotheca* and *Drummondita*.

The family is difficult to link up with any other. Most of them are woody

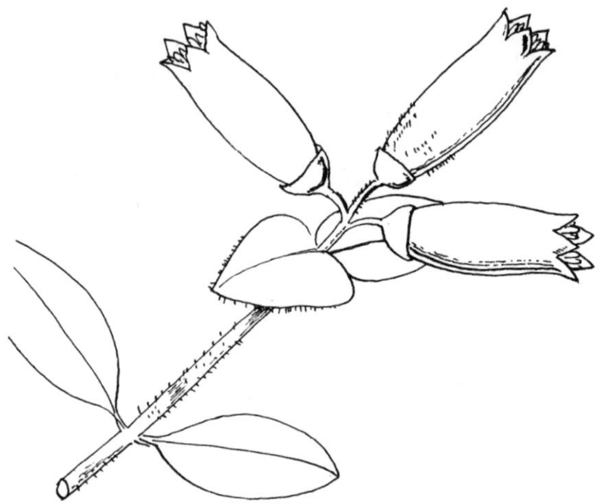

FIG. 329. Note the sympetalous corolla in *Correa speciosa* Ait. (*Rutaceae*), Australia.

and some have simple leaves, though several genera have pinnate or bipinnate leaves. Many have opposite leaves. There are no stipules.

Whilst free petals are usual, quite a number have them united into a sometimes considerable tube, raising part of the family in that respect fairly high in the evolutionary scale. Sympetalous corollas occur in several genera of the tribe *Cusparieae* (tropical America), and in the well-known cultivated greenhouse genus *Correa* (Fig. 329), as well as in *Phelline* (New Caledonia) and *Nematolepis* (Australia). In some of these the stamens are inserted on the corolla, especially in the tribe last mentioned, and in this group the disk is sometimes also tubular and even overtops the ovary, as in *Erythrochiton*. This combination of characters (sympetaly, epipetalous stamens, and tubular disk), associated sometimes with induplicate-valvate corolla-lobes, raises this group of the family to quite a high position and about equal to the sympetalous family *Loganiaceae*, though not at all related. Indeed it shows how very artificial is (or was) the group *Metachlamydeae* (*Sympetalae*, *Gamopetalae*), depending as it does (or did) on a single character, united petals. *Erythrochiton* is also remarkable in that the flowers are borne on the undersurface of the leaf, due to the adnation of the peduncle to the midrib, as shown in Fig. 327.

In all the family *Rutaceae* there is a strong tendency to deep vertical lobing of the ovary resulting in a gynobasic or subgynobasic style, this being no doubt a parallel development with the similar feature so common in many *Ochnaceae* in our woody subphylum and in *Boraginaceae* (*sensu stricto*) and *Lamiaceae* (*Labiatae*) in the herbaceous subphylum.

I do not consider *Rutaceae* to be at all related to *Geraniaceae*, though they

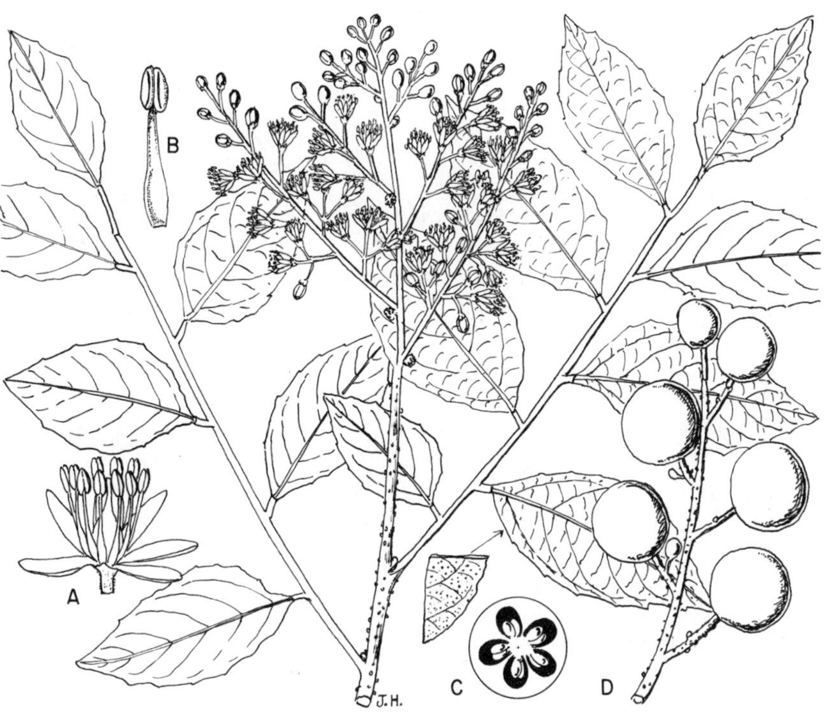

FIG. 330. Captain James Cook was honoured by Sonnerat, who named a genus after him (Sonnerat VOYAGE **3**, 258 (1806)), calling it *Cookia punctata*, because of its punctate leaves; previously, however, it had already been described by Louriro as *Quinaria lansium*, and the plant is now called *Clausena lansium* (Lour.) Sheels (family *Rutaceae*); a regrettable example of name-changing due to following the International Code of Botanical Nomenclature. **A**, flower. **B**, stamen. **C**, cross-section of ovary. **D**, fruits (orig.).

stand side by side in the Bentham and Hooker system, and both are included in the same subseries (Reihe) in the Engler and Prantl system. No doubt some botanists, inured to either of those systems, will consider this to be rank heresy. However, I would recommend them to look over the two families *Rutaceae* and *Geraniaceae* in a large herbarium such as that at Kew and see whether they could discover any cross-affinities amongst the genera!

Some of the more outstanding genera are those already mentioned as having a sympetalous corolla, whilst others have evolved in quite a different way. The most remarkable of these is perhaps the Australian *Diplolaena*, (Fig. 328), in which the flowers are densely collected into a head with a 3–4-seriate involucre of bracts, like a composite, the inner of which are petaloid, thus resembling a flower with several petals and numerous stamens. As one might expect from the crowding of the flowers, the calyx is completely reduced, and the petals are scale-like, their function of attraction

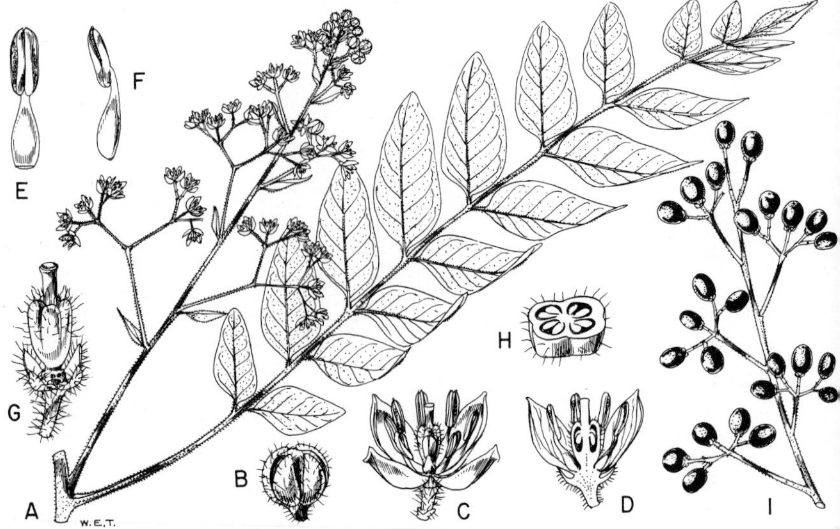

FIG. 331. *Clausena anisata* (Willd.) Hook. (*Rutaceae*), widespread in tropical Africa. **A**, inflorescence and leaf. **B**, flower-bud. **C**, flower. **D**, vertical section of flower. **E** and **F**, stamens. **G**, gynoecium. **H**, cross-section of ovary. **I**, fruits. (From Hutchinson and Dalziel, FLORA OF WEST TROPICAL AFRICA.)

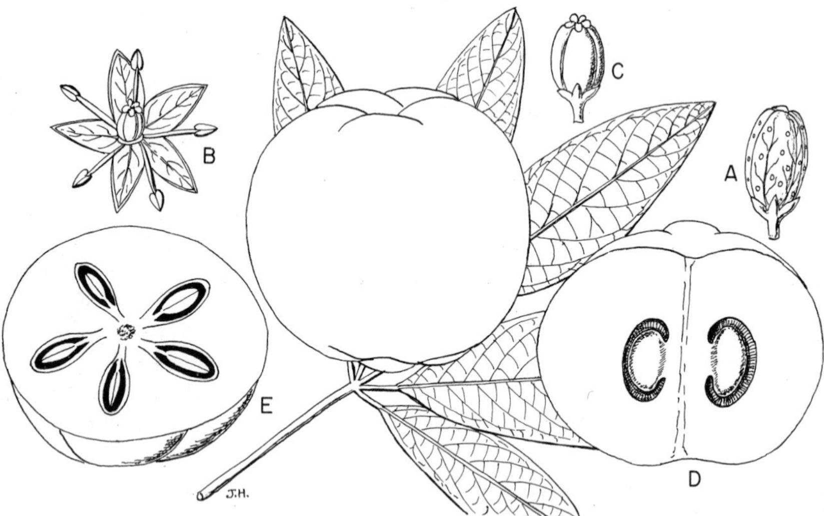

FIG. 332. White Sapote, *Casimiroa edulis* Ll. & Lex., family *Rutaceae* (adapted from Hooker); much cultivated in Nicaragua and other parts of Central America and Mexico, south California and the West Indies. The apple-like fruits have a soft yellow sweet custard-like pulp. Seeman recorded that in Nicaragua it was called "Matasana", a delicious and wholesome fruit. **A**, flower-bud. **B**, open flower. **C**, gynoecium. **D**, section of fruit. **E**, cross-section of same.

FIG. 333. *Simarouba amara* Aubl., tropical America, the type species of the type genus of *Simaroubaceae*. **A**, flower. **B**, vertical section of flower. **C**, stamen showing the scale at the base. **D**, the same side view. **E**, fruits. **F**, vertical section of seed.

being taken over by the petaloid bracts. The genus is a small one and is only found in S.W. Australia. A good spotting feature for most of the *Rutaceae* is, of course, the presence of pellucid gland-dots in the leaves. Except for the small tribe *Ruteae*, the family is confined to the tropics and subtropics and to temperate regions of the Southern Hemisphere, being especially abundant in Australia and South Africa. One feels after a review of the genera, that the family *Rutaceae* is something of a climax group, from the stock of which little further evolution has taken place. They are of great economic importance especially for the orange, the lemon, the grape-fruit, as noted above, and the White Sapote, *Casimiroa edulis* Ll. & Lex. (Fig. 332).

Simaroubaceae[1] will be a mere name to many students who live in temperate regions, for they are found almost exclusively in the tropics and subtropics. *Simarouba* (Fig. 333), the type genus, embraces nine species distributed from the West Indies to northern Brazil; trees with bitter bark; leaves alternate, abruptly pinnate; stipules absent; flowers dioecious, in axillary and terminal panicles; calyx-lobes 6–4, imbricate; petals 5, imbricate; disk hemispherical; stamens usually 10, filaments with a short scale at the base; anthers dorsifixed; female flowers with rudimentary stamens; ovary on the disk, deeply 5-partite; stigmas 5; ovule 1, pendulous; drupes 5–1, sessile; seed with fleshy cotyledons. Type species *S. amara* Aubl., tropical S. America.

[1] Including *Surianaceae* Arnott (1834). *Soulameaceae* Endlich. (1841). *Ailanthaceae* J. G. Agardh (1858). *Castelaceae* J. G. Agardh (1858). *Holacanthaceae* Jadin (1901). *Ptaeroxylaceae* Leroy (1959).

Fig. 334. *Ailanthus altissima* (Mill.) Swingle (*Simaroubaceae*), China, Tree of Heaven, often planted in Britain and other parts of Europe; Rumphius' name for it was *arbor caeli* which signified a tree so tall as to reach the sky, hence the common name; more properly applicable to the taller tropical species of the genus; the pollen from the staminate flowers causes hay fever; when young plants are annually cut back and grown for summer bedding they produce the next season leaves of enormous size (as much as 4 ft long). **A**, male flower-bud. **B**, male flower opened out. **C**, vertical section of female or sub-bisexual flower. **D**, cross-section of ovary and disk. **E**, fruit. **F**, female flower (orig.).

The carpels and styles of the more primitive genera, *Suriana*, *Cadellia*, *Guilfoylia* and *Rigiostachys*, are free, and except for *Rigiostachys*, the leaves are undivided. In *Guilfoylia* there is only one carpel. In many other genera the carpels are free, though the styles are partially or completely united, an indication of secondary apocarpy, as in many *Ochnaceae*. Other morphological peculiarities are the spine-tipped branches of *Castela* and the leafless habit of *Holocantha*, the large leafy orbicular early deciduous stipule-like lowermost leaflets of *Picrasma javanica* Bl. (see reference at foot of p. 396), the elongated peduncles with subumbellate flowers of *Samadera*, the flowers 5-merous in the females, 4-merous in the males of *Picrolemma*, the sub-bilabiate calyx of *Hannoa*, the petals connivent into a tube in *Quassia*, absent from *Alvaradoa* spp., the stamens up to 18 in *Pierreodendron*, opposite the petals in *Picrolemma* and *Picramnia*, unequal in *Suriana*; fruits semi-orbicular, woody and keeled in *Samadera*.

Fig. 334 is a drawing of *Ailanthus altissima* (Mill.) Swingle, the "Tree of Heaven", up to 100 ft high, which provides good autumn colour in Britain. The leaves appear late in spring and when rubbed exhale a disagreeable odour which renders them distasteful to animals. The flowers are either unisexual or bisexual, but often they are dioecious; only those with male

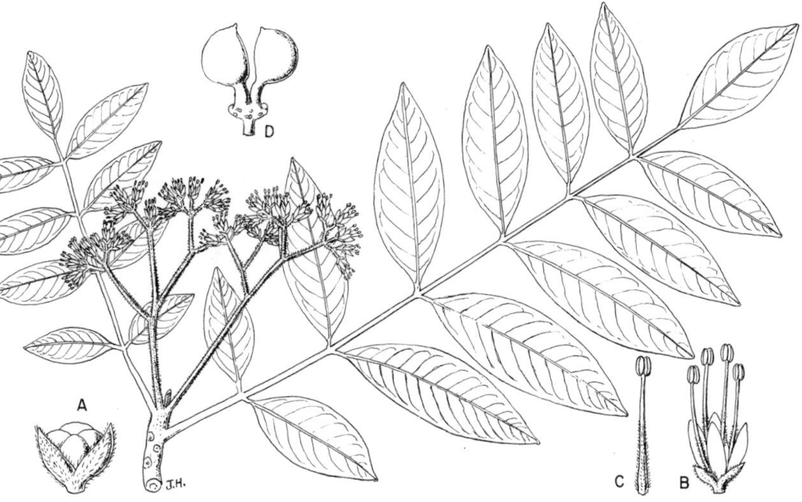

FIG. 335A. *Picramnia excelsa* (Sw.) Planch. (*Simaroubaceae*), West Indies and Venezuela. *Lignum Quassiae*, known in commerce as Jamaica Quassia. Quassia is the dried stem-wood of this species. **A**, flower bud. **B**, open flower. **C**, stamen. **D**, fruits (orig.).

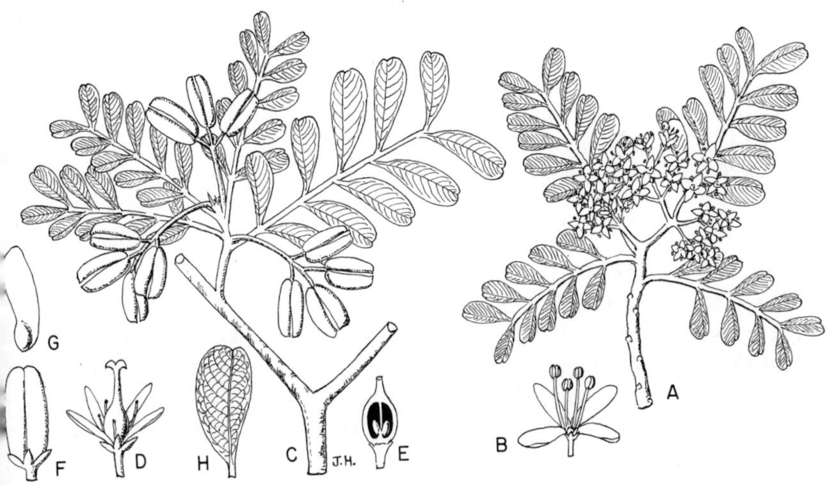

FIG. 335B. *Ptaeroxylon obliquum* (Thunb.) Radlk., South Africa and east tropical Africa. **A**, shoot with male flowers. **B**, male flower. **C**, shoot with fruits. **D**, female flower. **E**, vertical section of ovary. **F**, fruit. **G**, seed. **H**, leaflet. This genus was formerly included in *Meliaceae*, but finds its nearest relative in *Kirkia* Oliv., in the family *Simaroubaceae*.

flowers give off an offensive odour. Each bisexual or female flower produces 1–5 samaras, each 1-seeded, which are slightly twisted so that the fruit in sailing to the ground gyrates like a screw. These so-called "keys" are bright

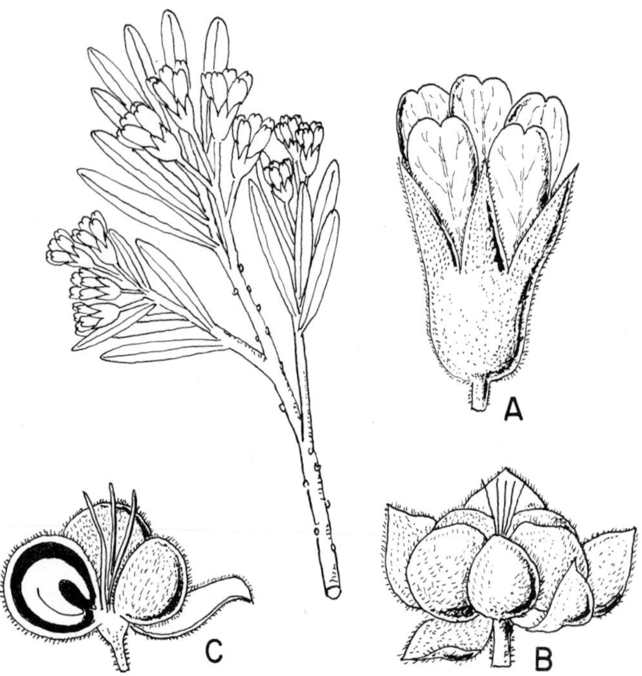

FIG. 336. *Suriana maritima* Linn.; the genus is sometimes regarded as a separate family, but is here retained in *Simaroubaceae* (as in Bentham and Hooker's GENERA PLANTARUM); the free carpels are probably not primitively so but this condition may be secondary (as in many *Asclepiadaceae* and *Apocynaceae*). **A**, flower. **B**, carpels in fruit. **C**, vertical section of same showing basal styles and curved embryo (orig.).

red or purplish brown in autumn; the stamens are 10 in the male flowers, 2–5 in the bisexual flowers; petals valvate.

Few anatomical characters are common to the whole family, the indumentum, when present, being of simple 1-celled hairs and many-celled gland-tipped hairs. The stomata are usually of the ranunculaceous, rarely of the rubiaceous, kind.

Simaroubaceae are most abundantly represented in tropical America, from Mexico to the Argentine. The largest genus is *Picramnia* (Fig. 335 A) (40 spp.), the second in number of species being *Simaba* (22), with one endemic species (*S. africana* Baill.) in west tropical Africa and formerly included in *Quassia*. Tropical Asia and Polynesia harbour several genera, one of the largest, *Soulamea* (8–10 spp.), also in the Seychelles. *Ailanthus* (15 spp.) ranges from India to New Guinea, N.E. Australia and the Solomon Islands. The genus *Brucea* (7 spp.) is common to tropical Africa, tropical Asia, and N.E. Australia. Small genera of restricted distribution are *Cadellia* (1 sp.), *Guilfoylia* (1 sp.) and *Hyptiandra* (1 sp.) in Australia, *Tetramyxis* (2 spp.)

and *Picroderma* (1 sp.) in Indo-China. In tropical Africa there are five small endemic genera, *Pierreodendron* (2 spp.), *Odyendea* (4 spp.), *Hannoa* (5 spp.), *Gymnostemon* (1 sp.) and *Kirkia* (8 spp.). The last mentioned ranges into the northern Transvaal. The most widely distributed genus is *Suriana*, a single species, *S. maritima* Linn. (Fig. 336), which grows on maritime shores, and by some botanists regarded as a separate family.

Anatomically the family **Burseraceae**[1] is considered to be homogeneous (Metcalfe and Chalk, 347). The indumentum consists of various types of

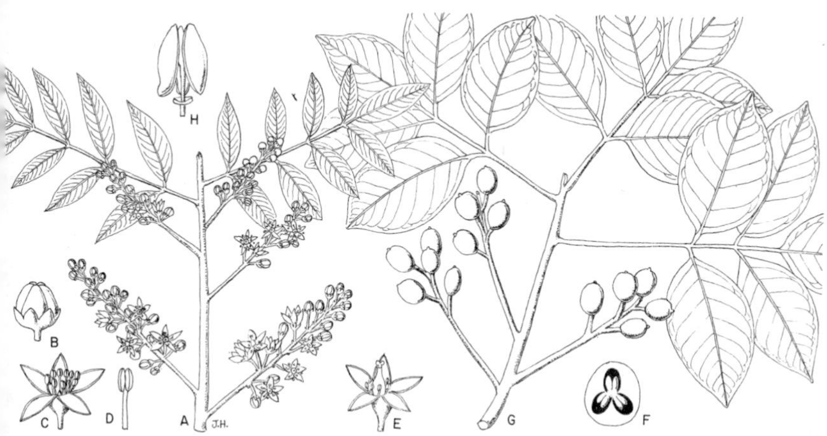

FIG. 337. *Bursera simarouba* (Linn.) Sarg., the type species of the type genus of *Burseraceae*. **A**, flowering shoot. **B**, flower-bud. **C**, male flower. **D**, stamen. **E**, bisexual flower. **F**, cross-section of ovary. **G**, shoot with fruits not yet opened. **H**, fruit (orig.).

hairs, simple, stellate, and glandular; rarely the hairs are hooked and unicellular (*Garuga*).

Bursera, the type genus (type species *B. simarouba* (Linn.) Sargent) (Fig. 337), is represented by about 100 species confined to tropical America except two species in S. United States; resiniferous trees; leaves imparipinnate or 1-foliolate, leaflets entire or toothed; flowers bisexual or unisexual, in panicles or racemes; sepals and petals 5 or 4 each, free, the latter imbricate; stamens 10–8, inserted outside the base of the annular entire disk; ovary 3-locular, ovules paired, axile; stigma 3-lobed; fruit globose or oblong, pyrenes bony, often solitary, 1-seeded, mesocarp sometimes fleshy and aril-like; seeds with much folded cotyledons.

The most divergent genera are *Tetragrastris* and *Trattinnickia*, in which the petals are united into a tube, and valvate. Of those with free petals, *Aucoumea*,

[1] Including *Balsameaceae* Dumort. (1829).

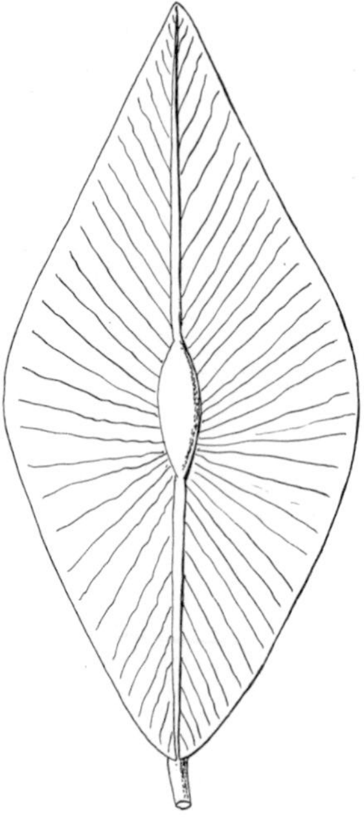

FIG. 338. The genus *Triomma*, Malaya, stands apar from other genera of *Burseraceae* by its thickly an broadly winged fruits (as shown in *T. malaccens* Hook. f., above).

Boswellia and *Bursera* have them imbricate, those of the remainder of th genera being valvate. Of these *Triomma* (Fig. 338) stands apart with it thickly and broadly winged fruits, whilst another divergent character, deeply concave receptacle, causing the calyx, petals and stamens to b perigynous, is a feature of *Garuga*, *Scutinanthe* and *Commiphora*.

Other outstanding characters may be noted: Lower pair of leaflets i some spp. of *Canarium*, *Garuga* and *Dacryodes*[1] resemble stipules; flower sometimes 6-merous in *Protium*; stamens 5, opposite the calyx-lobes i *Crepidospermum*, *Filicium* and *Nothospartium*; 5 and inserted above the disl in *Filicium*; anther-loculi separate in *Dacryodes*; ovule solitary in the locul in *Filicium* and *Hemprichia*; drupes gibbous in *Santiria*, decurved with th style sometimes towards the pedicel; cotyledons straight in *Hedwigia* multifid in *Boswellia*.

[1] See valuable paper on stipules by F. Weberling and P. W. Leenhouts, AKAD. WISSEN-SCHAF. UND DER LITERATUR 1965, n. 10

ORDER 48. MELIALES

(*Fam. Fl. Pl.* **1**, 356)

Family: **Meliaceae.**

This is undoubtedly a climax Order consisting of a single family perhaps evolved on parallel lines with RUTALES, but lacking the glands in the leaves and with a very distinctive androecium, the filaments being mostly united into a tube; its origin may be traced as follows: MAGNOLIALES → DILLENIALES → BIXALES → THEALES → CELASTRALES → **MELIALES**.

The hallmark for most of the family **Meliaceae**[1] is the stamens united into a tube, which often greatly resembles a sympetalous corolla, and probably functions biologically in a similar way. In the genus *Turraea* (Fig. 339), especially, the staminal tube is very long and slender.

In the most primitive group of genera, however, the tribe *Cedreleae*, the stamens are quite free or nearly so, and associated with this is a capsular fruit. In tribe *Swietenieae*, which contains the important mahogany timbers, *Swietenia* and *Khaya*, the stamens are united into a tube, and the ovules are numerous in the loculi, whilst in the remainder, *Trichilieae* and *Melieae*, the ovules are reduced to 2 or 1. The petals are usually free and contorted or imbricate, or sometimes more or less adnate to the staminal tube as in many *Malvaceae*, and then they are usually valvate in bud.

A few genera, also primitive from their leaf-form, have simple (not unifoliolate) leaves; these are *Turraea*, *Nymania*, *Vavaea* and *Nurmonia*.

Like those of *Rutaceae*, the leaves are without stipules, but they are very rarely glandular-punctate as in that family. Usually they are pinnate. It is felt with regard to *Meliaceae* that, as with *Rutaceae*, one is dealing with a climax group entirely confined to the tropics and subtropics. The latest monograph is that by that great German taxonomist, Harms, in Engler's DIE NATÜRLICHEN PFLANZENFAMILIEN (2nd Ed., 19b (1940)).

The type genus *Melia* embraces about a dozen species of trees throughout the tropics and subtropics and is often cultivated for ornament and shade; leaves simply pinnate or 2–3-times so, often tomentose with stellate hairs when young; leaflets toothed; panicles axillary; flowers white or purple; calyx 6–5-partite, imbricate; petals 6–5, free, imbricate; staminal tube subcylindric, mouth 10–12-fid, lobes 2–3-fid; anthers 12–10, included; disk annular; ovary 6–3-locular, style deciduous; ovules 2 in each loculus, superposed; fruit a drupe; seeds with or without endosperm. Type species *M. azedarach* Linn., tropics and subtropics (Fig. 340).

---

[1] Including *Cedrelaceae* R.Br. (1814). *Flindersiaceae* C. T. White ex Record (1931).

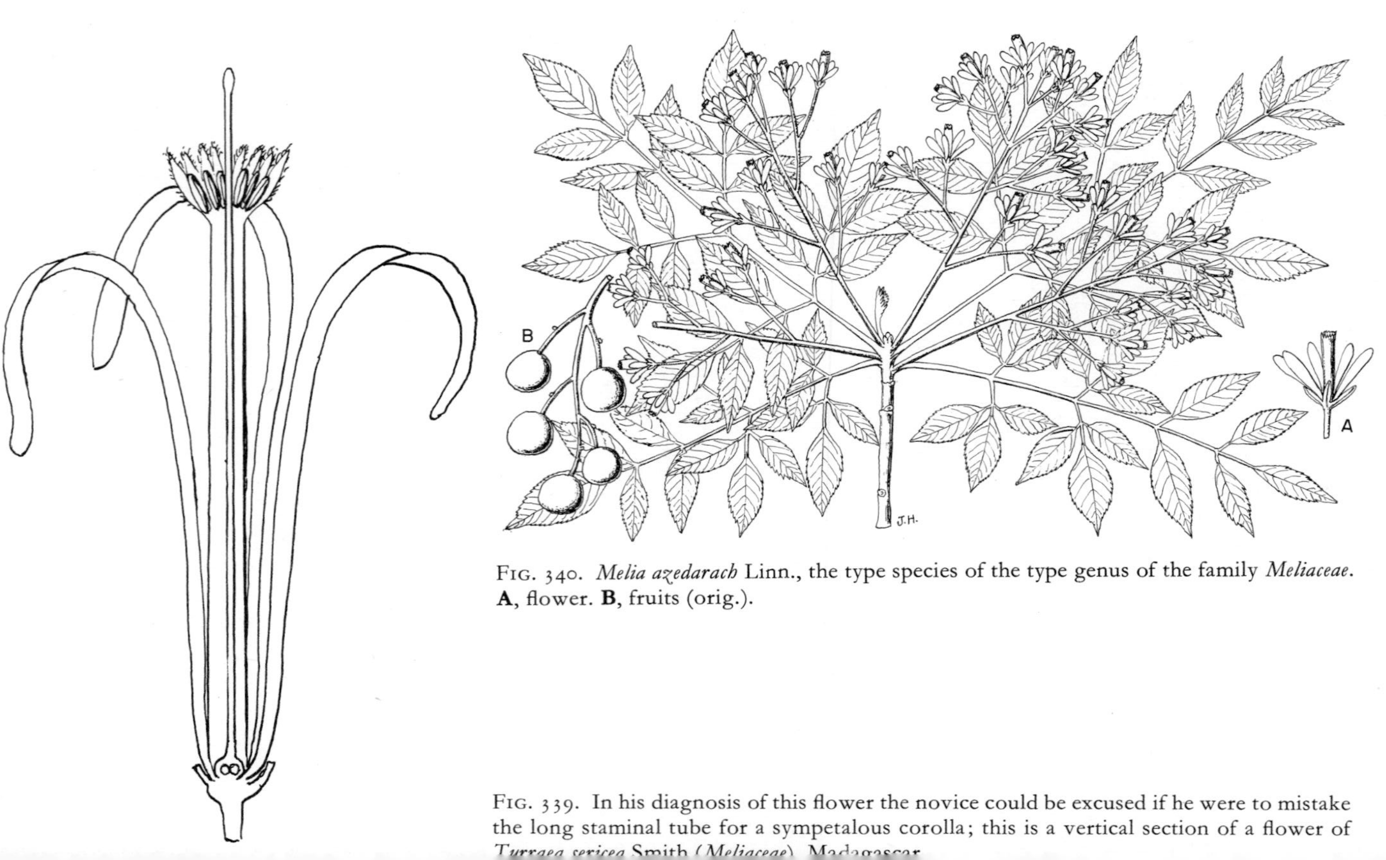

FIG. 340. *Melia azedarach* Linn., the type species of the type genus of the family *Meliaceae*. **A**, flower. **B**, fruits (orig.).

FIG. 339. In his diagnosis of this flower the novice could be excused if he were to mistake the long staminal tube for a sympetalous corolla; this is a vertical section of a flower of *Turraea sericea* Smith (*Meliaceae*), Madagascar.

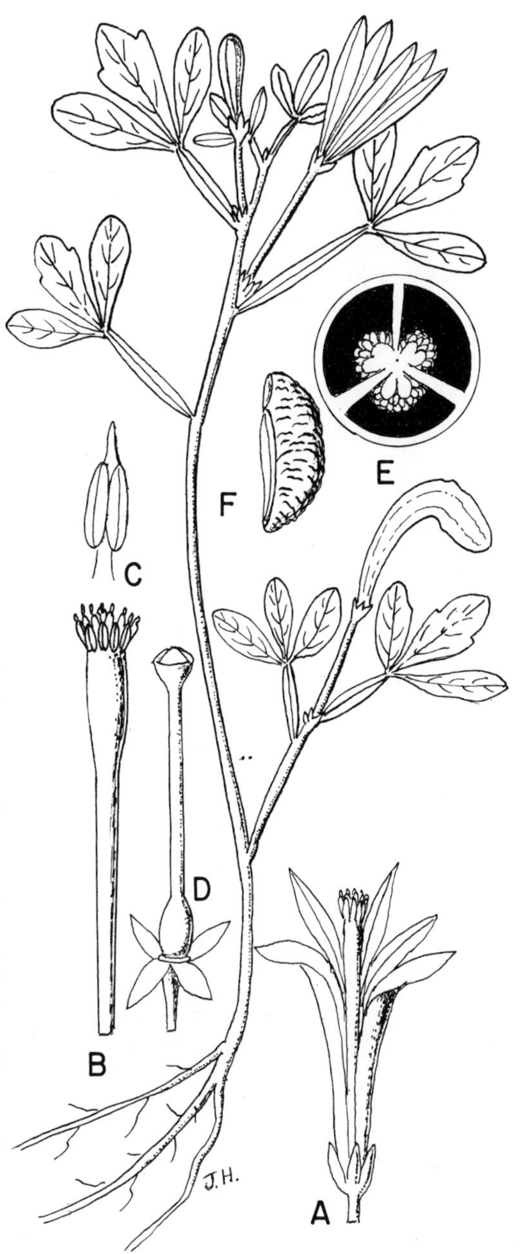

FIG. 341. *Naregamia alata* Wight & Arnot, south India, a remarkable reduction to almost a herb in an otherwise woody family, *Meliaceae*. **A**, flower. **B**, staminal tube. **C**, anther. **D**, gynoecium and calyx. **E**, cross-section of ovary. **F**, seed (orig.).

A few outstanding characters may be noted: Stem subherbaceous in *Munronia* and *Naregamia* (Fig. 341); leaves punctate in spp. of *Aglaia*; leaflets serrate in some spp. of *Cedrela*, *Ekebergia*, *Munronia* and *Melia*; some-

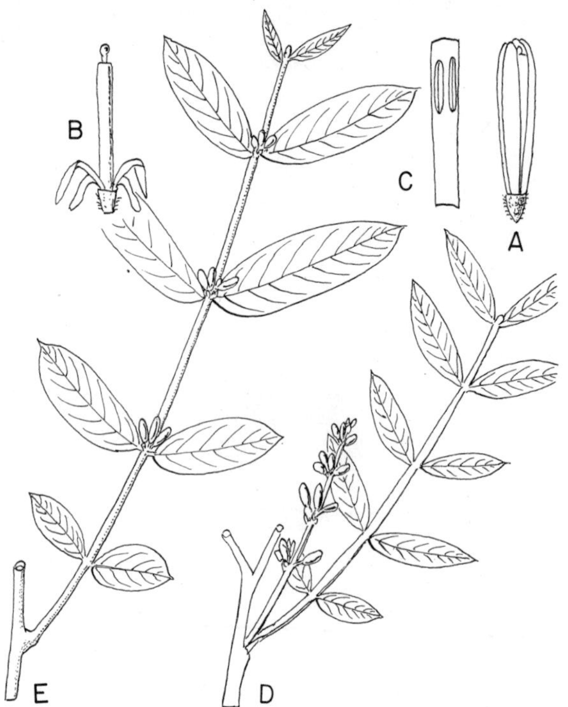

FIG. 342. *Chisocheton pohlianus* Harms (*Meliaceae*), New Guinea, a remarkable and unique example of epiphyllous flowers. In **D** the inflorescence is in the axil of the pinnate leaf; in **E** the flowers are borne on the rhachis between the leaflets of the pinnate leaf, due to the adnation of the peduncle with the rhachis. **A**, flower. **B**, note the rod-like staminal tube. **C**, part of the latter from the inside, showing position of the anthers (adapted from Harms).

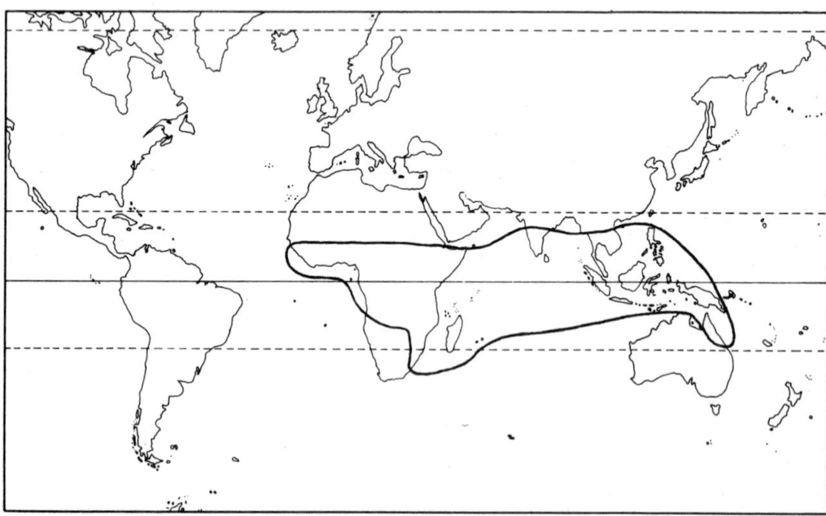

MAP 25. Range of the natural genus *Turraea* (*Meliaceae*); over 100 species have been described.

Fig. 343. Two species of the natural genus *Turraea* (*Meliaceae*) from widely separated regions: **A**, *T. floribunda* Hochst., flowers sweetly scented, tropical Africa; **B**, part of androecium. **C**, anther. **D**, disk. **E**, cross-section of ovary. **F**, young fruit. **G**, open fruit. **H**, seed. **J**, *T. villosa* Benn., India; **K**, staminal tube opened out. **L**, cross-section of ovary. **M**, fruit.

times pinnately divided and fern-like in *Quivisia*; stellate-tomentose when young in *Melia* spp. and *Aglaia*; flowers polygamous-dioecious in *Chisocheton* (Fig. 342) and *Aglaia*; petals connate in *Calodryum*, *Aglaia*, *Odontorrhena*, *Turraeanthus*, and spp. of *Moschoxylon*; merged into the staminal tube in *Munronia* and spp. of *Guarea*; stamens numerous in spp. of *Vavaea*; filaments free in *Cedrela* and *Cedrelopsis*, and spp. of *Walsura*; anthers transversely locellate in *Chisocheton* and *Clemensia*; connective long-produced above the loculi in *Elutheria*; disk absent from *Turraea*; ovary imperfectly 4-locular in *Elutheria*, loculi numerous in spp. of *Turraea*.

ORDER 49. SAPINDALES

(*Fam. Fl. Pl.* **1**, 358)

Families: **Melianthaceae, Sapindaceae, Podoaceae, Sabiaceae, Anacardiaceae, Aceraceae, Hippocastanaceae, Staphyleaceae, Akaniaceae, Julianaceae, Didiereaceae.**

This is another group of mostly trees and shrubs probably evolved on more or less parallel lines with MELIALES and RUTALES; it may be regarded as a climax of the pinnately leaved families with free petals, with some zygomorphy, or flowers often very reduced and polygamo-dioecious.

Phylogeny: MAGNOLIALES → DILLENIALES → BIXALES → THEALES → CELASTRALES → **SAPINDALES.**

In the first edition (1926) of my FAMILIES OF FLOWERING PLANTS (**1**, 202, Fig. 140) I excluded from the family **Melianthaceae** the genus *Greyia*, and placed it as a separate family next to *Escalloniaceae*, with which it is closely related, and certainly not with *Geraniaceae* or *Dirachmaceae* as suggested by Airy Shaw (Willis, DICT. 499). However, the latest Englerian SYLLABUS has ignored this and continues to include *Greyia* in *Melianthaceae*, which it resembles, if at all, only very superficially. They give the following "Key" for the family:

§ **Greyieae** (Greyiaceae). Blüten schwach ·|· Diskus ringförmig. Stam. 10. Ovar. 1-fächerig mit 5 parietalen Placenten. Blätter ohne Stipeln.—*Greyia* (3) Kapland; *G. sutherlandii*, prächtig blütender Strauch.

§ **Meliantheae.** Blüten deutlich ·|· Diskus einseitig. Stam. 5, selten 4. Ovar. 4 fächerig, fachspaltig. Blätter mit Stipeln.—*Bersama* (30) trop. und südl. Afrika, alle Sep. gleichgestaltet.—*Melianthus* (5) S. Afrika, 1 Sep. spornartig augesbildet; *M. maior*, beliebter Zierstrauch von Honigvögeln besucht.

This is only one of many more naïve treatments of several small families in the SYLLABUS, a few of which are noted in the present work.

Sapindus, the type genus of **Sapindaceae**[1] (type species *S. saponaria* Linn.) (Fig. 344), consists of 11 species in the tropics and subtropics; trees and shrubs, sometimes somewhat climbing; leaves alternate, simple, 1-foliolate or paripinnate; no stipules; flowers polygamous, in racemes or panicles; sepals 5–4, broadly imbricate; petals 5–4, nude or with 1–2 scales above the claw; disk annular or elevated; stamens 10–8 (7–4 or more); filaments free;

---

[1] Including *Saponaceae* Ventenat (1799). *Dodonaeaceae* Link (1831). *Aitoniaceae* Harvey (1859). *Koelreuteriaceae* J. G. Agardh (1858).

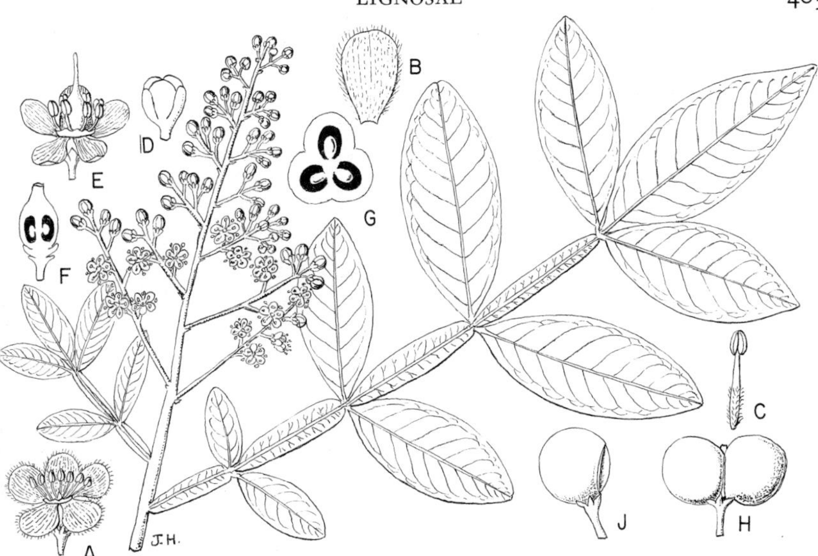

FIG. 344. *Sapindus saponaria* Linn., the type species of the type genus of *Sapindaceae*. **A**, male flower. **B**, petal. **C**, stamen. **D**, flower bud. **E**, bisexual flower. **F**, vertical section of ovary. **G**, cross-section of ovary. **H**, bilobed, **J**, one-lobed fruit (partly after Sargent).

anthers versatile; ovary 4–2-locular; style terminal, stigma 4–2-lobed; ovule 1 in each loculus, ascending; fruit dry or fleshy, indehiscent; seeds not arillate.

Outstanding genera are *Valenzuelia*, with opposite leaves, *Macphersonia* with bipinnate leaves; biternate or bipinnate in *Cardiospermum*, *Serjania* and *Paullinia*; stipules present in *Urvillea*, *Serjania* and *Paullinia*; sepals valvate in *Koelreuteria*; disk produced into 5 elongated horns in *Xanthoceras* (Fig. 345); stamens 12 or more in *Deinbollia*; fruiting carpels samara-like in *Urvillea*, *Serjania*, *Toulicia*; capsule 3-winged in *Bridgesia*; lobes of the fruit inflated in *Cardiospermum*, *Valenzuelia*, *Erythrophysa*, *Aitonia* and *Koelreuteria*.

Blighia sapida (see Fig. 346) was named by König and Sims[1] in honour of Captain Bligh, of Bounty fame. The species is a native of west tropical

---

[1] Charles Dietrich Eberhard König (1774–1851), mineralogist, was born in Brunswick. He was educated at Göttingen, and came to England at the end of 1800 to arrange the collections of Queen Charlotte. On completion of this he became assistant to Dryander, librarian to Sir Joseph Banks. In 1807 he succeeded Dr. Shaw as Assistant Keeper of the department of Natural History in the British Museum, and on Shaw's death in 1813 he took his place. He collaborated with Dr. Sims in editing the ANNALS OF BOTANY, of which only two volumes were published (1805–7). The genus *Koniga* (*Lobularia*) (*Brassicaceae*) was named after him by Robert Brown.

John Sims (1749–1831), botanist and physician was born at Canterbury in 1749, and educated partly at Burford in Oxfordshire, and partly under his father, who was a good

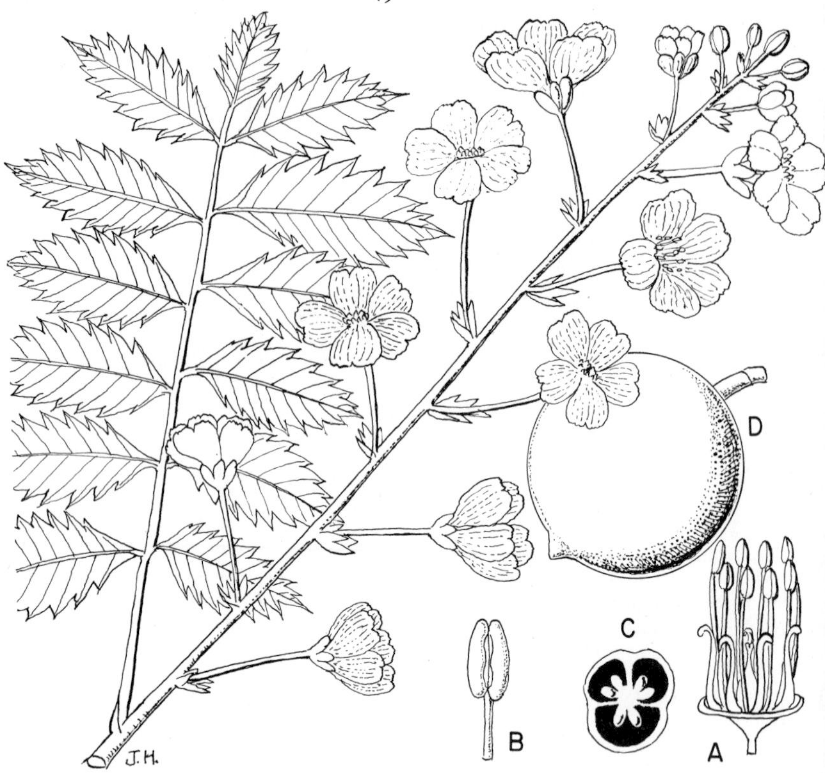

FIG. 345. *Xanthoceras sorbifolia* Bunge (*Sapindaceae*), N.E. Asia. **A**, flower with sepals and petals removed; note the horn-like disk-glands. **B**, stamen. **C**, cross-section of ovary. **D**, fruit (an open fruit is also shown in Fig. 348) (orig.).

Africa, whence seeds were brought by a slave ship to Jamaica in 1778. It was mentioned by Broughton in HORTUS EASTENSIS, a catalogue of plants in the garden of Hindon East, in the mountains of Liguanea, Jamaica, in 1794, and described by the authors from a specimen in Sir Joseph Banks' herbarium (now at the Natural History Museum).

In naming this plant after Bligh, König and Sims noted:

Secutus exemplum botanicorum qui Cookios et Bouginvillaeos non indignos censuere a quibus plantae denominarentur, novum hoc genus sacrum volo

classical scholar. In 1770 he proceeded to the University of Edinburgh, and after a spell at Leiden, graduated M.D. at Edinburgh in 1774. In 1776 he settled in London, and besides his medical duties he edited CURTIS'S BOTANICAL MAGAZINE from 1801 to 1826, and from 1805 to 1806, with König, the ANNALS OF BOTANY. Sims was a Fellow of the Royal Society, and one of the original Fellows of the Linnean Society. His name was commemorated by Robert Brown in the Mexican genus *Simsia* of the family *Asteraceae*. His herbarium was purchased by George Bentham and is at Kew.

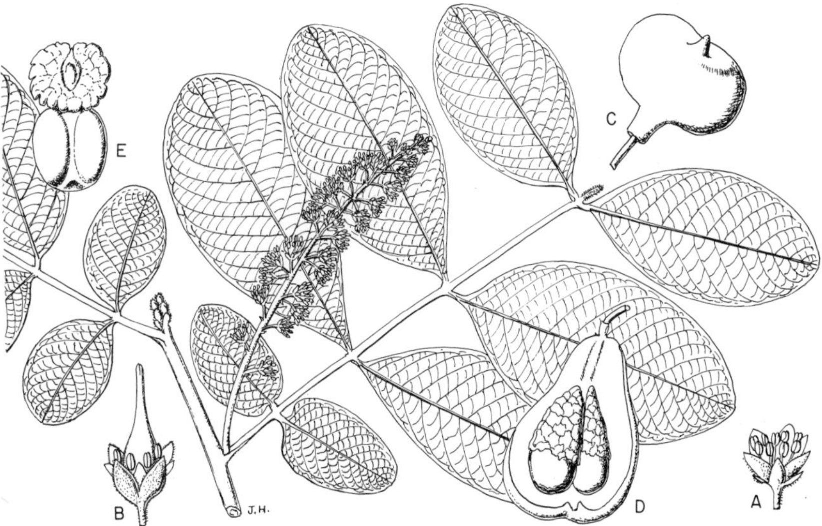

FIG. 346. *Blighia sapida* König & Sims (*Sapindaceae*), named in honour of Captain Bligh, of Bounty fame; fruit red, size of a small pear; seed black, the aril cream-yellow and edible, rather like a walnut; this aril a delicate article of cookery. **A**, male flower. **B**, female flower. **C**, young fruit. **D**, vertical section of fruit. **E**, seed and aril (orig.).

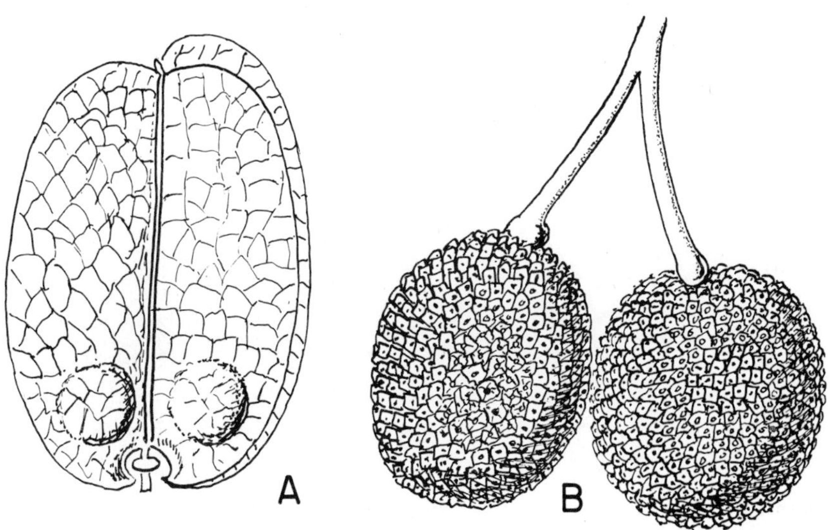

FIG. 347. **A**, Fruit of *Toulicia reticulata* Radlk. (*Sapindaceae*), Peru. **B**, Fruits of the Litchi, *Litchi chinensis* Sonn. (*Sapindaceae*); grows wild in Indo-China and has been an important fruit in S.E. Asia for over 2000 years; widely grown in the tropics and in California and Florida; they are canned for export.

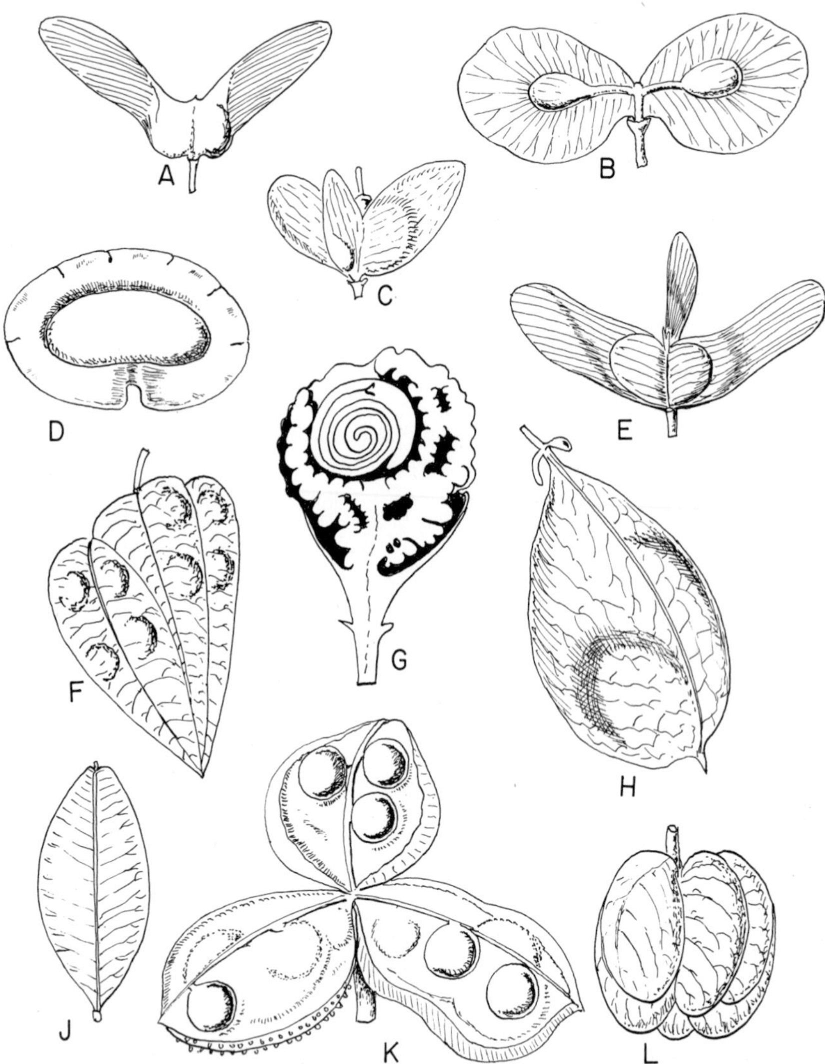

FIG. 348. Various fruits of the family *Sapindaceae*: **A**, *Atalaya hemiglauca* F. Muell., Australia. **B**, *Dipteronia sinensis* Oliv., China. **C**, *Bridgesia incisifolia* Bert. ex Cambess., Chile. **D**, seed of *Magonia pubescens* A. St. Hil., Brazil. **E**, *Thouinia decandra* H. & B., Mexico. **F**, *Koelreuteria paniculata* Laxm., China. **G**, vertical section of fruit of *Alectryon excelsum* Gaertn., New Zealand. **H**, *Cardiospermum grandiflorum* Sw., West Indies. **J**, *Urvillea ulmacea* H.B. & K., South America. **K**, *Xanthoceras sorbifolia* Bunge, N.E. Asia. **L**, *Aitonia capensis* Thunb., South Africa (orig.).

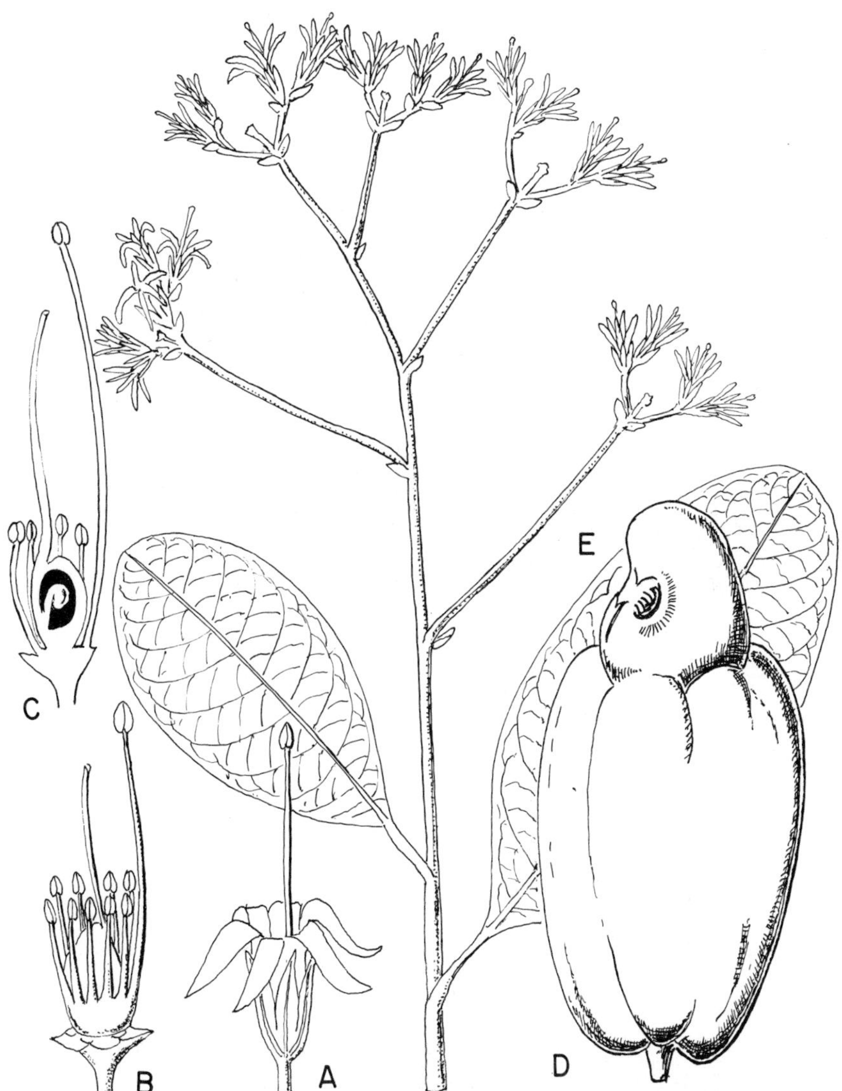

FIG. 349. Cashew Nut of Brazil, *Anacardium occidentale* Linn. (*Anacardiaceae*). **A**, male flower (the stamens hidden); **B**, bisexual flower with sepals and petals removed. **C**, vertical section of bisexual flower. **D**, swollen receptacle known as the Cashew Apple and which is juicy; the nut, **E**, is at the top, and its rich kernel is delicately flavoured, eaten in many countries and also used for preserves.

Guilielmo Bligh, navarcho, jam vero Novae Hollandiae gubernatori, viro, cura plantarum et officiis olim in Floram collatis, nulli navigatorum secundo.[1]

---

[1] (Translation): Following the example of the botanists who did not deem the Cooks and the Bouginvilles unworthy of having plants named after them, I wish to dedicate this new genus to William Bligh, the sea captain, now governor of New Holland; a man second to no sailor in the care of interesting plants and flower-service to botany.—König and Sims.

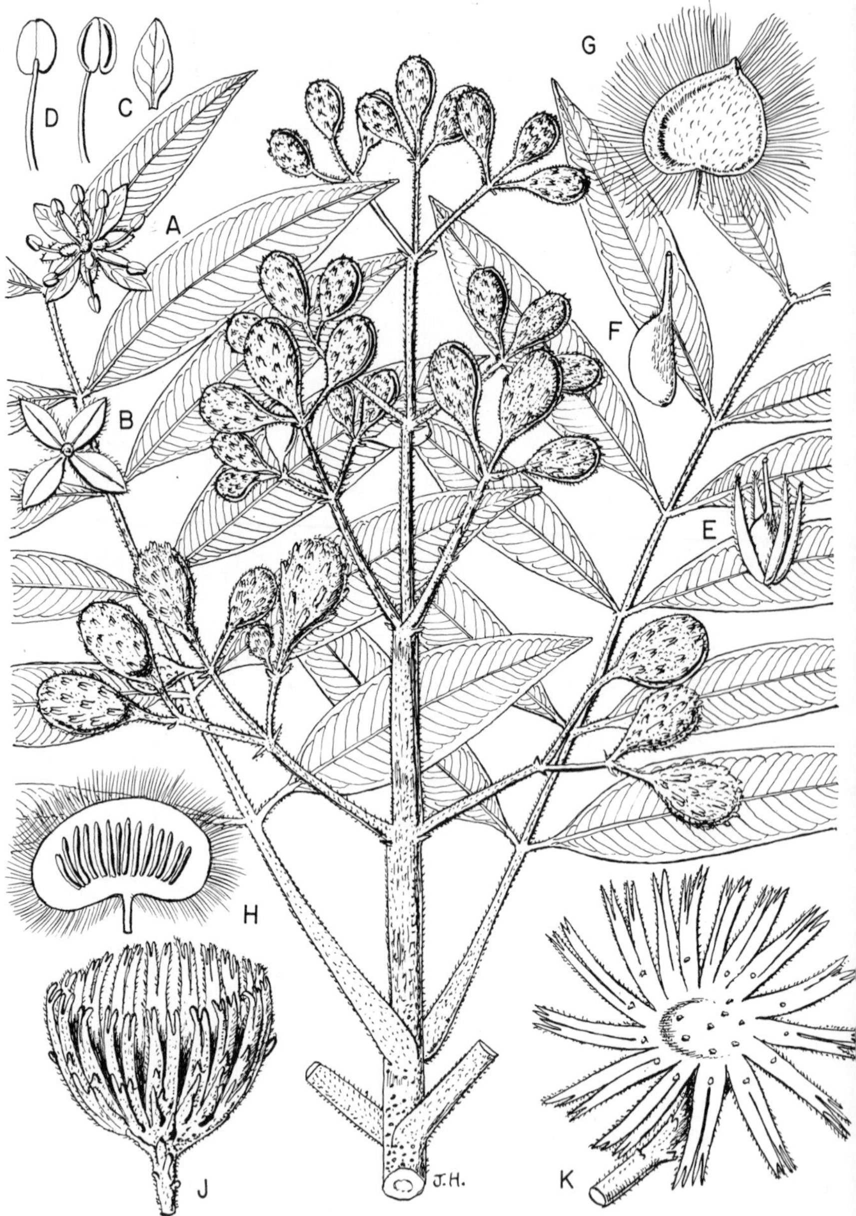

FIG. 350. Not a "fig" in the *Anacardiaceae* but almost equivalent to one; the very small female flowers of *Blepharocarya involucrigera* F. Muell. are enclosed by the inner bracts upon the inside of which they are inserted; a very remarkable Australian member of the family. **A**, male flower. **B**, calyx. **C**, petal. **D**, stamens. **E**, female flower. **F**, gynoecium. **G**, fruit. **H**, vertical section of fruit. **J**, involucre. **K**, involucre opened out showing scars of flowers.

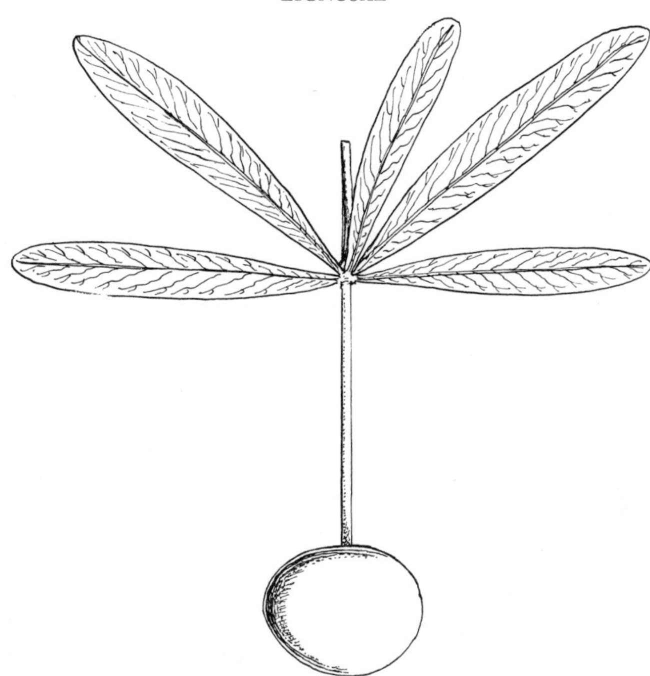

FIG. 351. Drawing of *Melanorrhoea glabra* Wall. (*Anacardiaceae*), Burma; a very rare instance of the petals of a flower persisting and enlarging in fruit and assisting in its distribution, after the manner of the sepals of a Dipterocarp.

There are four genera belonging to the family **Sabiaceae,**[1] in the tropics and subtropics, except Africa. The floral structure is peculiar. The stamens, and even sometimes the petals, are inserted opposite the sepals, an almost unique arrangement. The anthers are didymous, the loculi separated by a thick connective and dehiscing by a transverse slit or deciduous cap (calyptra). The seeds are without endosperm and the cotyledons much folded. In the largest genus, *Meliosma*, about 150 species, both in Asia and America, the petals are very unequal.

Anacardiaceae[2] are little known to people living in temperate regions, except for the glorious autumn colour of the leaves of some species of the genus *Rhus*, such as *R. typhina* Linn., and for the Poison Ivy, *R. toxicodendron*, and *R. vernix*, the leaves of which seriously affect some who touch them.

[1] Including *Millingtoniaceae* Wight & Arn. (1834). *Wellingtoniaceae* Meisn. (1836–43). *Meliosmaceae* Endlich. (1841).

[2] Including *Terebinthaceae* A. L. de Juss. (1789). *Cassuviaceae* R.Br. (1818). *Spondiaceae* Kunth (1824). *Spirolobae* Link (1831). *Pistaciaceae* Caruel (1879). *Blepharocaryaceae* Airy Shaw (1965).

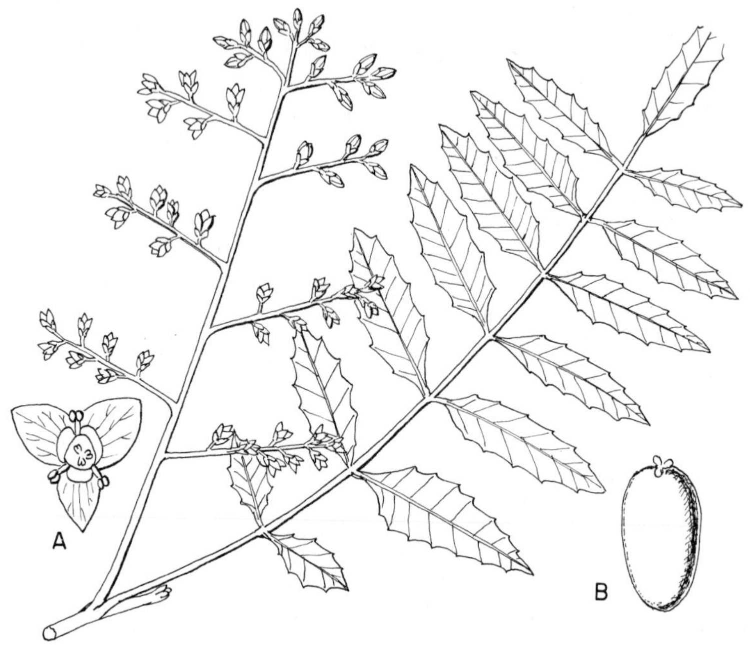

FIG. 352. *Conocladus dentatus* Jacq. (*Anacardiaceae*), a very poisonous plant in Cuba. **A**, flower. **B**, fruit (orig.).

Anacardium, the type genus, contains about 14 species of trees and shrubs, the latter sometimes very dwarf with a subterranean stem; leaves alternate, simple; flowers polygamo-dioecious, paniculate; calyx deciduous; petals 5, imbricate; torus stipe-like, enlarged in fruit; stamens 10–7, connate at the base; ovary 1-locular; style terminal; ovule lateral from near the base; drupe reniform on top of the thick fleshy greatly enlarged torus; pericarp oily; seed reniform, cotyledons convex.

Tapiria has a climbing habit; *Duvaua* is often spinescent; leaves opposite in *Bouea*; fruiting panicles with pedicels of numerous sterile flowers elongated and plumose in *Cotinus*; peduncles drupe-like in fruit in *Anacardium* (Fig. 349); inflorescence fasciated and comb-like in *Laurophyllus*; female bracts concrescent into large fig-like receptacles in *Blepharocarya* (Fig. 350); calyx spathaceous in *Gluta*; petals persistent and enlarged in fruit (resembling the calyx of some *Dipterocarpaceae*) in *Melanorrhoea* (Fig. 351), *Swintonia* and *Astronium*; petals absent from *Pistacia*; anther-connective dilated and bilobed in *Androtium*; ovary of free carpels in *Buchanania*, *Androtium* and *Pistacia* spp.; inferior in *Holigarna* and *Drymicarpus*; drupes winged in *Loxopterygium*, *Smodingium*; densely fringed with coloured hairs in *Ochoterenaea*, so all over in *Actinocheita*.

FIG. 353. *Amphipterygium adstringens* (Schlecht.) Schiede (*Julianaceae*), in fruit, Mexico. **A**, male flower. **B**, female flowers. **C**, vertical section of ovary.

The family **Aceraceae**,[1] formerly in *Sapindaceae*, has opposite leaves, the ovary 2-locular and compressed contrary to the septum, the fruit separating into 2 divergent winged indehiscent samaras. The family is confined to the Northern Hemisphere, *Acer* with over 120 species being the most widely distributed. *Dipteronia*, a single species, occurs in central China. In this the leaves are pinnate. The well-known Sycamore is *Acer pseudoplatanus* Linn., the wood of which is hard and durable. Maple is *Acer campestre* Linn., and the Sugar Maple, *Acer saccharum* Marsh, North America. Trees of this family are famous for their autumn colours, especially in eastern North America.

Hippocastanaceae[2] is a small family including only two genera, *Billia* in

[1] Including *Volataceae* Dulac (1867).

[2] Including *Castanaceae* Link. (1821). *Paviaceae* Horaninow (1834). *Aesculaceae* Burnett (1835). *Bretschneideraceae* Radlk. (1907).

Central and South America, and *Aesculus* in the temperate zone of the Northern Hemisphere. The well-known Horsechestnut, *Aesculus hippocastanum* Linn, is the most typical of the family, until recently mostly included in *Sapindaceae*. The leaves are opposite and digitately 5–9-foliolate, and the flowers are somewhat zygomorphic and in terminal panicles or racemes. Much detailed work on the American species of the family was published by J. W. Hardin (BRITTONIA **9**, 145–195 (1957)). He called attention to the fact that the genus *Ungnadia* is more or less intermediate between *Hippocastanaceae* and many genera of *Sapindaceae*, and it remains a question whether the two genera should not be restored to the family *Sapindaceae*, as formerly, a question for a future monographer.

In **Julianaceae**, which is generally regarded as related to *Anacardiaceae*, we need only note that *Juliania* (the type of the family!) is an illegitimate name and must be discarded in favour of *Amphipterygium* Standley.

Staphylea, the type genus of the small family **Staphyleaceae**,[1] embraces 10–11 species in the temperate Northern Hemisphere; shrubs; leaves opposite, 3–5-foliolate or pinnate, leaflets stipellate; stipules linear; flowers bisexual, white, pendulous, in panicles or racemes; pedicels jointed; sepals 5, equal, deciduous; petals 5, erect; disk lining the base of the calyx, lobed; stamens 5; ovary 2–3-partite to the base, lobes 1–locular; ovules numerous, 2-seriate; capsule membranous, inflated, 2–3-lobed, 2–3-locular, dehiscent inside the apex; seeds subglobose.

Tapiscia, *Huertea* and *Triscaphis* have alternate leaves, but the carpels are completely united and the fruit is a berry or drupe. In *Euscaphis* the carpels are free from the base.

ORDER 50. **LOGANIALES**

(*Fam. Fl. Pl.* **1**, 370)

Families: **Potaliaceae, Loganiaceae, Buddleiaceae, Antoniaceae, Spigeliaceae, Strychnaceae, Oleaceae.**

Even the author of this system hesitates to speculate on the origin of this Order, which, except for the more ancient ERICALES (with hypogynous stamens), seems to be the most primitive group of the woody sympetalous families in which the stamens are carried up onto the corolla-tube (epipetalous) and alternate with its lobes, and with a superior ovary; however,

---

[1] Including *Ochranthaceae* Endlicher (1841).

FIG. 354. *Potalia amara* Aubl., Brazil, the type species of the type genus of *Potaliaceae*. **A**, flower-bud. **B**, vertical section of the flower. **C**, cross-section of ovary. **D**, fruit. **E**, seed (orig.).

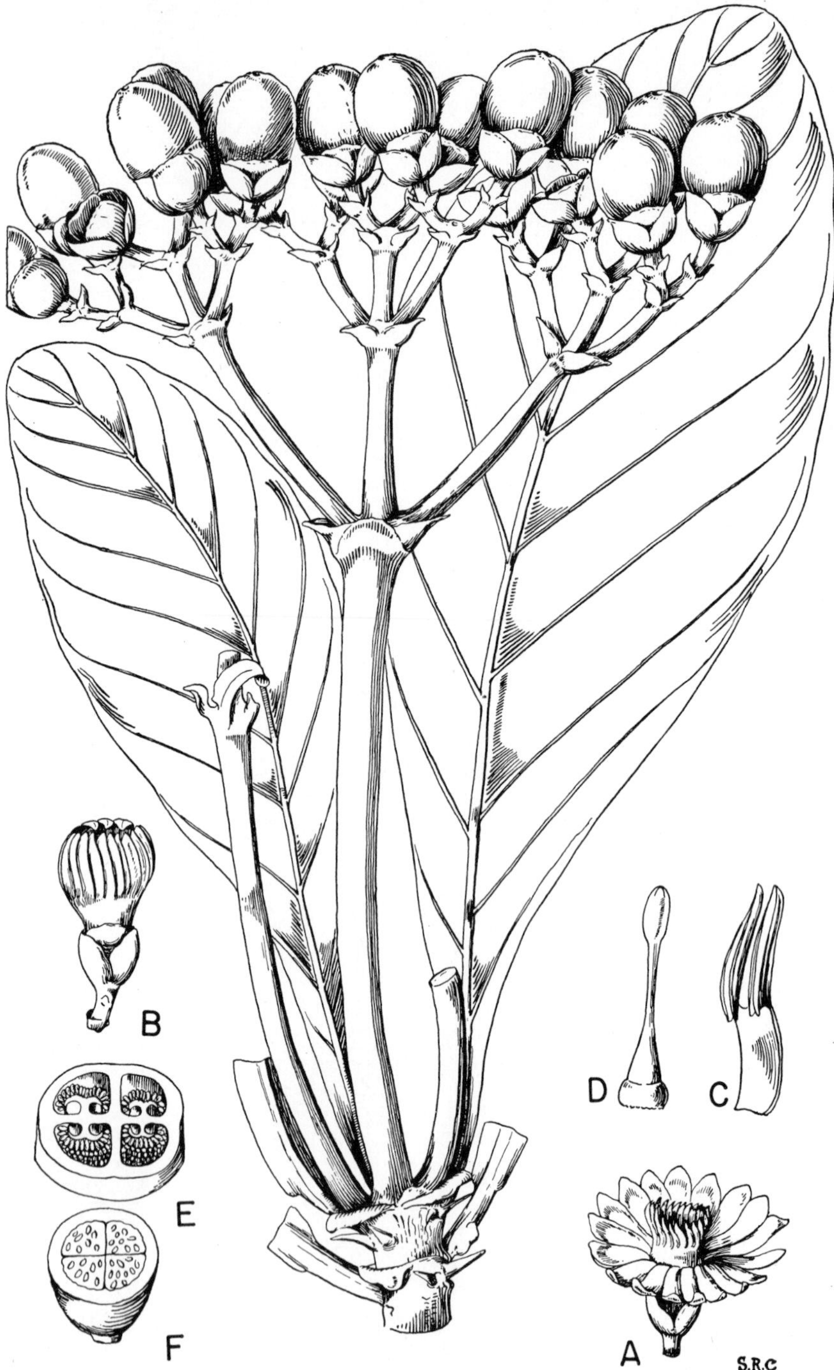

Fig. 355. A fine drawing by Miss Ross Craig of *Anthocleista vogelii* Planch. in fruit (*Potaliaceae*), widespread in tropical Africa. **A**, flower. **B**, androecium. **C**, stamens. **D**, gynoecium. **E**, cross-section of ovary. **F**, cross-section of fruit. (From Hutchinson and Dalziel, FLORA OF WEST TROPICAL AFRICA.)

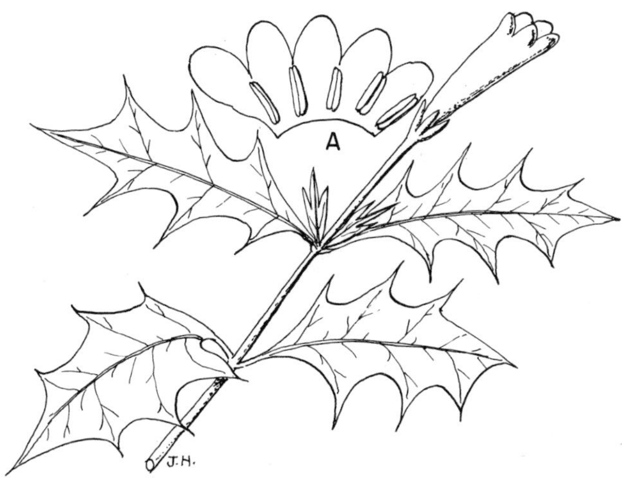

FIG. 356. An outstanding genus of the family *Potaliaceae*, *Desfontainia spinosa* Ruiz & Pavon, Peru. **A**, corolla-limb spread out.

whatever their origin, they seem to be the basic group for the vast family *Rubiaceae*, in which the ovary has become completely inferior. The most advanced family is *Oleaceae*, sometimes with the stamens reduced to 2, and even some apetaly (as in *Fraxinus*).

In my FAMILIES OF FLOWERING PLANTS, 2nd Edition, I divided the *Loganiaceae* of the Bentham and Hooker f. system into six families, *Potaliaceae*, *Loganiaceae* (*sensu stricto*), *Antoniaceae*, *Spigeliaceae*, *Strychnaceae* and *Buddleiaceae*.

The last mentioned is separated from the others mainly by anatomical characters, the absence of intraxylary phloem, and the indumentum when present is glandular, stellate or lepidote, the corolla-lobes being imbricate. In the remainder intraxylary phloem is present and the indumentum is never glandular.

In **Potaliaceae**[1] the corolla-lobes are contorted and vary from 16–5, indicating perhaps a relatively primitive group, though the fruit is advanced, a berry with the seeds immersed in pulp. *Potalia* (Fig. 354), the type genus of only one species, occurs in tropical South America, and has a cymose inflorescence and a corolla with 10–8 lobes coupled with a 4-merous calyx; *Fagraea* has a 7–5-merous corolla and a 4-merous calyx, and *Anthocleista* (Fig. 355) a 16–10-merous corolla and a 4-merous calyx. *Desfontainia* stands out by its spinose-dentate leaves and its solitary to few flowers, with the calyx, corolla and androecium and often the pistil 5-merous (Fig. 356).

---

[1] Including *Desfontainiaceae* Endlicher (1839).

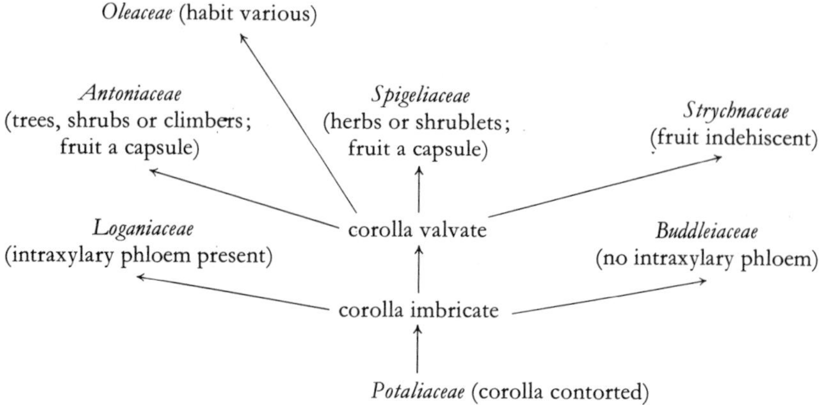

The Order LOGONIALES may be of mixed origin and difficult to trace backwards to any particular group. Further development is postulated in the diagram above.

Loganiaceae (*sensu stricto*) are thus reduced to seven genera as follows: *Geniostoma*, *Labordia*, *Logania* (Fig. 357), *Polypremum*, *Gelsemium* (Fig. 358), *Mostuea* and *Coinochlamys*. In the first four the seeds are not winged as they are in the remainder, and the most divergent and highly evolved genus is *Coinochlamys*, which has its flowers involucrate with two face-to-face large petaloid bracts. Although stipules are not very evident in the family, the leaves are sometimes connected at the base by a raised interpetiolar line or rim.

The family **Buddleiaceae** is typified by *Buddleia*, a large genus of about 260 species, several of them beautiful garden plants and when in flower especially attractive to butterflies; trees or shrubs, rarely herbs, often with a stellate or woolly indumentum; leaves connected by a transverse line or there are subherbaceous stipules; corolla-lobes 4, imbricate; stamens 4; ovary 2-locular; ovules numerous; capsule septicidally 2-valved, seeds compressed, fusiform or discoid, often winged; embryo straight in fleshy endosperm; the type species is *B. americana* Linn.

As restricted, three types of fruit occur in the family, a capsule in *Gomphostigma*, *Buddleia*, *Chilianthus*, *Emorya* and *Nuxia* (*Lachnopylis*), a drupe in *Adenoplea* and *Adenoplusia*, and a berry in *Nicodemia*.

I am myself responsible for the family name **Antoniaceae**, based on *Antonia* Pohl, a monotypic genus in Brazil and the Guianas: shrub or small tree; leaves opposite; cymes dense, terminal; calyx 5-partite, surrounded by numerous imbricate scales, the segments and scales dry with thin margins; stamens 5; capsule oblong, breaking up into 2 parts split along the inner face; seeds with a long wing at each end (for illustration see FAMILIES OF FLOWERING PLANTS, 2nd Ed. 1, 375, Fig. 228).

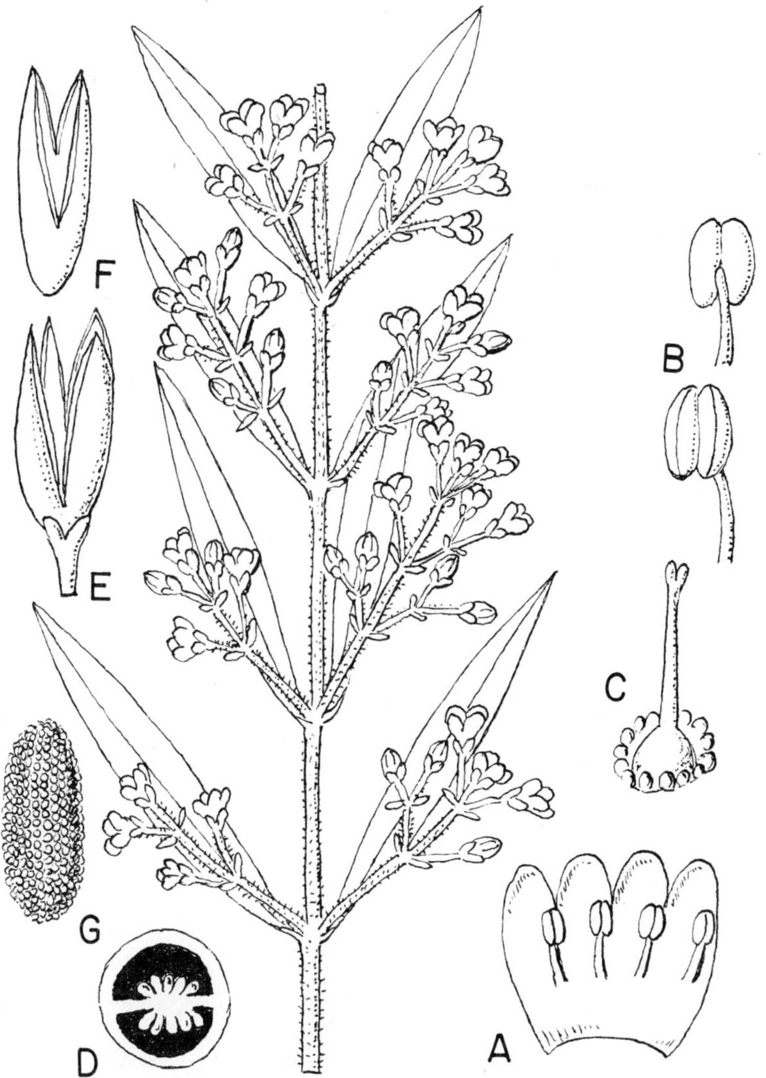

FIG. 357. *Logania albiflora* (Andrews) Druce (*L. floribunda* R.Br.), the type species of the type genus of *Loganiaceae*. **A**, corolla laid open. **B**, stamens. **C**, gynoecium and disk. **D**, cross-section of ovary. **E**, fruit. **F**, half of fruit. **G**, seed.

The genus *Usteria* in this family stands out in having a 4-lobed calyx, but more especially by the single stamen, and the outer calyx-lobe large and petaloid. In *Peltanthera* the anther-loculi become confluent and peltate when open.

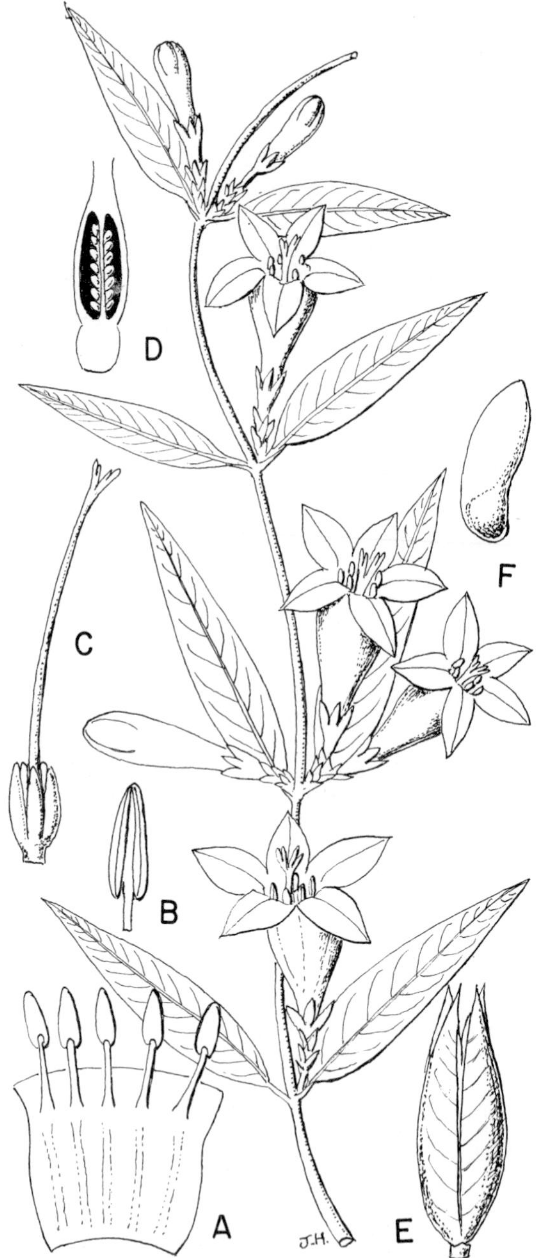

FIG. 358. *Gelsemium sempervirens* Ait. (*Loganiaceae*), North America. **A**, corolla-tube laid open. **B**, anther. **C**, calyx and style. **D**, vertical section of ovary. **E**, fruit. **F**, seed (orig.).

The family **Spigeliaceae**, founded by Martius in 1827, has an equal claim to be regarded as a separate group, based on the genus *Spigelia*, with about 80 species native of America and introduced into other warm countries.

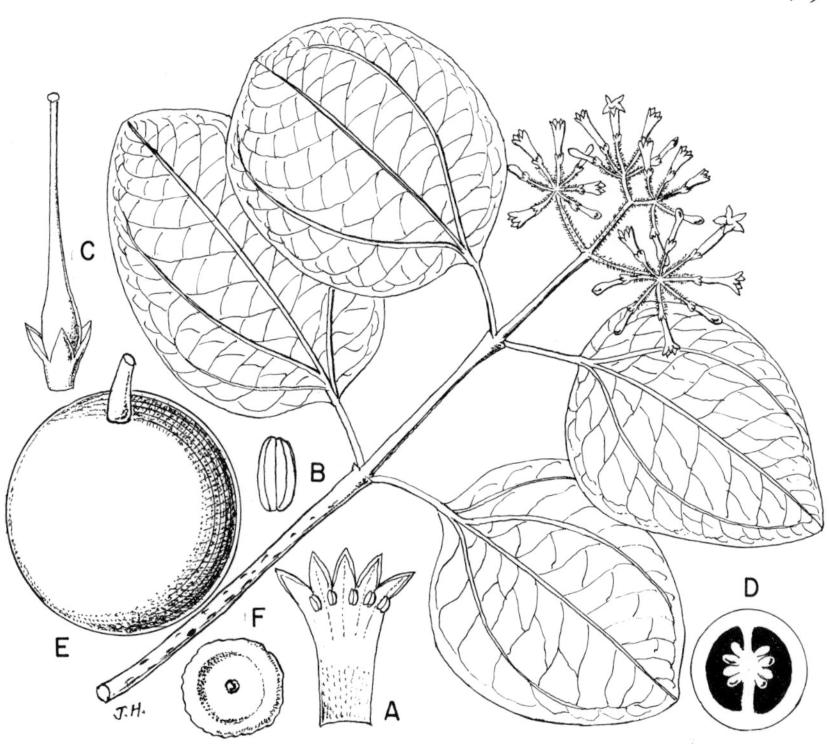

FIG. 359. *Strychnos nux-vomica* Linn. (*Strychnaceae*), India and Burma. **A**, corolla laid open. **B**, anther. **C**, calyx and gynoecium. **D**, cross-section of ovary. **E**, fruit. **F**, seed (orig.).

As in *Antoniaceae* the fruit is a capsule and the corolla-lobes are valvate, the stamens being inserted in the corolla-tube, and the seeds are not winged.

Spigelia differs from the other three genera in having a capsule circumscissile at the base, and more or less unilateral spikes; the species are perennial or annual herbs. The Indian Pink Root is *Spigelia marilandica* L., in the southern United States of America. *Mitreola* has a 5-lobed corolla, *Mitrasacme* and *Mitrasacmopsis* a 4-lobed corolla.

Finally in this alliance *Strychnos* (Fig. 359) and related genera, **Strychnaceae**, equally stand out by their indehiscent drupaceous or baccate fruit. *Strychnos* is a vast genus of about 400 species spread over the tropical regions of almost the whole world; they are readily recognised by their leaves which are 3–5-nerved from or above the base and the branchlets are often armed with axillary or supra-axillary spines or with tendrils; corolla-lobes 5 or 4, valvate; stamens 5 or 4; ovary 2-locular; stigma capitate; fruit a mostly globose berry, the seeds immersed in shiny pulp.

Couthovia and *Crateriphytum* have drupaceous fruits and large pinnately nerved leaves, whilst *Gardneria*, *Pseudogardneria* and *Scyphostrychnos* share the

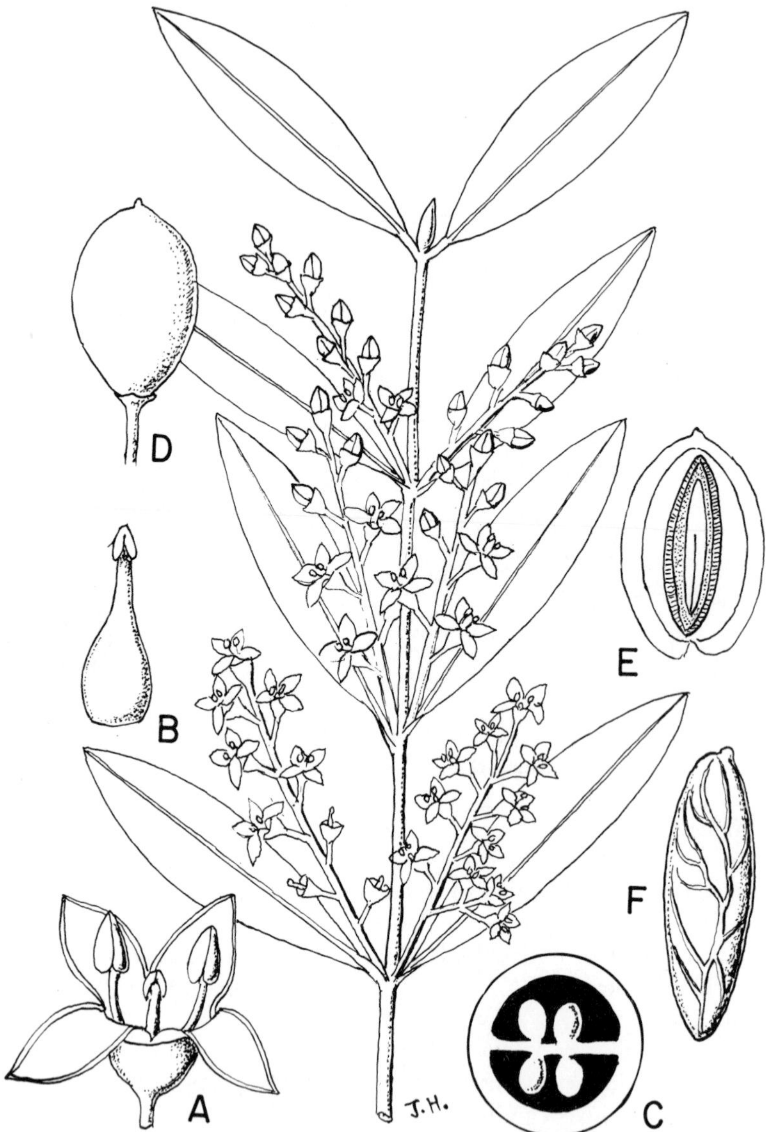

FIG. 360. The Olive, *Olea europaea* Linn., south Europe and north Africa, the type species of the type genus of the family *Oleaceae*, **A**, flower. **B**, gynoecium. **C**, cross-section of the ovary. **D**, fruit. **E**, vertical section of fruit. **F**, seed (orig.).

berry with *Strychnos* but are climbing shrubs with pinnately nerved leaves, the anthers of *Gardneria* being connivent or subconnate and 1-locular.

The Loganiaceous alliance tails out from an evolutionary point of view in

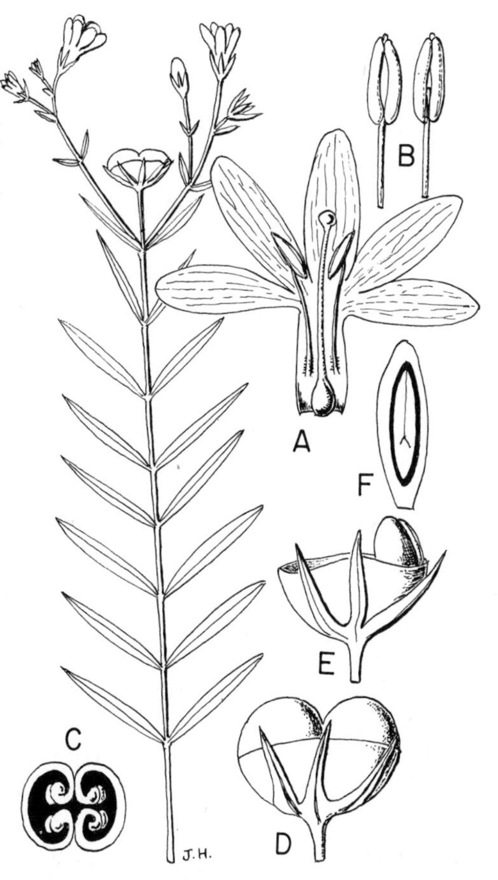

FIG. 361. The genus *Menodora* is remarkable in the family *Oleaceae* in having a capsule which opens by a transverse slit, as in some *Primulaceae*; *Menodora integrifolia* Steud. is a herb from a rhizome, native of Brazil; the genus occurs also in South Africa (see Map 26). **A**, corolla laid open. **B**, stamens. **C**, cross-section of ovary. **D**, fruit. **E**, fruit dehisced. **F**, vertical section of seed (orig.).

the better known Ash family, **Oleaceae**,[1] characterised, as every student of elementary botany learns, by usually having only 2 stamens. *Olea*, the type genus, embraces trees and shrubs with hard wood, sometimes with lepidote indumentum; the small flowers may be bisexual, polygamous or even dioecious; corolla-lobes 4, induplicate-valvate, or corolla absent; stamens 4 or 2, inserted either on the tube, or in the male flowers free, and in the latter case the anthers are introrse; ovary (as in the whole family) 2-locular; ovules 2 in each loculus; fruit a drupe with a single pendulous seed with flat cotyledons in fleshy sometimes slightly ruminate endosperm. Type species *Olea europaea* Linn. (Fig. 360).

---

[1] Including *Jasminaceae* A. L. de Juss. (1789). *Lilacaceae* Ventenat (1799). *Fraxinaceae* S. F. Gray (1821). *Jasmineae* Link (1829). *Forestieraceae* Endlicher (1837). *Bolivariaceae* Griseb. (1839). *Syringaceae* Horaninow (1847). *Turbinaceae* Dulac (1867).

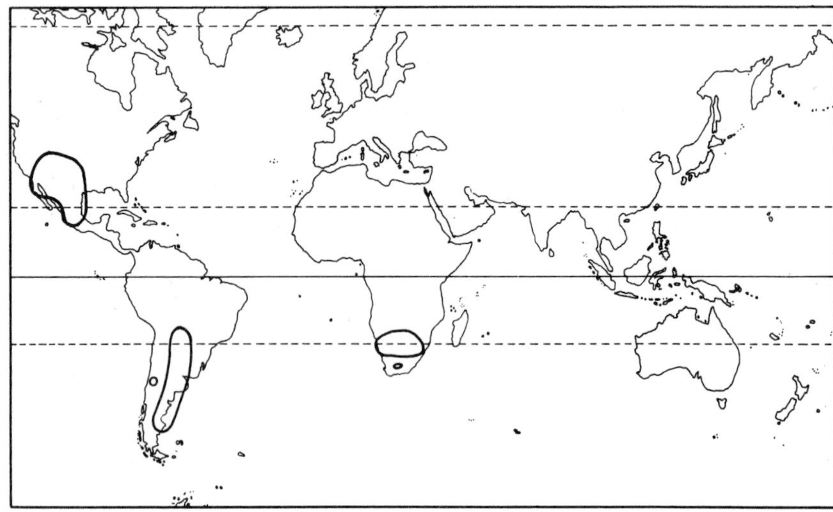

MAP 26. Discontinuous distribution of the natural genus *Menodora* (*Oleaceae*).

Outstanding characteristics of other genera are the climbing habit of most species of *Jasminum* and *Myxopyrum*; herbaceous stems from an underground rhizome in *Menodora* spp; the calyx is absent from some species of *Fraxinus* and *Forestiera*, whilst the corolla is absent from many species of *Fraxinus*, from *Forestiera*, *Olea* spp., and from the female flowers of *Olea dioica*. *Menodora* is remarkable in having a capsule which dehisces by a transverse slit (Fig. 361), whilst the fruit of *Parasyringa* is at first drupe-like but at length splits at the apex. The leaves are alternate in a few spp. of *Jasminum*. Stamens 4 in a few spp. of *Osmanthus*, *Linociera*, *Fraxinus* and *Forestiera*, Cotyledons contorted in *Schrebera* sp.

The family furnishes our gardens with some lovely shrubs and climbers, *Syringa* (Lilac), *Forsythia* and *Jasminum*, in addition to the utility hedge of Privet (*Ligustrum vulgare* Linn.). Olive fruits are those of *Olea europaea* Linn., S.E. Europe, North Africa and Asia Minor, and widely cultivated.

ORDER 51. **APOCYNALES**

(*Fam. Fl. Pl.* **1**, 379)

Families: **Plocospermataceae, Apocynaceae, Periplocaceae** and **Asclepiadaceae.**

More advanced than the LOGANIALES and consisting of climax families, especially *Asclepiadaceae*, in which the pollen has become waxy and collected

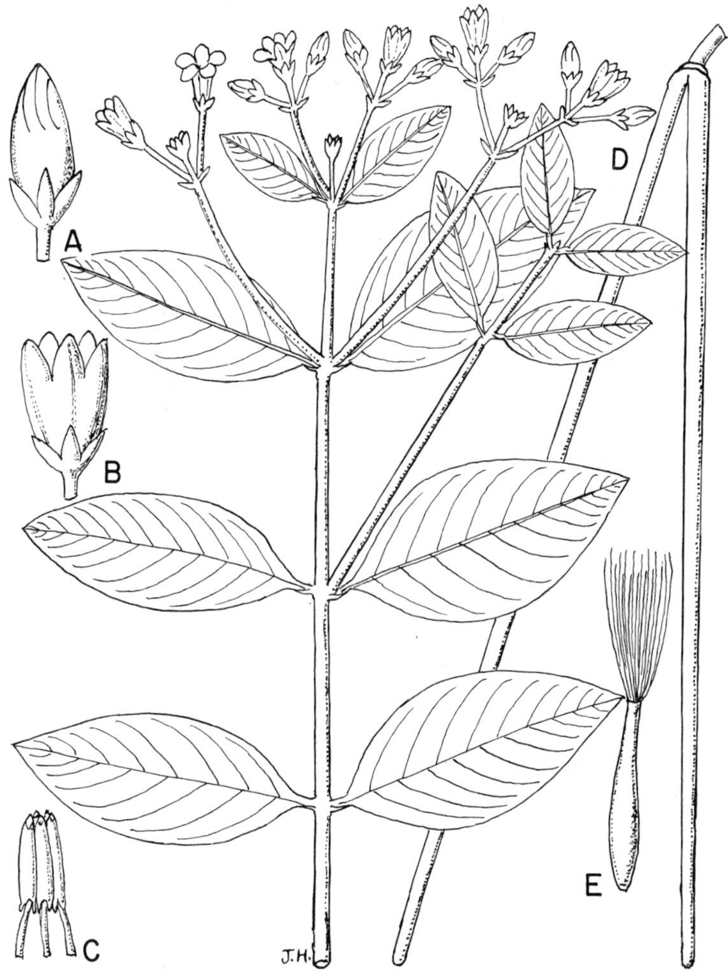

FIG. 362. *Apocynum androsaeifolium* Linn., North America, type species of the type genus of *Apocynaceae*. **A**, flower-bud. **B**, flower. **C**, stamens. **D**, fruit. **E**, seed (orig.).

into masses (pollinia) as in *Orchidaceae* in Monocotyledons; corona often present; secondary apocarpy is common in this group, especially in the fruiting stage.

Phylogeny: LOGANIALES→ APOCYNALES → **Asclepiadaceae** (climax family).

In **Plocospermataceae** the ovary is composed of 2 united carpels and is 1-locular with 4 parietal ovules in pairs, the lower pair erect, the upper pair pendulous, and the style is shortly bilobed; the fruit is a capsule, dehiscing

FIG. 363. A stylish Trevithickian drawing of *Strophanthus sarmentosus* A.P.DC. (*Apocynaceae*), from Hutchinson and Dalziel, FLORA OF WEST TROPICAL AFRICA. A, leafy shoot. B, flowers. C, anther. D, fruit. E, seed.

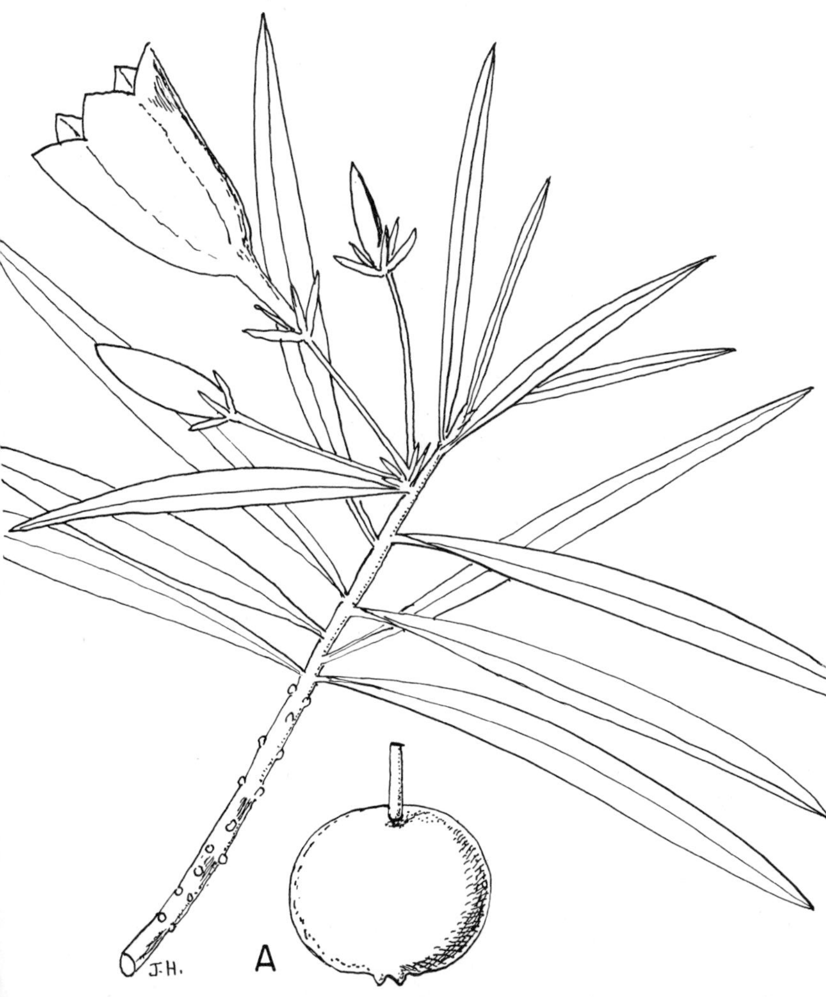

FIG. 364. The "Amancay", *Thevetia peruviana* (Pers.) Merrill (*Apocynaceae*), the milky sap and seeds of which are poisonous; flowers yellow; fruit, **A**, green and then bright black (orig.).

along both sides (2-valved from the apex), and the mostly solitary seed is long and subterete, with a dense tuft of hairs at the apex. These characters bring this monotypic Central American family within the orbit of the Order APOCYNALES rather than in the *Loganiaceae* (*sensu lato*), in which it was placed by Bentham in the GENERA PLANTARUM.

The type genus of **Apocynaceae**[1] is *Apocynum* Linn. Perennial erect herbs

[1] Including *Vincaceae* S. F. Gray (1821). *Plumeriaceae* Horaninow (1834). *Willughbeiaceae* J. G. Agardh (1858). *Emeticaceae* Dulac (1867).

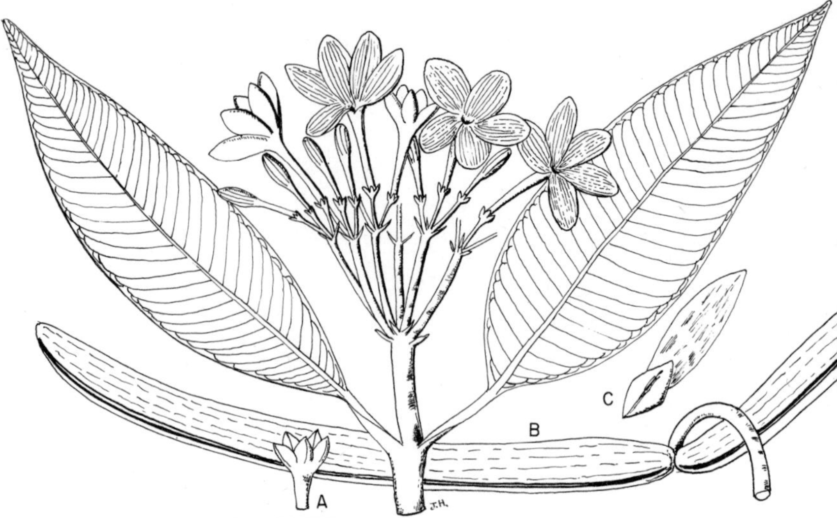

FIG. 365. *Plumeria rubra* Linn., the Red Frangipani (*Apocynaceae*). Visitors when they step ashore on some Pacific Islands, such as Tahiti, are often garlanded with these sweetly scented flowers. **A**, calyx. **B**, fruit. **C**, seed (orig.).

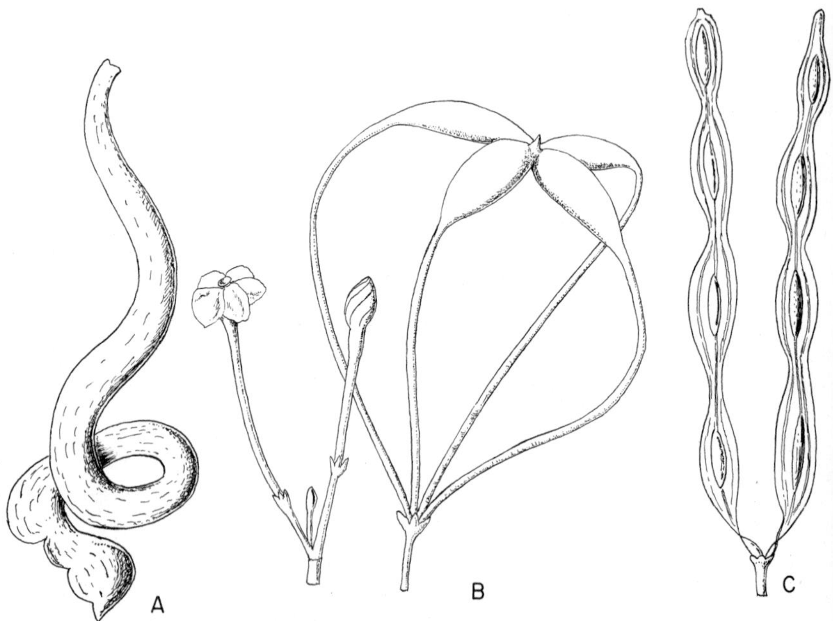

FIG. 366. **A**, fruit of *Tabernaemontana anguinea* Hemsl., Solomon Islands. **B**, flowers and fruit of *Lepinia taitensis* Decne. **C**, fruit of *Condylocarpon rauwolfiae* Müll., Brazil; some examples of secondary apocarpy in the family *Apocynaceae* (orig.).

or shrublets, often glaucescent; leaves opposite; flowers small, in terminal cymes; calyx deeply 5-lobed; corolla campanulate, 5-lobed, lobes dextrorsely contorted; stamens inserted near the base of the corolla-tube, included; anthers sagittate, connivent around the stigma and adherent to it in the middle, loculi produced and empty at the base; disk fleshy, 5-lobed around the base of the ovary; ovary of 2 carpels, free nearly to the base; style very short, stigma subglobose, slightly 2-lobed at the apex; ovules numerous; follicles elongated, free, slender; seeds small, crowned at the apex by a long caducous coma of hairs; endosperm very thin; cotyledons oblong, flat.

The type species of the genus is *A. androsaeifolium* Linn., about which William Curtis, the author of the BOTANICAL MAGAZINE, wrote the following very interesting account:

In addition to the powerful recommendation of beauty and fragrance, the Tutsan-leaved Dogbane interests us on account of the curious structure of its flowers, and their singular property of catching flies. The flowers of this Apocynum have a sweet honey-like fragrance which perfumes the air to a considerable distance, and no doubt operates powerfully in attracting insects; when a plant of this sort is fully blown, one may always find flies caught in its blossoms, usually by the trunk, very rarely by the leg; sometimes four or even five, which is the greatest possible number, are found in one flower, some dead, others endeavouring to disentangle themselves, in which they are now and then so fortunate as to succeed; these flies are of different species, the *Musca pipiens*, a slender variegated fly with thick thighs, is a very common victim; the *Musca domestica*, or house fly, we have never observed among the captives.

On looking into the flower we perceive five stamens, the anthers of which are large, of a yellow colour, and converge into a kind of cone; each of these anthers is arrow-shaped to nearly the top of the cone, their sides touch but do not adhere, below they separate a little, so as to leave a very narrow opening or slit between each; they are placed on very short filaments, which stand so far apart that a considerable opening is left between them, which openings, however, are closed up by processes of the corolla, nicely adapted to, and projecting into them; at the bottom of, and in the very centre of the flower, we perceive two germina, or seed-buds, the rudiments of future seed-vessels, surrounded by glandular substances, secreting a sweet liquid; on the summit of these germina, and betwixt the two, stands the stigma, in the form of a little urn, the middle of which is encircled by a glandular ring, which secretes a viscid honey-like substance; to this part of the stigma the *Antherae* interiorly adhere most tenaciously, so as to prevent their separation unless considerable force be applied; it is, as we apprehend, the sweet viscid substance thus secreted by the stigma, within the *Antherae*, which the fly endeavours to obtain, and to this end insinuates its trunk first into the lowermost and widest part of the slit, betwixt each of the *Antherae* above described, pushing it of necessity upwards: when gratified, not having the sense to place itself in the same position as that in which it stood when it inserted its trunk, and to draw it out in the same direction downwards, unfortunately for it, it varies its

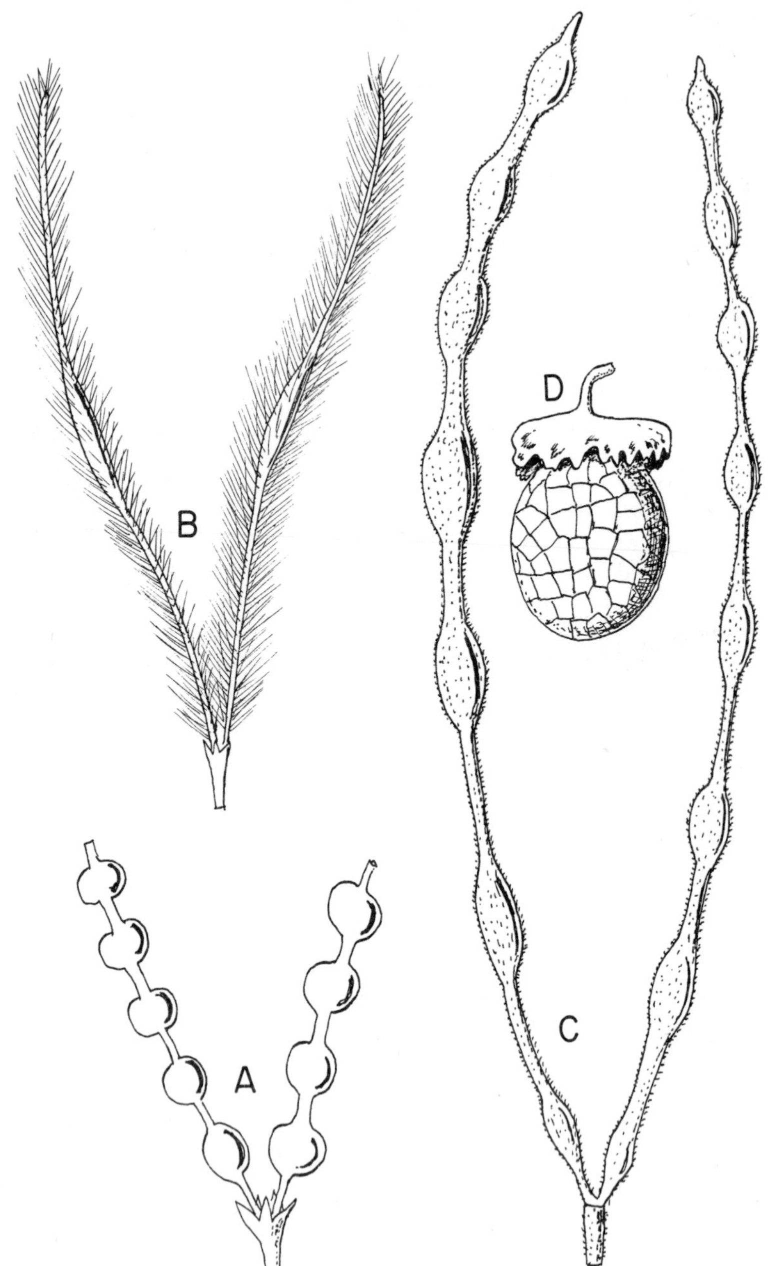

FIG. 367. **A**, fruit of *Alyxia concatenata* (Blanco) Merrill, Philippines. **B**, fruit of *Rhipidia amazonica* Markgraf, Brazil. **C**, fruit of *Parameria densiflora* Oliv., Malay Peninsula. **D**, seed of *Neokeithia conspicua* Van Steenis, Borneo.—All *Apocynaceae* (orig.).

FIG. 368. *Mandevillea hirsuta* (A. Rich.) K. Schum. (*Apocynaceae*), drawn from a specimen collected by the author in the marsh forest of the Aripo savannah, Trinidad. **A**, disk and gynoecium. **B**, disk gland. **C**, fruit. **D**, seed (orig.).

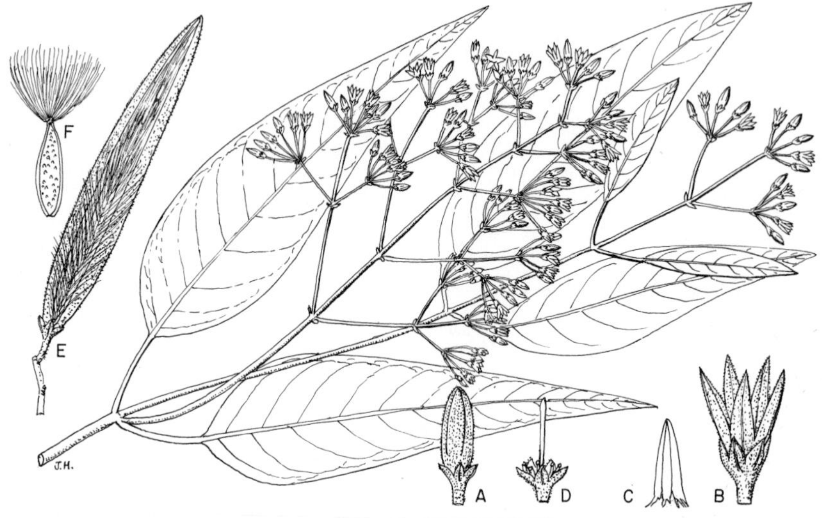

FIG. 369. The genus *Lyonsia* (*Apocynaceae*) was named by Robert Brown in compliment to Israel Lyons, a tutor from Cambridge who gave Sir Joseph Banks his first lessons in botany. This species, *L. straminea* R.Br., is the type of the genus, a common climber in eastern Australia. Brown said of Lyons: "Dixi in memoriam Israelis Lyons, Fasciculi plantarum circa Cantabrigiam nascentium auctoris". **A**, flower bud. **B**, flower. **C**, anthers. **D**, calyx and style. **E**, fruit. **F**, seed (orig.).

position, and pulling its trunk upwards, draws it into the narrow part of the slit, where it becomes closely wedged in, and the more it pulls the more securely it is caught, and thus the heedless insect, as Thomson calls it, terminates its existence in captivity most miserable.

There are few outstanding features in the very natural family **Apocynaceae** as follows: Branches fleshy in *Adenium* and *Pachypodium*; with spiny cushions below the leaves in *Pachypodium*; spiny in *Carissa*. Corolla-lobes subvalvate in *Parsonsia* and *Notonerium*; valvate in *Pseudochrosia*, *Neuburgia*, *Lyonsia* and *Urceola*. Ovary of 3–5 carpels in *Lepinia*, *Pleiocarpa* and *Notonerium*; more or less immersed in the disk and thus "semi-inferior" in *Epigynum*, *Ichnocarpum*, *Apocynum*, and here and there in *Holarrhena* and *Plumeria*; stigma densely penicillate-plumose in *Vinca*. Ovules erect in *Acokanthera* and *Vallesia*. Fruit entire and dehiscing by 2 valves in *Allamanda* and *Chilocarpum*; carpels dehiscing by 2 valves in *Aspidosperma*.

In my FAMILIES OF FLOWERING PLANTS the following note was provided regarding the family **Periplocaceae**: "In addition to the late Dr. N. E. Brown of Kew, Rudolph Schlechter, a German botanist, studied the *Asclepidiaceae* intensively. It seems worth while to reproduce his remarks (NOTIZBL. BOT. GART. BERLIN **9**, 23 (1924)) when he proposed the separation of the *Periplocaceae* as a separate family."

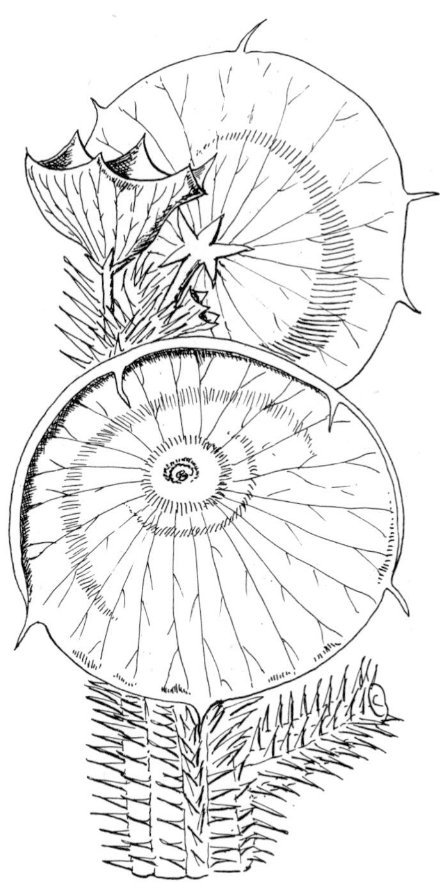

FIG. 370. *Hoodia gordonii* (Masson) Sweet ex Decne. (*Asclepiadaceae*), drawn by the author near the Orange River, South Africa, in 1928.

Here is a free translation of his notes:

"Again I have taken the opportunity to state that I consider the *Periplocaceae* to be a family in itself. The free filaments, the form of the anthers, the remarkable spoon- or bag-shaped pollen-containers which lead to tetrads of pollen-grains, and the stigmas are so different from those of the remainder of the *Asclepiadaceae*, that I consider the separation of both families to be not only justified but also necessary.

"In my view the *Periplocaceae* in the form of their flowers are actually closer to the *Apocynaceae* than the *Asclepiadaceae*. The result of all this is that we are dealing in this instance with a clearly defined association of genera which are found only in the Old World without a single one in America. Actually in the *Gamopetalae* (*Sympetalae*) are many families worse defined than the

Periplocaceae. I would draw attention to the *Symplocaceae*, *Styracaceae*, *Loganiaceae* and *Caprifoliaceae*, and others. Under the circumstances it seems to me correct here and in the future in further works that the family should continue to be distinguished from the *Asclepiadaceae*."

Nevertheless in the latest SYLLABUS (12th Ed.) of the Englerian system the *Periplocaceae* are again included as a subfamily in the *Asclepiadaceae*! I am of the opinion that many so-called families are just as distinct as the remainder of the group in which they are included, and there are many such in this latest SYLLABUS.

ORDER 52. RUBIALES

(*Fam. Fl. Pl.* **1**, 384)

Families: **Dialypetalanthaceae, Rubiaceae.**

A very large group of plants related to and perhaps derived from the Loganiaceous stock (an intermediate genus is *Gaertnera*); leaves constantly opposite, simple, entire, stipulate; corolla epigynous, sympetalous, actinomorphic; stamens epipetalous; ovary inferior (except in *Dialypetalanthaceae*).

Phylogeny: LOGANIALES → **RUBIALES**—most recent tribe *Rubieae* (*Galieae*), with foliaceous stipules resembling leaves.

The interesting genus *Dialypetalanthus*, Brazil, **Dialypetalanthaceae**, is fully illustrated, described, and its position discussed in my FAMILIES OF FLOWERING PLANTS, 2nd Ed. **1**, 384, Fig. 236. In this plant the petals are free and the stamens are epigynous, a combination of characters unknown in the large family *Rubiaceae*, in which it was originally placed. The large intrapetiolar stipules, so frequent in *Rubiaceae*, are quite foreign to *Myrtaceae*, *Rhizophoraceae* and *Melastomataceae*, families suggested as being related. I consider it to be a primitive type near *Rubiaceae* and closely linked with LOGANIALES.

Rubiaceae[1] is a very large and almost entirely tropical family. They seem to be the epigynous types evolved mainly from the Loganiaceous stock.

---

[1] Including *Aparinaceae* Hoffmansegg & Link (1820). *Operculariaceae* Dumortier (1829). *Gardeniaceae* Dumortier (1829). *Lygodysodeaceae* Bartling (1830). *Cinchonaceae* Lindley (1830). *Galiaceae* Lindley (1836). *Lippayaceae* Meisn. (1836–43). *Coffeaceae* J. G. Agardh (1858). *Stellataceae* Dulac (1867). *Naucleaceae* Wernham (1912). *Henriqueziaceae* Bremekamp (1957).

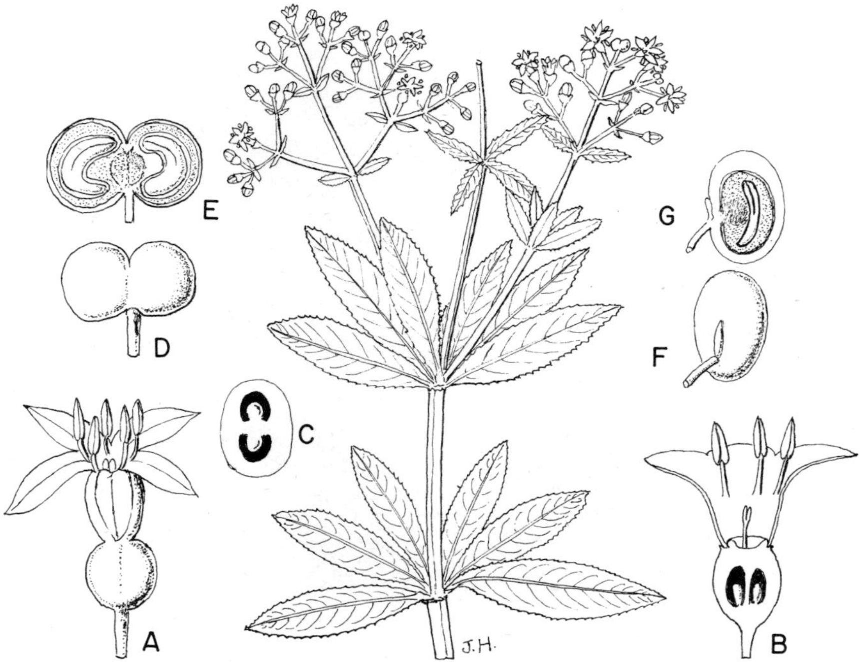

FIG. 371. *Rubia tinctorum* Linn., the type species of the type genus of the large family *Rubiaceae*. **A**, flower. **B**, vertical section of same. **C**, cross-section of ovary. **D**, fruit. **E**, vertical section of same. **F**, seed. **G**, vertical section of seed (orig.).

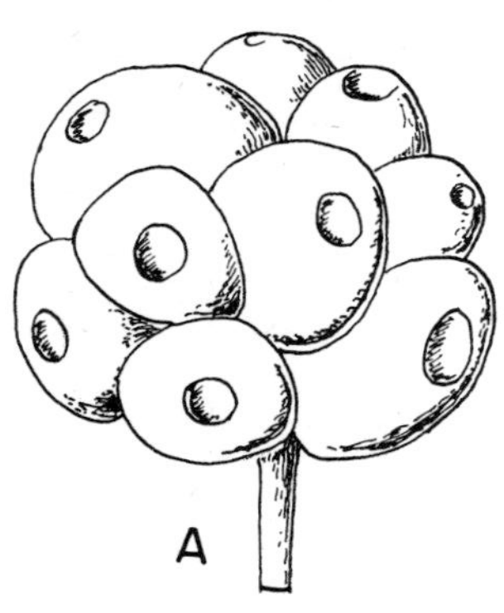

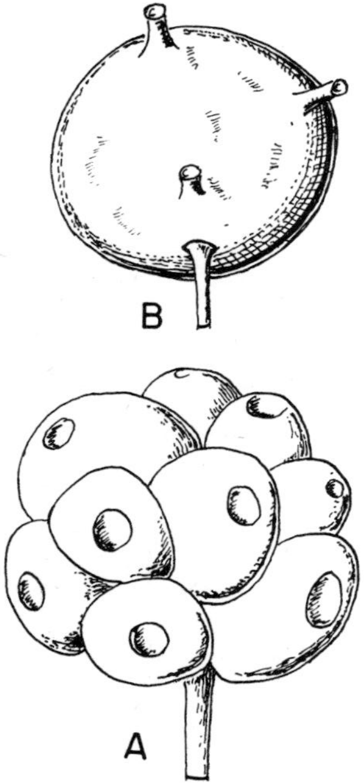

FIG. 372. **A**, fruits of *Morinda confusa* Hutch. (*Rubiaceae*). **B**, *M. longiflora* G. Don (*Rubiaceae*).

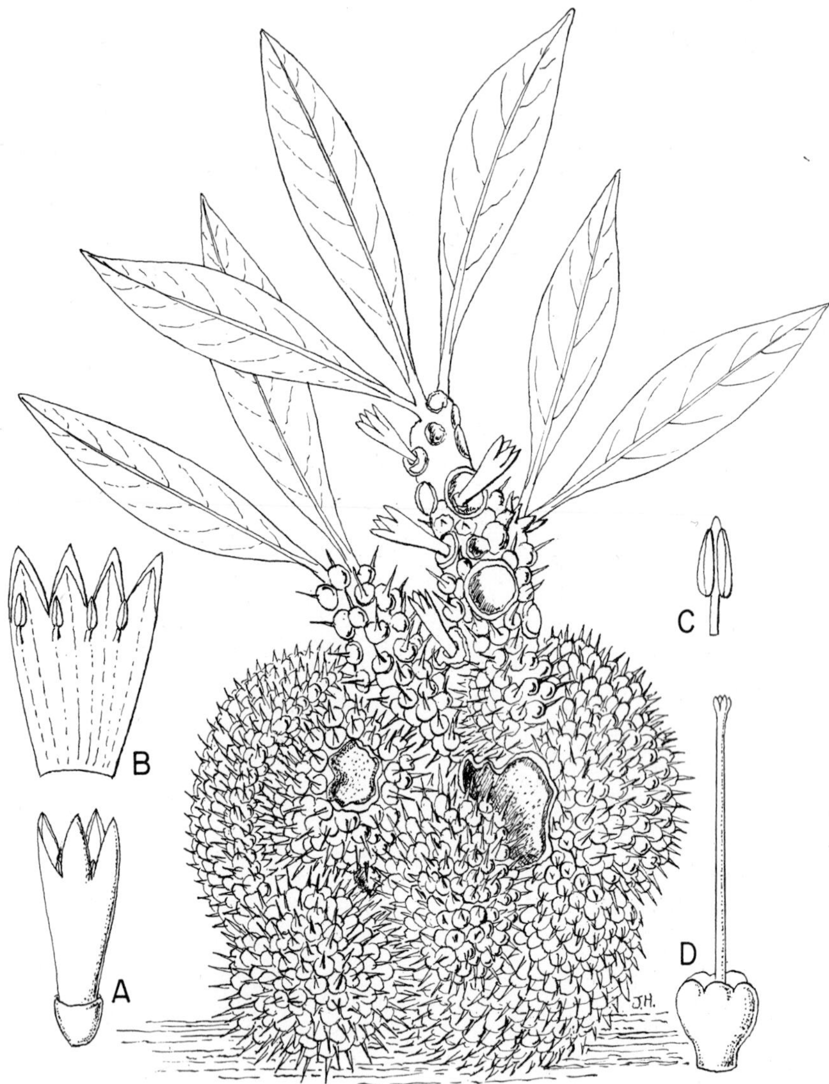

FIG. 373. *Myrmecodia beccarii* Hook. f. (*Rubiaceae*), Australia, which harbours ants. **A**, flower. **B**, corolla opened out. **C**, stamen. **D**, gynoecium (orig.).

The habit is chiefly woody, and the stomata of the leaves have special subsidiary cells parallel to the pore, this kind of stoma being often spoken of as the "rubiacous" type. The leaves are always opposite (or verticillate), and a remarkable fact about them is that they are never toothed or lobed. The type

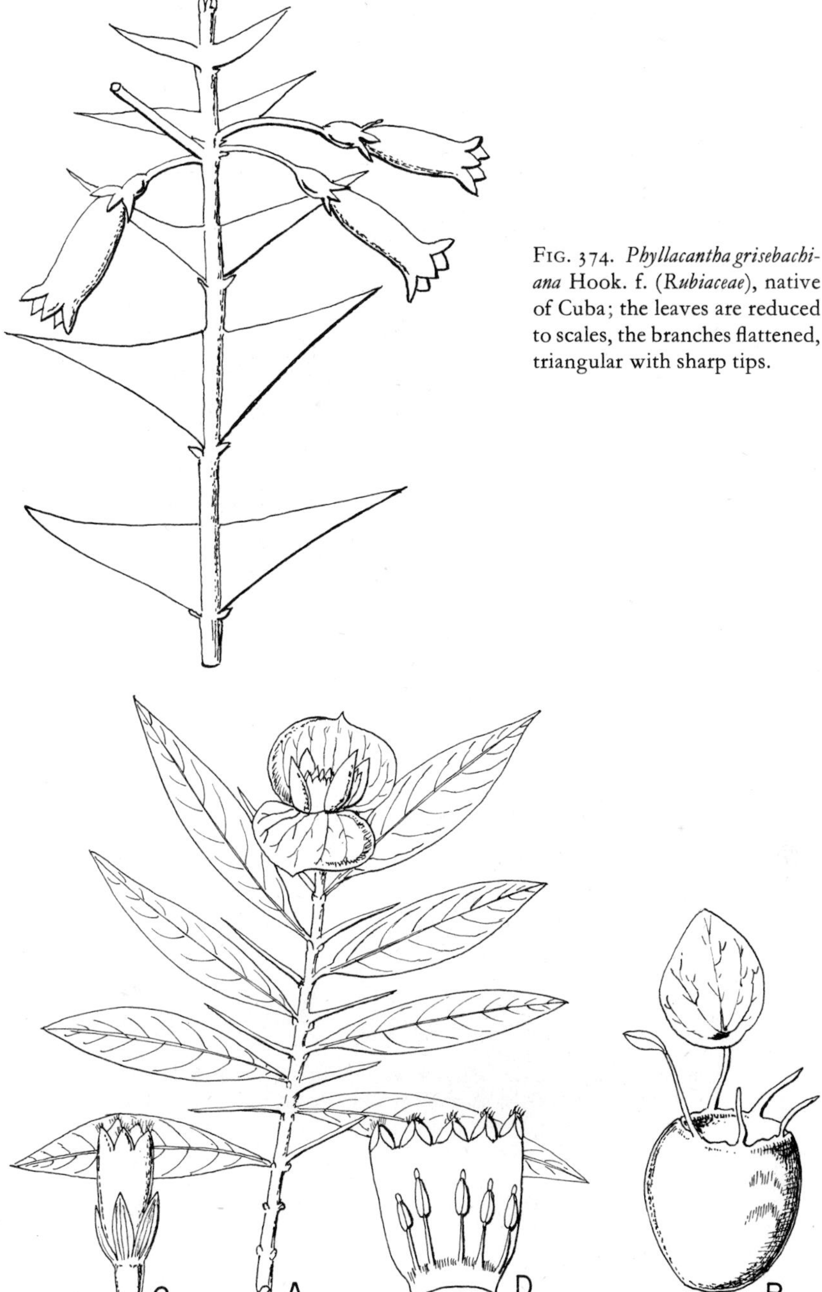

Fig. 374. *Phyllacantha grisebachiana* Hook. f. (*Rubiaceae*), native of Cuba; the leaves are reduced to scales, the branches flattened, triangular with sharp tips.

Fig. 375. **A**, *Didymochlamys whitei* Hook. f. (*Rubiaceae*), Colombia; originally described as having alternate leaves; they are really opposite, alternately normal leaves, alternately long-subulate (anisophyllous). **C**, separate flower. **D**, corolla laid open. **B**, *Temnopteryx sericea* Hook. f., tropical Africa, fruit with one large foliaceous calyx-lobe (orig.).

FIG. 376. *Warszewiczia coccinea* Klotzsch (*Rubiaceae*), tropical America; inflorescence about 30 cm long (lower and upper parts only shown); enlarged calyx-lobe scarlet; **A**, flower. **B**, corolla laid open. **C**, stamen. **D**, vertical section of ovary with style. **E**, cross-section of ovary. **F**, fruit. (Partly adapted from Martius FLORA BRAS.)

of stipule is advanced. It is either inter- or intra-petiolar, and is really composed of the union of two opposite stipules, the one from the petiole of one leaf, the other from the petiole of the second leaf. When intra-petiolar the four stipules are often united into one tube, as in *Gardenia*. One might suspect the *Rubieae* (*Galieae*), with their stipules resembling leaves, to have had a separate origin from the remainder of the *Rubiaceae* were it not for the

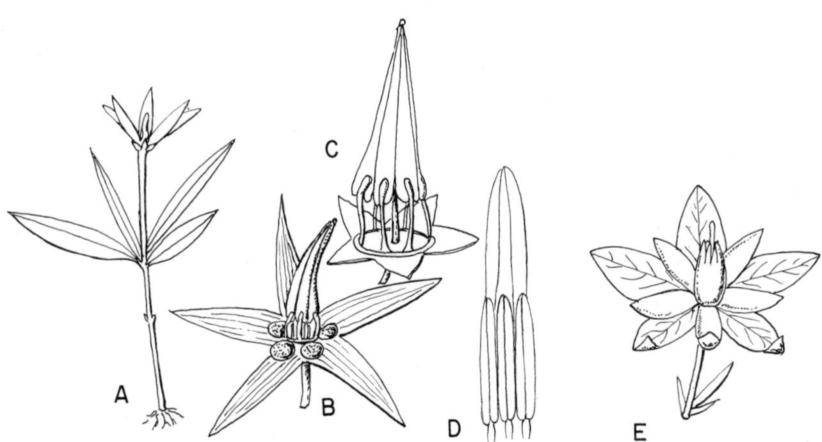

FIG. 377. **A**, *Argostemma concinnum* Hemsl., Thailand. A diminutive one-flowered herb 1–2 in. high. **B**, open flower. **C**, the same with corolla removed showing the connivent anthers. **D**, anthers from within. **E**, *Neurocalyx zeylanicus* Hook., Ceylon, with connate stamens (*Rubiaceae*).

existence of a linking genus, *Didymaea*, a native of Central America, which has quite the facies of *Galium*, but with small inter-petiolar stipules. A few species of *Rubia* also have opposite leaves. The *Rubieae* (*Galieae*), therefore, may be regarded as the most recent and advanced of the *Rubiaceae*, with the more advanced habit, climbing and herbaceous, having spread widely into temperate regions from their primitively tropical home.

The classification of the genera has up to the present been rather artificial, and it will perhaps have to remain more or less in this condition. Too much importance has been attached to the number of ovules, with the result that closely allied genera are widely separated. To give one example, the genus *Tarenna* (*Webera*), no. 162 in the GENERA PLANTARUM of Bentham and Hooker f., is very closely allied and scarcely distinguishable from *Pavetta*.

From a phylogenetic point of view it was unfortunate that in the Bentham and Hooker system one of the most advanced groups, the *Naucleeae*, was allotted the premier position. In the subtribe *Sarcocephaleae* of this alliance we have the very remarkable development of a capitate inflorescence in which the calyces of the individual flowers are united together, the fruit being a syncarp after the manner of some members of the *Moraceae*. Disregarding other characters which are not so far advanced, this seems to be the very ultimate stage which an inflorescence attains. In *Morinda* (see Fig. 372) and a few allied genera there is a similar condition, which has, however, not been quite so completely carried out.

The general tendency in the evolution of the inflorescence has been the

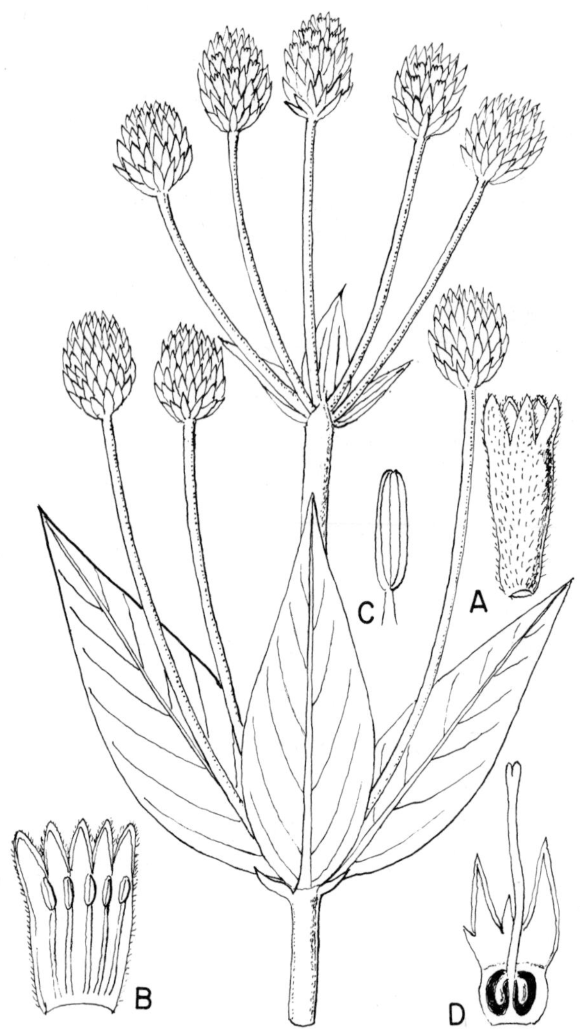

FIG. 378. *Calanda rubricaulis* K. Schum. (*Rubiaceae*), could be mistaken for a Composite or even *Amaranthaceae*. **A**, corolla. **B**, corolla opened out. **C**, anther. **D**, vertical section of ovary.

same as in *Asteraceae* (*Compositae*), i.e. into corymbs or umbel-like cymes. But in this case the involucre of bracts characteristic of *Asteraceae* is lacking, although it occurs in *Uragoga*. The capsular fruit of several tribes is generally associated with more ancient characters than those tribes which have a baccate fruit. For example *Mussaenda*, with fruit a berry and a rather small and usually inconspicuous corolla, is rendered attractive by the production of

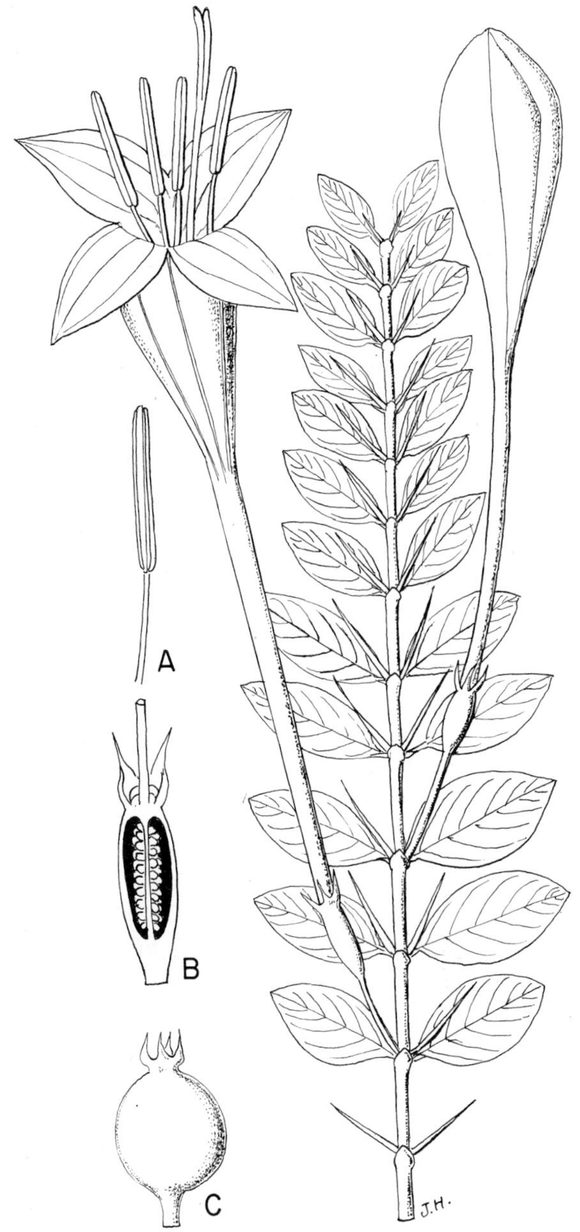

FIG. 379. *Catesbaea spinosa* Linn. (*Rubiaceae*), West Indies. **A**, stamen. **B**, vertical section of ovary. **C**, fruit.

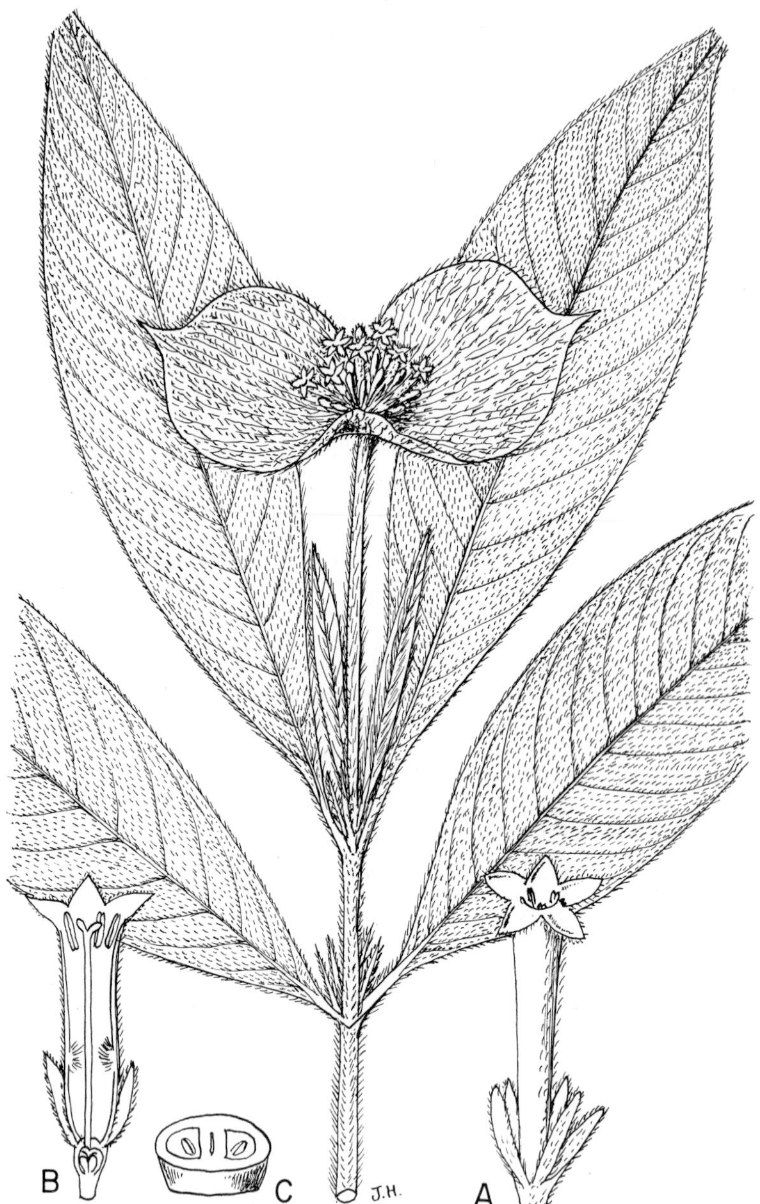

FIG. 380. *Cephaelis tomentosa* Willd. (*Rubiaceae*), in marsh forest near Aripo savannah, Trinidad; note the two large bracts subtending the cluster of flowers. **A**, flower. **B**, vertical section of the same. **C**, cross-section of fruit (orig.).

FIG. 381. *Coffea liberica* Bull ex Hiern (*Rubiaceae*), a larger-fruited species than the better *C. arabica* Linn., but used in blending with the latter. **A**, vertical section of flower. **B**, flower-buds. **C**, stamen. **D**, fruits. (From Hutchinson and Dalziel, FLORA OF WEST TROPICAL AFRICA.)

large and petaloid calyx-lobes. A primitive species of *Mussaenda* has a capsular fruit.

Those tribes in which numerous ovules are associated with a contorted corolla are probably the most primitive of Rubiaceous groups, and it will be remembered that in many *Apocynaceae*, a less advanced or perhaps parallel group, the corolla is also contorted. Probably tribe *Gardenieae* is the most primitive, and in *Gardenia* itself we find an ovary with parietal placentas, a relatively ancient type of syncarp. Most of the other tribes with numerous ovules have a valvate corolla, but both contorted and imbricate occur in tribe *Hamelieae*, and all types of aestivation are found in *Cinchoneae* in which the seeds are winged or appendaged. Quinine is obtained from the bark of *Cinchona* spp. (Fig. 383), without which life in the tropics for the white man was for any length of time at least very precarious.

A queer mixture of comparatively ancient and advanced characters occurs in the small South American tribe *Henriquezieae*, wherein the ovary is only half-superior and the corolla is slightly zygomorphic (family *Henriqueziaceae* Bremekamp)!

Here is a list of the more outstanding characters of certain genera of *Rubiaceae*: Stem tuberous in *Myrmecodia* (Fig. 373), *Hydnophytum*. Branches leafless with vertical flattened spines in *Phyllacantha* (Fig. 374). Supposedly

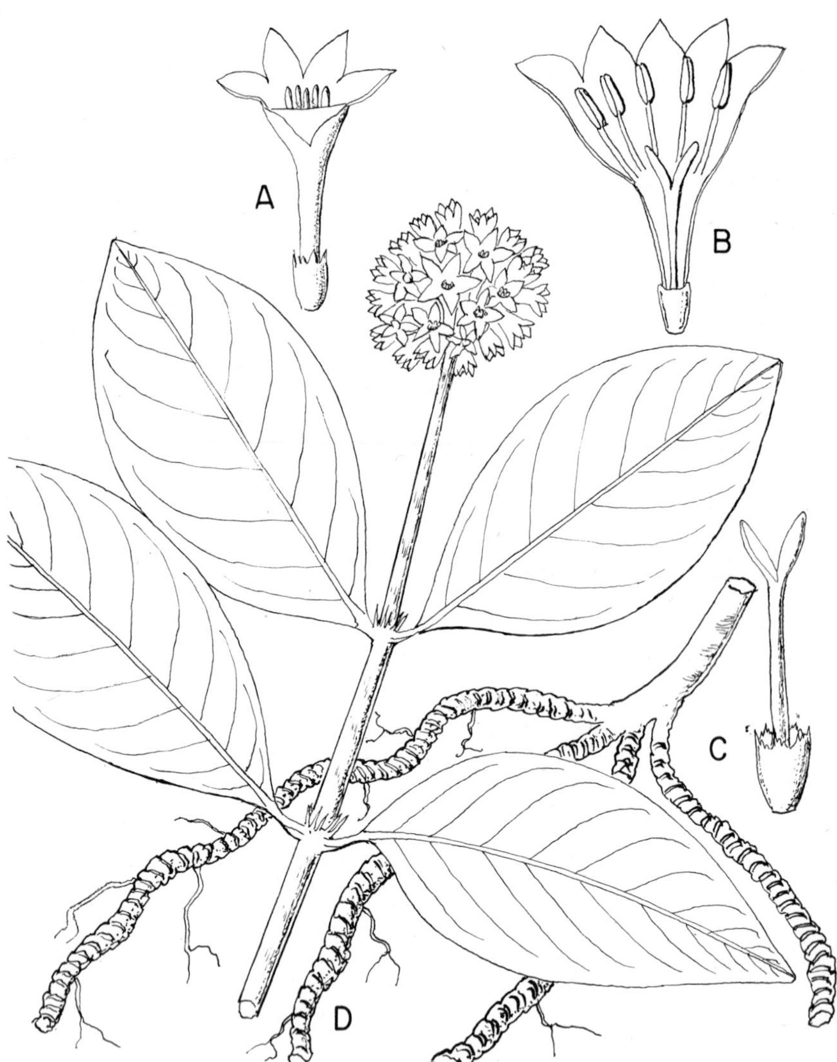

FIG. 382. Ipecacuanha, *Cephaelis ipecacuanha* (Brot.) A. Rich. (*Rubiaceae*), a small shrublet in moist forests of Latin America; the dried rhizome and roots are used; principal ingredient emetin, a white bitter colourless alkaloid; used chiefly as a diaphoretic, emetic, and expectorant. **A**, flower. **B**, vertical section of flower. **C**, ovary and style. **D**, rhizome (orig.).

FIG. 383. *Cinchona officinalis* Linn. (*Rubiaceae*), the principal source of Quinine; native of tropical America and much cultivated in tropical Asia and Africa. **A**, flower. **B**, fruit. **C**, seed (orig.).

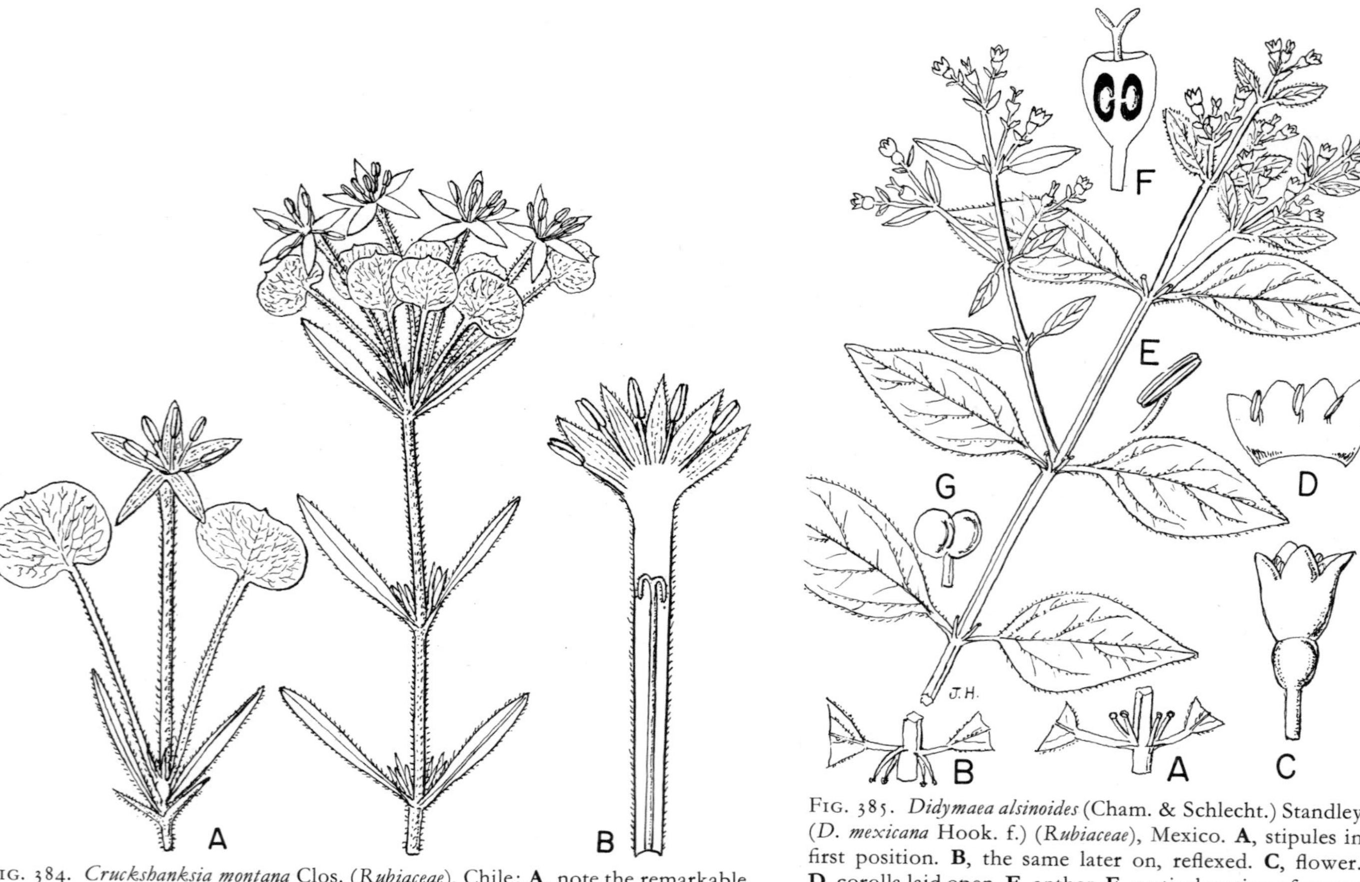

Fig. 384. *Cruckshanksia montana* Clos. (*Rubiaceae*), Chile; **A**, note the remarkable enlarged calyx-lobes. **B**, corolla laid open (orig.).

Fig. 385. *Didymaea alsinoides* (Cham. & Schlecht.) Standley (*D. mexicana* Hook. f.) (*Rubiaceae*), Mexico. **A**, stipules in first position. **B**, the same later on, reflexed. **C**, flower. **D**, corolla laid open. **E**, anther. **F**, vertical section of ovary. **G**, fruit (orig.). (See text.)

IG. 386. Miss Ross Craig's drawing of *Gardenia ternifolia* Schum. & Thonn. (*Rubiaceae*), rom Hutchinson and Dalziel, FLORA OF WEST TROPICAL AFRICA. **A**, cross-section of ovary howing the parietal placentas. **B**, vertical section of fruit. **C**, seed.

FIG. 387. *Gardenia taitensis* DC. (*Rubiaceae*), the national flower of Tahiti, Pacific Islands. **A**, cross-section of ovary. **B**, fruit (orig.).

FIG. 388. *Guettarda hirsuta* (Ruiz & Pav.) Pers. (*Rubiaceae*), Peru and Ecuador; note the remarkable inflorescence, resembling those of many *Boraginaceae*.

alternate leaves in *Didymochlamys* (Fig. 375) are really opposite but strongly anisophyllous; sinuately lobed or pinnatifid in *Pentagonia* and *Sickingia*; denticulate, serrate or crenate in *Heterophyllaea*, *Neurocalyx*. Stipules obsolete in *Limnosipania*; thick and coriaceous and obliquely wing-like in *Mesoptera*; calyptriform sheathing the young leaves in *Hymenocnemis*; leaf-like in tribe *Rubieae* (*Galieae*). Calyx-limb plumose in *Gaillonia* spp.; one lobe enlarged and coloured in *Calycophyllum*, *Monadelphanthus*, *Capirona*, *Schizocalyx*, *Pinkneya*, *Pogonopus*, *Pallasia*, *Howardia*, *Warszewiczia* (Fig. 376), *Mussaenda*, *Temnocalyx*. Corolla more or less bilabiate in *Ferdinandusa*, *Capirona*, *Henriquezia*, *Dichilanthe*, *Spathichlamys*; partite to the base in *Molopanthera*, *Synaptantha*, *Aulacodiscus*; lobes dextrorsely contorted in *Deppea*, *Cosmibuena* and a few others; horned or appendaged in *Rudgea* and *Corynanthe*; zygomorphic in *Dorothea*. Stamens more numerous than the corolla-lobes in *Praravinia*; declinate in *Tammisia*, *Henriquezia* and others; almost epigynous and persistent in *Synaptantha*; filaments monadelphous in *Capirona*, *Solenandra*, *Monadelphanthus* and *Strumphia*; very unequal in *Remijia*, *Ferdinandusa*, *Capirona*, *Henriquezia*, *Pallasia* and *Didymochlamys*; anthers more or less connate in *Argostemma* (Fig. 377), *Neurocalyx* (Fig. 377) and *Acrantha*; dehiscent by pores in *Argostemma* spp., *Neurocarpus* and

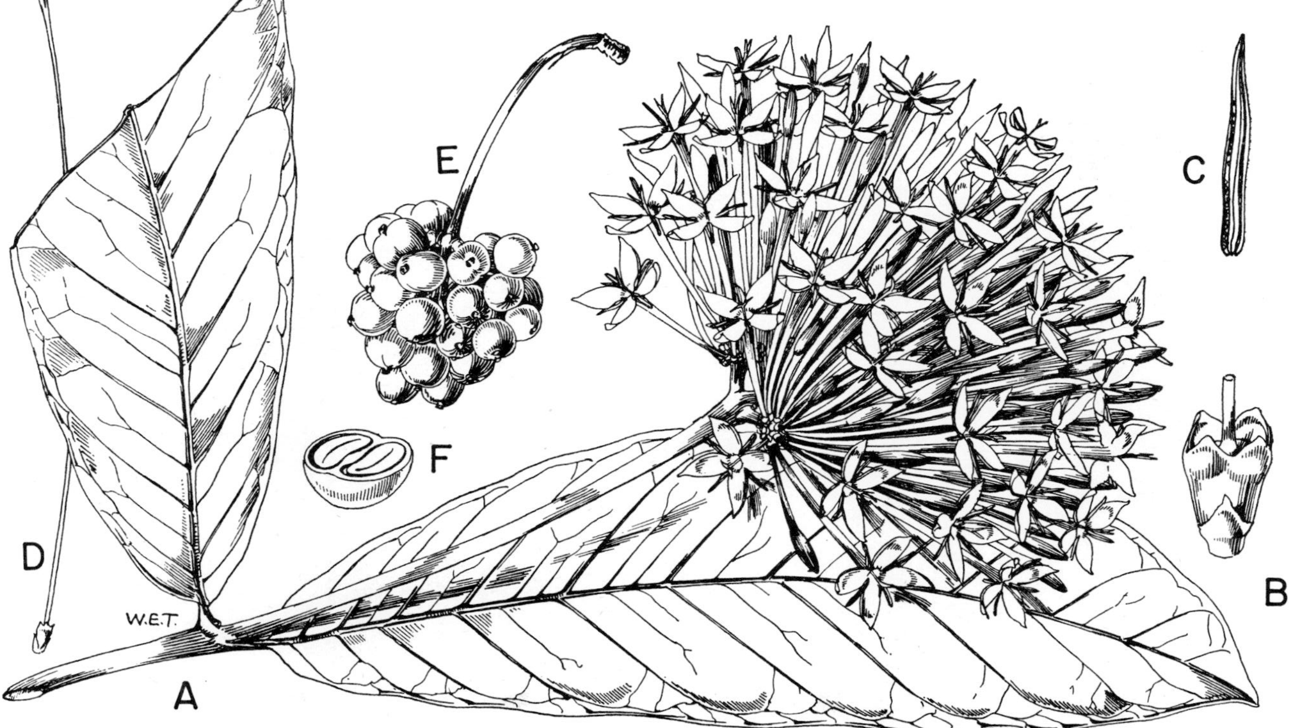

FIG. 389. *Ixora radiata* Hiern (*Rubiaceae*); a fine drawing by Trevithick for Hutchinson and Dalziel, FLORA OF WEST TROPICAL AFRICA. **A**, flowers. **B**, ovary and calyx. **C**, anther. **D**, ovary and style. **E**, fruits. **F**, cross-section of fruit.

FIG. 390. *Joosia umbellifera* Karst., belonging to a small but very distinct genus of *Rubiaceae*; a small tree with white flowers in Peru and Colombia; corolla very deciduous; note the scorpioid inflorescence, the induplicate-valvate corolla-lobes with crenate margins, and the winged seeds. **A**, corolla opened out. **B**, the same in bud. **C**, cross-section of the ovary. **D**, fruit, dehiscent and the valves spirally twisted. **E**, seed.

Rustia; transversely locellate in *Isertia*, *Dictyandra* and *Anomanthodium*. Ovary and capsule $\frac{1}{4}$–$\frac{3}{4}$ superior in *Henriquezia*, *Platycarpus*, *Rhachicallis*, *Synaptantha* and a few others; ovules paired in the loculi, one ascending, the other pendulous, in *Scyphiphora*. Capsule 2-valved in *Virecta*, with one valve persistent, the other caducous. Seeds without endosperm in *Henriquezia*, *Platycarpus* and various *Guettardieae*; arillate in *Isidorea* and *Galiniera*; comose at the apex in *Hillia*; endosperm ruminate in *Galiniera*, *Coptosperma*, *Polysphaeria*, *Rutidea* and various *Psychotrieae*.

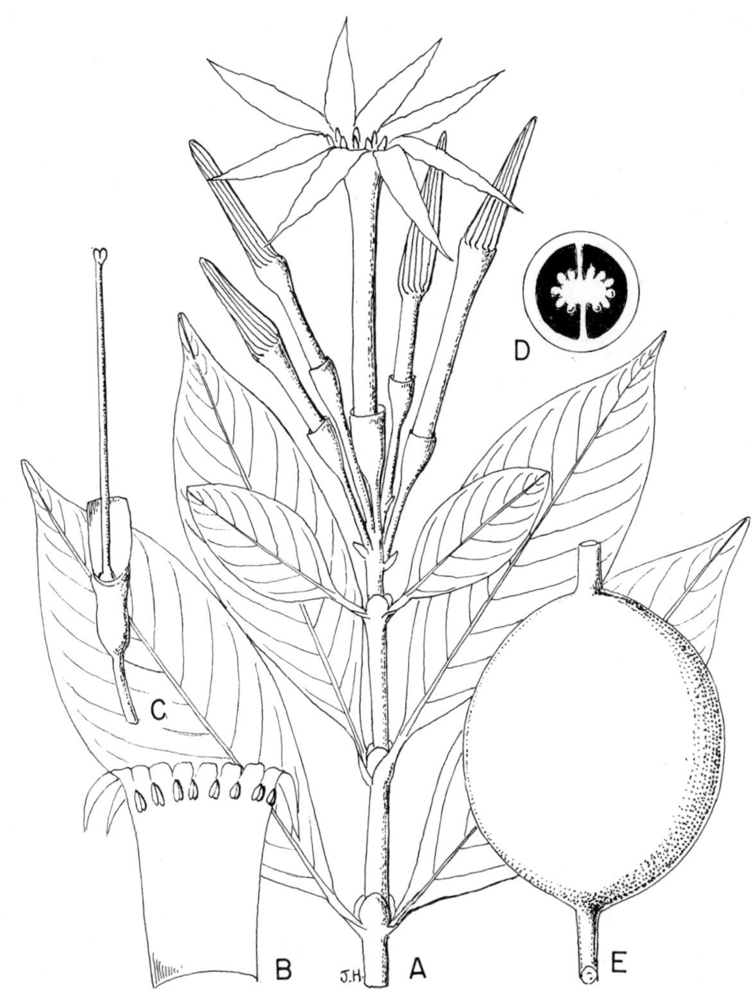

Fig. 391. *Kutchubaea insignis* Fisch. (*Rubiaceae*), Guyana and Brazil; flowers white, at length yellow, scented; note the 8 corolla-lobes, spirally twisted clockwise in bud. **A**, flowering shoot to show intrapetiolar stipules. **B**, corolla laid open. **C**, ovary and style. **D**, cross-section of ovary. **E**, fruit (orig.).

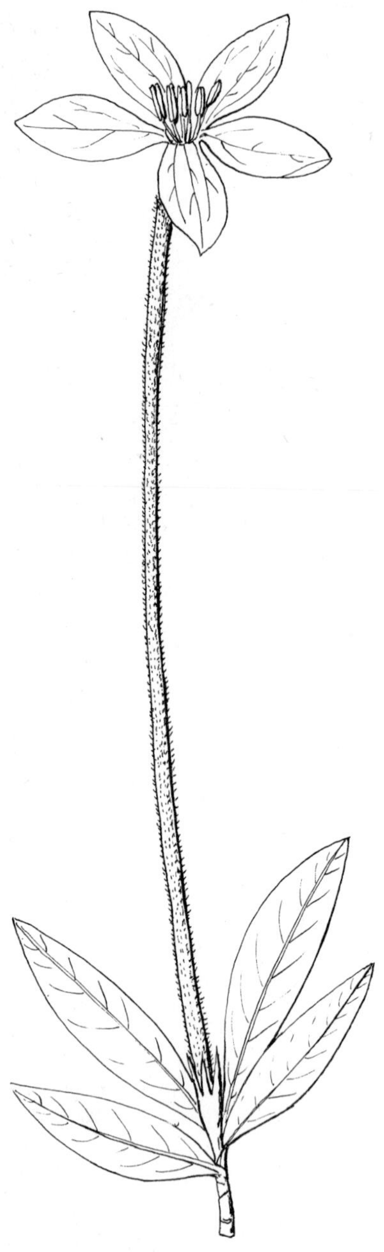

FIG. 392. *Lindenia rivalis* Benth. (*Rubiaceae*), native of Mexico; note the extremely long and slender corolla-tube (18 cm). (See also map of distribution, p. 452.)

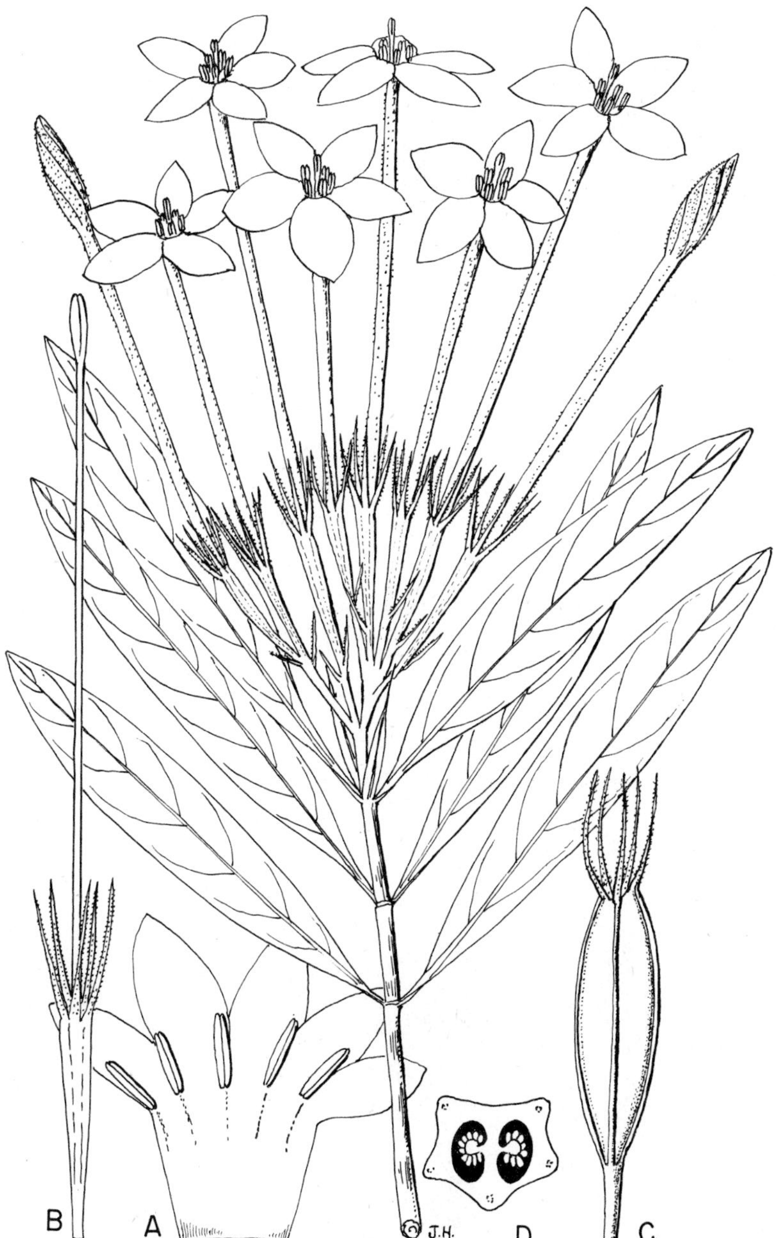

Fig. 393. *Lindenia vitiensis* Seem., occurs both in Fiji and New Caledonia; there are two or three related species in Central America (Mexico to Costa Rica) (*Rubiaceae*) (see Map 27). **A**, corolla-limb laid open. **B**, ovary, calyx and style. **C**, fruit. **D**, cross-section of ovary (orig.).

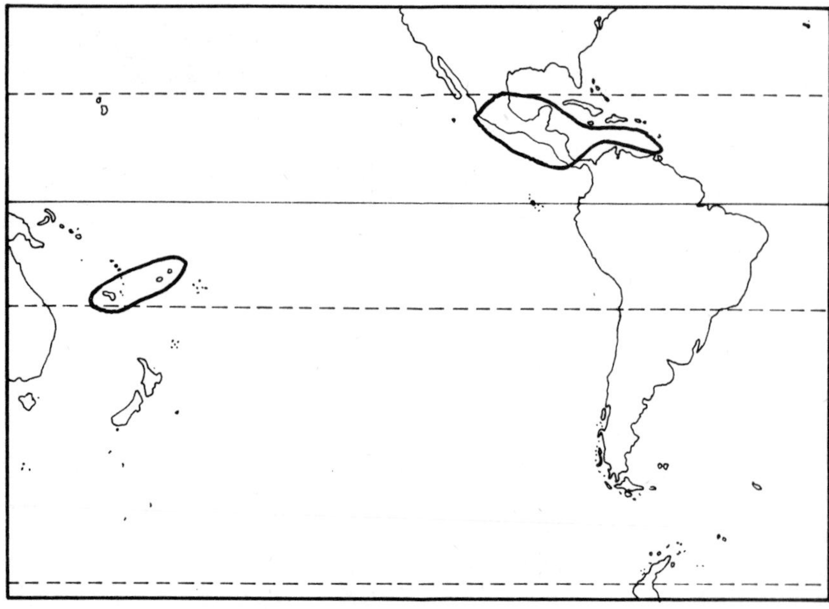

MAP 27. Remarkable distribution of the homogeneous genus *Lindenia* (*Rubiaceae*); one species, *L. vitiensis* Seem., in Fiji and New Caledonia, the other four species separated from it by the vast Pacific Ocean, in Central America and the island of Tobago. *L. rivalis* Benth., Mexico shown in Fig. 392.

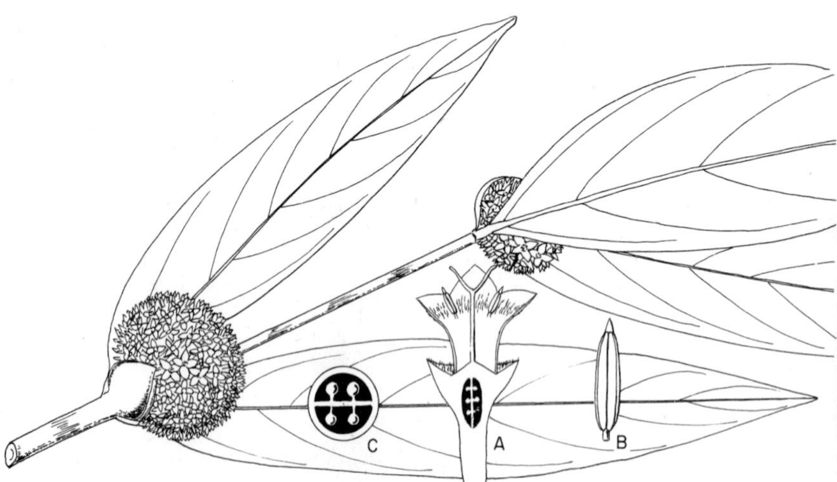

FIG. 394. *Maschalodesma arborea* K. Schum., New Guinea (*Rubiaceae*). **A**, vertical section of flower. **B**, anther. **C**, cross-section of ovary (orig.).

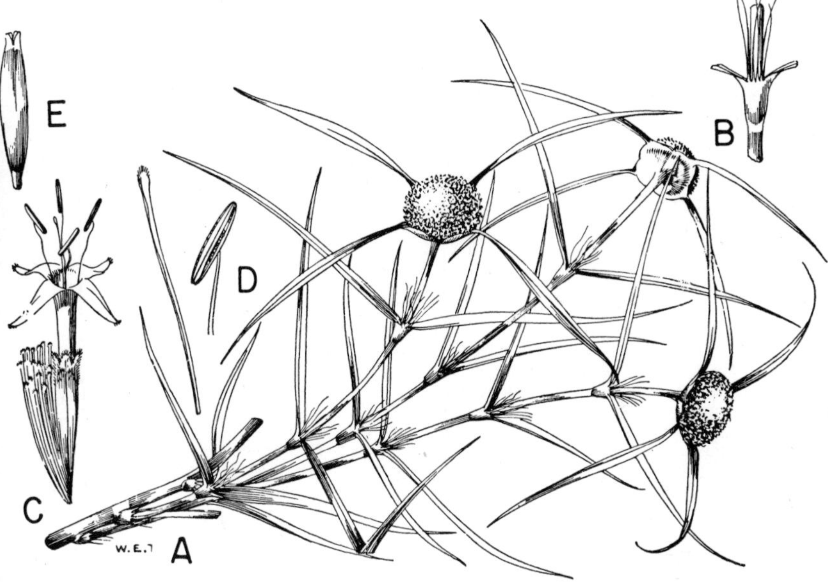

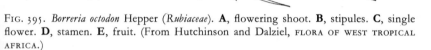

FIG. 395. *Borreria octodon* Hepper (*Rubiaceae*). **A**, flowering shoot. **B**, stipules. **C**, single flower. **D**, stamen. **E**, fruit. (From Hutchinson and Dalziel, FLORA OF WEST TROPICAL AFRICA.)

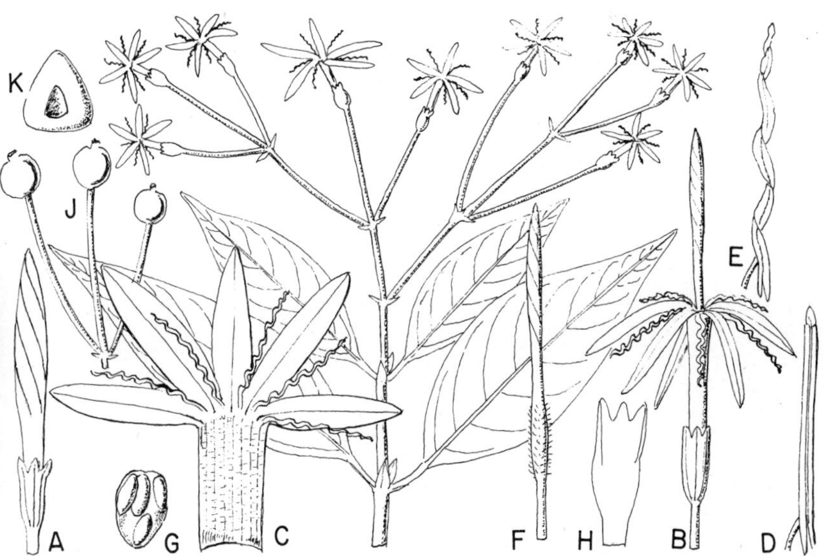

FIG. 396. *Tarenna spiranthera* (Drake) Homolle (*Rubiaceae*), Madagascar. **A**, flower-bud. **B**, flower. **C**, upper part of corolla laid open showing the spirally twisted anthers. **D**, anther before opening. **E**, anther becoming twisted. **F**, style. **G**, ovules. **H**, calyx opened out. **J**, fruits. **K**, seed. (Adapted from drawing by d'Apreval.)

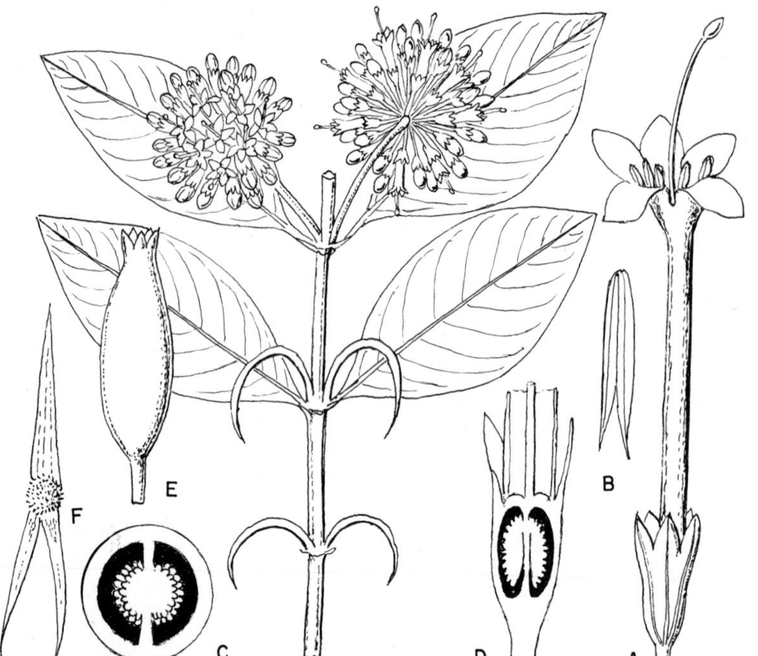

FIG. 397. *Uncaria gambir* Roxb. (*Rubiaceae*), Malaya; the lower inflorescences barren and transformed into hooks by which the plant climbs. **A**, flower. **B**, anther. **C**, cross-section of ovary. **D**, vertical section of ovary. **E**, fruit. **F**, seed winged at both ends (orig.).

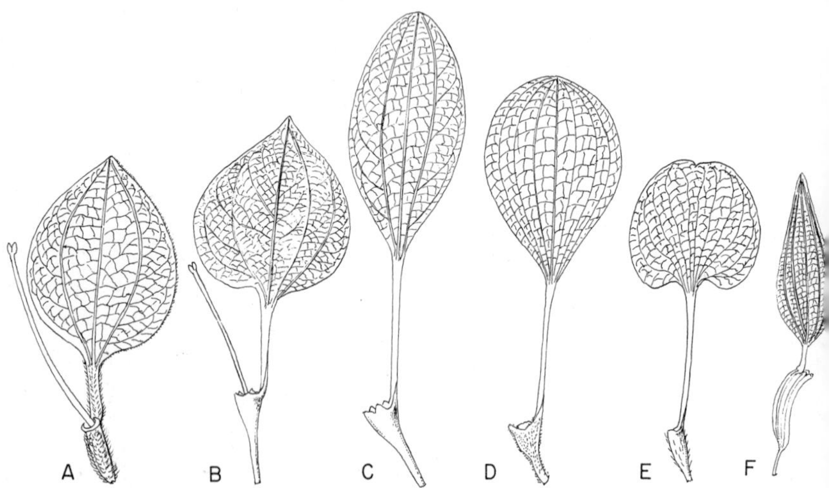

FIG. 398. Enlarged and mostly petaloid calyx-lobes of some *Rubiaceae*: **A**, *Pinckneya pubens* Michx., Florida. **B**, *Pogonopus tubulosus* (A. Rich.) K. Schum., Brazil. **C**, *Capirona wurdeckii* Steyermark. **D**, *Calophyllum spectabile* Steyermark, Guyana. **E**, *Calophyllum candidissimum* Vahl, Nicaragua. **F**, *Cosmocalyx spectabilis* Standley, Mexico (orig.).

Order 53. BIGNONIALES

(*Fam. Fl. Pl.* **1**, 387)

Families: **Cobaeaceae, Bignoniaceae, Pedaliaceae, Martyniaceae.**

Phylogeny: LOGANIALES → BIGNONIALES → Climax family *Martyniaceae* (herbs).

Cobaeaceae is a generically monotypic family referred by its original author to *Bignoniaceae*, but by later botanists to *Polemoniaceae*, except G. Don,[1] who regarded it as distinct from both, and with some justification. It differs from *Bignoniaceae* by the actinomorphic contorted corolla, by its long undivided anthers, 3 stigmas, its 3-locular ovary, septicidally 3-valved capsule, and nearly erect seeds. From all other *Polemoniaceae* it differs by its climbing habit, pinnate stipulate leaves with the end pair modified into tendrils, and by the septicidal capsule.

Though **Bignoniaceae**[2] follow after *Rubiaceae* the student should not presume that they are in any way related. They are not. Bentham and Hooker f. say of *Bignoniaceae*: "Arbores vel frutices alte scandentes, rarius frutices vel suffrutices erecti, rarissime herbae." These facts decide at once into which of my main divisions the family should be placed, and in which it occupies rather an isolated advanced position. It is thus far removed from the *Gesneriaceae* and *Scrophulariaceae*, near which it has usually been classified, for there are few members of *Bignoniaceae* which it might be claimed are really related to any of these two families. The most obvious, of course, are the few herbaceous genera such as *Amphicome* and *Incarvillea*. To use an oft repeated, indeed an almost hackneyed phrase in this book, the apparent similarity is "due to parallelism or convergent evolution". That is my interpretation of it and the system more or less stands or falls by it throughout.

The type genus is *Bignonia* Linn., now confined to a single species, *B. capreolata* Linn., native of North America. Evergreen climbing vine; leaves opposite, 2-foliolate, the rhachis ending in a branched tendril clinging to supports by small round disks; flowers few (2 or 3) in axillary clusters; bracts in pairs, ovate, much resembling leafy stipules; calyx campanulate, undulately lobulate; corolla tubular, slightly curved, with a spreading little oblique limb; stamens 4, included, inserted near the base of the tube; disk annular; ovary 2-locular, many-ovuled; capsule linear, compressed parallel to the partition, septifragally dehiscent with leathery valves; seeds elliptic,

---

[1] G. Don, EDINB. PHIL. JOURN. **10**, 109 (1824).

[2] Including *Crescentiaceae* Dumort. (1829).

FIG. 399. *Bignonia capreolata* Linn., the type species of the type genus of the family *Bignoniaceae*. **A**, note the remarkable transformation of the upper leaflets into disk-like suckers which adhere to other objects. **B**, one of the 4 anthers. **C**, gynoecium. **D**, fruit. **E**, seed (orig.).

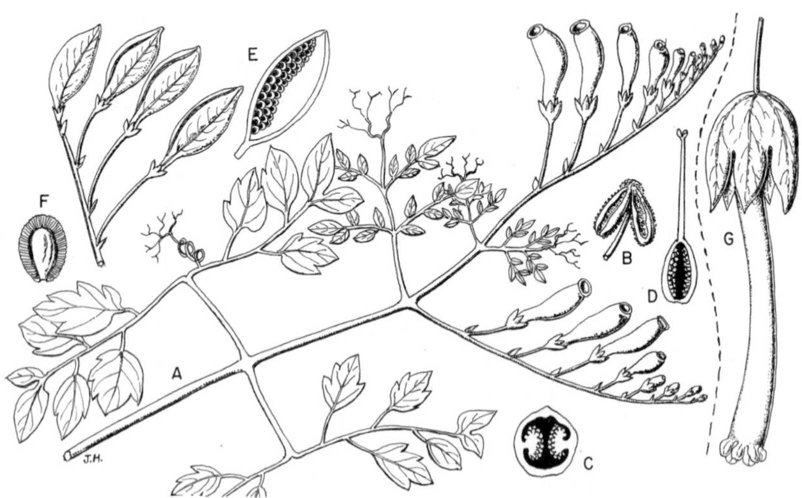

FIG. 400. **A**, *Eccremocarpus scaber* Ruiz & Pavon (*Bignoniaceae*), Chile and Argentina. **B**, anther. **C**, cross-section of ovary. **D**, vertical section of ovary. **E**, open fruit. **F**, seed. **G**, *E. longiflorus* Linn., Peru; note some leaflets transformed into tendrils (orig.).

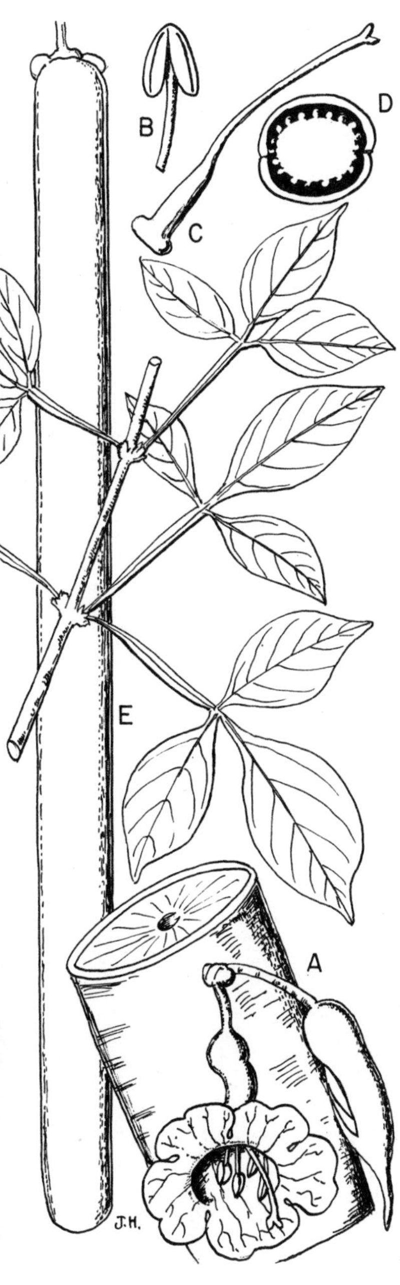

winged all around. The genus was named after Abbé Jean Paul Bignon, court librarian to Louis XIV (1662–1703).

The following exceptions are noted in the GENERA PLANTARUM: Infrafoliar spines present in *Parmentiera*; leaves 3- or 4-pinnately verticillate in *Diplanthera* and in some species of *Colea*; alternate or scattered in *Parmentiera*, *Phyllarthron* spp., *Crescentia* and *Kigelia*; flowers dimorphous, the upper sterile with a coloured calyx, the lower fertile with a green calyx in *Tourretia*; calyx double in *Amphilophium* and *Tourretia*, and in *Haplolophium* sp.; corolla deeply 2-lipped and shortly lobed in *Tynanthus* and *Amphilophium*; anterior lip small in *Tourretia*; lobes induplicate-valvate in *Haussmannia*, subvalvate in *Millingtonia*; only 2 perfect stamens in *Catalpa*, 5 in *Rhigozum* and *Cataphractes*; one anther-loculus small and empty in spp. of *Jacaranda* and *Colea*, glandular in *Millingtonia*; ovary 1-locular with 2 parietal placentas in *Eccremocarpus* and in tribe *Crescentieae*.

The fruits of *Bignoniaceae* are very different from those of *Scrophulariaceae*, the seeds are often winged, and there is no endosperm. The main centre of distribution is tropi-

FIG. 401. Palo de velas, the Candle tree of Panama, *Parmentiera cereifera* Seem. (*Bignoniaceae*); from the stem and branches hang long cylindrical fruits of a yellow wax colour, resembling candles. **A**, flower. **B**, stamen. **C**, gynoecium. **D**, cross-section of ovary. **E**, fruit. (Adapted from Fitch's drawing in Seeman.)

FIG. 402. *Phyllarthron bojerianum* DC. (*Bignoniaceae*), Madagascar. **A**, gynoecium and disk. **B**, cross-section of ovary. **C**, fruit. **D**, seed (orig.).

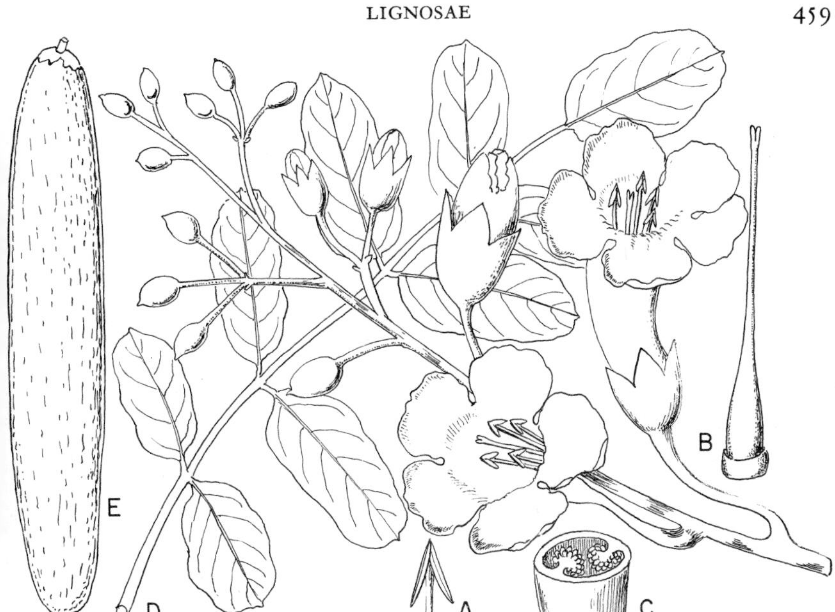

FIG. 403. *Kigelia africana* Benth. (*Bignoniaceae*), a feature tree in the tropical African landscape. **A**, anther. **B**, disk and gynoecium. **C**, cross-section of ovary showing parietal placentas. **D**, leaf. **E**, fruit which hangs down. (Adapted from drawing by Trevithick for FLORA OF WEST TROPICAL AFRICA.)

cal South America, being particularly plentiful in Brazil. *Scrophulariaceae*, on the other hand, are found mostly in temperate regions, the seeds usually have endosperm, are not winged, and are, as a rule, very small and numerous. On the whole my hypothesis is strengthened after considering the supposed affinity between these two families. Their floral diagrams, of course, may be very similar, but as stated in the Introduction these have influenced the minds of taxonomists long enough and helped to associate families in the same group which are not otherwise phylogenetically related. Indeed, Bentham and Hooker's further remarks on affinity have a bearing on the point:

Ordo inter *Personatas* sat bene limitatus, olim ad *Gesneraceas* et *Pedalineas* includendas extensus, ab iis tamen tam habitu quam characteribus facile distinctus, a prioribus imprimis seminum structura et situ, a *Pedalineis* ovarii structura interiore, et, generibus paucis exceptis, ab omnibus differunt septo inter placentas post anthesin aucto, placentis sub anthesi in medio septo utrinque approximatis vel contiguis post anthesin ad margines septi inter se distantibus. . . . Affinitas etiam observatur generibus paucis arboreis *Scrophularinearum*, e.g. *Wightiae*, cujus tamen placentae in medio septo constanter connatae.[1]

[1] (Translation): "A well-defined family among the *Personatae*, formerly included with the *Gesneriaceae* and *Pedaliaceae*, but easily separated from them by the habit, from the former

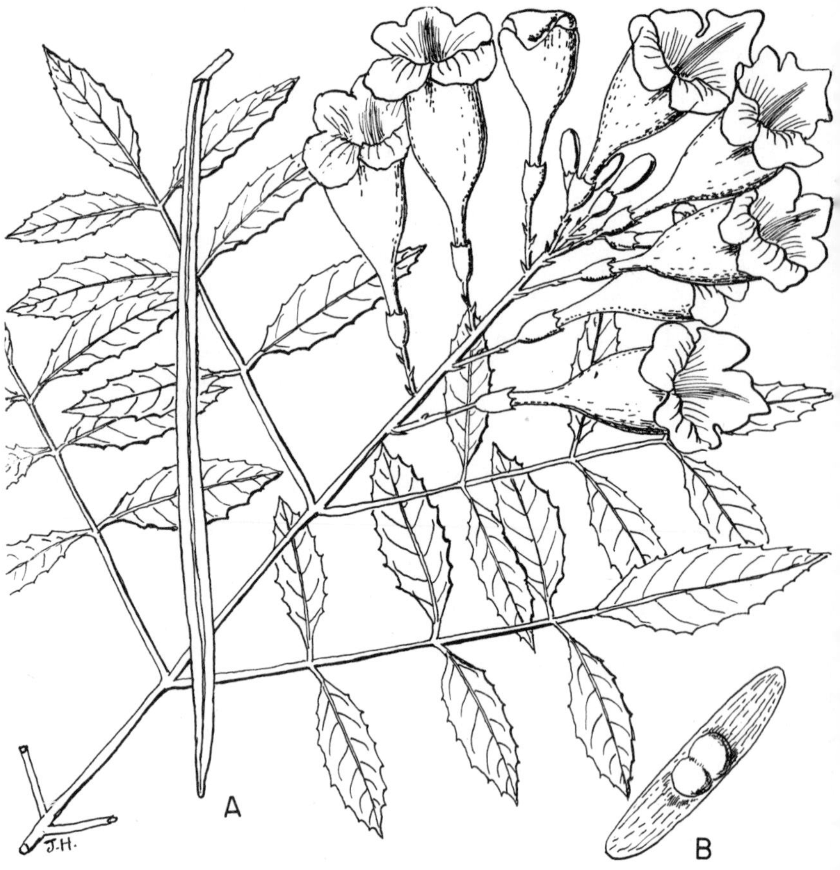

FIG. 404. *Tecoma stans* (Linn.) H.B. & K., tropical America and cult. (*Bignoniaceae*). **A**, fruit. **B**, seed (orig.).

Pedalium, the type genus of the small family **Pedaliaceae**,[1] embraces only two species, from tropical Africa to India; annual herbs; leaves opposite or alternate; flowers solitary, axillary, yellow; pedicels with 1–2 glands at the base, ebracteate; calyx 5-partite; corolla-tube equal and slender at the base, limb subbilabiate, lobes 5, subequal; stamens 4, didynamous; anther-loculi ovate, parallel, separate, pendulous from the apex of the connective; disk

especially by the structure and position of the seed, and from the *Pedaliaceae* by the internal structure of the ovary, and, with the exception of a few genera, different from all of them by the septum after flowering increasing between the placentas. . . . Relationships also observed amongst a few genera of the arboreal *Scrophulariaceae*, i.e. *Wightia*, in which, however, the placentas are connate in the middle of the septum."

[1] Including *Trapellaceae* Honda & Sakisaka (1930). *Sesamaceae* Horaninow (1834).

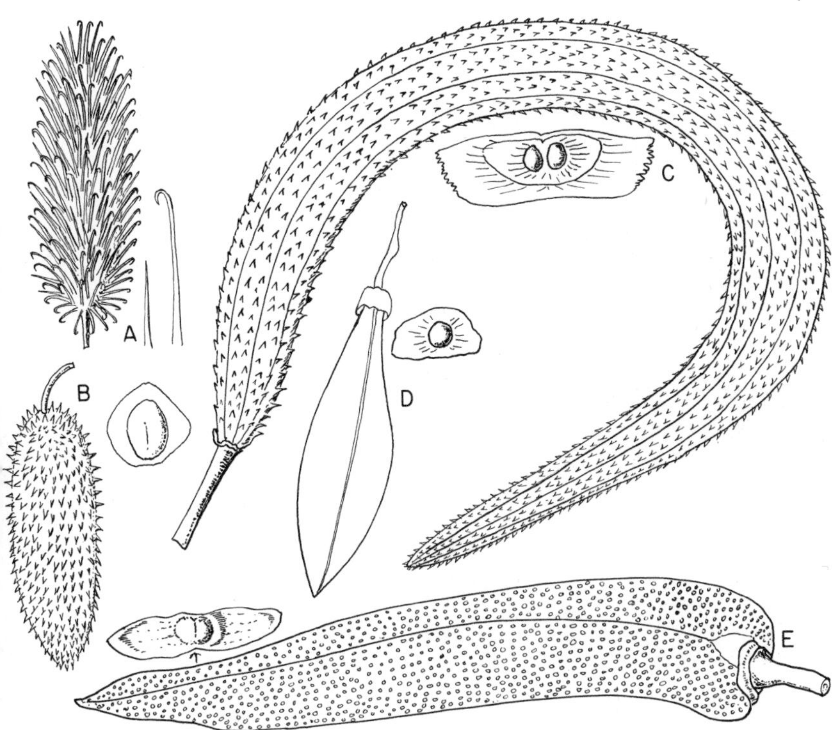

FIG. 405. Fruits and seeds of some *Bignoniaceae*. **A**, *Tourrettia lappacea* Willd., and bristles, South America. **B**, *Clytostoma callistegioides* (Cham.) Baill., with seed alongside. **C**, *Heterophragma adenophyllum* Seem., with seed, India. **D**, *Distictis lactiflora* DC., with seed, West Indies. **E**, *Ceratophytum tetragonolobum* (Jacq.) Sprague & Sandwith, with seed, Venezuela (orig.).

slight; ovary superior, 2-locular, with 2 ovules in each loculus; fruit 2-locular, hard and indehiscent, ovoid-pyramidate, angles armed with spreading conical spines; seeds oblong.

Outstanding genera are *Trapella* (Fig. 407), an aquatic Chinese plant with inferior ovary; *Pterodiscus*, a 4-winged indehiscent unarmed fruit; *Harpagophytum*, with fruit tardily dehiscent and flattened contrary to the septum and armed along the edges with 2 rows of long horny arms bearing recurved spines; *Holubia*, with a broad orbicular membranous wing but otherwise unarmed. *Sesamothamnus* (Fig. 408, **J**) has a very long, cylindric corolla-tube spurred at the base, the leaves small on short branchlets armed with spines, whilst *Stigmatosiphon* has an S-shaped corolla-tube not spurred at the base. I see no good reason for "declassifying" *Trapella* as a separate family.

The family **Martyniaceae** has sometimes been included in *Pedaliaceae*, but the late Dr. O. Stapf, F.R.S., a first-class taxonomic botanist, kept it apart and we are well content to follow his example. There are only three

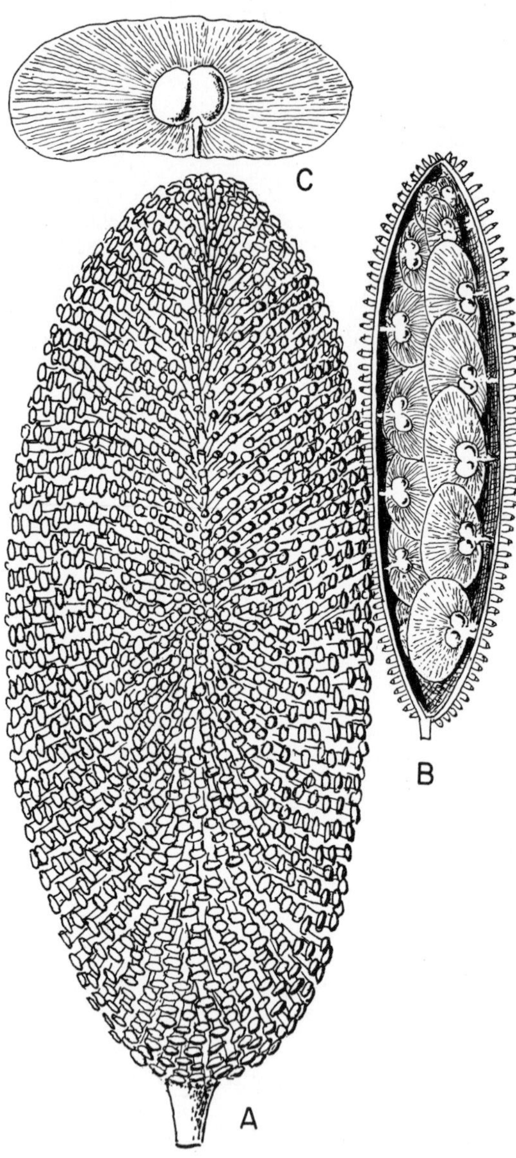

FIG. 406. **A**, fruit of *Pithecoctenium echinatum* (Jacq.) K. Schum. (*Bignoniaceae*). **B**, valve of same opened out showing arrangement of seeds (reduced). **C**, seed (orig.).

genera, all in America. Two of them have 4 stamens, *Proboscidea*, South America, with the corolla-tube broadened from the base, and *Craniolaria*, also South America, with a very long cylindric corolla-tube campanulate at the upper end. The third and type genus, *Martynia*, Mexico, has only 2 fertile stamens, and the corolla-tube broadened from the base.

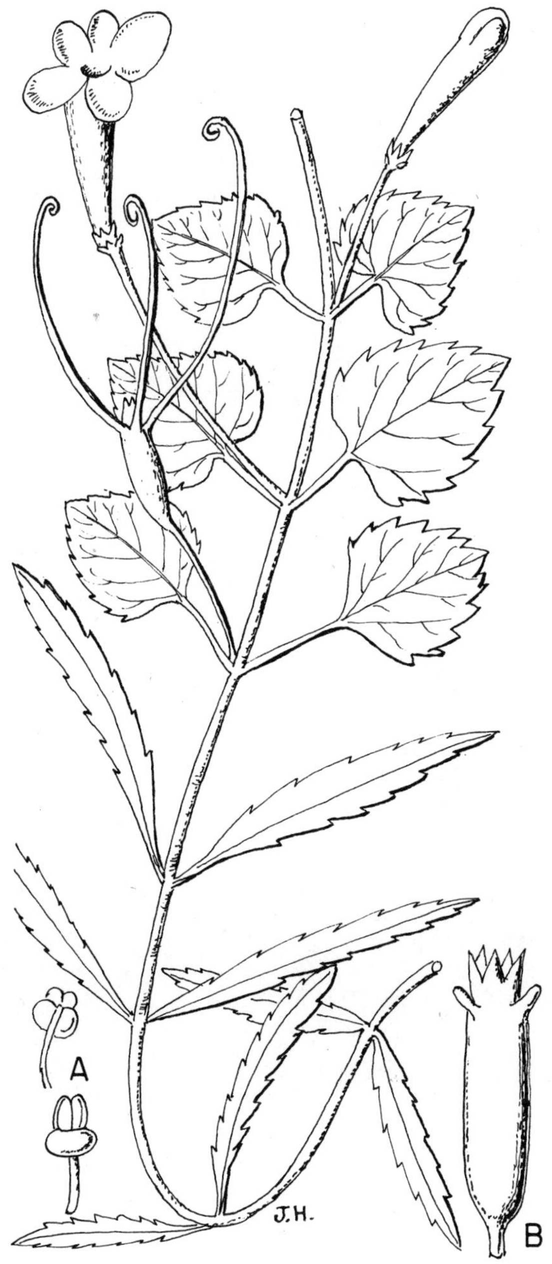

FIG. 407. *Trapella sinensis* Oliv. (*Pedaliaceae*), China, is well provided with hooks to aid its distribution by aquatic animals. **A**, stamens, front and back. **B**, young fruit (orig.).

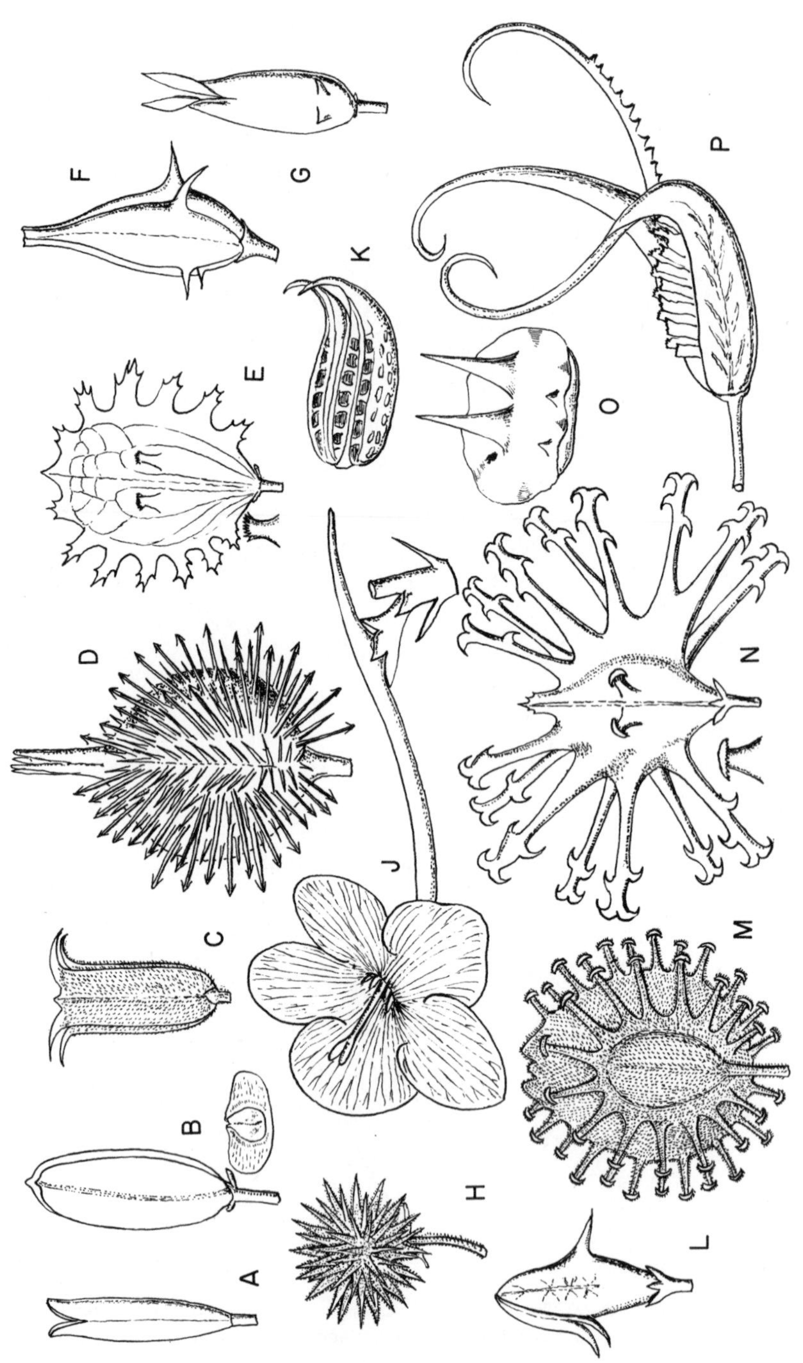
A
B
C
D
E
F
G
H
J
K
L
M
N
O
P

ORDER 54. VERBENALES

(*Fam. Fl. Pl.* **1**, 393)

Families: **Ehretiaceae, Verbenaceae, Stilbaceae, Chloanthaceae, Phyrmataceae.**

Phylogeny: LOGANIALES → VERBENALES → **Ehretiaceae** → **Phrymataceae** (herbs).

The basic group for *Verbenaceae* is **Ehretiaceae**[1] (conserved name) proposed as a family by Martius in 1827 (NOV. GEN. ET. SP. **2**, 138), followed by Lindley in his INTROD. NAT. SYST. 242 (1830). The type genus is *Ehretia*, described as follows:

Trees or shrubs; leaves alternate, entire or dentate; flowers small, in terminal cymes or panicles, rarely axillary and solitary; calyx small, 5-partite, segments narrow, imbricate or open; corolla-tube short, lobes 5, imbricate, spreading; stamens 5, inserted in the tube, exserted or rarely included; anthers ovate or oblong; ovary 2-locular, loculi imperfectly 2-locellate, or 4-locular; style terminal, shortly or deeply 2-lobed, stigmas terminal, capitate or clavate; ovules attached about the middle of the axis; fruit a small globose drupe, endocarp hard, divided into two 2-locular or four 1-locular pyrenes; seeds mostly straight, with little endosperm; cotyledons ovate, not plicate. Type species *E. tinifolia* Linn.

All the genera are trees or shrubs except *Coldenia*, which are herbs, often diffuse or prostrate.

In the large family **Verbenaceae**[2] we have reached the top of our funda-

---

[1] Including *Cordiaceae* R.Br. ex Dumort. (1829). *Sebestenaceae* Dulac (1799). *Duckeodendraceae* Kuhlmann (1950).

[2] Including *Viticaceae* A. L. de Juss. (1789). *Pyrenaceae* Ventenat (1799). *Nyctanthaceae* J. G. Agardh (1858). *Avicenniaceae* Endlich. (1841). *Durantaceae* J. G. Agardh (1858). *Petreaceae* J. G. Agardh (1858). *Symphoremataceae* van Tieghem (1898).

FIG. 408. Fruits of *Pedaliaceae* and *Martyniaceae*. **A**, *Sesamum alatum* Thonn. (*Pedal.*), tropical and subtropical South Africa. **B**, *Sesamothamnus busseanus* Engl. (*Pedal.*), with seed, tropical Africa. **C**, *Ceratotheca triloba* E. Mey. (*Pedal.*), South Africa and east tropical Africa. **D**, *Uncarina grandidieri* (Baill.) Stapf (*Pedal.*), Madagascar. **E**, *Harpagophyton peglerae* Stapf (*Pedal.*), South Africa. **F**, *Rogeria adenophylla* J. Gay (*Pedal.*), tropical Africa. **G**, *Rogeria longiflora* (Roy.) DC. (*Pedal.*), South Africa. **H**, *Josephina africana* Vatke, (*Pedal.*) east tropical Africa. **J**, flower of *Sesamothamnus lugardii* N.E.Br. (*Pedal.*), subtropical South Africa and Rhodesia. **K**, *Craniolaria annua* Linn. (*Martyn.*), tropical America. **L**, *Pedalium murex* Linn. (*Pedal.*), tropical Africa and Asia. **M**, *Harpagophytum peltatum* Baker (*Pedal.*), Madagascar. **N**, *Harpagophytum procumbens* (Burch.) DC. ex Meisn. (*Pedal.*), South Africa. **O**, *Dicerocaryum zanguebarica* (Lour.) Merrill (*Pedal.*), east tropical Africa. **P**, *Proboscidea altheifolia* (Benth.) Decne. (*Martyn.*) Mexico (orig.).

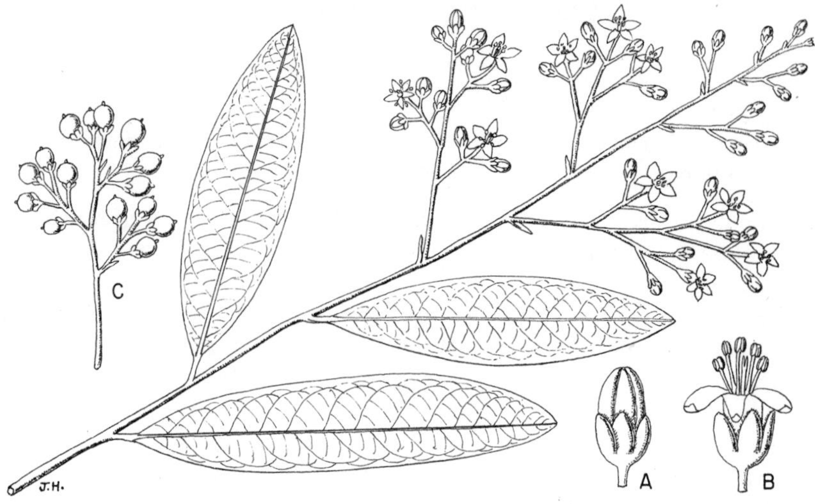

FIG. 409. *Ehretia tinifolia* Linn. (*Ehretiaceae*), West Indies. **A**, flower-bud. **B**, flower. **C**, fruits.

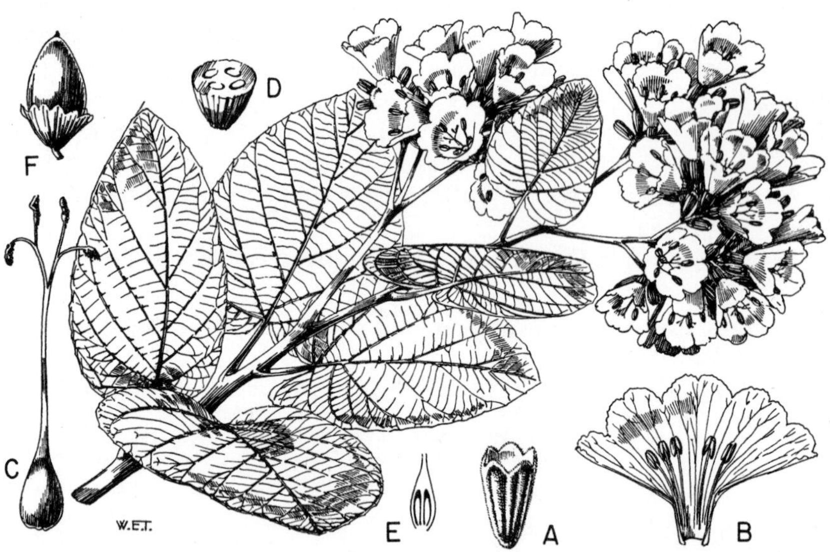

FIG. 410. *Cordia africana* Lam. (*Ehretiaceae*), tropical Africa. **A**, calyx. **B**, corolla laid open. **C**, gynoecium. **D**, cross-section of ovary. **E**, vertical section of ovary. **F**, fruit. (From Hutchinson and Dalziel, FLORA OF WEST TROPICAL AFRICA.)

mentally woody phylum, **Lignosae.** It is usually classified next to *Lamiaceae* (*Labiatae*), and it is perhaps almost unnecessary to point out to the student that parts of the two families seem rather similar because both of them represent climaxes of evolution in their respective groups. To those who would

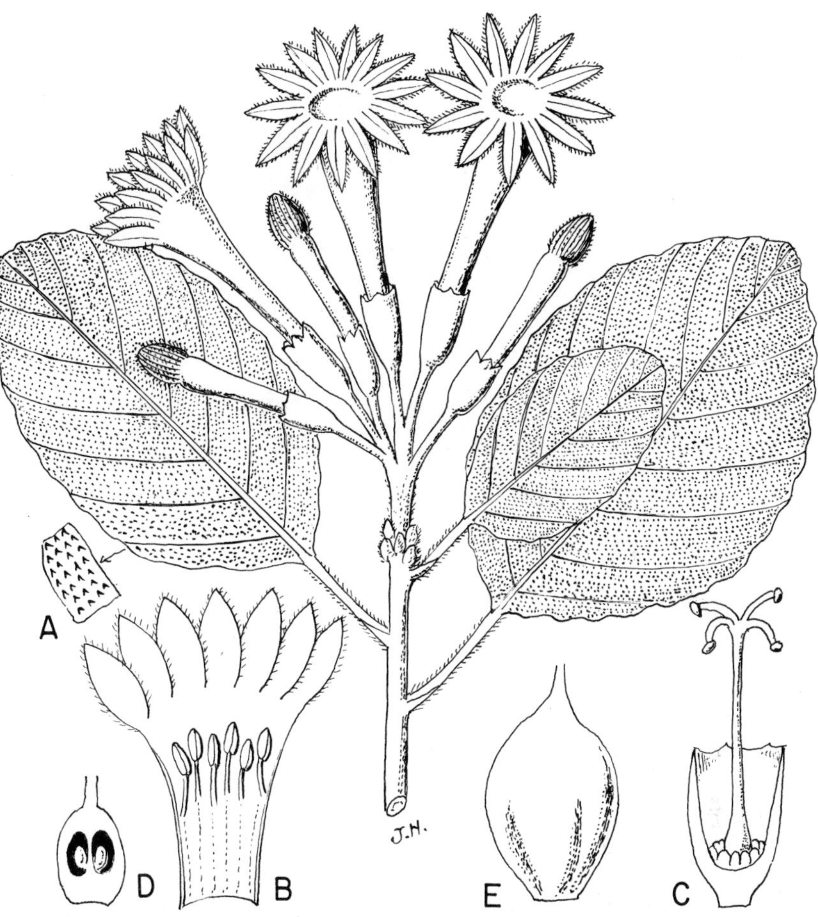

Fig. 411. An outstanding species of *Cordia* with more than five corolla-lobes, *C. angiocarpa* A. Rich., tropical America. **A**, portion of leaf showing the indumentum. **B**, part of corolla opened out. **C**, calyx, disk and gynoecium. **D**, vertical section of ovary. **E**, fruit. (Adapted from Martius FLORA BRAS.)

classify *Verbenaceae* in the same group as *Lamiaceae*, I would point out that it is a very far cry indeed from a Teak tree (*Verbenaceae*) to the humble Ground Ivy, *Nepeta hederaceae* (L.) Trev. (*Lamiaceae*). And the *Nepeta* is not at all related to *Verbena*, some species of which are herbaceous.

In *Verbenaceae* the leaves are mostly opposite, usually simple, but in *Vitex* they are digitately foliolate. There are no stipules. It seems more than significant that if we look for a primitive type of *Verbenaceae* the choice falls on the genus *Tectona* (Fig. 415), a hard-wooded timber tree, in which 5 stamens have been retained (as in *Ehretiaceae*), a character shared by another

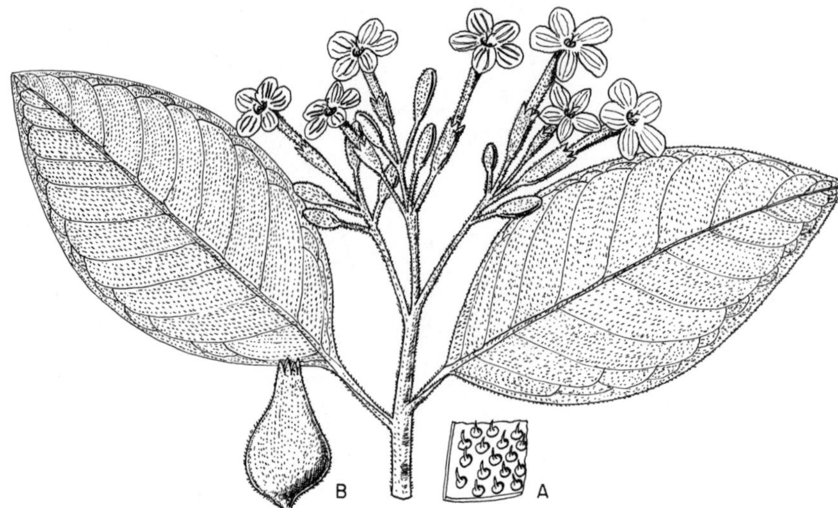

FIG. 412. *Cordia sebestena* Linn. (*Ehretiaceae*), American tropics. **A**, bulbous based setulae on the leaves. **B**, fruit (orig.).

woody genus, *Geunsia*. In all the other genera the fifth stamen is absent or rarely represented by a staminode, and there are sometimes only 2 stamens (as in some *Lamiaceae*). The ovary, unlike that of *Lamiaceae*, is not lobed, the style being terminal, and usually the ovary is composed of only 2 carpels.

In this phylogenetic system *Verbenaceae* are therefore regarded as a parallelism and not as a close relative of *Lamiaceae*. The test for this, besides the differences in the floral and fruit structures, is to see whether any genus of either family shows real (not superficial) relationship. I have tried but failed to find any such. Hence *Verbenaceae* top the linear sequence of **Lignosae**, and *Lamiaceae* that of **Herbaceae**.

The type genus of *Verbenaceae*, *Verbena* Linn., embraces about 300 species, mostly in tropical and extra-tropical America, with a few in the Old World (type species *V. officinalis* Linn.); shrublets or herbs with simple hairs or rarely glabrous; leaves opposite or rarely 3-verticillate or alternate, dentate to incised or dissected, rarely entire; spikes terminal, single or sometimes collected into corymbs or panicles, rarely axillary; flowers usually small, solitary in the bract-axils; calyx tubular, 5-ribbed, 5-toothed; corolla-tube straight or incurved; limb spreading, somewhat 2-lipped; lobes 5, posterior outermost, anterior innermost; stamens 4, didynamous, very rarely 2, included; anthers ovate, either all without appendage or the connective on the anterior produced into a clavate or glandular appendage, loculi parallel or slightly divergent; ovary entire or shortly 4-lobed, 4-locular, loculi 1-ovuled; style often short, 2-lobed, anterior lobe larger

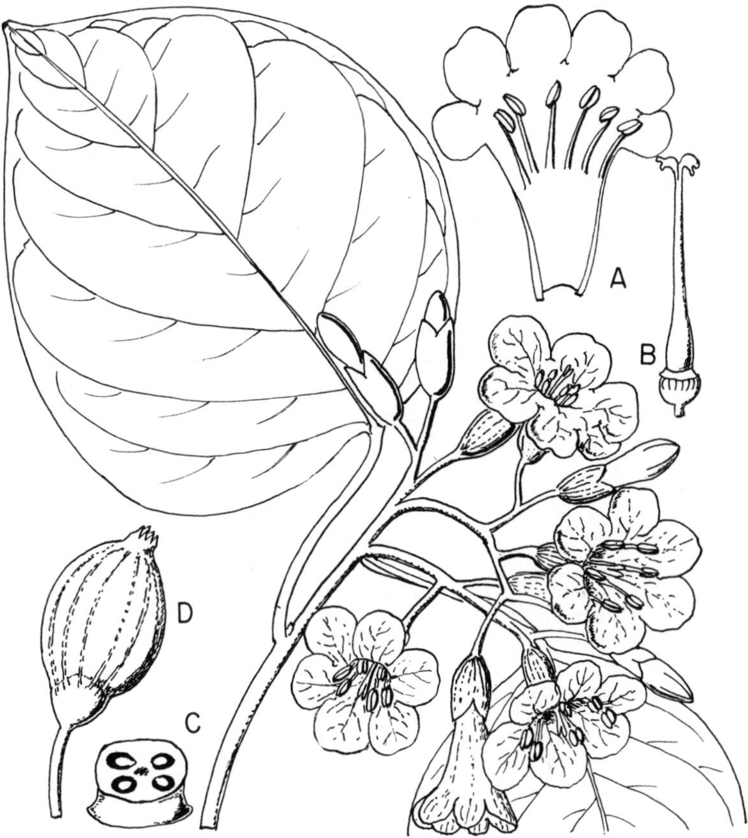

FIG. 413. *Cordia subcordata* Lam. (*Ehretiaceae*), common tree on beaches and near mangrove swamps and widely spread in the tropics; flowers orange-red; fruit with edible kernels; known as "Nawanawa" in Fiji. **A**, corolla opened out. **B**, gynoecium. **C**, cross-section of ovary. **D**, fruit (orig.).

and stigmatic, posterior often smooth; ovule inserted near the base; fruit enclosed by the calyx, dry, separating into 4 narrow pyrenes, pericarp crustaceous or hard; seed erect, without endosperm.

In my FAMILIES OF FLOWERING PLANTS I treated as separate families *Stilbaceae*, *Chloanthaceae* and *Phrymataceae*, which were tribes of *Verbenaceae* in Bentham and Hooker's GENERA PLANTARUM. These small families are mostly confined to the Southern Hemisphere. Thus the family is reduced to include only tribes *Verbeneae*, *Viticeae*, *Caryopterideae*, *Symphoremeae* and *Avicennieae*. A few exceptions may be noted: Leaves imparipinnate in *Peronema* Jacq. (Malaya), digitately compound in *Vitex* and *Rapinia*; alternate in *Dipyrena*, *Amasonia*, and *Stachytarpheta* spp. Corolla with 6–16 lobes

FIG. 414. *Verbena officinalis* Linn., the type species of the type genus of the family *Verbenaceae*; this family is placed at the end of the author's system, being regarded as the culmination of the fundamentally woody phylum, **Lignosae**. **A**, bract. **B**, flower. **C**, corolla laid open. **D**, anther. **E**, gynoecium. **F**, cross-section of ovary. **G**, one loculus of ovary showing erect ovule (orig.).

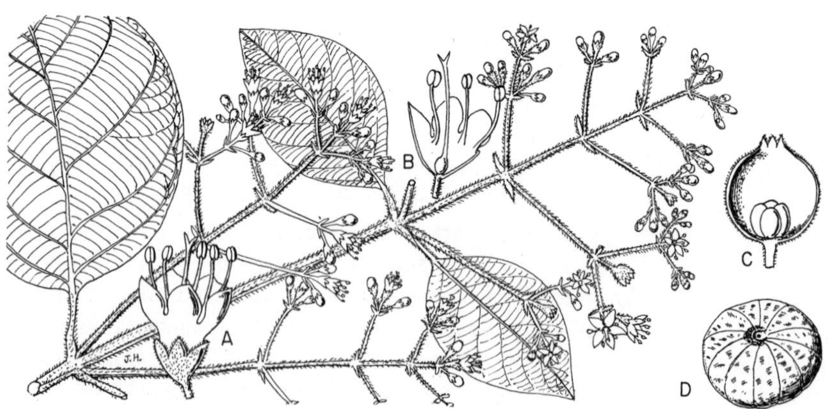

FIG. 415. The Teak tree, *Tectona grandis* Linn. (*Verbenaceae*), tropical Asia; one of the greatest money-makers in the timber trade. **A**, flower. **B**, vertical section of same. **C**, young fruit enclosed by the calyx. **D**, seed (orig.).

FIG. 416. *Baillonia amabilis* Bocquillon (*Verbenaceae*). In commemorating the name of this celebrated French botanist, Bocquillon stated "Hocce genus ego gratissimo animo dicabam clarissimo H. Baillon qui, multis operibus suis scientias botanicas singulis diebus auget et locupletat". **A**, flower-bud. **B**, flower. **C**, stamen. **D**, disk and gynoecium. **E**, fruit. **F**, portion of leaf, showing nervation. (Adapted from Baillon.)

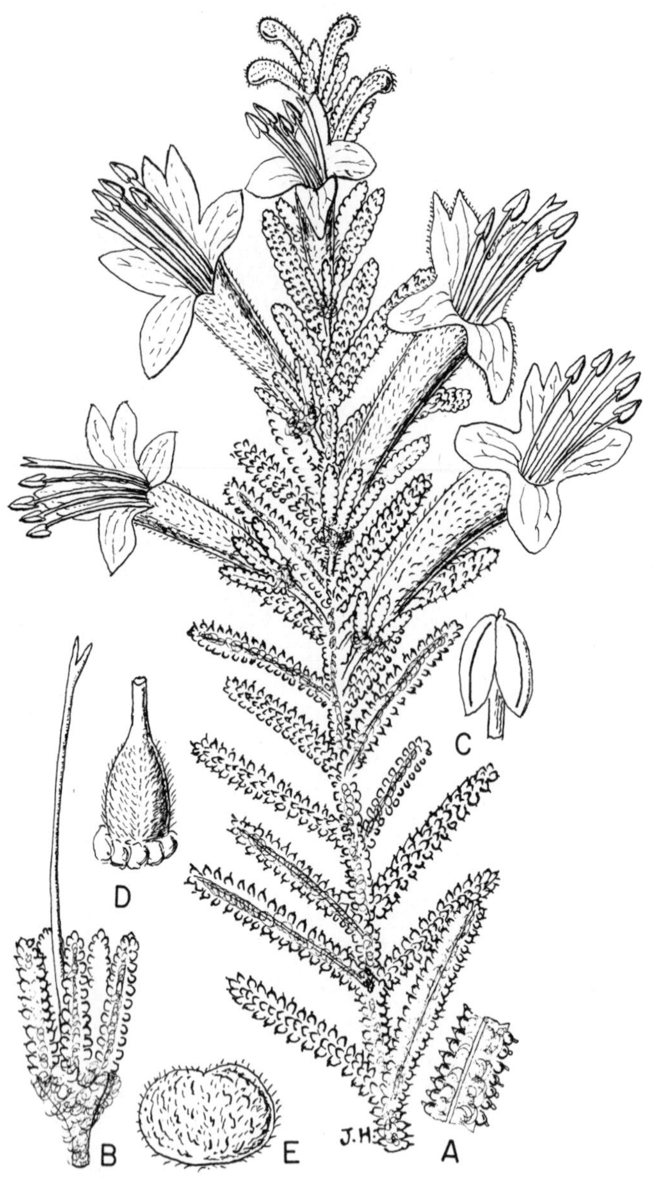

FIG. 417. *Chloanthes staechadis* R.Br., Australia, the type species of the genus (*Chloanthaceae*). **A**, portion of leaf showing the lower woolly surface. **B**, calyx and style. **C**, anther. **D**, disk and ovary. **E**, fruit (orig.).

in *Symphorema* (cf. *Cordia* in *Ehretiaceae*), sub 1-lipped (partly split on one side) in *Monochilus*. Ovary of 4 carpels in *Duranta* and 4 or 5 in *Geunsia*. Fruit subcapsular in *Caryopteris* and *Avicennia*.

There are four species of the type genus *Stilbe* Berg (**Stilbaceae**), all in South Africa (type species *S. vestita* Berg) (for Fig. see FAMILIES OF FLOWERING PLANTS, 2nd Ed. I, 396); erect shrubs; leaves verticillate, crowded, linear, margins recurved; spikes terminal, dense, ovoid to cylindric, sessile amongst the upper leaves; bracts rather similar to the leaves; bracteoles linear or lanceolate; flowers solitary to each bract; calyx 5-toothed or lobed; corolla-tube often slender, hirsute in the throat; limb equal, spreading, lobes 5, narrow, flat; stamens 4, subequal, inserted between the lobes; anther-loculi parallel, separate or at length rather confluent at the apex; ovary 2-locular; ovule 1, erect; style entire or 2-fid; fruit enclosed by the calyx, oblong, 2-locular, or one carpel abortive, indehiscent; seed laxly reticulate.

The type genus of **Chloanthaceae** is *Cloanthes* R.Br., with about 8 species, Australia (type *C. staechadis* R.Br., Fig. 417); shrublets or perennial herbs; woolly-tomentose or glandular-hairy; leaves opposite or ternately verticillate, decurrent, bullate; flowers axillary, solitary, shortly pedicellate, upper ones crowded into leafy spikes; bracteoles linear below the middle of the pedicels; calyx 5-lobed or almost 5-partite, lobes narrow, herbaceous, woolly-villous outside; corolla-tube elongated, limb 2-lipped, posterior lip erect at the base and 2-lobed, lobes spreading, anterior lip spreading, 3-lobed; stamens 4, subdidynamous, attached below the middle of the tube; anther-loculi parallel; ovary imperfectly or subperfectly 2-locular, loculi 2-ovuled; style 2-lobed; ovules laterally attached; fruit dry, subdrupaceous, endocarp hard, splitting into 2 pyrenes, 2-locular by spurious septa.

Phrymataceae Schauer (1847) occupies the ultimate place in our **Lignosae** phylum, though it is a genus of herbs, *Phryma*, and clearly related to *Verbenaceae*. It is especially interesting, in addition to its distinctive floral structure, because of its discontinuous distribution, which is shown in the map in my FAMILIES OF FLOWERING PLANTS (2nd Ed. I, 398), i.e. eastern North America and eastern Asia. This distribution recalls that of some woody plants, such as *Magnolia* and *Hamamelis*. The ovary is greatly reduced, 1-locular with 1 erect ovule. The calyx is strongly reflexed in fruit and appressed to the rhachis of the inflorescence, the 3 posterior lobes hooked at the apex (FAMILIES OF FLOWERING PLANTS, 2nd Ed. I, Fig. 246).

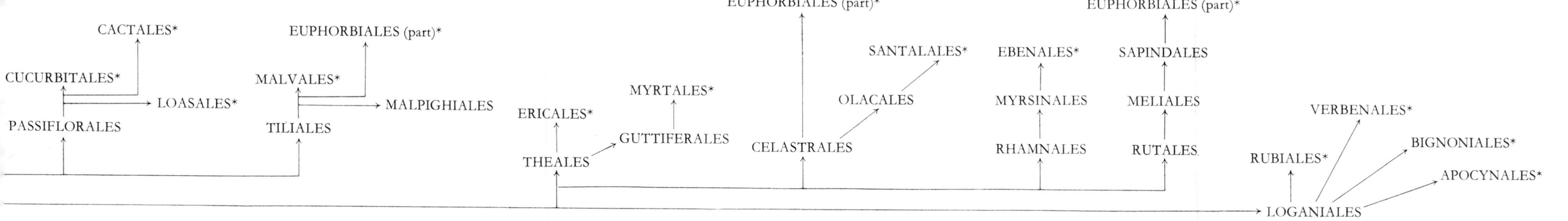

ı of evolution of the Orders of fundamentally woody Dicotyledons (**Lignosae**) as arranged in the pre-
to the student whilst reading the text. A group marked with an * is regarded as a complete climax from
: is unlikely to have taken place.

ORDER 55. **RANALES**

(*Fam. Fl. Pl.* **1**, 399)

Families: **Paeoniaceae, Helleboraceae, Ranunculaceae, Nymphaeaceae, Podophyllaceae, Ceratophyllaceae, Cabombaceae.**

RANALES → considered to be the most primitive group of herbaceous flowering plants, more or less on a parallel with MAGNOLIALES.

The Order RANALES, as defined in the present system, is considered to be the most primitive of the herbaceous groups of Dicotyledons, a parallel or duplicate group of the MAGNOLIALES, but in contrast almost entirely herbaceous. Indeed, except for some species of *Clematis*, which are soft-wooded climbers and probably the most advanced genus of the group, the whole Order is herbaceous. They are perennials with underground rootstocks nearly all dying down in winter, or during the dry season in more temperate climates. The paucity of annuals in the Order is very striking, and they belong to the most advanced genera such as *Nigella* (carpels united), and *Delphinium* (few to one carpel and flowers zygomorphic). So here at any rate it seems quite clear that the annual habit is more recent than the perennial, associated as it is with an advanced type of floral structure. It has also been shown that in the TILIALES alliance (a fundamentally woody group) there is a considerable number of annuals in the most advanced family, *Malvaceae*.

From *Ranunculaceae*, as usually circumscribed, it seems desirable, at any rate on phylogenetic grounds, to recognise at least three other families, *Paeonia* as 1, *Paeoniaceae*; *Helleborus* and its relatives as 2, *Helleboraceae*, both with numerous ovules and follicular fruits; and *Ranunculus* and its relatives as 3, *Ranunculaceae* (*sensu stricto*), with achenial 1-seeded fruits. It should be noted that there are no genera with zygomorphic flowers in *Ranunculaceae*, but some have been evolved in *Helleboraceae* (*Aconitum* and *Delphinium*). These three families were in the past usually treated as one, perhaps because of putting too much stress on one character, the apocarpous gynoecium (free carpels).

Paeoniaceae has been recognised as a separate family by several recent writers. The single genus *Paeonia* has always been something of a puzzle, and it may be regarded as rather an isolated primitive type of the Order RANALES and perhaps a link between the latter group and MAGNOLIALES, for some species are rather woody. The foliage is definitely similar to that of the Hellebores; the anthers are extrorse, and there is a large fleshy disk around the carpels sometimes at length nearly covering them and resembling a fig with an apical ostiole; a striking feature is the arillate seeds, which are also common in an early family of the **Lignosae**, namely *Dilleniaceae*. Could this character have been retained from as far down the scale as the *Cycadaceae*, which have arillate seeds?

The carpels in **Helleboraceae**[1] have remained free from one another except in some species of *Helleborus*, in which they are shortly connate at the base; they are completely connate into a capsular fruit in *Nigella*, and reduced to only one in *Glaucidium* spp., *Delphinium consolida*, *Actaea*, and *Cimicifuga* spp.

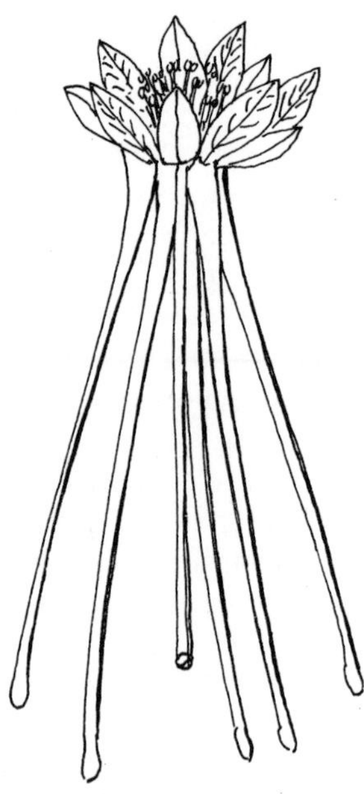

FIG. 418. *Aquilegia longissima* A. Gray, a highly evolved flower with extra long spurs in the otherwise primitive herbaceous family (*Helleboraceae*).

From *Helleborus* we may trace the origin of the Aquilegias, some with very long-spurred petals (see Fig. 418), the Winter Aconites (*Eranthis hyemalis*), *Nigella*, *Aconitum* and *Delphinium*, the last two especially representing a climax in floral development within the family. An interesting link between *Isopyrum* and *Aquilegia* is *Semiaquilegia* (Fig. 419), a genus with the petals only pouched at the base (and not spurred), but with the characteristic staminodes of *Aquilegia*. *Cimicifuga* is also an advanced genus of this group, with densely spicate flowers.

A few have medicinal properties, such as "Golden Seal" *Hydrastis canadensis* L., found in Canada and the eastern United States of America, and various species of *Aconitum*. Golden Seal was formerly common in rich woods and was a favourite remedy of the Indians and early settlers. It is now cultivated in the Pacific Northwest and North Carolina. The rhizomes contain several alkaloids, used as a tonic and for the treatment of catarrh and other inflamed mucous membranes.

Aconite is obtained from the tuberous roots of *Aconitum napellus* Linn., a familiar garden plant in Europe and long known to be poisonous. Only the roots are official, aconitine being the most important of the several alkaloids present. It is used externally for neuralgia and rheumatism, and internally to relieve fever and pain (A. V. Hill ECON. BOT., 2nd Ed., 245). The British plant was regarded as a separate species, *A. anglicum*, by the late Dr. O. Stapf. (Fig. 420).

The type genus is *Helleborus* Linn., of which there are about 18 species,

[1] Including *Nigellaceae* J. G. Agardh (1858). *Hydrastidaceae* Lemesle (1948).

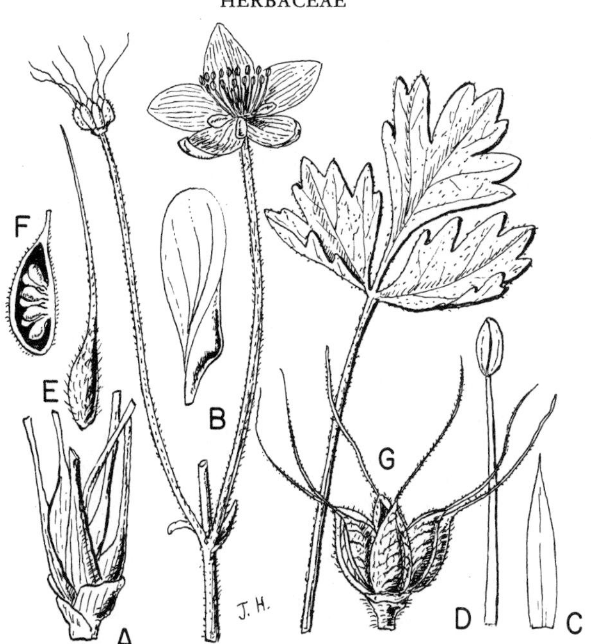

FIG. 419. *Semiaquilegia henryi* Drumm. & Hutch. (*Helleboraceae*) (from KEW BULL.); a genus with a more primitive type of petal, merely saccate and not spurred as in the more advanced genus *Aquilegia*. **A**, base of plant. **B**, petal. **C**, staminode. **D**, stamen. **E**, carpel. **F**, vertical section of carpel. **G**, fruit (orig.).

mainly in S.E. Europe (type species *H. niger* Linn., Fig. 421): herbs with a perennial rhizome; leaves palmately or pedately dissected or lobed, the cauline few, the uppermost resembling an involucre, or all bract-like; flowers sometimes precocious ("Christmas Roses"), rather large, white, green or lurid; sepals 5, broad, petaloid or subherbaceous; petals small, clawed, nectary-formed, lamina tubular at the base or bearing a scale; stamens numerous; carpels mostly few, free or united at the base, several-ovuled; fruits dehiscent at the apex on the adaxial side; seeds shining.

Here are a few examples of genera which diverge by certain characters from the type genus: Duration: annual in *Nigella*, *Komaroffia*, *Garidella*, *Leptopyrum*, *Delphinium* spp. Stem: climbing in a few Asiatic spp. of *Aconitum*; slightly woody in *Xanthorrhiza*; leaves peltate in *Asteropyrum* (Fig. 422). Flowers: in racemes or panicles in *Actaea*, *Beesia* and *Cimicifuga*; in *Eranthis* the upper leaf-segments form an involucre below the flower, the sepals are petaloid, and the petals are very small and nectariform; zygomorphic in tribe *Delphinieae*; sepals spurred in *Aquilegia*, saccate in *Semiaquilegia*; nectariferous in *Aconitum*; stamens few in *Caltha* spp., inner stamens sterile and scale-like in *Aquilegia* and *Semiaquilegia*; carpels more or

FIG. 420. *Aconitum anglicum* Stapf (*Helleboraceae*), Great Britain. **A**, longitudinal section of flower. **B**, nectary. **C**, lower sepal. **D**, lower petal. **E**, stamen. **F**, fruit. **G**, seed. (Adapted from BOTANICAL MAGAZINE.)

less united in *Nigella*, *Komaroffia*, *Garidella*; solitary in *Delphinium* section *Consolida*, *Actaea*, *Beesia*, *Cimicifuga* spp.; sometimes reduced to 2 and then divaricate in fruit in *Isopyrum*. Fruit baccate in *Hydrastis* and *Actaea*; seeds winged in *Glaucidium*, covered with transverse membranous scales or ridges in *Anemonopsis*, *Nigella* spp., and in nearly all tribe *Delphinieae*. As the family **Helleboraceae** is in this system separated from *Ranunculaceae*, the following key to tribes and genera is given as an example to the student of a phylogenetic arrangement.

Flowers actinomorphic ("regular"); petals small and narrow or imperfect or absent; seeds neither scaly nor winged or rarely so (*Glaucidium*)
1. HELLEBOREAE

Flowers zygomorphic ("irregular"); petals conspicuous; seeds often transversely ridged with scales, or winged 2. DELPHINEAE

Tribe 1. HELLEBOREAE

Flowers solitary, rarely few and subpaniculate, never racemose:
Leaves palmately nerved or palmately divided Subtribe **Calthinae**
Petals present but usually much reduced and nectariferous:
Upper leaf-segments not forming an involucre below the flower:
Sepals usually deciduous:
Petals several; leaves not peltate *Trollius* Linn.
Petals 5, club-shaped; leaves peltate *Asteropyrum* Drumm. & Hutch.
Sepals persistent, broad; petals trumpet-shaped or much reduced *Helleborus* Linn.
Upper leaf-segments forming an involucre below the flower *Eranthis* Salisb.
Petals absent, the sepals often then petaloid:
Ovules several, in 2 or more rows; fruits dehiscent:
Carpels more than 2; seeds not winged:
Ovules arranged all along the ventral suture of the carpel *Caltha* Linn.
Ovules arranged near the base of the carpel *Calathodes* Hook. f. & Thoms.
Carpels 2; seeds broadly winged *Glaucidium* Sieb. & Zucc.
Ovules 2 in each carpel, the latter baccate in fruit and becoming connate *Hydrastis* Ellis ex Linn.
Leaves ternately or somewhat pinnately compound:
* **Carpels** quite free from one another Subtribe **Isopyrinae**
Staminodes absent:
Petals present:
Sepals and petals numerous *Anemonopsis* Sieb. & Zucc.
Sepals 5 or 6:
Carpels more than 2:
Carpels sessile:
Caespitose perennials; carpels 3–5; petals not tubular:
Stems tunicated; flowers solitary; fruits ascending *Paraquilegia* Drumm. & Hutch.
Stems leafy, not tunicated; flowers 1–3; fruits spreading stellately *Paropyrum* Ulbrich
Annuals; carpels about 12; petals tubular *Neoleptopyrum* Hutch.
Carpels stipitate *Coptis* Salisb.
Carpels 2, divaricate *Isopyrum* Linn.
Petals absent *Enemion* Raf.
Staminodes present within the stamens, flat and membranous; petals

saccate or spurred at the base:
Petals at most saccate at the base *Semiaquilegia* Makino
Petals distinctly spurred at the base *Aquilegia* Linn.
* **Carpels more** or less united, especially in fruit; annuals
Subtribe **Nigellinae**
Carpels with long beaks; sepals petaloid, clawed; petals smaller than the sepals *Nigella* Linn.
Carpels not beaked or only slightly so; sepals not clawed:
Sepals coloured and more conspicuous than the petals, without transverse markings *Komaroffia* O. Ktze.
Sepals less conspicuous than the long-clawed transversely marked petals *Garidella* Linn.
† **Flowers** numerous in racemes or racemose-paniculate
Subtribe **Cimicifuginae**
Leaves orbicular, palmately nerved *Beesia* Balf. f. & W.W. Sm.
Leaves much divided:
Herbs; stamens more than 10:
Carpels dehiscent:
Inflorescence few-flowered; leaves vaginate *Souliea* Franch.
Inflorescence many-flowered *Cimicifuga* Linn.
Carpel solitary, baccate in fruit *Actaea* Linn.
Low shrub; stamens 5 or 10; carpels dehiscent
Xanthorrhiza L'Herit.

Tribe 2. DELPHINEAE

Posterior sepal spurred at the base *Delphinium* Linn.
Posterior sepal not spurred at the base, but hooded at the apex
Aconitum Linn.

In **Ranunculaceae**[1] there are no true stipules, though the leaf-base is sometimes broadened into a sheath resembling them (*Thalictrum* spp.). This is an important difference, amongst others, between *Ranunculaceae* and *Magnoliaceae*, in which there are always very distinct stipules. Outstanding forms of leaves are the much dissected submerged of the aquatic species of *Ranunculus* and the climbing habit of *Clematis*, in which the petiole, rhachis, and sometimes even the blade, are sensitive to contact. In *Clematis afoliata* Buch. (New Zealand) the whole leaf is reduced to a tendril and the work of assimilation is carried out by the green cortex of the stem (Fig. 424).

The type genus of *Ranunculaceae* is, of course, *Ranunculus*, well known to all flower-lovers in most parts of the north temperate zone and also in the

[1] Including *Anemonaceae* Bartling (1830). *Pharmaceae* Dulac (1867). *Kingdoniaceae* A. S. Foster ex Airy Shaw (1965).

FIG. 421. *Helleborus niger* Linn., the type species of the type genus of *Helleboraceae*. **A**, flower with sepals removed showing the tubular petals. **B**, petal. **C**, stamen. **D**, vertical section of carpel. **E**, fruiting carpel. **F**, seed. **G**, vertical section of seed (orig.).

mountainous regions of the Southern Hemisphere. It embraces a large number of species of perennial or annual herbs with mostly much-dissected long-stalked leaves, no stipules, white, yellow or red, terminal, often solitary flowers, sepals and petals free and of equal number, the latter when yellow often highly glossy above and with one (rarely more) nectariferous pit near the base, numerous free extrorse stamens, and an indefinite number of free carpels with separate styles, each carpel with one ascending ovule. The fruits are a bunch of 1-seeded achenes, the seeds rich in endosperm in which is embedded a tiny embryo with two small cotyledons. Type species *R. acris* Linn. (Fig. 425).

Ranunculus, then, is not only the type, but to us also in Europe, at any rate, the typical genus of the family. We have noted here and there that the genus after which a family is named is not always typical of the family as a whole; for example *Euphorbia* is the least typical of *Euphorbiaceae* (see p. 275), and if this family were split up it would become small indeed, though very rich in species.

Here are some outstanding characters in certain genera compared with those of *Ranunculus*: Duration: annual in *Myosurus* (and a few spp. of

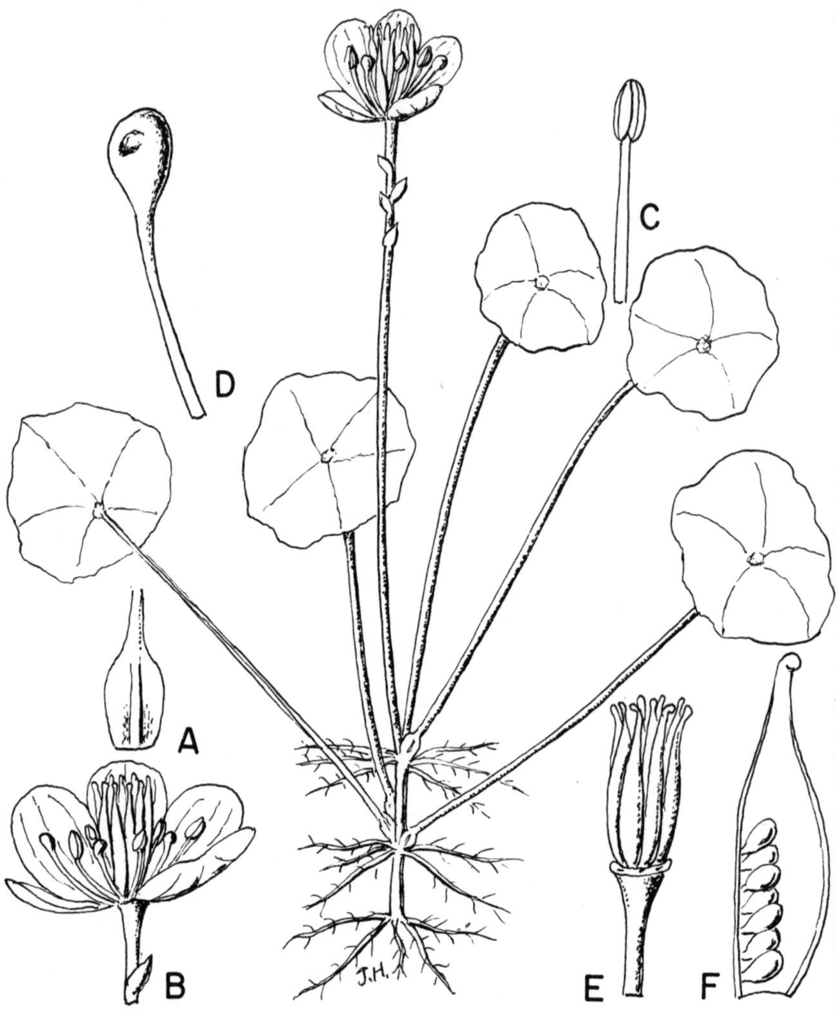

FIG. 422. *Asteropyrum peltatum* (Franch.) Drumm & Hutch., an outstanding example of the *Helleboraceae*; native of Szechuan and Hupeh, China, at 12 000 to 15 000 ft, in shady woods; note especially the club-shaped petals, **D**. **A**, base of petiole. **B**, flower. **C**, stamen. **E**, carpels. **F**, vertical section of carpel (after d'Apreval).

Ranunculus). Stem: woody and climbing in most *Clematis* and all spp. of *Naravelia*; slightly woody in *Clematopsis*. Leaves: opposite in tribe *Clematideae*, and in runner shoots of *Ficaria*; terminal leaflet tendriliform and 3-pronged in *Naravelia*; upper leaves forming an involucre to the flower in tribe *Anemoneae*, and some species of *Clematopsis*. Stipule-like lobules present in a few spp. of *Thalictrum*. Flowers: dioecious in species of

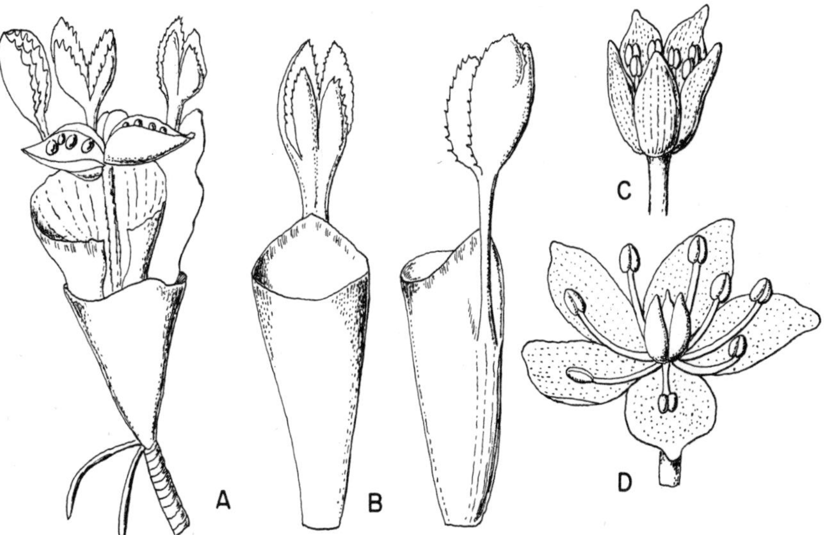

FIG. 423. *Caltha dioniifolia* Hook. f. (*Helleboraceae*), Magellan region. **A**, whole plant. **B**, leaves. **C**, young flower. **D**, mature open flower.

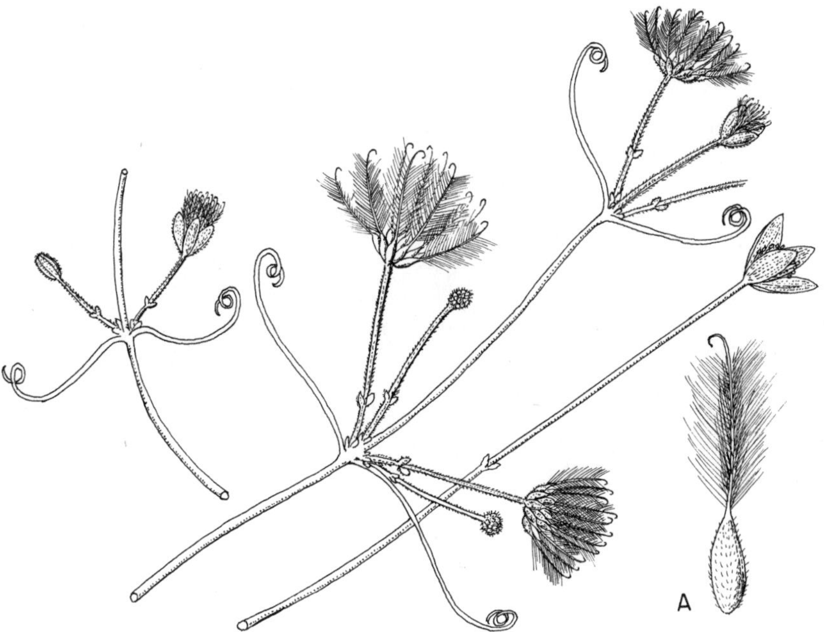

FIG. 424. *Clematis afoliata* Buch. (*Ranunculaceae*), unique among the New Zealand species, the leaves transformed into tendrils. **A**, fruiting carpel (orig.).

FIG. 425. *Ranunculus acris* Linn., lectotype of the type genus of *Ranunculaceae*. **A**, sepal **B**, petals. **C**, stamen. **D**, carpel. **E**, bunch of carpels. **F**, seed (orig.).

Clematis and *Thalictrum*, and in *Trautvetteria*, *Paroxygraphis* and *Hamadryas*. Sepals: induplicate-valvate in *Clematis* and *Naravelia*; more or less half-imbricate and half-valvate in *Clematopsis*; mostly petaloid in tribe *Anemoneae*; spurred or saccate in *Myosurus*. Petals: represented by petaloid staminodes in *Clematis* section *Atragyne*; absent from *Anemone* and most of *Clematis* and then sepals often petaloid. Stamens few in *Myosurus*, *Gampsoceras*, and spp. of *Ranunculus*. Fruit: baccate in *Knowltonia*; with long hairy tails in *Anemone* section *Pulsatilla*, and tribe *Clematideae*; embryo rather large in *Trautvetteria*; cotyledon solitary in *Ficaria*.

FIG. 426. *Myosurus minimus* Linn. (*Ranunculaceae*), a curious mixture of ancient and advanced characters (see text).

Myosurus (Fig. 426) has an interesting floral structure and a very wide distribution in isolated areas. It has been considered to represent a very primitive type of the family, partly because the floral axis is elongated just as in *Magnolia*. But the fact that the species are annuals and the sepals are spurred may indicate that the genus is not quite so primitive as it appears, the long floral axis having been retained from a more ancient stock. *Oxygraphis*, a small genus growing at very high elevations in central and northern Asia, is another ancient type with persistent sepals and numerous petals. Among the genera allied to *Ranunculus* perhaps the most striking is *Laccopetalum*, native of Peru, which, instead of a single nectary on the petal as in most Buttercups, has several nectaries scattered over the surface. In this connection it is interesting that some of the New Zealand species of *Ranunculus* (Fig. 427) have two or three nectaries on the petals. The floras of these two distant regions are known to be related.

Ranunculus has been a most successful genus and occurs nearly all over the world, and a few species have even adopted an aquatic habitat (Sect. *Batrachium*). A more advanced genus is *Gampsoceras* (Fig. 428), a monotypic in Asia Minor, in which the carpels are reduced to a single whorl and spread in a stellate manner, and the stamens are only 10 in number. The genus *Thalictrum*, and a few lesser known genera, are reduced apetalous types, and a few are wind-pollinated, the attractive parts of the flowers being the anthers, which, however, provide food for insects.

Tribes *Anemoneae* and *Clematideae* are very interesting from a phylogenetic point of view. The former is the older, and in it the petaloid sepals are imbricate and the leaves are alternate or radical. The latter is more recent

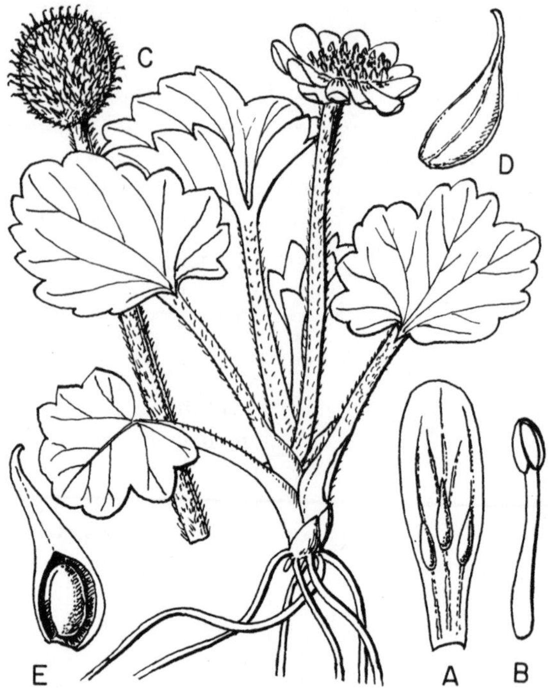

FIG. 427. *Ranunculus pinguis* Hook. f. (*Ranunculaceae*), endemic in the Auckland group of islands, south of New Zealand, found from sea level to 1200 ft; the petals vary from 5–10 in number, and they have 3 nectaries. **A**, petal. **B**, stamen. **C**, fruits. **D**, carpel. **E**, vertical section of carpel showing seed. (Adapted from Hook. f. FL. ANTARCT.)

with its usually climbing habit, opposite leaves and induplicate-valvate sepals. But there is an interesting link between these two tribes. *Clematopsis*,[1] a genus common to Madagascar and the ancient African plateau, has an aestivation neither wholly imbricate nor wholly valvate. Formerly in herbaria this genus was tucked away in *Clematis*.

A striking development in *Ranunculaceae* is the climbing habit of some species of *Clematis*. But the student who knows only the wild *Clematis* of the British Isles and a few garden plants may not be aware that there is a large number of herbaceous species. They belong to the *Alpina* and *Viorna* groups, and these probably represent the more primitive types of growth-form of the genus, for in many of them there are rudiments of petals. But the majority of the species of *Clematis* are apetalous.

Elsewhere[2] I have called attention to the type of wood found in *Clematis*

---

[1] KEW BULL. 1920, 12.

[2] *loc. cit.* 1923, 69.

FIG. 428. *Gampsoceras pinardii* Stev. (*Ranunculaceae*), eastern Mediterranean; a distinct genus with a single whorl of free long-beaked carpels and few stamens. **A**, petal. **B**, sepal. **C**, stamen. **D**, carpel in fruit (orig.).

and *Naravelia*, and it seems probable that this peculiar structure may be due to the fact that *Clematis* has been derived from herbaceous ancestors. Solereder[1] describes this wood as follows:

The primary medullary rays are broad, and do not become closed by interfascicular wood during secondary thickening, form continuous plates, which are somewhat broadened towards the exterior, and divide the mass of wood into a corresponding number of longitudinal segments. The secondary medullary rays are likewise broad, and behave in the same way as the primary rays. The vascular bundles are separated clearly from one another by the broad primary medullary

[1] SYSTEMATIC ANATOMY OF DICOTS., English edition, **1**, 18 (1908).

rays and the vascular bundles themselves are split up in a fan-like manner by the secondary rays.

We find a similar type of wood in the *Aristolochiaceae*, *Menispermaceae*, and *Berberidaceae* (*Berberis* and *Mahonia*), all of which are considered in the present system to have been derived from herbaceous ancestors.

Under *Magnoliaceae* (p. 3) the fact has been stressed that the stomata of the leaves of *Ranunculaceae* are not accompanied by special subsidiary cells. This in itself might not be of much importance, but coupled with the lack of real morphological relationship is perhaps significant. Though *Ranunculaceae*, as here understood, contains many beautiful garden plants, no member is of either economic or medicinal value. Buttercups (*Ranunculus*) are often harmful to stock and a nuisance in pastures to the farmer.

The Water-lily family, **Nymphaeaceae**,[1] is no doubt derived from the ancestral stock which also produced the hellebores and buttercups, but in this the torus has mostly become enlarged around the carpels. In some the petals sometimes show a gradual transition into stamens, a rare feature, and one which should be regarded as very primitive.[2]

A striking member of the family is *Victoria amazonica* Sowerby (syn. *V. regia* Lindl.), with its enormous floating leaves upturned at the margins and prickly below. It is difficult to imagine the feelings of the discoverer of this remarkable plant in the backwaters of the Amazon, one named Haenke, in the year 1801. It was not until 1837, however, that the plant became generally known in Europe, and was named in honour of Britain's famous queen. Several species of *Nymphaea* are of great ornamental value in water gardening.

The ovules are numerous except in one genus, *Nelumbo*, in which there are only 1 or 2. The carpels or ovary are more or less immersed in the enlarged torus, except in the genus *Nuphar*. Plants are armed with sharp prickles in *Eurale* and *Victoria*. The inner stamens are sterile in *Victoria*; seeds without endosperm in *Nelumbo*.

Podophyllaceae[3] contains those herbaceous genera previously associated in the family *Berberidaceae*, the latter restricted in the present classification to *Mahonia* and *Berberis*. The dried rhizomes of *Podophyllum peltatum* L. are the source of *Podophylloresin* in the eastern United States and Canada, and of *P. hexandrum* Royle (*P. emodi* Wall.) on the lower slopes of the Himalayas. In the eastern United States the drug obtained from the May Apple or Mandrake, as it is called, *P. peltatum* Linn., has long been used by country

---

[1] Including *Nelumbonaceae* Dumort. (1829). *Euryalaceae* J. G. Agardh (1858). *Saccaceae* Dulac (1867). *Nupharaceae* Nakai (1943). *Barclayaceae* Li (1955).

[2] The interested student should consult M. F. Moseley's Morphological Studies of the *Nymphaeaceae*, I. The nature of the stamens. PHYTOMORPHOLOGY **8**, 1 (1958).

[3] Including *Diphylleiaceae* C. H. Schultz (1832). *Leonticaceae* Airy Shaw (1965).

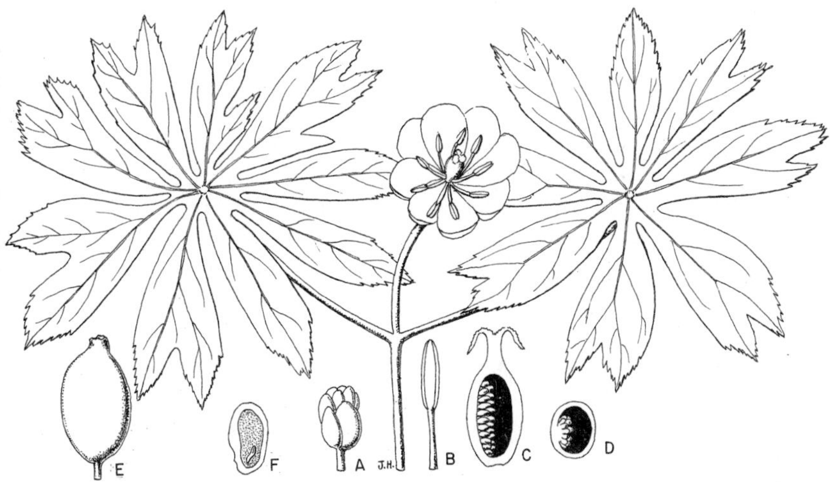

FIG. 429. *Podophyllum peltatum* Linn., North America, the type species of the type genus of *Podophyllaceae*. **A**, flower-bud. **B**, stamen. **C**, vertical section of ovary. **D**, cross-section of ovary. **E**, fruit. **F**, vertical section of seed (orig.).

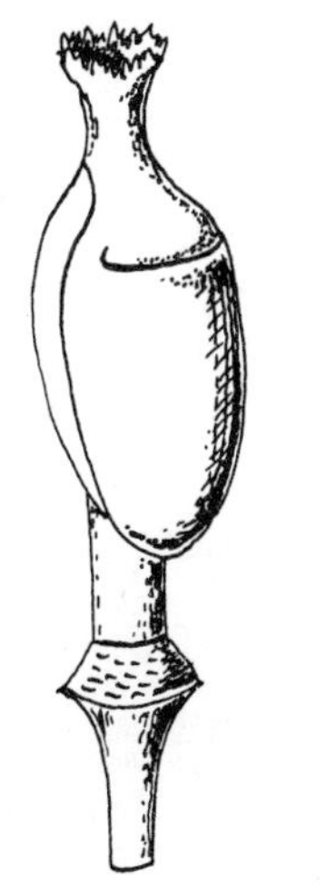

FIG. 430. *Jeffersonia binata* Bart. (*Podophyllaceae*), North America; note the almost completely circular transverse slit through which the seeds escape from the fruit.

people as an emetic and cathartic. The roots, which contain a resin, are collected in the fall or spring and cut into cylindrical segments and carefully dried (A. F. Hill ECON. BOT., 2nd Ed., 247).

There are 12 genera belonging to this family, of which a key is given in my FAMILIES OF FLOWERING PLANTS. The type is *Podophyllum*: herbs with creeping rhizomes; leaves peltate, palmately lobed, cauline leaves 1 or 2; flowers solitary or fasciculate, terminal, pedicellate, nodding; sepals 6, petaloid; petals 6–9, flat or corrugated in bud, larger than the sepals; stamens as many as or twice as many as the petals, free; anthers dehiscing lengthwise by slits; carpel 1, style hollow, stigma peltate; ovules numerous, many-seriate; fruit a berry; seeds immersed in the fleshy-pulpy placentas. Type species *P. peltatum* Linn. (Fig. 429).

Outstanding characters of other genera: a thick globose tuber in tribe *Leonticeae*. Leaves: bifoliolate in *Jeffersonia* and *Aceranthus*; peltate in *Diphylleia*. Flowers: solitary and scapigerous in *Jeffersonia* and *Plagiorhegma*; spicate in *Achlys* and the ovary with only 1 ovule; racemose or paniculate in *Bongardia*; perianth absent from *Achlys*. Carpel-wall early fugitive and exposing the young seeds in *Caulophyllum*; horizontally circumscissile in *Jeffersonia*; opening by an oblique valve in *Epimedium* spp., and *Plagiorhegma*; ripe seeds exposed on long thickened funicles and covered with "bloom" in *Caulophyllum* (Fig. 431).

Podophyllum is a natural genus of closely related species, and occurs both in eastern Asia and North America. *Achlys*, with two very similar species, closely connects the floras of the extreme parts of eastern Asia with western North America, whilst of very great phytographical interest is the occurrence of *Caulophyllum thalictroides* in the eastern United States of America and in eastern Asia (see Map 28). *Jeffersonia* and *Plagioregma* are two very closely allied genera found in these two regions respectively.

A more advanced and entirely aquatic family is **Cabombaceae**,[1] in which the submerged leaves are finely dissected and those floating are peltate. The sepals and petals are 3 each and very similar, and the carpels are often reduced to 2 or 3, while the stamens are few. Here we have, I consider, a further development of the *Helleboraceae*, and not of the *Nymphaeaceae*, to which family these plants have often been assigned. They are probably aquatic representatives of the former family and not of the *Ranunculaceae*, for they still retain 2 or 3 ovules on the nerves of the inner surface of the carpels and

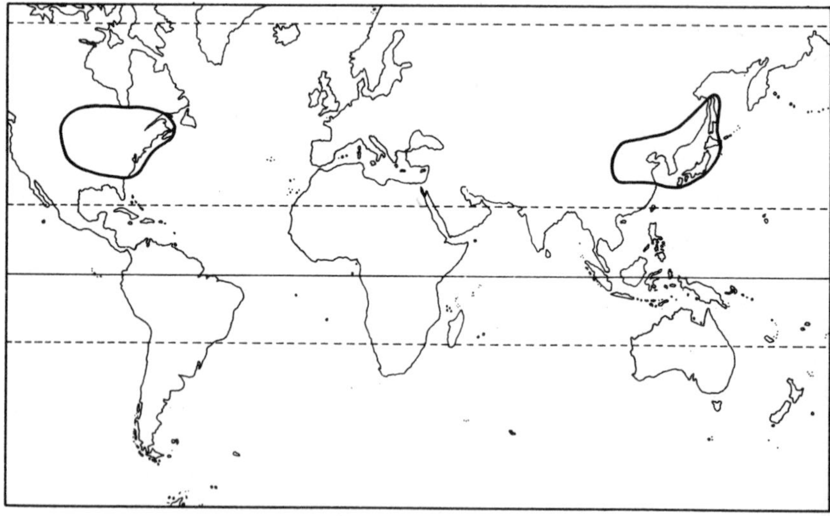

MAP 28. Remarkable discontinuous distribution of a single species, *Caulophyllum thalictroides* (Linn.) Michx. (*Podophyllaceae*).

[1] *Including Hydropeltidaceae* Dumortier (1822).

FIG. 431. The Blue Cohosh, Blue Ginseng, Squaw or Papoose Root, *Caulophyllum thalictroides* (Linn.) Michx. (*Podophyllaceae*), has an interesting discontinuous distribution, in eastern North America, and in N.E. Asia from Sachalin and Japan as far west as Szechuan in China (see map); the ovary-wall disappears in this monotypic genus soon after fertilisation, and the seeds, **E**, develop without its protection (orig.).

The Asiatic plant was described by Maximowicz as *C. robustum*, but I agree with the statement in the GENERA PLANTARUM "Species unica, in America boreali, Japonia et Mantchuria crescens". **A**, petal. **B**, stamen. **C**, gynoecium. **D**, vertical section of gynoecium. **F**, vertical section of seed, showing the minute embryo (orig.).

not on the infolded margins, a feature which may represent a very primitive type of placentation. Closed vascular bundles of the stem are characteristic of this family and *Nymphaeaceae*, and they are irregularly arranged as in Monocotyledons, perhaps a relic from a common stock with that group.

There are only two genera, *Cabomba*, with 6 stamens and usually 3 carpels, the submerged leaves much cut up, and *Brasenia*, with 18 to 12 stamens, carpels numerous to 6, and the leaves all peltate.

Order 56. BERBERIDALES

(*Fam. Fl. Pl.* **1**, 407)

Families: **Sargentodoxaceae, Lardizabalaceae, Menispermaceae, Nandinaceae, Berberidaceae, Circaeasteraceae.**

At this point in our phylogenetic system we pass on to a few families mostly in warmer countries, and whose flowers appear to be reduced types of the preceding RANALES. These are *Lardizabalaceae*, found only in eastern Asia and in far away Chile (see Map 29), *Sargentodoxaceae* and *Menispermaceae*. Most of these are climbers after the manner of *Clematis*, and they have a very similar kind of softly woody stem with very broad primary medullary rays, a feature also developed to a marked degree in the next Order ARISTOLOCHIALES, which appear to be reduced apetalous relatives, connected through one genus, *Saruma*, which has retained well developed petals.

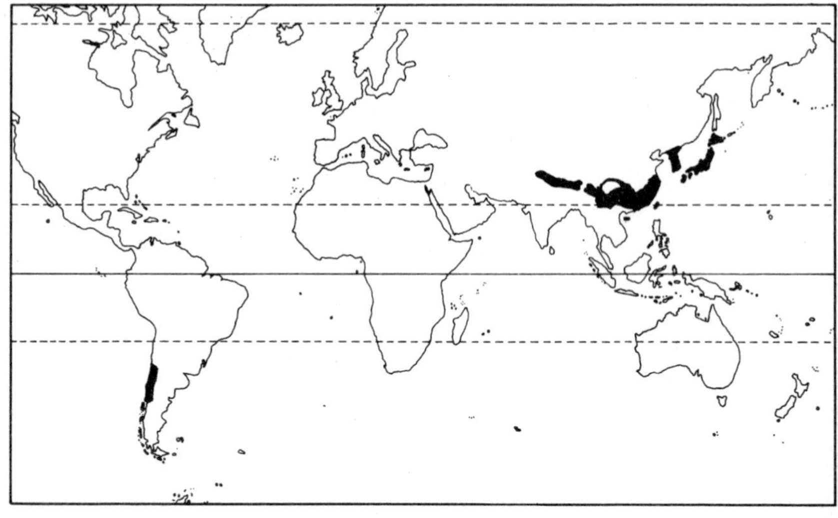

MAP 29. Distribution of the family *Lardizabalaceae* (shaded black).

Sargentodoxa, the only genus of **Sargentodoxaceae**, as its author (Dr. O. Stapf) pointed out, represents an extraordinary case of the superimposition of the characters of one family on those of another, almost a "family hybrid", if that were possible. In its external morphology the genus closely resembles a *Sinofranchetia* (*Lardizabalaceae*) with which, in an imperfect state, it was originally associated. It agrees with that genus in its male flowers and inflorescence. But the female flowers with regard to their gynoecium are quite different and do not conform to the *Lardizabalaceae*. Instead they are very like those of *Schisandraceae* (in the Order MAGNOLIALES), except that the

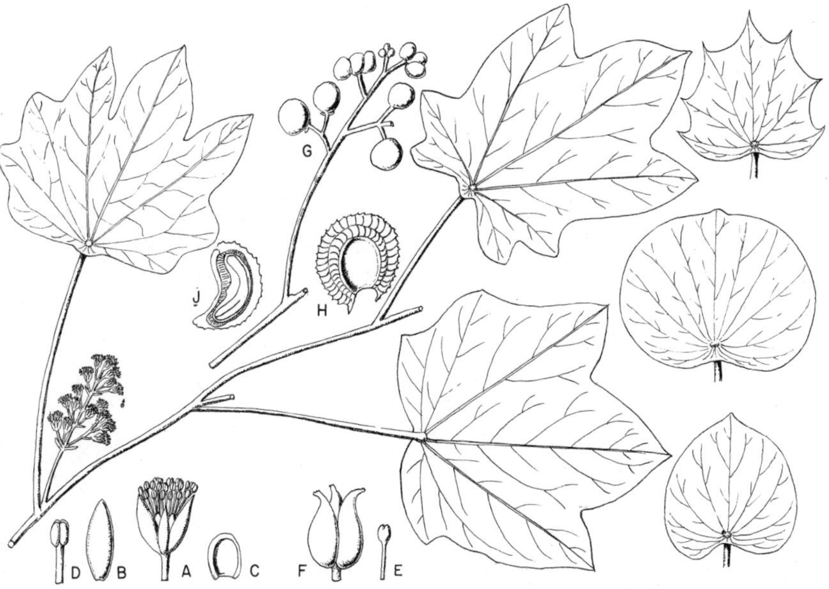

FIG. 432. *Menispermum canadense* Linn., N.E. Asia and United States of America, Canada, and Mexico, type species of the type genus of *Menispermaceae*. **A**, male flower. **B**, sepal. **C**, petal. **D**, stamen. **E**, staminode. **F**, gynoecium. **G**, fruits. **H**, seed. **J**, vertical section of seed; additional leaves show variation in this species.

carpels are 1-ovulate and the seeds different. As pointed out by Stapf "it is as if the gynoecium of a *Schisandraceae* had been grafted on a plant which externally is a *Sinofranchetia* (*Lardizabalaceae*)". It seems to the present writer to be a queer relic of an ancient stock whence both these families originated. Perhaps it represents an "experimental" stage which has persisted.

Lardizabalaceae is a small family of 8 genera with a rather singular distribution (see map): the moist woods at rather low levels of the Himalayas, central China, Japan and Korea, and a narrow strip of country in far off south Chile between the Andes and the Pacific. The members of the family still existing in these two areas are remarkably similar, the Chilean genera, however, differing from the Asiatic in their dioecious flowers. *Decaisnea*, with its pinnate leaves, is very distinct, but in all other features it agrees well with the rest of the family, especially by its fruits. The latter, together with the unisexual flowers and the longitudinal dehiscence of the anthers, serve to distinguish *Lardizabalaceae* from *Berberidaceae* (*sensu stricto*), with which it was united by Bentham and Hooker.

The type genus of the family **Menispermaceae** is *Menispermum*, consisting of only two species, the type, *M. canadense* Linn. (Fig. 432), in eastern Canada and eastern United States south to Mexico, and *M. dahuricum* DC., in N.E. Asia; scandent shrubs or subherbaceous; leaves shortly peltate, more or less ovate-triangular or angular-lobate to suborbicular and entire; inflorescence paniculate and axillary; flowers dioecious; male flowers: sepals 4–10, imbricate; petals 6–9, small, free; stamens 12–18 (rarely more), anthers basifixed, ellipsoid or subglobose, opening by a slit lengthwise; female flowers: sepals and petals as in the male; staminodes 6–12, thickened at the apex; carpels 2–4, free on a short gynophore, semi-ovoid; style almost nothing, stigmas curved outwards, fimbriate; drupes 2 or 3, reniform-orbicular or broadly semi-lunar and compressed, dorsally crenulate-tuberculate; seeds with copious endosperm and subterete annular-curved embryo and semi-terete cotyledons.

FIG. 433. *Cocculus balfouri* Schweinf. (*Menispermaceae*), Socotra. **A**, branch with leaves and cladodes. **B**, male flower expanded. **C**, stamens. **D**, female flower with petals removed. **E**, cladode with fruits. **F**, lateral view of fruit. **G**, end view of fruit. **H**, vertical section of seed. (Mostly after Balfour BOT. OF SOCOTRA.)

The late L. Diels monographed the family in Engler's PFLANZENREICH in 1910, and little taxonomic work has been done since then. He described two main divisions of the family, one in which the seeds are without endosperm, and the second with fleshy or sub-bony endosperm, and further divided the second group as to whether the cotyledons are foliaceous and thin, or not foliaceous and thick and fleshy. There is room for a much more workable classification, based partly on the different types of inflorescence and floral structure.

A few outstanding features may be noted: Stem tree-like in *Cocculus laurifolius*; herbaceous, low and erect from a woody rhizome in a few American species of *Cissampelos*; leaves 3-foliolate in *Burasaia*; sepals all united into a campanulate or globose calyx in *Cyclea*, the inner ones valvate in *Triclisia* and in some species of *Limacia*; inner 3 sepals connate and valvate into a corolla-like structure, the 6 petals very small in *Synclisia*; embryo spirally twisted in *Spirospermum*.

In the second edition of my FAMILIES OF FLOWERING PLANTS I reduced **Berberidaceae**[1] to only two genera, *Mahonia* and *Berberis*. In both, the anthers open by valves from the base upwards, the 6 stamens are opposite to the petals, the latter having two nectariferous glands on the inner face, and the few ovules in the single carpel are ascending.

Mahonia was formerly often included in *Berberis*, but seems to be a more primitive genus. In *Mahonia* there is only one kind of shoot, the long shoot; the leaves on these long shoots are normally developed and are either trifoliolate or imparipinnate and evergreen; the inflorescence terminates the long shoot; there are no thorns. In *Berberis*, however, there are two kinds of shoots, long shoots and short shoots, the former bearing metamorphosed leaves in the shape of thorns, in the axils of which arise short shoots which bear simple (unifoliolate) often deciduous leaves; the inflorescence terminates the short shoots. The unifoliolate leaf and articulated petiole of *Berberis* seem to suggest that it has been derived from *Mahonia*. In *Mahonia* considerable reduction of the leaf occurs in *M. trifoliolata* (Moric.) Fedde and *M. fremontii* (Torr.) Fedde, in the S.W. United States of America, in which the leaflets are reduced to 3 or 5.

There is only one instance of a hybrid between the two genera, x *Mahoberberis* Schneid., between *Mahonia aquifolium* (Pursh) Nutt. and *Berberis vulgaris* Linn. "It resembles *Mahonia* in the unarmed branches, in the solitary, not fascicled leaves on the shoots, and the occurrence of 3-foliolate or pinnate leaves; the influence of *Berberis* is shown in the usually simple leaves, thinner and serrulate on the older branches, while those of the shoots are more coriaceous and sinuately spiny; flowers and fruits not known" (Quoted from Rehder, MANUAL CULT. TREES AND SHRUBS, 2nd Ed., 295 (1956)).

Berberidaceae are mainly of ornamental value, though the fruits of *Berberis* and *Mahonia* are edible and can be made into jelly, those of *Mahonia aquifolium* Nutt. known as the "Rocky Mountain Grape".

The genus *Circaeaster* Maxim., the sole member of the family **Circaeasteraceae**, monotypic, *C. agrestis* Maxim., is a small annual found only in the N.W. Himalayas. It was placed by Bentham and Hooker in the *Chloranthaceae*, but seems to be much nearer *Berberidaceae* and *Papaveraceae*. The apetalous flowers recall those of another very advanced member of the RANALES, the genus *Achlys*, in *Podophyllaceae*. This rare plant has been the subject of much investigation and speculation as to its affinities, especially by the American anatomist, Professor A. S. Foster,[2] who has laid great stress on the dichotomous venation of the leaves.

---

[1] Including *Coelostigmaceae* Dulac (1867).

[2] A. S. Foster, The Morphology and Relationships of *Circaeaster*, J. ARN. ARB. **45**, 299 (1963); also Morphology of Anastomosis in the Dichotomous Venation of *Circaeaster*, AM. J. BOT. **53**, 588 (1966).

ORDER 57. ARISTOLOCHIALES

(*Fam. Fl. Pl.* **1**, 414)

Families: **Aristolochiaceae, Hydnoraceae, Rafflesiaceae, Nepenthaceae.**

Phylogeny: RANALES → BERBERIDALES (**Menispermaceae**) → **ARISTOLOCHIALES**.

From the previous group, interesting but unfamiliar to the average student, we pass on to equally little known and highly reduced families in which the ovary for the first time in this alliance is inferior, whilst in some the calyx has become much modified and attractive to insects as a compensation for the complete loss of petals, with one exception. This occurs in *Saruma* in which there have been retained fully developed petals; petals in the old group "Apetalae"!, though they are present in many other families such as *Euphorbiaceae*.

There are 10 genera belonging to **Aristolochiaceae.**[1] Although the family was placed in the *Monochlamydeae* ("Apetalae") by Bentham and Hooker, it is most closely related to certain petaliferous families such as *Menispermaceae*. As the anatomical stem structure is identical with that of *Menispermaceae*, it seems logical to postulate that the family as a whole has also arisen from herbaceous ancestors, such as RANALES, the stomata of the leaves having no special subsidiary cells just as in that group. The actinomorphic calyx (perianth) of some of the more primitive genera is associated with two whorls of stamens, the latter being reduced to a single whorl in the more advanced genera in which the calyx has become increasingly zygomorphic.

During study of this family for the FLORA OF WEST TROPICAL AFRICA, I was struck by the morphology of a few species which up to that time were included in *Aristolochia*. For these I established a different genus which I called *Pararistolochia* (Fig. 436), distinguished by having a perfectly actinomorphic 3-lobed calyx (perianth) and a very elongated, ribbed, hard, indehiscent fruit in contrast to the fruit of *Aristolochia* (*sensu stricto*) with rounded dehiscent fruits.

There are two kinds of Snake Root which had formerly a reputation as a cure for snake-bite: Virginian, *Aristolochia serpentaria* Linn., a native of moist fertile woods of the United States of North America, and the Texan, *A. reticulata* Nutt. Snake Root possesses general stimulant and tonic properties.

---

[1] Including *Asaraceae* Ventenat (1799). *Pistolochiaceae* Link (1829). *Pipaceae* Dulac (1967). *Sarumaceae* Nakai (1936).

FIG. 435. *Aristolochia somaliensis* Oliv. (*Aristolochiaceae*), tropical Africa, a primitive species of the genus with an actinomorphic (regular) calyx (perianth).

FIG. 434. *Aristolochia rotunda* Linn., the type species of the type genus of *Aristolochiaceae*, south Europe, and often naturalised in more northern countries. **A**, flower with calyx (perianth) removed. **B**, cross-section of ovary. **C**, fruit (orig.).

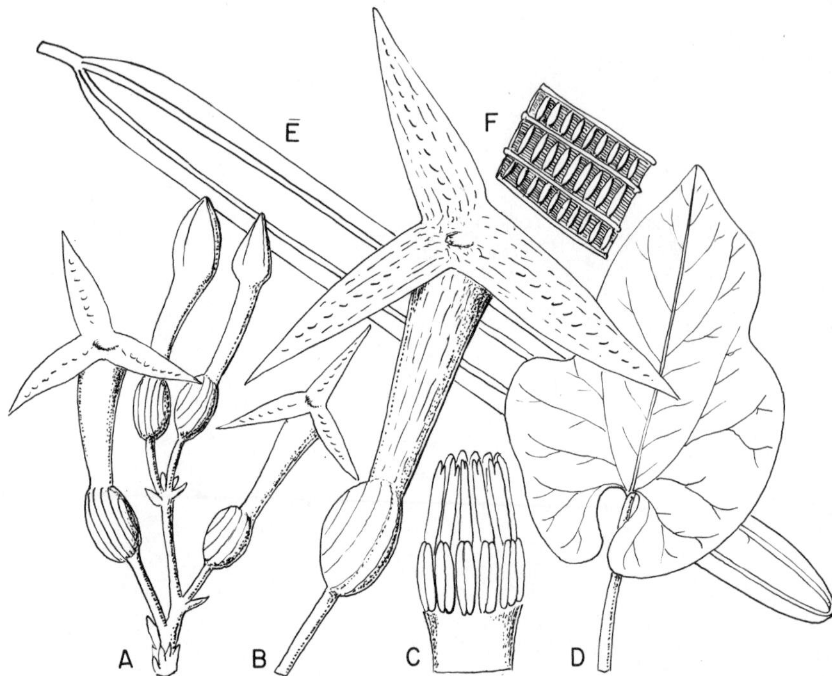

FIG. 436. *Pararistolochia triactina* (Hook. f.) Hutch. & Dalz. (*Aristolochiaceae*); forests of tropical west Africa; the genus is more primitive than *Aristolochia*, with an actinomorphic (regular) 3-lobed calyx (perianth), and especially the long ribbed indehiscent fruit. **A**, flowers. **B**, separate flower. **C**, androecium and styles. **D**, leaf. **E**, fruit. **F**, longitudinal section of fruit showing transverse seeds (orig.).

Parasitic related families are **Hydnoraceae** and **Rafflesiaceae**[1] (*Cytinaceae*). The flower of *Rafflesia arnoldii* is noteworthy as being the largest in the vegetable kingdom and is found only in the island of Sumatra in the Malay Archipelago. Wax models of this remarkable flower excite the wonder of visitors to the botanical museums at Kew and the British Museum (Natural History). Another representative of this family familiar to people in southern Europe is the brilliant scarlet *Cytinus hypocistus* Linn., which depends for its existence on the roots of *Cistus* shrubs (*Cistaceae*).

The opinions of Bentham and Hooker, on the one hand, and of the Englerian school, on the other, were as opposite as the poles in regard to the affinities of the **Nepenthaceae**. The former placed them amongst the *Monochlamydeae* (*Apetalae*) near *Aristolochiaceae*, the latter next to the *Saxifragaceae*. In my opinion *Nepenthaceae* have no relationship whatever with

[1] Including *Patmaceae* C. H. Schultz (1832). *Mitrastemonaceae* Makino (1911). *Apodanthaceae* van Tieghem (1898).

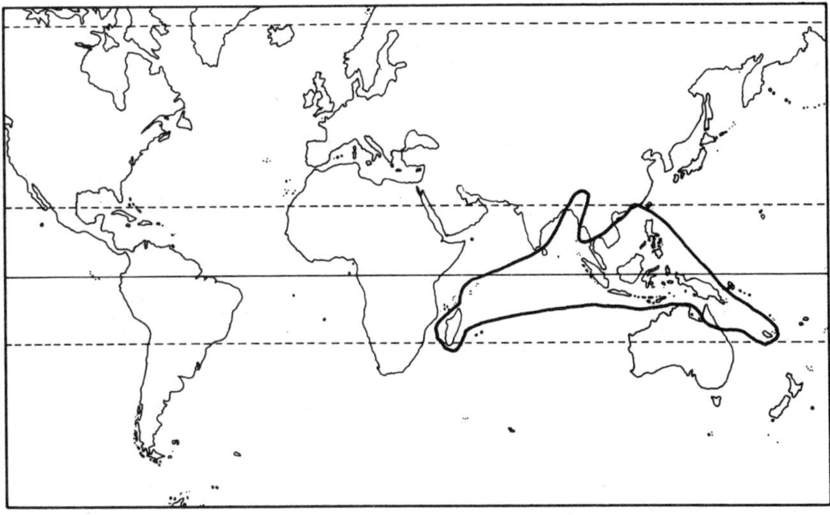

MAP 30. Distribution of the genus *Nepenthes*, the well-known "Pitcher Plants", emphasises the close connection between the floras of Madagascar, Ceylon and the Malay Archipelago. Although the seeds of this genus are adapted for wind dispersal, this could not account for the occurrence of two endemic species in the mountains of Madagascar and the Seychelles Islands. (Repeated from my FAMILIES OF FLOWERING PLANTS.)

the *Saxifragaceae* or any of the families segregated from it; but there is considerable evidence to show that they may be descendants from the same stock as the *Menispermaceae*, and should remain near the *Aristolochiaceae* as in the de Candolle – Bentham and Hooker system. Their dioecious flowers, devoid of petals, with the filaments connate into a column, the filiform seeds etc., are quite foreign to the *Saxifragaceae*. Presumably they were placed near the *Saxifragaceae* because somewhat similar leaf-pitchers occur in *Cephalotus* and in *Sarraceniaceae*; but this feature has no doubt been developed in families which are not otherwise related. There are other anomalies in the Engler system which are difficult to understand, such as the entirely false position of *Ancistrocladaceae*[1] next to *Begoniaceae*, and the *Cucurbitaceae*[2] between the *Rubiaceae* and the *Compositae*, discussed further on. Incidentally Airy Shaw's contention that *Dioncophyllum* (*Flacourtiaceae*) is related to *Nepenthes* is, in my opinion, quite outside the realm of possibility.

---

[1] In the latest SYLLABUS of the Englerian system (12th Edition, 1964) this family is placed at the end of the Reihe GUTTIFERALES.

[2] Now placed in this same SYLLABUS (*loc. cit.*) as a separate Reihe between the VIOLALES and *Myrtiflorae*! If the late Sir Winston Churchill had been a botanist instead of a world famous statesman he would surely have termed this and other groups in the Englerian system "taxonomic inexactitudes"!

ORDER 58. PIPERALES

(*Fam. Fl. Pl.* 1, 419)

Families: **Piperaceae, Saururaceae, Chloranthaceae.**

Phylogeny: RANALES → PIPERALES → to climax family **Chloranthaceae.**

The greatest reduction of the flowers and specialisation of families derived from the Ranalean basic stock seems to be reached in the Pepper family, *Piperaceae*, and a few other small families which seem to be related, such as *Saururaceae*, *Chloranthaceae* and *Lacistemataceae*. In all these there is neither calyx nor corolla, and the flowers are aggregated into dense spikes almost like catkins, in a similar manner to other families which went to make up the old group " Amentiferae ", the fundamentally woody members of which I have placed after the ROSALES in the woody phylum, **Lignosae**.

In **Piperaceae**[1] there is sometimes present a character which is such a hallmark of the Monocotyledons, i.e. the vascular bundles in the stem are scattered and not arranged in concentric rings as in most other Dicotyledons. This seems to me to be an indication of their Ranalean origin, *Ranunculaceae* being most closely related to the more primitive Monocotyledons such as *Alismatacese*. The accompanying diagram (p. 511) may make clear to the student the probable course of evolution of the RANALES and allied Orders and families.

Many species of *Piperaceae* have pungent or aromatic properties. Black and White Peppers are obtained from the fruits of *Piper nigrum* Linn., a climbing shrub of the Malabar coast of India, and widely cultivated in tropical countries. Black Pepper is obtained by grinding the fruits without removing the husk, and White Pepper by grinding after removing it. The thick, knotty roots of *Piper methysticum* Forst., known as Kava Root, are used in the Society and South Sea Islands in the preparation of a slightly narcotic and intoxicating drink which is reputed to quench thirst better than other liquid, besides acting as a sedative, a soporific, and a hypnotic, bringing about pleasant dreams and sensations. Long Pepper, *Piper longum* Linn., of Java and India was more highly esteemed by the Romans than black pepper and was also important in the Middle Ages. It is extensively used in the tropics in pickles, preserves and curries.

These monocotyledonous characters no doubt led Lotsy to the belief that some groups of Monocotyledons, such as *Araceae*, have been derived from

---

[1] Including *Peperomiaceae* Novák (1954).

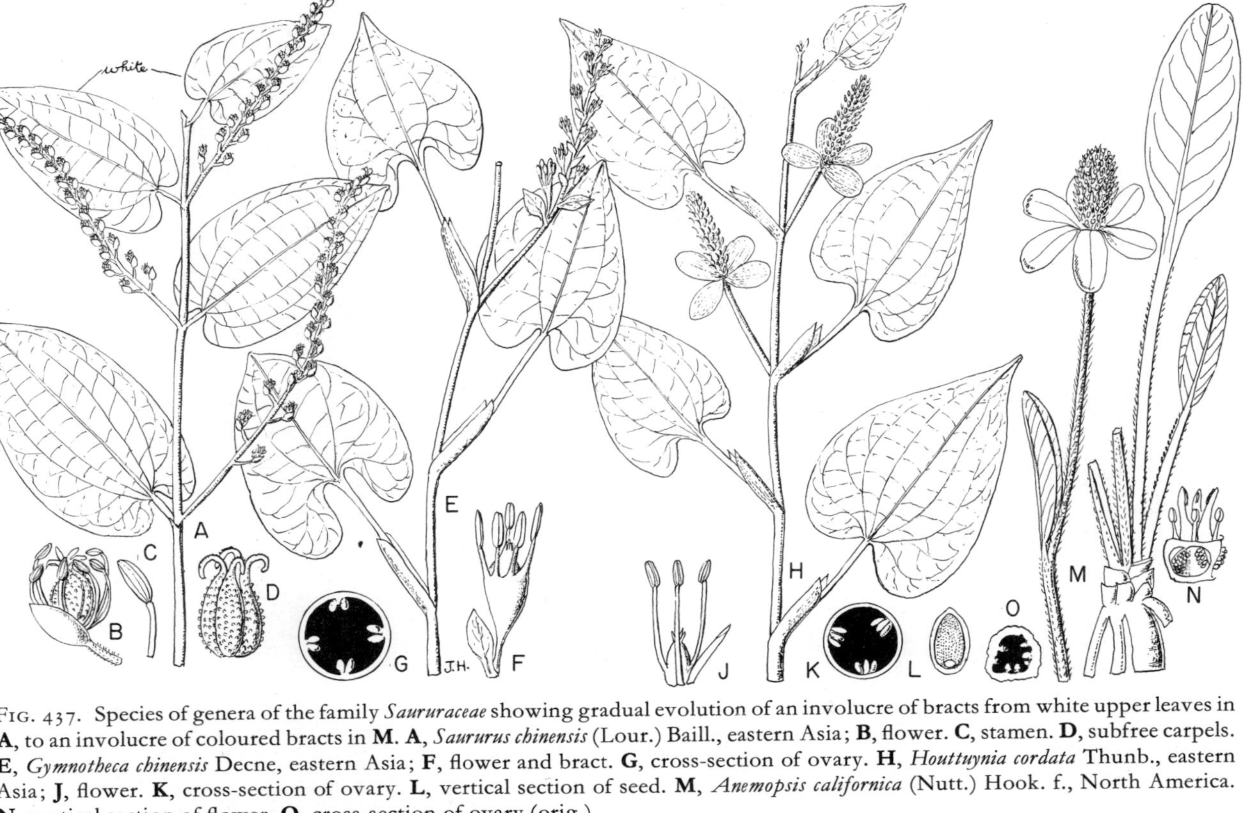

Fig. 437. Species of genera of the family *Saururaceae* showing gradual evolution of an involucre of bracts from white upper leaves in **A**, to an involucre of coloured bracts in **M**. **A**, *Saururus chinensis* (Lour.) Baill., eastern Asia; **B**, flower. **C**, stamen. **D**, subfree carpels. **E**, *Gymnotheca chinensis* Decne, eastern Asia; **F**, flower and bract. **G**, cross-section of ovary. **H**, *Houttuynia cordata* Thunb., eastern Asia; **J**, flower. **K**, cross-section of ovary. **L**, vertical section of seed. **M**, *Anemopsis californica* (Nutt.) Hook. f., North America. **N**, vertical section of flower. **O**, cross-section of ovary (orig.).

the PIPERALES. I am convinced that such general resemblance as there may be is merely superficial and entirely due to parallelism.[1]

Saururaceae is an interesting family and a good example for the study of the evolution of certain characters. For example the gradual development of an involucre of bracts as in the *Asteraceae* (*Compositae*) and in *Cornaceae* may be clearly traced. In the most primitive genus of the family, *Saururus* (see Fig. 437, **A–D**), the slender spike-like inflorescence has no involucre, but sometimes the uppermost leaves are white and attractive. In the very closely allied genus *Gymnotheca* (see Fig. 437, **E–G**), there are instead of these white leaves occasionally 2 or 3 leafy bracts at the base of the inflorescence. The involucre is more fully developed, however, in *Houttuynia* (Fig. 437, **H–L**) and *Anemopsis* (Fig. 437, **M–O**), and it consists of 4 or more much modified bracts at the base of the spike; in the former genus, which is Asiatic, the floral bracts are small and inconspicuous; in the latter, in the S.W. States of North America, they are spathulate and conspicuous, nearly all the leaves being radical and those of the stem reduced to large stipules (see Fig. 437, **M–O**). The stipules in *Saururus* and *Gymnotheca* are completely adnate to the petiole and are scarcely distinguishable as such. We may assume they are stipules by comparison with those of the genus *Houttuynia*, where they are only partially adnate to the petiole.

Little need be said about the next and small family **Chloranthaceae**, although I have examined it several times in great detail. But it seems most closely allied to *Saururaceae*. *Chloranthus*, a genus of about twenty species, occurs only in eastern Asia, extending eastwards into New Guinea; further east it is replaced by *Ascarina*, which ranges from the Philippines through New Caledonia to New Zealand and the Fiji Islands; whilst on the far side of the Pacific *Hedyosmum* takes on this peculiar family role, extending from Mexico mainly through western South America to Peru. In this genus the male flowers have advanced further than the female; they have no calyx (perianth), though in the female there is a small calyx united to the ovary, which is therefore inferior. This group of genera is no doubt very advanced. Judged from its present-day distribution, the family probably originated in the Burma-Indo-Chinese region (*Chloranthus*), and spread eastwards through the Pacific (*Ascarina*), culminating in *Hedyosmum* on the American continent, the last being the most advanced genus, with unisexual inflorescences.

Here are the characters of the type genus *Chloranthus* (about 20 spp. from Ceylon east to New Guinea and Japan): shrubs or perennial herbs; stem and branches joined at the nodes; leaves opposite, connected by a transverse line, sometimes verticillate; stipules sometimes conspicuous; spikes terminal, slender, sometimes branched; flowers falsely bisexual on account

---

[1] See FAMILIES OF FLOWERING PLANTS **2**, 4 (1934); 2nd Ed. **2**, 514 (1959).

of the male lateral and adnate to the base of the female; calyx and petals absent; stamens 3, the middle one 2-locular, the lateral 1-locular, connate into a 3-lobed mass; ovary nude; stigma subsessile, truncate. Type species *C. inconspicuus* Swartz, Ceylon to New Guinea.

ORDER 59. RHOEADALES

(*Fam. Fl. Pl.* **1**, 422)

Families: **Papaveraceae, Fumariaceae.**

Phylogeny: RANALES → (Helleboraceae) → **RHOEADALES** → (to local climax family *Fumariaceae*).

There are many indications that this Order has descended either directly from *Helleboraceae* or by way of the *Podophyllaceae*. For in *Papaveraceae* the genus *Platystemon* has torulose carpels which are only loosely united and which become quite free from one another in the fruiting stage (Fig. 438, **F**). But in general there is a considerable advancement from the RANALES, especially in regard to the gynoecium. With the above-noted exception, the ovary is syncarpous throughout **Papaveraceae**,[1] and it is chiefly by means of characters derived from it with regard to the relative position of the carpels and stigmas and the nature of the fruit that the genera are classified. *Papaveraceae* have "pollen flowers", that is flowers provided with an abundance of stamens, the pollen of which is eaten by insects, but there are no nectaries. It follows then that the more stamens there are the more insect visitors will be provided for, and hence greater opportunities for cross-pollination. This may seem a rather far-fetched view, but nevertheless we do find the greatest number of stamens in the most advanced and certainly the most successful genus, *Papaver*. If we follow up this reasoning we shall find that in the tribe *Platystemoneae*, there are few stamens associated with a primitive type of capsule, suggesting that the absence of nectaries and numerous stamens in the other *Papaveraceae* are secondary and are thus not primitive features in this family.

The woody or subwoody members of *Papaveraceae* are also the most advanced in the structure of their flowers, apparently confirming the fact that the herbaceous condition is here the more primitive. The genus

---

[1] Including *Chymaceae* Dulac (1867). *Pteridophyllaceae* Sugiura ex Nakai (1943). *Chelidoniaceae* Nakai (1952). *Hypecoaceae* Nakai (1948).

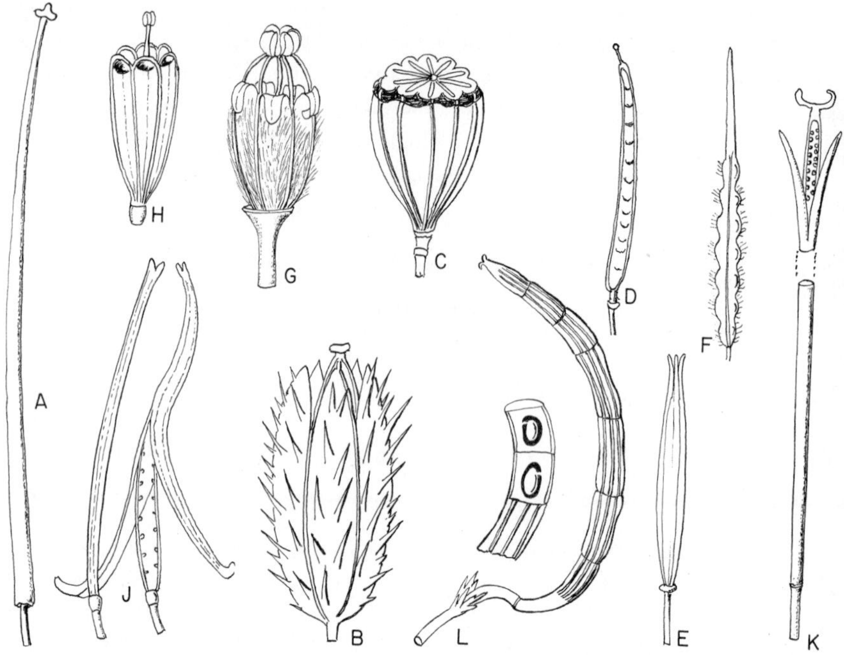

FIG. 438. Fruits of some *Papaveraceae*: note the tendency towards the evolution of the *Brassicaceae* (*Cruciferae*). **A**, *Glaucium flavum* Crantz, Europe. **B**, *Argemone mexicana* Linn., widely spread. **C**, *Papaver rhoeas* Linn., widely spread, often a weed in cornfields. **D**, *Chelidonium majus* Linn., Europe. **E**, *Meconella oregana* Nutt., North America. **F**, *Platystemon californicum* Benth., western United States of North America. **G**, *Meconopsis integrifolia* Franch., China. **H**, *Stylomecon heterophylla* (Benth.) G. Taylor, northern Asia. **J**, *Dendromecon rigida* Benth., western North America. **K**, *Glaucium calycinum* Bois., Persia. **L**, *Hypecoum procumbens* Linn., Mediterranean region and Orient (orig.).

Dendromecon (Fig. 438, **J**, fruit) is a shrub with leathery leaves, whilst *Bocconia* (but not *Macleaya*[1]) is sometimes arboreal. Again, this woody habit is associated with much-reduced, apetalous flowers which are arranged in panicles. A perigynous type of flower with the sepals coherent into a cap (calyptra) occurs in *Eschscholtzia*. The fact that the genus *Glaucium* has the ovary divided by a false septum is interesting as showing a tendency to the production of a type of ovary which has become such a fixed character in the more advanced climax family *Brassicaceae* (*Cruciferae*). *Glaucium* might be looked upon, therefore, as something of a link between the *Papaveraceae* and *Brassicaceae*. Long ago Bentham pointed out the origin of the peculiar position of the stigmas in some genera of *Papaveraceae*, and drew attention to the same feature being general in *Brassicaceae*. In *Platystemon*, etc., the stigmas

[1] The "Bocconia" of gardens is *Macleaya*—see KEW BULL. **1920**, 276.

are in the normal position, i.e. alternating with the placentas, as we should expect in this the most primitive tribe and the one most nearly related to the *Helleboraceae*, but in several other more advanced genera, such as *Glaucium*, the stigmas are in line with the placentas. It is important to note that we have a similar position of the stigma in some *Saxifragaceae*, which is also regarded as having been evolved from the RANALES.

According to Solereder the lack of glandular hairs and of special subsidiary cells accompanying the guard-cells is characteristic of *Papaveraceae*. Secretory organs containing a milky substance are widely distributed in the family.

Of paramount economic importance in the *Papaveraceae* is the Opium Poppy, *Papaver somniferum* Linn., one of the most helpful, and at the same time vicious drugs (Fig. 440). Opium is the dried latex obtained by making incisions in the unripe pods. Here I may quote from Hill's ECONOMIC BOTANY:

Opium is a very old narcotic. . . . Originating probably in Asia Minor, the use of opium soon spread westward. The drug was known to the Greeks, Romans, and Egyptians and perhaps to the earlier Lake Dwellers of Switzerland. In its eastward dispersal it had reached Persia, India, and China by the eighth century, and since then has spread all over the world. When properly utilized, opium and alkaloids derived from it are valuable medicinally, and have proved a great blessing to mankind in the relief of pain. Excessive use of the drug, however, and the resulting opium habit have been and still are the cause of unbelievable suffering and evil. No other drug has caused so much corruption and tragedy. In spite of every effort to stamp out the habit, it seems to be increasing. This is particularly true of the Orient, where opium has taken a toll of millions of lives. It has been estimated that over 900 000 000 people are still apt to use it. . . . The immediate effects of taking opium are pleasurable, and alluring dreams and visions are induced. Continued use, however, leads to delirium and death. The opium addict soon loses the will power necessary to resist the craving, the withdrawal pains being so severe that it becomes virtually impossible for him to continue his abstinence.

The seeds of the Opium Poppy, curiously enough, are edible and fed to cage birds as "Maw" seed. An important drying oil is obtained from the seeds, and the plant is grown for this purpose in northern France and Germany and in India. The first cold pressing yields a white edible oil, while a second, hot, pressing furnishes a reddish oil used for lamps, soap, and (after bleaching) for oil paints. "Bloodroot" is the rhizome of *Sanguinaria canadensis* Linn., and contains several remarkable and interesting alkaloids used in certain medicines.

Tribe *Hypecoumeae* (genera *Chiazospermum*, *Hypecoum* and *Pteridophyllum*) is probably as nearly related to *Podophyllaceae* as to *Papaveraceae*, especially to *Epimedium*, *Aceranthus* and *Bongardia*; furthermore, *Hypecoumeae* may have descended directly from the Podophyllaceous stock. This view as to

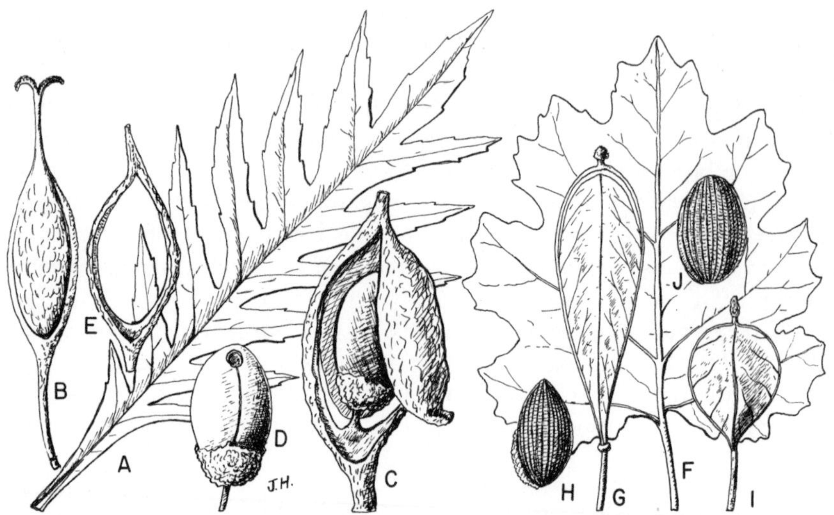

FIG. 439. **A–E**, *Bocconia arborea* S. Wats., Mexico. **A**, leaf. **B** and **C**, fruits. **D**, seed with basal aril. **E**, empty shell of fruit. **F–H**, *Macleaya cordata* (Willd.) R.Br., China and Japan. **F**, leaf. **G**, fruit. **H**, seed with lateral aril. **I–J**, *Macleaya microcarpa* (Maxim.) Fedde, China. **I**, fruit. **J**, seed (*Papaveraceae*). (After Hutchinson in KEW BULL. 1923, 242.)

the affinity with *Podophyllaceae* is perhaps strengthened by the possession of similar medicinal and chemical properties (See Watt DICT. ECON. PROD. INDIA **2**, 574).

The type genus, *Papaver* Linn., consists of herbs with milk-like juice, mostly in extratropical Northern Hemisphere; leaves mostly lobed or dissected; flowers very showy, nodding; sepals mostly 2; petals 4, rarely 6; stamens numerous; placentas of the ovary 4 to numerous, protruding towards the centre and bearing numerous ovules, rarely nerviform; stigmatic lobes radiating on top of the ovary and opposite the placentas; capsule globose to oblong, dehiscing by pores below the top and between the placentas; seeds scrobiculate. Type sp. *P. somniferum* Linn. (Fig. 440).

Characters occurring in relatively few genera and species: Stem woody in *Dendromecon*; sometimes arborescent in *Bocconia* spp. Leaves entire in *Dendromecon*, *Platystemon, Meconella*, *Hesperomecon*, *Papaver* spp., *Meconopsis* spp.; floral leaves subopposite in *Platystemon*, *Meconella*, *Hesperomecon* and *Dicranostigma*; leaves aculeate in *Argemone*. Indumentum of barbellate hairs in *Cathartica*, *Meconopsis* sect. *Polychaetia*; prickly in *Papaver* spp. and *Meconopsis* spp. Flowers scapose in *Sanguinaria*, racemose in *Eomecon*, subumbellate-racemose and leaf-opposed in *Chelidonium*; paniculate in tribe *Bocconieae*. Sepals coherent into a calyptra in *Eschscholtzia* and *Eomecon*; leathery, boat-shaped and subpersistent in *Bocconieae*. Petals subpersistent in spp. of *Platystemon*, persistent until ripening of the fruit in *Canbya*; absent from

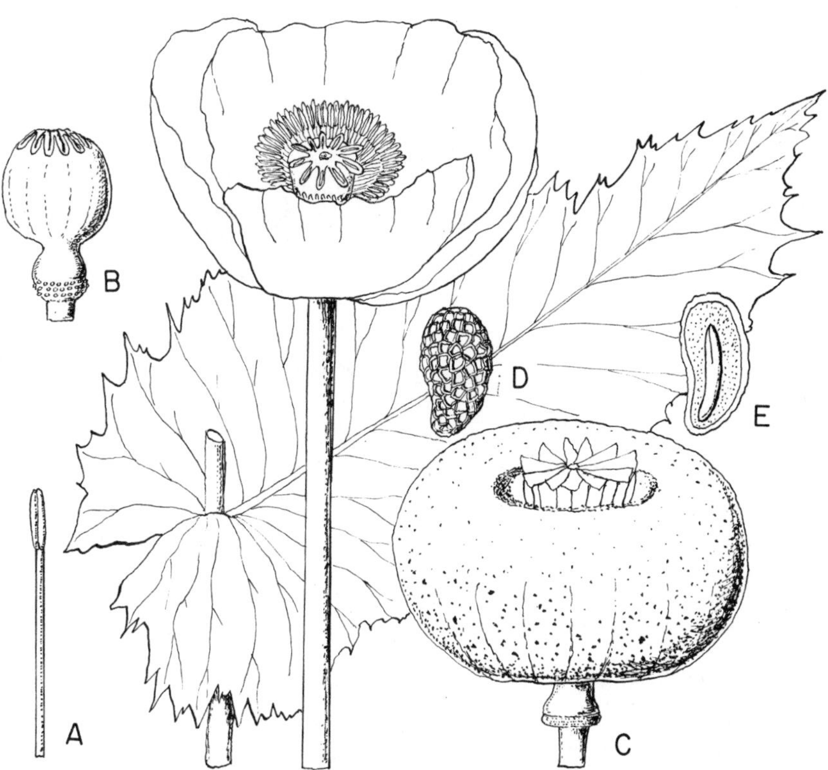

FIG. 440. The Opium Poppy, *Papaver somniferum* Linn. (*Papaveraceae*), provides one of the most useful and also potent drugs. **A**, stamen. **B**, gynoecium. **C**, fruit. **D**, seed. **E**, vertical section of seed (orig.).

tribe *Bocconieae*; perigynous in *Eschscholtzia*; 8–12 in *Sanguinaria*. Stamens subdefinite in *Meconella*, *Bocconia* spp., *Macleaya microcarpa* (Maxim.) Fedde, perigynous in *Eschscholtzia*. Carpels separate and torulose when mature in *Platystemon*; becoming spirally twisted in *Meconella*; valves remaining attached to placentas in tribe *Platystemoneae*, except *Romneya*. Seeds rather large and solitary in *Bocconia* and *Macleaya microcarpa* (Maxim.) Fedde (Fig. 439).

There are at least three main areas of concentration of the family: 1, The S.W. United States of America, especially California; 2, The eastern Mediterranean and Asia Minor; and 3, Tibet and western China. The S.W. United States shelter the whole of the tribes *Platystemoneae* and *Escholtzieae*, and several distinct small genera of the *Chelidonieae*. The bulk of tribe *Papavereae* are S.E. European and Asiatic, most of the Poppies occurring in the eastern Mediterranean, while the genus *Meconopsis* takes its place mainly in west central China and the Himalayas. The paucity of *Papaveraceae* in the

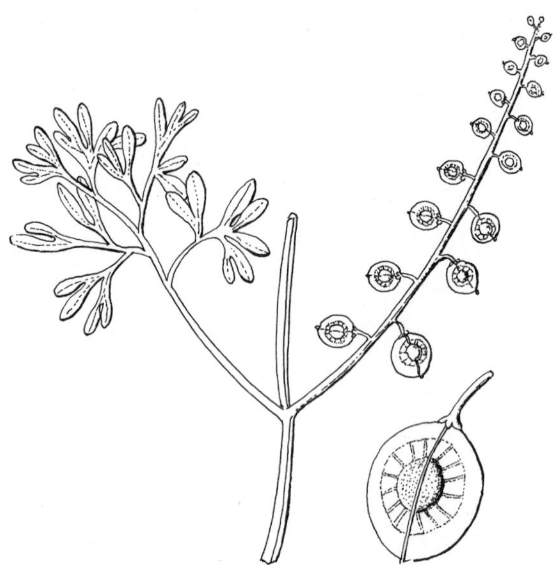

FIG. 441. The fruits of *Discocapnos mundtii* Cham. & Schl. (*Fumariaceae*) recall those of *Lobularia* in the family *Brassicaceae* (*Cruciferae*).

Southern Hemisphere is remarkable, one distinct species of Poppy in Australia and in South Africa, and three species of *Bocconia* in N.W. South America being the sole representatives, exclusive of weeds of cultivation. One small genus, *Stylophorum*, shows affinity between Atlantic North America (1 sp.) and N.E. Asia (2 spp.). Another, *Dicranostigma*, connects the floras of the N.W. Himalaya (*D. lactucoides*, at 10 000–12 000 ft) and western China (*D. franchetianum* and *D. leptopodum*). Two most interesting related genera, *Bocconia* and *Macleaya*, occupy, the one central and N.W. South America, the other central and western China. Although these two genera have even been regarded as one, it is probable that they have arisen quite independently of each other. Indigenous *Papaveraceae* appear to be lacking from temperate and eastern South America, New Zealand and the Antarctic Islands, Polynesia, Malay and southern India.

The number of botanists who still include the **Fumariaceae**[1] within the *Papaveraceae* is happily very small, and those that do are probably not interested in phylogeny, or they follow tradition. I wish many other pairs of families were as easily separable. It is true that there is one small group, the *Hypecoumoideae*, which forms something of a connecting link. But believing in evolution as we do what else should we expect? The old idea of the special creation of species is probably not quite eradicated from some minds.

[1] Including *Chylaceae* Dulac (1867).

Fumariaceae is a considerable advancement on the *Papaveraceae*. The flowers are mainly zygomorphic, the petals are often connivent or coherent, and two of them are usually spurred at the base, whilst another advanced feature is the union of the stamens into bundles of three each. The spurred petals are in the horizontal plane and not in the median plane as is generally the case in spurred flowers. Then in the fruits of some there are tendencies

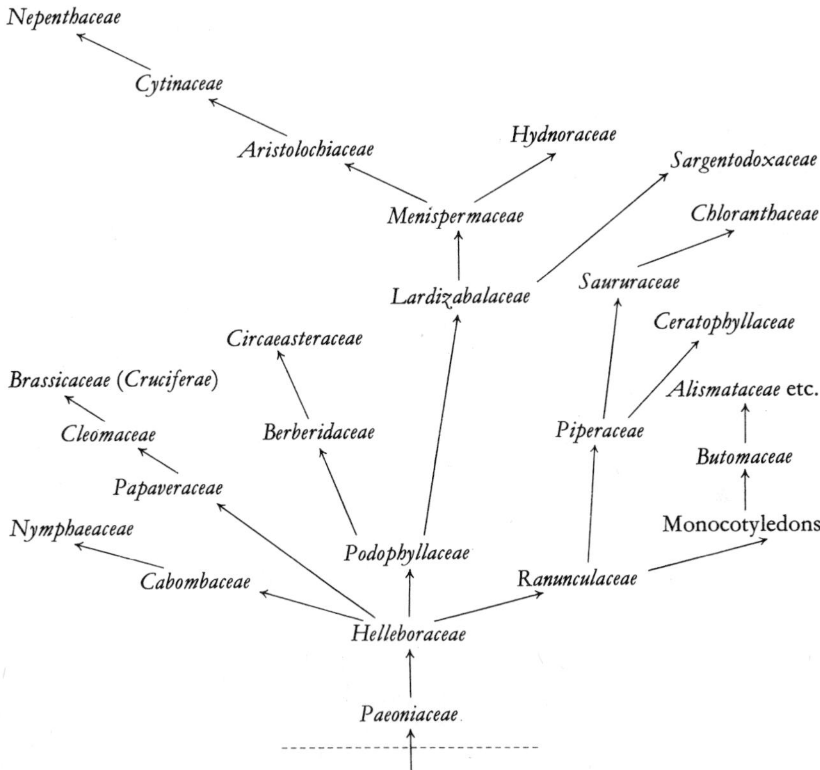

Diagram showing the probable course of evolution of the families directly derived from the *Ranales* stock. From a distributional point of view it is interesting to note that the basal stock occurs largely in temperate regions, that the moderately specialised groups have remained in the same areas, and that the reduced or very specialised groups occur in the tropics.

Growth-forms begin with perennials with underground rhizomes, leading up to climbing soft-wooded shrubs with broad medullary rays, and becoming apetalous; annuals are exceedingly rare in the lowermost families, and always characterised by an advanced type of floral structure.

in development very similar to that which has become so common in *Brassicaceae* (*Cruciferae*). *Hypecoum* (Fig. 438, **L**) has fruits transversely septate which break up into 1-seeded compartments as in *Hedysarum* (*Fabaceae*). In *Discocapnos* (Fig. 441) and *Platycapnos* the fruits are flattened disks like *Lobularia* fruits in *Brassicaceae*, and in *Ceratocapnos* they are dimorphic, the upper being pointed and capsular, the lower truncate and indehiscent. Here are a few more outstanding features of certain genera and species: Habit, climbing by leaf-tendrils in *Dactylicapnos*, *Corydalis claviculata* DC., *Phacocapnos*, *Cysticapnos*, *Adlumia*, *Ceratocapnos*, *Trigonocarpus*, *Fumaria* spp. and *Discocapnos*. Leaves pectinately pinnatisect and fern-like in *Corydalis cheilanthifolia* Hemsl.; trifoliolate in *Corydalis benecincta* W.W.Sm.; usually the terminal segments tendriliform and sometimes 3-pronged in the climbing spp. of *Corydalis*; leaves woolly-hairy in *Corydalis tomentosa* Hemsl. and *C. tomentella* Franch. Inflorescence dense and spike-like in *Platycapnos*; leaf-opposed in most of the climbing spp.; paniculate in *Corydalis gigantea* Trautr. & Mey. Petals neither saccate nor spurred in subfamily *Hypecoumoideae*; spur of the petal 2·5 cm long in *Corydalis schanginii* Fedtsch. Stamens not united in *Hypecoumoideae*. Ovules few (2) in *Sarcocapnos*. Fruits transversely septate and breaking up into 1-seeded compartments in *Hypecoum*; capsules bladder-like in *Cysticapnos*; twisted and torulose in *Corydalis ophiocarpa* Hook. f. & Thoms.; strongly torulose in *Corydalis pallida* Pers.; cotyledon 1 in *Corydalis tuberosa* DC.

ORDER 60. **CRUCIALES**

(*Fam. Fl. Pl.* **1**, 425)

Families: **Cleomaceae, Oxystylidaceae, Brassicaceae** (*Cruciferae*).

Phylogeny: RANALES (*Helleboraceae*) → RHOEADALES (*Papaveraceae*) → *Cleomaceae* → to climax family *Brassicaceae*.

As noted in my GENERA OF FLOWERING PLANTS (Vol. 2, p. 303), about half of the family *Capparidaceae*, as usually understood, are woody and have indehiscent fruits without a replum, and are clearly related to *Flacourtiaceae* (BIXALES), whilst the other half, subfamily *Cleomoideae*, greatly resemble certain *Brassicaceae* (*Cruciferae*), all being herbs with dehiscent fruits with a replum, i.e. a frame-like placenta from which the valves fall away in dehiscence, as in most *Brassicaceae*.

After much careful study in connection with that work, genus by genus,

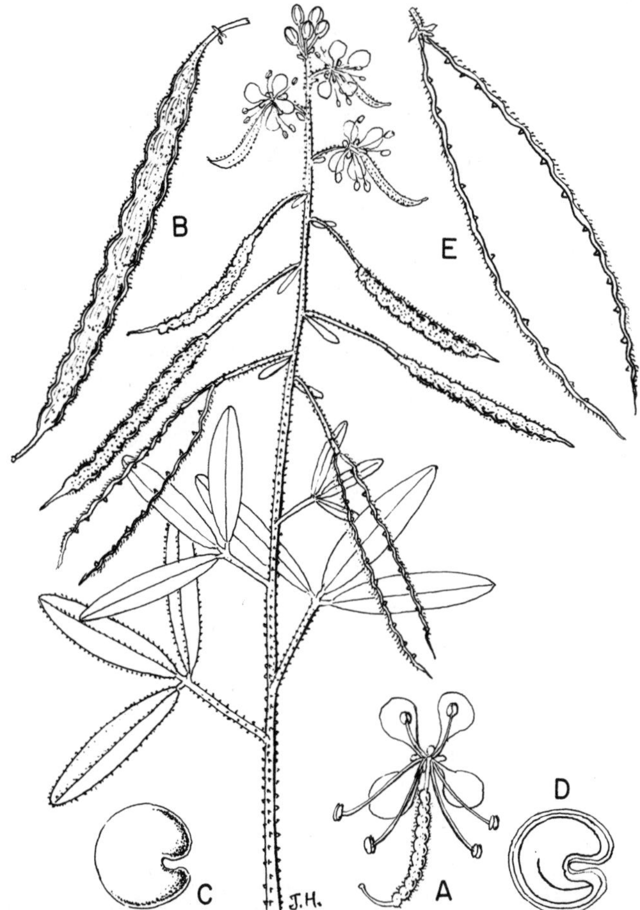

FIG. 442. *Cleome ornithopoides* Linn., eastern Mediterranean, the type species of the type genus of *Cleomaceae*. **A**, flower, **B**, fruit. **C**, seed. **D**, vertical section of seed showing the curved embryo. **E**, the replum after the valves and seeds have fallen away (orig.).

and species by species, in the Kew Herbarium, I came to the conclusion that phylogenetically at any rate two distinct families have hitherto been included in the *Capparidaceae*, and that subfamily *Cleomoideae* (type genus *Cleome* Linn.) should have family status immediately preceding *Brassicaceae*.

The type genus of **Cleomaceae** is therefore *Cleome* Linn.: embracing about 200 spp. in the tropics and warm temperate regions: Undershrubs, rarely small trees, or annual herbs, if glandular the glands often stipitate; leaves simple or 3–7-foliolate, leaflets entire or serrulate; flowers bisexual, solitary or in racemes, white, yellow or purple; calyx 4-toothed or 4-partite,

FIG. 443. An outstanding species of *Cleome*, *C. spinosa* Jacq. (*Cleomaceae*), tropical South America. **A**, young flower. **B**, cross-section of ovary. **C**, fruit. **D**, seed. **E**, vertical section of seed. (Adapted partly from BOTANICAL MAGAZINE.)

persistent or deciduous, sometimes splitting around the base; petals subequal, often rather 1-sided, entire, convolute, imbricate or open in bud; torus short, sometimes produced at the back into an appendix; stamens numerous to 6, rarely 4, inserted on the torus, all or only some bearing fertile anthers; filaments mostly unequal and declinate; ovary sessile or stipitate; ovules numerous on 2 parietal placentas; style very short or stigma sessile; capsule short or elongated, sessile or stipitate, 1-locular, valves membranous; seeds reniform, rough or woolly (type species *C. ornithopoides* Linn., eastern Mediterranean; Fig. 442).

The genera are arranged in two tribes, 1, *Cleomeae* (Fig. 443), with fruit more or less elongated or rarely bladdery, with numerous to several seeds, and 2, *Cleomelleae*, with trapezoid fruits compressed contrary to the septum, with few seeds, stamens 6, flowers racemose with leafy bracts.

The genera which diverge most from the type genus are *Podandrogyne*, with unisexual monoecious flowers, the lower female, the upper male; *Haptocarpum*, petals reduced to 2 and only 4 stamens; *Christatella*, petals coarsely toothed or laciniate at the apex; *Dactylaena*, only 1 stamen bearing an anther.

Key to Tribes and genera of **Cleomaceae**

Fruits more or less elongated and compressed in the same plane as the replum, or rarely bladder-like; seeds numerous to several CLEOMEAE

Fruits trapezoid, compressed contrary to the replum, with 8–4 seeds; stamens 6, all fertile; flowers racemose; bracts leafy; North America CLEOMELLEAE

Tribe CLEOMEAE
(*Key to genera*)

A. Two or more stamens bearing fertile anthers:

B. Petals entire or at most crenulate:

C. Petals more than 2:

D. Fruits not inflated; calyx rarely campanulate:

E. Torus short (ovary sessile) or if produced into a gynophore then the stamens free from the latter; stamens mostly all fertile:

F. Flowers bisexual; cosmopolitan genus CLEOME (*Physostemon*)

FF. Flowers unisexual, monoecious, the lower female, the upper male; S. America PODANDROGYNE

EE. Torus elongated into a gynophore and with the filaments adnate to it:

G. Inflorescence a raceme, sometimes with leafy bracts; stigmas subsessile or style very short; tropics and subtropics, and cult. GYNANDROPSIS

GG. Flowers solitary in the upper leaf-axils; stigma on a long filiform persistent style; herb with stipitate glands; N. and N.E. Australia JUSTAGO

DD. Fruits inflated; calyx sometimes campanulate; seeds large and smooth:

H. Small tree or shrub; flowers in racemes, large, yellow; leaves trifoliolate; California, Mexico ISOMERIS

HH. Perennial herbs covered with glands; flowers axillary, solitary; leaves simple, ovate-orbicular; Orient and N.E. Africa BUHSIA

CC. Petals reduced to 2; stamens 4, anticous, all fertile; fruit subsessile; Brazil. HAPTOCARPUM

BB. Petals coarsely toothed or laciniate at the top; stamens 14–6, declinate; sepals deciduous; N. America. CRISTATELLA

AA. Only one stamen bearing a fertile anther; leaves trifoliolate; flowers small, racemose, ebracteate; capsule glandular, shortly stipitate; West Indies through S. America to Argentina. DACTYLAENA

Tribe CLEOMELLEAE

Single genus in North America CLEOMELLA.

Oxystylidaceae,[1] new family, related to *Cleomaceae*, but ovary 2-locular, loculi 2-ovuled, ovules inserted on axile placentas, fruits 2-valved, valves deciduous and enclosing the seeds.

The type genus is *Oxystylis* Torr. & Frem., REPORT APP. 312 (1845). 1 sp. *O. lutea* Torr. & Frem., California to Nevada.

Annual herb, glabrous; leaves 3-foliolate; flowers bisexual or gynomonoecious, in short head-like axillary clusters, small, yellow; sepals linear, acute; petals ovate, shortly clawed; stamens 6, separated from the petals on the elevated and somewhat fleshy torus; ovary borne on a short stout stipe, didymously and unilaterally 2-lobed, 2-locular, loculi 2-ovuled on axile placentas; style elongated, pyramidal; fruit didymous, lobes obovoid-globose, indehiscent, crustaceo-coriaceous, 1- rarely 2-seeded, falling away from the persistent spine-like style-base and leaving a circular perforate scar on the corky thickened axis; seeds ovate, subcompressed, testa membranous, fleshy within; cotyledons linear-oblong, incumbent.

Wislizenia Engleman, Wisliz. MEM. TOUR. N. MEXICO 99 (1848); 2 or 3 spp. (or more), North America and Mexico; type *W. refracta* Engleman, N.W. Mexico to Arizona and Texas (see Fig. 444).

Annual rank-smelling herbs, glabrous; leaves minutely stipulate, 3-foliolate, stipules fimbriate; flowers in elongated bracteate racemes, yellow; sepals short, spreading, lanceolate, deciduous, imbricate; petals entire, shortly clawed, imbricate; torus short; stamens 6, all bearing anthers, subequal, inflexed in bud; filaments filiform, elongated, exserted; ovary long-

---

[1] **Oxystylidaceae,** fam. nov. affinis *Cleomaceae*, sed ovarium 2-loculare, loculis 2-ovulatis, ovulis axillaribus, fructus 2-valvis, valvis deciduis et semina includentibus differt.

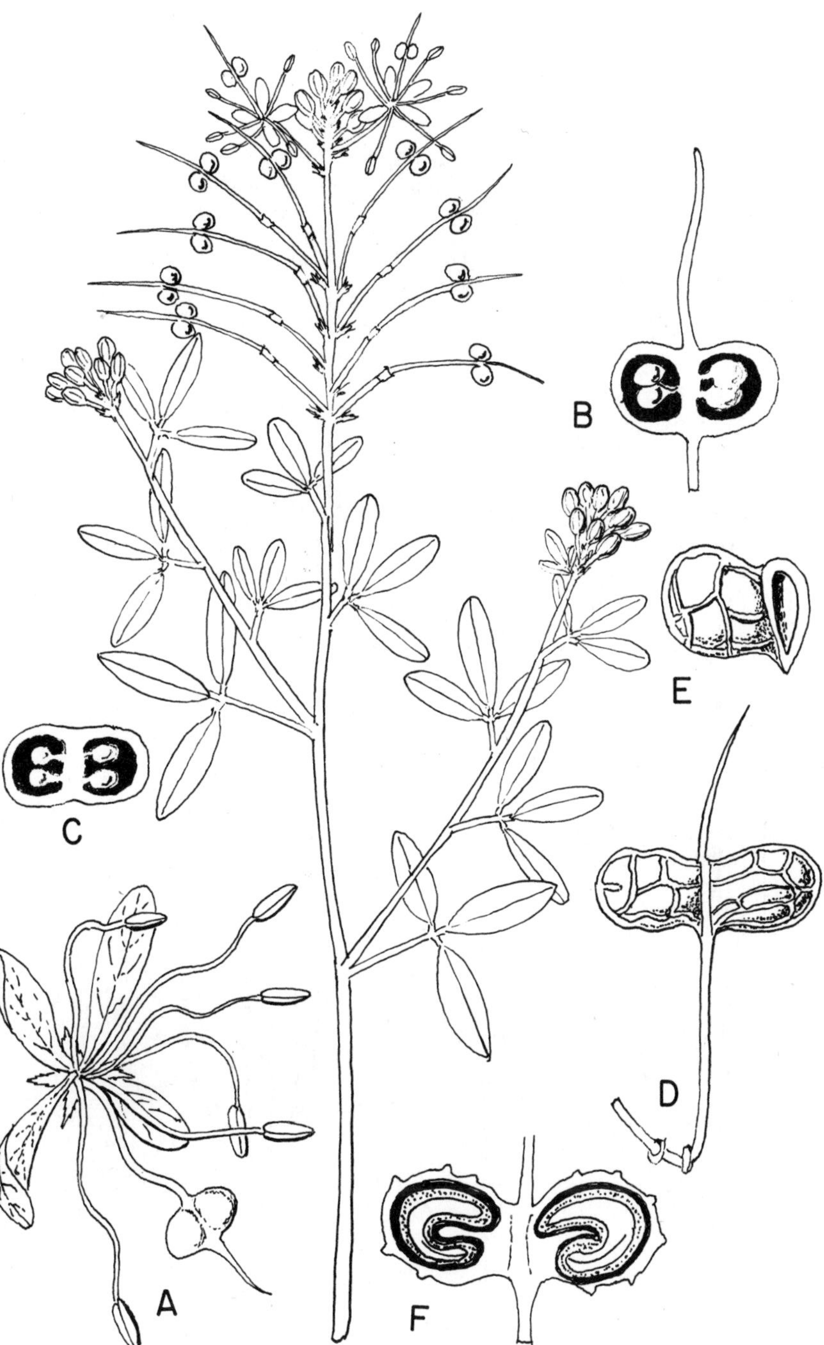

FIG. 444. *Wislizenia refracta* Engelm. (*Oxystylidaceae*), California to New Mexico and Texas. **A**, flower. **B**, vertical section and **C**, cross-section of ovary showing axile placentation. **D**, fruit (compressed contrary to the septum). **F**, vertical section of fruit (orig.).

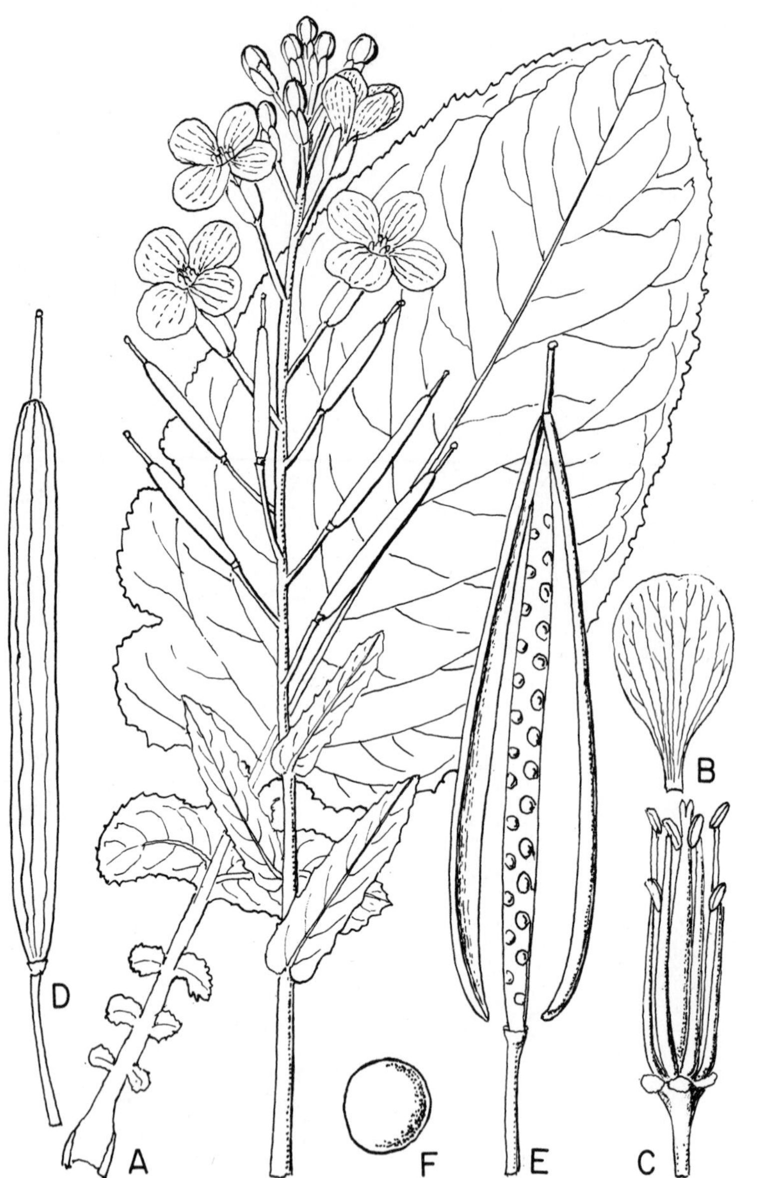

FIG. 445. *Brassica oleracea* Linn., the type species of the type genus of *Brassicaceae* (*Cruciferae*). **A**, lower leaf. **B**, petal. **C**, stamens and ovary. **D**, fruit. **E**, the same after opening. **F**, seed (orig.).

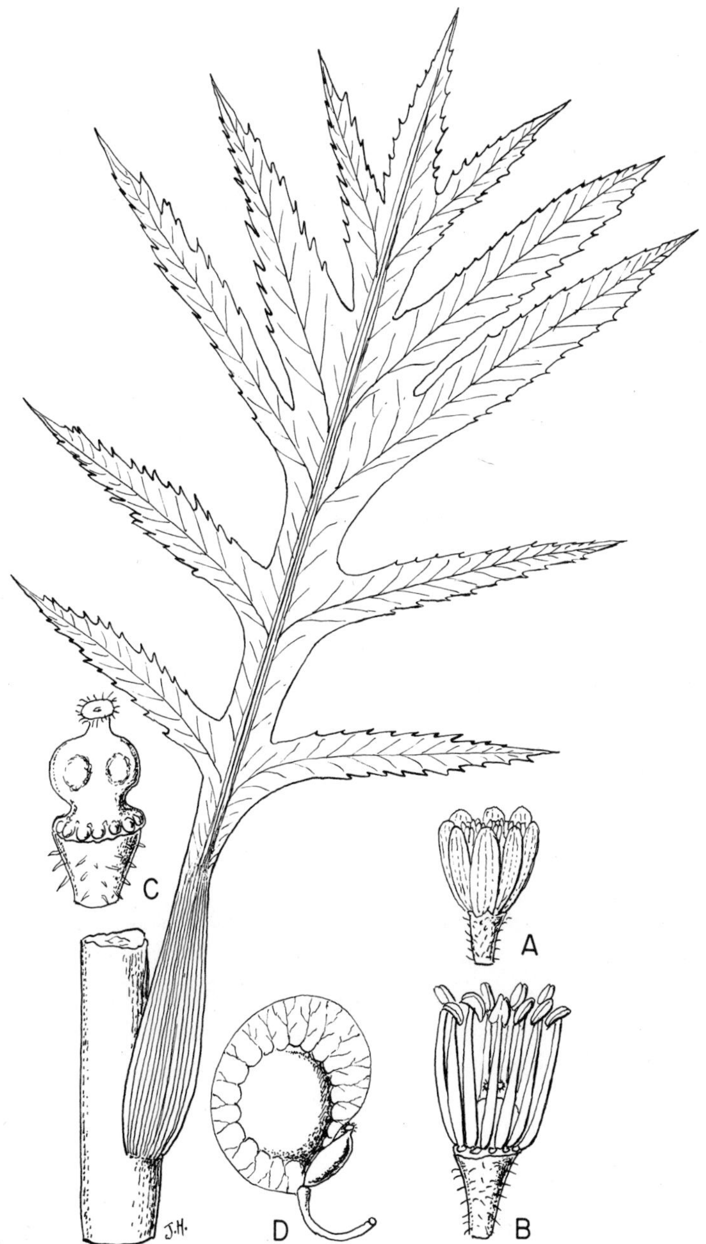

FIG. 446. *Megacarpaea polyandra* Benth. (*Brassicaceae*), Himalayas. An unusual genus in which the stamens vary in number from 6 to 16, with equal-length filaments; otherwise the genus is not primitive because of the advanced type of fruit, **D**. **A**, flower with 8 petals. **B**, showing the 10 stamens. **C**, gynoecium and glands (orig.).

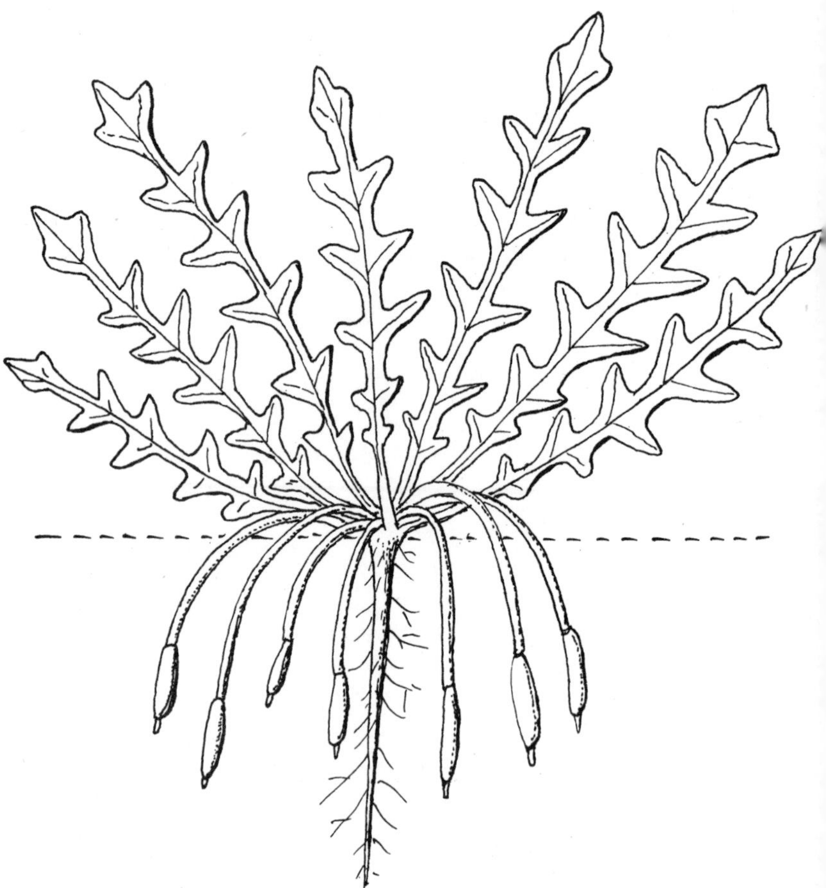

FIG. 447. *Geococcus pusillus* Drumm. (*Brassicaceae*), Australia, buries its fruits in the ground (orig.).

stipitate, didymous, 2-locular, loculi 2-ovuled on axile placentas; style filiform-subulate and persistent in fruit; capsule small, didymous, lobes transversely oblong, tuberculate, 2-locular, loculi 1-seeded; valves separating from the septum and enclosing the seed; stipe refracted on the pedicel in fruit; seeds conduplicate-reniform, smooth; embryo curved, with incumbent cotyledons.

Engleman remarked, "An interesting and quite anomalous plant, on account of its fruit with an almost complete dissepiment, and of stipules and bracts. Tuberculated valves of the capsule separating from the placentae, and though open, retaining the only (rarely 2) seed; placentae forming a complete dissepiment, which, in the perfectly ripe and dry state, finally becomes perforated in the centre."

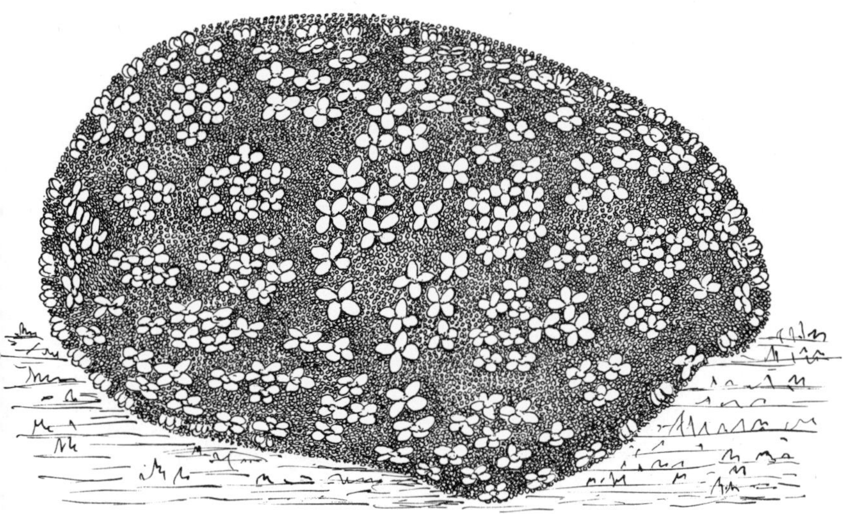

FIG. 448. A "Vegetable Sheep", *Xerodraba pycnophylloides* Skottsb. var. *microphylla* Schultz (*Brassicaceae*), Andes of Argentina; from a photograph by Coomber.

One of the most natural or homogeneous families of Dicotyledons is **Brassicaceae**[1] (known to generations of botanists as *Cruciferae*).[2] It seems to represent the final stage of reduction in this subphylum, in which the flowers have remained actinomorphic, the tetradynamous stamens having become a fixed and apparently very efficient contrivance for successful pollination. In consequence various members of the family are found almost throughout the world, many of them as rank growing weeds in cultivated or waste ground.

Perhaps in no other family are the genera so dependent on fruit characters, and a goodly number of the more outstanding are shown in our figures (Figs 449–452). The stomata of the leaves are characteristic throughout; they are surrounded by three subsidiary cells which are not, however, parallel to the pore as they are in the *Rubiaceae*, in the woody phylum.

---

[1] Also to be included in *Brassicaceae*: *Tetradynamae* H. G. Reichenb. (1830–32). *Raphanaceae* Horaninow (1847). *Cruciaceae* Dulac (1867). *Hectorellaceae* Philipson (1961).

[2] In the FAMILIES OF FLOWERING PLANTS I continued to use the name *Cruciferae*, but in my Revised KEY TO FAMILIES OF FLOWERING PLANTS OF THE WORLD, I decided to use the generic type name for all, such as **Fabaceae** (for *Papilionaceae*), **Clusiaceae** (for *Guttiferae*), **Aizoaceae** (for *Ficoidaceae*), **Lamiaceae** (for *Labiatae*), **Apiaceae** (for *Umbelliferae*), **Asteraceae** (for *Compositae*), **Arecaceae** (for *Palmae*), **Poaceae** (for *Gramineae*); most of these names may be used according to International Rules. I also continue to write **Capparidaceae** (not *Capparaceae*) for surely we cannot have *Epacraceae* (for **Epacridaceae**), *Bataceae* (for **Batidaceae**), not *Balanopaceae* (for **Balanopsidaceae**), and surely, surely not *Orchiaceae* (for **Orchidaceae**)!

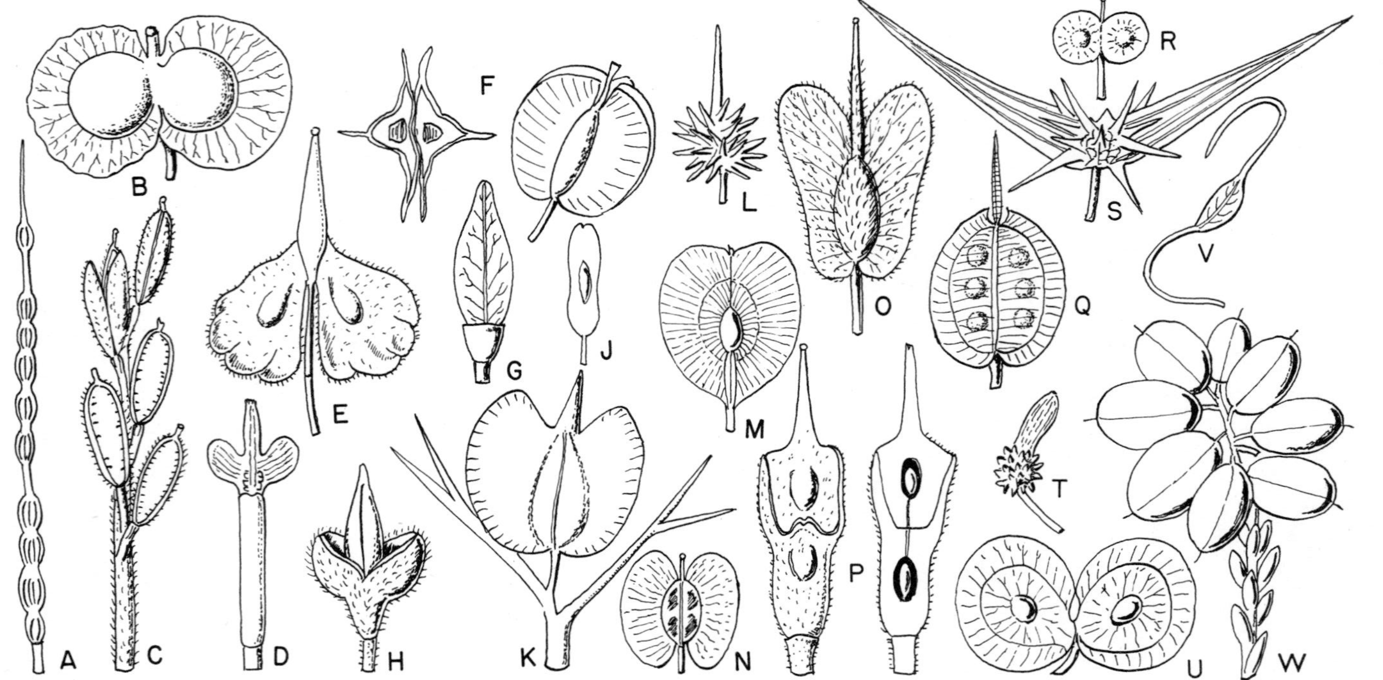

FIG. 449. Fruits of *Brassicaceae* (*Cruciferae*). **A**, *Raphanus raphanistrum* Linn., Middle Europe. **B**, *Cremolobus peruvianus* (Lam.) DC., Ecuador and Peru. **C**, *Pringlea antiscorbutica* R.Br., Kerguelen. **D**, *Fezia pterocarpa* Pitard, Morocco. **E**, *Urbanodoxa rhomboidea* (Hook.) Muschler, Peru. **F**, *Hexaptera pinnatifida* Gill. & Hook., Chile and Argentina. **G**, *Cakile maritima* Linn., central Europe, Mediterranean region, Australia, South America. **H**, *Otocarpus virgatus* Durieu, Algeria. **J**, *Isatis tinctoria* Linn., central and southern Europe. **K**, *Zilla macroptera* Coss., north Africa. **L**, *Succowia balearica* (Linn.) Medik., Mediterranean. **M**, *Fortuynia aucheri* Shuttl., Orient. **N**, *Aethionema arabicum* (Linn.) Andrz., Orient. **O**, *Psychine stylosa* Desf., north Africa. **P**, *Ceratocnemum rapistroides* Coss. & Balansa, Morocco. **Q**, *Schouwia schimperi* Jaub. & Spach, north Africa to Arabia. **R**, *Biscutella laevigata* Linn., southern Europe and north Africa. **S**, *Pugionium cornutum* (Linn.) Gaertn., Mongolia. **T**, *Schimpera arabica* Hochst. & Steud., Orient. **U**, *Megacarpaea gigantea* Regel, Turkestan. **V**, *Spirorhynchus sabulosus* Kar. & Kir., Orient. **W**,

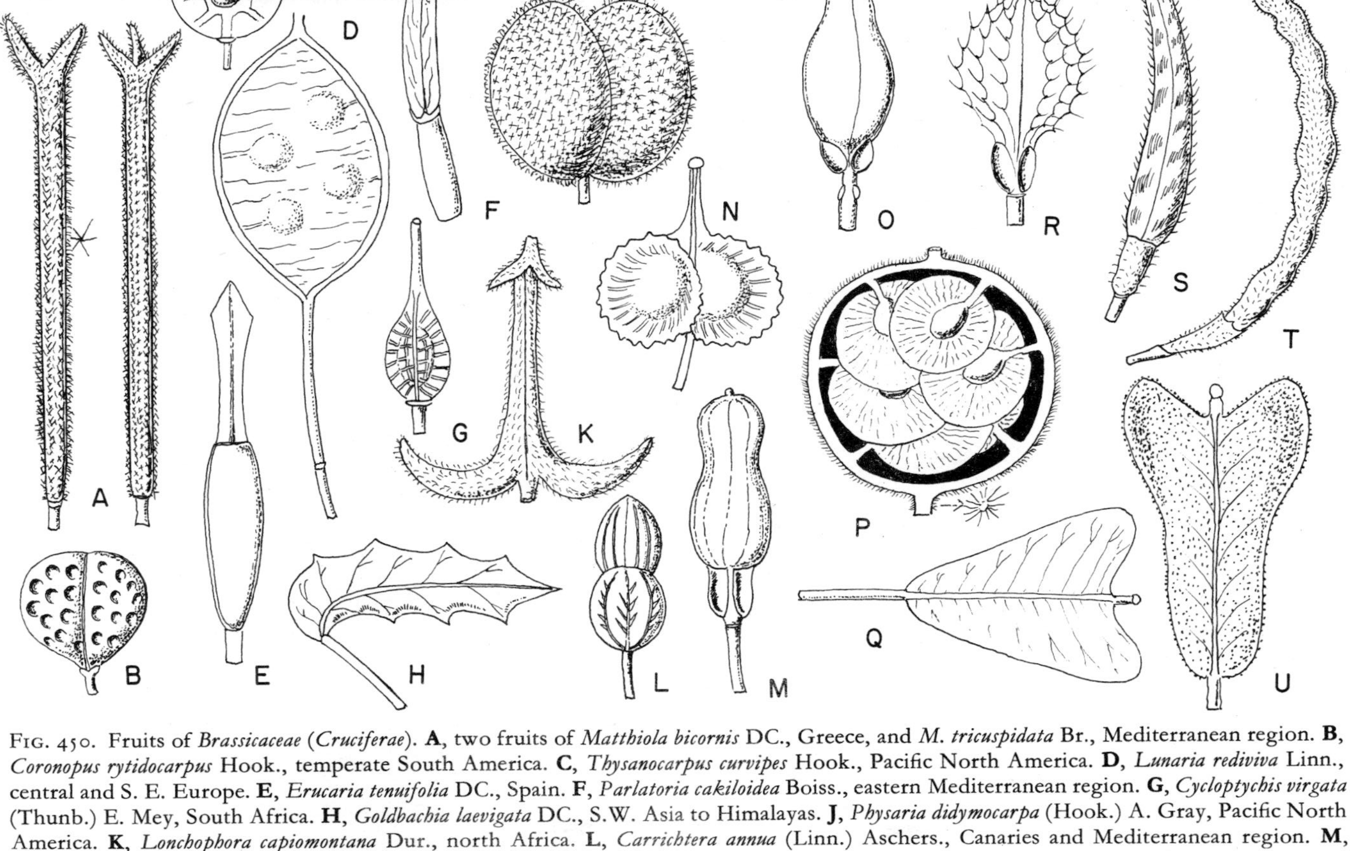

Fig. 450. Fruits of *Brassicaceae* (*Cruciferae*). **A**, two fruits of *Matthiola bicornis* DC., Greece, and *M. tricuspidata* Br., Mediterranean region. **B**, *Coronopus rytidocarpus* Hook., temperate South America. **C**, *Thysanocarpus curvipes* Hook., Pacific North America. **D**, *Lunaria rediviva* Linn., central and S. E. Europe. **E**, *Erucaria tenuifolia* DC., Spain. **F**, *Parlatoria cakiloidea* Boiss., eastern Mediterranean region. **G**, *Cycloptychis virgata* (Thunb.) E. Mey, South Africa. **H**, *Goldbachia laevigata* DC., S.W. Asia to Himalayas. **J**, *Physaria didymocarpa* (Hook.) A. Gray, Pacific North America. **K**, *Lonchophora capiomontana* Dur., north Africa. **L**, *Carrichtera annua* (Linn.) Aschers., Canaries and Mediterranean region. **M**, *Enarthrocarpus chevalieri* Baratte, Algeria. **N**, *Cremolobus pinnatifidus* Hook., Peru. **O**, *Physorrhynchus brahuicus* Hook., Orient, India. **P**, *Fibigia macroptera* Boiss., Asia Minor. **Q**, *Capsella bursa-pastoris* Moench, widely distributed weed. **R**, *Guiroa arvensis* Coss., Spain. **S**, *Enarthrocarpus pterocarpus* DC., Mediterranean region. **T**, *Enarthrocarpus arcuatus* Labill., Mediterranean region. **U**, *Lyrocarpa coulteri* Hook. & Arn., Pacific North America.

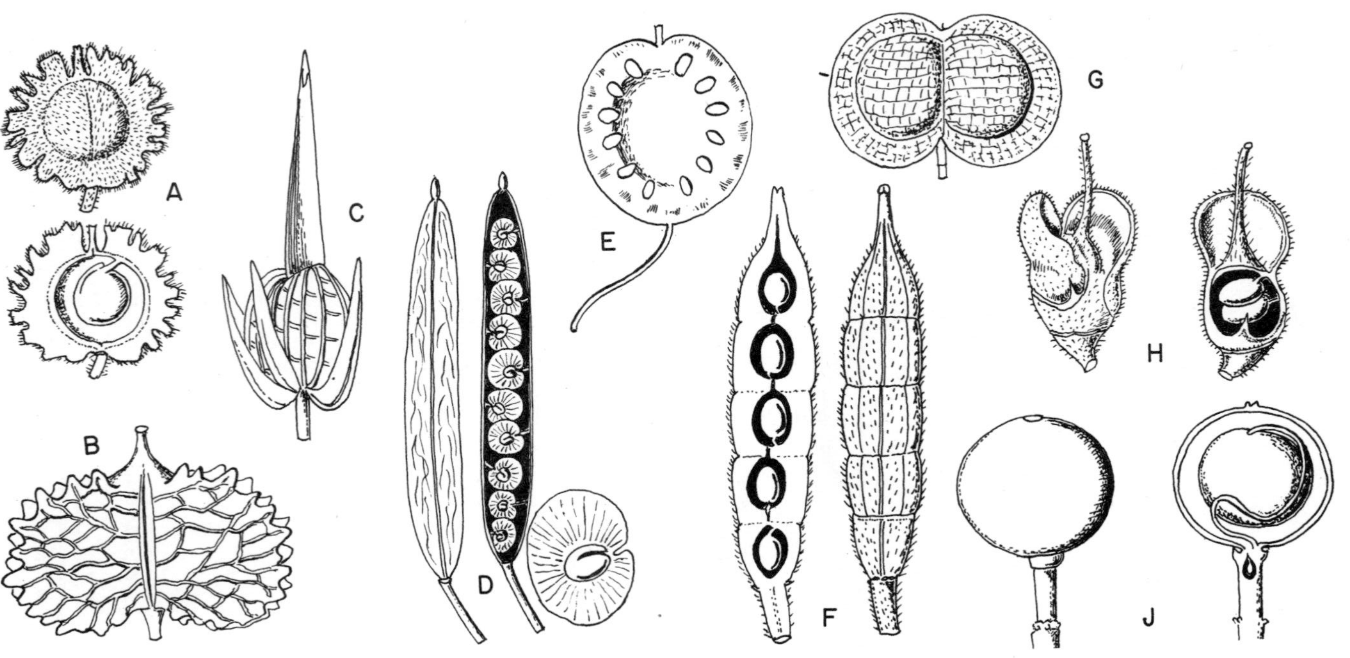

Fig. 451. Fruits of *Brassicaceae* (*Cruciferae*). **A**, *Clypeola cyclodontea* Delile, North Africa. **B**, *Coronopus violaceus* (Munby) O. Ktze., North Africa. **C**, *Rytidocarpus moricandioides* Coss., Morocco. **D**, *Oudneya africana* R.Br., North Africa. **E**, *Thysanocarpus curvipes* Hook., Pacific North America. **F**, *Enarthrocarpus clavatus* Delile, North Africa. **G**, *Schouwia schimperi* Jaub. & Spach, Arabia, Egypt and Central Sahara. **H**, *Anastatica hierochuntia* Linn., Mediterranean region. **J**, *Crambe kralikii* Coss., North Africa.

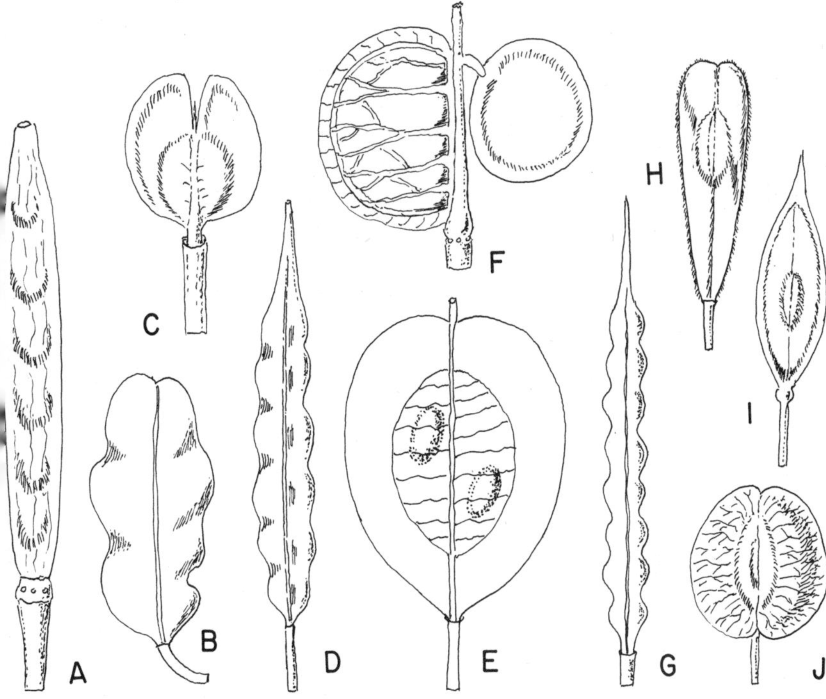

FIG. 452. Fruits of *Brassicaceae* (*Cruciferae*). **A**, *Arabis doumetii* Coss., North Africa. **B**, *Cossonia platycarpa* Coss., North Africa. **C**, *Lepidium rotundum* DC., Australia. **D**, *Cossonia africana* Dur., North Africa. **E**, *Brossardia papyracea* Boiss., Orient. **F**, *Iberis semperflorens* Linn., southern Europe, North Africa (and cult.). **G**, *Chorispora greigii*, Rgl., temperate Asia. **H**, *Isatis aleppica* Scop., eastern Mediterranean. **I**, *Heliophila scandens* Harv., South Africa. **J**, *Isatis gjurdjurae* Coss. & Dur., Algeria.

Natural evolution works in a mysterious way. It may not be just fortuitous that this highly evolved and climax family of herbs supplies the animal kingdom and humanity with several food plants and condiments, the latter helping to whet the appetite of mankind. Most important money-makers are the Cabbage, Cauliflower and Brussels Sprouts (*Brassica*), and from the seeds of this genus commercial oils are obtained, including rapes or colzas and mustards. The mustard, of "Mustard and Cress" sandwiches, is grown from the seed of *Brassica nigra* Linn., and the cress from that of *Lepidium sativum* Linn. Table mustard is made from the powdered seeds of *Brassica nigra* Linn. and *B. alba* Boiss., the British brand from the seeds without the husks, and the French kind from seeds ground whole with the husk. Before the introduction of Indigo dyes from India, the only blue dye known in Britain was obtained from "Woad", *Isatis tinctoria* Linn., which was grown chiefly in Lincolnshire and other eastern counties.

Type genus *Brassica* Linn.: Perennials, biennials or annual herbs, glabrous to setose hairy; rootstock fusiform; basal leaves often in a rosette, stem leaves alternate, entire or variously deeply divided; inflorescence racemose, rarely with bracts; flowers bisexual, actinomorphic; sepals more or less erect, inner somewhat subsaccate; petals yellow, rarely white, clawed; stamens always 6, anthers obtuse or acuminate; lateral nectaries sometimes very small, median usually large, semiglobose to filiform; ovary cylindric, with 5 or more ovules; stigma capitate or somewhat 2-lobed; fruit linear to oblong, straight or bent, biconvex in section, beaked; valves convex; seeds 1-seriate, globose or ovoid, pendulous; cotyledons conduplicate or concave. Type species *B. oleracea* Linn. (Fig. 445).

ORDER 61. RESEDALES

(*Fam. Fl. Pl.* **1**, 426)

Family: **Resedaceae**

Resedaceae[1] is an advanced family in which the petals are small and inconspicuous and valvate in aestivation. The family makes up for this deficiency in the size of its petals, however, by usually having a very pleasant odour, the most familiar example of this being the common Mignonette, *Reseda odorata* Linn. The seeds have no endosperm.

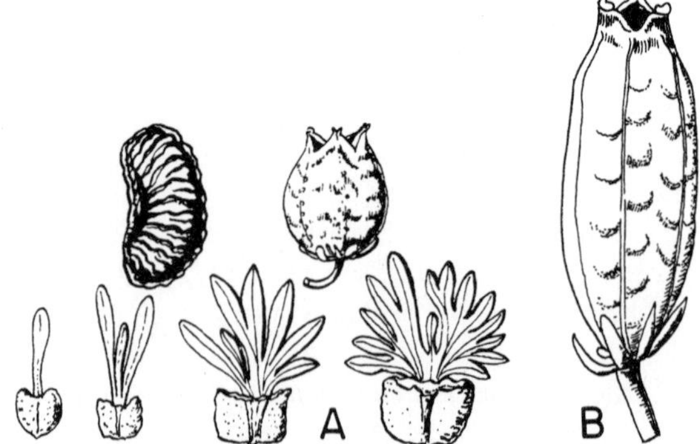

FIG. 453. **A**, parts of flower and a fruit and seed of *Reseda arabica* Boiss. **B**, the fruit of *Reseda villosa*. Note the gaping tops of the fruits.

[1] Including *Laciniaceae* Dulac (1867). *Astrocarpaceae* Kerner (1891).

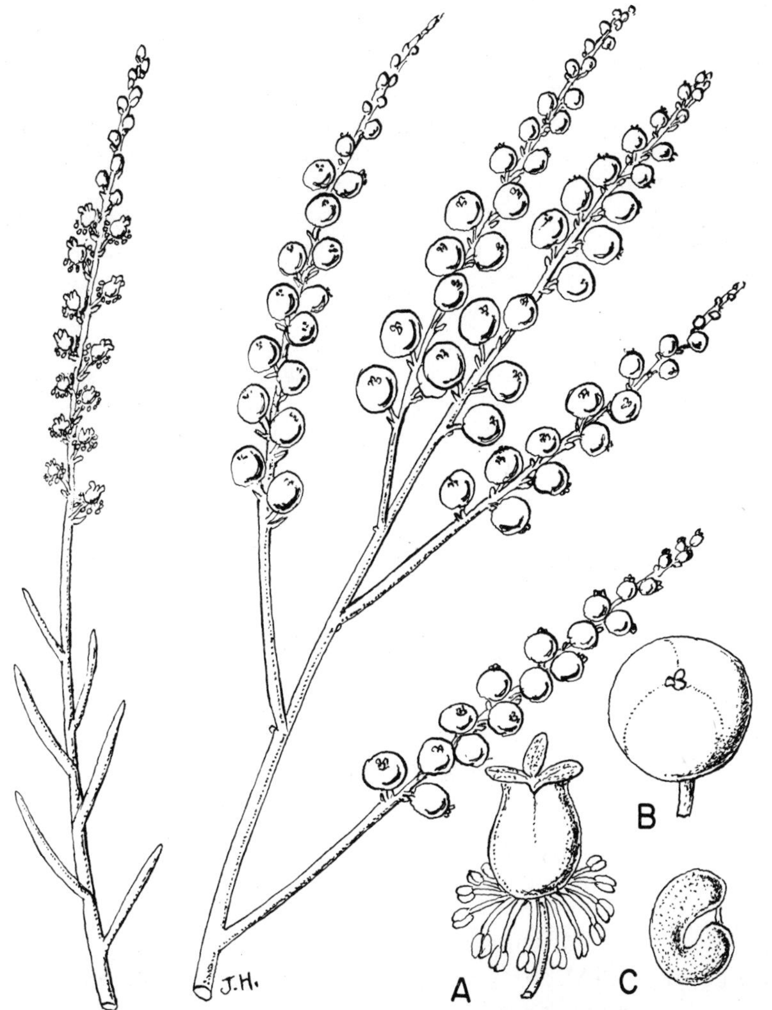

FIG. 454. *Ochradenus baccatus* Del., the only genus with a berried fruit in the family *Resedaceae*; a favourite food of camels in the dry regions of North Africa. **A**, flower. **B**, fruit. **C**, embryo (orig.).

It is allied to the *Brassicaceae* (*Cruciferae*), but with a tendency to zygomorphy of the flowers, the development of a disk, and some apetaly. The family is most highly represented in the countries surrounding the Mediterranean, a few reaching the frontier of India and N.E. tropical Africa; there is one genus, *Oligomeris*, common to the Northern Hemisphere and southern Africa. For the most part the family is partial to desert regions, especially abundant on calcareous soils. The most cosmopolitan and largest genus is

Reseda, the type of the family, with a great concentration of species in the eastern parts of the Mediterranean, with one or two distinct endemic species in the island of Socotra. *R. pruinosa* Del. is common in Arabia and Somaliland. Two of the most widespread species in the family are *Caylusea canescens* A.St.Hil. and *Ochradenus baccatus* Del. (Fig. 454), which occur in the desert regions from the Canary Islands and Cape Verde Islands through northern Africa to Arabia and Socotra. The other species of *Ochradenus* are of limited distribution and confined to the Near East (Persia to Somaliland). The monotypic genus *Randonia* is indigenous to N.W. Africa. According to Hildebrandt (note in Herb. Kew), *Ochradenus baccatus* Del. is a good camel food. It is the only genus with a berried fruit, and there are no petals. According to notes by collectors in the Kew Herbarium, this is a weak *Spartium*-like shrub which persists in the protection of thorn bushes; if growing in the open it is a small dense shrub but is usually quickly eliminated by camels or goats. On some bushes the fruits make a show in March, looking like pearls along the branches. The plants also have the pale green flowers at all stages of development at the same time.

ORDER 62. **CARYOPHYLLALES**

(*Fam. Fl. Pl.* **1**, 427)

Families: **Elatinaceae, Molluginaceae, Caryophyllaceae, Aizoaceae** (*Ficoidaceae*), **Portulacaceae.**

↗ SAXIFRAGALES
Phylogeny: RANALES → CARYOPHYLLALES → further evolution to *Primulaceae*, and *Gentianaceae*.

The Order CARYOPHYLLALES is fundamentally and predominantly herbaceous, more advanced than the basic group of the SAXIFRAGALES (such as *Crassulaceae*), and one which has been the centre of very considerable evolution. For example we may trace, although sometimes not very clearly and often with rather wide intervening gaps, a large portion of the old and artificial group *Monochlamydeae* or *Apetalae*, especially herbaceous parts of it, such as POLYGONALES and CHENOPODIALES, held together mainly by one character, the curved embryo, hence the ordinal name *Centrospermae* of the Engler system. From this group also have almost certainly been developed *Gentianaceae*, a family with a sympetalous corolla, and *Primulaceae*.

Elatinaceae[1] is a small family composed of only two genera, *Elatine* and *Bergia*, in which the stipules are paired, and they are distinguished from *Caryophyllaceae* by their septate ovary and seeds without endosperm. Their exact phylogenetic position is, however, rather doubtful, but I consider this is a much better position than that assigned to them by Engler, who placed them between the Dipterocarps and Tamarisks! If we accept the theory that

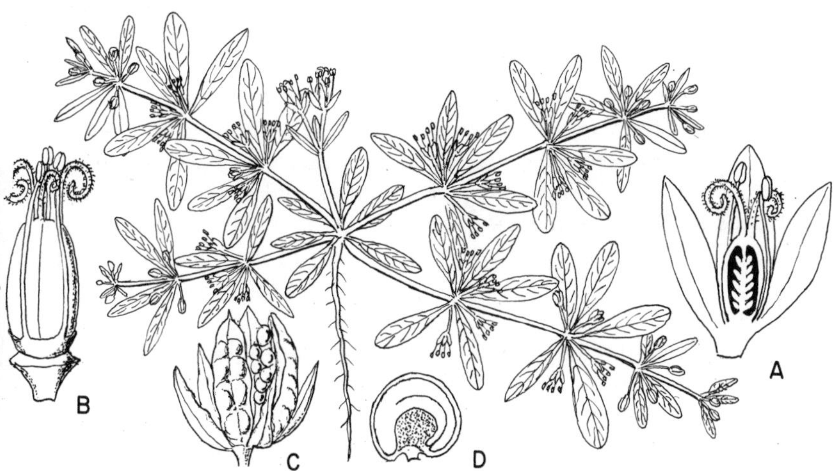

FIG. 455. *Mollugo verticillata* Linn., the type species of the type genus of *Molluginaceae*, a family considered in this system to be more primitive than *Caryophyllaceae* on account of its axile placentation. **A**, vertical section of flower. **B**, androecium and gynoecium. **C**, fruit. **D**, vertical section of seed.

the placentation typical of *Caryophyllaceae* (free central) has been derived from an axile one from which the dividing walls have disappeared, then this family might be regarded as representing a forerunner of the *Caryophyllaceae*.

The small family **Molluginaceae** is but little removed from the *Caryophyllaceae*; usually they have a several-locular ovary and the petals have become very small or absent. The majority are weedy plants of dry places in the tropics and warm temperate regions.

The type genus is *Mollugo* Linn.: Erect or spreading herbs, sometimes stellate-tomentose, often dichotomously branched; leaves all radical or alternate or mostly subverticillate, linear to obovate or spathulate; stipules membranous, fugacious, undivided; flowers axillary, fascicled or in axil-

[1] Including *Glinaceae* Link (1831). *Adenogrammataceae* Nakai (1942). *Gisekiaceae* Nakai (1942).

lary cymes, umbels or subracemose, greenish; sepals 5, persistent; petals none; stamens 3–5, rarely more, subhypogynous, often mixed with subulate staminodes; anthers linear-oblong, opening lengthwise; disk absent or small and annular; ovary 3–5-locular, styles 3–5, linear or clavate; ovules numerous, inserted on the inner angle; capsule membranous, enclosed by the calyx, 3–5-locular, 3–5-valved; seeds 1 or more in each loculus, sometimes with a small bristle-like aril.

In *Orygia* the petals and stamens are numerous and there are no stipules. In *Macarthuria* the petals are 5 or absent, and the stamens 8, also without stipules. In *Telephium* the petals and stamens are 5 each, the ovary 3-locular, and there are small scarious stipules. In several of the other genera (mainly South African) there are no petals, and the stipules when present are lobed or lacerate. In *Adenogramma*, also South African, the ovary is 1-locular with 1 ovule, and the verticillate leaves are without stipules. These characters are mentioned to show that there is great diversity in the floral structure in this small family, which from a phylogenetic point of view seems to be more primitive than *Caryophyllaceae*, from which the partitions of the ovary have disappeared.

From a phylogenetic point of view the **Caryophyllaceae**[1] have always been of great interest. The "spotting" characters for the family are the opposite simple leaves, the clawed petals, free-central placentation, and the endospermic seed with curved often quite peripheral embryo. The family is readily divided into two distinct groups, the one with free sepals (*Cerastium*, *Stellaria, Spergularia*, *Polycarpaea*, etc.), the other with united sepals (*Dianthus*, *Silene*, *Lychnis*, etc.).

Tribe *Polycarpeae*, especially, with its usually dry and scarious stipules and sepals and reduced petals, seems to show the path of evolution to the *Illecebraceae*. Tribe *Alsineae* may have given rise to the *Geraniaceae*, but the connections are not very evident. Tribe *Sileneae*, however, with their gamosepalous calyx, seem to point to the origin of families such as *Primulaceae*. With regard to the latter, it is supported by Gertrude E. Douglas in her "Studies in the Vascular Anatomy of the *Primulaceae*" (AM. J. BOTANY **23**, no. 3, 199–212 (1936)).

The type genus of *Caryophyllaceae* is *Dianthus* Linn., the type species being *D. caryophyllus* Linn. (Fig. 456), hence the family name from *Caryophyllus* P. Miller (not of Linnaeus), an illegitimate generic name: Herbs, mostly perennial, sometimes rather shrubby; leaves narrow and mostly grass-like; flowers terminal, solitary, cymose-paniculate or clustered, mostly rose or purple, rarely white or yellowish; calyx tubular, 5-toothed, finely and

---

[1] Including *Alsinaceae* Lamarck & de Candolle (1805). *Stellariaceae* Dumortier (1827). *Corrigiolaceae* Dumortier (1829). *Silenaceae* Bartling (1830). *Telephiaceae* Link (1831). *Dianthaceae* Burnett (1835). *Circumaceae* Dulac (1867). *Onychiaceae* Dulac (1867).

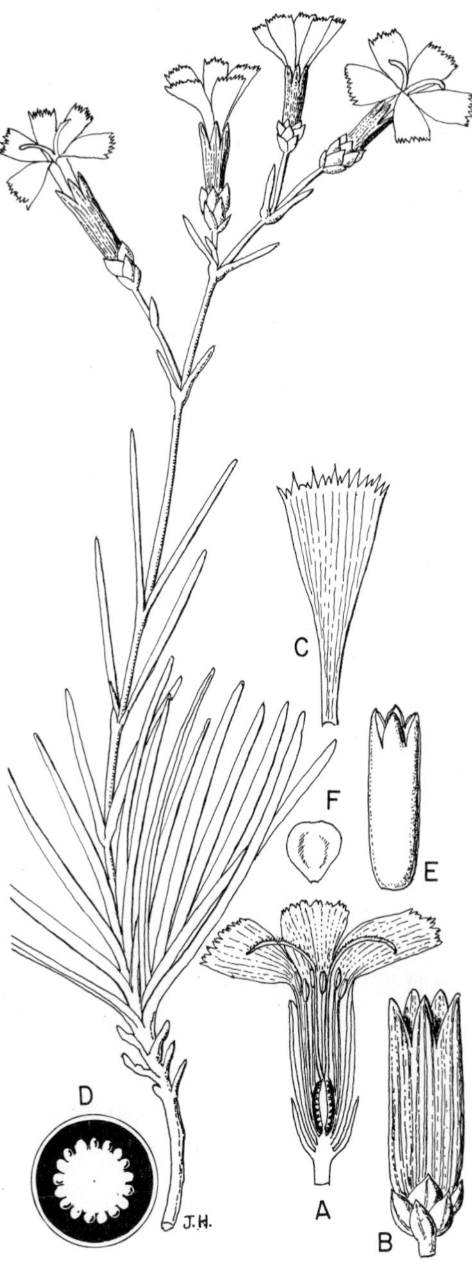

FIG. 456. *Dianthus caryophyllus* Linn., the type species of the type genus of *Caryophyllaceae*. **A**, vertical section of flower. **B**, bracts and calyx. **C**, petal. **D**, cross-section of ovary. **E**, capsule. **F**, seed (orig.).

equally multi-striate, girt by 2 or more bracteoles imbricate in pairs at the base; petals 5, long-clawed, limb entire to multifid; stamens 10, free; torus mostly more or less elongated into a stipe-like gynophore; ovary 1-locular; styles 2, free from the base; capsule cylindric or oblong, dehiscing at the top by 4 teeth or valves; seeds orbicular or discoid, overlapping on the columnar placenta; embryo straight, mostly excentric in the endosperm.

In Bentham and Hooker's GENERA PLANTARUM it was noted that

Caryophylleae typicae petaliferae foliis oppositis, staminibus definitis, ovario pro maxima saltem parte l-loculari multiovulato, et seminibus, facile distinguuntur.

Attention was also drawn to the relationship with *Molluginaceae*:

Mulluginearum species paucae petalis donatae primo intuitu Caryophylleas memorant et iis saepe adscribuntur, sed foliis non vere oppositis et ovario septato recedunt.

A few *formae abnormes* may be noted: Leaves pungent in *Acanthophyllum* and *Drypis*, and their fruits are subindehiscent and 1-seeded with peripheral embryo; very small and closely imbricate in *Pycnophyllum*; closely imbricate in *Lyallia*. Stipules absent from tribes *Sileneae* and most genera of tribe *Alsineae*, except *Spergula* and *Spergularia*; present and scarious, sometimes fimbriate in tribe *Polycarpeae*, except *Pycnophyllum*. Flowers dimorphic in some *Stellaria* spp., those with petals sterile, those without petals fertile; in globose spiny heads in *Sphaerocoma*. Petals absent from *Queria*, *Ortegia*, *Colobanthus*, *Microphyes*, *Cerdia* and from some species or even individual specimens of *Arenaria*, *Sagina*, *Spergularia* and *Loeflingia*. Stamens alternate with the sepals in *Colobanthus* (apetalous). Style scarcely divided in *Ortegia*, *Loeflingia*, *Pycnophyllum* and *Polycarpaea*. Fruits rather fleshy in *Cucubulus*, nut-like in *Sphaerocoma*.

Although **Aizoaceae** (*Ficoidaceae*) are widely separated in the Bentham and Hooker system, the authors of that work were well aware of its relationship with *Caryophyllaceae* and *Portulacaceae* etc., as shown by the following notes subtended to the description of the family:

Order inter Caryophylleas, Portulaceas, et Paronychieas quasi medius, cum his omnibus multis notis congruens, et vix nisi characteribus v. non constantibus v. levioris momenti distinguendus. A Caryophylleis differt ovario 2-∞-loculari saepe infero, foliis in perplurimis alternis, et non raro defectu petalorum; a Portulaceis calyce nunquam 2 sepalo et ovario 2-∞-loculari; a Paronychieis [= Illecebraceae], Amaranthaceis et Chenopodiaceis, habitu, ovario 2-∞-loculari v. si l-loculare evidenter l-carpellari stigmate simplicissimo, et capsulae dehiscentia; a Phytolacceis habitu et inflorescentia nunquam racemosa; a Polygoneis habitu, stipulis et ovario. Placentae in plerisque generibus Ficoidearum v. fere in toto Ordine e basi loculorum oriundae in angulo interiore v. liberae remanent v. axi adnatae, quomodo quoad placentationem Caryophylleis accedunt.

The family has become particularly well known in European countries and North America, especially on account of the South African genus *Mesembryanthemum*, which has been split up into a large number of small genera and is cultivated by many people in their cool greenhouses, especially in Britain and Holland. The authors of these genera were mainly the late Dr. N. E. Brown of Kew, Dr. L. Bolus in South Africa, and Tsr. G. Schwantes in Holland.

The type genus of the family is *Aizoon* Linn.: Herbs or shrublets, very often papillous, pubescent or tomentose, often with medifixed hairs; leaves alternate, rarely opposite, sessile or petiolate; stipules none; flowers bisexual, axillary, solitary or in divaricate cymes and secund, yellow; calyx-tube free from the ovary, lobes 4 or 5, spreading, imbricate or valvate, often coloured within; petals absent; stamens many, inserted in the throat of the calyx, arranged in bundles alternate with the calyx-lobes; filaments filiform, anthers oblong; ovary superior but enclosed by the calyx-tube, 4- or 5-locular; styles 4 or 5, free, filiform, papillous; ovules 2 to many in each loculus; capsule 5-locular, surrounded by the persistent calyx, loculicidally (rarely septicidally) 5-valved at the apex, valves gaping; seeds 2 or more in each loculus, small, with long funicles, compressed and subreniform; embryo curved, cylindric.

Except for the very numerous segregates from *Mesembryanthemum* there are not many genera left after the exclusion of tribe *Mollugineae*. Most of them are South African, *Galenia*, *Plinthus* and *Acrosanthes*, with loculicidal capsules, and the Australian *Gunnia* with a septicidal capsule. In *Sesuvium* the capsule opens by a transverse slit (as in some *Primulaceae*), while in *Trianthema* and *Cypselea* the capsule opens in the same way and the placenta is basal (as in all *Primulaceae*!). In tribes *Mesembryeae*, *Mesembryanthem* (*sensu latissimo*) and *Tetragonia* the ovary is completely inferior. In *Galenia* the stamens are in pairs, in *Aizoon* itself sometimes in bundles, and in *Cypselea* even reduced to one.

Portulacaceae[1] is a highly interesting family, for in the structure of its flowers it seems to point very clearly to the evolution of the more advanced *Primulaceae*. When the stamens are the same number as the petals, they are opposite to them and the ovary is 1-locular with a free basal placenta, both features of *Primulaceae*. And in *Lewisia* the capsule dehisces by a circumscissile slit as in the Primulaceous genera *Soldanella*, *Bryocarpus*, *Anagallis* and *Centunculus*. A further hall-mark of the family is the two sepals in all genera except *Lewisia*. And there is even slight sympetaly in species of *Claytonia* and *Calandrinia*, and more distinctly in *Montia* and *Calyptridium*.

---

[1] Including *Montiaceae* Dumort. (1829). *Spaetalumeae* Wyeth & Nuttall (1834). *Lewisiaceae* W. J. Hook. & Arnott. *Metabletaceae* Dulac (1867).

FIG. 457A. *Spraguea umbellata* Torr. (*Portulacaceae*). A very remarkable plant native of California and illustrated in the BOTANICAL MAGAZINE in 1859 (from which our black and white sketch is adapted); named after Mr Isaac Sprague, of Cambridge, Massachusetts, well known as a botanical draughtsman, and especially for the illustrations of A. Gray's GENERA OF PLANTS OF THE UNITED STATES. **A**, flower. **B**, the same with the two sepals removed. **C**, gynoecium. **D**, vertical section of ovary showing the free basal placentation.

The type genus is *Portulaca* Linn., which itself differs from the other genera by its semi-inferior ovary: Spreading or ascending fleshy herbs; leaves alternate or subopposite, flat or terete, often fasciculate-setose in the axils, the uppermost often forming an involucre below the flower; stipules scarious or setose; flowers terminal, yellow, purple or red; sepals 2, connate at the base and partly adnate to the ovary, deciduous; petals 4–6, free or nearly so; stamens 8 or more and opposite the petals; ovary semi-inferior, with numerous ovules; style deeply 3–8-lobed; capsule semi-inferior, the free part circumscissile-dehiscent; seeds reniform, shining, often granular; embryo peripheral. Types species *P. oleracea* Linn.

In *Portulacaria*, a South African shrub with opposite leaves, the ovule is solitary, and the fruit is winged and indehiscent. The stamens are numerous in *Grahamia*, a shrub with alternate leaves, these opposite in *Talinopsis*, and *Anacampseros*, with thick imbricate leaves. The androecium is reduced to a single stamen in *Monocosmia*, *Silvaea*, and in *Calyptridium*, which is also sympetalous with the stamen inserted on the corolla-tube. Although the flowers of this family have a mixed range of structure, it corresponds to their somewhat intermediate position between the *Caryophyllaceae* and the *Primulaceae*.

ORDER 63. POLYGONALES

(*Fam. Fl. Pl.* **1**, 431)

Families: **Polygonaceae, Illecebraceae.**

Phylogeny: RANALES → CARYOPHYLLALES → POLYGONALES → climax family *Illecebraceae*.

We need not try the patience of the student on the Order POLYGONALES except to emphasise the now generally recognised view that they are much reduced descendants of the CARYOPHYLLALES. Most of them have in common the curved embryo partially surrounding the endosperm, and there is usually a considerable reduction in the ovary, which is mostly 1-locular and 1-ovuled.

The peculiar stipular sheath (ochrea) is a good distinguishing feature for most of the **Polygonaceae**,[1] and a few of the most outstanding fruits are shown in Fig. 458.

[1] Including *Rumicaceae* Dumort. (1829). *Eriogonaceae* Meisner (1836–43). *Ocreaceae* Dulac (1867).

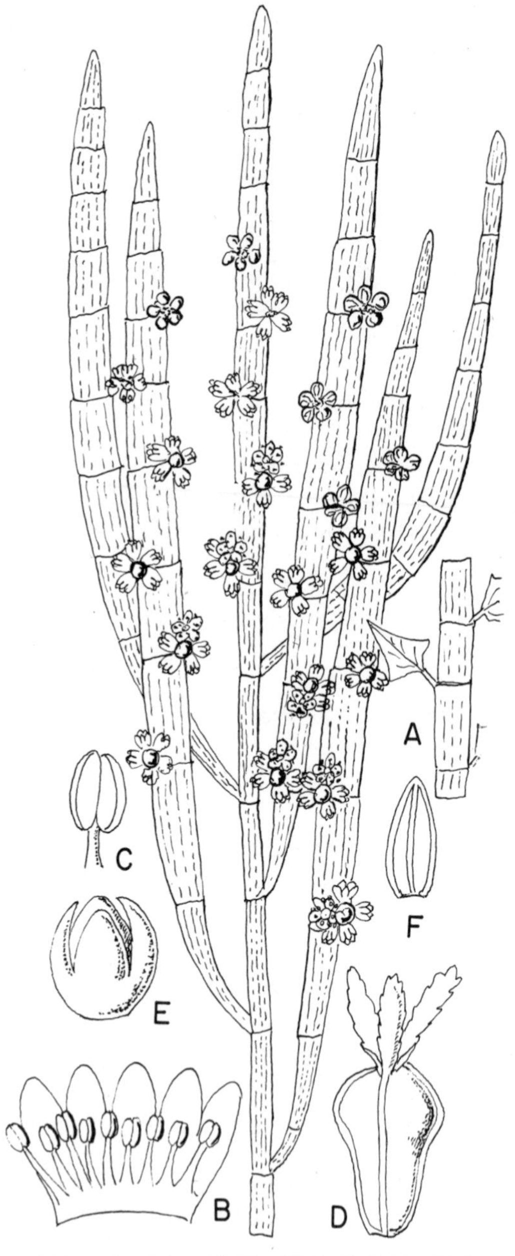

FIG. 457B. *Homalocladium platycladum* (F. Muell.) L. H. Bailey (*Polygonaceae*), native of the Solomon Islands, and cultivated in warm countries. **A**, young sterile leafy shoot. **B**, flower laid open. **C**, anther. **D**, gynoecium. **E**, calyx and nutlet. **F**, nutlet (orig.).

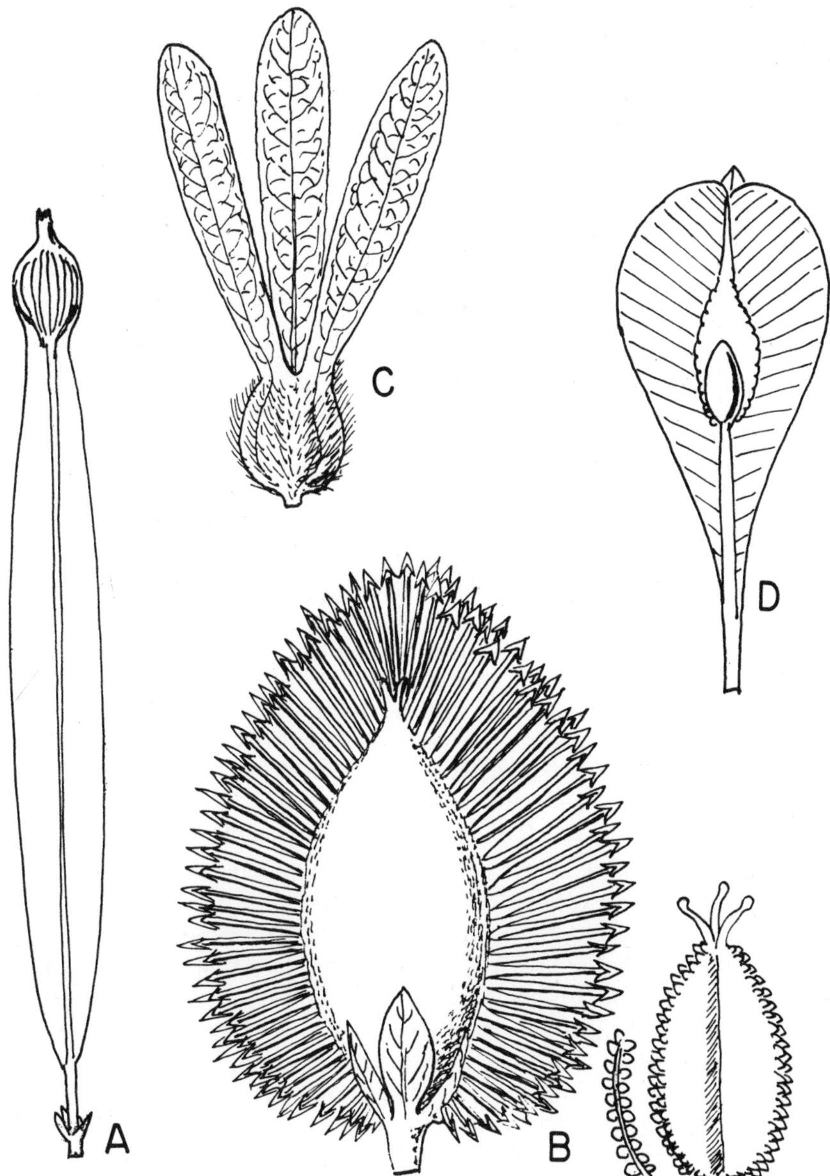

FIG. 458. Fruits of *Polygonaceae*. **A**, *Afrobrunnichia erecta* (Aschers.) Hutch. & J. M. Dalz., tropical Africa. **B**, *Harpagocarpus snowdenii* Hutch. & Dandy, tropical Africa. **C**, *Triplaris surinamensis* Cham., tropical South America. **D**, *Podopterus mexicanus* Humbl. & Bonpl., Central America (orig.).

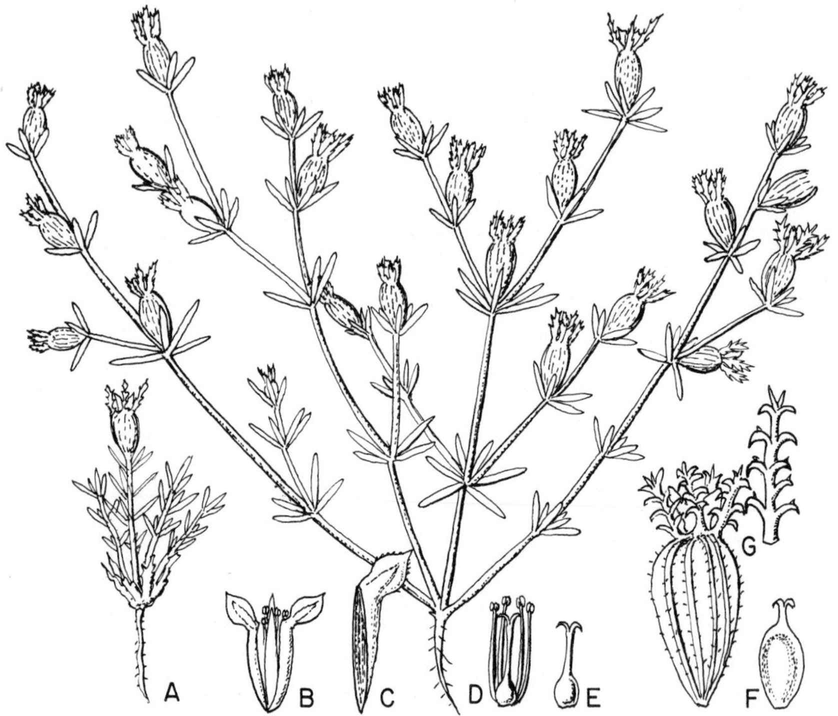

Fig. 459. *Pteranthus dichotomus* Forssk. (*Illecebraceae*). **A**, seedling showing the persistent calyx. **B**, flower. **C**, lateral sepal. **D**, stamens and gynoecium. **E**, gynoecium. **F**, fruit. **G**, receptacle with persistent calyx-lobes in fruiting stage (orig.) (see text).

Type genus *Polygonum* Linn.: Herbs, sometimes tall or climbing, sometimes prostrate and weedy, rarely aquatic; leaves alternate, subtended by mostly membranous stipules forming a sheath (ochrea) either truncate or oblique, entire, lacerate or ciliate; flowers bisexual or rarely polygamous, fasciculate, fascicles axillary or in spikes, racemes or panicles; pedicels jointed; calyx (perianth) deeply 5-lobed or partite, often coloured, covering the fruit and unchanged or rarely succulent or 3-winged; stamens 8 or 6, filaments free, often dilated at the base around an annular crenulate disk; anther-loculi separate, opening lengthwise; ovary compressed or 3-angled; styles 3 or 2, free or partly connate, stigmas capitate or subfimbriate; ovule often stalked; fruit a nut, compressed or 3-angled, covered by the persistent calyx; embryo excentric or lateral, usually curved, with narrow or oblong cotyledons. Type species *P. aviculare* Linn., widely distributed as a weed in fields and waste places.

Here are a few so-called *formae abnormes*: leaves opposite or verticillate in a few species of *Eriogonum*, in *Lastarriaea*, *Chorizanthe*, *Pterostegia* and sometimes in *Koeniga*; stem and branches flattened and forming ribbon-like cladodes jointed at the nodes in *Homalocladium platycladum* (Muell.) L. H. Bailey (*Muehlenbeckia platyclados* Meisn.), native of the Solomon Islands; calyx-lobes enlarged in fruit and forming wings like those of a Dipterocarp in *Triplaris* (Fig. 458, **C**); basally winged with the fruit at the top in *Afrobrunnichia erecta* (Aschers.) Hutch. & Dalz. (Fig. 458, **A**); stamens numerous in *Calligonum* and *Symmeria*; inserted on a central disk in the male flowers of *Ruprechtia* and *Symmeria*; gynoecium 4-merous in *Calligonum*; fruiting calyx (perianth) perfectly closed or solid over the nut in *Oxygonum*, *Emex* (outer lobes spreading and spinescent) and *Symmeria*, fleshy and berry-like in *Coccolobus*; fruits beset with harpoon-like bristles on the margin in *Harpagocarpus snowdenii* Hutch. & Dandy (Fig. 458, **B**).

In **Illecebraceae**[1] the leaves are mainly opposite and the flowers are very minute. Figure 459 is that of *Pteranthus dichotomus* Forssk. This remarkable desert plant was described and illustrated by Sibthorp in his monumental FLORA GRAECA (Vol. 2, t. 153 (1813)). It is a common plant in dry regions from Algeria east to Baluchistan, and is widespread in the valley of the Jordan. Sibthorp called it *Camphorosma pteranthus*, but the correct generic name is *Pteranthus* as named earlier by Forsskal. The swollen structures are not fruits but are the enlarged receptacle tipped by the persistent calyx-segments; note that the latter remain and form a collar around the base of the seedling (Fig. **A**) as in *Neurada* (Rosaceae) (see Fig. 54).

ORDER 64. **CHENOPODIALES**

(*Fam. Fl. Pl.* **1**, 433)

Families: **Barbeuiaceae, Phytolaccaceae, Gyrostemonaceae, Agdestidaceae, Petiveriaceae, Chenopodiaceae, Amaranthaceae, Theligonaceae** (*Cynocrambaceae*), **Batidaceae, Basellaceae.**

This Order embraces several small families about which little need be said. Their relationships are shown in the diagram on p. 540. In **Phytolaccaceae**[2] the genus *Phytolacca* has a number of free carpels, a feature which has lagged behind compared with those of several other members of the family. In my FAMILIES OF FLOWERING PLANTS I entirely disagreed that this

---

[1] Including *Paronychiaceae* A. St. Hiliare (1815). *Scleranthaceae* Bartling (1825).

[2] Including *Rivinaceae* C. A. Agardh (1825). *Endochromaceae* Dulac (1867). *Polpodaceae* Nakai (1942).

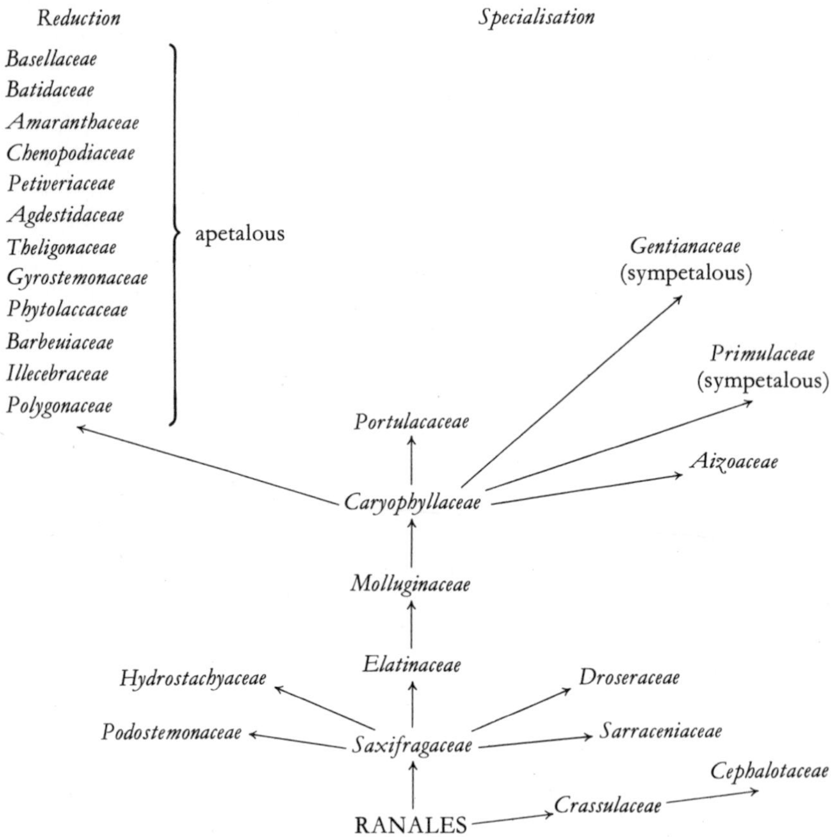

Diagram indicating the probable evolution and relationships of several closely related fundamentally herbaceous families, those on the left-hand side with greatly reduced apetalous and often unisexual flowers and many of them weeds, and on the right-hand side more specialised, retaining their petals and culminating in the climax sympetalous families *Primulaceae* and *Gentianaceae*; also many desert or semidesert succulent plants such as *Mesembryanthemum* (*sensu lato*) and allied genera (*Aizoaceae*), with mostly perigynous types of flowers.

genus was in any way related to *Sphenoclea* (*Campanulaceae*), a view since supported by Dutch[1] botanists and the late Professor Maheshwari. The genus *Theligonum* (*Cynocrambe*), the sole representative of the **Theligonaceae**, formerly regarded as one of the *Urticaceae*, seems to find its true affinity here. The expanded stipular base of the petiole is peculiar, as are the 2-parted valvate calyx of the male flower, the unilateral calyx of the female, and the remarkable almost basal attachment of the style.

---

[1] See FLORA MALESIANA **6**, pt. 1, 109 (1960).

Chenopodiaceae[1] is a large family in which the flowers are much reduced and the calyx is herbaceous in contrast with the usually dry and membranous calyx of the **Amaranthaceae.**[2] The connection between the *Chenopodiaceae* and the *Caryophyllaceae* is not so evident as that of *Amaranthaceae*, which is related to the tribe *Polycarpeae* in which the calyx is similarly dry and scarious. The monotypic allied family **Batidaceae** probably represents the highest evolution in this group. It has dioecious flowers arranged in dense cone-like spikes, opposite, fleshy leaves, and is a maritime shrub of tropical America and the Pacific. **Basellaceae**, another small family, are climbing relatives of the *Chenopodiaceae*, in which they were formerly included.

ORDER 65. **ONAGRALES**

(*Fam. Fl. Pl.* **1**, 446, as part of LYTHRALES, see notes below)

Families: **Onagraceae, Trapaceae, Haloragidaceae, Callitrichaceae.**

Phylogeny: RANALES → CARYOPHYLLALES → ONAGRALES.

As I have now included the family *Lythraceae* in the Order MYRTALES, after further study, it is necessary to call this Order ONAGRALES, based on the family *Onagraceae*. They appear to be advanced perigynous to epigynous types derived from the Caryophyllaceous stock through the subfamily *Sileneoideae*. This is "mere speculation", as non-phylogenists are so fond of remarking, but at least it may be intelligent!

In **Onagraceae,**[3] the Evening Primrose family, there is a definite number of stamens, the ovary is almost without exception inferior, and the style is solitary. That it is a relatively advanced group is shown by some very interesting characteristics peculiar to certain genera. In *Lopezia*, in Central America, for example, the stamens are reduced to two, only one bearing an anther and the other petaloid and sterile. Here there is a reduction to one fertile stamen as in most orchids and in *Centranthus* in *Valerianaceae*. A similar condition occurs in *Semeiandra* (Fig. 460), Mexico, but a little more advanced, for the basal portion of the filaments is adnate both to the style

[1] Including *Atriplicaceae* A. L. de Juss. (1789). *Corispermaceae* Link (1831). *Betaceae* Burnett (1835). *Salsolaceae* Moquin-Tandon (1849). *Salicorniaceae* J. G. Agardh (1858). *Farinaceae* Dulac (1867). *Dysphaniaceae* Pax (1927). *Halophytaceae* Soriano (1946).

[2] Including *Deeringiaceae* J. G. Agardh (1858). *Subscariosaceae* Dulac (1867).

[3] Including *Epilobiaceae* Ventenat (1799). *Circaeaceae* Lindl. (1930). *Oenotheraceae* Endlich. (1840). *Jussieuaceae* Drude (1887).

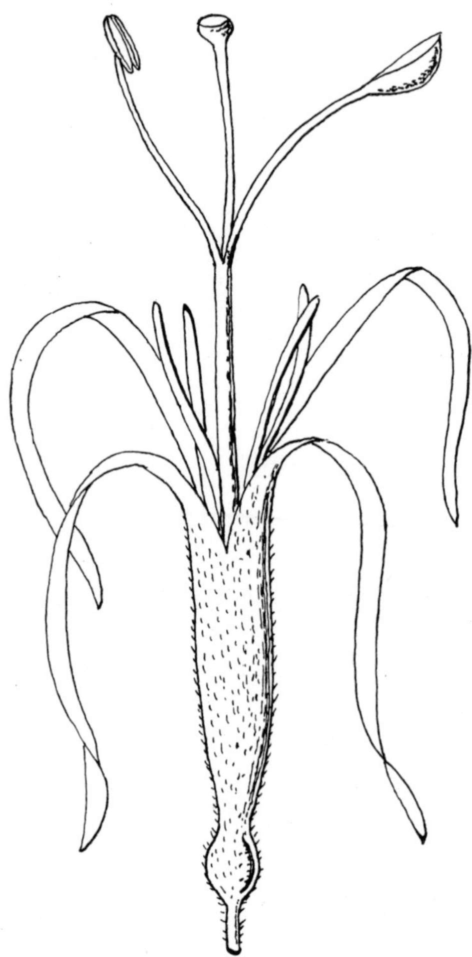

FIG. 460. *Semeiandra grandiflora* Hook. & Arn. (*Onagraceae*), Mexico; flower reduced to 2 stamens, one fertile, the other petaloid; petals linear and shorter than the calyx-lobes.

and to one side of the calyx-tube. In *Riesenbachia* even a further reduction is evident, the solitary stamen being accompanied by the absence of petals. These are only some of the interesting developments to be found in this family.

Besides the genus *Oenothera* (Fig. 461A), studied intensively by my late friend, Professor Ruggles Gates, F.R.S., the genus *Fuchsia* is too well known even to mention except for its interesting distribution, shown on the accompanying map (Map 31), which should gladden the heart of those who, like myself, support the theory of drifting continents. Of the 80 or so species of this truly natural (homogeneous) genus, all are found in Central and South America, except for three endemic species in New Zealand,

FIG. 461A. *Oenothera biennis* Linn., type species of the type genus of *Onagraceae*. **A**, lower leaf. **B**, vertical section of flower. **C**, stamen. **D**, cross-section of ovary. **E**, capsule. **F**, seed (orig.).

Fig. 461b. *Hauya elegans* Moç. & Sesse, Central America, the only genus of the family *Onagraceae* with winged seeds, **B**. **A**, fruit. (After Hemsl. BIOLOG. CENTRAL AMERICA.)

emphasising the close relationship of the flora of that region and far away Chile.

In tribe *Jussieueae* the calyx-tube is not produced beyond the top of the ovary and is persistent in fruit. In the remainder of the tribes the calyx-tube is more or less produced above the ovary, constricted and deciduous. Tribe *Epilobieae* is distinguished by its seeds which have a tuft of hairs at the apex (resembling some *Apocynaceae* in this respect – no affinity!). Tribe *Hauyeae* has winged seeds, and the remainder of the tribes lack the above characters. The fruit is a fleshy berry in *Fuchsia*, and the calyx-tube above the ovary is coloured (often white).

The type genus is *Oenothera* Linn.: Herbs, rarely shrublets, mostly erect, branched and leafy; leaves alternate, thin, entire to pinnately lobed; flowers axillary, solitary, sessile or pedicellate, rarely in pairs or crowded

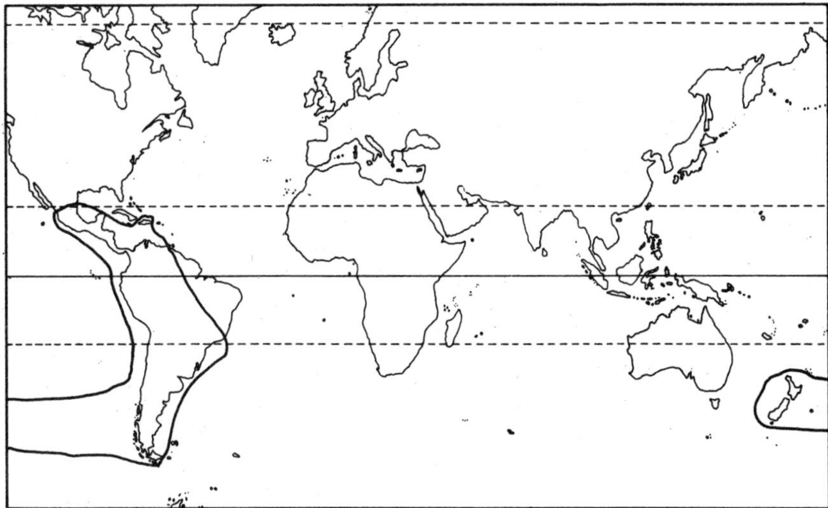

Map 31. Range of *Fuchsia* (*Onagraceae*), a very natural genus of about 80 species, 3 endemic in New Zealand, remainder in America from Mexico to Fuegia; a striking example of the close connection of the floras of New Zealand and far away Chile.

into a head, mostly showy, yellow, rose or purple; calyx-tube linear or clavate, 4-angled, produced above the ovary and 4-lobed; petals 4, obovate or obcordate; stamens 8, equal or alternately shorter; anthers linear, often elongated; ovary 4-locular, style filiform, stigma capitate, entire, 4-lobed or 4-partite; ovules numerous, in one or two series on the inner angle of the loculi, spreading or ascending; capsule various, membranous to rather woody, linear, oblong or clavate, terete, 4-angled or several-angled, many-ribbed or 4-winged, 4-locular, 4-valved from the apex to the middle, separating from the seed-bearing axis, seeds many to few, inserted on the axis or septa, nude or appendaged on the chalaza. Type species *OE. biennis* Linn. (Fig. 461A), North America, cult. and naturalised in many places.

There are not many exceptions to note: Flowers without bracts in *Circaea*, sometimes polygamous in *Fuchsia*; petals absent from *Ludwigia* spp., *Fuchsia* spp. and from *Riesenbachia*; only 2 in *Circaea*. Stamens 2, adnate at the base of the style to one side of the calyx-tube in *Semeiandra*. Seeds with a tuft of hairs (comose) at the top in *Epilobium* and *Zauschneria*; winged (as noted above) in *Hauya* (Fig. 461B); stamen 1 and 1 petaloid in *Semeiandra* (Fig. 460), *Lopezia*; 2 in *Diplandra*, 1 in *Riesenbachia*. Ovule solitary (or rarely 2–4) in each loculus, and the fruit nut-like in *Gaura*, *Stenosiphon*, *Heterogaura*, *Gongylocarpus* and *Circaea*; fruits with hooked bristles in *Circaea*.

The single genus *Trapa* is now considered to be sufficiently distinct to be regarded as a separate family, **Trapaceae.**[1] It consists of floating herbs with leaves of two kinds, those submerged being opposite and finely pinnatisect and resembling roots, the emerged leaves in a rosette, rhomboid and with a spongy inflated petiole. The turbinate bony fruit is armed with 2–4 short "spines" and is 1-seeded, the seed without endosperm but with very unequal cotyledons, one large, the other small and scale-like; on germination the radicle perforates the top of the fruit. Singhara flour is obtained from the fruits of *Trapa bispinosa* Roxb., and is a valuable food in N.W. India (FAMILIES OF FLOWERING PLANTS, 2nd Ed. **1**, 447, Fig. 290).

The most familiar of the **Haloragidaceae**[2] are the large species of *Gunnera* often planted around our lakes. Its leaves closely resemble those of a large rhubarb, and there are some handsome species on the island of Juan Fernandez, which sheltered Alexander Selkirk, the prototype of Robinson Crusoe. No doubt he used them for thatching his roof or as a sunshade or umbrella. Here again we find very considerable reduction in the number of stamens, whilst the majority have adopted an aquatic habitat, which in flowering plants is regarded as being a secondary one. In **Callitrichaceae**[3] (*Callitriche*) extreme reduction seems to have taken place, with the flowers unisexual, neither sepals nor petals, and in the male only 1 stamen subtended by a pair of bracts.

ORDER 66. **GENTIANALES**

(*Fam. Fl. Pl.* **1**, 450)

Families: **Gentianaceae, Menyanthaceae.**

Phylogeny: RANALES → CARYOPHYLLALES (*Caryophyllaceae*) → GENTIANALES → climax family *Menyanthaceae* (aquatic).

The family **Gentianaceae**[4] has much in common with its basal stock *Caryophyllaceae*, and perhaps also more remote affinity with some *Saxifragaceae*. The leaves are opposite and often connected by a transverse line, but never truly stipulate. The vascular bundles in the stem are bicollateral.

---

[1] Including *Hydrocaryaceae* Link (1821).

[2] Including *Cercodiaceae* A. L. de Juss. (1817). *Hippuridaceae* Link (1821). *Myriophyllaceae* C. H. Schultz (1832). *Gunneraceae* Endlich. (1837). *Hygrobiaceae* Dulac (1867). *Verticillaceae* Dulac (1867).

[3] Including *Dibracteaceae* Dulac (1867).

[4] Including *Chironiaceae* Horaninow (1847). *Amaracaceae* Dulac (1867).

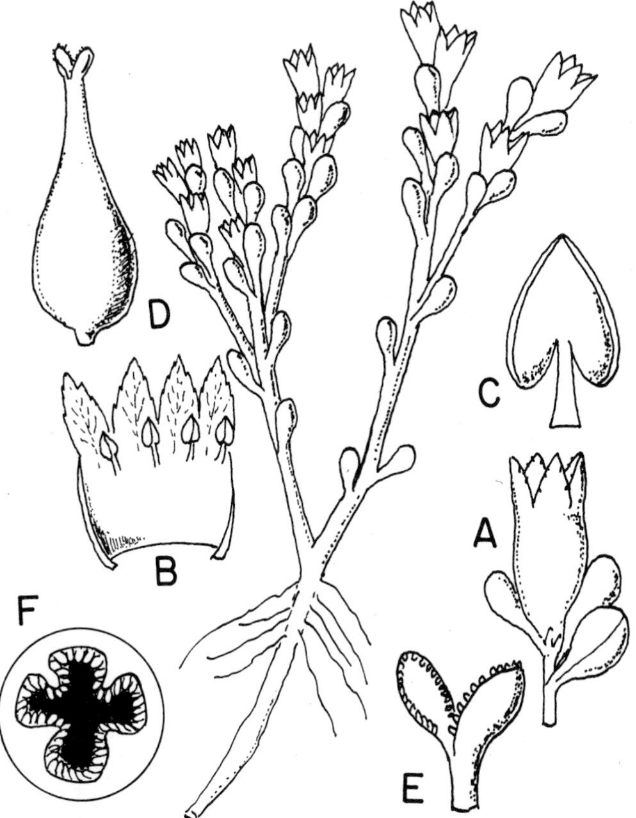

FIG. 462. *Obolaria virginica* Linn. (*Gentianaceae*), North America, has only 2 spathulate calyx-lobes. **A**, flower and upper leaves. **B**, corolla laid open. **C**, stamen. **D**, gynoecium. **E**, stigmas. **F**, cross-section of ovary (orig.).

In *Menyanthaceae*, usually included in *Gentianaceae*, the leaves are alternate, and the vascular bundles of the stem are collateral, and there are intercellular hairs as in *Nymphaeaceae*. *Menyanthaceae* are also more advanced in the aestivation of the corolla, which is induplicate-valvate, whereas in *Gentianacae* it is contorted or imbricate.

As so limited, *Gentianaceae* is a homogeneous group which every family should be so far as possible. Almost without exception they are herbaceous, and relying on the hypothesis upon which our classification is based I cannot agree with Bentham and Hooker[1] and reiterated by Rendle[2] that they

[1] GENERA PLANTARUM **2**, 799 (1876).
[2] CLASSIF. FL. PL. **2**, 46 (1876).

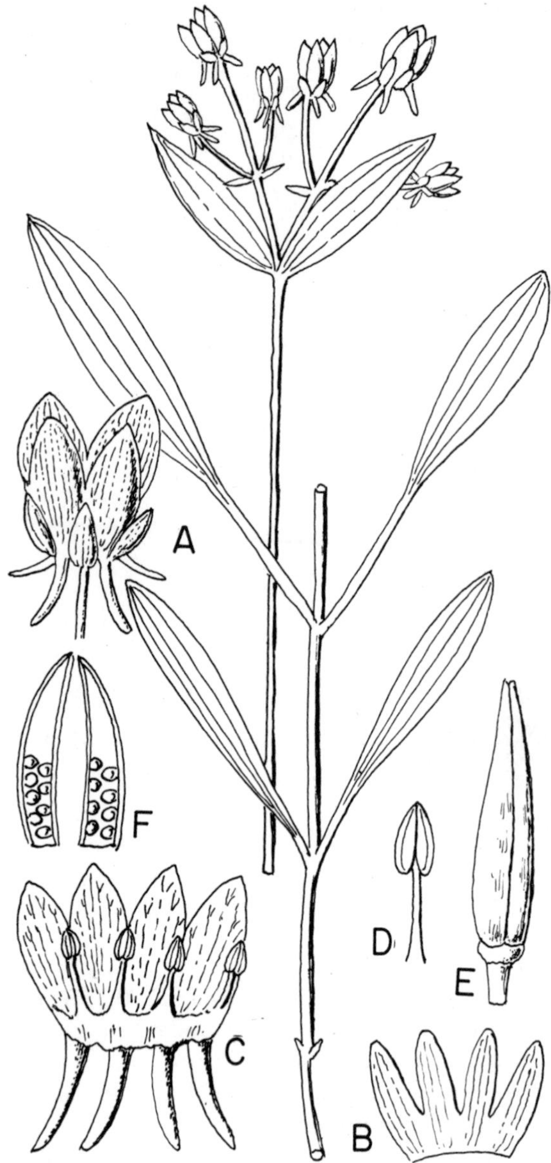

FIG. 463. *Halenia hintonii* Bullock (*Gentianaceae*), Mexico; note the basally spurred corolla-tube. **A**, flower. **B**, calyx. **C**, corolla spread out showing stamens. **D**, stamen. **E**, fruit. **F**, part of fruiting carpels laid open (orig.).

are related to *Loganiaceae*, from which in this system they are widely separated in the ligneous subphylum. As in *Polemoniaceae* the stamens are inserted at unequal heights within the corolla-tube, except in *Jaeschkea* and *Obolaria*,

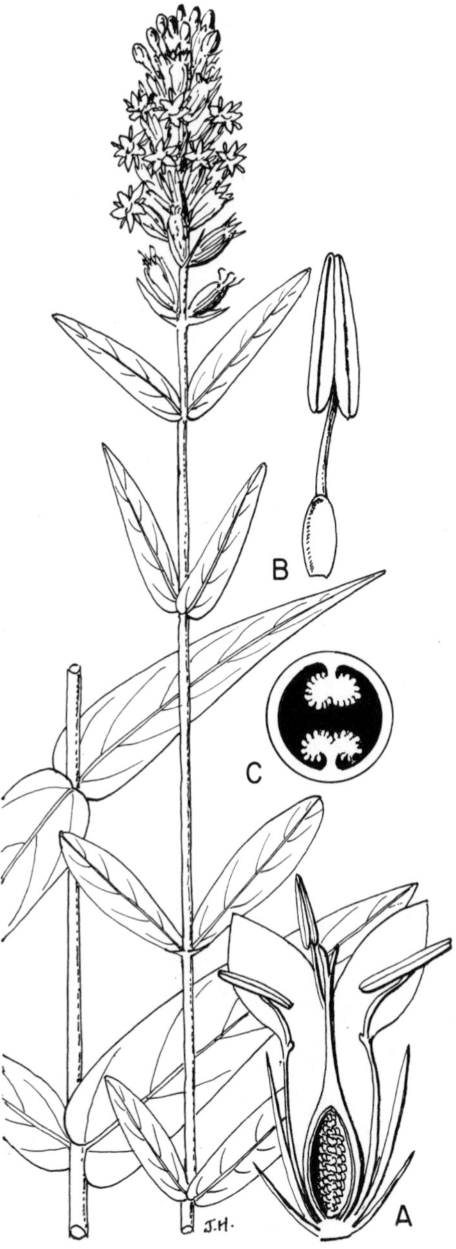

FIG. 464. *Coutoubea spicata* Aubl.; although it belongs to *Gentianaceae* it greatly resembles *Lysimachia* in the *Primulaceae*, no doubt due to parallel evolution. **A**, vertical section of flower. **B**, stamen. **C**, cross-section of ovary. (Drawn by the author from a specimen collected by him in the Aripo savannah in Trinidad, 1960.)

in which they are placed between the corolla-lobes. *Obolaria* (Fig. 462) is curious in other respects; there are only 2 sepals, which are leafy and spathulate, and the stem-leaves are scale-like, except the floral leaves which are

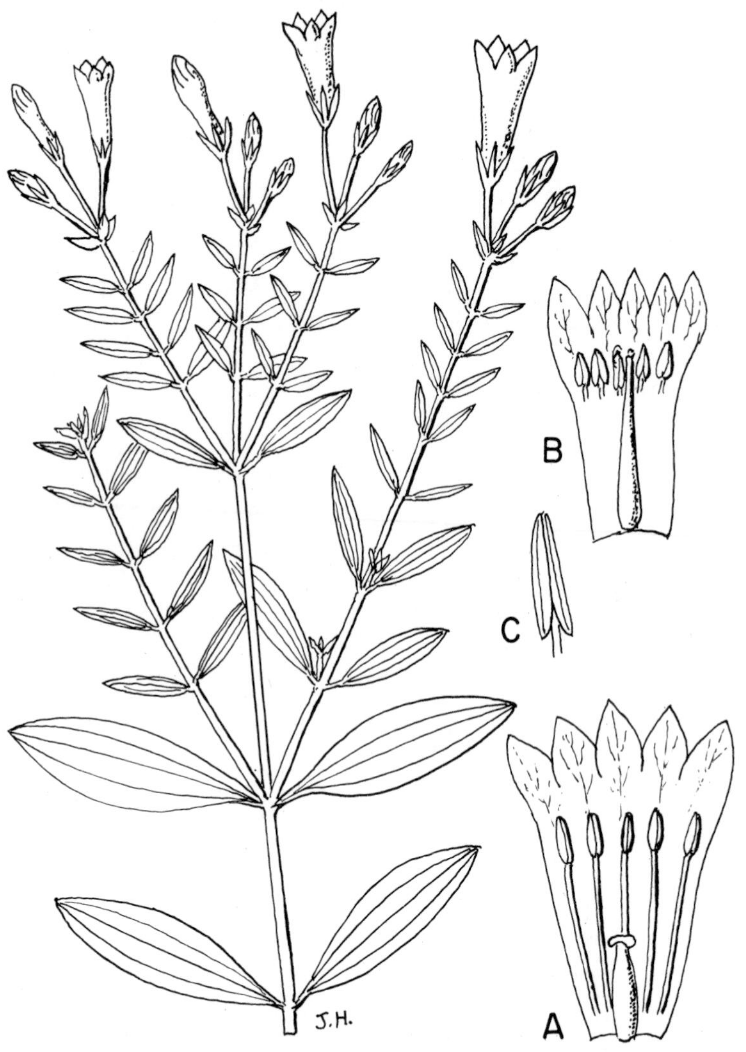

FIG. 465. *Hockinia montana* Gardn. (*Gentianaceae*), Organ Mts of Brazil; unique in the family on account of its heterostyled flowers, as in some *Primulaceae*. **A**, corolla opened out showing the short style and long stamens. **B**, the same showing the long style and short filaments. **C**, anther (orig.).

suborbicular. The one or two pits within the base of the corolla-tube and opposite each corolla-lobe, characteristic of *Swertia* and *Frasera*, are in *Halenia* (Fig. 463) sometimes produced into spurs rather like those of *Aquilegia* in *Helleboraceae*. The genus *Coutoubea* (see Fig. 464) (tropical America) seems to show relationship with *Primulaceae*, especially with

FIG. 466. *Chelonanthus chelonoides* Linn. f. (*Gentianaceae*), drawn from a specimen collected by the author in the marsh forests of the Aripo savannah, Trinidad; the genus is outstanding in the family.

Lysimachia and indeed even with *Plantago* (*Plantaginaceae*). There is a strong tendency to a saprophytic habit in various groups of the family. *Gentiana lutea* Linn. is of medicinal value.

The type genus is *Gentiana* Linn.; herbs; leaves opposite, mostly sessile; flowers axillary and terminal, usually sessile, erect, 2-braceolate or nude, often very showy, violet, purple, yellow or white; corolla-tube variously shaped, with small lobes between the larger ones, without a fringe at the throat; lobes dextrorsely contorted, 5, or rarely 4 or 6 or 7; stamens as many as corolla-lobes, inserted in the tube and rarely exserted; anthers free or connivent; ovary 1-locular with parietal placentas; style short, stigmas 2, distinct, spreading or revolute; capsule sessile or stipitate, 2-valved; seeds numerous, 1–2-seriate, globose to lenticular or winged, reticulate. Type species *G. lutea* Linn., Europe.

Divergent from the type genus: Leafless herbs, very small and simple in *Voyriella*, *Cotylanthera*, *Voyria* and *Obolaria*. Leaves or scales sometimes alternate in a few spp. of *Swertia*, *Voyria* and *Bartonia*; verticillate in a few spp. of *Curtia* and *Frasera*. Bracteoles large and foliaceous, connate at the base and adnate to the calyx-tube in *Zonanthus*. Flowers dimorphic in *Hockinia* (Brazil) (Fig. 465), in some the anthers subsessile with elongated style, in others with filiform filaments and the stigma sessile on the ovary (Fig. 465). Calyx-lobes broadly winged in *Canscora* spp. and *Shultesia*; calyx inflated and as long as the corolla-tube in *Prepusa*. Corolla-lobes sinistrorsely contorted in *Halenia*, imbricate in *Canscora*, *Bartonia* and *Obolaria*; 7–10 in *Lapithea*, 5–12 in *Sabbatia*; tube very long in *Tachiadenus*; lobes dorsally spurred or saccate in *Halenia*; corolla 3-lobed in *Pcynosphaera*, persistent on top of the capsule in *Blackstonia* and *Geniostemon*. Stamens inserted in the sinuses between the corolla-lobes in *Jaeschkea* and *Obolaria*; anthers opening by apical pores in *Cotylanthera* and *Exacum*; connate and introrsely dehiscent in *Tapeinostemon*, some spp. of *Voyria*, *Curtia* and *Hockinia*; connate and extrorsely dehiscent in some spp. of *Gentiana* itself; appendaged at the apex by a gland in *Sebaea* and *Belmontia*; plumosely setose at the base in one sp. of *Voyria*; spirally twisted in *Orphium*; perfect stamens reduced to 1 in *Hoppea* and *Schinziella*; seeds winged in *Voyria* spp.

Menyanthaceae, as stated above, have usually been included in *Gentianaceae*, but were treated as a separate family by Dumortier and others. The leaves are alternate, the corolla-lobes are induplicate-valvate, and the vascular bundles of the stem are collateral. The five genera are aquatic or marsh plants; the type genus, of course, is *Menyanthes*.

Order 67. **PRIMULALES**

(*Fam. Fl. Pl.* 1, 453)

Families: **Primulaceae, Plumbaginaceae.**

Phylogeny: CARYOPHYLLALES (*Caryophyllaceae*) → PRIMULALES.

As indicated in the diagram on p. 540, **Primulaceae**[1] are most probably derived from the Caryophyllaceous stock. We should look, therefore, for some real affinity of a part of the family with the existing *Caryophyllaceae*. This is not very obvious in the case of the largest genus *Primula*, but it is clearly indicated by *Lysimachia* and *Anagallis*, and the groups to which these two genera belong may be considered to be the most primitive of the *Primulaceae*. In these the corolla lobes are contorted (an ancient type of aestivation and common in *Caryophyllaceae*), and there are sometimes staminodes alternating with the stamens, these representing another whorl which is also so often present in *Caryophyllaceae*. Then genera such as *Asterolinum* and *Pelletiera* are very Caryophyllaceous in appearance. *Glaux*, a puzzle to young botanists, is more Crassulaceous in habit, with its subsucculent opposite leaves and no corolla.

It takes no less than nine tribes to accommodate the 22 genera of *Primulaceae*. Of these the genus *Cyclamen* (Fig. 467) stands out in having a tuberous rootstock (formed from the swollen hypocotyl). *Coris* (Fig. 468) differs from all the other genera only in its zygomorphic flowers; not worthy of family rank. *Samolus*, which otherwise recalls the habit of some *Boraginaceae*, has a semi-inferior ovary. *Hottonia* is aquatic, with pinnatisect leaves. The capsule opens by a transverse circular slit in *Bryocarpum*, *Anagallis* and *Centunculus*.

Bentham and Hooker said of *Primulaceae*: "Ordo valde naturalis, *Myrsineis* solis affinis, et ab eis distinctus habitu herbaceo, fructu capsulari et floribus semper hermaphroditis."[2]

Rendle, in his English interpretation of Engler and Prantl, states: "*Myrsinaceae* are closely allied to *Primulaceae*, from which they are distinguished by their woody habit, and the one- to few-seeded drupaceous fruit."

According to the present writer these two families are not at all related, their supposed affinity being due to the very similar floral diagrams, especially on account of the two groups having the stamens opposite to the corolla-lobes, and the same type of placentation (free basal). Too much

---

[1] Including *Lysimachiaceae* A. L. de Juss. (1789). *Coridaceae* J. G. Agardh (1858). *Stelitaceae* Dulac (1867).

[2] A very natural family (Order) related only to *Myrsinaceae* (*Myrsineae*), and distinct from it by the herbaceous habit, capsular fruit, and the flowers always bisexual (hermaphrodite).

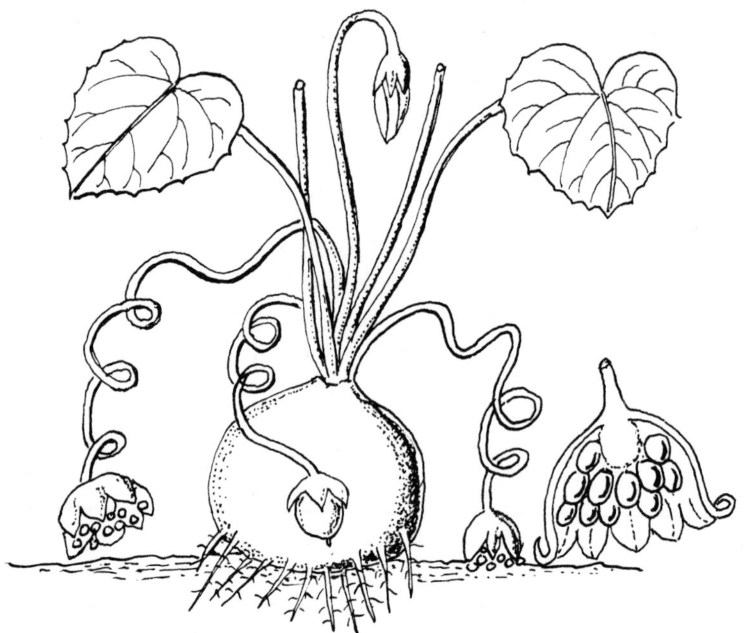

FIG. 467. *Cyclamen europaeum* Linn. (*Primulaceae*), makes doubly sure of its seeds reaching the soil.

notice has often been taken of floral diagrams, resulting in a certain amount of artificial classification.

Usually the first thing a student learns about *Primulaceae* is that one whorl of stamens is missing and that the members of the whorl retained are opposite the corolla-lobes. When he studies exotic families he learns the same about *Myrsinaceae*, and so a false impression of affinity is liable to be engendered.

It seems a very far-fetched view to regard the corolla of *Primulaceae* as a late development of the flower and that it arises from the backs of the stamens. A similar fantastic view has been held by some German botanists with regard to the petals in *Potamogeton* (*Monocotyledon*), and the same may be said of the so-called "Honigblätter" in *Ranunculaceae*, these in my opinion being ordinary petals such as we find in other families.

Type genus *Primula* Linn.: Herbs with perennial rhizomes; leaves all radical, mostly obovate-spathulate, entire, dentate or rarely lobed; no stipules; flowers umbellate or verticillate-racemose, very rarely solitary, dimorphic, some with anthers inserted high in the corolla-tube and with a short style, others with anthers low down and a long style; bracts involucrate; calyx tubular, often inflated or angular, 5-lobed, persistent; corolla hypogynous, tubular, lobes 5, imbricate; stamens 5, inserted in the throat

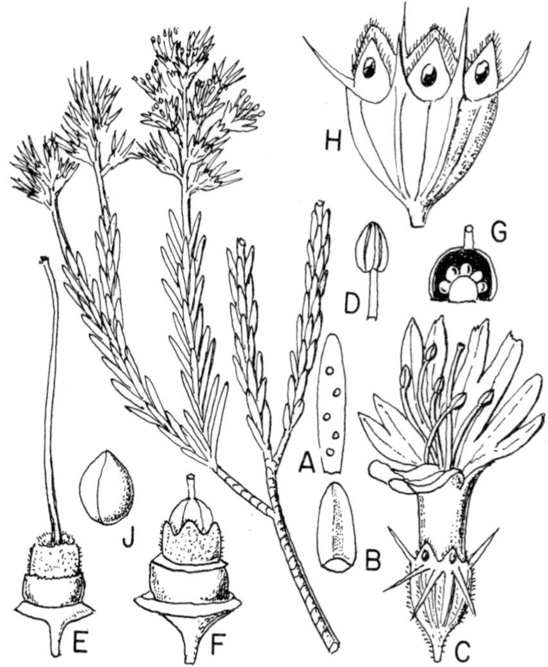

FIG. 468. *Coris monspeliensis* Linn. (*Primulaceae*); the genus is unique in the family in having zygomorphic flowers. **A**, leaf showing the glands. **B**, bract. **C**, flower. **D**, anther. **E**, disk, ovary and style. **F**, disk and ovary. **G**, vertical section of ovary showing basal placentation as in all other members of the family. **H**, calyx in fruiting stage, showing the eye-like glands on the lobes. **J**, seed (orig.).

or lower in the tube; anthers 2-locular, linear-oblong; ovary globose or ovoid; 1-locular, with free basal placenta; ovules numerous; style filiform, stigma capitate; capsule globose or ovoid-conical, apex 5-valved, valves entire or 2-lobed; seeds peltate, punctate, embryo transverse. Type species *P. veris* Linn., Europe (Fig. 469).

Here are some outstanding generic characters: Rhizome epigeal, large and tuberous in *Cyclamen*. Stems floating and leaves pinnatisect in *Hottonia*. Leaves subverticillate in *Trientalis*. Calyx and corolla 7-partite in *Bryocarpum*; 5–9-partite in *Trientalis*; calyx coloured and resembling a corolla (absent) in *Glaux*; tardily deciduous in *Bryocarpum* (Fig. 470). Corolla-lobes contorted in *Cyclamen*, *Lysimachia*, *Apochoris*, *Trientalis* and *Anagallis*; corolla zygomorphic in *Coris* (Fig. 468); minute and much shorter than the calyx in *Centunculus*, *Stimsonia*; 5-lobed or of 3 free petals in *Asterolinum*; perigynous in *Samolus*; lobes reflexed in *Cyclamen* and *Dodecatheon*. Ovary inferior in *Samolus*. Capsule opening by a circumscissile slit in *Soldanella*

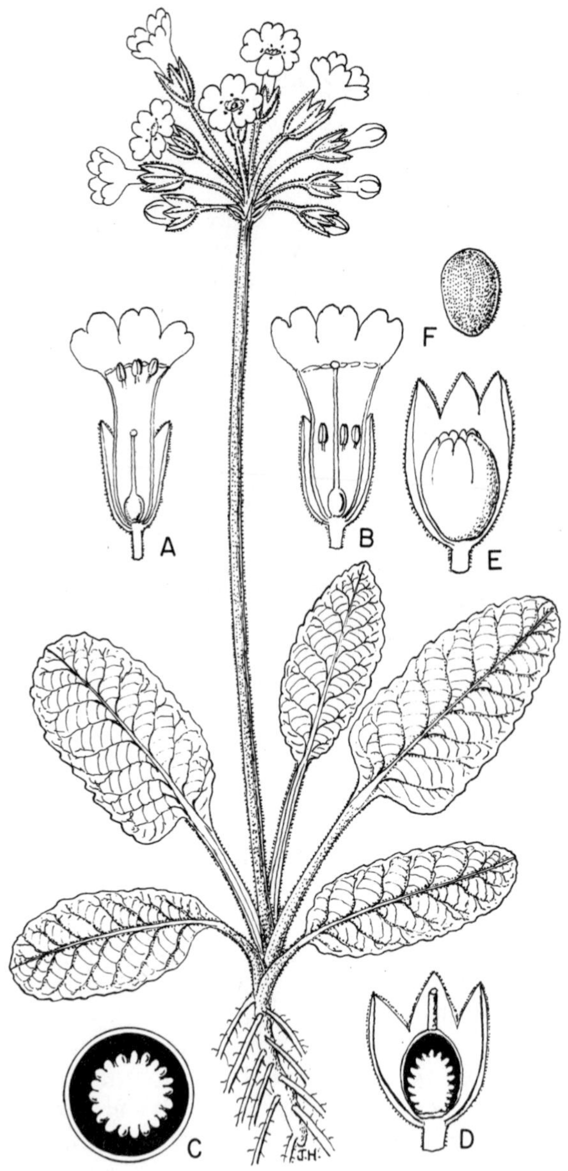

FIG. 469. *Primula veris* Linn., the type species of the type genus of *Primulaceae*. **A**, vertical section of short-styled flower. **B**, vertical section of long-styled flower. **C**, cross-section of ovary. **D**, vertical section of ovary and calyx. **E**, fruit. **F**, seed (orig.).

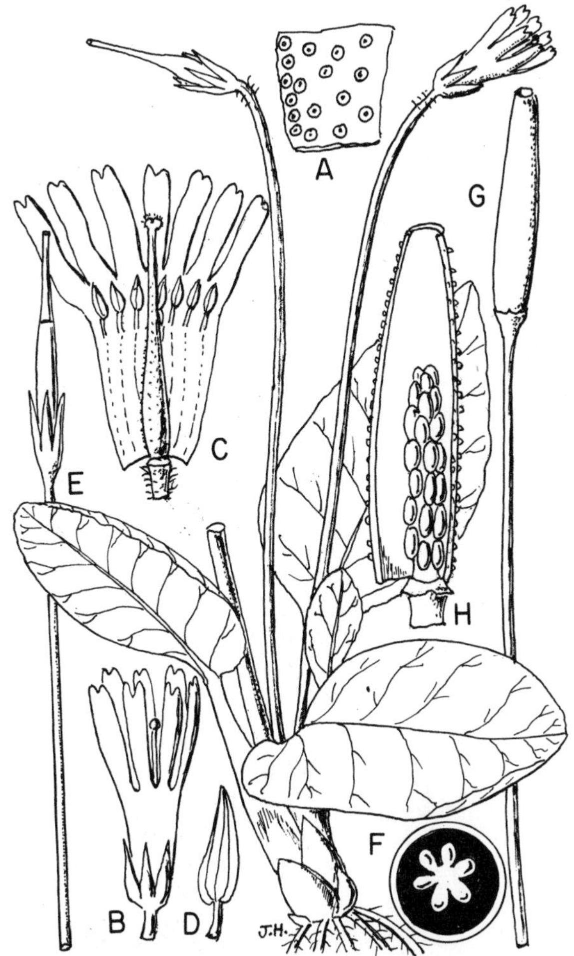

FIG. 470. A distinctive Primulaceous plant in the Himalayas, *Bryocarpum himalaicum* Hook. f. & Thoms. **A**, scales on lower surface of leaves. **B**, flower. **C**, the same with corolla laid open. **D**, stamen. **E**, calyx and gynoecium in advanced stage. **F**, cross-section of ovary. **G**, fruit. **H**, vertical section of fruit showing seeds (orig.).

(Fig. 471), *Bryocarpum*, *Anagallis* and *Centunculus*. Fruit subindehiscent in spp. of *Lysimachia*.

Plumbaginaceae.[1] The first exotic plant of which I learned the name when a boy was the lovely *Plumbago capensis* Linn., which flowered profusely every year in my father's greenhouse. There are about 10 species of this

---

[1] Including *Staticaceae* S. F. Gray (1821). *Armeriaceae* Horaninow (1834). *Pentaphytychaceae* Dulac (1867).

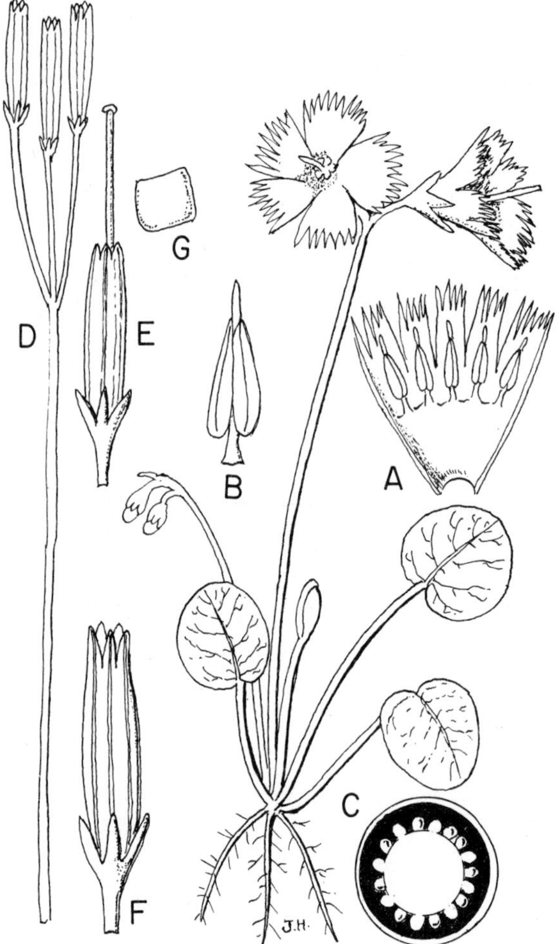

FIG. 471. *Soldanella alpina* Linn. (*Primulaceae*). **A**, corolla laid open, showing the stamens opposite the corolla-lobes (a family character). **B**, stamen. **C**, transverse section of ovary showing free basal placentation of ovules. **D**, fruits. **E** and **F**, the same. **G**, seed (orig.).

genus in the tropics and subtropics, and there is one in the Mediterranean region, *L. europaea* Linn. *P. zeylanica* Linn. (Fig. 472) is widespread in the tropics.

Limonium, with over 100 species, is the largest genus, and occurs chiefly in maritime districts and salt-steppes of the Old World. *Statice*, with over 50 species, is alpine, arctic and maritime in the north temperate zone and also in the Chilean Andes.

The two tribes into which the family is divided are distinguished as follows: *Plumbagineae*, with hypogynous stamens and styles free only in the

FIG. 472. *Plumbago zeylanica* Linn. (*Plumbaginaceae*), widely spread in the tropics. **A**, longitudinal section of flower. **B**, stamen. **C**, style-arms. **D**, calyx in fruit. **E**, sepal. **F**, fruit. **G**, cross-section of fruit. **H**, stalked gland. (From Hutchinson and Dalziel, FLORA OF WEST TROPICAL AFRICA.)

upper part, and *Staticeae*, stamens inserted on the corolla, and the styles free almost to the base. The genus *Armeria* is familiar in many maritime and mountain regions.

The family is placed next to *Primulaceae* mainly because the stamens are opposite to the corolla-lobes, and the basal placenta with a single ovule pendulous from a basal funicle. Bentham's remark as to affinity is very much to the point: "Ordo nulli arcte affinis nec cum ullo alio generibus intermediis connexus".

ORDER 68. PLANTAGINALES

(*Fam. Fl. Pl.* **1**, 455)

Family: **Plantaginaceae.**

Phylogeny: CARYOPHYLLALES (*Caryophyllaceae*) → PRIMULALES → PLANTAGINALES.

A family which has been moved about in various classifications is **Plantaginaceae.**[1] Bentham and Hooker f. placed it at the end of their *Gamo-*

---

[1] Including *Littorellaceae* S. F. Gray (1821). *Psylliaceae* Horaninow (1834). *Pyxidaceae* Dulac (1867).

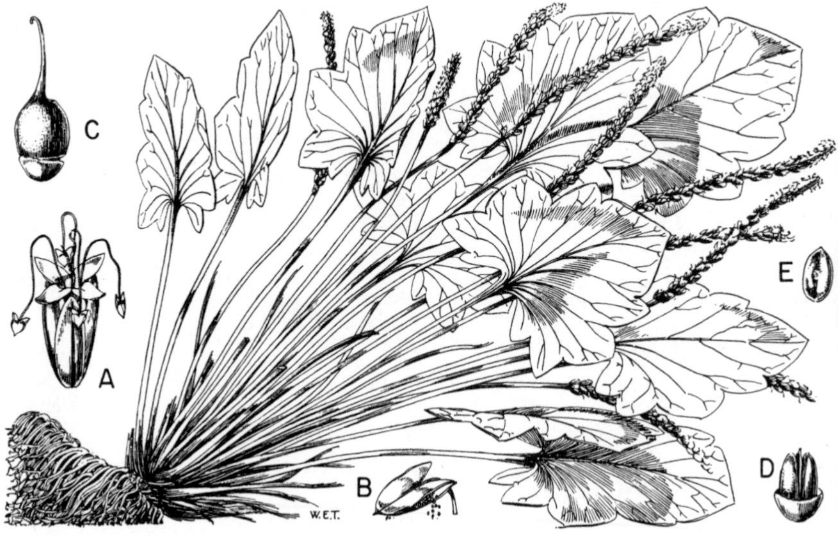

FIG. 473. *Plantago palmata* Hook. f. (*Plantaginaceae*), mountains of tropical Africa. **A**, flower. **B**, anther. **C**, pistil. **D**, open fruit. **E**, seed. (From Hutchinson and Dalziel, FLORA OF WEST TROPICAL AFRICA.)

petalae, with the following remark (at the foot of the CONSPECTUS COHORTIUM, Vol. 2): "Ordo anomalus Plantaginearum cohorti nulli associatur", while below the family description they wrote:

Ordo nulli prope accedit, etsi characteres generales *Gamopetalarum* ostendit. Ab Endlichero nonnullisque aliis cum *Plumbagineis* associatur; hae tamen longe distant inter alia staminibus petalis oppositis, stylo 5-mero et praesertim albumine farinaceo. A Decaisneo, Trait. Bot. 215, aliisque *Primulaceis* comparatur, sed praeter fructus dehiscentiam in utroque ordine saepe circumscissam characteres pauci conveniunt. Seminum structura et insertio eas Acanthacearum albuminosarum imprimis *Elytrariae* in mentem revocant, sed corolla et stamina valde dissimilia. Ordo parvus ad calcem *Gamopetalarum* seorsum relinquendus.[1]

This shows very clearly that Bentham and Hooker f. placed too much reliance on single characters, in this case that of the stamens being opposite

[1] Translation: "An anomalous family [order] . . . A family close to no other, even if the general charcters of the *Gamopetalae* are considered. Associated by Endlicher and others with the *Plumbaginaceae*; even these are a long way off on account of the stamens being opposite the petals, by the 5-partite style and especially by the mealy endosperm. By Decaisne and others compared with the *Primulaceae*, especially on account of the dehiscence of the fruit which is in each family circumscissile. The structure of the seeds and their insertion recalls those of the endospermous *Acanthaceae*, especially the *Elytrarieae*, but the corolla and stamens are very dissimilar. This small family (Order) is left at the end of the *Gamopetalae*."

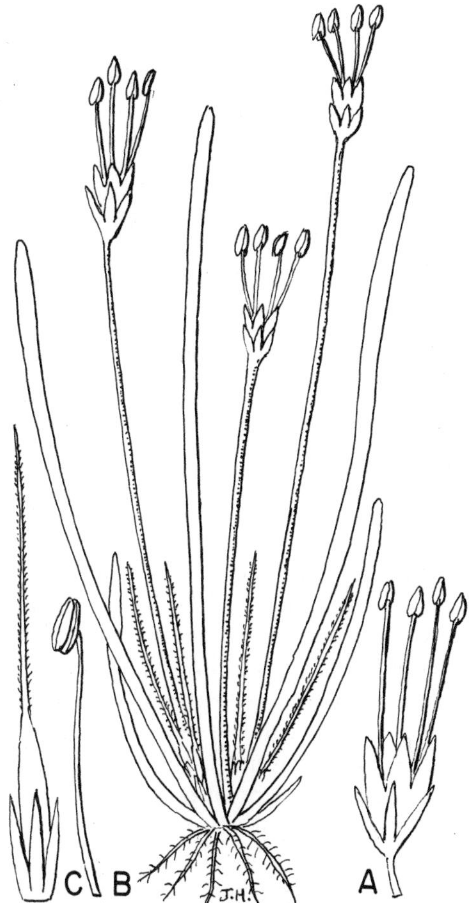

Fig. 474. *Littorella uniflora* (Linn.) Aschers. (*Plantaginaceae*); the flowers are unisexual; the males, **A**, on long pedicels, the females, **C**, sessile amongst the leaves. **B**, stamen (orig.). A similar condition occurs in the genus *Lilaea*, a monotypic family in the Monocotyledons. (See my FAMILIES OF FLOWERING PLANTS, 2nd Ed. **2**, 549, Fig. 350.)

the petals. It is easy now, of course, to say that either set of stamens might be dispensed with in one and the same group. Following this viewpoint, then, the family *Plantaginaceae* finds its closest relationship near the *Primulaceae* and *Plumbaginaceae*.

In the widely distributed type genus *Plantago* (Fig. 473) the fruits dehisce by a transverse circular slit (circumscissile), and the flowers are in spikes or heads, mostly all bisexual. In the other two genera the fruits are indehiscent, *Bougueria* with spicate-capitate flowers, a few at the top bisexual, the other female, and in *Litorella* (Fig. 474) the male and female flowers are quite separate, the males on a long pedicel and the females sessile among the leaves at the base of the males. A very similar separation of the sexes occurs in *Lilaea*, a monotypic family (*Lilaeaceae*) amongst the monocotyledons.

ORDER 69. SAXIFRAGALES

(*Fam. Fl. Pl.* **1**, 456)

Families: **Crassulaceae, Cephalotaceae, Saxifragaceae, Eremosynaceae, Vahliaceae, Francoaceae, Donatiaceae, Parnassiaceae, Adoxaceae.**

Phylogeny: RANALES → through *Crassulaceae* → SAXIFRAGALES → to *Adoxaceae* (climax family).

We now deal with a group of plants in which there has been considerable evolution, the ramifications of parts of it being rather difficult to trace. The most primitive family seems to be **Crassulaceae**,[1] which has retained free carpels with separate styles, as in *Helleboraceae* and *Ranunculaceae*. In some *Crassulaceae*, however, we meet with the very rare combination of a primitively apocarpous gynoecium and a sympetalous corolla; this phenomenon occurs in *Kalanchoe* (Fig. 475) and *Cotyledon*. Further up the scale in this system we shall see that apocarpy also occurs in the entirely sympetalous families *Apocynaceae* and *Asclepiadaceae*, but in these groups apocarpy is doubtless a secondary, and not a primitive feature, because a single style serves both carpels. *Crassulaceae*, therefore, is a family which appears to have undergone mainly ecological vegetative but little phylogenetic floral evolution. It is found chiefly in arid regions such as the South African Karoo.

The type genus is *Crassula* Linn., over 100 species, most of them in South Africa; type *C. perfoliata* Linn., dry regions of S.E. South Africa (Fig. 476): Herbs or shrubs, rarely annuals; branches and leaves mostly thick and fleshy, only a few thin and weak; leaves opposite, mostly sessile and often connate at the base, fleshy, entire and with cartilaginous margins, glabrous, pubescent or scaly; flowers on the small side, white, rose or yellow, mostly in cymes, rarely in heads, usually 5-merous; calyx partite or lobed; petals 5, free or shortly connate, erect or spreading, sometimes glandular at the apex; stamens 5, free; hypogynous scales various; carpels 5, free, with

[1] Including *Sempervivaceae* A. L. de Juss. (1789). *Isocarpellaceae* Dulac (1867). *Penthoraceae* van Tieghem (1898).

short styles and small stigmas; ovules numerous; fruits follicular, 5, with numerous, minute seeds; embryo terete in fleshy endosperm.

A few exceptions to the above may be noted: Leaves peltate in *Umbilicus rupestris* (Salisb.) Dandy; thin in *Penthorum*; alternate in *Sempervivum*, *Cotyledon* spp., *Sedum* spp. and *Monanthes* sp. Branches swollen and leafless in *Rhopalota* (Fig. 477). Calyx bladder-like in *Bryophyllum*. Petals sometimes absent from *Penthorum*; hypogynous scales petaloid in *Monanthes*. Carpels only 3 with 5 petals in *Triactina*; more or less connate in *Triactina*, *Penthorum* and *Dimorpha*; free parts of carpels dorsally dehiscent in these two genera.

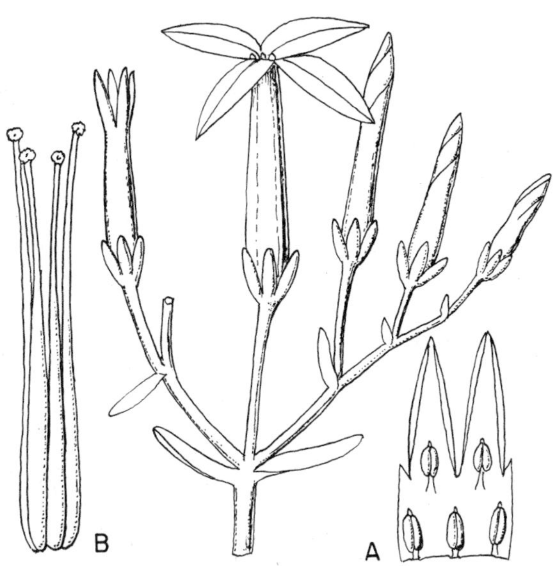

FIG. 475. *Kalanchoe dyeri* N.E.Br. (*Crassulaceae*), east tropical Africa, belongs to a genus showing an unusual combination of primitively free carpels and an advanced sympetalous corolla (orig.). **A**, upper part of corolla showing position of stamens. **B**, carpels.

In *Bryophyllum* adventitious buds spring from the edge of the leaves and develop into new plants. The common House-leek, *Sempervivum tectorum* Linn., is native of central and southern Europe, and is often found on roofs of sheds and dwellings.

The peculiar and very small family **Cephalotaceae**, in the south-west corner of Australia, seems a special development of *Crassulaceae*, with some of the leaves transformed into pitcher-like structures somewhat resembling those of *Nepenthaceae*, but not otherwise related to them!

In dealing with the *Saxifragaceae* of Bentham and Hooker, and partly of Engler, I excluded the woody groups formerly included in that family, i.e. the *Cunoniaceae*, the *Escalloniaceae*, the *Grossulariaceae* and *Hydrangeaceae*. The

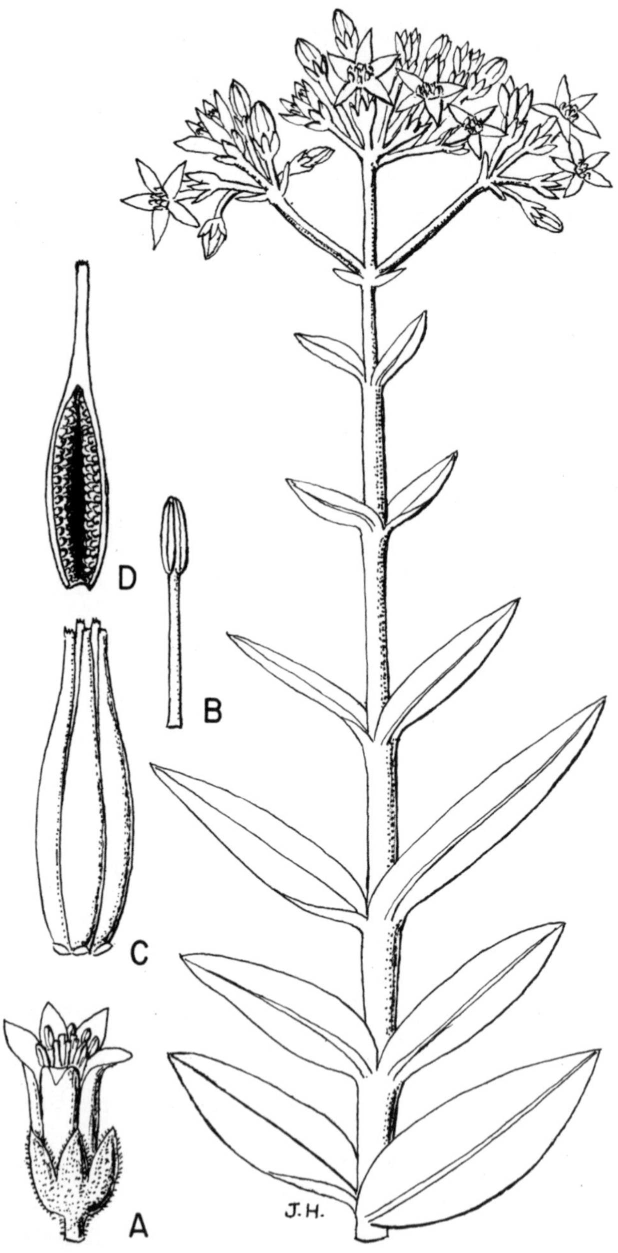

FIG. 476. *Crassula perfoliata* Linn., S.E. South Africa, type species of the type genus of *Crassulaceae*. **A**, flower. **B**, stamen. **C**, carpels. **D**, vertical section of carpel (orig.).

old conception of the family is an example of a group of plants sharing a number of characters without being phylogenetically related. As thus restricted, *Saxifragaceae* is a smaller, more homogeneous, almost entirely herbaceous, and comparatively ancient family.

The family *Saxifragaceae* was studied conjointly in 1927 by Mr. J. E. Dandy and myself, and a paper was published in the KEW BULLETIN for that year. At that time we continued to take a fairly wide conception of the family,

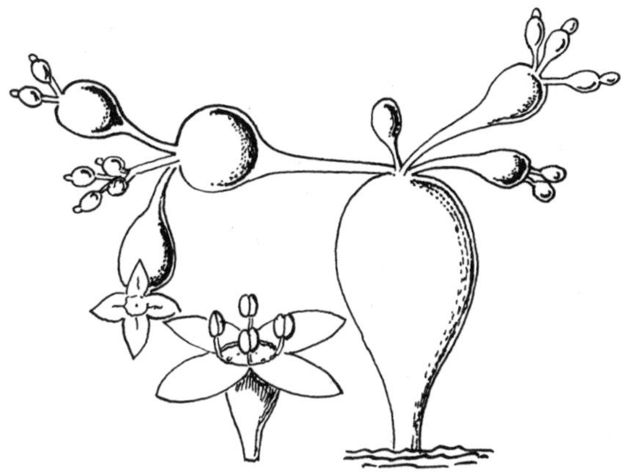

FIG. 477. *Rhopalota aphylla* N.E.Br., South Africa; a fleshy plant of striking habit in the family *Crassulaceae*.

following tradition, but later on in the second edition of my FAMILIES OF FLOWERING PLANTS Dandy raised the groups treated in that paper as subfamilies to family rank as follows: *Saxifragaceae* (*sensu stricto et herbaceo*), *Eremosynaceae*, *Vahliaceae*, *Francoaceae* and *Parnassiaceae*, and I added *Donatiaceae*. (For descriptions and figures of these small families see FAMILIES OF FLOWERING PLANTS, 2nd Ed. **1**, 460–466.)

This treatment may be regarded by some as splitting unduly, though it is often necessary that if a single tribe is removed from a large family, the other tribes may be just as distinct. Examples are *Rosaceae*, from which the tribe *Chrysobalanaceae* is treated by some as a separate family, though several of the other tribes are equally entitled to a similar status. The same may be said of the large family *Euphorbiaceae*, which could be split up into at least 12–15 families. I am not in favour of either of these families being so divided (see notes under *Euphorbiaceae*, p. 275).

Saxifragaceae[1] (*sensu stricto*) consists of about 28 genera, all herbs, in which the stigmas are dorsal to the carpels (a usual structure). This character

[1] Including *Bicornaceae* Dulac (1867). *Lepuropetalaceae* Nakai (1843).

is also shared by *Vahliaceae*, single genus *Vahlia*, which is distinguished by its apical pendulous placentas, and they are annual herbs with opposite leaves, contrasted with the parietal, axile or almost basal placentas of *Saxifragaceae*. *Eremosynaceae* shares the dorsal stigmas but the ovules are solitary on each of the two basal placentas of the 2-locular ovary.

The type genus of *Saxifragaceae* is *Saxifraga* Linn., on which an outstanding monograph was published by A. Engler and E. Irmscher in the PFLANZENREICH in 1916, a very notable achievement. They described no less than 302 species arranged in 15 sections. All but one of these have actinomorphic flowers, section *Diptera* having zygomorphic flowers. Even in this one genus the ovary may be quite superior to completely or almost completely inferior. One section, no. 14, *Tetrameridium*, has apetalous flowers and opposite leaves, and is represented only by a single species, *S. nana* Engler.

It may be that the Order SAXIFRAGALES, especially the family *Saxifragaceae*, is the basal stock from which have been evolved the much more advanced *Apiaceae* (*Umbelliferae*), and even part of *Primulaceae*. Those families, *Francoaceae* and *Parnassiaceae*, with stigmas opposite the placentas (commisural), share this remarkable and rare character with several genera of *Papaveraceae*.

In the type genus, *Saxifraga*, the sepals are usually 5 and imbricate; the petals 5 (rarely 4 or absent), always free from each other, imbricate in bud and persistent in fruit; stamens 10 (rarely 8), free, anthers didymous, the loculi dehiscing laterally; carpels usually 2 (rarely 3 or 5), free or variously adnate to the calyx-tube (hypanthium) or united into a usually 2-locular ovary, the introflexed margins bearing numerous ovules; styles free, at length spreading or reflexed; fruit a capsule, from superior to inferior, 2- (rarely 3–5-) beaked, 2-valved between the beaks; seeds very small with copious fleshy endosperm and minute terete embryo, cotyledons flat to convex. Type species *S. granulata* Linn., Europe (Fig. 478).

The late Professor Carl Otto Rosendahl made some cogent remarks about the splitting of genera in his Revision of the genus *Mitella* (Fig. 479) (*Saxifragaceae*) (ENGL. BOT. JAHRB. **50**, *Suppl.* 375 (1914)), which seem worth recording:

> The genus *Mitella* has experienced at the hands of the systematic workers a degree of splitting up into petty genera which is wholly inconsistent with its well-marked generic characters and which does violence to the lines of genetic development running through the group. The divisions in all cases have been made upon one or two characters which are obvious and artificial rather than fundamental, and the resulting genera, although easy enough to recognize, are wholly artificial and arbitrary.
>
> It has always been one of the common weaknesses of taxonomic work to employ single characters and greatly to overestimate their importance in distinguishing groups or constructing schemes of classification. The evil results of such

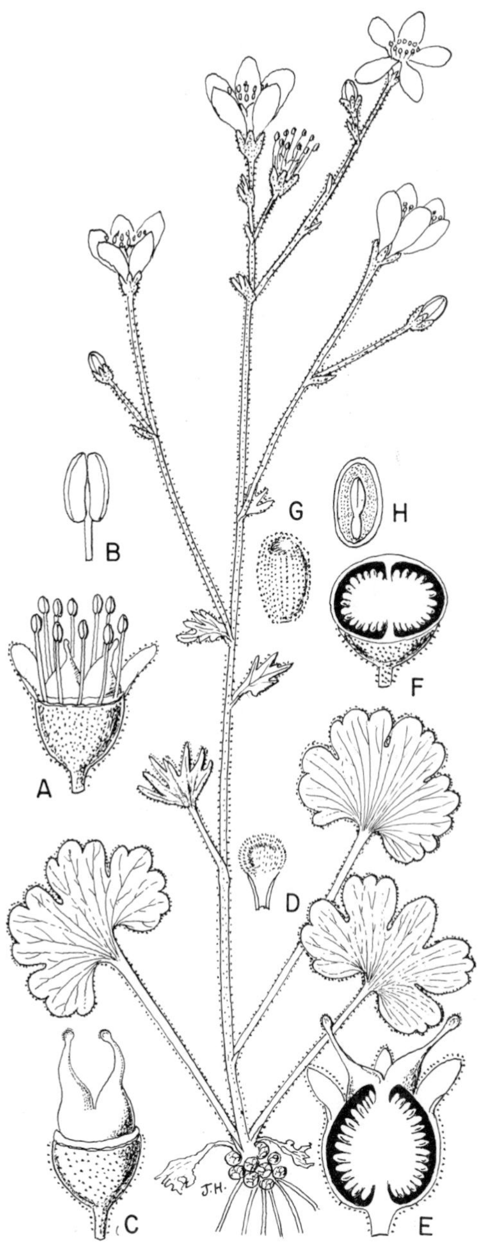

FIG. 478. *Saxifraga granulata* Linn., the type species of the type genus of *Saxifragaceae*. **A**, flower with petals removed. **B**, anther. **C**, gynoecium. **D**, stigma. **E**, vertical section of ovary. **F**, cross-section of ovary. **G**, seed. **H**, vertical section of seed (orig.).

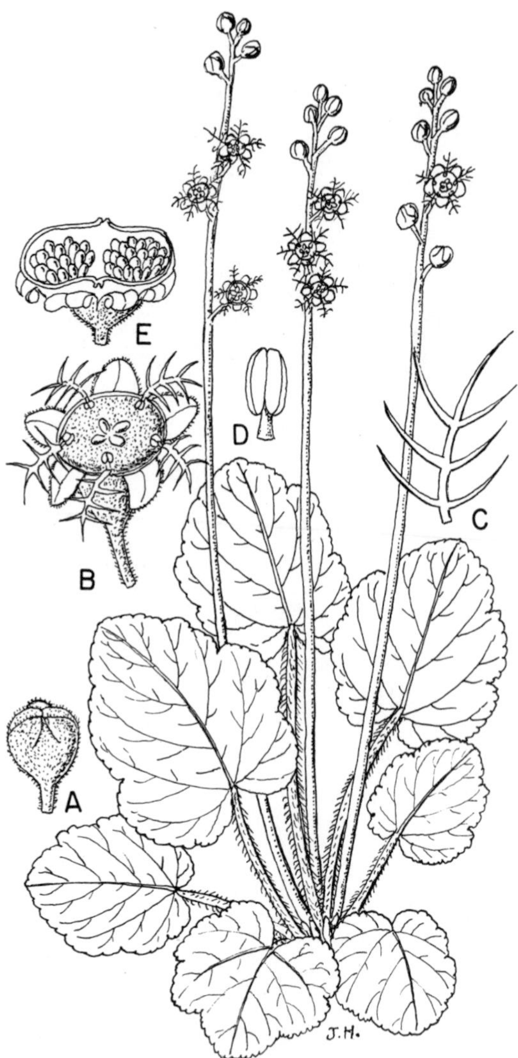

FIG. 479. *Mitella pentandra* Hook. (*Saxifragaceae*), North America. **A**, flower bud. **B**, open flower showing the stamens opposite to the pinnatisect petals, **C**. **D**, anther. **E**, open fruit and seeds (see special notes about the genus in the general text).

procedure are well illustrated in the breaking up of the genus under discussion. Another practice is that pursued in many floras of proceeding to slash and dismember families and genera on the basis of the material within the geographical limits of the particular flora, when the probabilities are that many, yes, often a large proportion, of the genera and species occur only outside such areas.

Rosendahl goes on to cite the account of the genus *Mitella* by P. A. Rydberg in the NORTH AMERICAN FLORA (1905) as follows:

> In his treatment of the group Mr. Rydberg carries the splitting-up tendency to the greatest extreme. Every section of the old genus, except one, is raised to generic rank, varieties are made into species, and many new species are described. Where Engler in 1890 recognised one genus and seven species, including one from Japan, this latest work recognises four genera and eighteen species exclusive of the Japanese ones.

In the KEW BULL. 1927, my former colleague, J. E. Dandy, after studying the whole family (i.e. *sensu herbaceo stricto*), from all parts of the world, agreed with Rosendahl; and after examination of the genus on my own account I entirely concur. It is, however, remarkable that in this small and natural genus of herbs some species have 10 stamens and some only 5, while in the latter case some have the stamens opposite to the petals, and in others they are alternate with them, differences which serve to distinguish families in other groups such as *Rhamnaceae* and *Primulaceae*.

ORDER 70. **SARRACENIALES**

(*Fam. Fl. Pl.* **1**, 467)

Families: **Droseraceae, Sarraceniaceae.**

The Orders most nearly related to the *Saxifragaceae* are the SARRACENIALES (*Droseraceae* and *Sarraceniaceae*) and the PODOSTEMONALES (*Podostemonaceae* and *Hydrostachyaceae*), all of them being more or less greatly modified in their vegetative parts and growing in special habitats. In these families there is little range in floral structure, and the most common type of placentation in the ovary is parietal. There are no special subsidiary cells to the stomata of the leaves.

In the Syllabus to the PFLANZENFAMILIEN, the *Sarraceniaceae*, *Nepenthaceae* and the *Droseraceae* are still kept together in Reihe 20, SARRACENIALES. The Reihe is described as follows (translation):

> Flowers spirally cyclic, heterochlamydeous (perianth double) or haplochlamydeous (perianth single), hypogynous, actinomorphic. Stamens numerous to 10–5–4, free or more or less united, in alternating whorls of variable number. Carpels 5–3, with centrally orientated, central or parietal placentas with numerous anatropous ovules. Seeds small, with endosperm and 1-celled archispores. Development of embryo sac normal. Shrublets or herbaceous plants with mostly spirally arranged undivided insectivorous leaves.

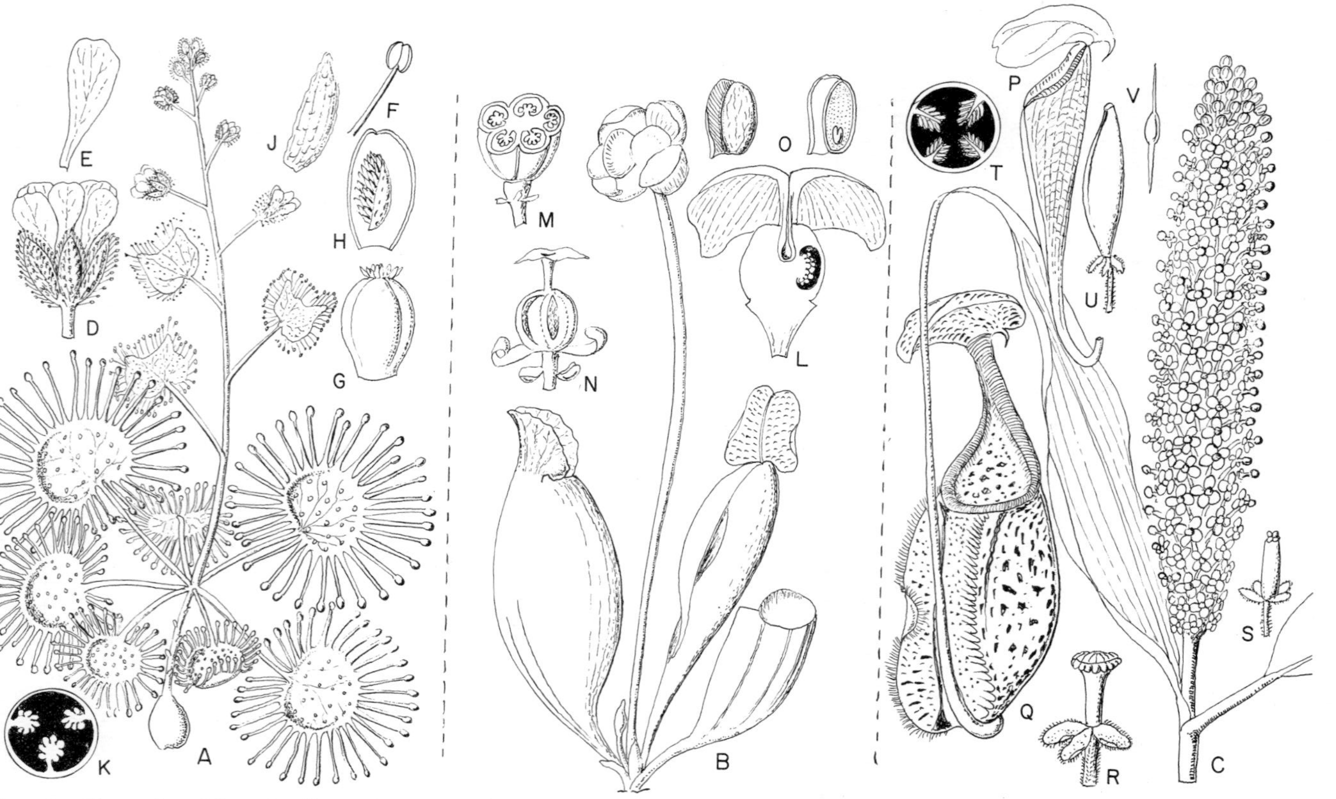

FIG. 480. Examples of three families included in the Reihe SARRACENIALES in the Englerian System. **A**, *Drosera gracilis* Hook. f. (*Droseraceae*), Tasmania. **D**, flower. **E**, petal. **F**, stamen. **G**, gynoecium. **H**, valve of capsule with seeds. **J**, seed. **K**, transverse section of ovary. **B**, *Sarracenia purpurea* Linn. (*Sarraceniaceae*), eastern North America. **L**, vertical section of flower. **M**, transverse section of ovary. **N**, fruit and anther. **O**, seed and vertical section. **C**, *Nepenthes rafflesiana* Jack (*Nepenthaceae*), Malaya. **P**, upper pitcher. **Q**, lower pitcher. **R**, male flower. **S**, female flower. **T**, transverse section of ovary. **U**, fruit. **V**, seed (see notes in text).

The Key to the families runs as follows (translation):

A. Leaves transformed into pitchers or bottle-like trap-apparatus. Placentas central:
  a. Flowers bisexual, heterochlamydeous or haplochlamydeous. Stamens numerous to 12, free. Pollen-grains single; anthers introrse. America *Sarraceniaceae*
  b. Flowers unisexual, haplochlamydeous. Stamens monadelphous; anthers extrorse. Pollen grains in tetrads; Indomalaya to Madagascar *Nepenthaceae*

B. Leaves covered with glands or glandular tentacles. Placentas parietal. Flowers heterochlamydeous. Pollen grains in tetrads *Droseraceae*

Here is the discussion provided by the editor of the SYLLABUS, word for word:

Die Ansicht (Eichler, Engler), dass die 3 Fam. einen natürlichen Verwandtschaftskreis darstellen, findet neuerdings (Markgraf) eine Stütze in dem Nachweis, dass die einzelnen Teile der so untershiedlichen Laubblätter homolog sind. Als möglicher Anschluss werden hierbei die Cistaceae und Passifloraceae in Anspruch genommen. Auch mit den Ranales und Papaverales wurden sie vielfach in Verbindung gebracht. Da aber auch in morphologischer und anatomischer Hinsicht (Shaw, Metcalfe, Markgraf) Beziehungen zu den Dioncophyllaceae bestehen, ersheint ein Anschluss an die Guttiferales (Cronquist) recht wahrscheinlich.—Möglicherweise ist die Anpassung an die Insektivorie aber eine in 2 gretrennten Verwandschaftsgruppen erfolgte Konvergenzerscheinung (Wettstein, Hutchinson), einerseits mit den Sarraceniaceae und den auf höherer Stufe stehenden Nepenthaceae, anderseits mit den Droseraceae, die infolge der andersartigen Ausbildung der Insektivorie, der parietal Plazentation, etc. sicher entfernter stehen und vielfach (Eichler, Wettstein, etc.) in die Nähe der Cistaceae und Violaceae gestellt werden. Byblis und Roridula werden heut allgemein den Rosales angeschlossen.

In our view this is a polygeneous Reihe which seems to depend almost exclusively on the presence of insectivorous leaves. The three families are otherwise not all related, and in the present system *Droseraceae* and *Sarraceniaceae* find their nearest relatives near the *Saxifragaceae* (*sensu herbaceo*), and *Nepenthaceae* in the ARISTOLOCHIALES, with which they agree in their stem-structure, and differ entirely from the other two families in their floral structure. Indeed the group as treated in the SYLLABUS is a taxonomic absurdity!

Droseraceae[1] is a small family of insectivorous plants of only 4 genera and about 90 species, most of them belonging to the genus *Drosera*. This genus is widely distributed throughout the temperate and tropical regions of both hemispheres. The other three genera, however, are widely separated

[1] Including *Dionaeaceae* Dumort. (1838). *Adenaceae* Dulac (1867). *Aldrovandaceae* Nakai (1949).

geographically; *Drosophyllum*, a shrublet with 2–4 times as many stamens as petals and free styles, in Spain, Portugal and Morocco; *Dionaea* (Venus' fly-trap), with stamens about 15 and with connate styles, confined to the S.E. United States of North America; and *Aldrovanda*, aquatic plant with jointed leaves recalling *Utricularia* in habit, with stamens the same number as the petals and parietal placentas, distributed from Europe through Asia to Australia. Most of the species of *Drosera* are small herbs inhabiting sphagnum-bogs or other damp places. A very full account of this interesting family will be found in Rendle's CLASSIF. FL. PL. **2**, 193 (1925).

The family **Sarraceniaceae** was described by J. M. Macfarlane in Engler's PFLANZENREICH **4**, 110 (1908). It consists of three genera, *Sarracenia* Linn., the type of the family, *Heliamphora* Benth, and *Darlingtonia* Torr. They are all endemic in America, but do not overlap in their distribution.

They are marsh-loving herbs with pitcher-like leaves somewhat resembling but not at all related to the real pitcher-plants, *Nepenthes*. Engler even went so far as to include *Nepenthaceae* in the same group as SARRACENIALES, in which he was followed by Rendle (CLASSIF. FL. PL. **2** (1925)).

Macfarlane, from a comparative study of the leaves of the three genera, considered that they are related to each other in advancing specialisation as follows: 1, *Heliamphora*, 2, *Sarracenia*, 3, *Darlingtonia*. On the contrary I should arrange them from a consideration of their floral structure: 1, *Darlingtonia*, flowers solitary with 5 petals, 15 stamens, 5–locular ovary, the style with normal radiating stigmas, the capsule 3-valved, and the seeds without wings; 2, *Sarracenia*, also with solitary flowers, 5 petals, numerous stamens, 5-locular ovary, and the style enlarged into an umbrella-like expansion, the capsule loculicidally 5-valved, and seeds shortly winged; and 3, *Heliamphora*, with flowers in braceate racemes, no petals, stamens numerous, 3-locular ovary with a simple style truncate at the apex, capsule 8-valved, and the seeds broadly winged.

Darlingtonia has a restricted range on the Pacific side of the United States, *Sarracenia* in eastern Canada and the eastern United States south to Florida, and *Heliamphora* in Guyana in South America.

ORDER 71. **PODOSTEMALES**

(*Fam. Fl. Pl.* **1**, 469)

Families: **Podostemaceae, Hydrostachyaceae.**

Phylogeny: RANALES → SAXIFRAGALES → PODOSTEMALES.

Podostemaceae[1] consists of over 20 genera and about 100 species of submerged herbs highly modified in association with their aquatic habitat, resembling mosses, hepatics or even algae. They are widely distributed in the tropics, growing attached by special organs (haptera) to stones and rocks in rapidly flowing water.

The flowers are bisexual, solitary or cymose, often enclosed when young in a spathe composed of partially connate bracts. There is a calyx but no petals, and the ovary has a central placenta bearing numerous ovules. (As I have not yet studied this family in detail, I would refer the student to Rendle's account in Vol. 2 of his CLASSIF. FL. PL., p. 326, Figs 158, 159, and the literature quoted therein.)

Hydrostachyaceae contains only one genus, *Hydrostachys*, formerly included in *Podostemonaceae*, found only in Madagascar and South Africa. They are also submerged aquatics with thick tuber-like stems bearing long simple or pinnately divided leaves and long-stalked spikes of naked dioecious flowers. The stamens are reduced to 1, and the ovary has 2 parietal placentas bearing numerous ovules. The fruit is a small capsule with numerous seeds devoid of endosperm.

ORDER 72. UMBELLALES

(*Fam. Fl. Pl.* **1**, 471)

Family: **Apiaceae** (*Umbelliferae*).

Phylogeny: RANALES → SAXIFRAGALES → with a fairly wide gap to UMBELLALES.

This highly natural and highly evolved family **Apiaceae**[2] is essentially for a specialist, and the present author has not much experience of it apart from routine naming and general herbarium work. He is fully aware of criticism due to his wide separation of the family from *Araliaceae*, and his reasons for this are given under that family on p. 123. He prefers to derive *Araliaceae* from the woody CUNONIALES and the *Apiaceae* from the herbaceous Saxifragaceous stock, no doubt "heresy" to many botanists.

---

[1] Including *Marathraceae* Dumortier (1829). *Philocrenaceae* Bongard (1835). *Tristichaceae* J. C. Willis (1915).

[2] Including *Angelicaceae* Burnett (1835). *Coriandraceae* Burnett (1835). *Smyrniaceae* Burnett (1835). *Umbellaceae* Dulac (1867). *Ammiaceae* Small (1903). *Hydrocotylaceae* Hylander (1945). *Daucaceae* Dostal (1949).

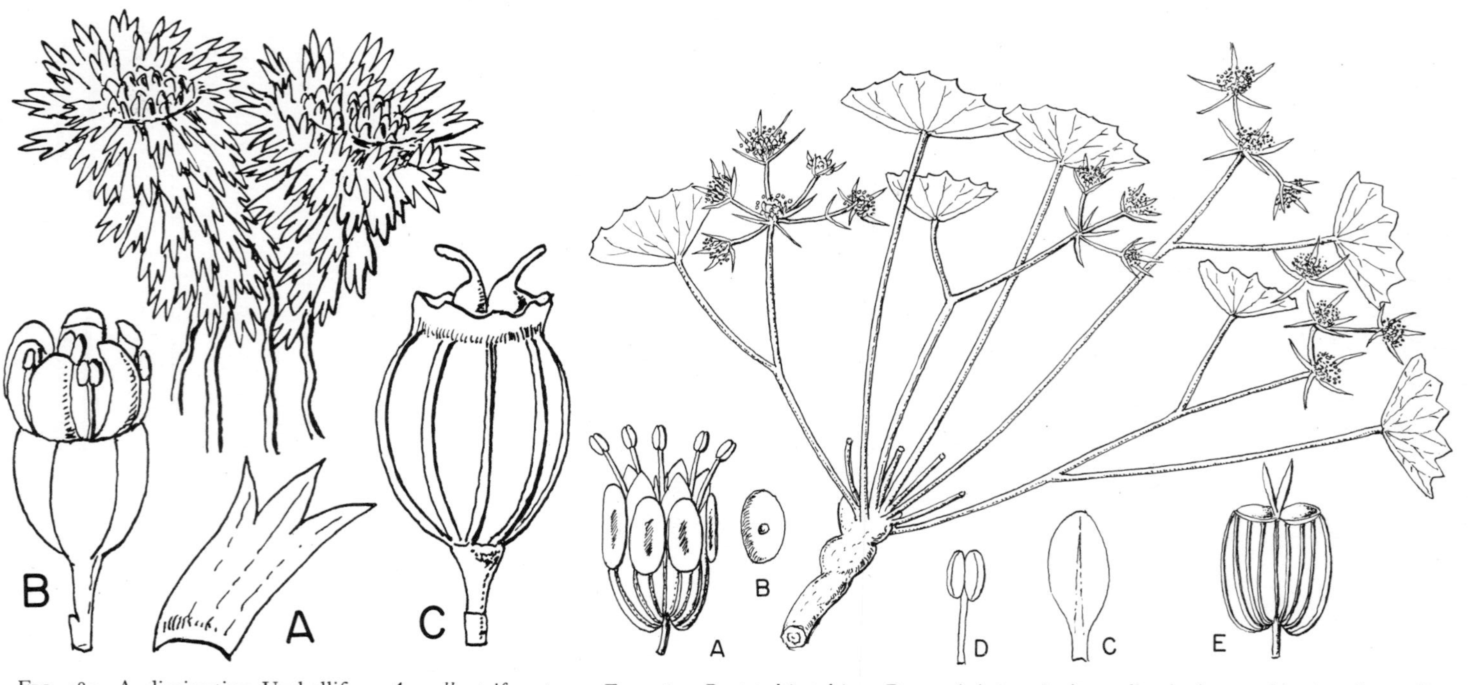

FIG. 481. A diminutive Umbellifer, *Azorella trifurcata* Gaertn. (*Apiaceae*), native of the Andes of South America. **A**, leaf. **B**, single flower. **C**, fruit.

FIG. 482. *Pentapeltis peltigera* Bunge (*Apiaceae*), Australia. **A**, flower showing the curious disk-like calyx-lobes. **B**, disk-lobe showing attachment. **C**, petal. **D**, stamen. **E**, fruit (orig.).

The family consists almost entirely of herbs with usually hollow stems, and the often very much divided leaves have no stipules. (The student will find a very good account of the family, which vies with *Poaceae* (*Gramineae*), *Asteraceae* (*Compositae*) and *Rubiaceae* in being the most natural (homogeneous), in Rendle, CLASSIF. FL. PL. **2**, 411.)

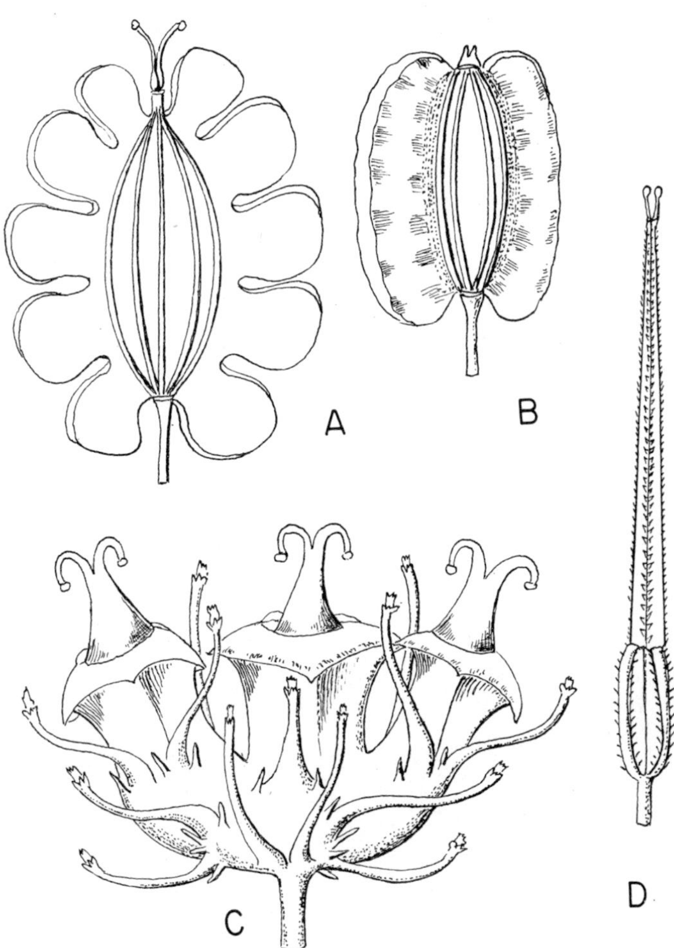

FIG. 483. Some fruits of *Apiaceae*: **A**, *Artedia squamata* Linn. f., Orient. **B**, *Thapsia villosa* Linn., S.W. Europe, N. Africa. **C**, *Thecocarpus meifolius* Boiss. **D**, *Scandix pecten-veneris* Linn.

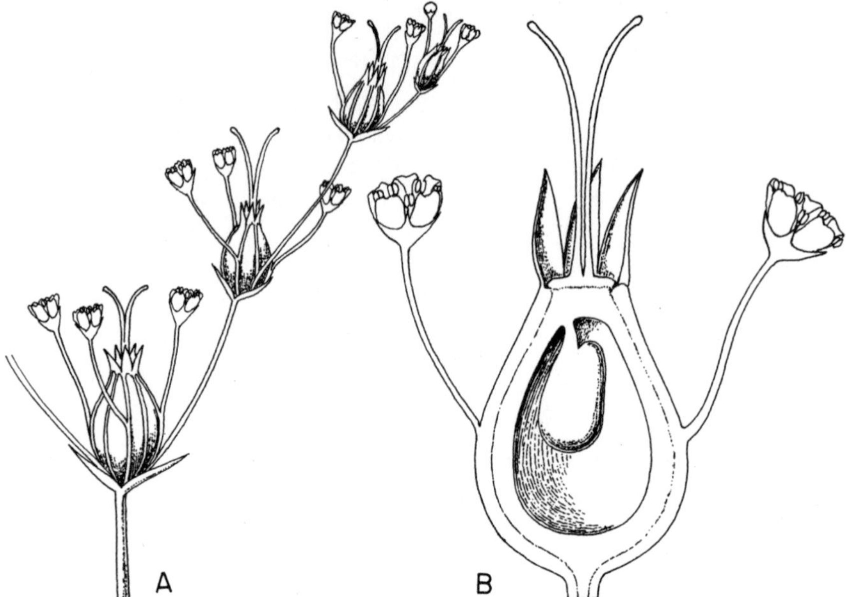

Fig. 484. This remarkable umbelliferous plant, *Pentagnia saniculifolia* Guss. (*Apiaceae*), Sicily, calls to mind "the lady with two strings to her bow and who could be happy with either were t'other fair charmer away", for the female flower has attached to it 2 or even 3 males, whose pedicels are partly adnate to a rib of the calyx (hypanthium). **A**, inflorescence. **B**, vertical section of female flower, with 2 males attached. (A similar phenomenon occurs in *Parthenium argentatum* (see p. 613) in the family *Asteraceae* (*Compositae*).)

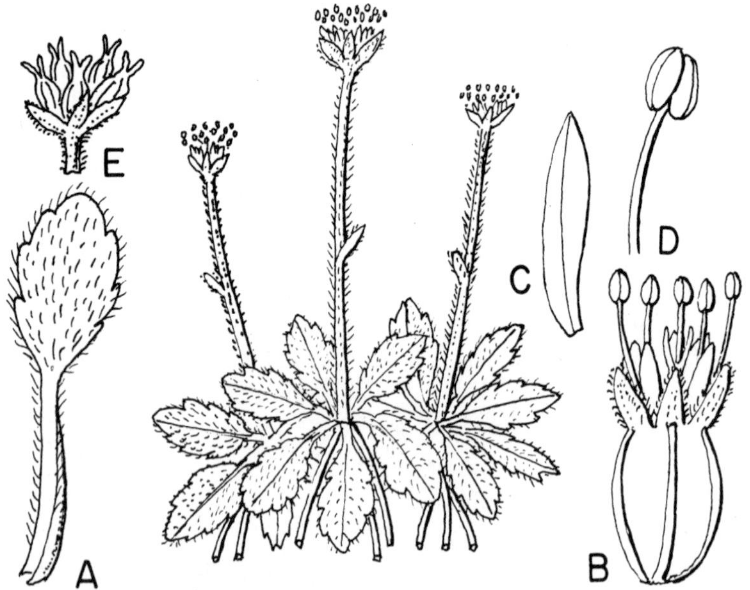

Fig. 485. *Actinotus bellidioides* (Hook. f.) Benth. (*Apiaceae*); a diminutive Umbellifer which grows in wet peaty soil at high altitudes in Tasmania. **A**, leaf. **B**, flower. **C**, petal. **D**, stamen. **E**, fruits. (Adapted from Fitch's drawing in Hook. FL. TASMANICA.)

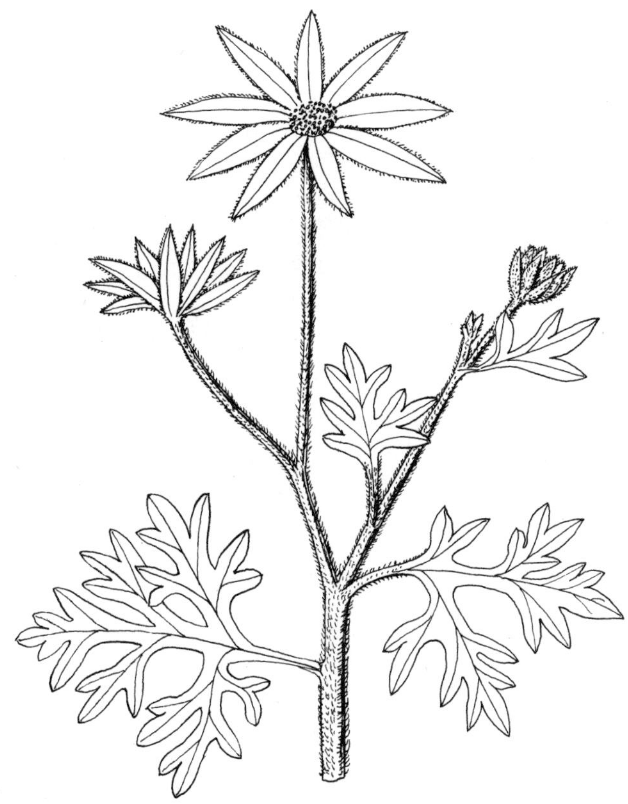

FIG. 486. *Actinotus helianthi* Labill. (*Apiaceae*), south Australia; known as "Edelweiss" (orig.).

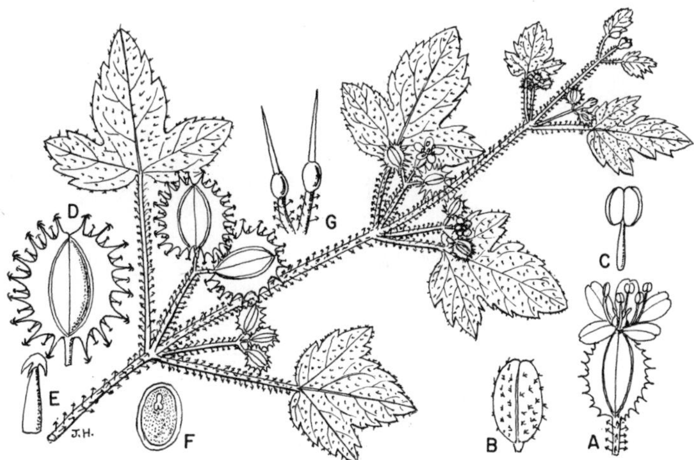

FIG. 487. *Dura oppositifolia* DC. (*Apiaceae*), Canary Islands, endemic. Note the opposite leaves and distinctive fruits. **A**, flower. **B**, petal from below. **C**, stamen. **D**, fruit. **E**, anchor-like process on margin of fruit. **F**, vertical section of seed. **G**, bristly hairs.

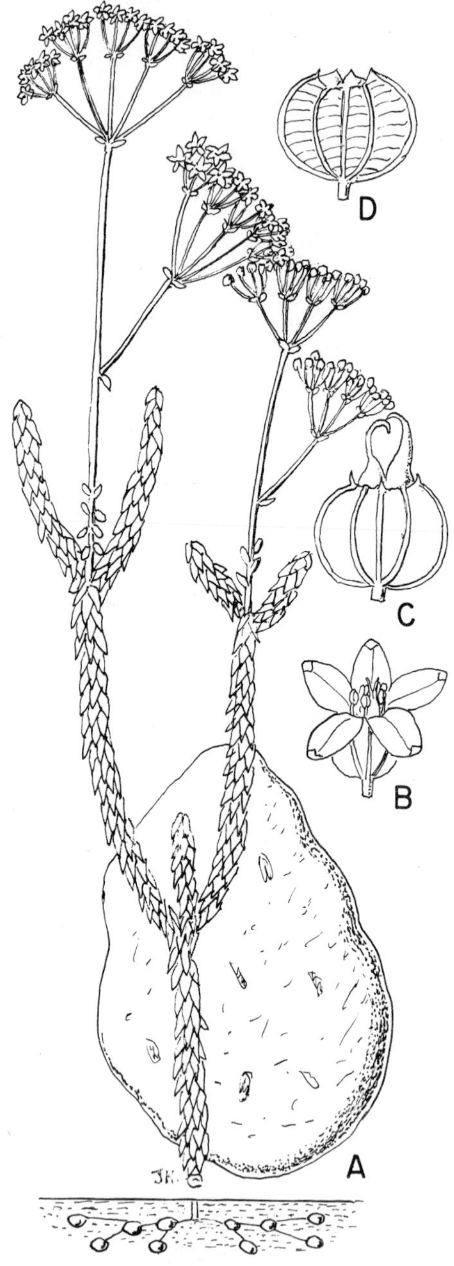

FIG. 488. *Platysace deflexa* (Turcz.) Norman (*Apiaceae*), a very distinctive species in Western Australia with underground tubers eaten by and known to the aborigines as "Yuke". **A**, tuber. **B**, flower. **C**, the same with petals removed. **D**, fruit. (Adapted from Hook. IC. PL.)

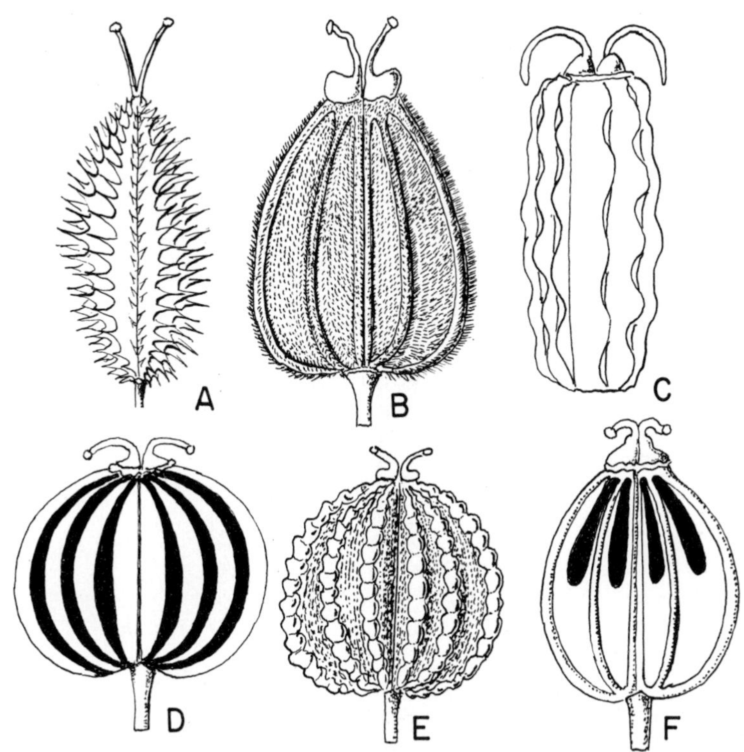

Fig. 489. Fruits of some *Apiaceae*. **A**, *Daucus carota* Linn. **B**, *Pimpinella anisum* Linn., eastern Mediterranean. **C**, *Cynoypterus terebinthinus* Raf., N.W. America. **D**, *Cicuta virosa* Linn., Europe, northern Asia, North America. **E**, *Conium maculatum* Linn., Europe, Orient. **F**, *Sison amomum* Linn., Europe, Asia Minor.

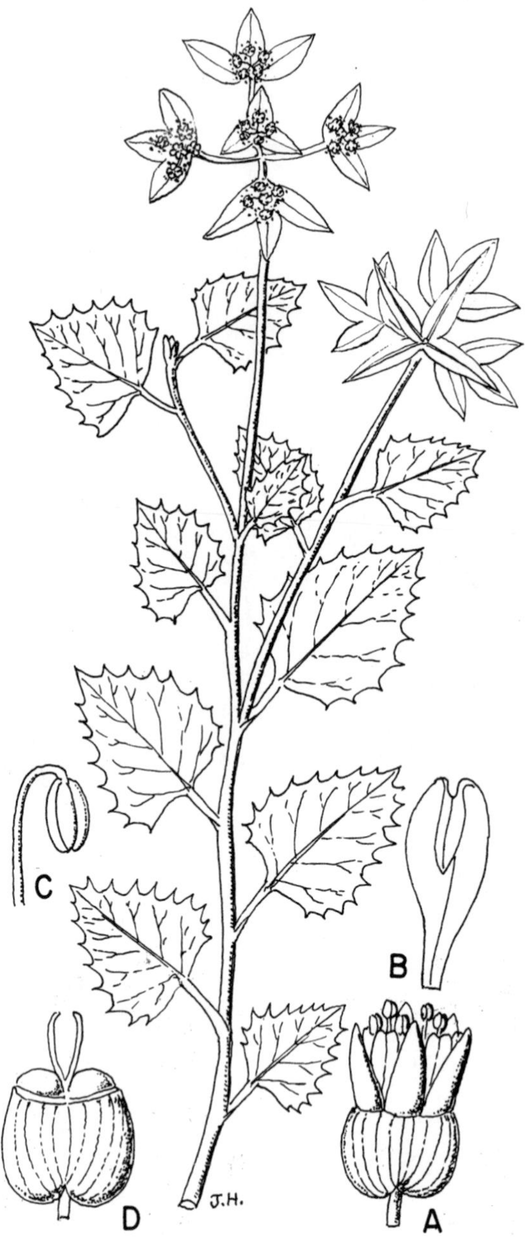

FIG. 490. *Xanthosia rotundifolia* DC. (*Apiaceae*), known in western Australia as the "Southern Cross" plant, on account of the arrangement of the partial umbels. **A**, flower. **B**, petal. **C**, stamen. **D**, fruit.

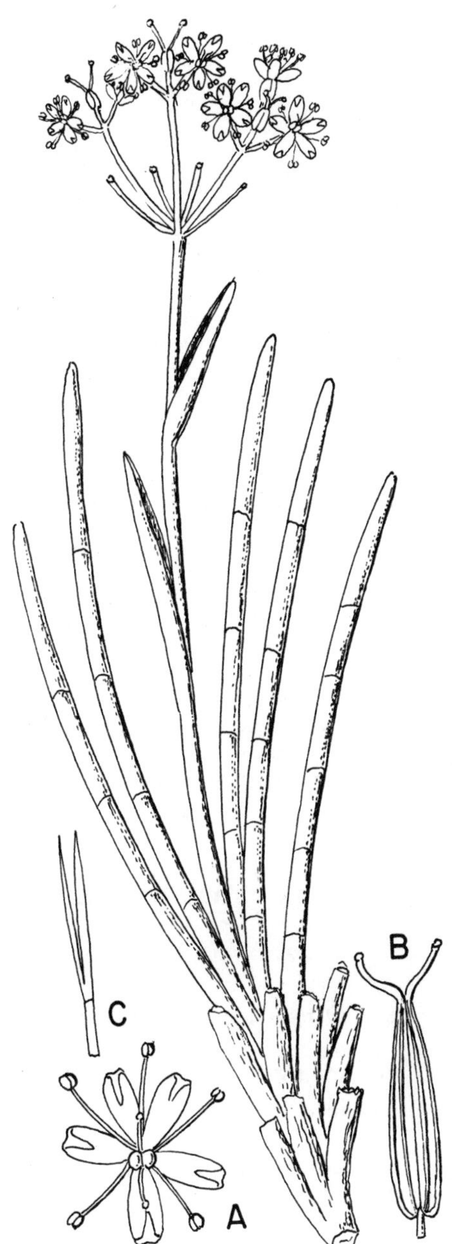

FIG. 491. *Ottoa oenanthoides* H.B. & K. (*Apiaceae*), Central America to Ecuador; leaves terete and jointed. **A**, flower. **B**, fruit. **C**, persistent axis of fruit (orig.).

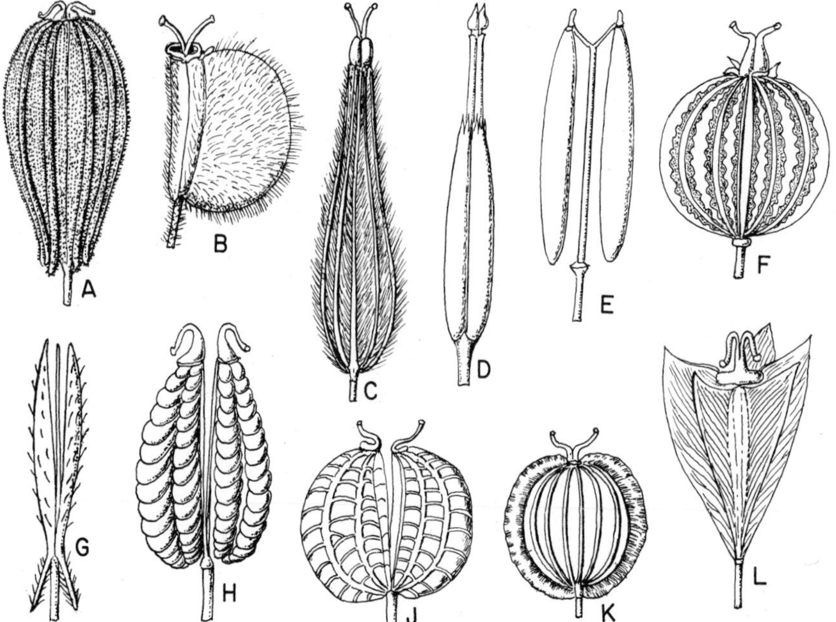

FIG. 492. Fruits of some *Apiaceae* (*Umbelliferae*). **A**, *Melanoselinum edule* Drude, Madeira. **B**, *Trachymene caerulea* R. Graham, Australia. **C**, *Athamanta mattioli* Wulf., S.E. Europe. **D**, *Anthriscus cereifolium* Hoffm., Europe to north Asia. **E**, *Anthriscus sylvestris* Hoffm., Europe to north Asia. **F**, *Coriandrum sativum* Linn., southern Europe and Orient. **G**, *Osmorrhiza clatonii* (Michx.) C.B.Cl. **H**, *Szovitsia callicarpa* Fisch. & Mey., Caucasus region. **J**, *Hydrocotyle asiatica* Linn., tropics and subtropics. **K**, *Peucedanum oreoselinum* Moench., central and southern Europe. **L**, *Pyramidoptera cabulica* Boiss., Afghanistan.

ORDER 73. **VALERIANALES**

(*Fam. Fl. Pl.* **1**, 471)

Families: **Valerianaceae, Dipsacaceae, Calyceraceae.**

Phylogeny: RANALES → SAXIFRAGALES → VALERIANALES → climax family **Calyceraceae**.

In Bentham and Hooker's system all the sympetalous families with an inferior ovary were grouped together in one series called *Inferae*, and those with a superior ovary disposed in two other series, the *Heteromerae* and *Bicarpellatae*. The *Inferae* were further subdivided into the RUBIALES, with two or more ovary-loculi, and the stamens inserted on the corolla, the

ASTERALES with one ovary-loculus and similarly placed stamens, and the CAMPANALES with the stamens mostly free from the corolla.

This classification, based only on one or two characters, was clearly artificial, on the one hand separating closely allied families, and on the other bringing into close proximity families which now seem to show little affinity, especially with *Asteraceae* (*Compositae*). These families are *Valerianaceae*, *Dipsacaceae* and *Calyceraceae*.

The transformation of the calyx in *Valeriana* and *Centranthus* is perhaps merely a parallelism of the pappus in the *Asteraceae* (*Compositae*). A similar development is found in the related but more advanced family **Dipsacaceae**, which is nearly on a par with *Asteraceae* (*Compositae*), again as a parallel and not a direct affinity. In this family the abortive ovary-loculi have disappeared, and the bracteoles have become united to form a cup around each individual flower, a feature never found in *Asteraceae*.

The spiny habit of *Morina* recalls that of some *Acanthaceae*. As stated above, a link between *Valerianaceae* and *Dipsacaceae* is perhaps the Himalayan genus *Triplostegia*, with subradical leaves and lax panicles of flowers. It has the habit and glandular hairs of some species of *Saxifraga*, and was regarded as a monotype in the mountains of northern India and western China, until a second species, *T. repens* Hemsl., was discovered at 11 000 ft in New Guinea!

Although the flowers of some **Dipsacaceae**[1] are arranged in heads almost as in *Asteraceae*, the relationship seems to end there. Each flower of the dipsacaceous head is surrounded by a little involucre (involucel) composed of two or more bracteoles. There is nothing like this in *Asteraceae*. In addition the ovule in *Dipsacaceae* is pendulous, not erect as in all *Asteraceae*, and the seed contains endosperm. It seems probable, therefore, that these three families have had quite a different phylogenetic history from that of *Asteraceae*, and that the supposed affinity is due to convergent evolution, especially of the inflorescence. To me it is clearly a case of superficial resemblance. The most likely stock from which they may have sprung is that of *Saxifragaceae*, though they are on a much higher plane than that family.

The difference given by Bentham and Hooker between *Valerianaceae* and *Dipsacaceae* is that in the former family the ovary consists of three loculi, only one of which is fertile, the other two being empty or rudimentary, and the seeds have no endosperm; whilst in the latter the ovary is 1-locular, and the seeds have endosperm, and the following is added as an additional character for *Dipsacaceae*: "Flores singuli involucello tubuloso calyciformi inclusi vel cincti, saepe capitati."

The two families are thus quite easily separated except for the genus

---

[1] Including *Morinaceae* J. G. Agardh (1858). *Involucellaceae* Dulac (1867). *Triplostegiaceae* Airy Shaw (1965).

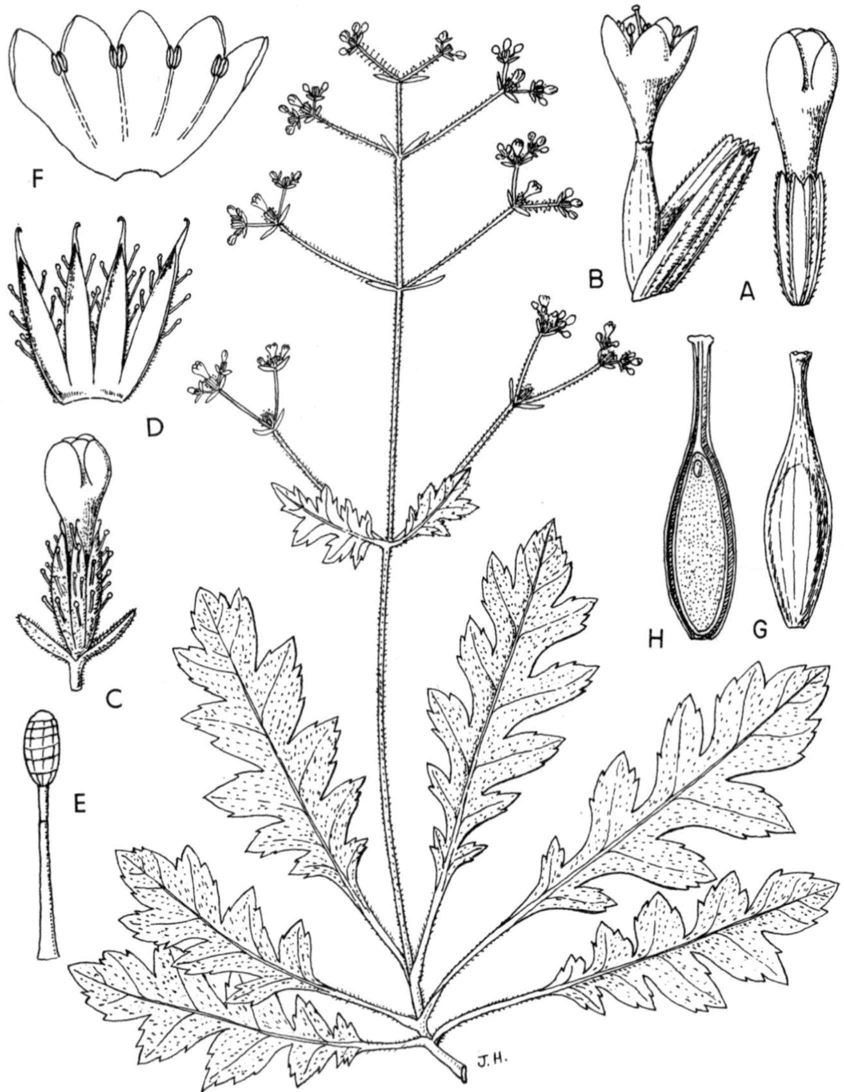

FIG. 493A. *Triplostegia glandulifera* Wall. (*Dipsacaceae*), northern India and western China. **A**, flower-bud showing involucel and corolla. **B**, flower with involucel. **C**, flower and involucre. **D**, involucre opened out. **E**, hair from involucre. **F**, corolla laid open. **G**, fruit. **H**, vertical section of fruit and seed (orig.).

Triplostegia (Fig. 493A), at first ascribed to the *Valerianaceae*, but transferred to the *Dipsacaceae* by Bentham and Hooker, and subsequently replaced in the *Valerianaceae* by Engler and Prantl. The habit and inflorescence of this genus is undoubtedly that of *Valerianaceae*, but this is deceptive, for there is actually a double involucel, the ovary is 1-locular, and the seeds have copious endosperm. Experienced taxonomic botanists know that habit alone is deceptive, and that similar inflorescences are evolved in many genera of very different relationship. Undoubtedly on the balance of characters *Triplostegia* should be classed with *Dipsacaceae*.

Progressive economy with nectar concealment and special distribution-mechanism is very clearly evident in the family **Valerianaceae.**[1] There are four stamens in *Patrinia*[2] and *Nardostachys*, the corolla-tube not being spurred at the base (except in one species of *Patrinia*), and in the other genera there are from 3 to 1 stamen. Four genera (*Astrephia*, *Phyllactis*, *Valerianella* and *Valeriana*) have no spur at the base of the corolla-tube, and in only one genus (*Valeriana*) the calyx-limb is pappus-like in fruit. *Plectritis*, *Fedia* and *Centranthus* have a spurred corolla, and the last mentioned genus represents the most evolved, with usually only one stamen and the calyx pappus-like and plumose in fruit. An interesting substitute for the pappus-like calyx is developed in *Patrinia*, which has the enlarged bracteole wing-like and membranous and closely appressed to the fruit. It may be significant

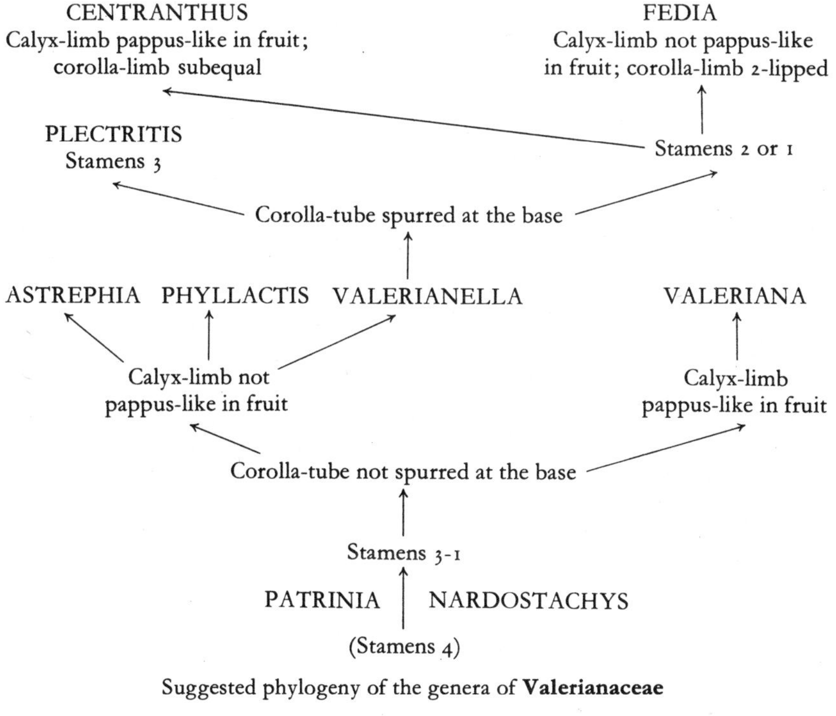

Suggested phylogeny of the genera of **Valerianaceae**

[1] Including *Stephanangaceae* Dulac (1867).

[2] There is only one stamen in *P. monandra* C. B. Clarke in the Himalayas.

that the habit of *Valeriana sedifolia* d'Urv., in the Falkland Islands, is that of a *Sedum* (*Crassulaceae*).

Calyceraceae[1] is a small family of three genera, somewhat more highly evolved than *Dipsacaceae*. The flowers are capitate with an involucre of bracts, but without the involucel mostly found in that family. The corolla-lobes are valvate, and the anthers are connate around the style as in *Lobeliaceae* and *Asteraceae*. There is a single pendulous ovule in the inferior 1-locular ovary. In *Boopis* the fruits are free from one another and are of one kind. In *Calycera* they are also free but of 2 kinds, some with hardened calyx and some unchanged. In *Acicarpha* the fruits of the outer flowers become united. Distribution temperate and subtropical South America.

ORDER 74. **CAMPANALES**

(*Fam. Fl. Pl.* **1**, 476)

Families: **Campanulaceae, Lobeliaceae.**

Campanulaceae[2] is not a very easy family to place. In the Bentham and Hooker f. system it formed an order (cohort) with *Stylidiaceae* and *Goodeniaceae*, and follows ASTERALES. In our phylogenetic scheme, however, this is no place for them and they are put in front of that group. Those authors' remarks on affinity refer only to the families mentioned, so they do not help in any way.

It is not a very big jump from *Saxifragaceae* to *Campanulaceae*, and it is from the stock of the former family that I believe them to have been derived. And *Campanulaceae* seem to be the most likely stock pointing to the evolution of that huge and wonderful family *Asteraceae* (*Compositae*), though the latter may be in small part polyphyletic. It is difficult indeed for anyone who knows the family fairly intimately, as I do, to believe that a *Vernonia*, a Sunflower (*Helianthus*), a *Baccharis* or *Brachylaena* (trees), and a Dandelion (*Taraxacum*), have all been derived from the same stock. But that question is more fully dealt with under the family itself (p. 600). *Lobeliaceae* are now generally treated as a separate family. It has definitely reached a higher stage

---

[1] Including *Boopidaceae* Cassini (1817).

[2] Including *Jasionaceae* Dumort. (1828). *Pongatiaceae* Endlich. (1838). *Cyphiaceae* A. P. de Candolle (1839). *Sphenocleaceae* Martius & A. P. de Candolle (1839). *Nemacladaceae* Nuttall (1843). *Cyphocarpaceae* Miers (1848). *Cyananthaceae* J. G. Agardh (1858). *Limbaceae* Dulac (1867). *Pentaphragmataceae* J. G. Agardh (1858).

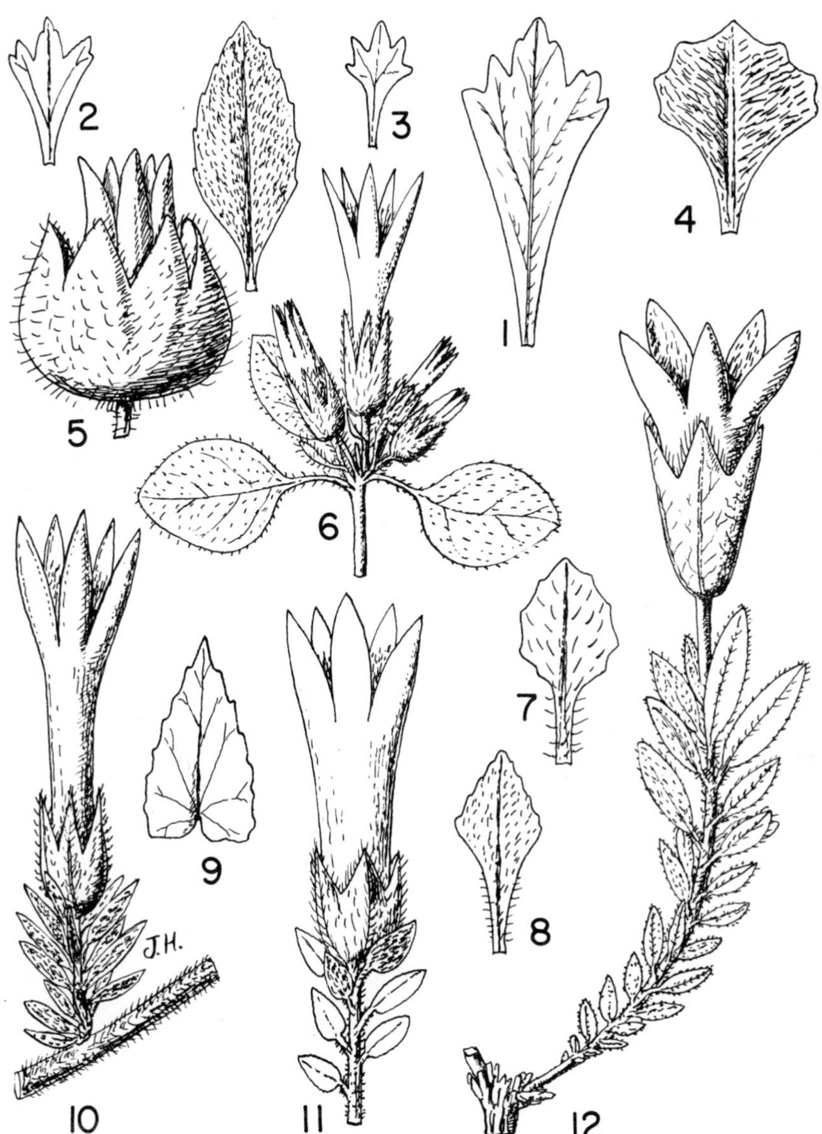

FIG. 493B. *Cyananthus* is the only genus in the family *Campanulaceae* with a superior ovary. Details of various species: **1** and **2**, leaves of *C. lobatus* Benth. **3**, leaf of *C. lobatus*, var. *farreri* Marquand. **4**, leaf of *C. formosus* Diels. **5**, fruit of *C. inflatus* Hook. f. & Thoms. **6**, *C. fasciculatus* Marquand. **7**, leaf of *C. hookeri* C.B.Cl. **8**, leaf of *C. incanus* Hook. f. & Thoms. **9**, leaf of *C. cordifolius* Duthie. **10**, *C. argenteus* Marquand. **11**, *C. obtusifolius* Marquand. **12**. *C. flavus* Marquand, Yunnan. (A drawing by the present author for KEW BULLETIN 254 (1921).)

FIG. 494. *Campanula latifolia* Linn., Europe to temperate Asia, the type species of the type genus of *Campanulaceae*. **A**, calyx and style. **B**, stamen. **C**, cross-section of ovary. **D**, fruit showing basal pores from which the seeds are liberated. **E**, seed.

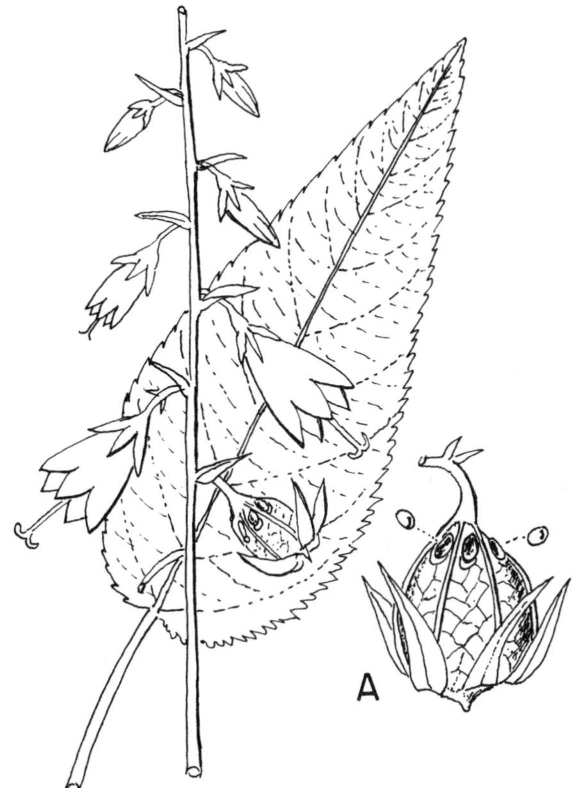

FIG. 495A. *Campanula rapunculoides* Linn., Europe (*Campanulaceae*). **A**, fruit showing the remarkable dehiscence by basal pores (the fruit being pendulous).

of evolution than *Campanulaceae*, and is a less perfect parallel with the *Asteraceae* (*Compositae*), representing a separate side-branch.

Campanulaceae are essentially herbaceous, often with a thick fleshy tap root, and they usually contain a certain amount of latex. There are over sixty genera and more than 1500 species, distributed mainly in the north temperate zone, though they are also numerous in South Africa, where they have adopted a heath-like habit. The ovary is inferior or semi-inferior (*Wahlenbergia*, etc.), but in one Asiatic genus, *Cyananthus* (Fig. 493B), it is quite superior. Perhaps at this point there is remote relationship with *Gentianaceae*, but the aestivation of the corolla is of an advanced type, valvate or induplicate-valvate.

Fruit characters are useful in the classification of the genera of *Campanulaceae*. In the majority the fruit is a capsule, in the small remainder it is a berry. The capsule opens in several different ways and the first series of Bentham and Hooker's system seems to be the more primitive type. In this

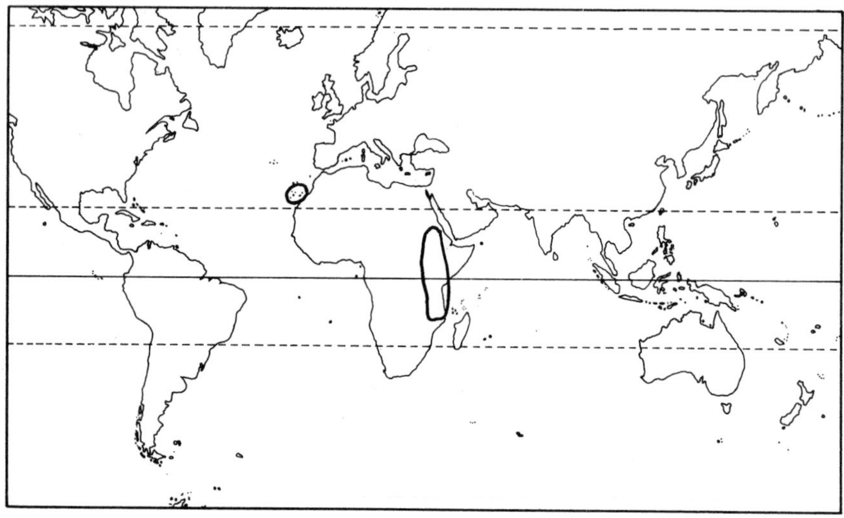

Map 32. Range of the natural genus *Canarina* (*Campanulaceae*), Canary Islands and mountains of tropical east Africa.

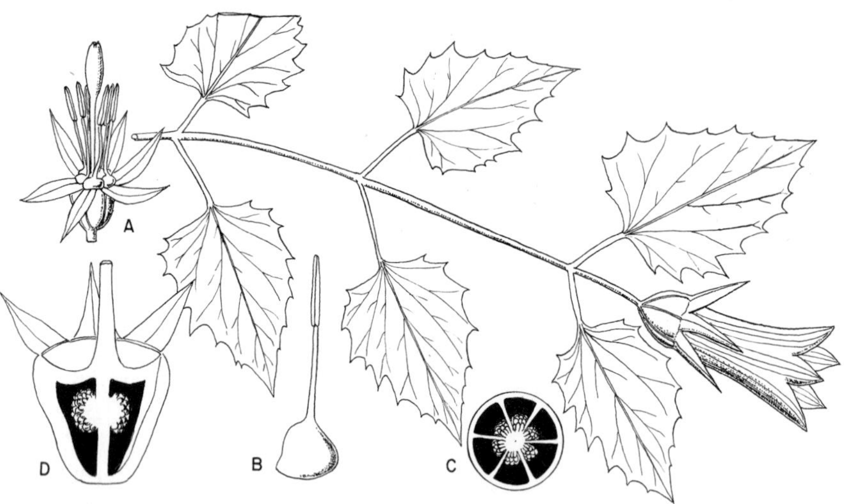

Fig. 495B. *Canarina eminii* Aschers. ex Schweinf., mountains of east Africa (*Campanulaceae*). **A**, flower, less corolla. **B**, stamen. **C**, cross-section of ovary. **D**, vertical section of ovary.

it dehisces loculicidally by apical valves within the calyx lobes. *Cyananthus*, already mentioned as having a superior ovary, has also this character. Though its anthers are connate, the filaments are free from the corolla and therefore hypogynous. *Jasione*, with its flowers in a head surrounded by bracts, heralds the evolution of an inflorescence which has become so fixed a characteristic of *Asteraceae* (*Compositae*). *Lightfootia* and *Wahlenbergia* are the two largest genera and very abundant in southern Africa.

Another group of genera has fruits which are either indehiscent, or they open by an operculum or transverse slit, and they may be indehiscent at the base or longitudinally split. These also are mainly south African.

A third batch of genera, to which *Campanula* belongs, have fruits which open by an operculum or by small solitary valves or pores between the ribs (see Fig. 495A).

Amongst the genera with baccate fruits is the very natural genus *Canarina* (Fig 495B), which has a discontinuous distribution in the Canary Islands and in the mountains of east Africa. They are climbing or decumbent plants with large flowers, and a tuberous rootstock.

The largest flowers, almost like a lily, are found in *Ostrowskia*, whilst in contrast are the small flowers of *Trachelium* arranged in a dense corymb. The last mentioned genus might be a pointer towards the evolution of the *Valerianaceae*.

Sphenocleaceae: With regard to my notes on the status of this taxon in my FAMILIES OF FLOWERING PLANTS, 2nd Ed. **1**, 476–7, where I declined to regard it as a distinct family, I was interested to see what had been done in the latest SYLLABUS (12th Ed.) of the Englerian System. Therein the family is retained together with the *Pentaphragmataceae*.

They are keyed out in the Reihe CAMPANULALES as follows, and I leave the student to judge for himself:

"Griffel mit Sammel- oder Fegehaaren; Ovar 5–2 (selten 1-) fächerig;
 Pflanzen mit Milchsaft ... *Campanulaceae*
Griffel ohne Sammel- oder Fegehaaren; Ovar 2-fächerig:
 Pet. dachig ... *Sphenocleaceae*
 Pet. klappig ... *Pentaphragmataceae*"

Regarding the last mentioned, Dr. Wagenitz[1] (responsible for CAMPANUALES) rather naïvely states: "Die systematische Stellung der Familie, die früher wie die vorige den *Campanulaceae* zugeordnet wurde, ist ganz unsicher. Wahrscheinlich gehört sie nicht zu den *Campanulales*"! (The exclamation mark is mine.)

---

[1] In case Dr. Wagenitz had not seen my notes I repeat them here: "As in Bentham and Hooker's GENERA PLANTARUM and Engler and Prantl's NATÜRLICHEN PFLANZENFAMILIEN, I prefer to retain the genus *Sphenoclea* in *Campanulaceae*, where its position has not been questioned except by Airy Shaw. Shaw says 'there is no evidence of affinity with *Campanulaceae*, with which it has hitherto been associated'. He does not qualify this negative statement, but considers it to be related to *Phytolaccaceae*. In my opinion, however, the resemblance to *Phytolacca* is entirely superficial and due to parallel evolution of the inflorescence. There are numerous similar inflorescences among flowering plants, and even that of *Michauxia*, in *Campanulaceae*, approaches it quite closely."

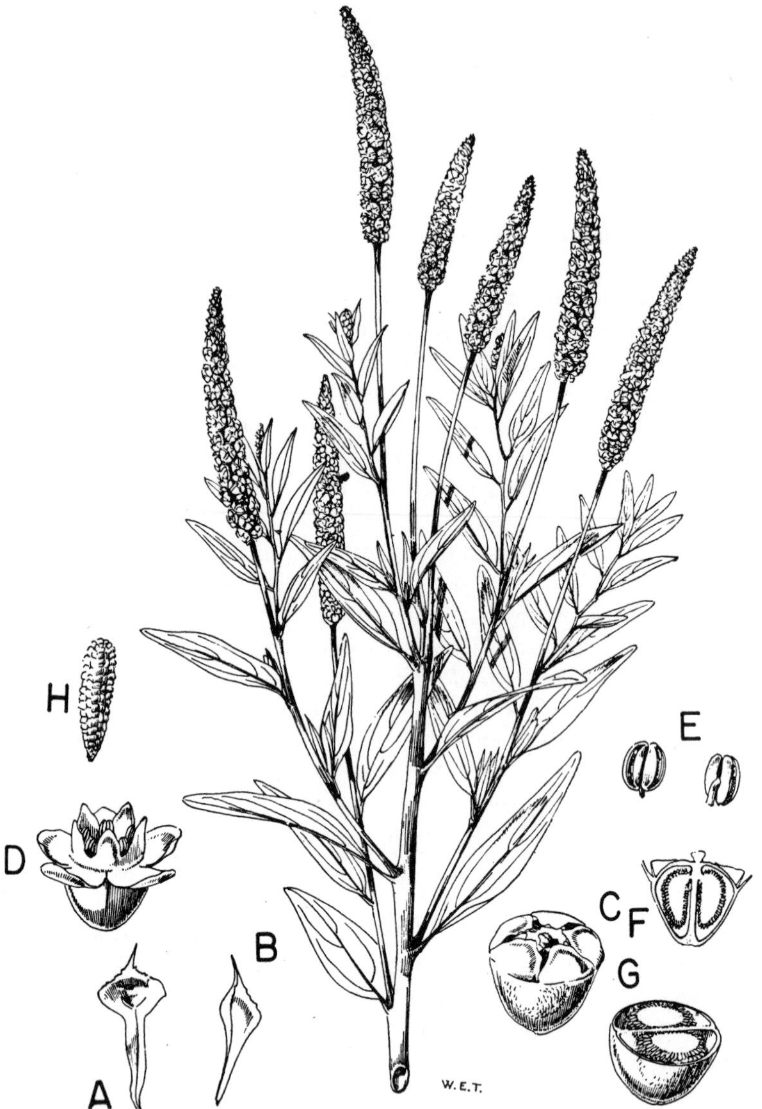

FIG. 496. *Sphenoclea zeylanica* Gaertn. (*Campanulaceae*), tropics generally. **A** and **B**, bracts. **C**, flower. **D**, the same open. **E**, anthers. **F**, vertical section of ovary. **G**, cross-section of ovary. **H**, seed. (From Hutchinson and Dalziel, FLORA OF WEST TROPICAL AFRICA.)

With respect to *Sphenocleaceae*, Airy Shaw states in his revision of Willis' DICTIONARY: "The widely assumed connection with *Campanulaceae* is probably illusory". It seems very improbable that all botanists previous to him should have suffered in this way. Indeed his original idea that *Sphenoclea*

(Fig. 496) is in any way related to *Phytolacca* is itself an illusion, as I pointed out in my FAMILIES OF FLOWERING PLANTS. In addition it should be noted that *Sphenoclea* has occurred in two different places in the FLORA MALESIANA, first as a family by Airy Shaw (Vol. 4, 27 (1948)), and then again as a tribe by a different author in *Campanulaceae* (Vol. 6, 109 (1960))!

Besides the above I gave the following table of characters:

In **Phytolaccaceae** (*sensu stricto*) there are no petals, the stamens, when definite in number, are alternate with the sepals (if petals were present they would therefore be opposite to them), a condition unknown in *Campanulaceae,* the ovary is superior, and the ovule is solitary in each carpel, the carpels in *Phytolacca* itself in fruit are free or connate and indehiscent.

In **Sphenoclea**, on the contrary, the corolla is sympetalous, the stamens are alternate with the corolla-lobes, the ovary is semi-inferior, 2-locular, and with large multi-ovulate pendulous placentas, the fruit is a capsule dehiscing by a transverse slit (circumscissile).

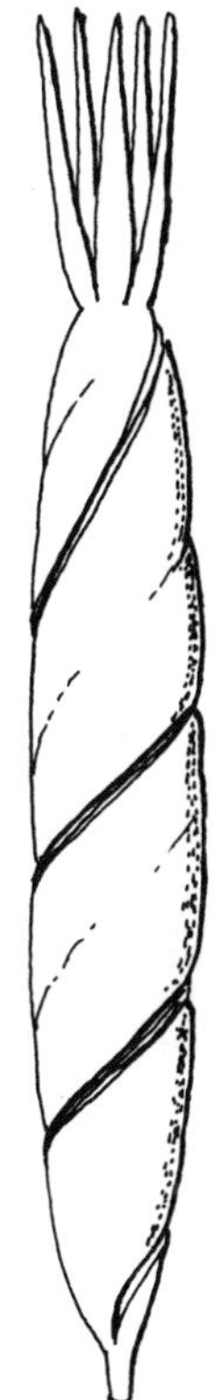

FIG. 497. Spirally twisted capsule of *Prismatocarpus tenellus* Oliv., South Africa (*Campanulaceae*).

I also added: "From a comparison of the embryological and anatomical features of *Sphenoclea* with those of *Phytolaccaceae*, K. Subramanyam has come to a similar conclusion to mine (see PROC. INDIAN ACAD. SCI. **31**, 60 (1950); also Maheshwari, The Embryology of Angiosperms, A Retrospect and Prospect, CURR. SCI. **25**, 106–10 (1956)). I also consider *Pentaphragma* (*Pentaphragmataceae*) to be equally correctly placed in *Campanulaceae*".

Type genus *Campanula* Linn. Herbs, perennial or very rarely annual; flowers terminal or axillary, or in a terminal panicle; calyx-tube adnate to the ovary, hemispherical to turbinate, 5-lobed or 5-partite; corolla campanulate, rarely funnel-shaped or subrotate, 5-lobed, lobes valvate or induplicate-valvate; stamens free from the corolla, anthers free; epigynous disk not prominent; ovary inferior, 3- or 5-locular, placentas many-ovuled; style 3- or 5-lobed; capsule crowned by the calyx-lobes, mostly flat and closed or rarely split with age on

FIG. 498. *Musschia wollastonii* Lowe, a genus of *Campanulaceae* endemic in Madeira; note the large number of pores through which the seeds, **B**, are liberated. **A**, stamen.

top, dehiscing laterally between the ribs by small valves or pores; seeds mostly numerous and very small. Type species *C. latifolia* Linn., Europe to temperate Asia (Fig. 494).

There are not many outstanding genera in this relatively natural family. Leaves opposite in *Campanumoea*, *Canarina*, and in odd species of a few other

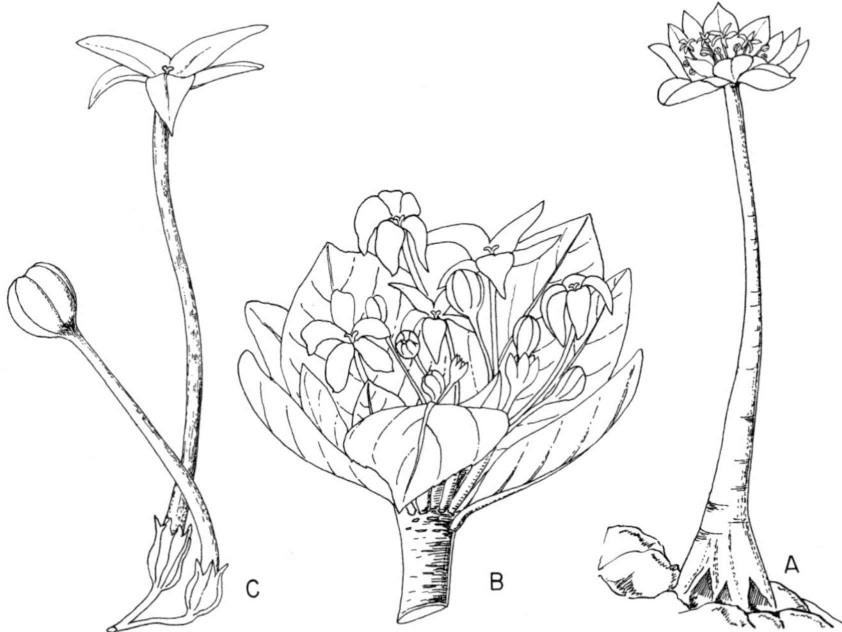

FIG. 499. *Brighamia insignis* A. Gray (*Lobeliaceae*), Hawaii, of weird habit, an unbranched fleshy stem with leaves crowded around the bunch of flowers at the top. **A**, habit of plant. **B**, leaves and inflorescence. **C**, flowers.

genera. Inflorescence capitate and involucrate in *Jasione* (resembling some *Asteraceae* but not at all related); densely spicate in *Sphenoclea* and in some species of *Phyteuma*; unilaterally scorpioid in *Pentaphragma* (not related either to *Begoniaceae* or to *Boraginaceae*!). Flowers dioecious in spp. of *Campanula* and *Specularia*. Sepals free and only the corolla-base adnate to the ovary in *Campanumoea*; calyx and corolla free from the ovary (therefore the latter superior) in *Cyananthus* and in spp. of *Lightfootia*. Epigynous glands alternate with the stamens in *Leptocodon*; fleshy epigynous cupular or tubular disk surrounding the base of the style in *Adenophora*. Ovary imperfectly 2–3-locular due to the early disappearance of the septa in *Githopsis*; ovules reduced to 4 and erect from the base in pairs in *Merciera*; pendulous from the apex of the loculi in *Siphocodon*. Fruit baccate (indehiscent) in *Campanumoea*, *Canarina*, *Peracarpa*, and *Pentaphragma*.

Several of these exceptional genera might equally be regarded as separate families if we accepted the family *Sphenocleaceae*!

Lobeliaceae,[1] as noted under *Campanulaceae*, are here regarded as sufficiently distinct to merit family rank. They differ from *Campanulaceae* by

[1] Including *Ciliovallaceae* Dulac (1867).

FIG. 500. *Lobelia cardinalis* Linn., North America, the type species of the type genus of *Lobeliaceae*. **A**, anthers. **B**, stigma. **C**, fruit. **D**, seed (orig.).

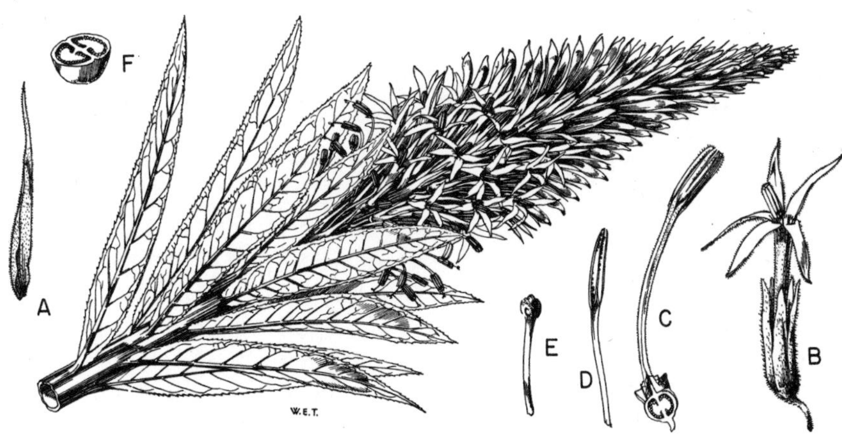

FIG. 501A. *Lobelia columnaris* Hook. f. (*Lobeliaceae*), mountains of west tropical Africa. **A**, bract. **B**, flower. **C**, vertical section of flower. **D**, stamen. **E**, style. **F**, cross-section of ovary. (From Hutchinson and Dalziel, FLORA OF WEST TROPICAL AFRICA.)

their zygomorphic corolla, and the anthers are always connate around the style, more or less as in *Asteraceae*, except in tribe *Cyphieae*.

There is a very remarkable group of them in the Hawaiian (Sandwich) Islands mostly with baccate fruits, whilst species of *Lobelia* in the east African mountains assume giant proportions, similar to species of *Senecio* in the same region. Of the insular genera the monotypic *Brighamia*, native of Hawaii, is of weird habit, with an unbranched fleshy stem and the leaves crowded around the bunch of flowers at the top. A sketch of this remarkable plant is given here (Fig. 499).

Most of the genera of *Lobeliaceae* are found in South America, particularly in the Andes, the family being mainly an austral one. The family is, of course, clearly an advanced type of *Campanulaceae*. The dwarf *Lobelia* used for bedding in temperate countries is *L. erinus* Linn., native of South Africa.

Type genus *Lobelia* Linn. (over 200 species). Herbs, shrubs or shrublets; leaves alternate; flowers solitary in the leaf-axils or bracts or in terminal racemes; bracteoles mostly very small or mostly absent; calyx-tube adnate to the ovary, obovoid to oblong-linear, 5-partite or 5-lobed; corolla-tube dorsally split to the base, lobes subequal, connivent or more or less distinctly bilabiate; tube of stamens mostly quite free from the corolla, 2 or all the anthers penicillate on top; ovary inferior, or semisuperior, 2-locular, placentas many-ovuled; stigma shortly 2-lobed, lobes rarely longer and at length revolute; capsule inferior to almost superior, 2-locular, loculicidally 2-valved within the persistent calyx-lobes; seeds numerous and very small. Type species *L. cardinalis* Linn., North America (Fig. 500).

ORDER 75. GOODENIALES

(*Fam. Fl. Pl.* **1**, 478)

Families: **Goodeniaceae, Brunoniaceae, Stylidiaceae.**

Phylogeny: RANALES → SAXIFRAGALES → CAMPANALES → GOODENIALES.

The Order GOODENIALES is rather a peculiar one, highly advanced, and of somewhat uncertain relationship. In **Goodeniaceae**[1] the pollen is exuded from the introrse anthers and deposited into a collecting cup (indusium) at the end of the style and before the flower opens, the cup then almost closing leaving a narrow opening covered by hairs. The style then bends down and occupies the mouth of the corolla, visitors to which become dusted with the powdery pollen. The stigmatic lobes later emerge to receive pollen in turn from insect visitors from other flowers, thus ensuring cross-pollination.

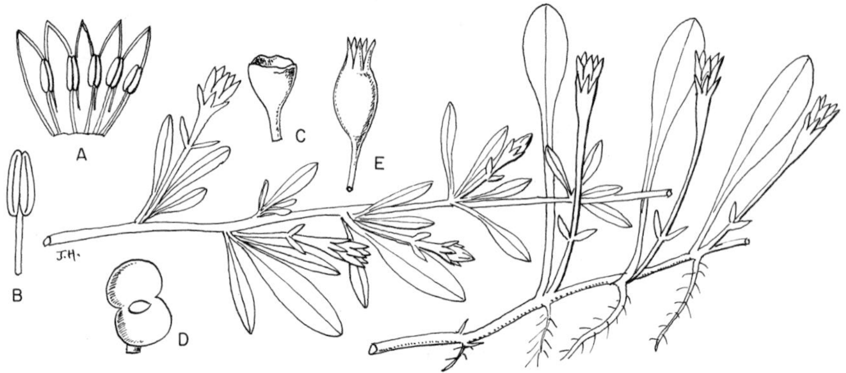

FIG. 501B. *Selliera radicans* Cav. (*Goodeniaceae*) grows in moist places near the sea in Chile, New Zealand, Tasmania, Victoria and New South Wales; flowers white; there is only one other species of this genus, *S. exigua* F. Muell., in west Australia. **A**, corolla laid open. **B**, stamen. **C**, stigma. **D**, stigma opened out. **E**, fruit.

The family is mostly austral in distribution, and the majority of the 11 or 12 genera are indigenous in Australia. The largest genus *Scaevola* is the most widely distributed, in Australia, Asia and Africa. The fruit of this genus is drupaceous. The herb *Selliera radicans* Cav. (Fig. 501B) grows in moist places near the sea and has a remarkable discontinuous distribution on both sides of the Pacific Ocean (see map in FAMILIES OF FLOWERING PLANTS, 2nd Ed. **1**, 478).

[1] Including *Scaevolaceae* Lindley (1830). *Goodenoughiaceae* K. Schum. (1894).

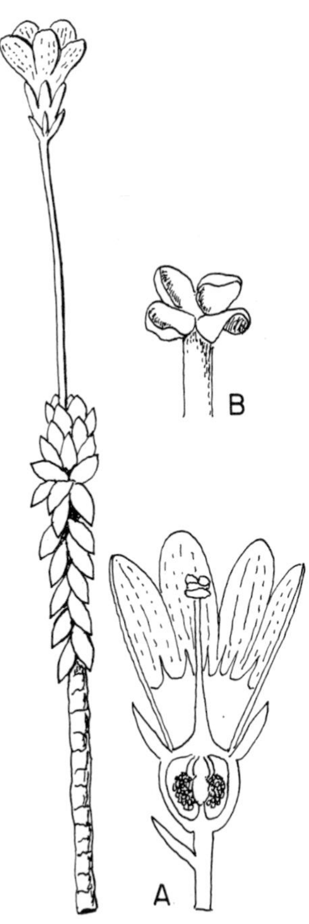

FIG. 502. The elder Forster, who was botanist on Captain Cook's second voyage around the world, was honoured by the son of Linnaeus, who named the plant *Forstera sedifolia* (family *Stylidiaceae*). **A**, vertical section of flower. **B**, stigmas.

Leaves opposite in a few spp. of *Scaevola*. Calyx free from the ovary but corolla adnate to its base in *Velleia*. Style 2–3-lobed in *Calogyne*; indusium deeply bilabiate in *Leschenaultia*, the upper lip shorter and glandular inside, furnished outside with a semi-annulus of hairs, lower lip glabrous or villous. Ovules pendulous in *Catosperma*.

The generically and specifically monotypic family **Brunoniaceae** was formerly included in *Goodeniaceae*, with which it shares the peculiar indusiate stigma. Bentham said of it in the GENERA PLANTARUM: "Species unica, per Australiam imprimis extratropicam late dispersa; genus anomalum a pluribus auctoribus pro ordine distincto habitum, notis tamen variis cum Goodenovieis plurimis connexum nec ulli ordini accedens".

The single species of *Brunonia* is a herb with radical leaves and the flowers densely capitate on a common peduncle, a sympetalous actinomorphic corolla with valvate lobes, anthers connate around the style (as in *Lobeliaceae*) and superior 1-locular ovary with 1 erect ovule; quite a unique concord of characters!

Stylidiaceae[1] is a small but highly evolved mostly Australian family, especially in regard to the androecium in which the stamens are reduced to 2 and are united with the style to form a column, but free from the corolla; the anthers are extrorse and sessile, the loculi at first divaricate but later confluent at the apex and opening by a continuous slit. The ovary is inferior and 2-locular (or only 1-locular at the very base). In three of the genera the corolla is actinomorphic, *Oreostylidium* (New Zealand), *Forstera* (Fig. 502), (New Zealand and Tasmania) and *Phyllachne*, common to subantarctic South America and New Zealand; and zygomorphic in *Stylidium* and *Levenhookia*, both Australian, but one species of *Stylidium* in eastern tropical and subtropical Asia.

[1] Including *Candolleaceae* Schoenland (1889).

In many species of *Stylidium* the column is sensitive to touch; in its normal position it is bent forwards and springs backwards when touched, after which it gradually resumes its original position. The fruit is a capsule dehiscing by 2 valves, or in *Phyllachne* it is indehiscent. The inflorescence in the family is generally a raceme or corymb.

ORDER 76. **ASTERALES**

(*Fam. Fl. Pl.* **1**, 481)

Family: **Asteraceae** (*Compositae*).

In a masterly essay on the Classification, History, and Geographical Distribution of **Asteraceae**[1] (*Compositae*), George Bentham[2] wrote of the family:

The *Compositae (Asteraceae)* are at once the largest, the most distinct, and the most uniform, and therefore the most natural, of all orders of Phaenogamous plants. Nearly ten thousand known species are separated from each other by characters most of which are usually considered as only of secondary importance; and I cannot recall a single ambiguous species as to which there can be any hesitation in pronouncing whether it does or does not belong to the order. . . . The androecium, gynoecium, and fruit, as to all the essential characters of number of parts and relative position of the seed and its embryo in every particular, are absolutely uniform throughout the order; or in the very few cases of a slight variation (as, for instance, in the shape of the cotyledons) the differences are no more than specific, varying in one and the same small genus. To distribute, therefore, these ten thousand species into thirteen tribes and above seven hundred and sixty genera, we are compelled to derive our characters from inflorescence and its rhachis and bracts, from the pappus or abnormal development of the rudimentary calyx, from the shape of the corolla, from sexual abortions, from appendages to

---

[1] Including *Cinarocephalaceae* A. L. de Juss. (1789). *Corymbiferae* A. L. de Juss. (1789). *Cichoriaceae* A. L. de Juss. (1789). *Nucamentaceae* Hoffmansegg & Link (1820). *Ritroneae* Hoffmansegg & Link (1820). *Synanthereae* Cassini (1826). *Acarnaceae* Link (1829). *Ambrosiaceae* Dumort. (1829). *Anthemidaceae* Link (1829). *Calendulaceae* Link (1829). *Coreopsidaceae* Link (1829). *Echinopaceae* Link (1829). *Eupatoriaceae* Link (1829). *Helichrysaceae* Link (1829). *Partheniaceae* Link (1829). *Peridiciaceae* Link (1829). *Cynaraceae* Burnett (1835). *Mutisiaceae* Burnett (1835). *Syngeneticae* Horaninow (1847). *Cassiniaceae* C. H. Schultz (1852). *Spurionucaceae* Dulac (1867). *Synantheraceae* Dulac (1867). *Carduaceae* Small (1903). *Arctotidaceae* Bessey (1915). *Heleniaceae* Bessey (1915). *Helianthaceae* Bessey (1915). *Inulaceae* Bessey (1915). *Lactucaceae* Bessey (1915). *Senecionaceae* Bessey (1915). *Vernoniaceae* Bessey (1915).

[2] G. Bentham J. LINN. SOC. **13**, 335–577 (1873).

the anthers, from the external form or appendages of the style-branches, and from very slight variations in the external form of the fruit, many of which, in other orders, are scarcely reckoned of more than specific value.

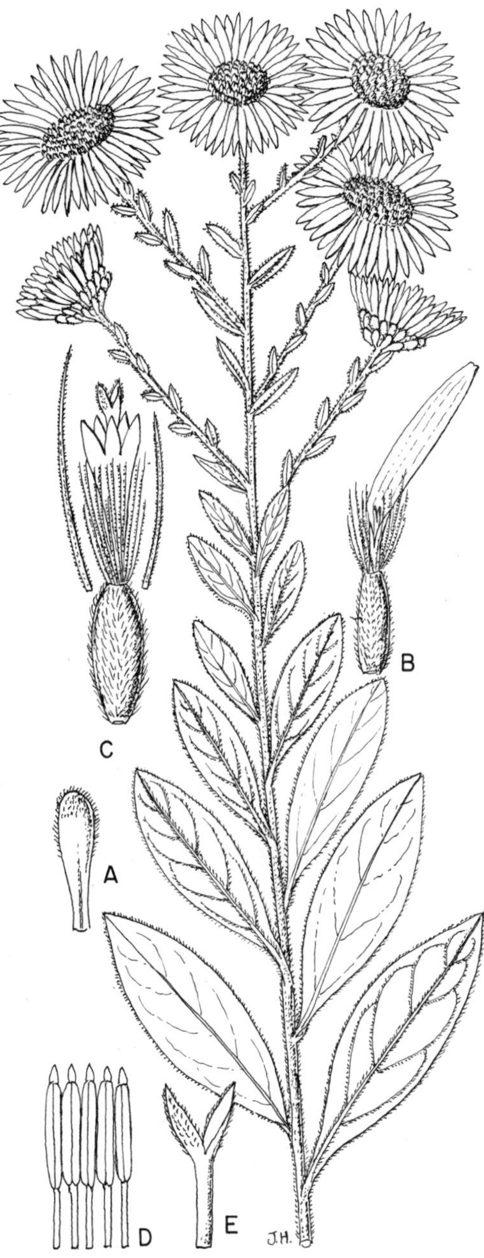

FIG. 503A. *Aster amellus* Linn., southern Europe, the type species of the type genus of *Asteraceae* (*Compositae*); flowers blue-mauve. **A**, bract of involucre. **B**, ray-flower. **C**, disk-flower and pappus bristles. **D**, stamens of disk-flower. **E**, style of same (orig.).

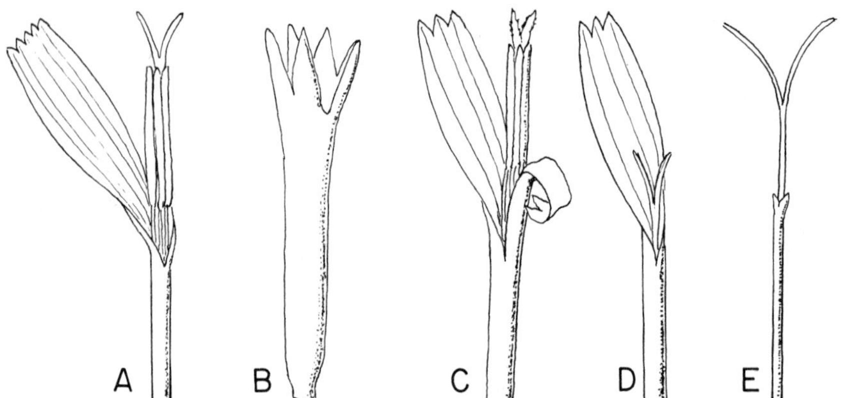

FIG. 503B. Types of corolla in *Asteraceae* (*Compositae*). **A**, Tribe *Cichorieae*. **B**, **C**, **D**, *Mutisieae*. **E**, filiform female flowers in various tribes.

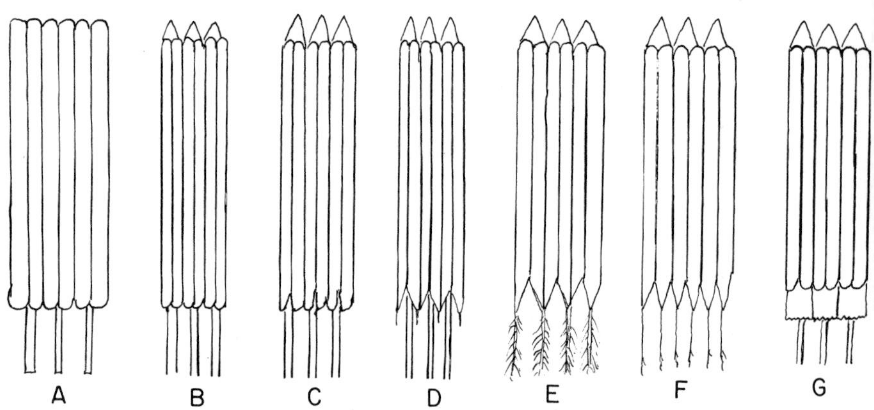

FIG. 503C. Types of anthers in *Asteraceae* (*Compositae*). **A–C**, Tribes *Eupatorieae* and *Astereae*. **D–F**, *Inuleae* and *Mutisieae*. **G**, *Cynareae*.

Asteraceae (*Compositae*) is one of the most interesting families of flowering plants. We may consider for a moment what they really represent and how they have come about. The head of flowers often has the appearance of a single flower, and this deception is sometimes intensified by the crowding of the heads into an inflorescence, which is frequently a flat corymb, as in *Tanacetum*, or even into a compound globular head, as in *Echinops*, the latter surely the acme of reduction, as each partial head is reduced to only one flower with its own involucre of bracts.

As the result of the crowding of the flowers and the abbreviation of the axis of the ancestral spike, the bracts are collected into a whorl or whorls

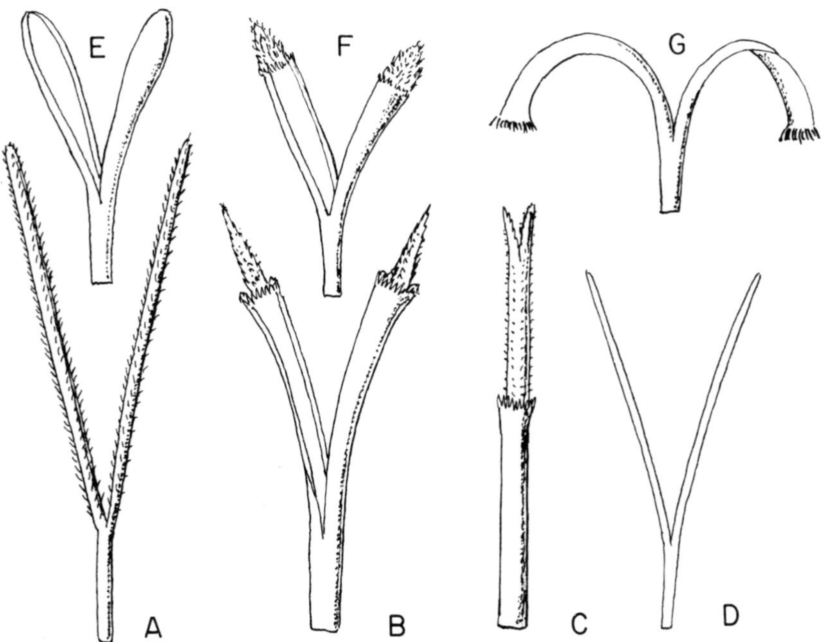

FIG. 503D. Style-arms of various tribes of *Asteraceae* (*Compositae*). **A**, *Vernonieae*. **B**, **G**, *Senecionideae*. **C**, *Cynareae*. **D**, *Cichorieae*. **E**, *Inuleae*. **F**, *Astereae*. (After Bentham J. LINN. SOC. **13**, 8–10 (1873).)

(the involucre), the calyx is reduced or much modified into a "pappus", or entirely suppressed, the corollas are small and often of two kinds, those in the periphery being ligulate and simulating petals, those within (the disk) actinomorphic and 5-merous, the anthers are coherent (syngenecious) and epipetalous, and the gynoecium, as indicated by the bifid or bilobed style, is composed of two united carpels, with a single erect ovule, the fruit (achene) containing a single seed with a large embryo and without endosperm. The bracteole usually subtending each flower in an ordinary spicate inflorescence is usually here in the composite head reduced or completely suppressed. And sometimes the ovule becomes aborted in either the ray or disk flowers (often called "florets" but they are perfect flowers), or in both, and in rare cases this results in the heads becoming unisexual (*Ambrosia*) and even dioecious (*Baccharis*, etc.).

Bentham, whose essay on the family quoted above should be read by every student, was of the opinion that in the diversity of the involucre and other parts of the flower-head we find some clues to the comparative antiquity of the different groups (tribes and subtribes) of *Compositae*. Thus an inflorescence and arrangement of flowers and bracts most nearly approaching an ordinary spike is to be found in tribe *Heliantheae*, which contains the

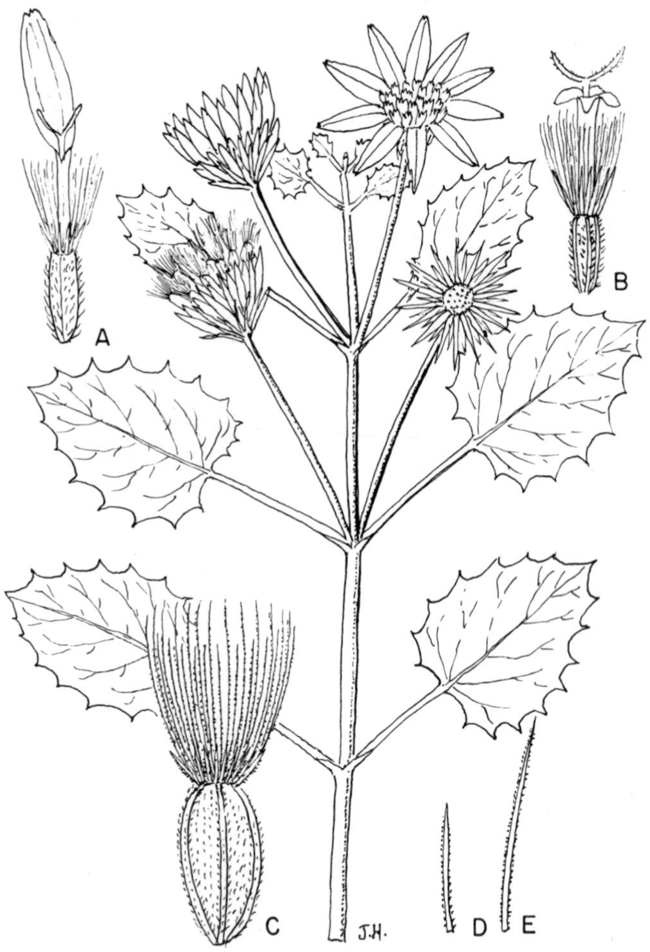

Fig. 504. *Engleria africana* O. Hoffm. (*Asteraceae*), Angola and S.W. Africa. The celebrated German botanist, Adolf Engler, deserved a more outstanding genus to be named after him than this by O. Hoffman, who classified the family *Asteraceae* (*Compositae*) in Engler and Prantl's DIE NATÜRLICHEN PFLANZENFAMILIEN. It is included here, not on account of its morphology, but as a mark of respect for this great botanist and botanical organiser. The genus is monotypic and belongs to Tribe *Astereae* and is closely related to *Pteronia* and *Fresenia*, both from South Africa. **A**, ray flower. **B**, disk flower. **C**, achene of disk flower. **D**, outer, **E**, inner pappus-bristles (orig.).

FIG. 505. Not every botanical artist can restore a dried herbarium specimen to such a life-like representation as here attained by Miss S. Ross Craig, equal to the high standard set by that famous draughtsman Walter Fitch in Hookerian days. This is *Helichrysum cameroonense* Hutch. & Dalz. (*Asteraceae*), which grows on the Cameroons Mountain, west Africa. **A**, bract of involucre. **B**, flower (floret). **C**, pappus-bristle.

FIG. 506. *Vernonia littoralis* Brandegee (*Asteraceae*), an endemic species which climbs over trees of the lower forest (about 2000 ft) on Socorro Island, in the Revillagigedo Archipelago, off the west coast of Mexico (orig.).

well-known cultivated *Rudbeckia*, the Sunflower, *Helianthus*,[1] and the Jerusalem Artichoke. The great consolidation and uniform structure of the floral organs are least evident in this group.

Aster Linn. is the type genus of the family, the type species being *Aster amellus* Linn. (Fig. 503A), southern Europe. Perennial herbs, rarely somewhat woody towards the base, very rarely annuals; leaves alternate; flower-heads usually very showy, solitary to paniculate or corymbose; ray-flowers usually present, blue, violet or white and mostly fertile, disk flowers yellow or very rarely purple, also mostly fertile; involucre campanulate or hemispherical, the bracts in several series and imbricate, the outer ones gradually smaller, rarely these herbaceous and subequal to the inner ones; receptacle flat or convex, mostly pitted (foveolate); ray-flowers ligulate, spreading or

[1] Linnaeus in his CRITICA BOTANICA (English translation) says of *Helianthus*, or "Flower of the Sun": "Who can see this plant in flower, whose great golden blossoms send out rays in every direction from the circular disk, without admiring the handsome flower modelled on the Sun's shape? And as one admires, presently the name occurs to the mind, even as, if one sees only the name, the admired picture of the flower comes before one."

FIG. 507. A remarkable genus of *Asteraceae* found only in the Hawaiian Islands, with the leaves in whorls and united at the base; there are two species, that shown being *Wilkesia gymnoxiphium* A. Gray (drawn by Miss M. Grierson), which grows on dry leeward slopes of the tabular summit above Waimea, at 3000–5000 ft; stem 8–14 ft, including the inflorescence of 2–3 ft; the genus was named after Captain Wilkes, the commander of the United States Exploring Expedition of 1838–42.

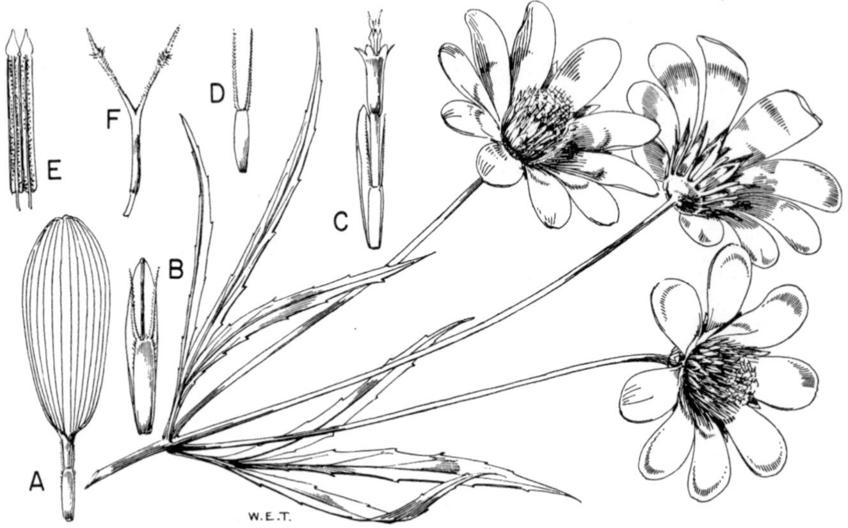

FIG. 508. A fine drawing of *Coreopsis guineensis* Oliv. & Hiern (*Asteraceae*) by the late W. E. Trevithick, who did most of the illustrations for our FLORA OF WEST TROPICAL AFRICA. **A**, ray flower. **B**, achene and scale of receptacle. **C**, disk-flower and scale. **D**, achene. **E**, stamens. **F**, style-arms.

recurved; disk-flowers actinomorphic, tubular, 5-fid; anther-base obtuse, entire; style-branches of the disk-flowers flattened, appendaged at the tip, the appendage lanceolate, papillous or hairy (see Fig. 503); achenes compressed, with mostly nerved margins, surfaces smooth or 1–2-(rarely 3–4-) ribbed; pappus-bristles slender, scabrid, copious, irregularly 2–3-seriate, usually more or less equal, rarely the outer shorter. The style-branches and anther-bases typical of tribe *Astereae* are shown in Fig. 503D.

This then is the genus with which all other genera may be compared, and they are a vast number, over 900. The name *Aster* is from the Greek name for a star, which the flower head is supposed to resemble.

Here are most of the so-called *formae abnormes* enumerated by Bentham (GEN. PL. **2**, 165): Capitula 1–few-flowered and crowded into head-like clusters in subtribe *Lychnophorineae* of tribe *Vernonieae*, in some subtribes of *Inuleae*, in subtribe *Lagascinae* of *Heliantheae*, in the genus *Syncephalanthus* in tribe *Helenieae*, in the genus *Oedera* in subtribe *Anthemidineae*, in subtribe *Gundeliineae* of *Arctotideae*, and in subtribe *Echinopsidineae* of tribe *Cynareae*. Fimbrillae of the receptacle much enlarged and united into a mass entirely enclosing the achenes in pits in *Albertinia*, *Balduina*, and certain African genera of *Arctotideae*, such as *Cullumia*, *Berkheya*, *Stephanocoma* and *Didelta*. Female flowers without a corolla in subtribe *Ambrosineae*, species of *Cotula* and in *Thespis*. Anthers scarcely coherent or free in subtribe *Ambrosineae*,

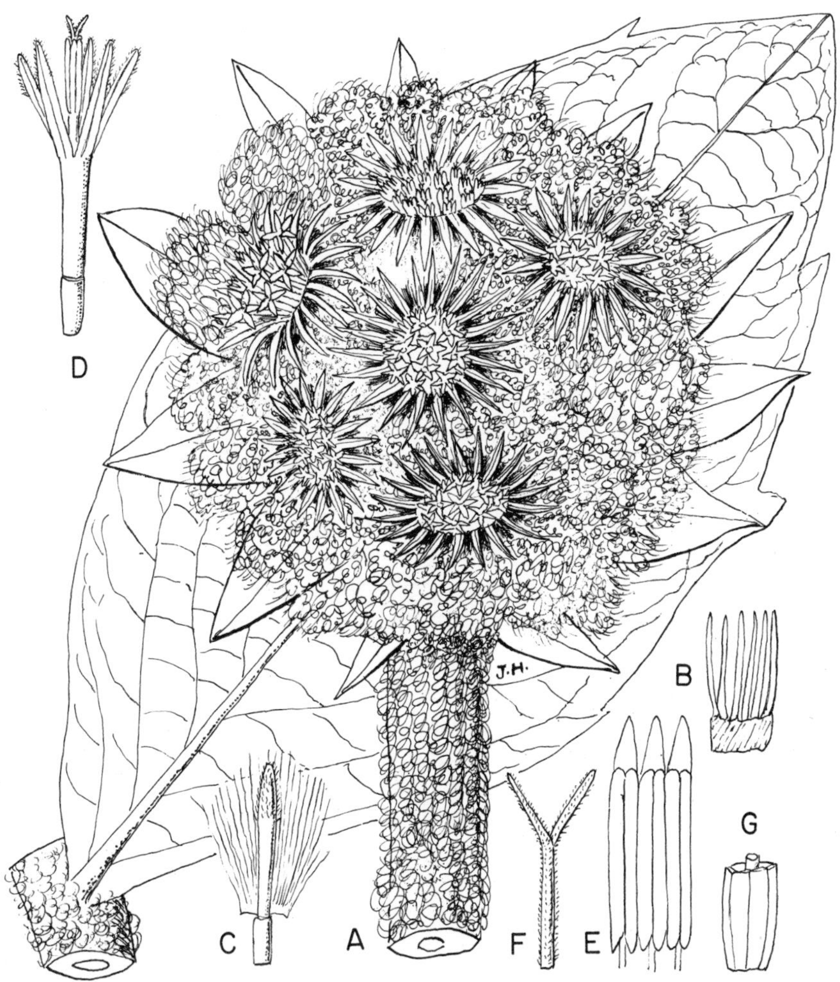

FIG. 509. In the genus *Sipolisia* (*S. lanuginosa* Glaziou ex Oliv.) (*Asteraceae*), Brazil, the flower-heads are almost buried in dense wool and crowded into a ball. **A**, tribe *Vernonieae*. **B**, processes on the receptacle. **C**, flower in bud with pappus opened out. **D**, flower without pappus. **E**, anthers. **F**, style. **G**, achene (orig.).

and in *Eleutheranthera*; present but destitute of pollen and altogether free in female flowers of *Petrobium*, *Podanthus*, *Balbisia*, and here and there in genera with dioecious or subdioecious flowers.

On quite broad lines the evolutionary history of the family may be followed by a study of the tribes and principal genera. These fall into the usual two main subfamilies, the one much more primitive than the other. The

FIG. 510. *Elvira biflora* DC. (*Asteraceae-Heliantheae*), tropical America. **A**, flower head, with 2 males and one female flower, subtended by 3 leafy bracts. **B**, one of the larger bracts. **C**, achene.

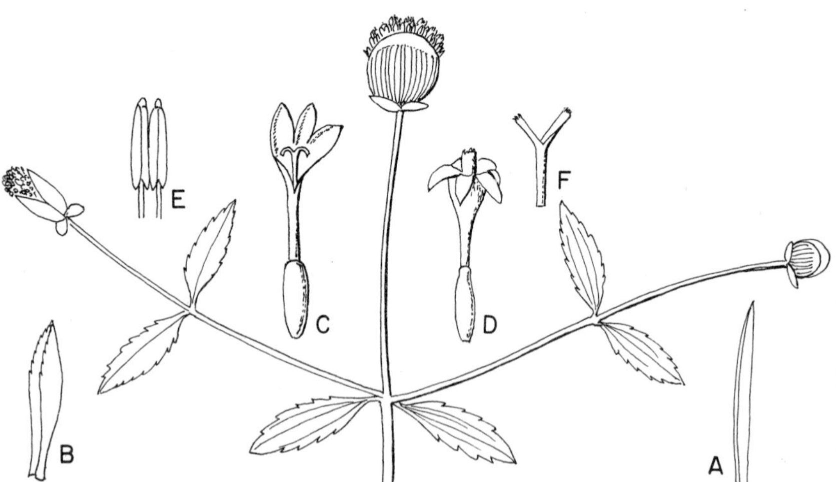

FIG. 511. In *Staurochlamys burchellii* Baker (*Asteraceae–Heliantheae*), Brazil, the inner bracts are united into two plate-like structures compressed face to face like a lady's purse. **A**, inner involucral bract. **B**, scale of receptacle. **C**, ray flower. **D**, disk-flower. **E**, anthers. **F**, style-arms (orig.).

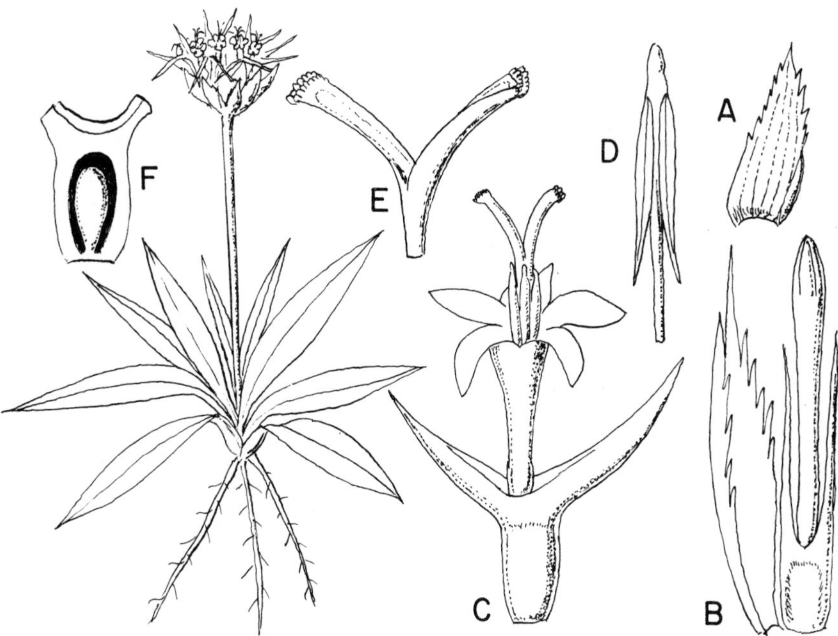

FIG. 512. *Nablonium calyceroides* Cass., Tasmania (*Asteraceae*), a diminutive species. **A**, involucral bract. **B**, inner bract and flower-bud. **C**, flower, note the horn-like pappus. **D**, anther. **E**, style-arms. **F**, vertical section of ovary (orig.).

first, *Helianthoideae*, are plants devoid of milky juice, in which the heads are heterogamous, i.e. with both ray zygomorphic (ligulate) and actinomorphic disk flowers, or the ray flowers absent; and the second, *Cichorioideae*, in which the heads are homogamous, with all the flowers zygomorphic, and in the latter group milk-like juice is often present. The second subfamily is obviously the more highly advanced, and evolved in line with more advanced families with sympetalous zygomorphic corollas, such as *Lobeliaceae*.

The most primitive tribe of the first subfamily is clearly *Verbesineae*; in many genera of this the inflorescence approximates most closely to an ordinary spike. The axis is elongated, there is an ordinary bract subtending each flower, and the "pappus" is often more calyx-like than in most other tribes. A typical example is the genus *Rudbeckia*. Most of the flowers in this tribe are yellow, a primitive colour (cf. *Ranunculus*), being little removed from green. On the other hand they are most pronounced in the *Cichorieae*, which, other things being equal, are probably the most modern group, and they have often a milk-like juice, a character also found in advanced climax families such as *Campanulaceae*, *Apocynaceae*, *Asclepiadaceae* and *Euphorbiaceae*.

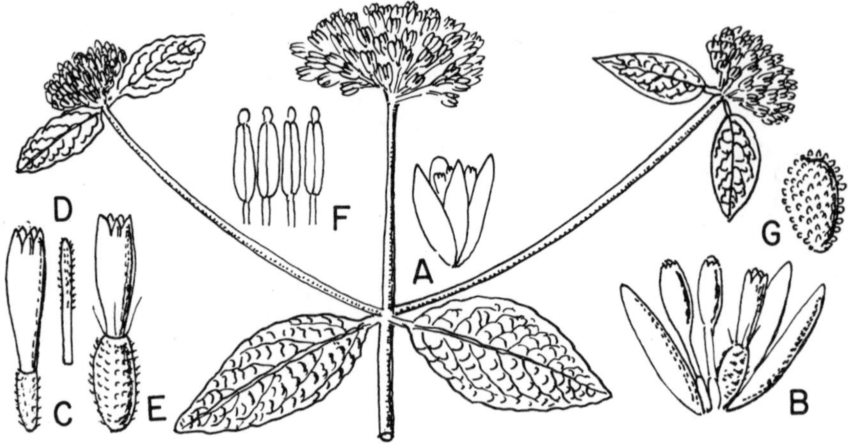

FIG. 513. The aptly named *Lantanopsis hoffmannii* Urb., West Indies, though resembling a *Lantana* (*Verbenaceae*), is nevertheless a "Composite" (*Asteraceae*). **A**, single flower-head. **B**, the same in more detail. **C**, male flower. **D**, style. **E**, female flower. **F**, stamens. **G**, achene (orig.).

In *Heliantheae* the involucral bracts are often quite foliaceous and in several series spirally arranged, the organ subtending each flower is frequently like an ordinary bracteole, sometimes even quite leafy, and the pappus, when present, is just like a small calyx, indicating that this tribe is more primitive than the Senecios, the Asters, and the Vernonias.

Tribal characters in *Asteraceae* (*Compositae*) are mainly confined to the shape of the style-arms of the bisexual flowers of the disk, and the nature of the anther-bases, combined with other minor features. The truncate style-arms and the yellow flower-colour of the *Heliantheae* are repeated in the nearly related tribe *Senecionideae*, though there is a great advancement in the arrangement of the involucral bracts, which are mostly reduced to a single whorl, sometimes partly united into a tube, and in quite a large number the ray-flowers have been dispensed with. A remarkable growth form in this tribe is found in the tree Senecios of the east African mountains, which are considered to be giant herbs and to be highly evolved climax members of the genus, the species being very closely related to more herbaceous forms found in the same region.

I shall not attempt to steer my readers through the whole of the tribes and subtribes of the family *Asteraceae* (*Compositae*) even were I able to do so at present, though the family has off and on been "an old love" of mine for nearly 60 years or more. I shall have to content myself with a consideration of the main groups, dipping into them only here and there.

First of all it is necessary to state quite irrevocably that I do not regard *Senecio* as the most primitive genus or ancestral type, as postulated by the

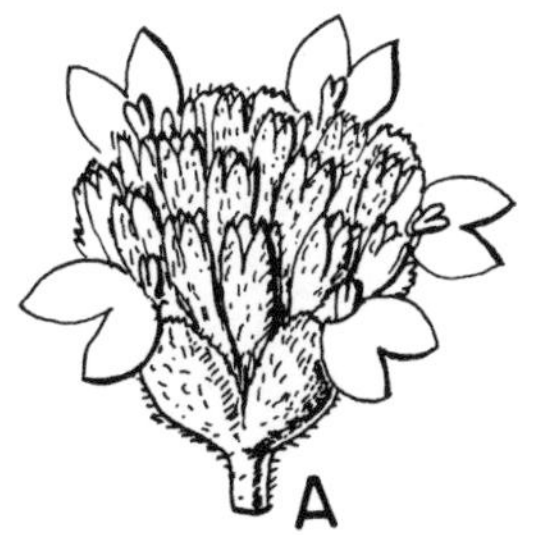

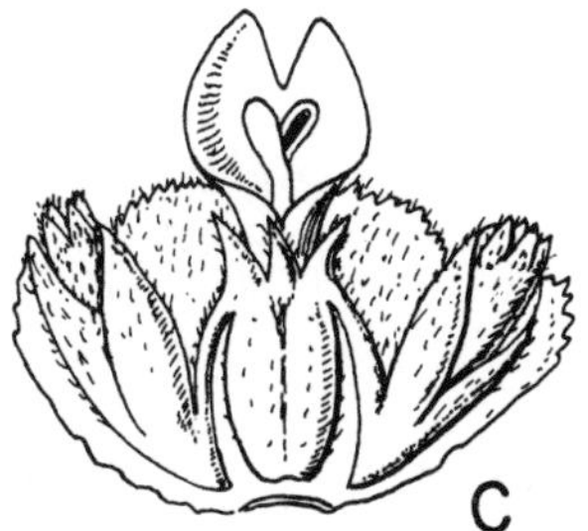

FIG. 514. The picture of the young lady who "could be happy with either (a sailor or soldier) were t'other fair charmer away" is again brought to mind (see Fig. 484) by this remarkable arrangement in the flower-head, **A**, of *Parthenium argentatum* A. Gray (*Asteraceae*), Mexico. The middle flower in **C** is female and fertile and has attached to it on each side a male flower, and they fall away together when ripe from the head and are blown about by the wind. **B** shows a young male flower with subtending bract.

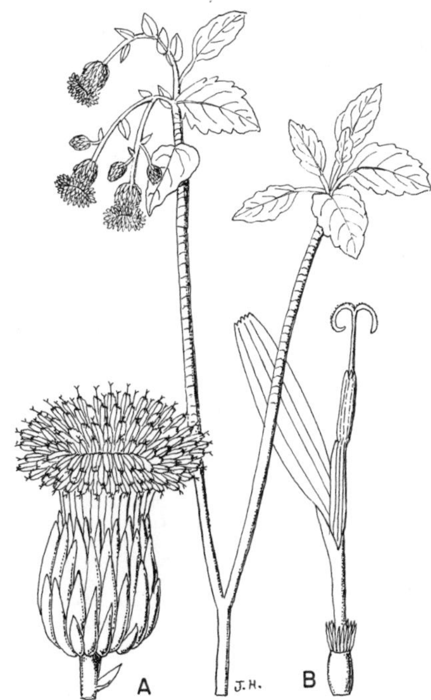

FIG. 515. *Dendroseris macrophylla* Don (*Asteraceae*), endemic in the Island of Juan Fernandez. **A**, single flower-head. **B**, single flower.

late Dr. James Small[1] of Belfast. In my opinion we should expect to find, in the most primitive existing group of *Asteraceae*, an inflorescence with bracts subtending the flowers, from which the orthodox capitulum may have been derived, together with the nearest approach possible to an ordinary calyx. We find none of these characters in *Senecio*, or indeed in the whole tribe of which *Senecio* is the largest and the most widespread member.

But these characters are to be found in the family, and they are not difficult to detect even without the aid of a microscope. The tribe *Heliantheae* possesses these characters, and in my opinion this group represents the most ancient of the *Asteraceae*. In *Rudbeckia*, for example, the axis of the inflorescence is elongated and there is a bract below each flower

[1] The Origin and Development of the *Compositae* (NEW PHYTOLOGIST 1917–19).

Fig. 516. *Sonchus angustissimus* Hook. f. (*Asteraceae*); another fine drawing by Miss S. Ross Craig from the FLORA OF WEST TROPICAL AFRICA. **A**, bract of involucre. **B**, flower (floret). **C**, style. **D**, scheme. **E**, pappus-bristle.

as in many ordinary spicate inflorescences. Though the calyx ("pappus") in this genus has been reduced to a ring or crown it is not of the ordinary pappus-type of bristles. And bristles occur but rarely in tribe *Heliantheae*.

In considering the evolution of *Asteraceae* the colour of the flowers may be of considerable significance, as it is mostly associated with important differences in the style-arms and anther-bases. Yellow is the basic colour of the *Heliantheae*, being little removed from green. Petals were first of all green or partly so and derived from green leaves in the most primitive flowering plants. In the more advanced tribes *Vernonieae* and *Eupatorieae* the colour is never yellow or very rarely slightly so. (It should be remembered that these notes are couched in broad terms with no reference to exceptions.)

Associated with the conical type of receptacle, the bract subtending each flower, and the primitive kind of calyx, there is in the *Heliantheae* a well marked type of style-arm, and here there is agreement with *Senecio* and with nearly the whole tribe *Senecionideae*. The style-arms of *Heliantheae* are nearly always truncate and penicillate at the apex, and of the kind known as the "*Senecio*-type". In addition the bracts of the involucre are in several series and little modified from ordinary green foliage leaves.

Tribe *Senecionideae* is considerably advanced in an evolutionary sense from tribe *Heliantheae*. The receptacle is much reduced and disk-like, there are no bracts subtending the individual flowers, and the involucral bracts are reduced to a single series and have become calyx-like, frequently with a considerable amount of cohesion. In addition *Senecio* is the largest and most widespread genus of *Asteraceae* and is therefore an advanced and highly successful type well adapted to hold its own (ask a gardener and he would probably point to Groundsel (*Senecio vulgaris* Linn.!)).

Order 77. **SOLANALES**

(*Fam. Fl. Pl.* **1**, 484)

Families: **Solanaceae, Retziaceae, Convolvulaceae, Nolanaceae.**

After making a careful survey of the genera of **Solanaceae**,[1] I came to the conclusion that it, too, is fundamentally herbaceous and derived from herbaceous ancestors. Of the 66 genera in Bentham and Hooker's GENERA

---

[1] Including *Cestraceae* Schlechtendal (1833). *Sclerophylaceae* Miers (1848). *Atropaceae* Miers (1849). *Narcaceae* Dulac (1867). *Goetzeaceae* Miers ex Airy Shaw (1965).

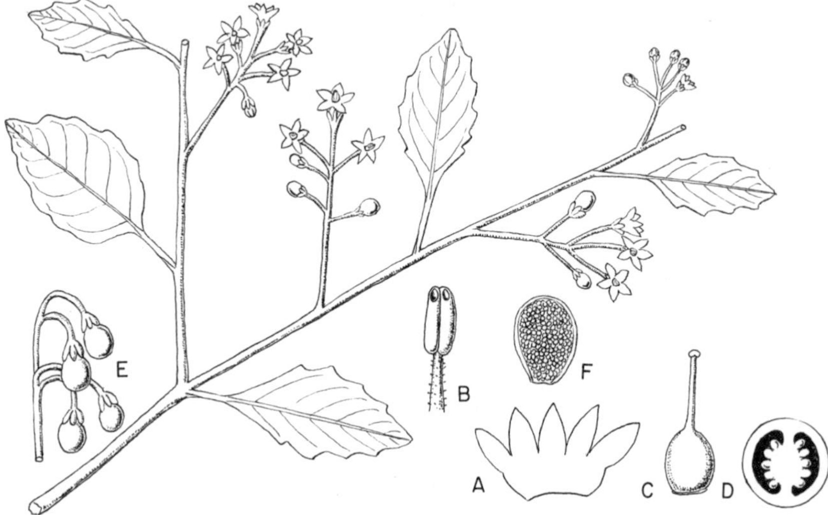

FIG. 517. *Solanum nigrum* Linn., a weed of cultivation and in waste places, the type species of the type genus of *Solanaceae*. Note the extra-axillary inflorescence. **A**, corolla opened out. **B**, stamen. **C**, gynoecium. **D**, cross-section of ovary. **E**, fruits. **F**, seed.

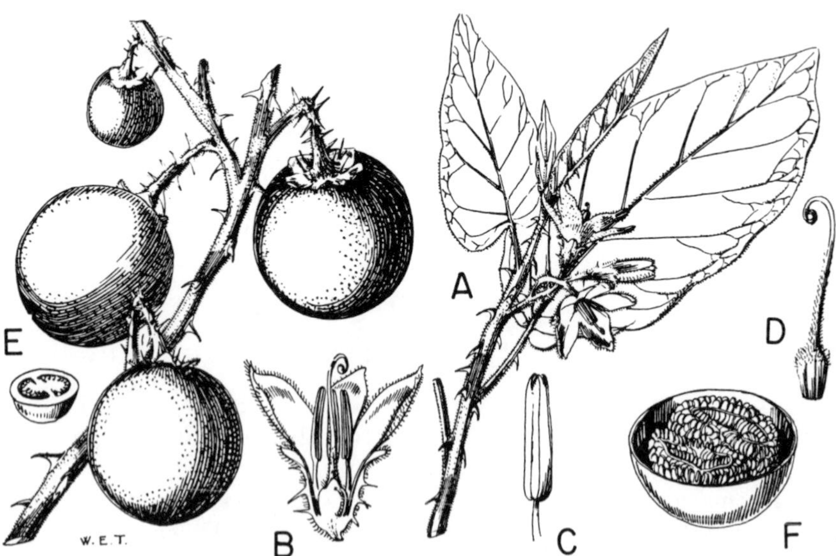

FIG. 518. *Solanum incanum* Linn. (*Solanaceae*), tropical Africa. **A**, flowers and leaves. **B**, vertical section of flower. **C**, anther showing apical pores. **D**, gynoecium. **E**, cross-section of ovary. **F**, cross-section of fruit. (From Hutchinson and Dalziel, FLORA OF WEST TROPICAL AFRICA.)

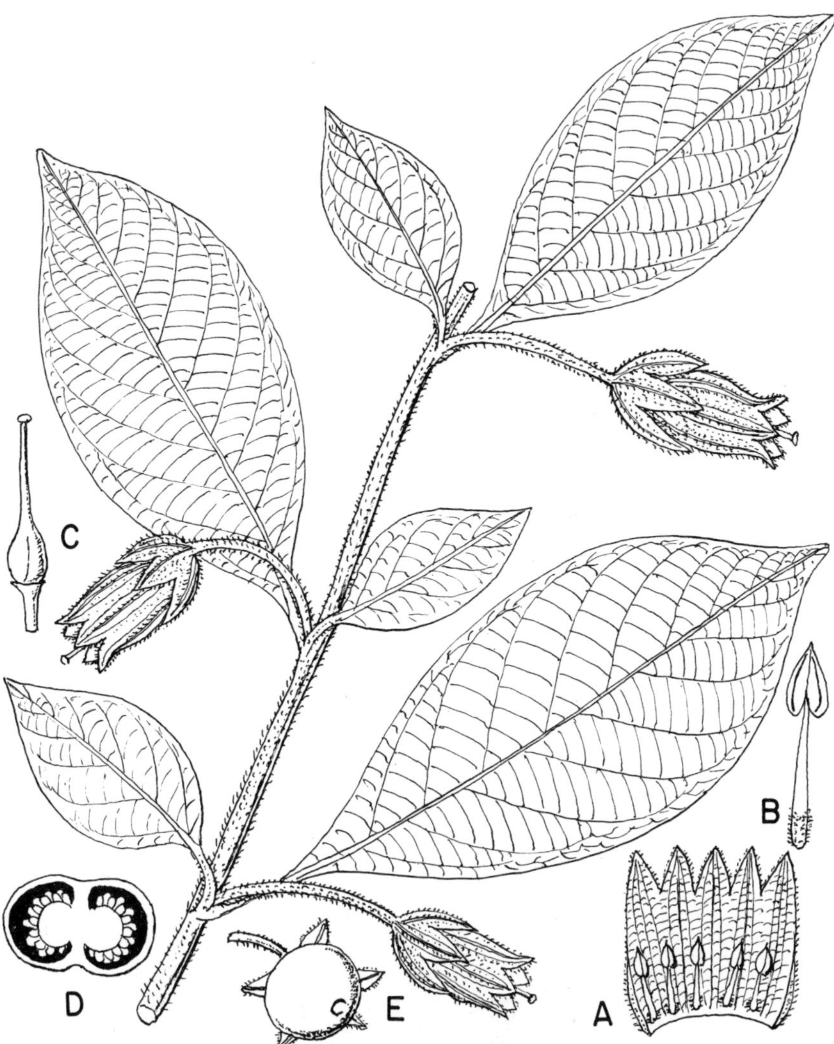

FIG. 519. *Atropa belladonna* Linn., Belladonna or Deadly Nightshade (*Solanaceae*), an old and important drug plant (see text). **A**, corolla opened out. **B**, stamen. **C**, gynoecium. **D**, cross-section of ovary. **E**, fruit (orig.).

PLANTARUM, about 34 are herbs, 4 are herbs or shrubs, about 18 are shrubs (sometimes climbers), and the remainder small soft-wooded trees. More than half of the species of the whole family, however, belong to the genus *Solanum* (Figs. 517, 518), with great diversity in habit, from small annual herbs to fairly big trees. A constant anatomical feature is the intraxylary phloem in the stem, a feature which occurs also in *Gentianaceae*. Another

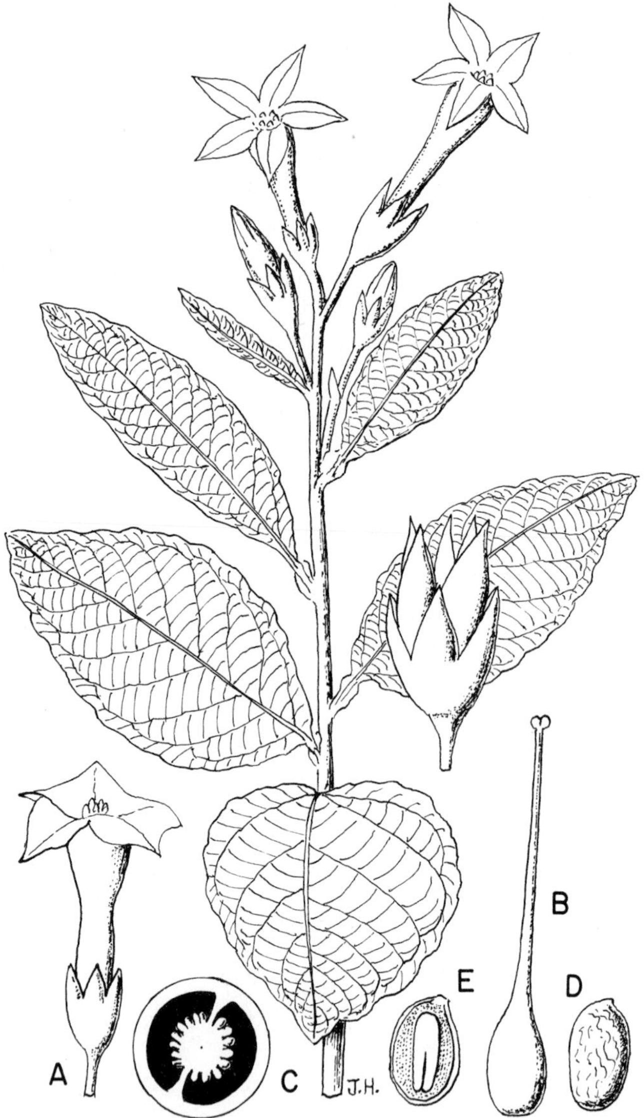

FIG. 520. The Tobacco plant, *Nicotiana tabacum* Linn. (*Solanaceae*). **A**, flower. **B**, gynoecium. **C**, cross-section of ovary. **D**, seed. **E**, vertical section of seed (orig.). The lower leaves are very much larger.

character much emphasised in some text books is the usually oblique position of the carpels in relation to the floral axis, though this may not be of much phyletic importance. It is common, however, in *Saxifragaceae*, the basic group from which *Solanaceae* is shown in the phylogenetic diagram to have been probably derived. In *Scrophulariaceae* the carpels are not oblique to the axis. Stellate hairs are quite general in the family *Solanaceae*, especially in the genus *Solanum*. According to Solereder the stomata are not accompanied by any special subsidiary cells. If we pin our faith to the more ancient type of aestivation (contorted) of the corolla-lobes, then Bentham and Hooker's tribe *Atropeae* seems to be basic. The stamens are all perfect, and in *Atropa* itself (Fig. 519) they are inserted at the base of the corolla. And the most advanced tribe which closely approaches *Scrophulariaceae* is undoubtedly *Salpiglossideae*, with frequently quite a zygomorphic corolla (for example *Schizanthus*), and there are only four or two perfect stamens (now treated by me as a separate family, *Salpiglossidaceae*; see p. 631; Fig. 536). The main centre of distribution for the family *Solanaceae* is Central and South America, though *Solanum* occurs over most parts of the world.

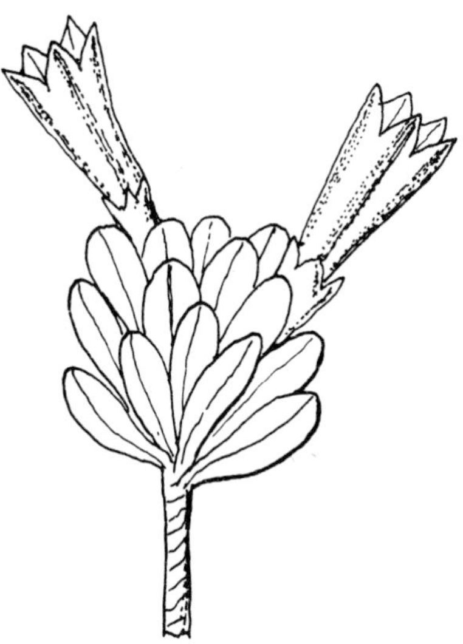

FIG. 521. A diminutive solanaceous plant, *Combera minima* Sandwith, a native of Chile.

Solanaceae are of great economic importance, in the first rank being the Potato (*Solanum tuberosum* Linn.), the Tomato (*Lycopersicum esculentum* Mill.), Tobacco (*Nicotiana tabacum* Linn.), and important medicinal plants are Deadly Nightshade (*Atropa belladonna* Linn.), Henbane (*Hyoscyamus niger* Linn.) and *Datura* spp. Others are of great ornamental value.

Belladonna or Deadly Nightshade, *Atropa belladonna* Linn. (Fig. 519), is an old and important drug obtained from the dried leaves and tops and to some extent the roots. It is a native of central and southern Europe and Asia Minor, and is extensively cultivated as a drug plant in the United States of America, in Europe and India. The leaves are collected during the flowering season and dried. In Britain the plant is usually found in waste places especially among ruins and by roadsides. The drug is used externally to relieve pain and internally to check excessive perspiration, coughs, etc., and to dilate the pupil of the eye.

Henbane, *Hyoscyamus niger* Linn., is a coarse evil-smelling herb native of Europe and Asia, and often found as a weed in other parts of the world. The leaves and flowering tops contain several poisonous alkaloids, among them hyoscyamine and scopolamine. The drug is used as a sedative and hypnotic.

A full account of the taxonomic history of the genus *Retzia* (Fig. 524) was

FIG. 522. A delightful effect of light and shade in this drawing by Miss S. Ross Craig, at the same time showing all its botanical features which should render easy the identification of this west African Solanaceous plant, *Discopodium penninervium* Hochst. **A**, flower. **B**, vertical section of flower. **C**, transverse section of ovary.

given by Marloth[1] and by R. A. Dyer,[2] and shows the divergent views of botanists since it was first described. From a position in the *Convolvulaceae* it was raised to family rank and later placed in or near the families *Apocynaceae*, *Solanaceae* (Bentham and Hooker's GENERA PLANTARUM) and *Scrophulariaceae*. Marloth followed Bartling[3] and treated it as a separate family, **Retziaceae**, and the present author has followed suit in his new edition of the KEY TO FAMILIES.[4]

The genus was named by Thunberg in honour of Andr. Joh. Retzius, Professor of Natural History at Lund, and author of a FLORA OF SCANDINAVIA (1742–1821). In turn Retzius named the genus *Thunbergia* (*Acanthaceae*) after Thunberg.

Retziaceae Bartling (partly). Upright shrub with very crowded verticillate leaves; no stipules; leaves about 6 in a whorl, sessile, linear, entire, the margins

---

[1] Marloth FL. SOUTH AFRICA **3**, 1, 122, t. 32 (1932).

[2] R. A. Dyer *in* FLOWERING PLANTS OF SOUTH AFRICA **24**, t. 942 (1944). The plant was also figured by Schnizlein, ICONOGR. **2**, t. 148 (1840).

[3] Bartling Ord. 192, in obs. partly excl. *Lonchostoma* Wikstr.

[4] Hutchinson KEY TO FAMILIES OF FLOWERING PLANTS OF THE WORLD (1968).

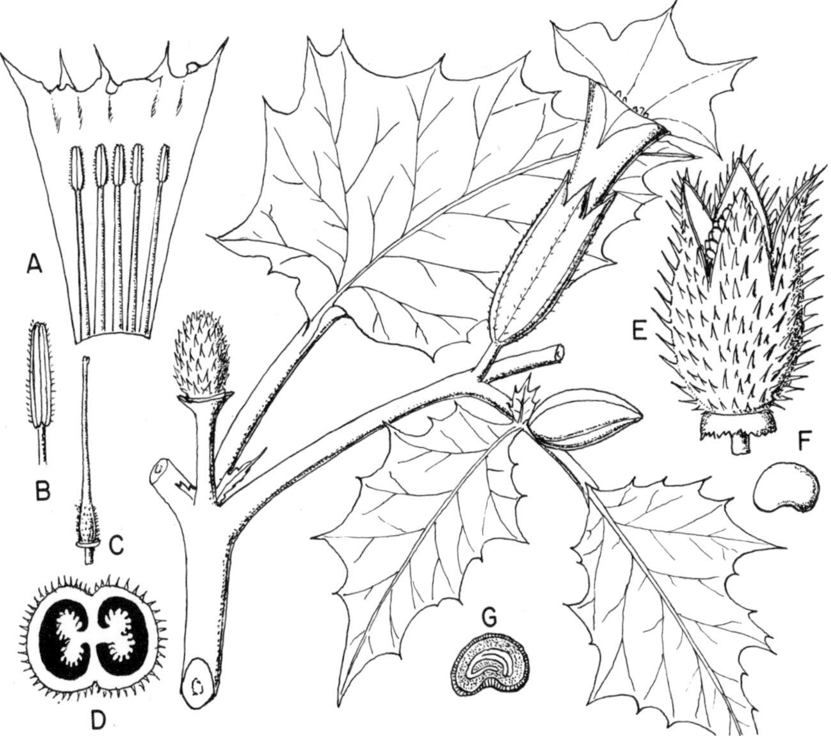

Fig. 523. *Datura stramonium* Linn. (*Solanaceae*). **A**, corolla laid open and stamens. **B**, anther. **C**, gynoecium. **D**, cross-section of ovary. **E**, fruit. **F**, seed. **G**, longitudinal section of seed (orig.).

very strongly recurved, villous below when young, orange coloured in the upper part when young; flowers bisexual, densely clustered on very short shoots, sessile, erect and partly hidden among the leaves; calyx tubular, lobes 5, unequal, linear, valvate; corolla actinomorphic, sympetalous, narrowly tubular and straight, usually 5- (6- or 7-) lobed, lobes induplicate-valvate in bud, villous; stamens mostly 5, alternate with the corolla-lobes, inserted at the mouth of the tube with very short filaments; anthers 2-locular, introrse, sagittate, opening by slits lengthwise; disk annular, thin, small; ovary 2-locular in the lower part, the placenta extending from the base half the length of the chamber, the latter incompletely septate in the upper part; stigma terminal, very small, not lobed; ovules 2 in each loculus, one ascending, the other descending from the axile placenta; capsule (*fide* Marloth) oblong, acuminate, septicidally 2-valved from the apex, the valves bifid, each part bearing one seed; embryo straight in ample endosperm.

One genus and species, *Retzia capensis* Thunb.; south-west Cape Province of South Africa (Mts from Sir Lowrey's Pass to Bredasdorp Division).

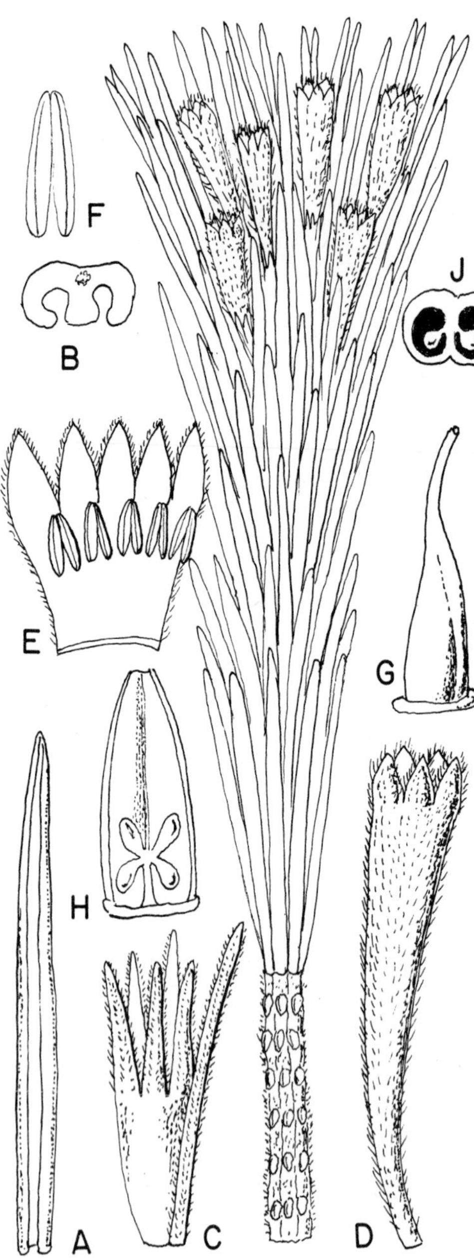

FIG. 524. *Retzia capensis* Thunb. (*Retziaceae*), South Africa. **A**, leaf showing the recurved margins. **B**, section of leaf. **C**, calyx and bract. **D**, corolla. **E**, upper part of corolla opened out. **F**, anther. **G**, gynoecium. **H**, vertical section of ovary. **J**, cross-section of ovary (orig.).

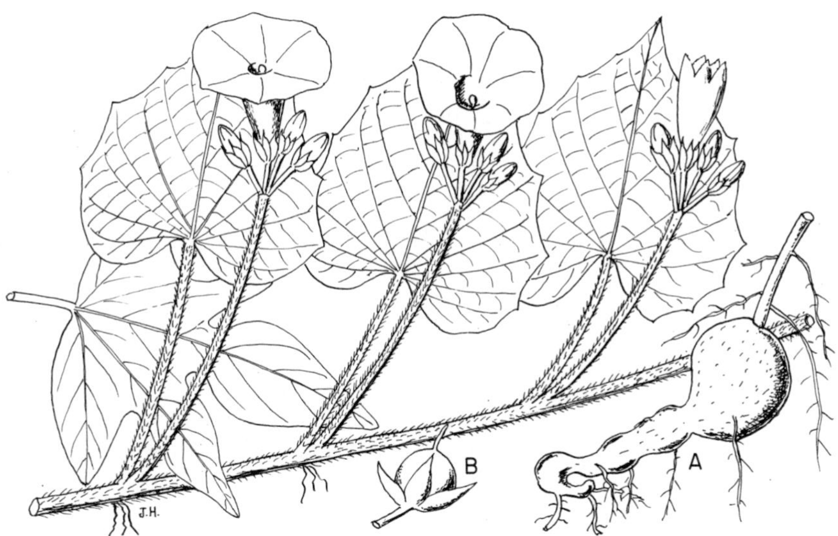

FIG. 525. *Ipomoea batatas* Linn. (*Convolvulaceae*), the species from which the Sweet Potato has been derived; an important food in the tropics. **A**, rootstock (potato). **B**, calyx and ovary.

Though the corolla of **Convolvulaceae**[1] has remained actinomorphic (regular), and is thereby not so far advanced as that of *Salpiglossidaceae*, the gynoecium is further evolved than in that family. That is why I placed it in my first arrangement higher than *Solanaceae*. The aestivation of the corolla is also generally on a higher plane, the lobes being induplicate-valvate, as in *Menyanthaceae*. As a rule the ovary is bicarpellary, and the ovules are reduced to two in each loculus and they are erect from the inner angle.

This is again a family of herbs and twining plants, very rarely shrubby or arboreal. The leaves are alternate and exstipulate. Pollen characters assist in the definition of some of the genera, which in such a natural family are separated by very slender morphological characters. Tribe *Dichondreae* (of Bentham and Hooker) is outstanding in having a deeply lobed ovary with a gynobasic style as in *Boraginaceae* and *Lamiaceae* (*Labiatae*); and **Cuscutaceae**, besides being aphyllous and parasitic, has imbricate corolla-lobes (see p. 654).

Except for its great ornamental value, *Convolvulaceae* have few economic plants of much importance. The best known is the Sweet Potato, *Ipomoea batatas* Linn. (Fig. 525), an important food plant in the tropics; and several are used in medicine; some are troublesome weeds.

---

[1] Including *Erycibaceae* Endlich. (1841). *Dichondraceae* Dumort. (1829). *Poranaceae* J. G. Agardh (1858). *Contortaceae* Dulac (1867). *Humbertiaceae* Pichon (1947).

FIG. 526. *Convolvulus arvensis* Linn., the type species of the type genus of *Convolvulaceae*, widely spread, often as a corn-field weed and on waste-places.

Type genus *Convolvulus* Linn. Erect, prostrate or climbing or twining herbs, shrublets sometimes spiny with mostly more or less silky indumentum; leaves entire, dentate, or lobate; flowers axillary, single or rarely in cymes; bracts mostly narrow or small; sepals mostly subequal; corolla tubular, limb plicate or rarely 5-lobed; stamens inserted near the base of the corolla and shorter than it, equal or unequal, filaments filiform, often dilated at the base; anthers oblong; ovary 2-locular, loculi 2-ovuled; style filiform, stigmas 2, distinct; capsule globose or ovoid, 2-locular, 4-valved or irregularly split; seeds glabrous; cotyledons broad, mostly emarginate, plicate. Type species *C. arvensis* Linn., temperate regions, often as a weed ("Bindweed") (Fig. 526).

Outstanding genera are: Calyx gamosepalous in *Wilsonia* (Australia). Corolla-lobes imbricate in *Cressa* and *Wilsonia*. Filaments of stamens dilated at the base into papillous scales over the ovary in *Lepistemon* (tropical Africa and Asia); loculi of the anthers separated from the broad connective in *Lysiostyles* (tropical South America). Stigma large and subsessile on the ovary in *Erycibe* (Asia and tropical Australia); style-branches 4 in *Evolvulus* Linn. (widely distributed), numerous in *Polymeria* R.Br. (Australia). In *Nephrophyllum* A.Rich. (see Fig. 527) the fruit is 1-seeded and matures below the surface of the soil, and the cotyledons are linear and persistent above ground. Fruits enclosed by the enlarged unequal 2 outer sepals in *Calycolobus africanus* (G. Don) Heine, tropical Africa (Fig. 528).

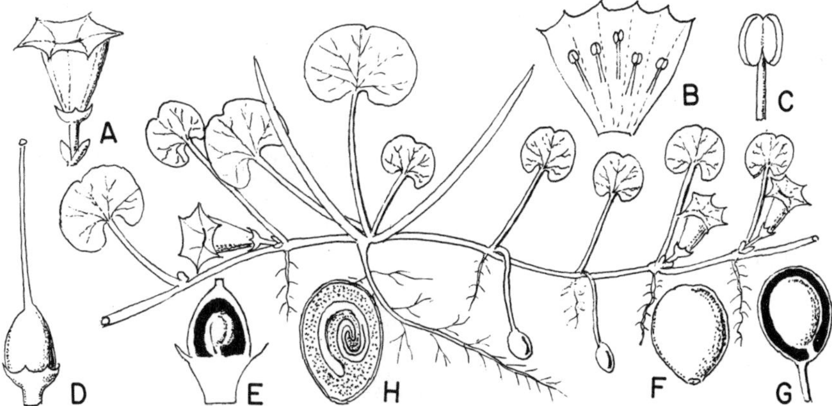

FIG. 527. *Nephrophyllum abyssinicum* A. Rich. (*Convolvulaceae*), Ethiopia. Note especially the 2 linear cotyledons which persist above, and the fruits which mature below the surface of the soil. **A**, flower. **B**, corolla laid open. **C**, anther. **D**, calyx and gynoecium. **E**, vertical section of ovary. **F**, fruit. **G**, vertical section of fruit showing the single seed. **H**, vertical section of seed showing the coiled embryo. (Adapted from A. Rich. FL. ABYSSINIA.)

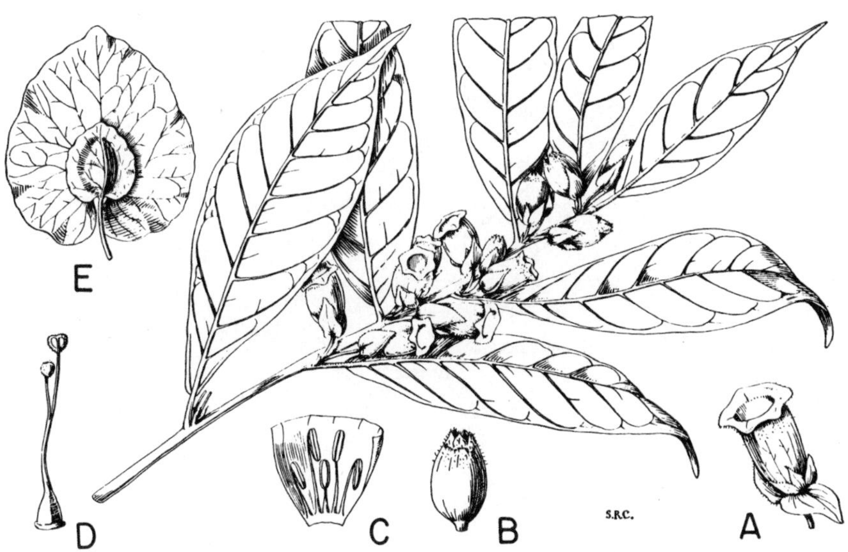

FIG. 528. *Calycolobus africanus* (G. Don) Heine (*Convolvulaceae*). **A**, flower. **B**, corolla in bud. **C**, open lower part of corolla. **D**, gynoecium. **E**, fruit enclosed by the enlarged bracts. (From Hutchinson and Dalziel, FLORA OF WEST TROPICAL AFRICA.)

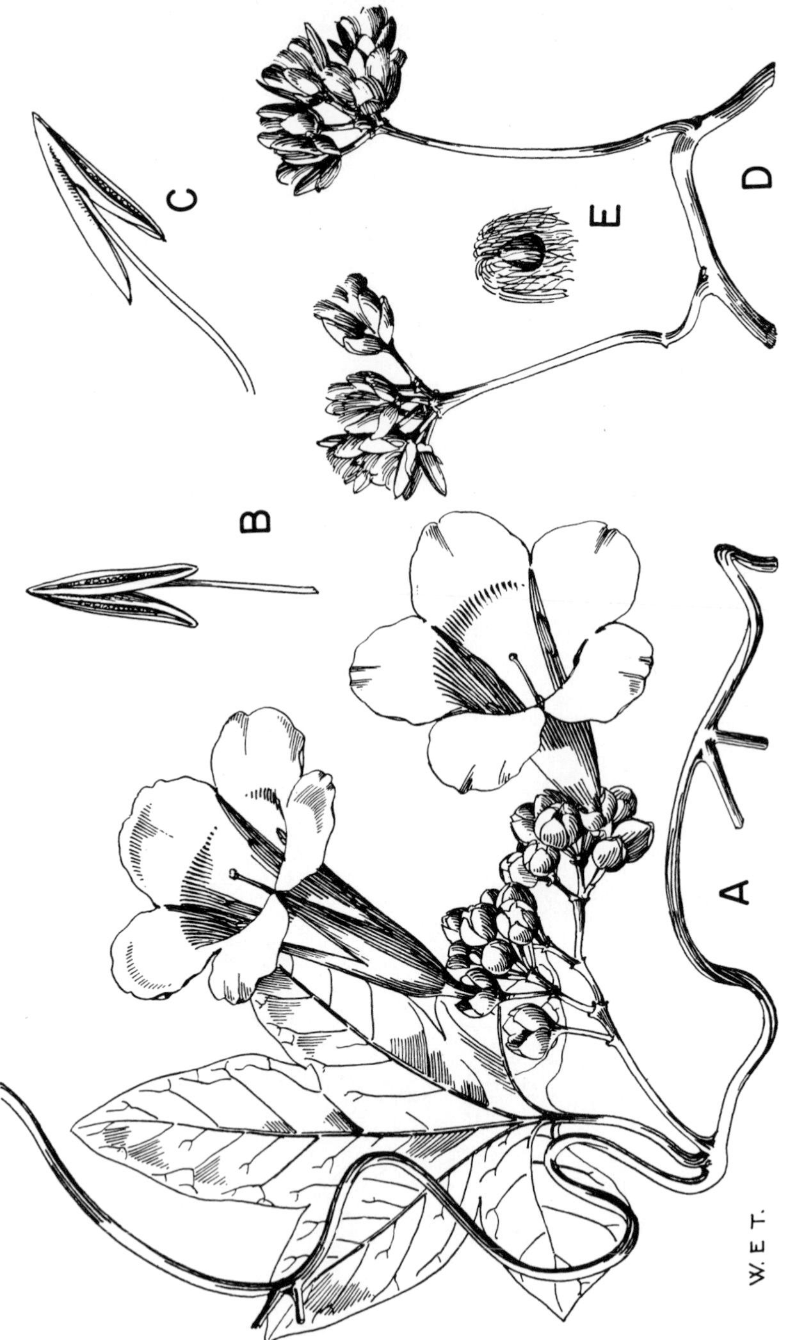

FIG. 529. *Ipomoea mauritiana* Jacq. (*Convolvulaceae*), tropics generally. **A**, flowering shoot. **B** and **C**, stamens. **D**, fruits. **E**, seed. (From Hutchinson and Dalziel, FLORA OF WEST TROPICAL AFRICA.)

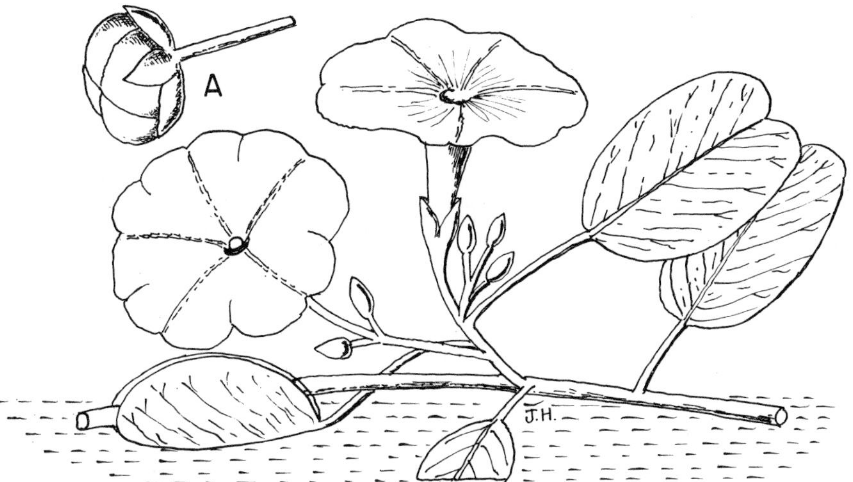

FIG. 530. *Ipomoea pescaprae* (Linn.) Sweet (*Convolvulaceae*), common on most tropical shores. **A**, fruit.

When I published the first edition of my FAMILIES OF FLOWERING PLANTS I did not consider it necessary to suggest any very radical changes in the status of the families of the *Metachlamydeae* (*Gamopetalae*), for in this respect they are much about the same in the Bentham and Hooker and the Engler and Prantl systems. My own intensive studies were therefore concerned almost entirely with the *Archichlamydeae* (*Polypetalae* and *Apetalae*). So with regard to the **Nolanaceae** of Dumortier, I merely followed Bentham and Hooker in treating them as a tribe of *Convolvulaceae*. Since then, however, the late I. M. Johnston made a monographic study of the group, and he considered them to be worthy of family rank, a status maintained for them by Lindley and others, with which I now fully concur.

This comparatively small group, now reduced to two genera (*Alona* and *Nolana*) and about sixty species, is of considerable interest, because it seems to occupy a basic position in this part of the *Metachlamydeae* (*Gamopetalae*) on account of the usually pentamerous gynoecium. I should regard this character as the "persistence of a generally primitive condition" rather than "a reversion to it", these being Johnston's alternatives. The tendency to reduce the number of carpels to two in these higher plants is so general, that once this reduction is carried out in any particular stock it seems likely to remain a fixed character.

Johnston describes the fruit of *Nolanaceae* as "bony, basically pentamerous, schizocarpic or consisting of three to numerous one- to eight-seeded nutlets that are uniseriate or pluriseriate in superimposed series". He follows several previous authors in considering them as more closely connected with *Solanaceae* than *Convolvulaceae*, regarding their relationship as being so close that they might even be treated as a well marked group subordinate to the *Solanaceae*.

Order 78. **PERSONALES**

(*Fam. Fl. Pl.* 1, 487)

Families: **Scrophulariaceae, Salpiglossidaceae, Acanthaceae, Gesneriaceae, Orobanchaceae, Lentibulariaceae, Columelliaceae.**

Suggested Phylogeny: RANALES → SAXIFRAGALES → SOLANALES → PERSONALES → climax families *Orobanchaceae*, *Lentibulariaceae* and *Columelliaceae*.

Scrophulariaceae[1] are closely related to the *Solanaceae* through *Salpiglossidaceae*, which has similarly zygomorphic flowers. As in most of these families one group is clearly more primitive. This was called Series A. *Pseudosolaneae*, in Bentham and Hooker's GENERA PLANTARUM, and subfamily *Pseudosolanoideae* in the PFLANZENFAMILIEN. In this there are generally still retained 5 perfect stamens and the leaves are alternate. Of these the genus *Verbascum* is a well known example. In the remainder of the family the stamens are often reduced to 4 or 2, and the leaves are often opposite.

As stated under *Solanaceae*, some text books draw attention to the orientation of the carpels in relation to the floral axis in this family and in *Scrophulariaceae*. In the latter the carpels are symmetrically arranged with reference to the axis. Too much reliance on such a character, however, might result in an artificial classification.

So far as the arrangement of the tribes is concerned, the two main systems of classification are not ideal from a phylogenetic point of view. Both, however, fortunately begin with the *Pseudosolaneae* and end with the *Rhinanthideae*, many of the latter being hemiparasites, such as *Pedicularis*, and *Euphrasia*, or parasites such as *Harveya* and *Hyobanche*.

---

[1] Including *Pedicularidaceae* A. L. de Juss. (1789). *Personatae* Ventenat (1799). *Rhinanthaceae* Ventenat (1799). *Antirrhinaceae* de Candolle & Duby (1828). *Melampyraceae* Lindley (1829). *Sibthorpiaceae* D. Don (1833). *Aragoaceae* D. Don (1835). *Chelonaceae* D. Don (1835). *Veronicaceae* Horaninow (1847). *Digitalidaceae* J. A. Agardh (1858). *Personaceae* Dulac. (1867). *Verbascaceae* Bonnier (1926). *Ellisiophyllaceae* Honda (1930). *Paulowniaceae* and *Halleriaceae* Nakai (1949).

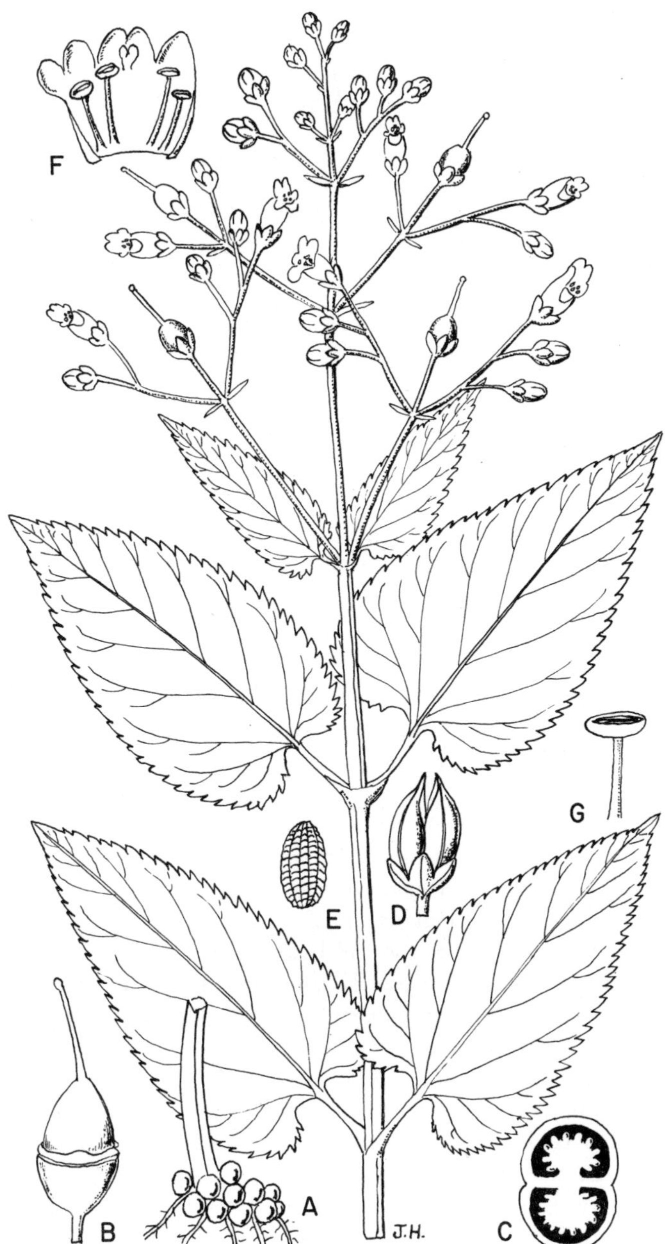

FIG. 531. *Scrophularia nodosa* Linn., the type species of the type genus of *Scrophulariaceae*. **A**, root nodules. **B**, gynoecium. **C**, cross-section of ovary. **D**, capsule. **E**, seed. **F**, flower laid open. **G**, stigma (orig.).

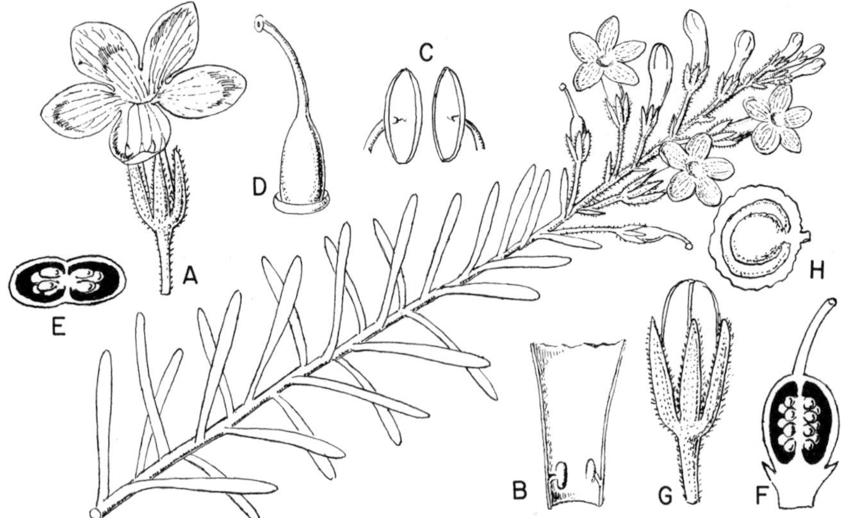

FIG. 532. *Campylanthus salsaloides* Roth (*Scrophulariaceae*). **A**, flower. **B**, part of corolla-tube showing position of the stamens. **C**, stamens. **D**, gynoecium. **E**, cross-section of ovary. **F**, vertical section of ovary. **G**, fruit. **H**, seed (for interesting distribution of the genus see Map 33).

From a habit point of view this group marks, of course, a climax, and is a pointer to the even more completely parasitic family **Orobanchaceae**, which contains no chlorophyll and has only scale-like leaves. The stems in this family are usually simple and in the upper axils of the scale-leaves (bracts) are solitary pedicellate flowers, or rarely the scape bears only 1 flower. As in most *Scrophulariaceae* there are only 4 stamens, the corolla is zygomorphic and 2-lipped. But in contrast with that family the ovary is only 1-locular, with 6–2 parietal placentas. The family is clearly an advanced group derived from the same stock as *Scrophulariaceae*.

The type genus of *Scrophulariaceae* is *Scrophularia* Linn. Herbs or shrublets, often evil-smelling; leaves opposite or the upper alternate, often pellucid-punctate; flowers in terminal lax cymes; small, greenish-purple to yellow; calyx deeply 5-lobed or partite; corolla-tube ventricose, globose or oblong; lobes 5, short, flat, 4 erect, the posterior 2 mostly longer; perfect stamens 4, didynamous, inserted on the tube, declinate, included or exserted; posterior staminode at the apex of the tube scale-like or absent; anther-loculi confluent into one transversely; style slender, stigma minute or rarely capitate; capsule septicidally dehiscent, valves entire or 2-lobed; seeds rugose. Type species *S. nodosa* Linn., Europe.

Here is a list of genera of *Scrophulariaceae* with rather outstanding characters: Leaves verticillate in *Ixianthes*; remarkably dimorphic in *Hemiphragma*,

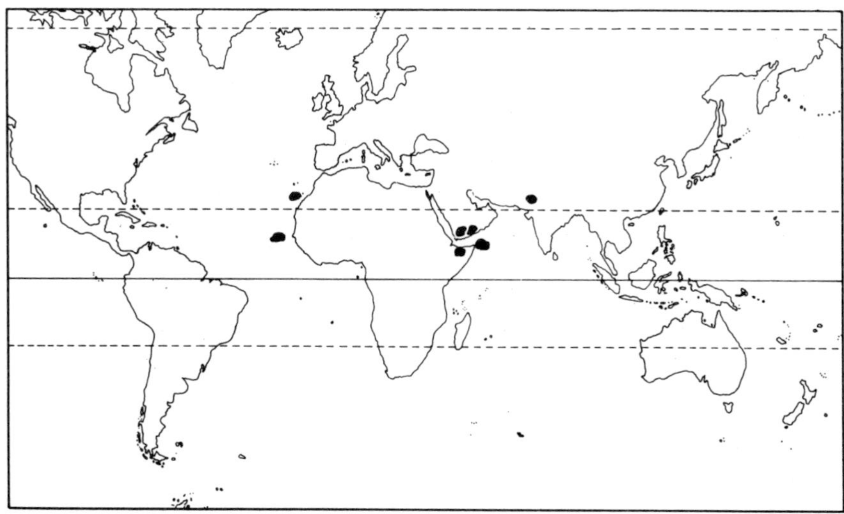

MAP 33. Discontinuous range of the natural genus *Campylanthus* (*Scrophulariaceae*); 5 species: *C. salsaloides* Roth., Canary Islands and Cape Verde Islands. *G. spathulatus* A. Chev., Cape Verde Islands. *C. spinosus* Balf. f., Socotra and Somaliland. *C. junceus* Edgew., Arabia and Somaliland. *C. ramosissimus* Wight, Scind.

the cauline are orbicular, the axillary fasciculate and linear. Flowers dimorphic or all cleistogamous in *Vandellia* spp. Corolla absent from one species of *Synthyris*; lip entire, concave or slipper-shaped in *Calceolaria*. Stamens equal in number to corolla-lobes in *Verbascum*, *Bacopa* and *Scoparia*, and sometimes in *Leucophyllum*, *Capraria* and *Sibthorpia*. Fruit a berry in *Halleria*, *Teedia*, *Leucocarpus*, *Dermatocalyx*. Capsule tardily dehiscent and 1-seeded in *Tozzia*. Seeds without endosperm in *Wightia* and *Monttea*.

Salpiglossidaceae[1] new family. In the BOTANICAL REGISTER Vol. 21, sub t. 1770 (1835), G. Bentham included *Salpiglossideae* as a tribe in the

---

[1] **Salpiglossidaceae** fam. nov. Herbae vel frutices, sapissime plus minus viscosae; folia alterna, exstipulata; inflorescentia normalis cyma simplex (racemus unilateralis) vel ramosa, nunc in capitulum densum contracta, nunc elongata racemiformis, nunc ad pedunculum uni-pauciflorum reducta, terminalis vel oppositifolia vel false axillaris; calyx 5-dentatus vel 5-lobus, aestivatione vix imbricatus; corollae-tubus elongatus vel campanulatus; limbi laciniae 5, planae, induplicato-plicatae vel subplicato-imbricatae, saepius plus minus bilabiatae, 2 posticis exterioribus; stamina fertilia 4, didynama, vel 2, quinti summi rudimentum breve vel nullum, rarissime 5; antherae biloculares, loculis dorso appositis distinctis vel demum apice in unum reniformem coalitis; stylus simplex, apice in stigma pulvinatum integrum emarginatum vel breviter et crasse bilobum dilatatus; capsula bivalvis, valvulis integris vel demum bilobis, membranaceis coriaceis vel subcarnosis; semina ovoidea, oblonga, reticulato- vel tuberculato-rugosa; embryo rectus vel saepius leviter curvatus. Genus typicum *Salpiglossis* Ruiz et Pavon, PRODR. FL. PER. ET. CHIL. **94**, t. 19 (1794).

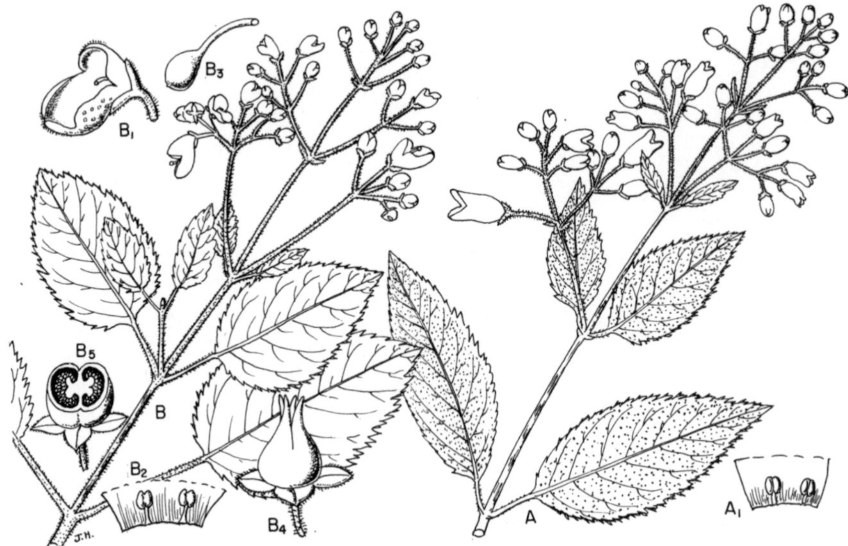

FIG. 533. Two species of *Jovellana* from widely separated regions: **A**, *J. punctata* Ruiz & Pavon, Chile; and **B**, *J. sinclairii* Kranz, New Zealand, showing the close connection of these now remote areas in the southern Pacific ocean. $\mathbf{A_1}$, base of corolla and two stamens of *J. punctata*. $\mathbf{B_1}$, flower of *J. sinclairii*. $\mathbf{B_2}$, base of corolla and two stamens. $\mathbf{B_3}$, gynoecium. $\mathbf{B_4}$, calyx and fruit. $\mathbf{B_5}$, cross-section of ovary (orig.).

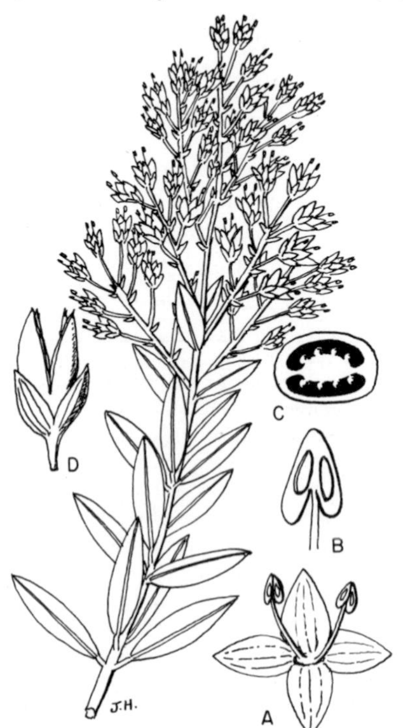

FIG. 534. The genus *Veronica*, widely spread in the Northern Hemisphere, is represented in New Zealand by numerous shrubby species of the very closely related *Hebe*; this is *Hebe elliptica* (Forst.) Pennell. **A**, flower, **B**, anther, **C**, cross-section of ovary, **D**, fruit (orig.).

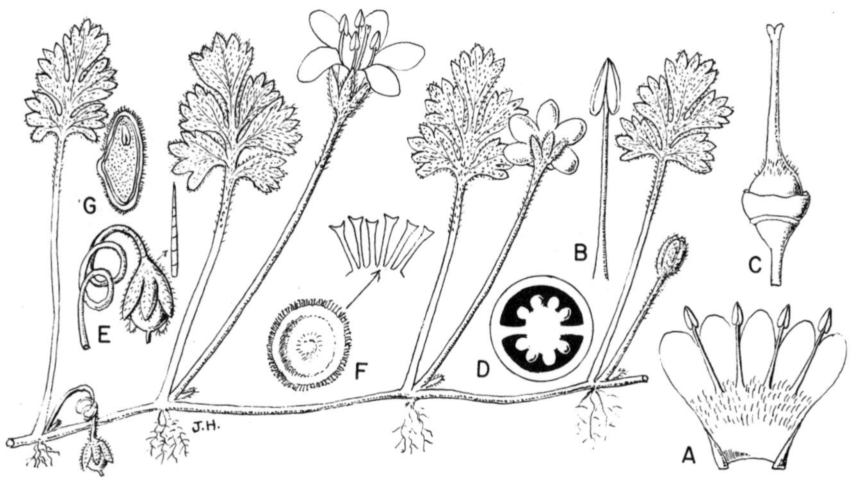

FIG. 535. *Ellisiophyllum pinnatum* (Wall.) Makino (*Scrophulariaceae*), occurs at high elevations from the Himalayas through S.W. China and Japan into the Philippines. **A**, corolla opened out showing the 4 stamens. **B**, stamen. **C**, disk and gynoecium. **D**, cross-section of ovary. **E**, fruit, which buries itself in the soil. **F**, seed and enlarged hairs from the same which anchor it in the soil. **G**, vertical section of seed. (Partly adapted from Makino in JAP. BOT. MAG.)

family *Scrophulariaceae*. Then in 1846 in de Candolle's PRODROMUS Vol. 10 he contributed the account of this tribe, maintaining it also in *Scrophulariaceae* as a suborder *Salpiglossideae*, distinguishing it from the other two suborders *Antirrhinideae* and *Rhinanthideae*.

In the GENERA PLANTARUM, however, he changed his mind and transferred *Salpiglossideae* to the family *Solanaceae* with the following statement:

Tribus tamen *Salpiglossidearum*, staminibus didynamis cum vel absque quinto minore embryone saepe recto allisque notis *Scrophularineisque* nonnullis prope accedit iisque a pluribus auctoribus adscribitur; inflorescentia tamen et habitus *Solanacearum*, et corollae aestivatio inter his ordinibus subvaga fere semper more *Solanacearum* plus minus plicata vel valvata.

Recently, in revising my KEY TO THE FAMILIES OF PLANTS OF THE WORLD, the genera belonging to *Salpiglossideae* consistently arrived next to *Scrophulariaceae*, and so I came to the conclusion that it would be better placed in this phylogenetic system as a separate family. This may not at first commend itself to taxonomists who have been accustomed to find it in *Solanaceae*. In my opinion, however, its exclusion from either family leaves each of them better defined.

In addition to the type genus **Salpiglossis** Ruiz & Pavon, the following

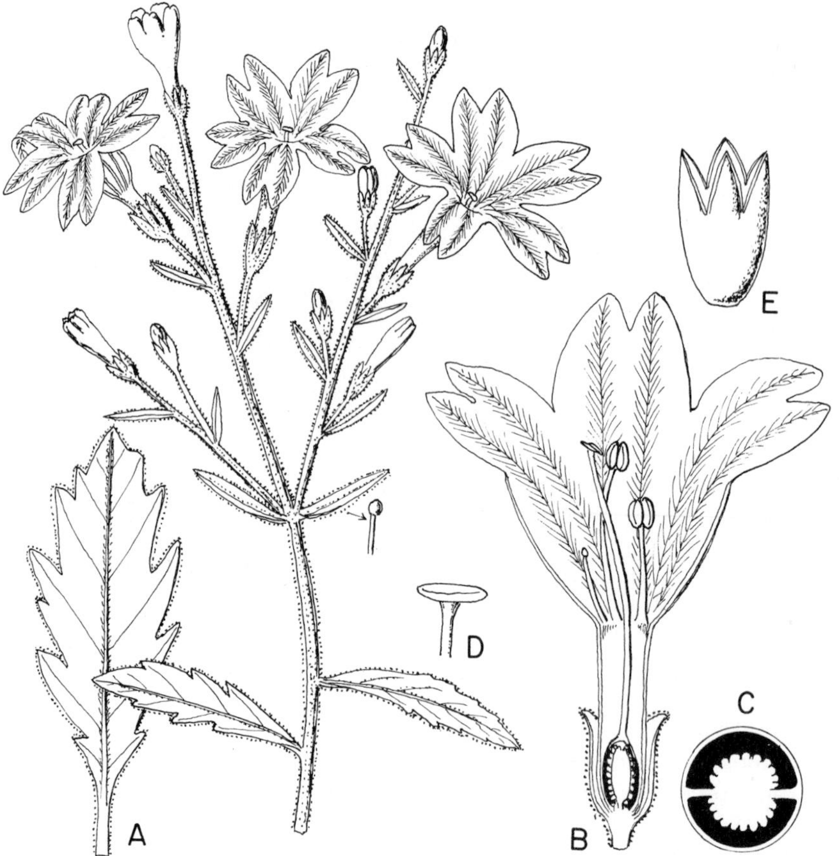

FIG. 536. *Salpiglossis sinuata* Ruiz & Pavon, Chile, type species of the type genus of the family *Salpiglossidaceae*. **A**, lower leaf. **B**, vertical section of flower. **C**, cross-section of ovary. **D**, stigma. **E**, capsule.

belong to the group: **Petunia** Juss., Central and South America; **Bouchetia** DC. ex Dunal, southern United States to southern Brazil; **Nierembergia** Ruiz & Pavon, Mexico and Texas and extratropical and subtropical South America; **Leptoglossis** Benth., extratropical and western South America; **Reyesia** Clos, Chile; **Schizanthus** Ruiz & Pavon, Chile; **Browallia** Linn., tropical America; **Streptosolen** Miers, north tropical South America; **Brunfelsia** Linn., West Indies and South America; **Schwenkia** Linn., South America and tropical Africa; **Duboisia** R.Br., eastern Australia and New Caledonia; **Anthocercis** Labill., Australia; **Anthotroche** Endl., Australia.

Acanthaceae[1] is a very homogeneous family mostly found in tropical and subtropical forests, often in damp or marshy places. Cystoliths are often present in the epidermis or parenchyma of the stem and leaves. With few exceptions the leaves are opposite, and there are no stipules. A few, including the type genus *Acanthus*, are xerophytic, the leaves or bracts of which are often more or less spiny. Arborescent species are very rare, but some are climbers, such as most species of *Mendoncia* and *Thunbergia*. In these the calyx is reduced to an annulus or split into subulate teeth, its protective function being transferred to the large foliaceous valvate bracteoles. A similar reduced calyx occurs in the small more distantly related Brazilian genus *Clistax* Mart., also with large compensating bracteoles. Large bracteoles also occur in *Boutonia* DC. (*Periblema* DC.), in which they are

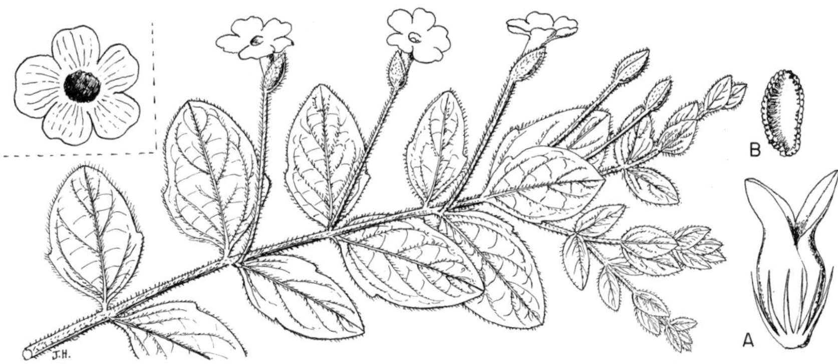

FIG. 537. *Thunbergia capensis* Retz., the type species of the family *Acanthaceae*; this genus is named after the famous Swedish traveller and botanist, Karl Thunberg, a pupil of Linnaeus, who collected extensively in South Africa and wrote a FLORA CAPENSIS. **A**, fruit. **B**, seed. Inset, a flower of "Black-eyed Susan", *Thunbergia alata* Boj., widespread in the tropics (orig.).

united into a tubular involucre enclosing a single flower, also with a reduced calyx. The corolla is mostly zygomorphic, but in *Thunbergia* (Fig. 537) and *Ruellia* and a few others the limb is almost equally 5-lobed. Generally the corolla is more or less deeply 2-lipped, but in *Acanthus* and related genera the posterior lip is completely absent, the corolla being unilateral to the base, the limb being abaxial and forming a platform for insects, and the upper lip is replaced by the large adaxial calyx-lobe.

Type genus *Acanthus* Linn. Tall armed herbs or shrubs; leaves radical or opposite, sometimes large, sinuate-dentate with sharp teeth or pinnately lobed, very rarely subentire; flowers white or blue, in dense terminal bracteate spikes; bracts either large and spiny-dentate or small and entire, rarely

[1] Including *Thunbergiaceae* van Tieghem (1908). *Mendonciaceae* Bremekamp (1953).

obsolete; bracteoles narrow, entire or spiny-dentate; calyx 4-partite, 2 outer segments large, veiny or cartilaginous at the base, posterior 3–5-nerved, entire, anterior 2–4-nerved, entire or 2-toothed, lateral 2 innermost and much smaller; corolla-tube very short, the posterior side split to the base, the anterior expanded into a large lip broadly 3–5-lobed, lobes inflexed in bud; stamens 2, inserted towards the base of the corolla, filaments rigid; anthers connivent, 1-locular, dorsifixed, bearded lengthwise; disk obsolete; style shortly bifid; ovary 2-locular, ovules 2 in each loculus; capsule ovoid or oblong, shining, with very thick septa; seeds 4 or fewer, flat, embryo with large flat cotyledons and without endosperm. Type species *Acanthus mollis* Linn., southern Europe and cult. (Fig. 538).

The plants of the family **Gesneriaceae**[1] are generally herbaceous or only slightly woody and a few tree-climbers, with opposite, exstipulate leaves and attractive solitary to cymose flowers. In some the leaves are unequal in pairs (anisophyllous) or alternately very small and stipule-like, thus appearing to be alternate. The lovely Gloxinias of our greenhouses do not belong to that genus but are hybrids of *Sinningia speciosa* Hiern belonging to this genus with a tuberous rootstock, and the flowers axillary and solitary or fasciculate. In the genus *Gloxinia* there are no tubers and the roots or rhizomes are creeping, the flowers in bracteate racemes.

A most remarkable genus is *Streptocarpus*, in which the adult plant consists of a single leaf, which is nothing but an enlarged and foliaceous cotyledon, the second cotyledon perishing after germination. Nutrition is supplied by adventitious roots which emerge from the base of the leaf and from which also arises the flower-bearing shoot. The flowers of many of the genera are mostly zygomorphic and the stamens are then generally 4, didynamous and inserted on the corolla. But in *Ramonda* (*Ramondia*) the corolla is subactinomorphic, 5- or 6-lobed, and accompanied by as many stamens as lobes (isomerous), and the stamens are attached at the base of the corolla-tube. These characters are also present in *Championia*, *Conandron*, *Niphaea* sp. and *Bellonia* sp., and these genera seem to be the most primitive in the family.

Many *Gesneriaceae* are of great horticultural value, especially *Sinningia* ("Gloxinia") with a great variety of beautiful hybrids, and the beautiful so-called African "Violets", species and varieties of *Saintpaulia*, natives of tropical east Africa. As the genera of this family are at present very much *sub judice*, it would be unwise for me to make any further comments about them. Although mostly in the tropics and subtropics, the family is represented in southern Europe by two genera, *Ramonda* (four species) and *Haberlea*, from the Pyrenees and the Balkans.

---

[1] Including *Didymocarpaceae* D. Don (1822). *Cyrtandraceae* Jack (1823). *Ramondiaceae* Godron (1850). *Replicataceae* Dulac (1867).

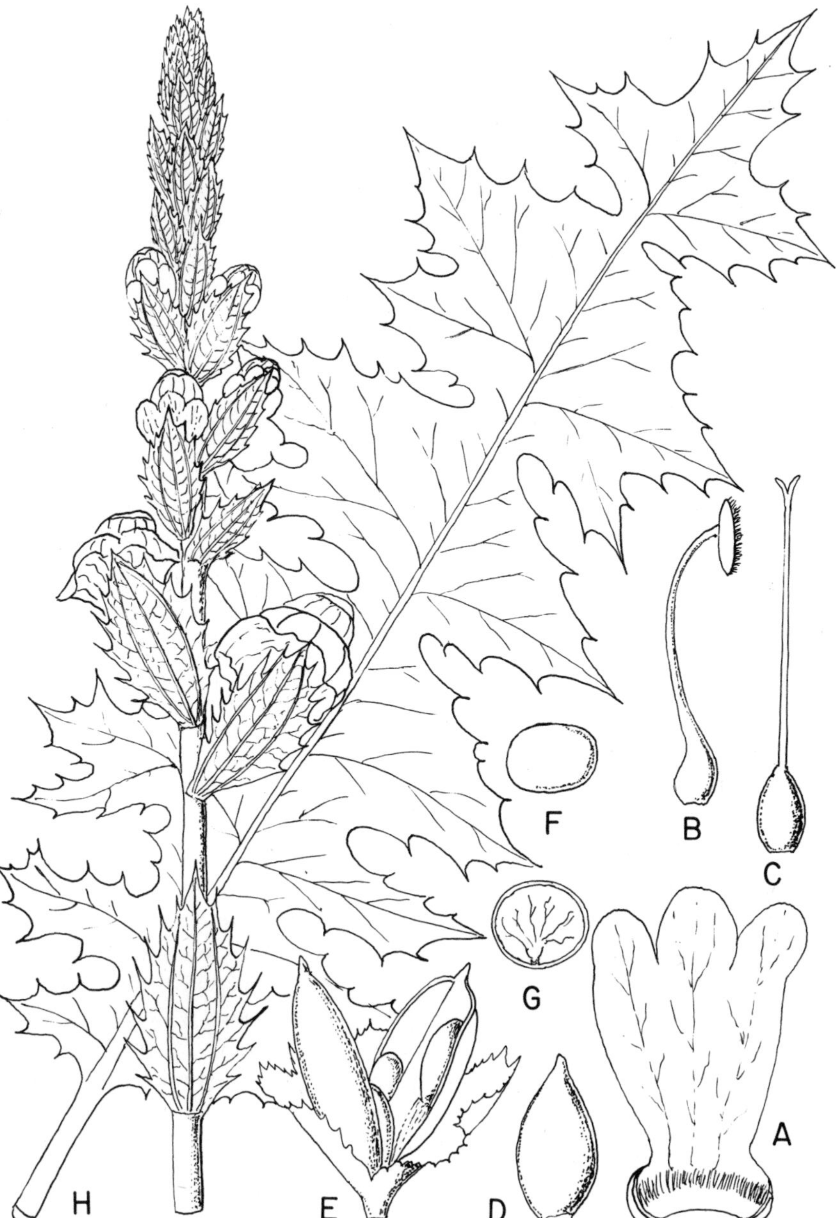

FIG. 538. *Acanthus mollis* Linn., southern Europe and cult., the type species of the type genus of *Acanthaceae*. **A**, corolla composed of one abaxial lip. **B**, stamen (anther 1-locular). **C**, gynoecium. **D**, young fruit. **E**, open fruit. **F**, seed. **G**, vertical section of seed. **H**, leaf (orig.).

FIG. 539. *Nelsonia canescens* (Lam.) Spreng. (*Acanthaceae*); the genus named by R. Brown* after David Nelson, of the Royal garden at Kew, who accompanied Captain Bligh on his voyage to introduce the Bread-fruit from Tahiti to the West Indies. **A**, corolla. **B**, fruit from within (orig.).

*Accompanying the description R. Brown wrote "Dixi in memoriam Davidis Nelson, Hortulani meritissimi, qui in ultimo itinere Cookii plurimas novas species plantarum detexit, postea expeditioni priori Cel. Navarchi Bligh adjunctus, in insula Timor accubuit" (R. Brown PRODROMUS 480 (1810)).

Lentibulariaceae[1] is a small and highly interesting family of insectivorous herbs of diverse habit, often marsh and aquatic plants. The four genera embrace about 200 species, in tropical and temperate regions, but absent from very dry parts and from oceanic islands. The largest and most widely spread genus is *Utricularia* with about 150 species, a certain number of them aquatics. "These are partly submerged and are rootless, with finely dissected leaf-like organs on which are borne bladders. The mouth of the bladder is closed by a valve, which opens inwards in response to a stimulus conveyed by sensory hairs, and immediately closes again forming a trap for small aquatic animals, the products of decay of which are absorbed by hairs lining the wall of the bladder."[2] The flowers of *Utricularia* are in racemes, which in aquatic species rise above the water. Other species are land-plants, often growing among moss with long runner-like shoots on which the

---

[1] I am indebted to Mr. Peter Taylor for critical notes incorporated in the above account.

[2] Quoted from Rendle CLASSIF. FL. PL. **2**, 541 (1925).

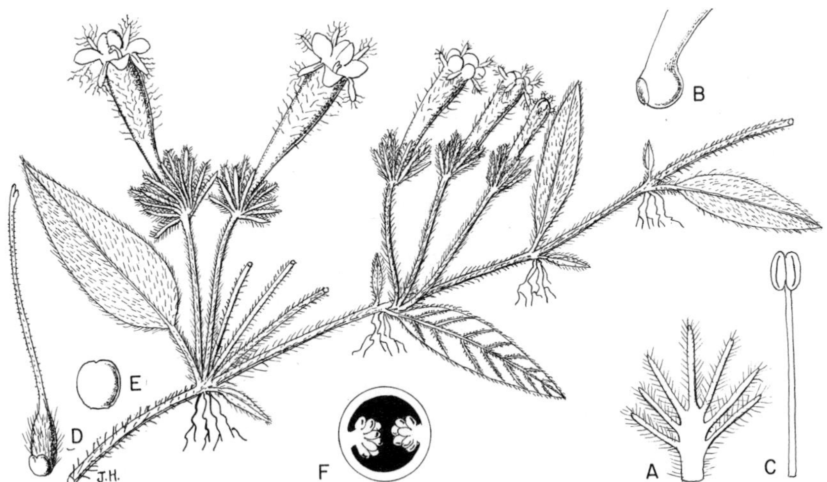

FIG. 540. *Trichantha minor* Hook. (*Gesneriaceae*), Ecuador; note the deeply divided calyx-lobes, **A**, and the peculiar recurved appendages between the corolla-lobes. **B**, base of corolla-tube. **C**, stamen. **D**, gynoecium and gland. **E**, gland. **F**, cross-section of ovary (drawn from a plant cultivated at the R.H.S. Gardens, Wisley, England) (orig.).

bladders are borne; others are epiphytic with much branched rhizomes. The terrestrial and epiphytic species have simple foliar organs.

The ovary of all the genera is superior, 1-locular, with the mostly numerous (rarely reduced to 2) ovules arranged on a free basal or free central placenta (as in *Primulaceae* and *Caryophyllaceae* respectively).

The genus *Polypompholyx* is closely related, differing in the 4 calyx-segments in two series, its two species confined to the southern parts of Australia. The genus *Genlisea*, tropical America and Africa, has 5 calyx-segments in a single series and all terrestrial, with rosettes of leaves and traps which are modified leaves of complicated structure preventing the escape of small creatures. The fruit dehisces by more than one transverse slit.

The fourth genus, *Pinguicula*, is widely distributed and has a rosette of sticky-glandular leaves which trap insects. The corolla is obliquely zygomorphic, usually with a longish spur, and the anthers dehisce by a horizontal slit.

In the GENERA PLANTARUM of Bentham and Hooker the family is placed after *Orobanchaceae* following on after *Scrophulariaceae*, with comments on affinity as follows:

Ordo distinctissimus, a diversis botanicis nunc *Primulaceis* nunc *Scrophularineis* approximatus. Ordinis Personatis accedit corolla, staminum situ et indole, stigmate, capsulae dehiscentia, et saepe ovulis seminibusque, nec differt nisi placenta globosa e fundo loculi unici ovarii oriunda, et hoc solo charactere *Primulaceis*

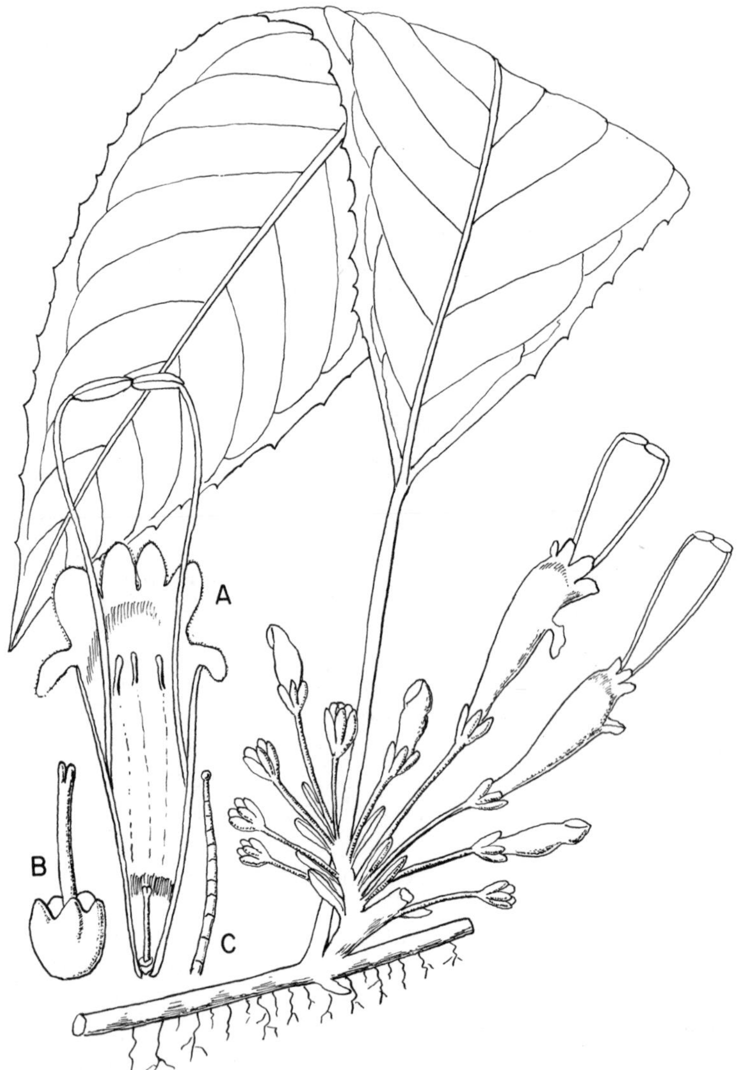

FIG. 541. *Agalmyla parasitica* (Lam.) O. Ktze. (*Gesneriaceae*), Malaya; note the remarkable connivent anthers of the only two stamens, and the presence of 3 staminodes. **A**, corolla laid open. **B**, disk and style. **C**, jointed hair (orig.).

convenit. Stigmata, capsula, semina, embryo, uti corolla et androecium, omnia ab illis *Primulacearum* longe distat.

This opinion was the opposite of that of Dr. Alexander Dickson (TRANS. ROY. SOC. EDINB. **25**, 646 (1869)), who considered the ovary to be composed

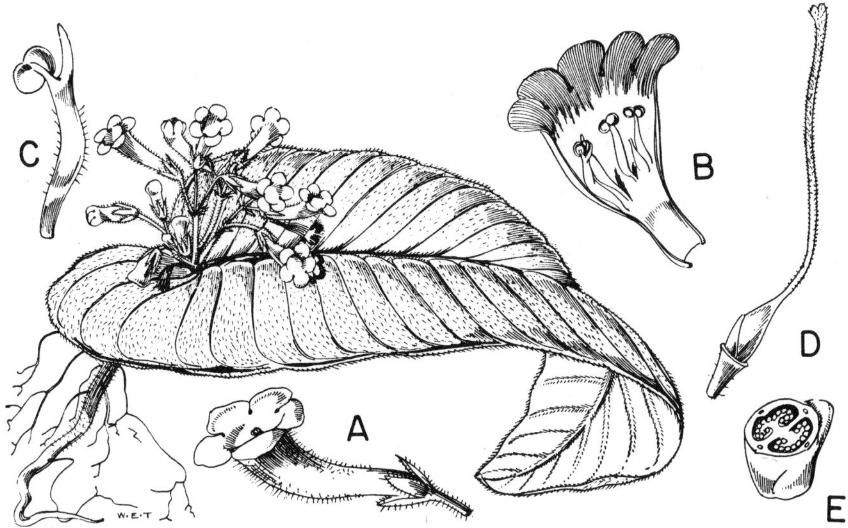

FIG. 542. *Acanthonema strigosum* Hook. f. (*Gesneriaceae*), grows on the Cameroons Mts. at 2000 ft and in Fernando Po, west Africa; closely related to the better known genus *Streptocarpus*; drawn by Trevithick for the FLORA OF WEST TROPICAL AFRICA. **A**, flower. **B**, corolla opened out. **C**, stamen. **D**, gynoecium. **E**, cross-section of ovary.

of 5 carpels as in *Primulaceae*, and that therefore the *Lentibulariaceae* were related to that family. Dickson remarked (*loc. cit.*) "On the whole it seems to me that we have as little right to associate *Lentibulariaceae* with *Scrophulariceae* on account of bilabiate floral envelopes and more or less didynamous stamens, as a zoologist would have to associate the Echnida with Hedgehogs or with Porcupines, on account of the remarkable correspondence in their prickly defence"!

ORDER 79. GERANIALES

(*Fam. Fl. Pl.* **1**, 494)

Families: **Geraniaceae, Limnanthaceae, Oxalidaceae, Tropaeolaceae, Balsaminaceae.**

Phylogeny: Probable derivation of the Order: RANALES → GERANIALES, climax families *Tropaeolaceae* and *Balsaminaceae.*

For many years students were taught by followers of the Englerian system that the GERANIALES were the progenitors of the *Euphorbiaceae*; and

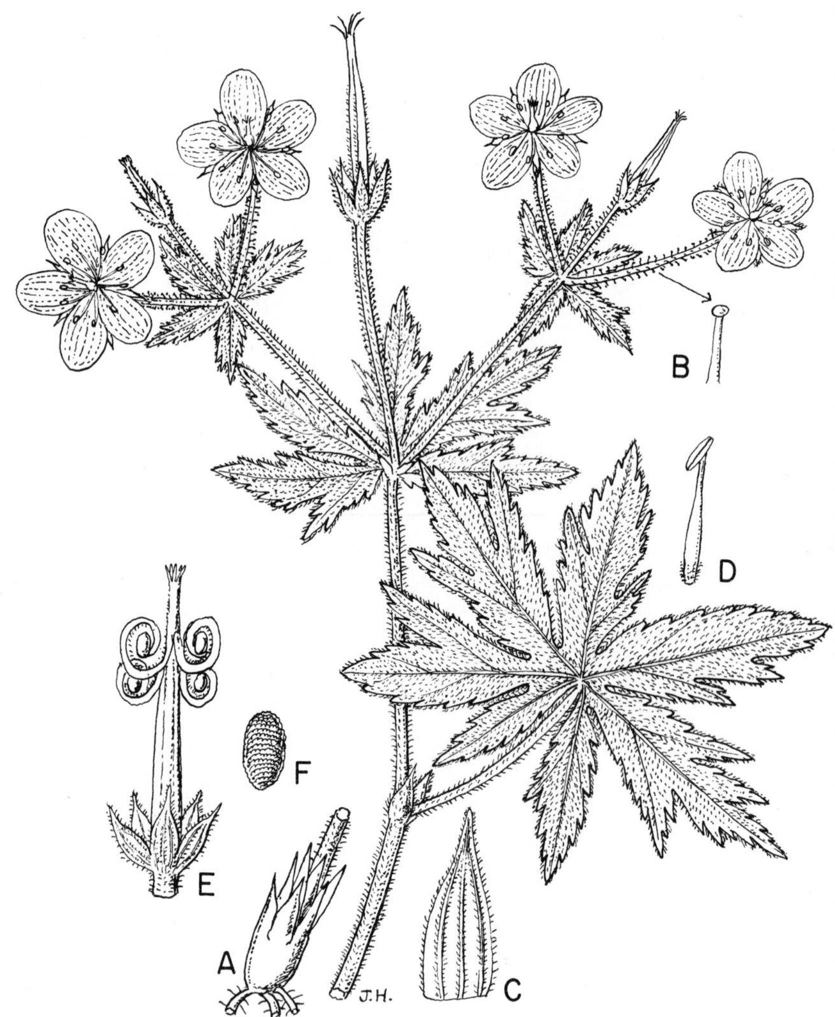

Fig. 543. *Geranium sylvaticum* Linn., the type species of the type genus of *Geraniaceae*, Europe to Siberia, naturalised in North America. **A**, base of stem. **B**, gland from pedicel. **C**, sepal. **D**, stamen. **E**, capsule. **F**, seed.

so the latter family formed Unterreihe 5, *Tricoccae*, of Engler's GERANIALES. As already mentioned (p. 275), *Euphorbiaceae* is here considered to be a family of very mixed origin, though it is difficult to detect relationship of any part of it with any of the families composing Engler's GERANIALES. Far better places in which to seek for the origin of *Euphorbiaceae* would be *Flacourtiaceae*, *Tiliaceae*, *Sterculiaceae*, *Malvaceae*, CELASTRALES, OLACALES, and

SAPINDALES. One might even be tempted to include also the family *Menispermaceae*, for a species of *Cocculus*[1] was mistaken by a great authority on the *Euphorbiaceae*, whom I have always held in great respect, to be a new genus of tribe *Phyllantheae*!

The Order GERANIALES in both Bentham and Hooker's and in Engler and Prantl's classifications is heterogeneous from our point of view, and contains many very widely different families. What, may we ask, is there in common between a *Geranium*, on the one hand, and a Mahogany tree (*Meliaceae*) or a *Simarouba* (*Simaroubaceae*) on the other? There was little more than the ventral raphe, a mere thread, to bring together this large group of families.

In this work I have restricted the GERANIALES to what I consider to be a more homogeneous and better defined group composed of the families enumerated above.

The family **Geraniaceae**[2] is familiar to many, and it is now perhaps rather late in the day to remind the student that the so-called garden bedding "Geranium" belongs not to that genus but to *Pelargonium*. The family is

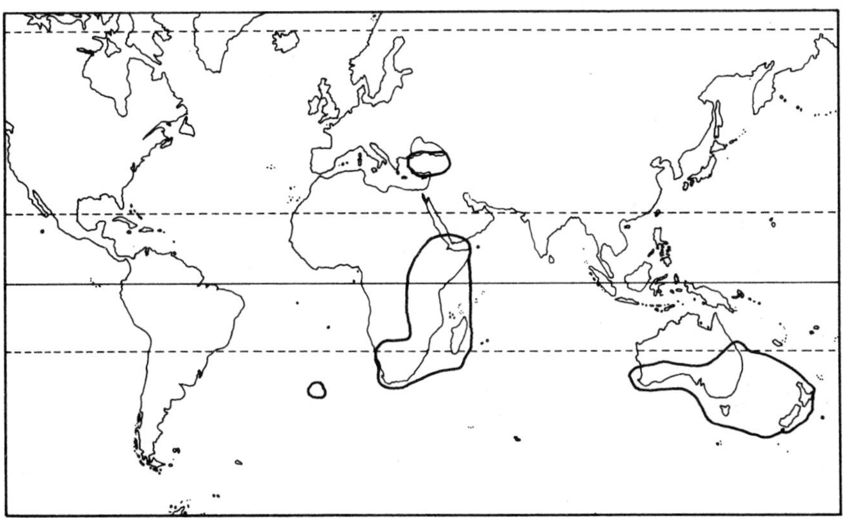

MAP 34. Distribution of the genus *Pelargonium* (*Geraniaceae*). Most of the species occur in South Africa; there is one isolated species in Asia Minor, very few in tropical east Africa and extending into the Yemen; only one species in Australia, Tasmania and New Zealand; one in Tristan da Cunha.

[1] *Bricchetia somalensis* Pax = *Cocculus laeaba* DC. See Hutchinson FLORA TROP. AFR. **6**, 1, 441 (1911).

[2] Including *Biebersteiniaceae* Endlich. (1841). *Rhynchothecaceae* Endlich. (1841). *Erodiaceae* Horaninow (1847). *Rostraceae* Dulac (1867).

now usually limited to the tribes *Geranieae* and *Pelargonieae*, and, so circumscribed, is a very natural group. It seems possible that this family and its higher evolved relatives listed above may have descended from the Ranalean stock, the connections having disappeared. The general habit and leaf-characters of *Geraniaceae* are similar to those of many *Ranunculaceae*.

FIG. 544. Fruit of *Erodium pachyrrhizum* Coss. & Dr. (*Geraniaceae*), Algeria, admirably adapted to penetrate and remain in the soil.

Many modern authors have treated as separate families the tribes of the family *Geraniaceae* in Bentham and Hooker's GENERA PLANTARUM, *Limnantheae* as *Limnanthaceae*, *Oxalideae* as *Oxalidaceae*, *Tropaeolum* as *Tropaeolaceae*, and *Balsamineae* as *Balsaminaceae*. The other two tribes, *Vivianieae* and *Wendtieae*, have usually remained in the family though they seem to differ from typical *Geraniaceae* to an even greater degree. They are therefore in this system also treated as separate families, *Vivianiaceae* and *Ledocarpaceae* respectively, the latter being the name to be used according to International Rules. The former is here placed in the PITTOSPORALES, the latter in the MALPIGHIALES. Since the publication of the GENERA PLANTARUM, Balfour f. added with considerable hesitation *Dirachma*, a peculiar monotypic Socotran genus. In my opinion this is not correctly placed in or near *Geraniaceae* and is here referred to the Order TILIALES (p. 230).

The family *Geraniaceae* is thus reduced to six genera, which together form a very homogeneous and quite natural group with its main concentration at the southern end of Africa, particularly in Cape Province, and also in the temperate regions of the Northern Hemisphere.

Type genus *Geranium* Linn.: Herbs, rarely somewhat shrubby, often spreading and almost stemless; branches jointed at the nodes; leaves opposite and sometimes anisophyllous, or alternate, dentate or palmately (rarely pinnately) lobed or dissected, stipulate; peduncles axillary, 1- or 2-flowered; flowers actinomorphic; sepals 5, imbricate; petals 5, hypogynous, imbricate, often beautifully veined; disk-glands 5, alternate with the petals; stamens 10, all fertile or rarely 5 without anthers, free or shortly connate at the base; ovary 5-lobed, 5-locular, beaked, beak narrowed into style with 5 branches; ovules 2 in each loculus, more or less superposed; capsule septifragally dehiscing into 1-seeded lobes, tails elastically revolute from the base up-

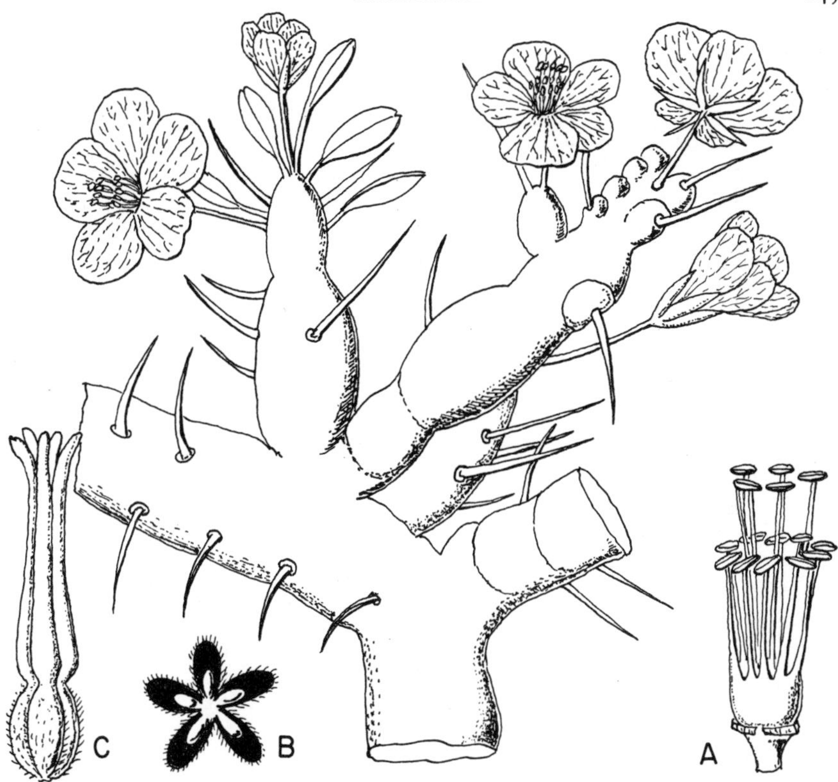

FIG. 545. *Sarcocaulon rigidum* Schinz (*Geraniaceae*), South Africa. **A**, stamens. **B**, cross-section of ovary. **C**, gynoecium (orig.).

wards; seeds with thin or no endosperm; embryo with the radicle incumbent on the folded or convolute cotyledons. Type species *G. sylvaticum* Linn., Europe to Siberia, naturalised in North America.

Apart from the widespread genera *Geranium* and *Erodium*, the main centre of distribution is South Africa, where many of the species take on remarkable forms. The tendency to the evolution of a zygomorphic flower shown in the genus *Erodium* is much more fully developed in *Pelargonium*, a genus with a great concentration of species at the Cape. The spur of the sepals adnate to the pedicel in *Pelargonium*, most clearly demonstrated by cutting a cross-section of the latter, is a unique feature. The migration of this genus from the Southern to the Northern Hemisphere is an interesting possibility (see Map 34).

The small family **Limnanthaceae**, formerly included in *Geraniaceae*, whilst retaining its actinomorphic corolla, has valvate sepals and the stamens double their number. Its carpels lack the beaks characteristic of many *Geraniaceae*, and there is some similarity to certain *Caryophyllaceae*. In the

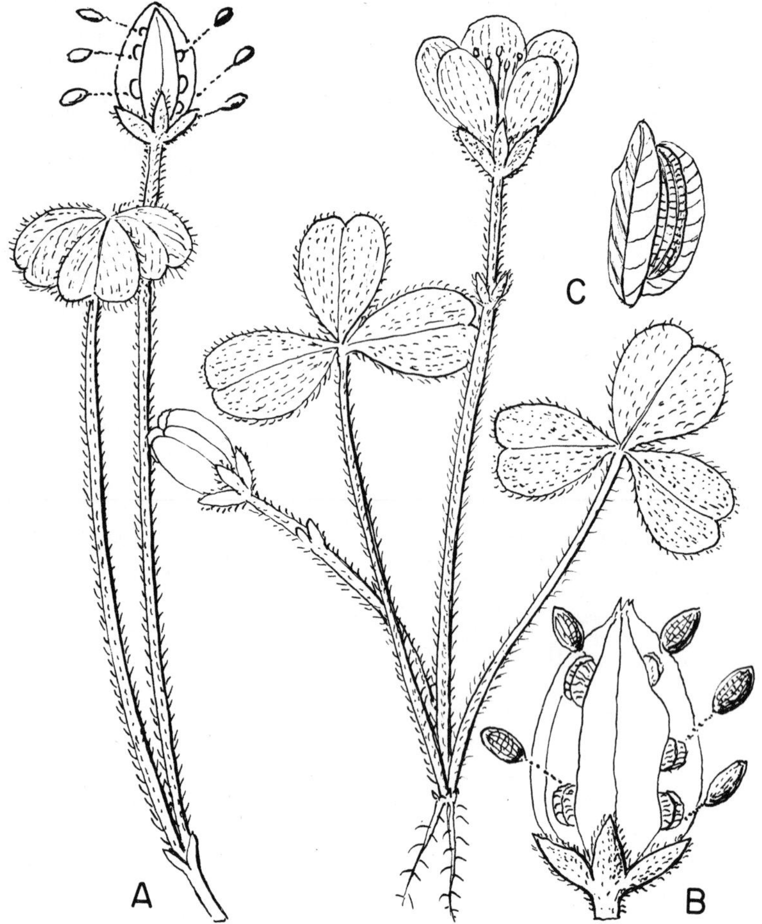

FIG. 546. *Oxalis acetosella* Linn. (*Oxalidaceae*), showing the interesting way in which the seeds are ejected from the capsule. **A**, specimen in fruit. **B**, fruit and seeds. **C**, seed (orig.).

German system this small family of herbs was actually placed in the SAPINDALES because of its dorsal raphe! It is indeed a far cry from a horsechestnut to a *Limnanthes*.

Oxalidaceae,[1] another small family but very rich in species in southern Africa, have compound leaves and frequently flowers of two kinds, some perfect and others minute and apetalous. The type species is *Oxalis acetosella* Linn., which ejects its seeds in an interesting way (Fig. 546). I excluded the genera *Averrhoa* and *Connaropsis* (see *Averrhoaceae*, p. 385).

[1] Including *Antitypaceae* Dulac (1867). *Hypseocharitaceae* Weddell (1861).

The genus *Tropaeolum*, the sole member of **Tropaeolaceae**,[1] is represented in tropical and subtropical America by a wealth of species similar to *Pelargonium* in southern Africa on the other side of the Atlantic ocean. Here, however, the spurred sepal has remained free from the pedical. One may speculate from the theory of continental drift that *Pelargonium* and *Tropaeolum*, both being recently evolved genera, have multiplied after the continents of Africa and South America were separated.

Balsaminaceae[2] (*Impatiens* and *Hydrocera*) have also strongly zygomorphic flowers with unequal petals. They are most numerous in tropical Asia. *Impatiens* is of great sentimental interest to British botanists because it was with this genus that Sir Joseph Dalton Hooker busied himself during the last few years of his long life, dissecting and making drawings of the floral parts almost to the last.

Order 80. **POLEMONIALES**

(*Fam. Fl. Pl.* **1**, 500)

Families: **Polemoniaceae, Hydrophyllaceae, Cuscutaceae.**

Phylogeny: RANALES → CARYOPHYLLALES → POLEMONIALES → Cuscutaceae.

The Phlox family, **Polemoniaceae**, is mainly of horticultural value, especially the genus *Phlox*, in which there are many beautiful garden plants such as the many colour varieties of *Phlox drummondii* Hook. The numerous species are endemic in North America and N.E. Asia. Though in my FAMILIES OF FLOWERING PLANTS (Vol. 1, p. 121) I regarded them as most nearly related to GERANIALES, I would now modify this view and derive them more or less from the Caryophyllaceous Stock.

In *Polemoniaceae* the corolla-lobes are dextrorsely contorted in aestivation. In the genus *Collomia* the flowers are in terminal heads surrounded by an involucre composed of the upper leaves. Both *Phlox* and *Collomia* differ from the other genera in having the stamens inserted at unequal heights in the corolla-tube. Most of the genera are herbs, but the species of *Cantua* are trees or shrubs of western South America.

---

[1] Including *Cardamindaceae* Link (1831).

[2] Including *Hydroceraceae* Blume (1825). *Crispaceae* Dulac (1867). *Impatientaceae* Barnhart (1895).

Fig. 547. A species such as this, *Phlox bifida* Beck, North America, seems to indicate that the family *Polemoniaceae*, to which it belongs, is not far removed from *Caryophyllaceae* (especially genera such as *Lychnis* and *Silene*) (orig.).

The genus *Phlox* is the most familiar. There is great similarity between some species of *Phlox*, such as *P. bifida* Beck (Fig. 547), and some *Caryophyllaceae*, such as species of *Silene* or *Lychnis*.

That they are not in a very advanced stage of sympetaly seems clear from the fact that the stamens are often inserted at unequal heights within the corolla-tube. The contorted aestivation of the corolla-lobes agrees with that of many *Caryophyllaceae*, and the student would probably concur in the view that a *Phlox* with free petals bears a striking resemblance to some of that family. Indeed even a few of the specific names bear testimony, and I cannot believe that these pointers indicate merely superficial resemblances. These are *Gilia dianthiflorus* (Benth.) Greene (*Gilia dianthoides* Endl.), *Gilia pharnaceoides* Benth., and *Gilia liniflora* Benth., all of which are strikingly like certain *Caryophyllaceae*. The genus *Polemonium* itself is rather high in its own family, with its pinnate leaves.

The geographical distribution of **Hydrophyllaceae** is very similar to that of *Polemoniaceae* (p. 647), and the two families seem to be closely related. The frequent occurrence of unilateral scorpioid racemes or cymes (see Fig. 548) seems to point to *Boraginaceae* (*sensu stricto*[1]). The style is never gynobasic as in that family, this being a more advanced character shared also by the more climax family *Lamiaceae* (*Labiatae*) (p. 659). The genus *Phacelia* embraces about a third of the species, the remainder being distributed among about seventeen other genera.

Hydrophyllaceae R.Br., Franklin Narrat. J. POLAR SEA APP. 764 (1823): A homogeneous family showing very little diversion from the type, *Hydrophyllum*, a genus with about 7 spp. confined to North America; perennial herbs with long slender tuber-like roots, radical leaves pinnately or palmately lobed and dentate, few stem-leaves, terminal often long-pendunculate scorpioid-dichotomous or subcapitate cymes, a subrotate or tubular-campanulate corolla, the tube with 5 pairs of linear appendages opposite each lobe; lobes contorted; ovary 1-locular with 2 erect placentas, style shortly 2-fid at the apex; ovules 2 on the inner face of each placenta; capsule 2-valved, with 4–1 globose seeds.

In a few genera, such as *Hydrolea*, *Wigandia*, etc., there are two separate styles, whilst in the remainder these are more or less united from the middle upwards. *Codon* (Fig. 552) is an outstanding genus of two spp. confined to S.W. Africa, with 12–8 merous flowers and densely prickly stems and leaves.

Tricardia (Fig. 551), a monotypic genus found in California, Arizona and Utah, differs from all the other genera by the two series of sepals, three of

---

[1] i.e. excluding *Ehretiaceae* (p. 465).

FIG. 548. *Hydrophyllum virginianum* Linn., the type species of the type genus of *Hydrophyllaceae*; Eastern United States of America and Canada; note the evolution of a scorpioid cymose inflorescence leading on to the family *Boraginaceae* (*sensu stricto*). **A**, flower. **B**, corolla opened out showing the nearly hypogynous stamens. **C**, anther. **D**, disk and gynoecium. **E**, cross-section of ovary. **F**, seed. **G**, vertical section of seed. (orig.).

FIG. 549. *Nemophila insignis* Benth. (*Hydrophyllaceae*), California; perhaps pointing back to *Geraniaceae* (see text). **A**, gynoecium (orig.).

which are large, orbicular, cordate at the base, and become enlarged, membranous and reticulate in fruit.

The genus *Romanzoffia* (Fig. 550) bears a great resemblance to some species of *Saxifragaceae*, with mostly radical long-petiolate orbicular-reniform coarsely dentate leaves and secund-racemose flowers. *Hesperochiron* is similar in habit, but with solitary flowers from the axils of the leaves; the 2–3 spp. are confined to western N. America.

In a few genera the single flowers or the inflorescences are sometimes leaf-opposed, though this character seems of moderate generic value.

It seems probable that *Hydrophyllaceae* are of somewhat mixed descent, though they have escaped the attention of family splitters. In the family "tree" they are shown to be descended with the *Polemoniaceae* from the *Geraniaceae* and allied families; but there is also a strong possibility that a small part has come from the *Saxifragaceae*. The morphology and general aspect of some of them bear this out in a striking way. The following genera

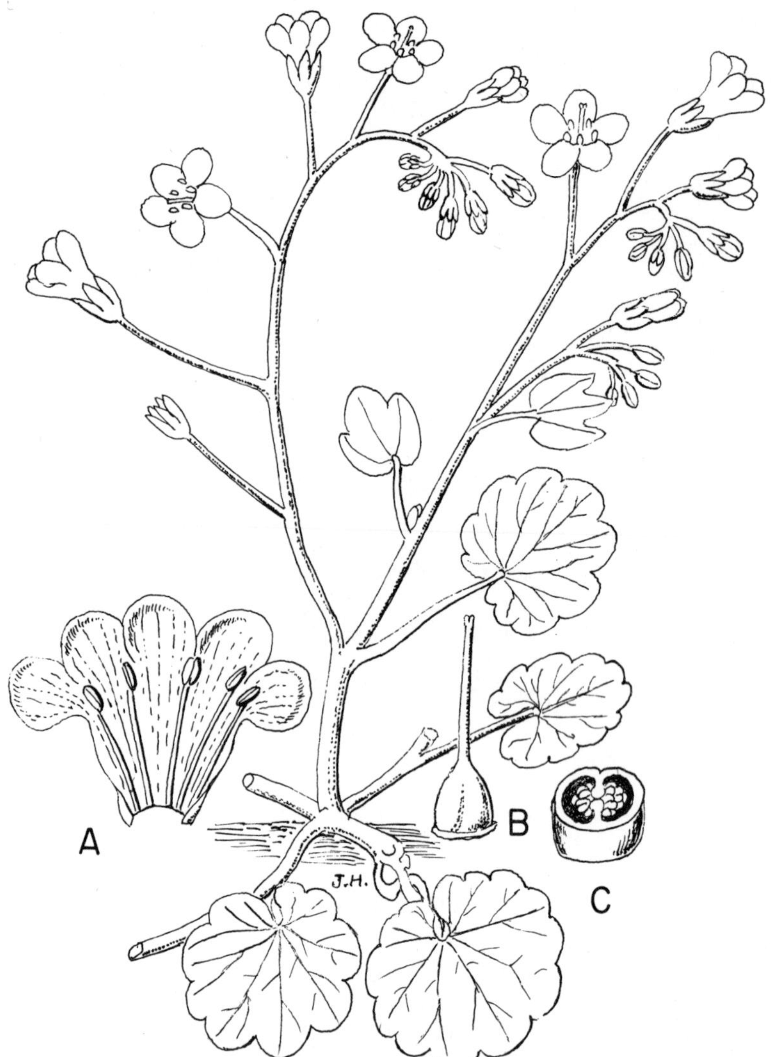

FIG. 550. *Romanzoffia sitchensis* Cham. (*Hydrophyllaceae*), perhaps shows affinity with *Saxifragaceae*. **A**, corolla opened out showing the nearly hypogynous stamens. **B**, gynoecium. **C**, cross-section of ovary (orig.).

of *Hydrophyllaceae* or part of them are definitely "Geraniaceous": *Nemophila* (for example *N. insignis* Dougl., Fig. 549) and *Conanthus grandiflorus* Benth. On the other hand, the following (or part of them) are "Saxifragaceous": *Hydrophyllum*, *Phacelia* and *Romanzoffia* (the last having a very striking resemblance to *Saxifraga* spp.).

Fig. 551. *Tricardia watsonii* Torrey (*Hydrophyllaceae*), distinguished especially by the unequal calyx-lobes, **A**. **B**, corolla laid open, showing the almost hypogynous stamens. **C**, anther (orig.).

Some of the remaining genera are too far removed from their basic stock to have retained any similarity to their ancestors, but they point very definitely to some higher up the scale. Such are *Phacelia* spp. (*P. sericea* A.

FIG. 552. *Codon royenii* Linn. (*Hydrophyllaceae*), dry regions of South Africa; note the number of calyx-lobes, corolla-lobes and stamens. **A**, flower. **B**, gynoecium. **C**, vertical section of ovary. **D**, fruit. **E**, seed. **F**, vertical section of seed (orig.).

Gray, N.W. America, very like an *Echium*; also *P. tanacetifolia* Benth., California; whilst *P. humilis* Torr., N.W. America, is little removed from *Heliotropium*), and again I hesitate to believe that these pointers are merely superficial resemblances.

I prefer to place the small family **Cuscutaceae**, single genus *Cuscuta* Linn., in this Order, rather than near *Convolvulaceae*. They are rootless nevergreen parasites, with thread-like stems, often forming a mass on other plants, corolla-lobes imbricate, fruits opening by a transverse slit or irregularly splitting, and the seeds with the linear embryo surrounding the endosperm.

ORDER 81. BORAGINALES

(*Fam. Fl. Pl.* **1**, 502)

Family: **Boraginaceae.**

Phylogeny: RANALES → GERANIALES → **BORAGINALES**.

Under *Ehretiaceae* (p. 465) reasons are given for separating it from **Boraginaceae.**[1] Bentham and Hooker say of *Boraginaceae*:

Ordo naturalis et accurate limitatus, nulli nisi *Hydrophyllaceis* arcte affinis, et ab his facile distinguitur ovarii carpellis constanter 2-nec ∞-ovulatis, placentis nunquam dilatatis et albumine dum adsit ratione embryonis tenuiore. Cum *Convolvulaceis*, *Labiatis* vel *Verbenaceis* saepe comparatur, sed ab omnibus essentialiter distinguitur ovuli micropyle vel embryonis radicula supera nec infera, et saepissime primo intuitu inflorescentia et habitu recognoscendus.

Cordieae apud auctores plures ordinem formant a *Borágineis* distinctum et eorum sensu *Convolvulaceis* affiniorem ob cotyledones plicatas; haec tamen plicatio in *Cordieis* flabellatim longitudinalis est vel rarius subirregularis absque albumine, nec ut in *Convolvulaceis* potius transversa vel sinuosa vel spiralis, albumine inter plicas intruso.[2]

---

[1] Including *Buglossaceae* Hoffmansegg & Link (1809). *Heliotropaceae* Schrader (1820). *Asperifoliaceae* H. G. Reichb. (1830–32). *Onosmotaceae* Horaninow (1834). *Scorpiaceae* Dulac (1867). *Tetrachondraceae* Skottsberg (1912). *Wellstediaceae* Novak (1942).

[2] Translation: A natural family ("order") and well defined, closely related to *Hydrophyllaceae*, and from them easily distinguished by the carpels being constantly 2- and not ∞-ovulate, by the placentas never being dilated, and by the endosperm when present thinner than the embryo. Often compared with *Convolvulaceae*, *Labiatae* or *Verbenaceae*, but from all essentially different by the micropyle of the ovule or the superior and not inferior radicle of the embryo, and very often recognised at a glance by the inflorescence and habit.

Tribe *Cordieae*, according to several authors, forms a separate family ("order"), and in their view allied to *Convolvulaceae* on account of the plicate cotyledons; however, the folding in *Cordieae* is lengthwise and fanwise or rarely rather irregular and without endosperm, not as in *Convolvulaceae*, rather transverse or flexuose or spiral, with endosperm between the folds.

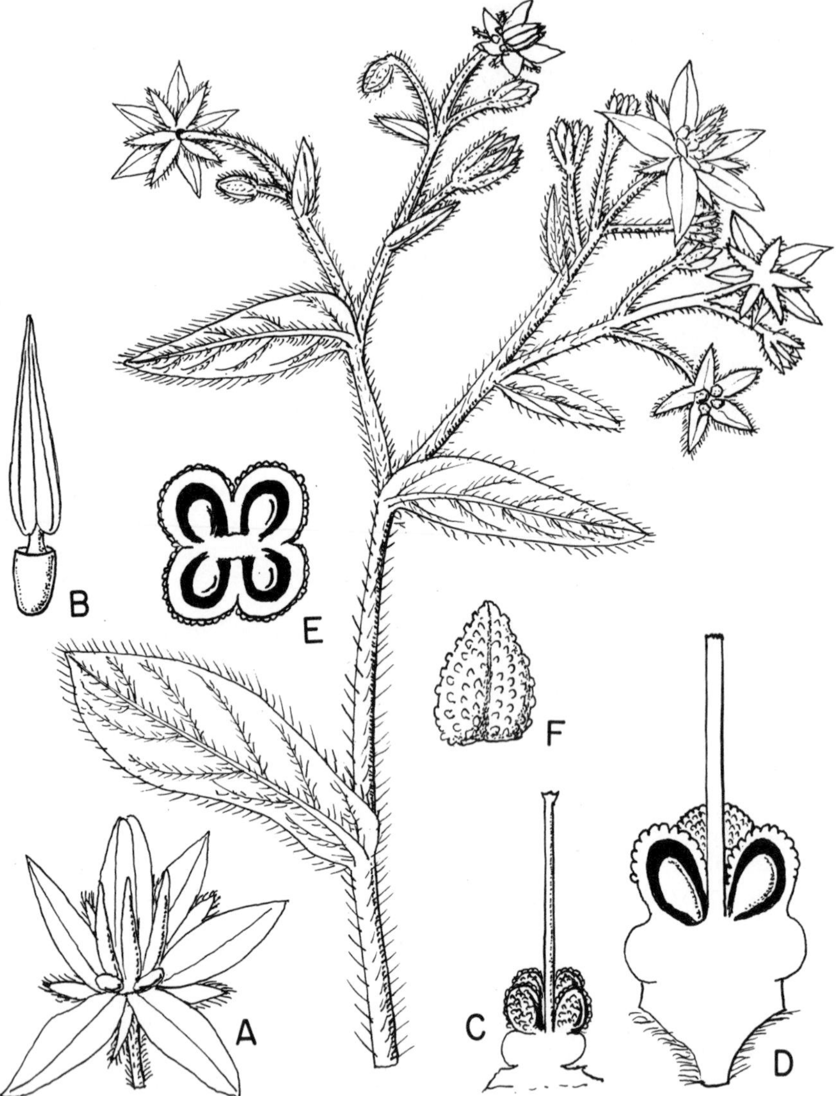

FIG. 553. *Borago officinalis* Linn., the type species of the type genus of *Boraginaceae*, Europe. **A**, flower. **B**, stamen. **C**, gynoecium. **D**, vertical section of gynoecium. **E**, cross-section of ovary. **F**, nutlet (orig.).

It will be observed that attention was drawn to the differences of tribe *Cordieae* from the rest of the family, and the somewhat similar characters of cotyledons to those of *Convolvulaceae*, besides the absence of endosperm.

It may be noted than van Tiegham, as pointed out by Rendle, drew atten-

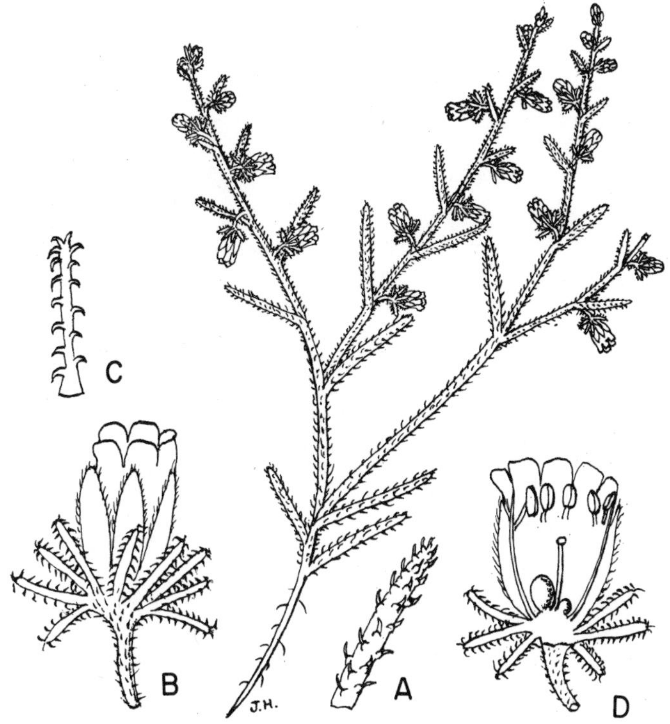

FIG. 554. *Harpagonella palmeri* A. Gray (*Boraginaceae*), California and Lower California east to Arizona; note the remarkable involucre. **A**, enlarged part of stem. **B**, flower. **C**, segment of involucre. **D**, vertical section of flower (orig.).

tion to the marked characters of Tribe *Heliotropieae* of *Boraginaceae*, i.e. the ovary with a terminal style which is simple or bilobed, the stigmatic surface consisting of a swollen hairy ring below the apex of the style, the latter terminal on the ovary and not gynobasic; ovule descending, anatropous; fruit drupaceous and seed with endosperm.

From a phylogenetic point of view, therefore, it may be desirable that this group should be given family status, leaving the true *Boraginaceae* better defined, with gynobasic style and its fruit of separate (generally 4) nutlets.

Here is a list of genera with aberrent or outstanding characteristics: Leaves all opposite in *Antiphytum*; lower or most of them so in *Trichodesma* and in a few spp. of *Eritrichium*. Calyx much enlarged and spreading stellately below the fruit in *Patagonula*, *Caccinia*; lobes deeply divided and hooked (harpagonate) in *Harpagonella* (Fig. 554). Corolla-limb 2-lipped in *Echiochilon*. One anther much larger than the others in *Caccinia* and *Heliocarya*; filaments with a broad scale in *Borago*; anthers connivent or coherent into a

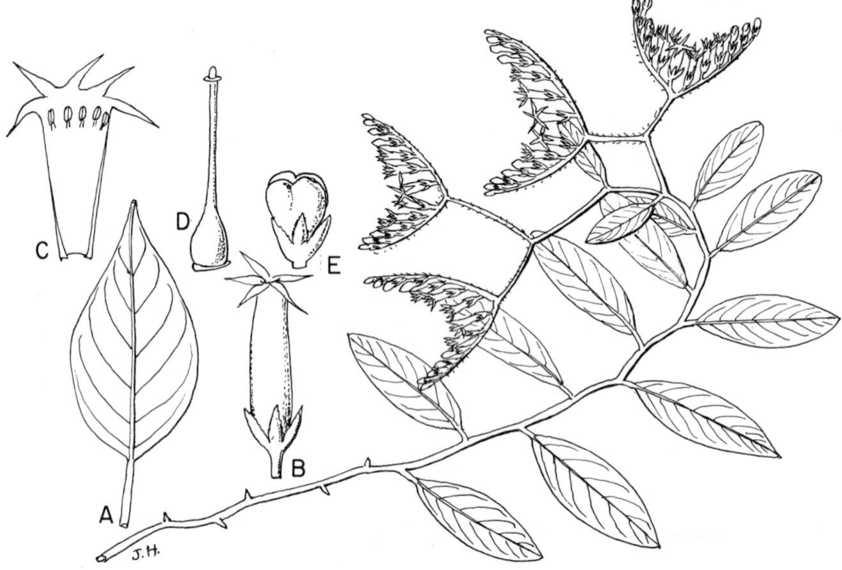

FIG. 555. *Tournefortia volubilis* Linn. (*Boraginaceae*); named by Linnaeus after Tournefort (1656–1708), often referred to as the founder of the genus (see INTRODUCTION, p. xvi). The drawing is that of the type species of the genus, a scrambler in the West Indies and Central America. **A**, larger leaf. **B**, flower. **C**, corolla laid open. **D**, disk and gynoecium. **E**, fruit (orig.).

cone in *Trichodesma*, *Borago*. Ovary 2-lobed and 2-ovuled in *Harpagonella* and *Rochelia*.

Harpagonella palmeri A. Gray is an outstanding very small annual in South California, as described by its author (PROC. AMER. ACAD. **11**, 88 (1876)):

Calyx 5-parted, except between two of the sepals, which coalesce to the middle; below the sinus of the coalescent divisions is an external tufted appendage which at length develops into the soft-spiny horns. The two lobes of the ovary on the side of the flower next to the three nearly separate and unchanged sepals (which we may designate the lower side of the flower) are uniformly and early abortive; the other portion of the calyx accrescent, and soon gibbous-involute into a sort of coriaceous burr, of about 2 lines in length, armed with a few (usually 7) spiny horns of a line or two in length, which spread in all directions, and are beset for nearly their whole length with short and very stiff backwardly directed hooked bristles; the burr closing on the ventral side, and completely covering a fertile nut; the other nut is free, and is certainly sometimes fertile, but more commonly, although enlarging, it seems to fail to mature a seed. The adaptive character of this little plant, viz. the transference of the burr-like apparatus for the dissemination of the seed from pericarp to the calyx, and the investment of the latter of only one of the two ripening nutlets, is most remarkable. (See Fig. 554.)

ORDER 82. LAMIALES

(*Fam. Fl. Pl.* **1**, 503)

Families: **Myoporaceae, Selaginaceae, Globulariaceae, Lamiaceae** (*Labiatae*).

The small families preceding the *Lamiaceae* listed above are closely related and are keyed out with a drawing of each in my FAMILIES OF FLOWERING PLANTS (2nd Ed. **1**, 503). They all differ from *Lamiaceae* by their alternate leaves and entire or only slightly lobed ovary, with a terminal style; **Myoporaceae**,[1] four genera, are mostly in the Southern Hemisphere; **Selaginaceae**,[2] several genera in Africa and the Mascarene Islands; **Globulariaceae**[3] embrace the genus *Poskea* (*Cockburnia*) in Socotra and Somaliland, with a spicate inflorescence; *Globularia*, southern Europe and Mediterranean to the Baltic, and *Lytanthus*, Atlantic Islands, both with capitate inflorescences.

Lamiaceae[4] (*Labiatae*) are undoubtedly the climax of the sympetalous herbaceous families, and have an evolutionary trail even longer than the *Asteraceae* (*Compositae*), though *Acanthaceae* and even *Scrophulariaceae* run them very close. The leaves are always opposite or verticillate, resulting usually in a quadrangular stem and branches, without stipules, and very frequently bearing ethereal oil "which is excreted mainly beneath the cuticle in various kinds of capitate hairs, and especially in the shortly stalked, bladder-like integumental glands" (Solereder). The limb of the sympetalous corolla is 2-lipped or oblique, the lobes being imbricate, the posticous (adaxial) one being outside, the anticous (abaxial) inside in bud, the stamens reduced to 4 or 2, with sometimes the missing stamen or stamens represented by staminodes. The ovary is deeply and vertically 4-lobed, the lobes in lateral pairs in relation to the axis, and the style is in consequence gynobasic, except in tribes *Ajugeae* and *Prosthanthereae*. The ovule is solitary and erect in each lobe of the ovary. Fruit of four 1-seeded nutlets, seeds erect; endosperm is absent from or very scanty in the seeds, embryo straight, cotyledons usually flat.

Bentham and Hooker f. say of them in their GENERA PLANTARUM (**3**, 1161): "Ordo naturalis ab omnibus facile distinguitur exceptis Verbenaceis quibuscum arcte connectitur." They give as reasons for this opinion the

---

[1] Including *Bontiaceae* Horaninow (1834). *Spielmanniaceae* J. G. Agardh (1858).

[2] Including *Hebenstreitiaceae* Horaninow (1834).

[3] Including *Confluaceae* Dulac (1867). *Alyphaceae* Hoffmansegg & Link (1820).

[4] Including *Nepetaceae* Horaninow (1834). *Menthaceae* Burnett (1835). *Labiaceae* Dulac (1867). *Scutellariaceae* Caruel (1886). *Labiatalaceae* Boerlage (1899).

fact that in the genera of *Prostanthereae* and *Ajugoideae* (*Lamiaceae*) (*Labiatae*) the ovary is only shortly lobed and that these tribes are not therefore really separate from the *Viticeae* of *Verbenaceae*. This comparison is considered to be of little account according to the principles on which this phylogenetic system is based.

Here, in our classification, the *Lamiaceae* (*Labiatae*) are placed at the top of the herbaceous subphylum, and the *Verbenaceae* in a like position at the head of the woody subphylum, and again the belief must be expressed with the now oft repeated phrase "that the apparent affinity of these two families is not real but due to convergent evolution".

The stomata of the leaves are often provided with subsidiary cells lying transversely to the pore, a character in common also with *Verbenaceae*, it is true, but also a constant feature in *Acanthaceae*. Just how much phylogenetic value can be attributed to it is problematical.

The type genus of *Lamiaceae* (*Labiatae*) is *Lamium* Linn.: annual or perennial herbs, often spreading or decumbent at the base; leaves often cordate, dentate or subincised, the floral similar or the upper shorter and more sessile; verticillasters densely many-flowered; bracteoles few; flowers purple, white or rarely yellow, in some species often dimorphous, some perfect, others cleistogamous; calyx tubular- or turbinate-campanulate, sub–5-nerved, mouth equal or oblique, teeth 5, often subulate at the apex, equal or the posterior longer; corolla-tube exserted or rarely shorter than the calyx, with or without a ring of hairs inside, widened at the throat; limb 2-lipped, posterior lip erect, ovate or oblong, concave or arched, entire or rarely 2-lobed at the apex, anterior spreading, lateral lobes short, truncate or rarely oblong with a tooth-like appendage, or blunt, intermediate lobe emarginate, contracted at the base; stamens 4, didynamous, anterior longer, ascending below the hood; anthers approximate in pairs, 2-locular, loculi divergent, at length divaricate, often hirsute on the back or tip; disk equal all around; style 2-lobed, lobes subulate, subequal; nutlets truncate, margins acute or rarely obtuse, smooth or minutely tuberculate.—Europe, north Africa, and extratropical Asia. Type species *L. album* Linn., Europe and widely dispersed (Fig. 556).

In this, one of the most homogeneous of families, there are few exceptions, or *formae abnormes*, as Bentham called them, to note: Flowers scattered in a raceme in a few species of *Scutellaria* and *Teucrium*; in heads in *Hyptis*; posticous segment of the calyx deciduous in *Scutellaria* and *Perilomia*; calyx at length spread out below the fruit in a few species of *Phyllostegia*, *Stenogyne* and a few of the tribe *Ocimoideae*; anticous stamens, and not the posticous ones, reduced to staminodes in *Mosla* and *Hypogomphia*; stamens monadelphous in *Coleus*; connective of the anther long and filiform in *Salvia* and related genera; style 4-lobed in *Cleonia*; ovary stipitate above the disk in *Scutellaria*; only shortly lobed in tribes *Prostanthereae* and *Ajugoideae*;

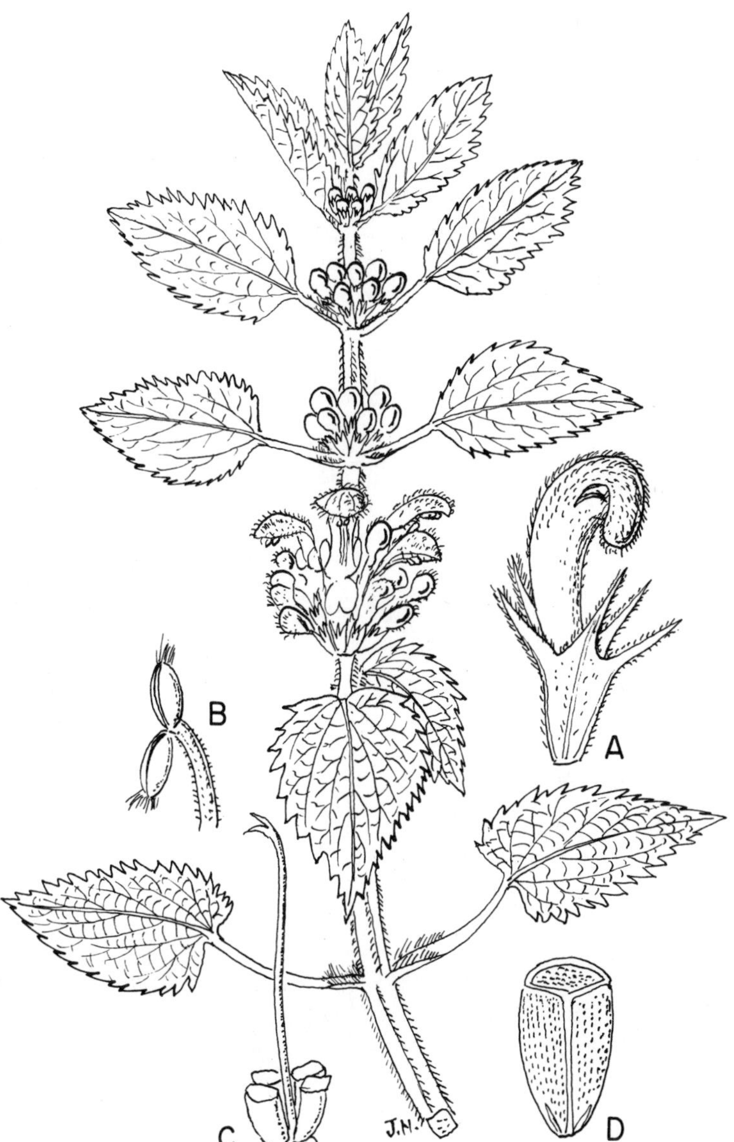

FIG. 556. *Lamium album* Linn., lectotype of the type genus of *Lamiaceae*. **A**, flower bud. **B**, anther. **C**, gynoecium. **D**, seed (orig.).

nutlets furnished with a dorsal cyathiform appendage in *Tinnea*, on the inner face in *Marsypianthes*, depressed-globose in *Salazaria* and *Scutellaria*, fleshy in *Gomphostemma*; areole introrsely lateral in tribes *Prostanthereae* and *Ajugoideae*, obliquely extrorse in *Lavandula*.

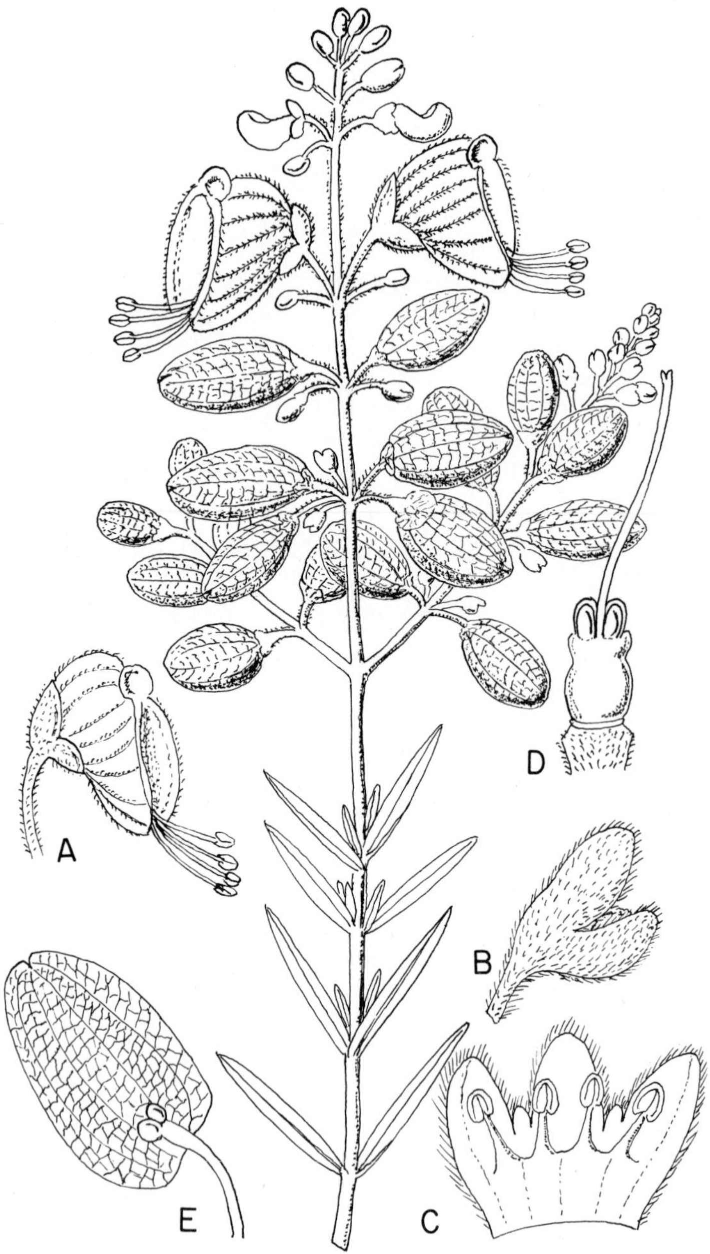

FIG. 557. *Alvesia rosmarinifolia* Welw. (*Lamiaceae*), tropical Africa; note the bladdery calyx in fruit. **A**, separate flower. **B**, calyx. **C**, corolla-bud opened out with stamens. **D**, gynoecium showing the gynobasic style. **E**, half of enlarged calyx showing the nutlets (orig.).

"A hypogynous disk is usually present, mostly 4-lobed, the anterior pair of lobes serving to secrete nectar. The flowers [of some] are resupinate by torsion of the pedicel, or in species of *Ajuga* and *Teucrium*, by torsion of the corolla-tube" (Rendle). The bracts are sometimes coloured, as in *Salvia*, in which there are only 2 stamens. The persistent calyx usually envelops the ripe nutlets which it often protects by closing over them. In the genus *Alvesia* (Fig. 557), tropical Africa, the calyx enlarges and becomes bladder-like and reticulate, as in some species of *Astragalus* (*Fabaceae*). In the genus *Otostegia* the upper lip of the calyx is small and composed of a single lobe, and the lower lip of 4 sepals is large and spreading.

A few genera are of economic use on account of the volatile oils which they contain. Such are Thyme (*Thymus*), Marjorum (*Origanum*), Sage (*Salvia*), Rosemary (*Rosmarinus*), Lavender (*Lavendula*), Patchouly (*Pogostemon*), Mint (*Mentha* spp.); and some are highly decorative greenhouse plants and for bedding, such as *Coleus*, with leaves of many colours, and also *Salvia* spp.

Rendle notes that in species of *Ajuga*, *Lamium*, and others, a small portion of the receptacle becomes separated with the nutlets and forms an elaiosome, in the same way as in some *Boraginaceae*, which tends to strengthen the connection between that family and *Lamiaceae* (*Labiatae*).

INDEX

Bold type signifies Orders and Families, although Family names appearing in footnotes to the text are in italic.

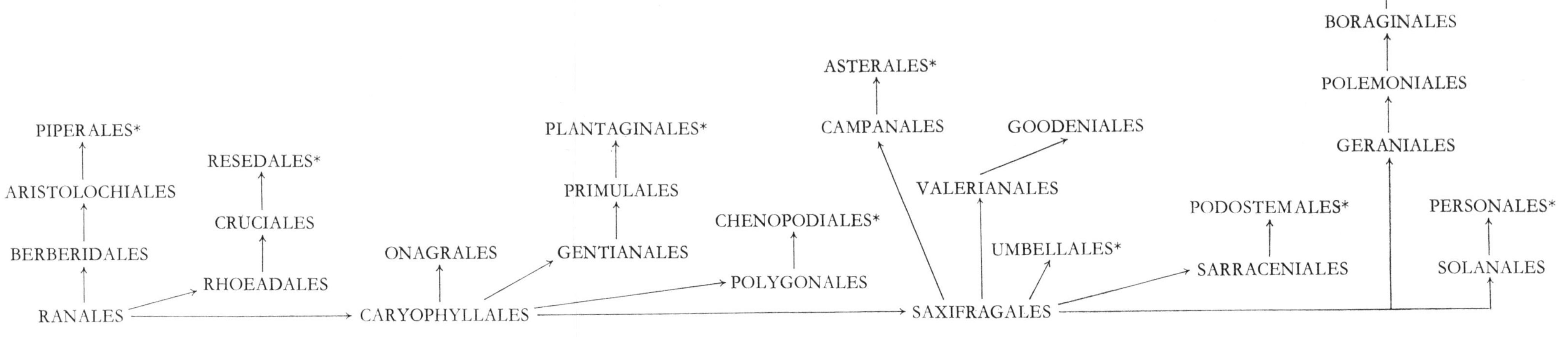

Diagram representing the probable path of evolution of the Orders of fundamentally herbaceous Dicotyledons (**Herbaceae**) as arranged in the preceding pages and designed to be visible to the student whilst reading the text. A group marked with an * is regarded as a complete climax from the stock of which further development is unlikely to have taken place.

B

D

E

F

G

H

I

J

K

L

M

N

O

P

Q

R

S

T

U

V

W

X

Z

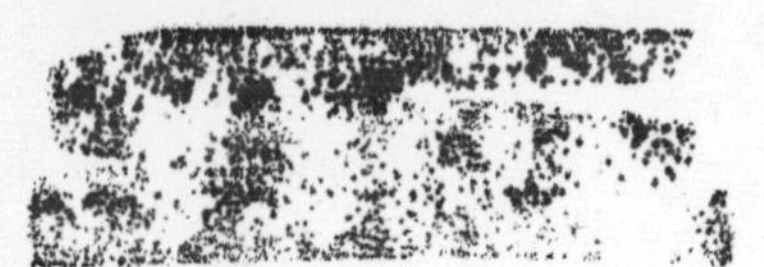